RADIO! RADIO!

Jonathan Hill

For Juliet, Samantha, Cavyll *and* Sabrina

I would like to thank sincerely the following people and organisations for their help during the writing of Radio! Radio!,

Pete Ansell
Trefor Ball
Trevor Baylis
Alan Bedmall
Robert & Pauline Brain
B.B.C. Written Archives Centre
British Broadcasting Corporation
Brit. Library Newspaper Library
British Vintage Wireless Society
Frank Brittain
Gordon Bussey
Jim Butterworth
Douglas Byrne
Roger Campbell
Mick Carter
Malou Cartwright
Bill Caten
Lewis E. Cearley Jnr.
Chalk Pits Museum
Ken Chorley
Gilly Christian
Paddy Clarke
Louis & Iris Coakley
David Cochrane
John Coleman
Chevie Crandell
Eric Darker

Geoffrey Dixon-Nuttall
David Dolbey-Jones
Susan Ellison
John Fenwick
Jim Forster
Keith Geddes
John Gillies
Carl Glover
Carol Gooderham
Mark Gooderham
Bob Gordon
Ron Ham
Terry Harvey
Robert Hawes
Frank Hawkins
Fred Hay
Ian Higginbottom
David Hill
G.E.F.M. Hill
Pat Hill
M.J. Hillier
Suzanne Hobbs
Tony Hopwood
John Howes
R.W. Jessup
Sarah Jewell
Fary Kazemi

Mike Kemp
Colin King
Pat Leggatt
Jem Lineham
Rupert Loftus-Brigham
Joan Long
M.-O. Valve Company Ltd.
Marconi Co. Ltd.
Lucy Mason
William T. Manns
McMichael Radio Ltd.
Ed Millis
Milne Museum
Brian Moseley
John Narborough
Duncan Neale
Hiroaki Otsuka
David Oxland
John Petrie-Baker
Plessey Co. Ltd.
Jack Pope
Practical Wireless Magazine
Public Records Office
R.T.E. Broadcasting Museum
Radio Rentals Ltd.
Karen Radford
Sandy Rand

David Read
Gill Read
Christine Reid
Medwyn Roberts
Roberts Radio Ltd.
John Rodgers
Roy Rodwell
David Rudram
Science Reference Library
Robert Seaman
Gerald Sexton
Jonathan Shirley
Bob Smallbone
Suzanne Smith
Enrico Tedeschi
Noriyoshi Tezuka
Ray Turner
Ken Tythacott
Vintage Wireless Museum
Fred Ward
Bob & Ruth Warner
Gerry Wells
Ann Westerlin
John Marmaduke Western
David Wickham
Vicki Wilkinson
Andrew Wylie

and especially
Peter Missiuro
*who is entirely responsible for opening my eyes to the delights of post-war radio design
and for showing me that radio collecting* can *continue beyond 1939!*

British Library Cataloguing In Publication Data.
A catalogue record for this book is available from the British Library.

First edition published in 1986 (ISBN 0 9511448 12).
Reprinted 1987, and 1988.
Second edition published in 1993 (ISBN 0 9511448 20).

This expanded (third) edition published in 1996 by
Sunrise Press, 2-4 Brook Street, Bampton, Devon EX16 9LY.

Correspondence relating to the subject matter of this book is welcomed, and can be sent to the
author c/o the above address.

ISBN 0 9511448 71.

Designed & produced by Jonathan Hill.

Printed in England, 1996, Maslands Printers, Tiverton, Devon EX16 5HW.

CONTENTS

Preface To The Third Edition

In this third and extended edition of *Radio! Radio!* (with 75 entirely new pages and 50 new illustrations) I have added a large section on transistors, not only because this year marks the 40th anniversary of the release of the first British transistor radio, but also because interest in the subject has grown tremendously recently amongst collectors and historians.

The transistor directory which begins on page 242, contains a listing and basic description of nearly 3,000 different models made in Britain or imported between the years 1956 and 1972 (the 'Golden Age' of the transistor radio in this country).

While researching for this third edition, I was particularly pleased to have made contact with Mick Carter who in the mid-1950s was a member of Pye's pioneering Transistor Section working on the development of Britain's first transistor radio, the Pam 710. His account of these times (see pages 288-291) has provided us all with a rare and fascinating first-hand insight into a missing part of radio's story, and underlines the point that writing books and doing research isn't just about spending one's life wading endlessly through piles of dusty old magazines and reference volumes — it's about people too and their own unique contribution they make to history, whether large or small.

Just as I was about to go to press with this book, a very interesting twist to the Pam 710 story came to light. I was sent a somewhat blurred photograph of what can only be described as a 'PYE 710' (all photographs of great mysteries are, of course, traditionally blurred — *eg.* those of the Loch Ness Monster, UFOs *etc.* — but I have included it anyway in the hope that one of my readers will be able to throw some light on it. See *fig.940, page 293*). I am assured by the set's owner that while it is housed in a Pam 710 cabinet which contains a Pam 710 chassis (it is even marked as such), it bears the Pye badge on the front plus the green flock surround only found (up till now) on Pye's own version, the P123BQ. So, did Pye release the 710 badged up with their own trade-name on the front?

Among other recent discoveries made since the publication of the second edition of *Radio! Radio!* in 1993, have been the wonderful Horophone time-signal receiver which I have described as the 'Holy Grail' of early wireless receivers (*see pages 238 to 241*) and also a complete Edwardian amateur transmitting and receiving station (*see pages 234 to 237*). Between these two pre-WWI items and the section on transistors, both ends of the evolutionary scale of radio have now been more fully covered.

Jonathan Hill, Bampton, Devon. October 1996.

The B.V.W.S.

As mentioned in the preface to the second edition (see opposite), the British Vintage Wireless Society was founded on Sunday April 25th 1976, so this year its 1000 plus members are celebrating the 20th anniversary.

The very first annual general meeting of the B.V.W.S. was held in the grounds of the King's Road School, Chelmsford on Sunday May 29th 1977, and pictured below on that occasion are some of the society's original members (all 27 of them plus dog) together with an imposing array of early wireless equipment — in those days we were not allowed to buy from each other, but had simply to admire the display! This comprised mainly 'museum quality' pieces from the early 1920s, items like a B.T.H. Radiola I and a Marconiphone Crystal 'A' *etc.*, beautiful to look at, and of course now beyond the reach of most collectors' pockets!

The hut behind the group was used by the school as a sports changing room and store, but it originally stood a few miles away at Writtle where it housed the Marconi Scientific Instrument Company's experimental transmitter, call-sign 2MT 'TWO-EMMA-TOC'. This pioneering station was operated on 700 metres by Director and Chief Announcer Captain Peter P. Eckersley, and first went on the air on February 14th 1922, several months before the B.B.C. was formed. (*For full details, see page 34*).

(*Photo: Andrew Hill*).

Preface To The Second Edition

The first edition of *Radio! Radio!* was published in 1986 and altogether some 6,000 copies were printed and subsequently sold. Since then I have been surprised to find that the demand for the book has not stopped. The numerous requests I have received for producing this revised second edition have certainly shown that interest in history is still gaining ground, as with each passing year, many hundreds of new collectors join those already captivated by this fascinating subject.

Much new archive material comes forward all the time and on this page I briefly acknowledge the minor role played by two early radio experimenters whose stories I should have included when this book was originally written. The first was Mahlon Loomis. He was an American dentist from Washington D.C. who, in the early 1860s, carried out several experiments with a system of wireless communication using two copper gauze-covered kites flown on copper wires from adjacent mountain tops in West Virginia - this was long before Guglielmo Marconi 'invented' wireless (see page 12). The gauze of the transmitting kite became charged by atmospheric electricity and by means of a switch, was discharged to earth, and a reciprocal current pulse was registered on a galvanometer in the circuit of the receiving kite several miles away. Loomis believed that he had a marketable product, and was even granted a patent for "establishing an electric current for telegraphic or other purposes without the aid of wires, batteries or cables". Unfortunately, he was unable to find the necessary financial backing needed to support and to exploit his ideas - he just failed to get an appropriation of $50,000 from Congress. If he had, the history of radio may have been rather different.

The other experimenter omitted from the first edition was Robert Goldschmidt, who, just before WW1, carried out a series of unscheduled broadcasts of both speech and music from a transmitting station he had set up at Laeken in Belgium. He began broadcasting in March 1914 using an arc transmitter and continued for a few months until the station was dismantled when German troops crossed the Belgian frontier on August 3rd. Both Loomis and Goldschmidt deserve further investigation and perhaps one day may appear next to Marconi and other pioneers in the radio 'hall of fame'.

Considered redundant in most electronic circuits by the mid-1970's, the valve in recent times has made a remarkable comeback - not in radio though, but in domestic hi-fi amplification. The current demand for the *valve-sound* in music reproduction has meant the re-establishment of a valve supply industry principally from manufacturers based, not in this country, but in China - some of whom are employing English valve-making equipment once considered obsolete and sold off. Alongside the manufacture of new valves, 'vintage' valves are being resurrected and incorporated into the circuits of state-of-the-art audio equipment. The most extreme case of the old-with-the-new can be found in Audio Note's *Gaku-On* monoblock amplifiers. Upon their launch in 1993, these retailed at an astonishing £128,125 and each feature a pair of semi-ancient (and collectable) directly-heated 845 power triodes, which were once designed for bomber transmitters and popularly used by the American Airforce during and after WW11 (see the feature in *Hi-Fi News & Record Review*, May 1993).

It would be difficult to discuss radio collecting as a hobby in this country without mentioning the British Vintage Wireless Society and the contribution it has made to preserving and promoting radio history. Founded in 1976, today its combined membership of nearly one thousand strong must hold the most comprehensive archive of British radio history that exists in the world, and many members are acknowledged to be leading experts in their particular fields. For a new collector today, help and advice is therefore readily at hand. There is a bookcase full of reference material on the subject, as well as several established vintage radio-type magazines. There are regular vintage radio gatherings round the country, specialist auctions, museums and numerous shops which buy and sell old radios. It's a well organised hobby, even for those who have no wish to join a club. But in the early 1970s, before a few of us got together and founded the B.V.W.S., we were among only a handful of collectors in isolated pockets, with no contemporary books to help us and only the occasional reference to the vintage days of radio through such articles as Colin Riches' *"Going Back"* which appeared in *Practical Wireless*. We would scour street markets and antique fairs for old sets and were surprised when we chanced upon anybody else doing the same on our patch.

In 1972, things began to change when an electronics technician from the Physics Department of Bristol University with a love of vintage cars and a flair for repairing the radios that went inside them started a vintage car radio repair business from home. Within a couple of years Tudor Gwilliam Rees opened a specialist vintage radio business at premises in Broad Street, Bristol, by which time he had also branched out into domestic models, repairing and supplying parts and complete sets, and accessories such as headphones and loudspeakers. By the middle of 1975 he was sending out an annual catalogue and a monthly newsletter to his growing list of customers detailing his vintage radio services and the radios currently available in the shop - issue number 5 (from September 1975) notes several round Ekcos *"Five in stock - all different models, £7.00 to £15.00"*. On sale too were period sales catalogues, leaflets and literature, plus a huge variety of vintage radio components including a selection of valves from his stock of 40,000. There was useful information for newcomers to the hobby (*"Valve of the Month"* and *"Radio Wrinkle"* sections), and customers were encouraged to conduct research into radio history in their local area and to contribute short articles.

Following a meeting the year before, Tudor Rees threw open his shop again on Sunday March 7th 1976 for a general get-together with the idea of stimulating the formation of a vintage wireless society or at least providing a stopgap until one was formed. On that particular occasion only 5 collectors managed to make the effort. Despite this, three of us, Tony Constable, Tim Richie and myself (all from London) decided to pursue the idea. The historical inaugural meeting of the British Vintage Wireless Society was duly arranged by Tony at his house in Ealing for 3pm on Sunday April 25th 1976. Besides Tony (who was the driving force behind the B.V.W.S.) and myself, the founding committee comprised John Gillies, Dennis Grey, Ian Higginbottom and Norman Jackson - Tim Richie never showed up and was never heard of again! Being heavily involved in the business side of vintage radio, Tudor Rees felt that he shouldn't be a part of a committee running a club. However, he was happy to have been instrumental in providing a base for its launch and helped out in those early days by printing a membership application form in his newsletters and reviewing and promoting the Society's activities.

Other pioneer vintage radio-based businesses started up around this time: *The Vintage Radio Mart* in Greenwich, *Gramophones et Alia* in Fortune Green Road, Cricklewood and *Rupert's* in Ealing. These three, along with Tudor Rees' shop in Bristol and the infant B.V.W.S., formed the basis of the radio collecting scene that has developed today.

Here, then, for collectors old and new, is the second edition; with a new easy-to-read subject index, the few previous inaccuracies ironed out, and a list of all the radio models illustrated abstracted and put together in the form of a simple A-Z directory, so it's now much easier to look up that old radio!

Jonathan Hill, Bampton, Devon. July 1993.

Introduction To The First Edition

Radio has been a part of home entertainment for well over 60 years. For most people in Britain in the pioneering broadcasting days of the 1920s, their first experience of a 'wireless set' came after the introduction of official broadcasting in 1922, when the British Broadcasting Company opened its first transmitting station in London. Although the wireless rapidly found its way into the homes of people all around the country, the technical development of transmitting and receiving equipment had not suddenly occurred overnight. The behind-the-scenes evolution of radio was a long and gradual process which started in the laboratories of Victorian scientists experimenting with electricity and magnetism, and developed through the research of both amateurs and professionals investigating *wire-less* systems of communication. These used at first telegraphy and later telephony, and until after the First World War were employed mainly for maritime, military and other official purposes - all long before radio was conceived around the early 1920s as a broadcast entertainment for the general public.

At the end of 1922, there were just four B.B.C. stations on the air transmitting within the medium-wave 'Broadcast Band', these being in London, Birmingham, Manchester and Newcastle. There were comparatively few 'listeners-in'; some 35,000 people had taken out a receiving licence, and these mainly lived within the immediate local area served by each transmitter. Most people listened-in on headphones to a simple crystal set, but for the better off there were battery operated multi-valve sets which could drive a horn loud-speaker. Within a few years, more stations were opened serving individual towns and cities and by the end of 1924 there were 21 stations and getting on for a million licence holders. In 1925, a high power long-wave station opened at Daventry in Northamptonshire marking the experimental beginning of the Regional Scheme which, serving whole regions rather than just single towns and cities as before, was to bring the B.B.C.'s programmes to practically the whole country. By the early 1930s broadcasting had become a national institution with the introduction of the National and Regional Programmes, and the wireless, now powered from the mains, had become an indispensable part of family life and the centrepiece of home entertainment.

Programme details and transmitter wavelength information of B.B.C. stations appeared in *The Radio Times*. At first in the 1920s, stations were known by their own particular call-signs, most famous of which was the B.B.C.'s first station in London, 2LO. Dials were calibrated in degrees only which meant that listeners-in had to make a note on a separate card of their own particular tuning dial settings for each station they wanted to hear; for example, 2LO on 361 metres might be 120 degrees and 5IT (Birmingham) on 420 metres might be 165 degrees and so on. Station names did not appear printed on the dial until the early 1930s and this made tuning-in very much easier and enabled listeners to select at will a whole galaxy of stations, not just in this country, but also from Europe by merely pointing the cursor at the station required. Foreign station listening was tremendously popular with British listeners throughout the 1930s and many stations became household words during this period. Could you say where some of those stations were? - stations such as Hilversum, Konigswusterhausen, Motala, Huizen, Kosice and Sottens.

The number of European broadcasting stations grew tremendously during the 1930s, but in Britain by 1936 the number of B.B.C. stations had fallen to 15. The Home Service arrived in 1939 sweeping away the National and Regional Programmes just before the outbreak of the Second World War, and was joined in the immediate post-war years by the Light and the Third Programmes which all lasted until 1967 when a 'trendier' sounding Radio 1, 2, 3, and 4 network took over.

By this time, valve receivers had been superseded by the transistor, and the television service, started in 1936, suspended in 1939 and re-introduced in 1946, gradually in post-war years established the television as the centrepiece of home entertainment and displaced the radio.

For those without an atlas, here are the locations of the foreign broadcasting stations referred to: Hilversum (Holland), Konigswusterhausen (Germany), Motala (Sweden), Huizen (Holland), Kosice (Czechoslovakia) and Sottens (Switzerland).

Jonathan Hill. London W3 9AH. April 1986.

KEY TO ABBREVIATIONS USED IN CAPTIONS

3-v	3-valve receiver etc.
+R	Plus valve rectifier
+MetR	Plus metal rectifier
+Bar	Plus Barretter
+West	Plus Westector
6-Tr	6-transistor receiver etc.
HF	High frequency stage
DET	Detector stage
LF	Low frequency stage
AC	Alternating current mains powered
DC	Direct current mains powered
AC/DC	Alternating or direct current mains powered
M/Batt	Mains and battery powered
Batt	Battery powered
SHet	Superheterodyne receiver
TRF	Tuned radio frequency ('straight') receiver

SW	Short waveband
2SW	2 short wavebands etc.
MW	Medium waveband
LW	Long waveband
VHF	Very high frequency band
AM	Amplitude modulation
FM	Frequency modulation
0-100 deg	Tuning calibrated in 0 to 100 degree markings
Mtrs	Tuning calibrated in metres
Kcs	Tuning calibrated in kilocycles
Mcs	Tuning calibrated in megacycles
StN	Tuning showing station names
300/500m	Wave-range 300 to 500 metres etc.
A.T.I.	Aerial Tuning Inductance
LT	Low tension battery
HT	High tension battery

Early Developments In Communication

The sending of messages over long distances by pre-arranged signals has been practised since ancient times. For centuries, fire and smoke and other primitive devices were in widespread use in various parts of the world, and in Britain right up to the late 18th century, at a time when signalling by flags was considered a sophisticated method of communication, it was still common to light beacons on high ground in order to give signals and warnings. But then these simple and basic methods of communication rapidly began to be supplemented at first by mechanical and later in the mid to late 19th century by quite advanced wired electrical devices such as the telegraph and the telephone. However, it was only in the last few years of the 19th century that the beginnings of an efficient *wireless* communications system began to emerge, an offshoot of which ultimately led to the development of radio broadcasting in the 1920s. (The term 'radio' as applied to a form of communication, was first suggested by J. Munro in an article entitled "RADIO-TELEGRAPHY" which appeared in *The Electrician* in 1898).

One of the earliest mechanical signalling devices used in Britain was the semaphore telegraph which was first established in 1774 between London, Portsmouth and Newmarket. In 1826 another semaphore telegraph was erected on hills between Liverpool and Holyhead and comprised a 70 mile chain of eleven signalling stations placed about 7 miles apart. A signal could be sent from one end to the other and back again in just over twenty three seconds. Various other forms of semaphore were soon being developed in Europe and Russia but they all suffered from the serious limitation of being rendered useless in fog, mists, storms and of course at night.

In the late 18th century, unsuccessful attempts at producing electrical machines for signalling were also made but it was not until the development in the 1790s of a continuous source of electric current (the Voltaic cell) and Oersted's discovery in 1819 that a magnetised needle was deflected by an electric current flowing through a wire placed near the needle, that the possibilities of developing a successful electrical signalling system were realised. Oersted's discovery laid the foundation of the wired telegraph and soon several scientists including Schilling and von Steinheil were endeavouring to perfect a communications system in which the movement of a magnetised needle could be used to indicate transmitted messages.

In England in 1837, the British physicist Charles Wheatstone in association with William Fothergill Cooke, took out a patent "for improvements in giving signals and sounding alarms in distant places by means of electric currents transmitted through metallic circuits". Wheatstone's system used a five-needle telegraph. By changing the direction of the current, five pivoted needles could be made to move, two at a time, either to the left or to the right and point towards a letter of the alphabet marked on the dial of the instrument. It was first fully adopted in 1839 by the Great Western Railway when it was used to connect the stations at Paddington and West Drayton.

In America, in the year that Wheatstone's needle telegraph was patented in England, Samuel Morse with his partner Alfred Vail produced an experimental system of electric telegraphy which used an automatic printer to record incoming messages on a continuous roll of paper tape. To enable this to have a more practical use he invented a code, the Morse Code, tapped out by a Morse key. The received Morse symbols (dots and dashes) were at first embossed on the tape by a steel needle, but in a later development ink was used to print them and the printer became known as the Morse Inker. Alternatively in place of the inker or in conjunction with it, a Morse Sounder was

used which was either a bell producing a ring or an instrument producing a click every time a dot or a dash was received. Morse also invented the relay which reinforced feeble signals at the receiving end by means of a current produced by a local battery. Although the results of his system were satisfactory, it was not until 1842 that Morse won support from the American Government and established the usefulness of his invention. Congress advanced money for the setting up of a telegraph system between Baltimore and Washington and a year later the service began.

In 1843, the Wheatstone needle telegraph from Paddington to West Drayton was extended to Slough and opened to the public for the first time, becoming the world's first commercial electrical communications system. For one shilling, the public could enter the telegraph offices at the termini and view this new wonder of science, and for a further shilling they could even send a telegram.

From the start, the British railway telegraph was intertwined with the public telegraph system and soon several rival telegraph companies and telegraph lines had been established. By 1868, 16,000 miles of line had been erected in Britain and the wires had already become a familiar sight, strung up on telegraph poles running alongside the railway or beside roads. At first, the charges made for sending telegrams were thought excessive, and the inconvenient situation and opening times of many telegraph offices made the public a little hesitant to use the system. However in 1870, the Post Office took over the whole telegraph network under the Telegraph Acts of 1868 and 1869 and at once began a great scheme of reorganisation by amalgamating the rival companies into one uniform and fair system. The Post Office completely disentangled the railway telegraphs from the ordinary public telegraph system and set about the immediate construction of 6,000 miles of new telegraph lines. Lines were laid to Post Offices in outlying suburbs and business hours extended, and by the turn of the century the telegraph system had been even extended to remote villages.

For several years following its adoption in 1839, the Wheatstone needle telegraph was widely used in Britain, with the number of needles soon being reduced to two and then to one and used in conjunction with a code of needle movements. In this form it was still being employed as a railway telegraph a hundred years later. However, within the Post Office and in most other fields, the Morse Code, tapped out by the Morse key or later by high-speed automatic machines or supplemented with teleprinters which had their own codes, became the universal language of telegraphic communication.

COMMUNICATION BY CONDUCTION

Other systems of telegraphic communication were being experimented with during the 19th century and these included three methods which did not use wires to connect the transmitting and receiving points. In 1843, Samuel Morse successfully transmitted across the Susquehanna River using the river itself as the conductor rather than wires, and similar wireless experiments sending signals through water by conduction were later made by several other investigators including J.B. Lindsay who used the river Tay at Dundee in Scotland. Lindsay's work subsequently came to the attention of William H. Preece and sparked off a great interest in the subject of communication without wires. In 1870, Preece was appointed Divisional Engineer to the General Post Office and later (in 1892) became Engineer-in-Chief, and in that capacity he ultimately sponsored the young Guglielmo Marconi when he came to England with an improved system of wireless telegraphy (see 1896).

Having begun a wired telegraph on land, it was inevitable that experimenters were drawn towards laying lines to places overseas. In 1851, the first successful undersea telegraph cable was laid across the English Channel and from its inauguration on November 13th it continued in public service for the next twenty four years. Links were also made between the Isle of Wight and Hampshire, England and Holland, and Scotland and Ireland, and soon, short-distance undersea cables were being laid in many other parts of the world.

The success of these short-distance cables inspired thoughts of linking the American and European Continents, although the bulk of scientific and commercial opinion was at first very much against such a scheme: laying some 2,000 miles of continuous cable seemed far too big an undertaking and fraught with potential disasters. However, after a short-lived triumph in 1858, (the cable parted within a few months), success came in 1866 when more permanent sub-marine links were establised with the laying of a cable between Ireland and Newfoundland. Over the next few years undersea telegraph cables were being laid all around the globe and they revolutionised the transmission of public, private and commercial communications between the continents and soon the phrase "sending a cable" had become part of the English language.

In 1882, the undersea telegraph cable linking the Isle of Wight with the mainland broke down, and Preece, who had some first hand knowledge of telegraphing through water, stepped forward to help. A 6 ft. square plate of copper was immersed in the sea at the end of Ryde Pier and from there an overground wire passed westwards through Newport ending in a second copper plate in the sea at Sconce Point. On the mainland shore at Hurst Castle, another wire led from a third immersed copper plate and ran through Portsmouth and Southampton terminating in a fourth copper plate in the sea off Southsea Pier, thus completing the circuit. Using a Morse key and the power from thirty Leclanche cells, two-way Morse Code communication was sucessfully established between Southampton and Newport with Preece using both a sounder and a telephone earpiece to hear the signals.

Normally, Morse signals at the receiving end would have been recorded by an inker or heard on a sounder only, but as in the Isle of Wight experiment, telephone earpieces were now beginning to be used as well. In 1876, Alexander Graham Bell had sent the first practical message on his newly invented telephone and by the end of the decade, public telephone services had been introduced in both America and Europe. In 1879, the first British telephone exchange (with lines to just a handful of 'subscribers') was opened in London at 36 Coleman Street by the Telephone Company Limited (Bell Patents), and this was quickly followed by further installations at Leadenhall Street and Palace Chambers. In the same year a rival company, the Edison Telephone Company of London, Limited (Edison Patents), was formed and opened exchanges at Lombard Street and Queen Victoria Street, and soon other companies were operating exchanges in various parts of the country. In 1889, the principal rival exchanges in Britain were amalgamated into one company under the title of the National Telephone Company which then provided a service to about 24,000 subscribers, and having a control of the telephone patents, gradually acquired most of the telephone services in Britain. By 1890, with many trunk lines already laid between cities and large towns, it was possible to speak from London to the Midlands and the North of England. In 1896, in a move to secure public control, the Post Office purchased these lines, leaving local exchanges mainly in the hands of the National Telephone Company. On January 1st 1912, the Post Office took over the whole of the National Telephone Company's service, bringing under State control virtually the whole of Britain's local and trunk telephone system, which then comprised some 1,565 exchanges and over 560,000 subscribers. The effects of this unified system were quickly apparent, for in the three years up to the outbreak of the First World War, the Post Office opened no less than 450 exchanges in small villages and rural areas.

WIRELESS BY ELECTRO-MAGNETIC INDUCTION

In 1831, the British chemist, physicist and electrical pioneer Michael Faraday made a discovery which was to become one of the fundamental principles of electrical, and later, radio engineering: the electro-magnetic induction effect between two entirely separate circuits. Many years later in 1880, Professor John Trowbridge of Boston, Massachusetts, first suggested that one of the principles of Faraday's discovery might be used for a form of wireless communication between ships at sea. He experimented with using a large coil of multi-stranded wire stretched from the yard arms and connected to a powerful battery or dynamo in one ship, and a similar coil connected to a telephone earpiece on the receiving ship. He achieved some measure of success, finding during experiments that signals were strongest when the two coils were parallel to each other. But the problems of this system were too great to be overcome for the further apart the ships were, the larger the radius of the coil needed to be, and in order to produce an audible signal in the telephone earpiece of a ship even half a mile away, coils with a radius of about 800 ft. would have been required.

Preece was also interested in the work being done by Trowbridge on wireless communication by induction, and from about 1885 carried out various experiments in different parts of Britain. He used the inductive properties of two circuits parallel to each other and determined how far apart the parallel wires in each circuit could be separated before the inductive influence ceased. Preece achieved quite a measure of success, but only over comparatively short distances of a few miles. Like Trowbridge's, for practical purposes his system too was limited, for although wireless communication was established between the two circuits, the length of the actual wire that went to make up each circuit could be quite considerable. Very long wires laid parallel to each other were needed at the transmitting and receiving stations and in order to increase the distance over which signals were transmitted, it was necessary to increase proportionally the length of the parallel wires opposing each other. As the wires had to be approximately as long as the distance between them, development of the system as a means of long-distance communication reached an unpractical dead-end. Preece however had gained familiarity and knowledge of the problems of conductive and inductive wireless communication through his experiments and this enabled him at once to recognise the potential worth of Marconi's system when he saw it for the first time in 1896.

Faraday's principle of electro-magnetic induction did lead to more positive and practical inventions though, including the dynamo and the transformer. But it was of more use to early radio science when in 1851 the induction coil was developed by the Parisian instrument maker H.D. Ruhmkorff. Towards the turn of the century the induction coil evolved into a standard piece of equipment used in wireless telegraphy to produce a spark across the spark gap of a transmitter and thus radiate electro-magnetic waves (radio-waves).

WIRELESS BY ELECTRO-MAGNETIC RADIATION

The theory of the existence of electro-magnetic waves was first worked out mathematically by the Cambridge physicist, James

Clerk Maxwell in 1864, but they were not demonstrated experimentally until 1879 when David Edward Hughes discovered the essential features of wireless communication during a series of experiments in which he became the first person in history to transmit and receive radio-waves in a communications system using electro-magnetic *radiation*, rather than electro-magnetic conduction or induction.

Hughes was a Professor of Music but he was also very keen on telegraphy and science, and had several inventions to his credit including an efficient printing telegraph and the carbon microphone. While working in his laboratory in Great Portland Street, London, Hughes noticed that his microphone was picking up sounds from a faulty circuit in his induction balance (fig. 1) while being completely unconnected to it by wires.

fig. 1 . Hughes' Induction Balance. 1879. Crudely made from deal, card, cork, brass wire and matchsticks. 4¾ in. x 15 in. x 11 in.

To investigate further, he made a simple automatic spark transmitter consisting of a battery, an induction coil and a clockwork contact breaker to interrupt the current passing through the coil and so send out signals in short bursts (fig. 2). Although he thought he was transmitting "aerial electric waves" which he believed travelled through the air by conduction, Hughes had in fact successfully produced radio-waves. With his transmitter running, he was able to take his receiver (consisting of a battery, a telephone earpiece and his microphone: a steel needle lightly touching a small piece of coke which acted as a detector, fig. 3) down Great Portland Street and receive good signals up to a distance of about 60 yards, after which they began to fade until at about 500 yards they disappeared altogether.

fig. 2 . Hughes' Clockwork Contact Breaker (or 'Interrupter'). 1879. Deal base with brass clock parts. 4½ in. x 6 in. x 3½ in. Part of Hughes' automatic spark transmitter.

Unfortunately, he did not proceed to carry out a full scientific investigation and without visual proof, his claims were not accepted by his scientific colleagues as being any more than well known electro-magnetic induction effects, the principle Michael Faraday had demonstrated in the early 1830s.

fig. 3 . Hughes' Microphone. 1879. Glass jar, with turned boxwood lid, housing a steel needle in contact with a small piece of coke. 4 in. high x 2½ in. dia. This acted as a crude detector of electro-magnetic waves and together with a battery and a telephone earpiece, formed part of Hughes' 'receiver'. It was used to receive experimental signals sent out from his automatic spark transmitter which comprised a clockwork contact breaker, an induction coil and a battery.

Discouraged, Hughes did not publish the results of his experiments for several years and the unique opportunity of developing a practical wireless communication system earlier was missed.

It was left to a German scientist, Heinrich Hertz, to give the scientific community the visual proof they needed. In 1887, Hertz successfully verified Maxwell's theory by generating, transmitting and detecting electro-magnetic waves (or Hertzian Waves as they soon became known to 19th century science) in his laboratory at the Technical High School, Karlsruhe, Germany where he was Professor of Experimental Physics.

Hertz's transmitter, or 'oscillator', consisted of a high voltage induction coil which was used to build up a charge across a spark gap, each side of which was connected to a large metal plate. When the charge had built up sufficiently, a spark jumped the gap and energy in the form of very high frequency electro-magnetic waves was radiated into space from the metal plates which formed in effect, a dipole aerial.

On the other side of Hertz's laboratory was his receiver, or 'resonator', which comprised a large hoop of thick metal wire broken by a small adjustable spark gap. Every time the oscillator produced a spark, a corresponding spark would instantly appear across the spark gap of the resonator, even though both instruments were completely unconnected by wires.

In a series of experiments, Hertz measured the length and velocity of the waves and he was able to demonstrate their susceptibility to reflection (by bouncing them off a large metal plate placed at the far end of his laboratory) and refraction (he bent them out of a straight course by passing them through a wedge of pitch), showing that they behaved in accordance with light waves.

Hertz published the results of his experiments and they were soon being repeated by scientists in other parts of the world, including Oliver Lodge in England and Professor Augusto Righi of Bologna University in Italy, and it was as a student of Righi's in 1894 that the young Guglielmo Marconi first became interested in the new science surrounding electro-magnetic waves.

In 1889, the English physicist Oliver Lodge began to employ a spark gap as a detector of weak electrical discharges. Lodge had originally employed a spark gap in his experiments with lightning and had observed that the spherical knobs used in standard lightning protectors often became fused together by the current discharged between them. On further investigation he discovered that even an extremely feeble spark was sufficient to produce the effect, providing that the spheres were almost touching. The adhesion of the two spheres was demonstrated by an electric bell and a battery in series with them: every time a spark occurred, the spheres joined and the bell rang and immediately broke the contact with its vibrations, therefore restoring the gap to its original condition. Unknown to him, Lodge had discovered a principle that was later to be applied to one of the basic components used in the apparatus of wireless communication when this new technology emerged towards the end of the 1890s: the filings coherer. (The word 'coherer' at least, was Lodge's invention).

fig. 4 . Branly-Lodge Coherer. 1894. One of Lodge's 'filings' coherers based on those by Branly of 1890. Glass tube, brass fittings, deal base. 2 in. x 7 ½ in, x 4 in.

The filings coherer was invented in 1890 by Professor Edouard Branly, not during the course of investigations into methods of communication, but into the influence of electro-magnetic discharges on various forms of imperfect contacts. Although Branly was unaware of it at the time, his coherer was the first practical device for detecting the presence of radio-waves and in this capacity was used by Lodge when he gave the first public demonstration of wireless transmission and reception in 1894. Branly's coherer consisted of a horizontal glass tube containing metallic filings loosely packed between two metal plugs. At each end of the tube a wire was placed in contact with the plugs and this completed a circuit through which an electric current could be passed. In their normally loose condition, Branly found that the filings allowed the passage of only a small current, but as soon as electric sparks were generated in a nearby Hertzian oscillator, the filings suddenly became much more conductive, and allowed a much greater current to pass through them. A mechanical shock in the form of a slight tap on the glass tube re-set the filings back to their original poor conductive condition. Later, electro-mechanical tappers were developed for this purpose. Branly had re-discovered what David Hughes had observed in 1879: that a loose contact in an electric circuit was sensitive to electro-magnetic waves. Hughes' microphone had one loose contact (a steel needle resting lightly on a piece of coke) while Branly's metal filings formed a number of loose contacts in its electrical circuit.

By June 1894, Oliver Lodge had been working on electro-magnetic waves for over four years and had reached the conclusion that they could be used in a form of wireless communication. In that month he gave the world's first public demonstration of wireless transmission and reception at the Royal Institution in London. Using his spherical oscillator as the transmitter (fig. 5), he radiated electro-magnetic waves of about 18 cms over a distance of up to 150 yards. In his receiver, Lodge had replaced Hertz's thick wire ring with two metal plates (a dipole aerial) and the small spark gap with a filings coherer based on Branly's (fig. 4). The filings coherer was more sensitive than the spark gap and it could detect weaker signals at much greater distances. During his demonstrations he also employed a 'Spiral Wire Coherer' which he had developed in 1890 (fig. 6).

fig. 5 . Lodge's 'Spherical Oscillator'. 1894. Part of one of the transmitters used by Oliver Lodge when he gave the world's first public demonstration of wireless transmission and reception in June 1894 in front of an audience at the Royal Institution. Ebonite support rods, wood cleats, miniature brass spheres, large nickel sphere. 6 in. diameter.

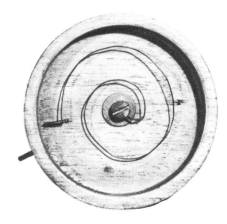

fig. 6 . The underside of Lodge's 'Spiral Wire Coherer' which was used in his Royal Institution lecture in June 1894 as a detector of wireless signals. Made by Lodge's assistant, E.E. Robinson in c.1890. Turned mahogany base. 3 in. diameter.

MARCONI'S EARLY EXPERIMENTS

Lodge's transmitting and receiving system was similar to the ones soon to be used by other wireless pioneers, including Marconi in Italy who, in 1894, was beginning to make his own independent experiments with Hertzian waves at his family's country retreat, the Villa Grifone at Pontecchio, near Bologna.

Marconi was just 20. He was keen on physics, chemistry and above all, on electricity, although he had had very little formal education and had failed to gain a place at Bologna University. However, he was allowed to attend lectures given there by Professor Righi who was a neighbour and friend of the Marconi family. Since reading about the experiments of Hertz, Righi had been working on the relationship between the behaviour of very high frequency electro-magnetic waves and light. He was one of the few scientists who had a thorough grasp of Hertz's work in this field and was able therefore to give Marconi a practical understanding of how to generate, radiate and detect electro-magnetic waves. Marconi also had access to Righi's laboratory and apparatus, and to his library where Marconi read about Hertz's work in detail both in contemporary articles and in Righi's own memorial paper to Hertz, who had died in January 1894.

Marconi though was interested in using Hertzian waves for wireless telegraphy and in the attic at the Villa Grifone he began to put together apparatus borrowed from Righi's laboratory. To generate sparks, Marconi used an induction coil whose secondary winding was coupled to a double spark gap of Righi's own design and this was to form the basis of Marconi's early transmitters. The spark gap used four spheres, with the two larger central ones immersed in oil coupling the discharge to them from the two smaller outer spheres and producing a train of sparks of high intensity and regularity. The primary winding was connected to a battery and a Morse key, and the transmitted signals were picked up by a coherer-type receiver. Marconi had read about Branly's coherer and no doubt about its use in Lodge's pioneering demonstration of wireless transmission in June 1894. Although it was more efficient than a spark gap detector, Marconi still found it relatively insensitive and unpredictable in response. So he set about improving it and achieved greater sensitivity by reducing the distance between the two metal plugs, using filings sieved to a uniform size, and heating the glass tube just before sealing it to create a partial vacuum. (Branly's coherer operated under atmospheric pressure). A mechanical tapper was used to re-set the filings.

By the summer of 1895, Marconi had succeeded in transmitting signals a matter of only a few yards. Until then he had been using horizontal dipole aerials but soon he began experimenting with an elevated aerial and a buried earth at both the transmitting and receiving ends (fig. 7). By August, using this improved system, he was able to extend significantly the range of his transmitter and at once he came to realise the commercial possibilities of using electro-magnetic waves for long-distance wireless communication.

EXPERIMENTS BY OTHER SCIENTISTS

From around the mid-1890s, many other scientists began experimenting with the transmission and reception of electro-magnetic waves. In 1895, the English scientist, Ernest Rutherford, detected signals from a Hertzian oscillator sent over a distance of just under a mile to his Cavendish Laboratory in Cambridge. He used a sensitive magnetometer (an instrument for measuring magnetic field strength) which changed its deflection when a pulse of electro-magnetic energy arrived at the receiving aerial and this idea was later modified by Marconi in 1902 when he designed his Magnetic Detector (see 1902).

In Russia, the physicist Admiral Popoff transmitted over a distance of 5 miles from a Hertzian oscillator set up at Petrograd (Leningrad) using a modified version of Branly's coherer. The incoming signals triggered off a relay which in turn caused a hammer to strike both a bell and the coherer, re-setting its filings and stopping the flow of current. The relay worked with a current supplied from its own local battery and enabled the hammer to strike with the same force irrespective of how strong the transmitted signals were. Popoff later used a Morse inker in place of the bell to obtain a permanent visual record of the signals received and the system he employed (a coherer, a relay and either a Morse inker or sounder) was within a short time to become the standard approach to receiver design.

fig. 7 . Model of Marconi's experimental transmitter used in Bologna during the summer of 1895, showing the spark gap, induction coil and an elevated copper sheet aerial supported by a bamboo frame.

Wireless Telegraphy & Telephony, And The Years Leading Up To Broadcasting, 1896 - 1921

1896

By 1896, Marconi had further improved his equipment and now believed that he had devised a sound, workable system of wireless telegraphy. It was in Marconi's mind to use this specifically for marine communication and having failed to interest the Italian Ministry of Posts & Telegraphs, he sailed for Britain, which at that time was still the world's leading naval power and boasted the world's largest merchant marine. It was also the hub of international trade, finance, insurance and marine intelligence. One other reason for choosing Britain was that he had strong, and probably more importantly, well-off family connections here.

fig. 8 . The young Guglielmo Marconi photographed in London shortly after his arrival in February 1896. In front of him on the desk is the wireless apparatus he brought over from Italy. A Righi oscillator (part of the transmitter) is on the left, while on the right, a Morse sounder sits on top of a wooden box which contained a self-tapping coherer and a relay, making up the receiver. On the front of the box are two copper strips which acted as the receiving aerial.

Accompanying him on his voyage was Marconi's Irish-born mother, Annie, who had been a great support to him during his initial experiments in Italy and who was now determined to see him succeed. Annie was the grand-daughter of John Jameson who had emigrated from Scotland and had founded the Jameson Irish Whiskey distillery in Bow Street, Dublin in 1780. She was also related to the Haig and Ballantyne whisky families of Scotland. Annie had married against family wishes in 1864 and had settled with her silk merchant husband, Giuseppe Marconi, in Bologna, the place where they had first met when as a young girl she had been sent to Italy to study singing. In the intervening years, she had made the occasional conciliatory visit to Britain, and Marconi, at the age of about five, is thought to have come with her on one of these visits and even attended school in Rugby for a short time.

It was against this background that Marconi set foot in England in February 1896. From the moment of his arrival, he was helped and guided by his mother's cousin, H. Jameson Davis who found accommodation for him in Hereford Road, Bayswater. The wireless equipment Marconi had brought over from Italy had been damaged during examination by British Customs officers, and over the next few months he was able to repair, set up and adjust it and prepare the provisional specification of a patent for "improvements in transmitting electrical impulses and signals and in apparatus therefor" which he filed on June 2nd 1896. Although he has often been credited with "inventing wireless", Marconi, who was then just 22, did not in fact invent any new device. He simply adapted and improved the discoveries of many other men like Hertz, Lodge, Branly, and Righi, set them free from the laboratory and combined them into the first practical and commercial system of wireless communication.

A good example of the way Marconi worked is demonstrated by what he did with Branly's coherer. Although Lodge was the first to use the coherer as a detector in wireless reception, he did not feel that he had made an invention and did not therefore apply for a patent. Branly too had not patented it, for he did not realise its worth. Marconi on the other hand improved the coherer and was later able to get the basic patents for its use in wireless, ably demonstrating his ability as an opportunist rather than as an inventor. By improving on important discoveries rather than doing fundamental laboratory work, Marconi was able to succeed in gaining possession of many principal wireless patents and thereby raise the companies he formed to a dominant position which far exceeded any of his competitors.

Answering the question, "Who invented wireless?", Judge William Townsend of the United States Circuit Court gave this answer in May 1905 during an action brought by Marconi's Wireless Telegraph Company of America against the De Forest Wireless Telegraph Company. "Other inventors, venturing forth on the sea of electrical movement, met the rising tide of the Hertzian waves and allowed them to roll by without appreciating that this new current was destined to carry onward the freight and traffic of world commerce. They noted the manifestations, suspected their possibilities, disclosed their characteristics, and hesitated, fearing the breakers ahead, imagining barriers of impracticable channels and shifting sand bars. Marconi, daring to hoist his sail and explore the unknown current, first disclosed the new highway."

Soon after Marconi's arrival in England, H. Jameson Davis arranged a meeting with the well-known electrical engineer, A.A. Campbell Swinton, who gave Marconi a letter of introduction to William H. Preece, the Engineer-in-Chief of the General Post Office. Preece himself was a keen experimenter in many branches of electricity, and having heard about the young Marconi was naturally very anxious to see an early demonstration of his system. This, Marconi gave in July. His spark transmitter was set up on the roof of the General Post Office in St. Martin's le Grand in London, and in front of Preece and several officials, he succeeded in sending an unofficial telegram a distance of just over half a mile to his wireless receiver on the Embankment. The Post Office, and especially Preece, were impressed, and it was primarily due to Preece's interest and encouragement that for nearly a year during the critical early stages of the development of Marconi's system, the Post Office worked closely with Marconi and willingly supported his experiments out of public funds, Preece putting his own private laboratory at Marconi's disposal as well as some of his staff.

On September 2nd, Marconi demonstrated his apparatus on Salisbury Plain to Post Office officials and representatives of the Army and Navy and this time achieved an improved range of just under 2 miles using directional parabolic metal reflectors at both the transmitting and receiving ends, with the apparatus earthed to ground. The directional properties of the parabolic reflector meant that messages could be beamed directly to the receiver which allowed some form of secrecy: something the Military were very interested in. His transmitter, sending out waves of about 2 metres in length, comprised a Righi double spark gap oscillator, an induction coil and a battery, with a Morse key inserted into the primary of the induction coil. For his receiver he used a Branly-type coherer, an electric bell and a relay in a similar arrangement to that used by Popoff. The use of directional aerials and parabolic reflectors had first become very familiar to Marconi in Righi's laboratory at Bologna when they were originally being used in Hertzian wave experiments. Although Marconi soon abandoned the idea of directional aerials and short-waves in favour of large, high elevated aerials and longer waves, he was to return to the idea on later occasions.

At the end of September, Preece introduced Marconi and his wireless system to the scientific community in a lecture to the British Association entitled "Telegraphy Without Wires", and on December 12th, Preece repeated his lecture to the general public for the first time, at Toynbee Hall in London, and gave a practical demonstration with Marconi acting as his assistant.

fig. 9 . Jackson's Coherer. c.1895. Used by Capt. Henry Jackson during his wireless telegraphy experiments of 1895/6. Brass mounting and fittings, ebonite tube. 3 in. high.

Meanwhile, other experimenters were also having some measure of success. For several months from December 1895, Captain Henry Jackson had been conducting a series of experiments into wireless telegraphy on board H.M.S. *Defiance*, the Naval Torpedo Training School at Devonport, using a coherer of his own design (fig. 9). In the spring of 1896, he successfully transmitted and received Morse Code messages, and this reinforced his original idea, first put forward in 1891, that electro-magnetic waves should be used for Naval communication. (In 1899, wireless telegraphy was first introduced into the British Navy, largely through the efforts of Jackson but using Marconi's system).

In Germany during 1896, Dr Slaby, a professor at the Technical High School of Charlottenburg in Berlin, was experimenting with electro-magnetic waves as a means of communication but had only succeeded in transmitting over a distance of about 100 yards. It was not until he came over to England in the following year to witness and actually take part in experiments using Marconi's apparatus that he was able to improve his own system. In the early 1900s, the Telefunken Company, using Slaby's patents together with those of Arco and Braun in a high-quality wireless telegraphy system, became one of Marconi's major competitors.

1897

In the early days of wireless telegraphy, spark transmitters and receivers were untuned. Waves were sent out from transmitters at no defined frequency and receivers themselves responded to a wide range of frequencies and were incapable of being selectively tuned to the required station to the exclusion of all others. Two or more spark transmitters in the same vicinity would therefore cause mutual interference. With the foreseeable growth in the number of wireless transmitters, one major problem to be solved therefore was how to make a transmitter radiate a wave of definite frequency and how to make the receiver respond selectively only to that particular frequency.

Much pioneering work was done on this subject by Oliver Lodge who discovered that by adding an inductance coil to an aerial, selectivity was greatly increased. On May 10th, Lodge took out a patent for a method of tuning entitled "IMPROVEMENTS IN SYNTONIZED TELEGRAPHY". His patent was for a complete system of wireless telegraphy specifically designed to transmit at a particular frequency and as such described the very first tuned circuit (see 1900).

In the same month, Marconi conducted experiments across the Bristol Channel assisted by Post Office engineer George S. Kemp. For these experiments, Marconi made a new multiple spark gap consisting of four brass balls, each about 2 in. diameter spaced about ¼ in. apart in an ebonite frame. The results achieved were very much better than with his original Righi spark gap oscillator and he later improved his induction coil by winding it with thicker wire "in order to get a thicker and heavier spark". On May 11th signals were transmitted a distance of over 3 miles from Lavernock Point, South Wales to a receiver set up on the Island of Flat Holm in the Bristol Channel, using aerials consisting of metal cylinders supported on masts. A week later, on May 18th, Marconi was able to send signals right across the Bristol Channel from Lavernock Point to Brean Down in Somerset, some 10 miles away. This time he used high flying kites covered with tin foil as the transmitting and receiving aerials. These were the first in a series of wireless experiments that Marconi carried out over water, and he later wrote, "It was soon obvious that signalling by wireless could be more easily carried out across stretches of water than over land. As it is precisely in those circumstances that ordinary telegraphic communication was least adequate, the sea was clearly the natural field for the development of wireless telegraphy." Marconi's aim therefore was to provide wireless telegraphic communication for ships at sea. Preece, too, sympathised with this, and in June announced to an audience at the Royal Institution that enough had been done to prove the value of Marconi's system and to show that for shipping and lighthouse purposes it would be a "great and valuable acquisition".

On July 2nd, the full patent for Marconi's system of wireless telegraphy was granted and in the same month he returned to Italy and gave several successful demonstrations of his wireless telegraphy apparatus to the Italian Government and to the Navy. While he was away, the Wireless Telegraph & Signal Company, Limited was formed on July 20th. Earlier in April, H. Jameson Davis had begun to make behind the scenes moves to persuade Marconi that instead of working towards a contract with the British Post Office, a private company should be set up using capital from the Jameson and Davis families to develop the commercial possibilities of Marconi's wireless telegraphy system and to work towards establishing regular wireless telegraphic services both nationally and internationally.

As soon as this proposal had been put to him, Marconi had quite properly confided in Preece who had acted immediately in a belated attempt at securing the rights to Marconi's system on behalf of the British Government. However, while Preece's recommendation of a £10,000 offer was still under discussion by the Treasury, the Wireless Telegraph & Signal Company was incorporated. Its offices were at 28 Mark Lane, in the City of London and H. Jameson Davis, representing the interests of the family, became its first Managing Director. Marconi transferred all except the Italian rights to the new company, and in exchange received £15,000 plus £60,000 in paid-up shares and a three-year contract worth £1,500 employing him as an engineer. The remaining £40,000 in ordinary shares was subscribed mostly by the Jameson and Davis families.

Since it had been Preece who had freely offered Marconi Post Office facilities and staff, and had given him every support and encouragement during his first 12 months in this country, a feeling of resentment over the fact that they had not acquired the rights to his system lingered between the Post Office and the Wireless Telegraph & Signal Company: Preece had been so convinced of the commercial possibilities of Marconi's system, that he had already lent Marconi one of his most trusted assistants (George Kemp), but even following the setting up of the new company, Kemp and Marconi continued to work closely together until Kemp's death in 1933.

Marconi's new financial independence from the British Post Office came at just the right moment, for on August 6th, Preece was obliged to write to Marconi and inform him that the Post Office was no longer able to support his experiments out of public funds. However, although they had been outmanoeuvred by the Wireless Telegraph & Signal Company, the Post Office's discontent was not directed personally at Marconi, who for a time continued to work with them. Having returned to England, Marconi conducted further experiments on Salisbury Plain during September and October, and using a high single wire aerial supported in turn by a balloon and a kite, he was able to transmit messages to a receiving station taken by a Post Office official to Bath, 34 miles away.

On November 1st 1897, the Wireless Telegraph & Signal Company set up their first British wireless telegraphy transmitting station in the grounds of the Royal Needles Hotel, Alum Bay, Isle of Wight and experiments were conducted between here and a chartered wireless-equipped steam tug cruising in the neighbourhood of Bournemouth, Boscombe, Poole Bay and Swanage. Readable signals were received at a distance of as much as 16 miles in all weathers, and were recorded on a Morse inker: Marconi expressing delight, in a letter to Preece dated December 26th 1897, that he was "able to prove repeatedly beyond a doubt that the thickest fog does not in the slightest way diminish the distance to which signals can be transmitted".

1898

During 1898, interest in Marconi's wireless system was greater than ever, and requests for demonstrations came from every quarter. In May, a short-distance experiment was set up at the request of Members of Parliament and this was carried out across the Thames between the House of Commons and St. Thomas' Hospital on the opposite bank.

On June 3rd, the first official paid wireless telegram was sent by Lord Kelvin who had come to view the Marconi transmitting station on the Isle of Wight. The telegram was transmitted by wireless telegraphy to a newly erected wireless station at Madeira House, Bournemouth, some 15 miles away. From here the message was then sent by conventional wired postal telegraph to the Physical Laboratory at Glasgow University. Lord Kelvin had insisted on paying a one shilling royalty as he wished to show his appreciation of the system and to illustrate its commercial possibilities. (Telegrams sent by wireless were subsequently called 'Marconigrams', and were

known by this term until well into the 1920s). Towards the end of the year, the wireless station at Bournemouth was removed to the Haven Hotel, Poole Harbour where it was maintained as an experimental station until 1926.

In July 1898, the Company received a request from the *Dublin Daily Express* to report the Kingstown Regatta held in Dublin Bay. A shore receiving station was erected in the grounds of the Harbour Master's house in Kingstown and a steamer, the *Flying Huntress*, was chartered and equipped with a spark transmitter. While the regatta was in progress, reports in Morse Code were transmitted from the steamer and the messages were received at the Harbour Master's house. From here they were telephoned to Dublin 6 miles away and were published in the editions of the evening newspaper.

Having been informed by some of her Cabinet Ministers of the House of Commons demonstration, Queen Victoria now showed great interest in Marconi's wireless system. At her request, a station was erected at Ladywood Cottage in the grounds of Osborne House, near Cowes on the Isle of Wight (where she had arrived for Cowes week) so that she might communicate with her son, the Prince of Wales, who was on board his wireless-equipped yacht, *Osborne*. During the sixteen days that the system was in use, over 500 messages were passed between the Queen and the Prince, and other members of the Royal family, who were all reported as being "exceedingly pleased with the demonstration". The *Osborne* also made contact with the Royal Needles Hotel station, which was some 8 miles away at the time.

In August, at the request of Lloyd's, the maritime insurance and intelligence association, an experimental wireless station was erected at Rathlin Island lighthouse and another on the opposite mainland at Ballycastle, Co. Antrim, so that Lloyd's could report shipping in that area. A few years later in September 1901, when wireless telegraphy (mostly using Marconi's system) was beginning to be widely used for maritime communication, Lloyd's awarded a large contract for the permanent installation of Marconi's wireless apparatus at their signalling stations around the coast of Britain and abroad, to report passing ships and to facilitate commercial telegraphic traffic to and from ships (see 1901). Lloyd's had until then conducted ship to shore signalling by means of a series of flags hoisted according to international code: a primitive method that had been in use for centuries.

THE FIRST 'WIRELESS AMATEURS'

In the late autumn of 1898, a young 17-year-old wireless enthusiast named Claude Willcox set up his own experimental wireless station in the garden of his parents home in Warminster (fig. 10). In doing so, Willcox became one of the very first 'wireless amateurs' and was one of a small section of the British public who pursued scientific hobbies during their leisure hours and who were now keenly following the achievements of Marconi and other wireless pioneers like Oliver Lodge, whose activities were regularly reported in the Press. In the summer, it had been announced that Lodge had invented a form of telephonic relay which was designed to operate a telephone earpiece. Weak signals were fed through the relay's coil which was caused to move in a magnet's field and thereby amplify the signal. This actually anticipated the moving-coil loud-speaker eventually developed in the early 1920s.

Detailed accounts of scientific experiments often appeared in such publications as *The Electrical Review, The English Mechanic & World of Science* and *The Times* and the excitement generated by reading about these experiments prompted many ordinary people to take up wireless as a hobby and to try and repeat some of the experiments in their workshops at home. Willcox was one of the few who were lucky enough to be able to afford commercially manufactured scientific apparatus but for most, such equipment was a luxury and they had to be content with constructing apparatus from improvised 'bits and pieces'.

fig. 10 . Claude Willcox, pictured here with his transmitter in 1899, was one of Britain's first 'wireless amateurs' and set up an experimental spark transmitting station in 1898 at the home of his parents in Warminster, Wiltshire. Over the years, his station grew to impressive proportions, and in 1913 was featured on the cover of Gamage's first *Directory of Experimental Wireless Stations* (fig. 21). By then, he had become Director of the Warminster Motor Company, which later during the First World War manufactured wireless apparatus for the Army under the name of the British Telegraph Instrument Company. By the end of 1922, Willcox had progressed to telephony, and operated his own amateur broadcasting station, call-sign 2FL, transmitting talks and musical items in the late evening as soon as the B.B.C. had closed down for the night.

1899

During a gale in January, the East Goodwin lightship was badly damaged by heavy seas. By chance only a few weeks before, both she and the South Foreland lighthouse near the port of Dover some 12 miles away had been equipped with experimental Marconi wireless apparatus by arrangement with Trinity House, and as a result, a report about the damage was able to be quickly sent. On March 3rd, during the early hours of the morning, the lightship was again in difficulties when in dense fog she was rammed by the London steamship *R.F. Matthews*. By being able to transmit an immediate distress call to the receiving station at the South Foreland lighthouse, the first sea rescue through wireless took place and all hands were promptly saved. The incident made world-wide news and gave Marconi's system a great boost.

On March 27th, the English Channel was for the first time spanned by wireless telegraphy when communication was maintained between the British Association meeting at Dover Town Hall via a land line to the South Foreland wireless station, and the French Association meeting at Boulogne via a land line to a wireless station at Wimereux. At this time, Marconi was directing his attention towards increasing the range of communication and the spanning of the Channel by wireless aroused even more Press attention than the East Goodwin rescue, and filled newspaper columns with descriptions, comments and wild prophecies. By increasing the height of the aerial it was possible to send messages over far greater distances, but since there was a practical limitation to the height of masts on both land and sea, improving sensitivity of receivers was another avenue receiving attention.

In July, Marconi's system of wireless telegraphy was used for the first time by the British Navy when H.M.S. *Alexandria*, *Europa* and *Juno* were fitted with apparatus during manoeuvres. The Admiralty were so impressed with the experiment that

a year later, in July 1900, they awarded a contract to Marconi for equipping 26 Navy ships and 6 land stations and their maintenance for a period of 14 years (the life of Marconi's British Patents).

In October, the War Office officially adopted Marconi equipment, and on November 2nd, following the outbreak of the Boer War, five portable stations that were originally supplied by Marconi for installation on board ship, were sent out to the field in South Africa to form the first Wireless Telegraphy Section, R.E. Following their use at the reliefs of Kimberley and Ladysmith in 1900, they were subsequently transferred to the Navy.

On November 15th, the steamer *St. Paul*, bound for England from America, established communication with the Royal Needles Hotel station when over 60 miles away. On board the ship was Marconi, who had been in America superintending wireless coverage of the International Yacht Race for the *New York Herald*, and who on the homeward journey had installed his apparatus on the *St. Paul*. Several Marconigrams were received from the ship and these were telephoned to the Totland Bay Post Office for despatch by wire to various parts of Britain. Messages were then transmitted from the Royal Needles Hotel to the *St. Paul* giving news of the Boer War in South Africa and news of the sinking of the U.S. cruiser *Charleston*. These reports were assembled and printed on board in a souvenir issue newspaper called *The Transatlantic Times*, which was sold direct to passengers while they were still at sea.

During 1899, premises were acquired for the Wireless Telegraph & Signal Company in Hall Street, Chelmsford, specifically for the manufacture of Marconi's wireless apparatus. Until then, the few pieces of transmitting and receiving equipment that had been ordered had been made up as and when required using various modified apparatus bought from well-established science laboratory suppliers. These were supplemented by parts made by Marconi, Kemp and their assistants but with the forseen rapid expansion of wireless communication, it was decided to set up a large-scale wireless factory to cope with the quantity production of standardized equipment. In September, a transmitting station was installed at the Hall Street works, while at Dovercourt near Harwich a station was erected for communicating with ships at sea, bringing the total number of such shore-based installations carried out by the Wireless Telegraph & Signal Company since their first one at the Royal Needles Hotel, to around a dozen.

Developments in wireless continued to take place in other countries. In Germany, Ferdinand Braun was granted a patent for his system of wireless telegraphy which was manufactured by Siemens and Halske. During experiments, Braun successfully established communication between his spark transmitter set up on the North German coast at Cuxhaven and his receiver comprising the standard type of coherer, relay and Morse inker arrangement on the island of Heligoland nearly 40 miles away.

In Italy, the mercury-iron 'Italian Navy' coherer was first developed for wireless reception (fig. 11). It comprised a glass tube with an iron plug at one end and a carbon plug at the other, bridged by a globule of mercury. Normally a coherer had a 'latching' action in which once it had been made conductive by an incoming signal, it would remain in that condition until re-set (de-cohered) by a mechanical shock. With this coherer, the resistance of headphones in series with it was sufficient to make it 'self-restoring', with current only being conducted so long as the signal was present. Marconi was to use one of these coherers in Newfoundland when he received the first transatlantic signals from Cornwall in 1901.

In America, Marconi's Wireless Telegraph Company of America was incorporated on November 22nd for the purpose of exploiting Marconi patents in the United States. Other developments were also taking place in that country and one of the most important of these was the introduction of the Continuous Wave High Frequency Alternator by Nikola Tesla. Continuous waves (C.W.) were a sequence of electro-magnetic waves of uniform amplitude produced without interruption or variation. From the earliest days of wireless, the need for a source of continuous oscillations was recognised by several pioneer wireless experimenters, for the spark method of oscillation sent out damped waves in bursts with breaks during each burst where no waves were being sent out and this had serious limitations. Continuous waves had the following advantages over spark oscillations.

(1) they were well adapted to high speed transmission by automatic machinery, and C.W. transmitters were capable of very much greater ranges,

(2) sharper tuning was possible. Spark oscillations spread out their energy over a wide band of frequencies whereas a C.W. transmitter sent out a very narrow band of frequencies lending itself to sharp tuning. A well designed transmitter would cause minimum interference to other operators using the same waveband,

(3) they were to be absolutely essential for the quality transmission of wireless telephony when it developed later.

Tesla's alternator produced a frequency of 30,000 cycles per second and although at this stage of development it was only capable of sending C.W. over a distance of about 20 miles, it did mark the beginning of the successful development of C.W. transmission which ultimately led to the age of wireless telephony and broadcasting.

fig. 11 . 'Italian Navy' Coherer. c.1899. A 'self-restoring' mercury-iron coherer, originally devised by P. Castelli, a signalman in the Italian Navy. The illustration shows the original one used by Marconi during his transatlantic wireless telegraphy tests of 1901. Ebonite base, brass fittings, glass tube containing an iron plug and a carbon plug bridged by a globule of mercury. Base, 1¼ in. x 3¼ in. 2 in.

1900

On April 25th, the Marconi International Marine Communication Company, Limited, was formed to develop the Marconi system for ship to ship, and ship to shore two-way wireless telegraphy communication, not only in this country but also throughout the world. Wireless installations built in the future by this company were to remain Marconi property and the equipment was to be operated by Marconi personnel. Ship owners requiring Marconi's wireless telegraphy facilities would therefore lease a system that used standardized apparatus and operating methods.

To train personnel, the world's first wireless technical school was set up during the following year at Frinton-on-Sea, Essex to supplement students' engineering knowledge with the theory and working principles of Marconi's system. Except in the case of a distress call, Marconi operators were under strict instructions not to accept any messages from wireless stations not equipped with Marconi apparatus, and this essentially created a private, closed system.

In 1900, the parent Wireless Telegraph & Signal Company was re-named Marconi's Wireless Telegraph Company, Limited, and in October, work began on the erection of a new high-power transmitting station at Poldhu in Cornwall for long-distance communication with ships at sea. The station at first used a circular 210 feet high aerial supported by twenty masts, but this was later wrecked by a severe gale in September 1901. It was hurriedly replaced by a fan-shaped aerial array, supported by two masts, and this in turn was replaced in 1903 by an aerial supported by four timber towers.

Since Oliver Lodge had filed his tuning patent in 1897, Marconi had himself been experimenting with making Lodge's method more practical. On April 26th, Marconi filed his own patent (No.7777) for an improved method of tuning which made receivers much more sensitive and much more selective than ever before. The 'four sevens' patent became one of the most famous in wireless history for with it, Marconi was able to bring a series of successful suits against most of his early rivals and further reinforce his dominant patent position in the world of commercial wireless communication. Among the improvements detailed in the patent specification was the addition of what we recognise as a tuning dial, and his new tuning circuit not only enabled messages to be received at far greater distances, but also enabled a number of wireless transmissions to be carried on without interference being caused between them. Marconi paid no royalties to Oliver Lodge for manufacturing equipment which, although based upon the four sevens patent, ultimately derived from Lodge's 1897 patent for syntonized telegraphy and much bitterness grew up between the two men which was not resolved until 1911 (see 1911).

Marconi applied for patents on practically everything he did, and by the mid-1900s his companies had won world-wide prestige and were in a dominant patent position with the Marconi name on three fundamental wireless patents: on improved types of vertical aerials, on the Magnetic Detector and on methods of selective tuning.

In America, Reginald A. Fessenden, a Canadian-born Professor of Electrical Engineering working for the U.S. Weather Bureau, made his first experimental attempts at transmitting wireless telephony (his own voice) by a spark transmitter over a distance of 1 mile on Cobb Island. Although the experiments were crude and scarcely capable of development, Fessenden persevered with the basic idea and within a few years, this time using a high frequency alternator, he was able to transmit wireless telephony over a distance of several miles (see 1906).

In England, while experimenting with an electric arc lamp at the Central Technical College on London, the scientist W. Duddell found that it could be made to produce a steady musical note by connecting its two carbons to a condenser and a coil of wire. He went on to discover that by altering the size of the condenser and the coil, the note of his 'singing arc' could also be altered. This musical note was caused by an oscillation set up in the circuit containing the arc, condenser and coil, but the frequency he produced was far too low to be of practical use in wireless transmission, and it was left to Valdemar Poulsen a few years later to discover a way of raising the frequency, so that it could be used for C.W. transmission (see 1903).

1901

During 1901, Marconi coastal transmitting stations each equipped with Marconi apparatus throughout, were opened at Caistor, Crookhaven, Holyhead, Lizard, Malin Head, Niton,

North Foreland, Port Stewart and Rosslare for communication with ships at sea. On May 21st, the first permanent installation of wireless telegraphy equipment in a British ocean-going merchant vessel was made on board the S.S. *Lake Champlain* of the Beaver Line on the day she sailed out of Liverpool for Halifax, Canada with about 1,200 people on board. Wireless communication was established with the Marconi coastal transmitting station at Holyhead and later with Rosslare, arousing tremendous interest among the passengers and crew on board who crowded around the tiny wireless cabin from morning to night.

In September, Lloyd's signed a contract with Marconi's for the erection of permanent wireless installations around the coast of Britain and abroad. At that time, Lloyd's had a huge network of over one thousand agents in all the major seaports of the world and a great many of the minor ones whose duties were to report by cable shipping movements and arrivals. The use of wireless therefore would not only vastly improve efficiency, but would also enable direct communication with ships at sea. It was one of the conditions of the contract that Marconi equipment was to be used exclusively and that communication was not to be made with ship and shore stations using systems made by other manufacturers except in the case of a distress call. These restrictions were applied to all installations of Marconi apparatus and even though other systems were being developed by other competitors, the Marconi companies were to have a virtual monopoly in ship to ship and ship to shore traffic for several years (see 1908).

During 1901, the Lodge-Muirhead Syndicate was formed as a limited liability company to manufacture and sell wireless apparatus based on Oliver Lodge's syntonic and other wireless telegraphy patents. Since 1894, when he gave the world's first public demonstration of wireless transmission and reception, Lodge had been at work perfecting his system. At the 1894 demonstration, Lodge had met Dr. Alexander Muirhead who with his brother Henry was a partner in a well-known firm of telegraph instrument manufacturers with a factory at Elmer's End in Kent. It was largely through Alexander Muirhead's involvement that Lodge's apparatus developed into a commercial system, but unlike that of Marconi's, it never went into full-scale operation and was essentially a side-line for both parties. Lodge's system was designed for low-power operation over relatively short distances. The Syndicate provided equipment but not trained operators. Instead, printed instructions were included so that purchasers could install and operate the equipment themselves. There was no mass-production, for while Marconi installations ran into many hundreds during the Edwardian period, those by Lodge-Muirhead amounted to less than a dozen over a period of some ten years, with most of these being Government owned stations in the Far East, Burma, Africa, and the West Indies. In this country, only three installations were brought into service: at Elmer's End and Downe in Kent (experimental stations owned by the Syndicate), and at Heysham Harbour for communication between steamers owned by the Midland Railway plying between Heysham Harbour and the Isle of Man. The Syndicate was finally dissolved in 1911 (see 1911).

On September 28th 1901, R.A. Fessenden filed a patent in America for his 'heterodyne' principle of circuit design. Ahead of its time and remaining unexploited for several years, Fessenden's heterodyne circuit eventually gave rise to E.H. Armstrong's 'supersonic heterodyne' principle which was patented in 1918 and ultimately became the standard approach to receiver design throughout the world (see 1924).

In December 1901, a great surge of public interest was created by the news that while conducting experiments at the old Military Barracks, Signal Hill, St. John's, Newfoundland, Marconi had received the first wireless signals ever to be transmitted across the Atlantic Ocean. They comprised a series of S's (... ... ...) and were sent by Dr. Ambrose Fleming from the new Marconi station at Poldhu, Cornwall on receipt of a message by sub-marine cable to begin transmitting. They were heard by Marconi and his assistant Kemp about twenty-five times through a telephone earpiece (fig. 12) in conjunction with an 'Italian Navy' coherer, and were picked up by a flying aerial wire suspended 400 feet in the air from a kite. It had been decided not to use the usual recording method of a relay and a Morse inker (which would have made a permanent record of the incoming signals on paper tape) since the human ear was far more sensitive, and this led to more than a few sceptical comments. The results of the transatlantic experiments were not totally accepted by all those within the scientific community or the technical Press, some believing that they were merely due to atmospherics or to the presence of a Cunard ship fitted with Marconi apparatus and sailing within range of St. John's at the time. However, the tremendous distance involved (over 2,000 miles) was far greater than anything so far achieved and the excitement over this great event fired the imagination of many people throughout the world. The cable companies on the other hand were understandably worried that this newcomer to the world of overseas communication might soon become a serious rival to their long established monopoly and were beginning now to show some signs of nervousness and apprehension.

fig. 12 . Telephone earpiece made by Collier-Marr Telephone & Electrical Manufacturing Co. Ltd., Manchester. 1901. It uses two diaphragms located on either side of a central ebonite-cased bobbin and placed between the two poles of a horse-shoe magnet. The one illustrated is the actual earpiece used by Marconi in conjunction with the 'Italian Navy' coherer (fig. 11) to hear the famous transatlantic wireless telegraphy tests of December 12th 1901. To improve sensitivity, the magnet has an extra winding. Overall size, 6 in. x 2 in. x 2 in.

1902

One of the most important advances in the efficiency of shipboard wireless reception took place in 1902 when Marconi patented his 'Magnetic Detector' (fig. 13), which was widely used as standard receiving equipment on board English and most European ships from 1903 to 1912: the first being installed in the Italian cruiser *Carlo Alberto*. The Magnetic Detector was found to be much more sensitive than any of the coherer type and because of its great reliability was generally preferred by wireless operators who affectionately referred to it as "Maggie". The introduction of the Magnetic Detector marked the end of the coherer era and made possible the reception of wireless messages at much greater speeds although the one disadvantage was that signals could only be heard as sounds in a telephone earpiece and could not be recorded on paper tape.

In the detector, an endless band of soft iron wire was passed around two pulleys which were driven by a clockwork motor at about 5 inches per second. The lower straight portion of the band passed through a coil of wire, one end of which was connected to the aerial and the other end connected to the earth.

Outside this coil was a second coil, the ends of which were connected to a telephone earpiece, and immediately above the two coils were two horseshoe magnets. As a portion of the soft iron wire passed under the magnets that portion became temporarily magnetised by induction and as the same portion passed away from the magnets, it lost its magnetism. When transmitted waves reached the aerial a tiny current passed through the first coil which caused the rate at which the soft iron wire lost its magnetism to alter slightly, and this in turn caused a small current to flow through the second, outer coil, and a consequent sound was heard in the earpiece.

In October, tests were carried out between Poldhu and a tuned wireless receiving station on board the American liner *Philadelphia*, en route from Southampton to New York. With the receiving aerial fixed to the main mast, readable messages were received up to a distance of 1551 miles and were recorded on paper tape by an ordinary Morse inker, and test letters were received as far as 2009 miles amply proving to all the long distance over which Poldhu was capable of transmitting.

Having been granted a subsidy of £16,000 by the Canadian Government to support his experiments, Marconi formed the Marconi Wireless Telegraph Company of Canada, Limited and commenced the construction of a long-distance high-power station at Glace Bay in Nova Scotia. In December 1902, an experimental transatlantic service began when messages were exchanged for the first time between here and Poldhu in Cornwall.

fig. 13 . 'Magnetic Detector', by Marconi's Wireless Telegraph Co.Ltd., Hall Street, Chelmsford. 1902. Solid teak case, ebonite wire reels, brass fittings and clockwork motor to drive an iron wire loop (label says "Rewind every half-hour"). 9½ in. x 19 in. x 8 in.

1903

On August 22nd, the Poldhu station began transmitting a regular Morse news service to shipping on a fixed wavelength of 2,800 metres and as experiments continued, it became possible in October to supply the Cunard steamship *Lucania* with news direct from shore during her entire crossing from New York to Liverpool. The number of shore-based wireless stations which had been erected or were in the course of erection by Marconi's and its associated companies in Britain and in countries abroad now exceeded fifty, and the Marconi system was now in regular use on board over forty merchant ships owned by ten major shipping lines. At Seaforth Sands near Liverpool, the first Marconi Service Depot was established to cope with the repair and maintenance of the Company's equipment, and in the same building a technical school room was set up to train service personnel.

A new development now took place in high frequency C.W. generation when, using the singing arc developed by Duddell in 1900 (see 1900), the Dane, Valdemar Poulsen succeeded in raising the arc's frequency so that it could be of practical use in wireless transmission. Poulson did this by placing the flame of the arc in a strong magnetic field induced by an electric

current and burning the arc in hydrogen or coal gas. During the coming years, it was successfully developed as a reliable C.W. generator and was used in many high-power, long-distance wireless stations as well as in a smaller portable form by wireless amateurs. From 1906, the Poulsen Wireless Telegraphy System employed the Pedersen 'Tikker', which was a C.W. detector specially designed by Professor Pedersen for use with the arc.

1904

Realising the need for an internationally recognised distress signal, Marconi's issued a general order that from February 1st 1904, the call to be given by ships in distress, or in any way requiring assistance, was to be "C.Q.D.", made up of the old telegraphic general call "C.Q." with the additional letter 'D' for distress.

fig. 14 . 'Fleming Diode'. c.1904. An experimental 'diode', used as a detector and rectifier of wireless signals. Turned boxwood socket, brass terminals. 8¾ in. high x 2¼ in. diameter.

On August 15th, the *Wireless Telegraphy Act, 1904* became law giving the Post Master General responsibility for administering wireless telegraphy in Britain and Ireland. The establishment of any wireless telegraphy station for transmitting or receiving on land or on board any British ship was only permitted under a special licence granted by the Post Office and failure to comply with this Act could mean a term of imprisonment of up to twelve months with hard labour. Up to this time the number of wireless telegraphy stations around the British Isles (including transmitting and receiving stations run by amateur experimenters) had been growing steadily and the Government saw that legislation was needed in order to secure adequate control of all such installations. The Act was the first piece of legislation of its kind in history, and it remained in force until July 31st 1906, after which date it was extended on a year-to-year basis under the *Expiring Laws Continuance Act until replaced by the Wireless Telegraphy Act, 1924.* Although the 1904 Act made no mention of wireless *telephony* or broadcasting (neither of which at the time were even remotely developed in Britain), the powers of the Post Office to control these were later seen as an extension of the Act. (This can be traced back to a High Court judgement in the early 1880s which established that a telephone was a 'telegraph' within the meaning of the Telegraph Acts of 1863, 1868 and 1869 in which the Post Master General was given a virtual monopoly to operate all forms of telegraphic communication).

On November 16th 1904, Dr. John Ambrose Fleming, Scientific Adviser to Marconi's, filed a patent for his 'diode valve' which was the first true rectifier used for the detection of electro-magnetic waves (fig. 14). In the following year, Fleming sent five of his prototype diodes to Marconi at Poldhu for a service trial, and they were so successful that Marconi's designed and later manufactured a receiver specially for the valves which by then had been put into commercial production by the Edison Swan Electric Company (see 1910).

1905

From January 1st, Marconigrams could be accepted from members of the public at any British Post Office for transmission to ships via the Marconi coastal stations. Since Lloyd's had equipped their coastal signalling stations with wireless, those who wished to receive progress reports about the passage of any vessel merely had to contact the Secretary of Lloyd's in London.

By now, the British Navy had some 80 ships equipped with Marconi's wireless telegraphy system and these were capable of receiving transmissions from the Poldhu station as far away as their bases in Gibraltar, the Mediterranean and the Atlantic. Transmissions could also be picked up from the new high-power station at Norddeich in Germany, which in 1905 began regular wireless telegraphy transmissions and sent out a programme of news and weather reports in Morse Code.

With regard to amateurs, provision was now made for the issuing of experimental wireless licences and the Post Master General, Lord Stanley, displayed a very sympathetic attitude and gave an undertaking that no request for a licence would be refused unless the refusal had been personally approved by him. And so, applications began to be received by the Post Office, and during the year, the first official printed licences were issued. On the application form, the applicant merely had to enter details of his wireless qualifications and experience (if indeed he had any), and clearly state "the particulars of the nature and objects of the experiments which it is desired to conduct". If the applicant satisfied the Post Master General that he was a bona-fide experimenter, then the licence would be granted with "no rent or royalty charged".

While working at the Glace Bay station in Canada, Marconi had devised a horizontal inverted-L form of aerial, which was found to have marked directional properties and which was a great improvement on other types of aerial used in long-distance long-wave wireless telegraphy. He patented his idea, which was an early step in the development of the Beam System of transmission (see 1927), and, using this new type of aerial, it was decided to build a new high-power station at Derrygimla, Clifden on the West coast of Ireland to take over the transatlantic service from Poldhu (see 1907).

1906

From 1906, 'crystal detectors' using crystalline minerals began to be developed for wireless reception and the first experimental crystal receivers were produced. Some thirty-three years after he had first reported the discovery of crystal rectification during his experiments in Germany from 1873 to 1874, Professor Braun patented a psilomelan (hydrated oxide of manganese) crystal detector on February 18th 1906. In England a few days later,

on February 21st, Dr. L.W. Austin patented his tellurium/silicon detector and in America in March, General H. Dunwoody of the United States Signal Corps patented a carborundum/steel detector for receiving spark transmissions. Carborundum was not a 'natural' crystal but was a compound of carbon and silicon first discovered accidentally in 1891 by an American chemist while attempting to make artificial diamonds. Dunwoody's detector used a contact comprising a disc of polished steel, and it proved to be so reliable that in America especially it was soon being widely and successfully used in many ships' wireless installations. (On this side of the Atlantic for a few more years at least, Marconi's Magnetic Detector continued to be unrivalled in maritime use, although crystal detectors were being looked at with growing interest and were soon adopted by the Military). To those wireless operators on board ship who worked with carborundum detectors, a good sensitive piece of this crystal was considered a most treasured possession and it became common practice that whenever an operator changed ships, the crystal went with him.

By June 6th 1906, sixty-eight amateur experimental licences had been granted and a list giving the details of the licence holders was prepared by the Post Master General and published on June 13th. This was the first such list ever compiled and it contained the names of several eminent men including Dr. John Ambrose Fleming, who being Scientific Adviser to Marconi's and having to his credit the world's first valve patent, could hardly be described as an "amateur experimenter".

The world's first successful experimental broadcast of wireless telephony took place in America in December between stations at Brant Rock and Plymouth, Massachusetts, a distance of about 11 miles. Using a high frequency alternator made by General Electric, R.A. Fessenden transmitted a programme in which he played the fiddle, sang Christmas carols and played Handel's Largo on the phonograph. Although the signals were very weak they travelled further than expected, and they were heard by several startled ships' wireless operators out in the North Atlantic who of course until then had heard nothing but Morse Code through their telephone earpieces.

1907

On January 29th, a second important development in valve technology took place when Lee de Forest filed a patent for his three electrode 'Audion triode' (fig. 15). It was a 'soft' (low vacuum) valve which was not only capable of rectification and detection, but also of amplification, although this third property was not fully exploited for a few years.

A new development also took place with crystal detectors. During the year in America, the 'Perikon detector' first appeared: the term being derived from PERfect pICK and CONtact. It was patented by Greenleaf Whittier Pickard and originally applied to a rectifying contact between a crystal of synthetic fused zincite and a brass point. Later, Pickard applied the name to designate a contact between natural zinc and copper pyrites and by the 1920s, 'perikon' generally meant a crystal detector comprising any two compatible crystals.

The successful use of crystal detectors in wireless reception caused a good deal of research work to be done in Edwardian England, and the quest for new rectifying combinations of crystals and contacts proceeded rapidly. Molybdenite, various pyrites, anatase, galena, hessite, cassiterite, bornite and a host of others were experimented with by scientists such as Professor Pierce, Dr. Eccles, P.R. Coursey and L.W. Austin, and many were found to be 'radio-sensitive'.

But in later years, the gradual development of the thermionic valve as a detector, rectifier and amplifier, with its ever increasing role during World War One in a 'hard' (high

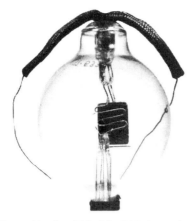

fig. 15 . De Forest 'Audion Triode'. 1907. Screw base, glass bulb. 2 in. diameter.

vacuum) form, caused a waning of the experimental interest which until then had been shown in the crystal. Although carborundum/steel and perikon detectors played an important part in Military wireless reception during the war, it was not until the advent of official broadcasting from the B.B.C. in the early 1920s that a widespread revival of interest in the crystal occurred: an interest which achieved a summit of popularity then with the mass introduction of the domestic 'crystal set' which gave tens of thousands of ordinary people their first taste of 'listening-in' (see 1922).

A new and important piece of receiving equipment was introduced by Marconi's during 1907. Patented by Charles S. Franklin, the 'Multiple Tuner' (fig. 16) was capable of tuning over the wavebands 80/150, 150/1,600, 1,600/2,000 and 2,000/2,600 metres. It was extensively used as part of the wireless receiving equipment on board ships, normally in conjunction with the Marconi Magnetic Detector. In the 'stand-by' position, operated by a switch on top of the panel, the detector was connected directly to the aerial circuit which enabled a watch to be kept over a very wide range of wavelengths.

fig. 16 . 'Multiple Tuner', by Marconi's Wireless Telegraph Co. Ltd., Hall Street, Chelmsford. 1907. Patented by C.S. Franklin. The receiver has three circuits (aerial, intermediate and detector), each of which had to be tuned. Rough tuning of the circuits was obtained simultaneously by a control which linked the three stud switches in the front, and then finer individual adjustments could be made by means of the variable condensers mounted on top of the case. Polished ebonite, brass fittings, mahogany base. 5¼ in. x 19 in. x 8 in.

Following on from Fessenden's pioneering success with wireless telephony the previous year, an enthusiastic British amateur called H. Anthony Hankey used a 250 watt portable Poulsen arc transmitter during the summer of 1907 to broadcast wireless telephony for the benefit of the War Office. His transmitter was powered by a dynamo connected to a 4-cylinder petrol engine, and was set up at Aldershot with General French and his staff listening-in on a crystal receiver in the neighbourhood of Midhurst. Hankey's programme consisted

of a number of songs and monologues which he personally conducted, and in a letter published in *Wireless World* on May 11th 1932, Hankey said that he believed that this was the first occasion that pure wireless telephony had been used in Britain.

On October 17th, the new high-power long-wave station at Clifden was opened for Morse Code communication with the Glace Bay station in Nova Scotia. Clifden used the improved inverted-L directional aerial, and the public could now for the first time send Marconigrams from Britain to Canada. The Clifden station was in operation until, during the Irish Civil War, on the night of Tuesday July 25th 1922, it was attacked by anti-Treaty Irregulars who caused irrepairable damage to the equipment.

1908

In 1908, the Lloyd's contract of 1901 became null and void when the *International Convention on Wireless Communication at Sea*, signed in 1907, became effective. The Convention was held largely at the insistence of the United States and Germany, both of whom had by then developed their own efficient wireless communication systems. In the United States, the United Wireless Company, using a system based on De Forest patents, operated a network of stations handling marine traffic on the Atlantic and Pacific coasts, and in Germany, the Telefunken Company, using Slaby-Arco-Braun patents, were establishing a European maritime network. Having suffered from what they saw as unfair competition from Marconi's, both these countries had called for unrestricted interchange of communication between all wireless stations regardless of the type of system installed.

During 1908, a new 5 kW spark transmitting station was completed for the British Admiralty at Horsea near Portsmouth, with the result that it now had the power to control the movement of its fleet by wireless telegraphy over a very large area of the seas. The signals were now picked up by 'cage' aerials introduced and generally adopted by the British Navy that year.

"S.O.S" was officially adopted as the international distress call, replacing "C.Q.D", although the majority of wireless operators on board British ships clung on to the old distress call until as late as 1912. (Wireless operator Phillips used both "C.Q.D." and "S.O.S." on the sinking Titanic. See 1912).

In Italy, Professor Q. Majorana transmitted speech from Rome to Sardinia and Sicily using a C.W. arc oscillator and his 'liquid microphone'. One difficulty experienced in early wireless telephony experiments was due to large currents which had to be handled by the microphones and this often caused them to overheat. Some circuits employed two microphones in which if the one in operation began to get too hot, the other cold one could be switched into the circuit. But in a few years (see 1913), the introduction of the valve oscillator brought about vast improvements since its frequency could be as high as 1,000,000 cycles per second and this could then be modulated by the output of a microphone placed in a low current part of the circuit so that it would not get hot.

1909

The controlling power of the Admiralty was further reinforced when a new 100 kW transmitting station was built at Cleethorpes, while the power of the Horsea station was increased to the same level during the year.

Experiments in wireless telephony continued. In March, a Poulsen arc transmitter at Lyngby put out an experimental wireless telephony transmission of phonograph records and speech in English, Dutch, French and German on 1,000 metres. Later, in June, the Cullercoates station in Newcastle conducted wireless telephony test transmissions with Lyngby, although according to Hankey who listened-in on a crystal receiver fitted with a perikon detector, "a bad cough appeared to be troubling the operator!"

On September 29th, Marconi's Wireless Telegraph Company entered into an agreement with the Post Office which provided for the transfer to the Post Office of all the Marconi coastal stations in Britain. The Postmaster General was granted a licence to use the Company's patents and the Company received a payment of £15,000. In December, Marconi delivered a lecture at the Royal Academy of Science in Stockholm, Sweden, and here, jointly with Professor Braun, he was awarded the Nobel Prize for Physics in recognition of his outstanding work in wireless communication.

1910

One of the most spectacular cases of the use of wireless as a means of communication at sea was demonstrated with the arrest of the notorious 'Doctor' Crippen and his mistress Miss Le Neve on board the Canadian Pacific liner *Montrose*. Having recognised the pair on his ship, Captain Kendall instructed his wireless operator to contact Scotland Yard via his company's offices in Liverpool, England and from that moment until the arrest, the police and the Press were kept in constant touch with the ship by wireless, with the public eagerly following the story as it unfolded in the newspapers.

Since 1905, the number of amateur experimental wireless licence holders had been gradually increasing, and in May 1910, the Post Master General announced in the House of Commons that in company with official stations, he had now found it desirable to lay down a general rule that all experimental stations "should have a distinctive call-sign and that each station, when signalling, should begin each transmission with the call-sign of the station with which it desires to communicate and end it with its own call-sign". Notification was sent out to all those concerned in the form of a very polite letter stating the licensee's allotted call-sign, and asking the licence holder if he had any objection.

Two other events which had some significance to amateurs also occurred in 1910. In London, A.W. Gamage Ltd. of Holborn, began supplying complete wireless telegraphy outfits (fig. 17) to supplement their range of component parts which had been introduced in 1908 to enable the amateur to make up his own equipment. A.W. Gamage was one of the few concerns catering specifically for the amateur experimenter and all their wireless equipment was made for them by Ward & Goldstone Ltd. of Pendleton, Manchester. A pair of transmitters and receivers bought from Gamages were set up at a church bazaar in Bristol in the summer of 1910 by an amateur named Gilbert Tonkin (call-sign TBX). Helped by a few of his friends, he charged the public sixpence a time for the amusement of sending wireless Morse signals a distance of some 300 feet.

In France, daily wireless telegraphy transmissions of time-signals began from the Eiffel Tower Observatory (call-sign FL) making Paris the "time centre of the world", and enabling clocks and watches to be set very accurately. (On February 5th 1924, the British Broadcasting Company inaugurated the Greenwich 'dot-seconds' time signal system, later known more familiarly as 'the pips', see 1924). There were now two European wireless transmitting stations with which the wireless amateur of the Edwardian period could conduct experimental long-distance reception tests. Although the lower powered Norddeich station was more difficult to receive, it was said that the reception of Norddeich (see 1905) distinguished certain amateurs from the lesser members of the tribe who contented themselves with the comparatively powerful transmission from the Eiffel Tower.

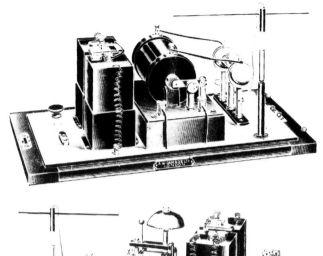

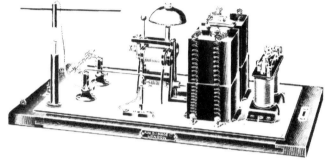

fig. 17 . The 'Atlantic' wireless telegraphy outfit manufactured by Ward & Goldstone Ltd., Pendleton, Manchester and sold by A.W. Gamage Ltd., Holborn, London EC. c.1910. The spark transmitter (top), had a range of about 250 ft. and comprised a condenser, a spark gap, a Morse key, and an 8 ft. extending aerial. The same type of aerial was fitted to the receiver which had a self-tapping coherer connected to a bell relay. Terminals were also provided for connecting a Morse printer and power was obtained from two pairs of dry cell batteries. Each unit was mounted on a mahogany base, into which was set a screw-thread which allowed the units to be conveniently supported on a standard camera tripod. Price £6.0s.0d complete with lockable mahogany covers (not shown). 18 in. x 7 in. (base).

Many amateurs were forced by financial circumstances to make up their wireless apparatus from scrap materials and to improvise with whatever came to hand. A typical amateur receiver of this period consisted of a loose-coupled tuner, and an electrolytic detector, comprising a small glass jar, a platinum spear-point sealed in a glass tube and an adjustable silver bottom plate: these being immersed in a weak solution of sulphuric acid. One owner of such a set up reported that in one spell of 'listening-in' which lasted eight hours, all he heard was one time signal from the FL station in Paris. Obviously a very keen and patient man!

A typical home-constructed transmitter of this period was operated by an amateur in Birmingham and consisted of an old motor car trembler ignition coil, a pair of brass door knobs for the spark gap, a copper helix as the tuning inductance and some old photographic plates and sheets of tin foil making up the condensers. Apparently, it worked quite well. But not all amateur wireless equipment was thrown together out of bits and pieces. Many wireless amateurs were also keen model makers, and much of their early home-made equipment was precision-made too.

At this time, wireless amateurs could read about their subject in magazines such as *The English Mechanic & World of Science*, *Model Engineer*, *Work* and occasionally in the *Boy's Own Paper*, but they had to wait until April 1911 for the first issue of a publication exclusively devoted to wireless: *The Marconigraph*. This was the house magazine of Marconi's Wireless Telegraph Company in Chelmsford, and although it contained a large amount of specialist information possibly only of interest to wireless engineers and operators, it could also be ordered, price 2d, by members of the public through most book sellers and newsagents. (It later became *Wireless World* in April 1913 and began including more items of an experimental and amateur nature and therefore catered more for general interest).

During the year, several experimental wireless telephony transmitters were made by Marconi's to the design of H.J. Round (fig. 18). They employed an arc which was burned in an atmosphere of hydrocarbon vapour, enclosed in a cylindrical arc chamber with a mica observation window set into it. One of the electrodes was kept turning by a clockwork mechanism in order to improve the steadiness of the burning, but although these transmitters were known to have been successfully demonstrated over distances of up to 100 miles, the design was never put into any quantity production.

fig. 18. Wireless Telephony Arc Transmitter and Receiver, by Marconi's Wireless Telegraph Co. Ltd., Hall Street, Chelmsford. 1910. (des: Capt. H.J. Round). Mahogany case, wood and ebonite panels, brass fittings. Note rear fuel reservoir on right hand side. 14 in. x 15½ in. x 19 in.

fig. 19. Marconi-Fleming Valve Receiver, by Marconi's Wireless Telegraph Co. Ltd., Hall Street, Chelmsford. c.1910. Two commercial pattern Fleming diodes, marked "Royal Ediswan Fleming Oscillation Valve. 4v", were provided with this receiver, either of which could be selected by means of a switch. Mahogany case, ebonite panel, brass fittings. 10¾ in. x 16 in. x 1¾ in.

Marconi's also produced the Marconi-Fleming Valve Receiver (fig. 19), in which two of Fleming's diode detectors were used, either one of which could be selected by means of a switch. The performance of the set depended upon the critical adjustment of two sliding resistors on the left-hand side of the set which controlled the heating of the valve's filament and the bias applied to it.

1911

During the summer of 1911, Marconi engineers at Hendon Aerodrome carried out the first regular experiments in air-to-ground wireless communication. From a 'plane circling the aerodrome piloted by Robert Loraine, Morse messages were successfully sent from a spark transmitter to a ground station erected in the Grahame-White sheds below. With petrol vapour and sparks flying in all directions this must have been a potentially hazardous situation but no fire accidents were reported. From about 1915 with the use of enclosed spark gaps and keys and later, valve transmitters, air-to-ground communication safely developed.

In October 1911, the differences between Lodge and Marconi were resolved. Lodge's patents were purchased by Marconi's for an undisclosed sum and Lodge accepted a nominal position as Scientific Adviser to the Company and a salary of £1,000 per annum for the remaining life of his syntony patents. One of the conditions of the purchase was that the Lodge-Muirhead Syndicate (hardly formidable opposition) would cease its operations and be dissolved.

1912

On April 15th, the White Star liner *Titanic* was ripped open by an iceberg just five days into her maiden voyage and over 1,500 men, women and children perished in the icy waters over the Grand Banks of the North Atlantic. Fortunately, the ship was equipped with Marconi wireless apparatus, and the Chief Wireless Telegraphist, Jack Phillips, was able to transmit a distress call using both "C.Q.D." and "S.O.S.". Principally due to this action, over 700 lives were saved and the value of wireless at sea dramatically demonstrated.

During the year, the British Government entered into an agreement with Marconi's for the erection of a chain of high-power long-wave wireless telegraphy stations around the British Empire (known as the Imperial Telegraph Service), but the First World War intervened and political wrangling further delayed the scheme until the second half of the 1920s (see 1927).

Over the years, the Marconi Works at Hall Street in Chelmsford had been slowly extended to keep pace with the development of the business. But in 1912, in order to allow for future developments, entirely new premises were designed, and within 17 weeks of the plans leaving the drawing-board, Marconi's new wireless factory opened in New Street, Chelmsford. On May 16th, the Company's administrative headquarters were moved to a new home at Marconi House in the Strand, London.

1913

A further demonstration of the life-saving value of wireless at sea was given on October 9th when the British steamship *Volturno*, fully laden with a miscellaneous cargo of oil, gin, straw, rags and chemicals and carrying over 600 emigrants from Rotterdam to New York, caught fire in mid-Atlantic. Once again, with wireless on board, help was quickly summoned and over 500 lives were saved, ten vessels having come in response to the wireless call. The *Volturno* episode prompted a famous cartoon in *Punch*, with Mr Punch saying to Marconi, "Many hearts bless you to-day, Sir. The world's debt to you grows fast." Marconi himself had said many times that the aspect of wireless which gave him, personally, the greatest gratification was its use in saving life at sea.

During 1913, some important new developments in valve technology took place. The first true 'hard' (high vacuum) triode valve (the Tungsten Wire Audion No.2) was developed by Irving Langmuir following his work on processes for creating high vacuum lightbulbs at the General Electric Research Laboratories in America. Later in World War One, because of their superior operation and efficiency as compared to the soft (low vacuum) valves which by the end of the war were practically obsolete, hard valves became the standard type.

One soft valve which did see active service during the war was designed by Captain H.J. Round of Marconi's in 1913. It was produced in two types, 'C' and 'T', and was first employed as a high frequency amplifier. Later, as an oscillator, it was used in the first practical wireless telephony transmitter for air-to-ground communication (see 1915). The grid was a long cylinder of fine mesh nickel wire surrounded by the anode cylinder, also made of nickel, while the filament was of platinum coated with a mixture of barium and calcium oxides. The coating of oxides was found to give good electron emission at low voltages: a principal first discovered by Wehnelt in 1904 and which eventually was generally adopted in both mains and battery valves towards the end of the 1920s. After continual use, the 'softness' of the Round valve diminished and so by heating the pinched neck of the glass envelope which contained a small piece of asbestos, gas was given off and the softness once again restored.

Another soft valve, developed in its final form in 1913, was the Lieben-Reisz 'Gas Relay' (fig. 20). Like the Round valve, it employed an oxide coated filament and while being

intended originally to be an amplifier of speech currents, it was successfully employed as a high frequency continuous wave oscillator by Alexander Meissner of the Telefunken Company in Germany, who on April 9th 1913 took out the world's first patent for using a valve in this way. The essential idea involved the coupling together of the input and output circuits to produce 'feed-back' whereby the small amount of energy from the anode circuit that was fed back to the input circuit caused it to oscillate. Later in June 1913, Meissner employed his feed-back circuit to produce carrier waves for the transmission of wireless telephony between Berlin and Nauen. The basic feed-back principle could also be used in simple receiving circuits, however the idea here was to use feed-back in a controlled way to obtain extra gain while stopping short of the actual point of oscillation. Feed-back was widely used in domestic valve wireless receivers during the 1920s in 'reaction' or 'regenerative' circuits and these too had their origin in 1913. On June 12th, C.S. Franklin took out a patent for a reaction circuit in which he employed a tuned grid and a tuned anode circuit, and in October, E. Armstrong patented his regenerative circuit which he had first demonstrated while still a student at Columbia University in America at the end of January.

fig. 21 . Claude Willcox's amateur wireless station, call-sign WUX, at 21 George Street, Warminster, Wiltshire. 1913. The transmitter used a gas quenched mercury break and a synchronised spark gap.

In the spring of 1913, a number of amateur wireless enthusiasts got together and formed the Derby Wireless Club, which was the first of many such organisations to be set up in Britain over the next ten years. Its formation reflected the growing public interest in wireless throughout the country and by now the number of experimental wireless licence holders was approaching 1,000, evidence of this being shown in A.W. Gamages' publication, *A Directory of Experimental Wireless Stations in the United Kingdom Licensed by the Postmaster General*. The directory's cover illustration showed station WUX (fig. 21). This was installed at 21 George Street, Warminster, and was operated by Claude Willcox who had been one of the very first wireless amateurs in the late 1890s (see 1898). In the directory were listed 405 transmitting stations together with their call-signs and details of the amateurs who operated them, and a description of 360 amateur receiving stations: among them was a station belonging to John Scott-Taggart (call-sign LUX) whose name was to become a household word amongst wireless-constructors during the 1920s and 1930s (see 1922 and 1932).

To the authorities, the number of licences already issued to experimenters seemed large, and concern was now shown that the situation might get out of hand if some new rules were not introduced. A new provision now laid down by the Post

fig. 20 . Lieben-Reisz 'Gas Relay' Valve, 1913. 11½ in. high x 4¾ in. dia. A small quantity of mercury amalgam was placed in the side tube, and this could be heated when necessary to produced a vapour which kept the pressure inside the valve constant.

Office stated that "licences to conduct experiments should only be issued to persons having the necessary qualifications". This went against Lord Stanley's original assurances a few years earlier when all the experimenter had to do was merely register, and with rumours circulating that the Post Office was drawing up rigorous legislation to clamp down on amateurs, wireless enthusiasts throughout the country began to realise the need for taking collective action. Also in May 1913, the Post Office had imposed a charge of £1.1s.0d on all new licences (whether for transmitting or for receiving), in the hope of dissuading those who were not really bona-fide experimenters from applying.

It was against this background of discontent that the London Wireless Club was formed on July 5th 1913 "to bring together all amateurs interested in wireless telegraphy and telephony". The founder members were Rene Klein, L. Francis Fogarty, A.P. Morgan and Leslie McMichael, who later went on to found his own wireless manufacturing company, L. McMichael Ltd.

fig. 22 . Home-constructed crystal set with open cat's whisker/galena detector, tuning coil with slider, brass fittings, mahogany base. 5 in. x 6½ in. x 4¾ in. Typical of the amateur-built type of receiver of pre-war years.

The wireless world was still essentially one of sparks, of communication by Morse Code, just as it had been since the end of the 19th century. The technicalities of wireless telephony were such that it had not developed as rapidly as wireless telegraphy and few people had heard the human voice transmitted by wireless. Wireless telephony was very much in its embryo stage at this time and the London Wireless Club was one of the few bodies to have expressed any interest in it.

With its formation, the total number of wireless clubs around the country had now grown to six, and the honorary secretaries of three of them (the Derby, the Birmingham and the London) co-wrote a letter published in *The English Mechanic & World of Science* attacking the Post Office's licensing system and offering an alternative solution to the licence problem. They considered that the fee of £1.1s.0d was too much for the majority of amateurs to be able to afford, and was especially hard on those who were already carrying out extensive and costly experiments. They suggested that a fee of 5s.0d or perhaps 7s.6d would be more reasonable.

On July 25th 1913, the 3 honorary secretaries held a meeting with the Secretary of the Post Office when the question of the experimental wireless licence was discussed formally for the first time. However, little seems to have transpired from this meeting and the licence fee remained fixed at the original figure.

At its first General Meeting held at the City of Westminster School on September 23rd 1913, the London Wireless Club changed its name to the Wireless Society of London, for it was felt that the word 'club' conveyed a misleading impression. The Chairman of this first meeting was Frank Hope-Jones, the Managing Director of the Synchronome Company and designer of the Horophone crystal set (fig. 23). He was a very prominent member of the British Horological Society and had recently come into the public eye by the firm stand he took against the Post Office over another constricting piece of legislation which he described as a "preposterous proposal". This was that the Post Office was intending to levy a tax or royalty on those who desired to listen to the international service of time signals transmitted from the Eiffel Tower station. Although he was biassed to a certain extent by commercial interests, Hope-Jones did express generally held fears that following this legislation, the Post Office would take drastic steps to repress what it called the "irresponsible amateur".

By the time the Wireless Society of London held its second meeting on November 13th 1913, many prominent scientists and eminent men from the Institution of Electrical Engineers had joined its ranks and it had also been recognised by the British

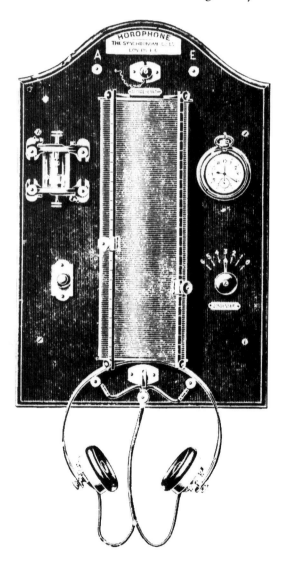

fig.23. The Horophone Type 'A' crystal set, produced by the Synchronome Co. Ltd., London EC in 1913. The Horophone employed a cast aluminium, glass-enclosed cat's whisker/galena detector and was specifically designed to receive time-signals, weather reports and news in Morse code from Paris, Norddeich and other high-power wireless telegraphy stations within a radius of about 800 miles. A two-detector version (the Type 'B') was also made. (*For full details, see pages 238 to 241*).

Association. Although its main body was now swelled by professionals, the Wireless Society of London still represented the voice and opinion of the amateur wireless experimenter and during the immediate pre-war period, its activities were considered important enough to be regularly reported in nearly a dozen technical journals.

1914

As war approached, it was seen that little at this stage could be achieved with the Post Office negotiations. On August 1st, just a few days before Britain declared war on Germany, the activities of the various wireless clubs and societies around the country were curtailed when the Post Master General ordered all experimental wireless apparatus in use to be dismantled and all aerial wires taken down and removed from their masts. Amateurs were informed that they could expect visits from Post Office officials to check that this order had been carried out.

Under the terms of Regulation 22 of the *Defence of the Realm Consolidation Act, 1914*, dated November 28th, restrictions were introduced banning the manufacture, the purchase, the sale and the possession of all wireless apparatus intended for the transmission or reception of wireless telegraphy, even if the operator held an experimental licence. A few amateur wireless stations were subsequently issued with a special permit allowing them to operate under Government control for official purposes, but the vast majority were eventually to be closed down for the duration of the war.

However, there were some amateurs who refused to abide by the Post Office's ruling and left their apparatus intact and kept their aerial wires visible for everyone to see. This had the result that the police began to receive reports from worried members of the public that there were "wireless spies" in their midst. Immediately after war had broken out, courts-martial were set up to put on trial anyone found in unauthorised possession of wireless apparatus. In one case, a keen member of the Birmingham Wireless Association was found guilty and sentenced to six months imprisonment for possessing a small portable transmitter at his home in Filey, Yorkshire. The severity of the sentence, particularly when it was made known that according to an expert Post Office witness, the transmitter was not capable of sending more than a mile, prompted many angry letters of protest to the Press. In the end, the sentence was reduced to two months, but only because the prisoner had already spent seven weeks in a cell awaiting trial.

In 1914, having been the subject of many tentative experiments and trials for a number of years, wireless telegraphy was beginning to be more widely used by the Military as a useful addition to visual and line signalling. At the beginning of the war, with the British Army on the move in France, cumbersome horse-drawn wagon and pack types of long-range wireless telegraphy sets were in use by the cavalry divisions and brigades, but with the coming of static trench warfare by the middle of October 1914 in which the opposing armies dug themselves in and were to face each other across no-man's-land for four years, the demand arose for efficient short-range equipment which would be more compact and portable and much less obtrusive. A huge network of telephone and telegraphy line communication had originally been laid down in the trenches but the enemy's barrage soon began to destroy it and wireless telegraphy (and later on in the war, wireless *telephony*) came into its own. An efficient organisation of trench wireless telegraphy grew up using 50 watt, 120 watt and 1.5 kW spark transmitters depending on the range required and it quickly became indispensable to the infantry, artillery and anti-aircraft gunners.

1915

In July 1915, more positive measures with regard to amateur wireless equipment were taken when the Post Master General announced that "in order to simplify the control of wireless apparatus and to avoid the inspection of private premises, all wireless apparatus (whether licensed or not), which is not required for public purposes shall be removed into Post Office custody for the period of the war, under the authority contained in the Defence of the Realm Act regulations".

As war progressed, the need for wireless operators, telegraphists and signallers became urgent and wireless amateurs were now called upon to fill many important posts in all three Services, joining the Wireless Sections as instructors, technicians and operators. For the thousands of men that these wireless amateurs of pre-war days trained, joining the Services during World War One gave them their first real experience of wireless, and for many that survived, this initial contact was to spark off a life-long fascination for the subject. Back in civilian life in the immediate post-war years, these men were to form the backbone of a growing body of enthusiastic wireless experimenters and, as the nucleus of the 'listening public', they gave great support and encouragement during the early and uncertain stages of British broadcasting.

THE DEVELOPMENT OF VALVES & TELEPHONY

Valves now began to be employed in Military receivers and transmitters and by 1917 they were in general use for wireless telephony communication. From a design patented on October 23rd 1915, the 'R' type high vacuum valve was first produced by the French Company, E.C. & A. Grammont of Lyon. These were designated 'TM Fotos' and the layout of their 4-pin 'B4' metal base was to become a standard design among British and European-made triodes until well into the post-war years. Because valves were vulnerable and were also the most expendable part of the circuit, they had to be easily removeable for replacement. For quite a few years following their introduction, they were usually mounted on the control panel by means of a 'socket' comprising four individual metal tubular contacts (one for each pin) protruding above, or sometimes below, the surface of the panel. From the early 1920s, one-piece moulded sockets with insulated metal contacts superseded the tubular contact type.

In the summer of 1915, the first one-way spoken message from an aeroplane to a ground station was achieved by the experimental section of the R.F.C. at the Wireless School, Brooklands, under the guidance of C.E. Prince, but at this stage in development, no attempt was made at receiving ground-to-air communication. The wireless telephony transmitter used here, (fig. 24), employed a single 'Round' valve and could also be used for Morse Code by simply moving a plug. It had been adapted by Prince (later to be given the O.B.E.) from a ground set originally demonstrated by Marconi's in 1914. The aerial was loose-coupled to the valve circuit which oscillated continuously and a microphone was used to modulate this current by varying the resistance in the aerial/earth lead. The operating wavelength was about 300 metres and using a trailing-wire aerial of about 75 feet, the set achieved an air-to-ground range of about 20 miles for wireless telephony and about 60 miles for Morse.

During World War One then, the first serious scientific experiments were conducted in Britain into wireless telephony and the success of these was due in particular to the rapid development of the valve.

From America, the Atlantic Ocean had once again been crossed by wireless, but this time it had been the human voice that had been transmitted. In October 1915, the American Telephone & Telegraph Company working with the Western Electric Company managed to send speech from the American Navy station in Arlington, Virginia across to the Eiffel Tower station, some 3,500 miles to the east. Despite only a few faint words being heard, the world's first transatlantic wireless telephony transmission was heralded as a success. But at this stage, long-distance telephony equipment was far from perfected; the transmitter used on this historic occasion employed several hundred 15 watt valves, many of which kept burning out and had to be hurriedly replaced.

fig. 24 . 'Aircraft Telephony Transmitter'. 1915. A single valve set adapted by C.E. Prince from a 1914 ground set by Marconi's Wireless Telegraph Co. Ltd. Also fitted with Morse key. Solid teak case, ebonite panels, nickel-plated fittings, milliampermeter on front. 13¼ in. x 7¾ in. x 5¼ in. (closed).

1916

In 1916, while working for Marconi's, H.J. Round had developed the V24 high frequency valve principally for use in marine communications equipment and even twenty years later it was still being manufactured for replacement purposes. By 1916, Round had been put in control of seven Admiralty wireless direction-finding stations installed on the eastern coast of Britain and these soon played a decisive role in the war when on May 31st during the battle of Jutland they provided essential information on the movements of the German fleet. The Marconi International Marine Communication Company had secured the patents of the Bellini-Tosi direction-finding system in 1912, and this was much improved on during the war by Round.

WIRELESS IN THE TRENCHES

By the middle of the war, the high vacuum valve was being successfully developed as a detector and an amplifier, but its growing use by the Military did not immediately cause the crystal to become obsolete. In fact, one of the most well known and widely used wireless receivers of the First World War period was a crystal receiver, the Mark III Short Wave Tuner, which had a tuning range of between 100 and 700 metres. (Until towards the end of the 1920s, the term 'short-wave' generally stood for wavelengths below 700 metres and it was not until then that the term 'medium-wave' was substituted. See 1929). The Mark III Tuner was designed by Marconi's Wireless Telegraph Company Ltd. in 1915, and manufactured too by

a number of other firms from 1916 including the W/T Factory, Robert W. Paul, Johnson & Phillips, and A.T.M. Co. (fig. 27). It was used by R.F.C. ground stations for the reception of Morse Code signals transmitted from aeroplanes flying above the battlefields of the Western Front. The pilots job was to direct the gunfire of artillery batteries on the ground via an R.F.C. wireless operator attached to each battery. With a clear view of the battle scene below, the pilots would transmit in Morse the coded position of the enemy using their Sterling No.1 spark transmitter of 1915 (fig. 25) and the message would be relayed on to the gunners who would then take the appropriate action.

fig. 25 . Sterling 'W.T. Spark Transmitter, No.1', by W/T Factory, W.D., Soho. 1915. This transmitter was widely used in British spotter aircraft from 1916 in conjunction with the 'Mark III Short Wave Tuner' (fig. 27) for one-way air to ground wireless telegraphy communication. It was developed by Fl./Lieut. B. Binyon RNAS and the Sterling Telephone & Electric Company. During operation, the front door was closed and in conjunction with an enclosed Morse key (not shown), danger of igniting petrol vapour from the engine by the transmitter's spark was averted. Nickel-plated fittings, black ebonite panels, teak case. 7 in. x 8 in. x 5 in.

Very little has been published about the men who served as wireless operators in the trenches, upon whose skill and endurance depended the accurate shooting of the artillery and upon that, the saving of the lives of many thousands of British and Allied infantry, and whose ground jobs with the R.F.C. were commonly believed to be 'soft billets'. I am very grateful therefore to 1st Air Mechanic William Manns (fig. 26) for supplying me with much of the following first-hand information on the time he spent on the Western Front attached to the 1/1st Welsh Heavy Battery.

William Manns was born in London on August 20th 1896 and joined the Royal Flying Corps in October 1915. For his training he was initially sent to the Polytechnic Institute in Regent Street, London where he learnt Morse Code and elementary electricity and magnetism. In order to accommodate the large number of men studying there, the Polytechnic's swimming baths were emptied to house rows of tables and chairs so that up to 150 recruits could receive instruction at the same time. Most of the men were billeted at Olympia and Manns remembers that the march to Regent Street for breakfast every morning was the worst part of the day. Usually they had one session of Morse Code training in the morning with most of each afternoon being spent in darkness while they practiced with signalling lamps. Before tea there would be a lecture on magnetism followed by one on electricity at about six o'clock. Lunchtimes were spent doing physical exercises or aerial erection practice in Regents Park: they never did any route marches, the walk to breakfast every morning being "quite sufficient!".

fig. 26 . 1st. Air Mechanic William T. Manns (sitting) with his assistant, 2nd. Air Mechanic R. Davidson. Zeggers-Cappel, August 1918.

In April 1916, Manns finished his training in London, having attained a Morse speed of 22 words per minute, and he then spent a fortnight at Test Hill, Weybridge which until then had been used as a race track. Here he got his first taste of the sort of operating conditions he was likely to encounter in France, albeit simulated. Test Hill was covered with dug-outs and places simulating the muddy terrain of the Western Front and with an RE8 observation aeroplane circling overhead, Manns put theory to practice, receiving signals and operating a Mark III Tuner for the first time.

In May, he went to the School For Wireless Operators at Farnborough which by this time had taken over from the Polytechnic as the main establishment for wireless tuition. The demand for, and the general recognition of the importance of wireless at the Front was marked by the fact that at the outbreak of the war only one Military aeroplane was equipped with a transmitter with less than a handful of wireless ground stations. By the time the Farnborough School had been established for a few months, there were 306 aeroplanes and 542 ground stations equipped with wireless, although at this stage of development the aeroplanes could only transmit and the ground stations could only receive.

At Farnborough, Manns was recruited for No.5 Squadron R.F.C. and was sent to join them at Dover. They then moved to Wye in Kent attached to the 20th Signals Regiment where part of his job was to fit the aeroplanes with Sterling spark transmitters and train the pilots to send Morse to a standard

of 7 words per minute. During his stay in Wye, it was found that he could do shorthand and typing and so Manns was collared for an office job. He would have stayed in it permanently if he had not resisted strongly, for he did not want to be sent to France as a clerk. After a few days he was taken to the H.Q. of the 1/1st Welsh Heavy Battery T.A. Royal Garrison Artillery and rather unceremoniously left alone to find his own feet. For the next 18 bloody months he was to see intensive action with this battery on the Western Front (particularly while stationed at Ypres) but miraculously he came through it all without so much as a scratch and never thought for a moment that he would be killed, although sometimes while under particularly heavy shelling, he admitted to having "got the wind up".

On arrival at the H.Q. he was issued with the following equipment which being heavy and cumbersome had to be carried about by motor transport or, more usually, by horses:

1 mast: 8 sections of iron tube 3 inches in diameter to make a 30 ft. mast, halliard and top plug, top and bottom guy ropes, 6 pegs, 1 hammer and a 5 ft. picket; 1 aerial on a winch with an insulated lead-in wire; 1 spare aerial; 2 aerial insulators; 2 earth mats; 6 cloth ground strips, 24 ft. by 2 ft., and a Morse lamp for signalling to aeroplanes; 1 tool kit; message forms, carbon paper and pencil; cord; Mark III Tuner including 2 pairs of Browns headphones, calibration and instruction card, technical notes in the use of the wireless station, circuit diagrams, 4 'S' cells for the buzzer and potentiometer, copper gauze earth mat, perikon crystals (zincite and chalcopyrites), carborundum crystals (silicon carbide) and a spare set of crystals.

The technical notes issued to Manns with this equipment were expected to be rigorously adhered to but, as Manns says,

fig. 27 . A.T.M. 'Mark III Short Wave Tuner', by Automatic Telephone Manufacturing Co. Ltd., London. 1916. A 'short-wave' crystal receiver for headphone use, covering the 100/700 metre wave range, used by R.F.C. ground stations in World War One. The panel houses Perikon and carborundum/steel detectors, a buzzer, and terminals for connecting the receiver to an auxiliary triode detector/amplifier. The lid contains a spare crystal compartment, a watch and a bracket for holding charts (charts missing in photograph). Solid mahogany case with polished interior, outside covered in black painted canvas. 8 in. x 14 in. x 12 in.

they were "wonderfully drawn up in an armchair in the safety of base camp and were often impossible to follow to the letter when under heavy shell fire in the battlefield". The 30 ft. aerial mast, with its 8 telescopic sections was extremely cumbersome to use and Manns says he "did not use that wretched thing whether there was a push on or not", he usually found a tree or other high place to fix his aerial instead.

Retrieving the copper earth mats, which he found easy enough to bury under the earth when setting up a station for the first time, proved an impossible task when moving location because the soil had by then become compressed into rock hard mud on top of them. Manns used to knock a nail in for the earth connection for subsequent stations and that worked just as well.

As a wireless operator receiving 4s.0d per day, Manns lived with the artillery gunners, sharing the same risks and hardships of trench warfare. Whenever possible, he operated near the map room so that the officer-of-the-day who had overall responsibility for communication could liaise with him. An observation aeroplane flying above the battlefield would direct the gunners towards the enemy targets by sending coded signals via Manns with his Mark III Tuner far below. The enemy's gun-smoke, giving away the position of its batteries, was known as a 'fleeting target', and would be clearly visible from the air as would be any enemy infantry or motor transport movement.

A wireless operator's work demanded continual alertness and close attention and more often than not was performed under heavy gunfire in a hastily constructed dug-out, rocking with the concussions of exploding shells which frequently put the aerial out of action, whereupon he was expected immediately to go outside and repair the damage, and this could mean going out more than a dozen times during one shoot. Through all this, he had to distinguish those signals coming from the particular aeroplane with which he was working from the numerous signals coming from other transmitters and a precise record had to be kept of the time and nature of each signal received and the result of the action taken by the gunners.

A careful check was being continually kept by the Central Wireless Station and each Squadron's H.Q. on whether the messages were being sent and received correctly. Only once was Manns' station reprimanded for inefficient reception, having receiving just 57 per cent of signals sent during one particular week, and that was the week when Manns was on leave.

At that time, ground wireless operators were also equipped with several strips of white cloth for use when signalling to the aeroplanes. Manns was supplied with a Mark III Tuner which could be used for reception purposes only. He did not have a transmitter to communicate to the aeroplane flying above but had to use either the cloth strips laid out on the ground in a coded pattern, or a Morse signalling lamp.

During a push, there was not time to build even the flimsiest shelter, the operator advanced with the gunners, rigged up his aerial and took cover in the nearest shell hole. In the long days of summer, Manns was sometimes on duty from 3am to 10pm with only a brief spell of relief when an artillery telephonist took over, and sometimes this was only for a few minutes. The telephonist however was not trained in wireless reception, and Manns had to give him enough instruction to enable him to get by. If there was a lull in the fighting, the battery used the time for calibrating and positioning their guns, with an aeroplane circling overhead directing the practice fire via the ground wireless operator.

In February 1918, Manns was joined by 2nd Air Mechanic R. Davidson who, sent out as his assistant, provided a welcome division of the work. Happily, both Manns and Davidson survived the war, but during the first four years of hostilities there was a yearly average of over 400 casualties amongst R.F.C. wireless operators, and this rose to nearly 500 during the months from May to November 1918. It was not a large number in itself, but compared to the numbers on the establishment, it represented a very large percentage: unusually large for a 'soft billet'.

After the war, many Mark III Tuners appeared on the surplus market and must have provided hundreds of people with their first taste of listening-in both before and after official broadcasting from the B.B.C. began in November 1922.

1917

With the war giving impetus to wireless research, Military wireless equipment continued to be developed and several notable transmitters and receivers were introduced including the Telephone Wireless Aircraft, Mk.II (fig. 28), the Aircraft Receiver Mk.III (fig. 29), the Mk.II Front Receiver (fig. 30) and the C.W. Mk.III Transmitter (fig. 31).

In April, the Mark III Amplifier became available and this was produced specifically for use with the Mark III Tuner. It was designed by the British Signals Experimental Establishment and employed two valves, the White soft valve and a de Forest Audion, but few of these amplifiers ever found their way to the Front.

fig. 28. Right: 'Telephone Wireless Aircraft, Mk.II', by General Electric Co., U.S.A. 1917. A 2-valve 20 watt telephony transmitter, fitted as standard in British aircraft towards the end of the war. Wood case covered in grey-painted cloth. 7 in. x 8 in. x 6 in. Left: A remote ON/OFF control with terminals for microphone, headphones and earth wires, (plugs into right hand side of transmitter).

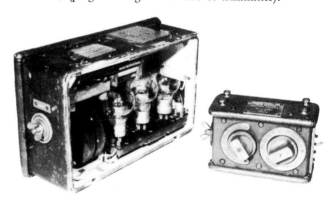

fig. 29. Left: 'Aircraft Receiver Mk.III', by Automatic Telephone Manufacturing Co. Ltd., London. 1917. A 3-valve receiver widely used in British aircraft in the latter stages of the war in conjunction with the General Electric Mk.II telephony transmitter (fig. 28). Wood case covered in black-painted cloth. (Receiver illustrated date-stamped "1918". Front of case removed to show components). 7 ½ in. x 12½ in. x 5 in. Right: Matching remote control unit, 'Tuner Aircraft Mk.III', by W/T Factory, W.D., Soho. 1917. 4 in. x 6 ½ in. x 3 in.

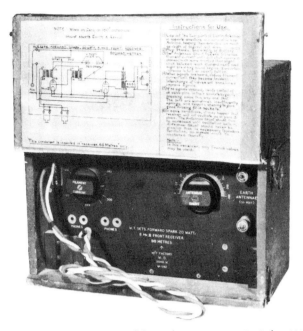

fig. 30 . 'Mk.II Front Receiver', by W/T Factory, W.D., Soho. 1917. A 20 watt spark receiver, employing two 'R' valves: an oscillating detector and an LF amplifier. Tunes to 80 or 65 metres. Wood case covered in black-painted cloth. 10 in. x 18 in. x 6 in.

fig. 31 . 'C.W. Mk.III Transmitter'. 1917. A 2-valve portable transmitter operating between 500/2000 metres. Ebonite panel, wood case covered in black-painted cloth. 13½ in. x 12½ in. x 9½ in. (including stand).

In the R.F.C., continuous-wave valve transmitters were brought into general use and immediately increased the ground-to-air and the air-to-ground range, and by the following year some 600 aircraft and 1,000 R.F.C. ground stations were using wireless communications equipment.

1918

During the year, the General Electric Company released the Osram R2A which was one of the very last 'soft' valves to be produced in this country (fig. 32).

In May 1918, the Dutch lightbulb manufacturers Philips introduced their first valve in Holland: the '1 Deezet' (1DZ), named after Dr. Hanso Idzerda. Idzerda was an electrical engineer who had set up business in 1914 to manufacture wireless apparatus and it was he who managed to persuade Philips (until then solely manufacturers of lightbulbs) to begin producing wireless valves. In 1919, the transmitting station in the Hague belonging to Idzerda's company, call-sign PCGG, began broadcasting a series of concerts which soon became compulsive listening-in for thousands of people in Britain and on the Continent (see 1919).

The First World War was now drawing to a close. For four years the opposing armies had viewed one another across the narrow belt of no-man's-land which separated their front lines, but in the summer of 1918 the great Allied break-through began with a French attack in July and a British attack in August led by 450 tanks, and within a few months the Germans had surrendered.

fig. 32 . Osram R2A, by the General Electric Company, London. 1918. A 'soft' valve filled with helium, mainly used in British Naval installations during the last year of the war. 1.1 amps, 3.3 volts, 28/38 anode volts. Brass screw-thread fitting. 3¼ in. high. Its appearance marked the final development of the 'soft' valve in England.

1919

Several months after the Armistice, the first relaxation of official restrictions on wireless occurred. In a letter to manufacturers of electrical apparatus dated March 24th 1919, the Secretary of the Post Office announced that restrictions were now lifted on the sale of certain component parts including spark coils and headphones. This was on condition that the purchaser gave a written undertaking that the experimental apparatus in which the parts were to be used would not be employed for wireless work unless written permission had first been obtained from the Post Office. In the next month, the Post Office began issuing special licences to clockmakers for the reception of time-signals, but the applicant had to prove that the licence was only going to be used in conjunction with his business before it was granted.

On July 5th 1919, all pre-war licences were cancelled but the Post Office did not start to replace these until October 21st 1919 when, under pressure from the wireless societies and clubs, they announced that informal authority could now be granted for the use of receivers only and amateurs could reclaim their wireless apparatus confiscated by the Post Office during the war. Accompanying this relaxation in restrictions, the Experimenter's Licence (for reception only) was introduced at 10s.0d per annum. Applicants for this new licence had to be of British nationality and had to produce a birth certificate to that effect. They were first required to submit a description of the apparatus they proposed to install, and if they sought to use thermionic valves, a diagram had to be sent showing the circuit layout. If any applicant wanted to buy complete factory-built apparatus (the manufacture of which was still controlled by official permit), he was required to give full particulars of the equipment and the name and address of the firm from whom he bought it. There were restrictions too on the size of the aerial used, the length being limited to 100 feet for a single stranded wire and 140 feet for a double or multi-stranded wire.

A week after the Experimenter's Licence was introduced, the Wireless Society of London held its first post-war Annual General Meeting at the Institution of Civil Engineers at Westminster on October 28th. Many societies and clubs were very keen to resume their activities soon after the war had ended, and in the audience that evening were some two hundred amateurs and their guests from as far away as Plymouth and Derby, providing further evidence of the growing national interest in wireless.

On show at the meeting were a few pieces of equipment made by Society members but the display mostly comprised factory-made wireless apparatus of the official type with Military C.W. and telephony receivers forming a major part of the exhibition. There was a lot of interest in valves made by the Edison Swan Electric Company and a valve display showing an 'R' valve in various stages of production which was described by John Scott-Taggart. British Thomson-Houston Co. Ltd. showed valves from the U.S., Germany and France, and there were various exhibits from Marconi's Wireless Telegraph Company including a Type 55 7-valve amplifier, direction-finding apparatus for ships, and pieces of captured German equipment such as trench spark sets and valves. The exhibition gave many their first chance of examining such apparatus at close quarters, and although a private affair, it was the first wireless exhibition ever to be held in Britain.

But with only a licence for receiving having been granted to the amateurs, there was not much for them to listen to apart from the international time-signals or Morse Code from official Government or Military stations. But on November 6th 1919, the situation took a definite turn for the better when the world's first pre-announced wireless telephony broadcast was transmitted from station PCGG in the Hague, Holland. The station had been set up by Hanso Idzerda and was owned by his company, Nederlandsche Radio Industry, who were designers and manufacturers of wireless equipment. Idzerda thought that he could use the transmitter for increasing the popularity of wireless broadcasting in Holland, stimulate the need for wireless receivers and so promote his commercial business: an idea which was fundamental too in the setting up of the British Broadcasting Company three years later. The day before, Idzerda had published details of the first of his forthcoming 'Soiree-Musicales' in the *Nieuwe Rotterdamsche Courant* and although of an irregular nature at first, the programmes, consisting of speech and music transmitted on 1,150 metres long-wave, were well received not only by the Dutch, but by hundreds of listeners in England too who soon began calling them the 'Dutch concerts'.

In November 1919, a Post Office announcement that new transmitting licences would shortly be introduced caused great excitement among the amateurs but again they had to wait, until August 1st 1920.

Immediately after the war, Marconi's began concentrating their research efforts in high-power wireless telephony transmission and soon commercial 250 watt, 1.5 kW, 3 kW and 6 kW sets were being manufactured. In 1919, they built an experimental 2.5 kW telephony transmitter at Ballybunion in Ireland under the direction of H.J. Round. Although it utilised only three main valves whose power was a fraction of that used by the Arlington transmitter in 1915, they succeeded in transmitting the voice of Marconi Engineer W.T. Ditcham to a receiving station at Louisbourg, Nova Scotia. The wavelength used was 3,800 metres and Ditcham's was the first European voice to be sent across the Atlantic by wireless. Spurred on by these excellent results, Marconi's then decided to build a 6 kW wireless telephony transmitter at their Chelmsford works to test long-distance transmissions on long-waves and this came into use in January 1920.

1920

On January 29th, the Wireless Society of London held its second private wireless exhibition. There were far fewer pieces of equipment of a Military or professional nature on show, and the accent now was on 'domestic' wireless for amateur home use. The exhibits included a Wireless Pocket-Book (a miniature crystal set designed by Capt. H. de A. Donisthorpe and manufactured by R.M. Radio Ltd. in the form of a pocket-book and claiming a range of 300/3,000 metres), a Gamage's Polaris Miniwaver, Mediwaver and Maxiwaver single-valve unit set capable of tuning between 450/30,000 metres (fig. 34), a Model No.2 valve detector unit by A.W. Knight and valve units and various components by F.L. Mitchell & Co. Ltd. Also shown at the exhibition was one of the very first domestic portable valve receivers: a 2-valve set for headphone use designed by R.C. Clinker and made by B.T.H. at Rugby (fig. 33).

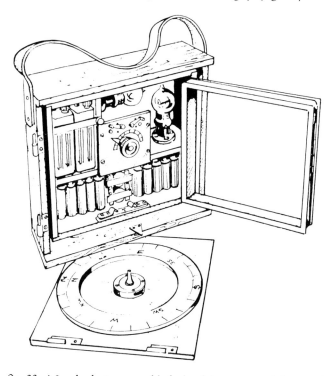

fig. 33. A 2-valve battery portable for headphone use, made by British Thomson-Houston Co. Ltd. Spring 1920. (des: R.C. Clinker). This very early domestic portable was designed to receive Press news, time signals and meteorological reports sent out from long-wave transmitting stations, and had a standard tuning range of 1,500/15,000 metres, extendable down to 400 metres. The receiver, together with all the necessary HT and LT batteries, was housed in a 13 in. x 14 in. x 5 in. oak case which had a removeable hinged front door, on the back of which was a printed compass scale. When required for use, the door was lifted from its hinges and laid flat on a table and the scale lined up along the meridian by means of a compass. The set was then positioned onto the pivot screwed in the centre of the door and swung around so that the pointer at the bottom of the cabinet indicated the bearing of the station required. This was then roughly tuned in by means of a variometer, and to obtain fine tuning, the hinged square-wound 'retroactive' coil (right) was swung out to the required position. (Drawing: Norman Jackson).

fig. 34 . Left: Gamage's 'Polaris Mediwaver', by A.W. Gamage Ltd., Holborn, London EC. 1919. (des: H. Powell Rees). A 1-valve battery receiver for headphone use, tuning between 750/3,300 metres. Mahogany case 8 in. x 8¼ in. x 8¼ in. Right: An add-on unit, the 'Polaris Miniwaver', was used to lower the combined wave range of the two units to between 400/700m. (In 1920, a third unit, the 'Polaris Maxiwaver', was introduced to extend the combined wave range to as high as 30,000 metres).

On February 23rd 1920, the power of the Chelmsford transmitter was increased to 15 kW and a regular service now began which consisted of two daily half-hour programmes of news, talks and music organised by G.W. White, an assistant to Round and Ditcham. These unofficial broadcasts were transmitted on 2,800 metres long-wave and since this was the same wavelength as that used by the Poldhu Station, a large number of wireless operators at sea were able to pick them up on their ships' receivers. Many amateurs too were listening-in around the country, and most of those who had previously bought or made apparatus for receiving the 2,600 metre time-signals from the Eiffel Tower transmitter also found that their receivers could tune to the Chelmsford wavelength. The programmes were a great success and they gave many their first chance of hearing broadcasts radiating from an English transmitter. The excitement of the Chelmsford broadcasts and the anticipation of future broadcasting developments, encouraged a national demand for wireless apparatus and during 1920, a domestic Wireless Industry began to be established based on the idea of manufacturing receivers specifically for home entertainment, and not for any Military or professional use.

In the immediate post-war years, the future of wireless communication was thought to lie with the *long* waveband, especially as there were already many well established official long-wave stations transmitting in this country and in Europe. Many receivers, like the Gamages Polaris unit set referred to above, were even brought out covering wavelengths as high as 30,000 metres, in order "to provide for future contingencies". Many who tuned-in were doing so on surplus Military wireless equipment left over from the war and now sold by the Disposal Board War Office, and some unwary amateurs were caught out by unscrupulous dealers offloading inefficient, obsolete or totally unsuitable equipment. Much of it had originally been designed for receiving the 'short' (medium) waveband only, and the circuits therefore had to be modified to receive the long waveband. Around this time, articles giving details of the necessary circuit changes often appeared in the Press and one, published in *Wireless World*, gave details of how to modify the Mark III Tuner and left little more than a dozen of the original parts intact, and that included the wooden case! The Mark III Short Wave Tuner also appeared as a commercial 1-valve long-wave receiver when in 1920, W.R.H. Tingey bought up a parcel of them and used many parts, including the case, to produce the Tingey Valve Tuner No.22 (fig. 35). Here again, the manufacturers had an eye to what they considered to be future broadcasting developments and provided this receiver with a circuit capable of tuning up to 30,000 metres.

However, when national broadcasting began from the British Broadcasting Company in November 1922, the *medium* waveband was chosen, and together with sets only capable of receiving long-waves, military surplus receivers like the Mark III Tuner which had been designed for the medium waveband but had then been changed soon after the war to cover the long waveband, had to be re-converted to receive the shorter 'Broadcast Band' (350 to 425 metres).

fig.35. Tingey 'Valve Tuner', instrument number 22, made by W.R.H. Tingey, London EC. 1920. A 1-valve battery receiver for headphone use, tuning between 800/30,000 metres. Made using parts from surplus Mark III Short Wave Tuners, (*see fig.27*). Canvas-covered mahogany case, 8 in. x 14 in. x 12 in.

The event which really put the idea of using wireless as a broadcast entertainment firmly on the map occurred on June 15th 1920. Sponsored by the *Daily Mail* for a reported figure of £1,000, the Australian soprano, Nellie Melba (fig. 36), sang a concert from the Chelmsford works which was heard by listeners all over the British Isles and many countries abroad, and led to Marconi's receiving thousands of letters and telegrams of praise. One newspaper reported, "Punctually at 7.15pm the words of Home Sweet Home swam into the receivers. Those who heard it might have been in an audience in the Albert Hall."

As well as in England, the concert was heard in Paris, Rome, Warsaw, Madrid, Berlin, Stockholm and Tabriz in Persia. But although dramatic and momentous at the time, the Melba concert did little to speed up the establishment of a national broadcasting system in Britain and several problems were to occur before the British Broadcasting Company was set up.

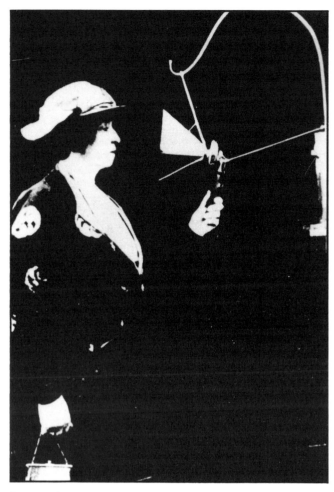

fig. 36 . The Australian soprano, Nellie Melba, on the night of her famous broadcast from Marconi's Chelmsford works in New Street. June 15th 1920. Clutching her handbag, (which surely is far too small to accommodate the £1,000 performance fee?), she is singing into an improvised Peel Connor carbon granule microphone manufactured by the General Electric Company. The makeshift cone was hastily made by H.J. Round from an old cigar box and was autographed by Melba after her broadcast.

Meanwhile, the public continued to listen-in with interest to the broadcasts from Chelmsford, which in the last week of July enabled the passenger liner *Victorian* to establish a long-distance telephony record for a ship at sea. Having been equipped by the Marconi International Marine Communication Company with an experimental 3 kW two-way wireless telephony transmitter, the *Victorian*, sailing from England *en route* for Canada, had first established telephonic communication with Chelmsford on July 21st 1920 when she was some 600 miles distant. The following day, she was able to entertain her passengers with concerts and Press Association news bulletins transmitted from Chelmsford and picked up on her telephony receiver. The programmes were relayed to passengers through a Brown H1 loud-speaker drive unit connected to a phonograph horn set up in the first-class passenger lounge. On the following days, the Chelmsford concert was again received until on July 26th, it was heard for the last time when the *Victorian* was over 2,100 miles away, establishing a new record. The *Victorian* also broadcast her own daily and nightly programmes of wireless telephony concerts comprising records played on a gramophone and she received many Morse Code requests for encores from ships scattered about the North Atlantic over a radius of nearly 800 miles.

On August 1st 1920, new experimental transmitting licences were introduced (the first one was issued to the Radio Communication Company at Slough, call-sign 2AA), and the 1,000 metre wavelength was allotted to amateurs for the transmission of wireless telephony with the maximum power restricted to 10 watts. In the same month, further experimental broadcasts of news items were conducted by the Press Association and to receive them, multi 'R' valve sets using frame aerials were installed in newspaper offices at Newcastle, Preston, Sheffield and Belfast. The frame aerial, a long length of wire wound around a square wooden frame usually a few feet across, was not as efficient as an outdoor aerial but was used where space outside was limited.

A new source of telephony now became available for amateurs to tune-in to. In 1919, Croydon Aerodrome had become Britain's main civil airport and during 1920 was supplied by Marconi's with a two-way telephony transmitting station and a Bellini-Tosi direction-finder sited 3 miles away at Mitcham. This was remotely controlled from the Croydon control tower, and by tuning to 900 metres, amateurs could listen-in to conversations with aeroplanes in flight as they made the journey to and from Paris.

Across the Atlantic in November, the Westinghouse Electric & Manufacturing Company in Pittsburg, Pennsylvania, transmitted the returns of President Harding's election by wireless telephony, thus beginning the advent of broadcasting in the United States. The public had been prepared for this by announcements in the newspapers and many thousands of amateur experimenters were therefore ready with their receivers and managed to obtain the news long before the papers had time to publish the results. The success of this first national broadcast encouraged Westinghouse to organise and maintain a daily service from its Pittsburg station, call-sign KDKA, which became the pioneering broadcast station in the United States.

But in England, things now took a turn for the worse when on November 23rd, the Post Master General, Albert Illingworth, informed the House of Commons that permission to broadcast from Marconi's Chelmsford works was being withdrawn owing to "the considerable interference with other stations", in particular with the Post Office's new arc transmitting station at Leafield near Oxford, which was then being used for telegram, Press and Foreign Office Morse transmissions to Cairo, India and America on 12,200 metres. The irony of this was that Leafield itself was a greater source of interference, owing to the harmonics generated by the arc system (see 1922).

1921

On September 21st, due to the lapse of Regulation 22 of the *Defence of the Realm Consolidation Act, 1914*, wireless apparatus could now be freely manufactured, sold and purchased without permit or restriction, although an Experimenter's Licence would still be necessary for those wishing to install a wireless receiver. An arrangement was made however for 'toy' sets to be used without a licence, providing that such apparatus had been approved by the Post Master General and had been stamped or marked to that effect before sale. (Toy sets were defined as "receiving or transmitting apparatus of the Hertzian oscillator type, not intended for connection to earth or to any aerial other than small rods and with a range not exceeding 50 yards").

By the winter of 1921, the Dutch concerts were in serious trouble, and it looked as though these were going to cease altogether owing to financial difficulties. But an appeal was made in the September 3rd 1921 issue of *Wireless World* by W.W. Burnham, Managing Director of the wireless manufacturers Burnham & Co. (later Burndept Ltd.), and sufficient funds came in to enable PCGG to continue broadcasting. Comments were also raised in the appeal that it was abominable that no British station, such as the one at Chelmsford, was allowed to transmit a short concert or a brief news bulletin even once a week while in America, broadcasting was well under way. Even the time-signal broadcasts from the Eiffel Tower station were now being livened up with speech and music.

As a minor concession, Marconi's were then granted permission for transmitting calibration signals from Chelmsford for half an hour a week, but the English amateur was justifiably feeling rather snubbed by the Post Office and thought that his contribution to radio science was often going unseen and unheard. Despite various important successes, including the first reception of transatlantic short-wave (200 metres) transmissions by the English amateur W.F. Burne (call-sign 2KW) of Sale, Cheshire on December 8th 1921, and the amateurs' considerable technical contribution during World War One, to many, the Post Office still exhibited a "deplorable attitude".

fig. 37 . 'Burndept 1', a two-unit set for headphone use manufactured by Burnham & Co., Deptford, London SE. 1921 (des: Frank Phillips). Left: A tuner unit with three loose-coupled plug-in coils, and a variable condenser housed in a walnut case with an ebonite control panel. Mounted on a walnut base, 7 in. x 7 in. x 13½ in. Right: A 1-valve amplifier unit with an ebonite control panel and walnut case, 5 in. x 8 in. x 10 in. One of Burnham & Co.'s first valve sets, which no doubt would have received the Dutch Concerts that the firm's Managing Director, W.W. Burnham, raised funds to save.

Since the spring, negotiations had been going on between the Post Office and the Wireless Society of London (now representing the majority of wireless societies and clubs around the country), with a view to establishing weekly high-power calibration transmissions, wireless telegraphy and, more especially, wireless telephony. This led to a petition being presented to the Post Master General, F.G. Kellaway on December 29th 1921, pleading the amateur's case:

"We, the undersigned, on behalf of the Wireless Society of London, and of most of the other societies of the country, representing in the aggregate a large number of citizens interested in wireless telegraphy, ask you to be good enough to give consideration to our views as follows:

"We wish to express our thanks for the courtesy and consideration which the authorities have always shown to the amateur radiotelegraphists of this country, and to state that we fully realise the difficulties that are inherent to the carrying on of wireless operations in a small and crowded country such as our own where the stringent regulations are obviously necessary to prevent undue interference.

"We also wish to express our satisfaction at the permission recently given to the Marconi Company to send special calibration signals from Chelmsford for the benefit of our members for a period of half an hour every week.

"We desire, however, to express our regret that wireless telephony has not been included in this arrangement and to say that we hope that this restriction may be reconsidered, either with reduced power, or perhaps on a short wavelength of 200 or 300 metres, so as not to cause interference. We would point out that it is telephony in which the majority of our members are chiefly interested at the present time, this being the most recent achievement in wireless, and that in which, for moderate distances at all events, improvements such as avoidance of distortion and the production of really articulate loud speakers and such like, are most required. It is therefore primarily to serve the scientific purpose of improving the receiving arrangements that we desire to have telephony included. We would, however call attention to the following general consideration, which in our opinion, should not be overlooked by the authorities in dealing with this question.

"It should be remembered that wireless telegraphy was, in the first instance, originated and has since been largely developed, by men who, at any rate to begin with, were not even electrical engineers or electricians, and still less qualified telegraphists. Many of these, when they began experimenting, were in this particular line pure amateurs, though no doubt some of them gradually attained to professional proficiency. New inventions and important improvements are still being made by this class of person and the more numerous they are the more chance there is for good and useful work to be done. In this connection it is noteworthy that it is entirely due to amateurs that all records have recently been broken by the successful transmission and reception of signals across the Atlantic on 200 metre waves. To attract such workers in the first instance and to keep them interested, it is necessary to make the occupation interesting and even entertaining; hence the need for wireless telephonic speech and even music. Furthermore the requirements of the large number of such amateur users have led to the establishment of numerous factories for the manufacture of wireless instruments and apparatus, where skilled engineers and workmen are employed and many experiments are carried out and where quite important improvements in instruments and methods are constantly being effected. Were it not for the demands of numerous amateurs, such manufacturing concerns would not exist and advance in the art would be checked. There is also the advantage, in the case of any future wars, of the existence of a number of persons skilled in wireless.

"The education value of wireless should not be overlooked. Just as the advent of the motor car has undoubtedly done more to disseminate a knowledge of mechanics throughout the population than all the millions of money spent annually on technical education, so also the practice of wireless is teaching thousands the principles of electrical science and of physics, and this without any expense to the State.

"That the French authorities recognise the force of these considerations is evidenced by the transmissions of speech and music that have already commenced under Government auspices from the Eiffel Tower. It is understood that it is intended to make these a regular feature like the time signals and meteorological reports and it will be somewhat lamentable if England, where Wireless Telegraphy originated and whose Greenwich time is the time of the world, but who sends out no wireless time signals, should again fall behind other countries by reason of failure to move with events.

We are,
Your obedient servants."

Here, the petition was signed by the Committee of the Wireless Society of London and representatives of some 65 other Societies and Clubs affiliated with it.

THE BROADCASTING YEARS

1 The 1920s

1922

THE WRITTLE STATION, 2MT

Having carefully considered the petition presented to him by the Committee of the Wireless Society of London only a few weeks before, the Post Master General announced on January 25th 1922 that he had authorised Marconi's Wireless Telegraph Co. Ltd. to arrange a short weekly programme of wireless telephony and Morse calibration signals for the benefit of the several thousand amateur wireless experimenters around the country who were eagerly waiting for something interesting to listen to. The service would be provided by Marconi's subsidiary, the Marconi Scientific Instrument Co. Ltd., from an experimental station housed in a wooden hut in the Essex village of Writtle, a few miles from Chelmsford and would have the call-sign 2MT ("TWO-EMMA-TOC"). This company had been set up by Marconi's on November 1st 1919 to repair and bring up to date all obsolete apparatus belonging to Marconi's and to manufacture and sell amateur telegraphic and telephonic equipment under licence. During the first week of January 1922, they had exhibited components, valves, batteries and receiver units including a complete set of six, at the Model Engineer Exhibition held at the Horticultural Hall in London. Also at the exhibition were stands from six other wireless manufacturers who displayed domestic wireless equipment designed solely for "amateur use in the home". The other exhibits were by G.Z. Auckland & Sons, a selection of components for the amateur to build "a domestic wireless installation"; Bower & Co., components and French 'R' valves; Burnham & Co., their Ultra-Five receiver and honeycomb tuning coils, together with the actual transmitter used to broadcast the Dutch concerts from the Hague; Economic Electric Co., various pieces of electrical and wireless apparatus; A.W. Gamage, components and unit receivers, and F.O. Read & Co., HF and LF amplifiers and other wireless apparatus. Leslie McMichael also had a stand at the exhibition, but showed almost exclusively ex-Government apparatus from the Disposal Board War Office including Townsend wavemeters, Mark III Tuners, condensers and valves.

The Writtle station began its regular Tuesday night broadcasts on February 14th at 7pm. From 7pm to 7.25pm, three five minute sections of C.W. Morse were transmitted on 1,000 metres long-wave (the same wavelength allocated to amateur transmitters) with a power of 1 kW, 500 watts and 250 watts respectively. This was followed at 7.35pm by an opening concert of songs by Robert Howe and records played on a Cliftophone gramophone, transmitted on the relatively long wavelength of 700 metres with a power of 250 watts. The wireless telephony transmissions were strictly limited to a maximum of half an hour per week and like the Morse transmissions were divided into sections. Between each section was a break during which the Writtle station closed down for a couple of minutes so that the announcers could maintain a listening watch on 2MT's wavelength for any important Government messages or "S.O.S." calls. For the benefit of wireless enthusiasts who wanted to try to tune-in to the test broadcasts, *Wireless World* had, a week before, published full details of the opening programme. Excellent reception was reported by those living within about a 15 mile radius of Writtle who were able to pick up the broadcasts on simple crystal sets while as far north as Forfar in Scotland, loud-speaker reception was obtained on a 5-valve set although signal fading was quite marked. Another, more serious problem encountered by many

of those tuning-in on valve receivers was interference, and this was especially experienced by amateurs living on the English Channel coast who were often prevented from receiving 2MT because of jamming from ship and coastal-based Naval wireless installations. Around the London area, the first three items of the opening concert were heard quite clearly, although after that, harmonic interference from the Post Office's arc transmitter at Leafield on 12,200 metres entirely wiped them out.

Interference continued to be a problem and so a few months later, on Tuesday May 30th, 2MT's 700 metre wavelength was changed to 400 metres medium-wave and the rather dreary section of Morse calibration signals on 1,000 metres long-wave was dropped altogether, with the wireless telephony section opening the programme at its new time of 8pm. 2MT's new medium wavelength meant that the circuit designs of long-wave only receivers had to be modified in order for Writtle to be received. This change would be necessary anyway as plans had been announced by the P.M.G. earlier in the month proposing the establishment of a national domestic broadcasting service which would employ a number of wireless telephony transmitting stations using allocations between 350 and 425 metres on the medium waveband: soon to become popularly known as the 'Broadcast Band'.

Until the Writtle station closed down on January 17th 1923, the 'ether' around the Essex area was filled with "first class amusement", which included on October 17th, the first ever wireless play: a short scene from Cyrano de Bergerac directed by a Miss Agnes Travers.

The station's Director and Chief Announcer was Captain Peter Pendleton Eckersley. An R.F.C. Wireless Equipment Officer during the war, he later joined the Experimental Section of the Marconi Company's Aircraft Department and went on to become the B.B.C's Chief Engineer. It was largely due to Eckersley's boyish enthusiasm and imaginative personality that these Tuesday evening programmes became compulsive listening-in and although the Writtle station operated for less than a year, it was a tremendous success and helped to convince many, including the Post Office, that broadcasting as an entertainment had great public benefit and, as a new art, had very definitely arrived.

THE BRITISH BROADCASTING COMPANY

Shortly after Writtle went on the air in January, the Post Office granted Marconi's a licence for the installation of a 100 watt wireless telephony broadcasting station at their Head Office at Marconi House in the Strand, London. Its call-sign was to be 2LO.

The transmitter and a single 20 ft. x 20 ft. studio were housed on the top floor of Marconi House in what used to be an old cinema theatre, and from here the first experimental tests began at 9.25pm on the night of Thursday May 11th with the opening message, "Hullo C.Q. 2LO calling. Please stand by." There then followed a rather ambitious outside broadcast of a boxing match between Carpentier and Lewis at Olympia in West London. The commentary was relayed live by telephone by *Daily Mail* reporters at the ringside and was sent out via the transmitter at Marconi House on 360 metres. However, there was not very much to describe as Carpentier won after only

A.J.S. 4-valve battery receiver, 1923, with an S.G. Brown Model H1 horn loud-speaker.

one minute of the first round, although the general opinion afterwards was that the broadcast had been a great success, brief as it was. 2LO was not alone in broadcasting the fight as the Radio Communication Company at Slough (call-sign 2AA) had their own commentator, Jack Dempsey, at the other end of a telephone line at Olympia.

Initially, subsequent test broadcasts from 2LO were restricted by the Post Office to hour-long studio programmes of speech, sent out in the late morning or late afternoon to a limited reception area around London. Like Writtle, periods of a few minutes silence were included which had the advantage of allowing the engineers time to smooth out any technical problems which might have (and usually had!) occurred. The station's Chief Announcer was Arthur Burrows, who in mid-November, when 2LO was inaugurated as the first station of the British Broadcasting Company, became its Director of Programmes. He was soon to become one of the famous Wireless Uncles: 'Uncle Arthur' to the thousands of children listening to him on Children's Hour every evening.

On May 18th, the first of a series of meetings was held between the Post Office and the representatives of firms interested in the Post Master General's proposed broadcasting plan, with the idea of forming a *single* licensed broadcasting company rather than having many firms operating their own separate stations, each under a different licence. In America, where controls were non-existent, the situation had become chaotic with a very large number of stations transmitting on a narrow band of wavelengths, and the Post Office naturally sought to prevent a similar situation arising in Britain. Also, any licence granted to such a joint company would only be for two years, thereby giving the Post Office the safeguard of being able to review the entire situation after a limited period. The geography of the British Isles played an important part too in this decision. Given that each station was to be of a certain power and range, it was thought impossible to operate more than eight transmitters in mainland Britain without causing interference between them.

From mid-summer, more variety was introduced into the broadcasts from 2LO with programmes of concerts and musical evenings now permitted. The original power of around 100 watts was raised to 1.5 kW and the reception range of the transmissions greatly extended to encompass many more of the 11,000 amateur 'listeners-in' who had already been issued with Experimenter's Licences.

In September, from the 2nd to the 8th, the International Radio Exhibition took place at the Central Hall, Westminster. This was the first exhibition open to the public solely devoted to wireless and was supported by over 40 British and foreign manufacturers showing complete receivers, components and accessories. At the end of the month, from September 30th to October 7th, the first All British Wireless Exhibition was held at the Horticultural Hall, London SW1. Supported by 52 British wireless manufacturers, it was then the most representative trade gathering ever to be held in Britain and was aimed primarily at the requirements of experimenters and amateur listeners-in. The general public flocked to the Hall, not to make a critical examination of the apparatus on show, but to witness the new phenomenon of broadcasting itself.

Among the exhibits on show were the first three sets from Marconi's made specifically for domestic and not for Government, marine or other official use. They were the Marconiphone V2 2-valve receiver (fig. 60), the Marconiphone Crystal A crystal set (fig. 64) and its smaller version, the Marconiphone Crystal Junior (fig. 68). 'Marconiphone' was the trade name used until the end of December 1923 by Marconi's on all their broadcast receivers produced for the domestic market. The Marconiphone Company Limited was set up on December 29th 1923 and

within a couple of days all the business in connection with the sale and distribution of Marconiphone receivers and accessories together with the Marconiphone trade name had been transferred to them (see 1923).

The original chassis of the V2, the Crystal A and the Crystal Junior were not in fact made by Marconi's but by the firm of Plessey, who up to that time, using two rooms in shared premises in Holloway, had specialised in the manufacture of tools and jigs. Early in 1922, Marconi's had been looking for firms to manufacture domestic wireless sets under contract, and in July, Plessey won an order from them for 5,500 crystal sets and 5,000 V2 valve receivers. It was worth £30,000 and transformed Plessey overnight, establishing them in the forefront of the emerging Wireless Industry, enabling them to quickly expand and, within twelve months, to move to a large permanent factory site of their own at Ilford.

On October 18th, the British Broadcasting Company was at last formed. It comprised 300 British manufacturers and dealers in wireless receivers and accessories headed by the so-called 'Big Six': British Thomson-Houston Co. Ltd., the General Electric Co. Ltd., Marconi's Wireless Telegraph Co. Ltd., Metropolitan-Vickers Electrical Co. Ltd., the Radio Communication Co. Ltd., and the Western Electric Co. Ltd. It was registered on December 15th 1922 and although its licence was not issued until January 18th 1923 it was retrospective and gave permission to broadcast for an initial period of two years as from November 1st 1922, two weeks before the actual inauguration of broadcasting.

The B.B.C. was a limited liability company licensed under the Wireless Telegraphy Acts to conduct a broadcasting service "to the reasonable satisfaction of the Postmaster General". It was constituted with a capital of £100,000, of which £60,000 was contributed in equal parts by the six main wireless manufacturing firms who each had representation on the Board of Governors. John C.W. Reith was appointed as General Manager of the Company, and in October 1923 joined the Board as Managing Director. The Chairman received an annual remuneration of £500, and each of the Governors received £200 - all payments free of income tax! Smaller firms were represented by Sir William Bull (Director of Siemens) and Walter W. Burnham (Managing Director of Burndept) and the remaining 40,000 £1 shares (limited to 10,000 to any one applicant) were made available to any bona-fide British manufacturer wishing to join the Company, whether it was a long-established firm with impressive factory premises or one of the growing number of 'back-room' concerns with just a few employees. Each shareholder had to pay an initial goodwill deposit of £50, although this clause was subsequently abolished on October 1st 1923. Dividends were limited to 7.5 per cent and revenue was derived both from a half share of the 10s.0d Broadcast Licence introduced on November 1st 1922 and from royalties levied on certain wireless equipment sold to the public.

And so, on Tuesday November 14th, the British Broadcasting Company first began broadcasting from their single studio on the top floor of Marconi House in the Strand. The London station retained its call-sign 2LO, and with the programmes being beamed on 361 metres from a cage aerial perched high on the roof, listeners in London and the Home Counties were soon tuning-in to the first evening's entertainment: two copyright news bulletins each of about a thousand words, and two weather reports, put out at 6pm and at 9pm. The announcer was the station's Director of Programmes, Arthur Burrows, and at the start of each programme he informed listeners-in that he would read the 'messages' through twice, first quickly and second slowly, asking them to write in and say which pace they considered better. With the official programmes over, he then began a little informal talk by saying, "You know, this broadcasting is going to be jolly good fun!"

Both the news and the weather reports soon became important features of the B.B.C.'s daily programme. An agreement was reached with four British Press agencies (Reuter's, the Press Association, the Central News and the Exchange Telegraph Company), for them to supply a daily summary of the world's news, and the Meteorological Department of the Air Ministry agreed to supply the B.B.C. with two weather reports every night.

THE B.B.C.'S BROADCASTING POLICY

The B.B.C.'s broadcasting policy was primarily one of public service rather than of pure commercial interest, and headed by Reith, it strove for political independence and impartiality. The Company began by serving the most densely populated areas in each main part of the country first, to gauge the popularity of broadcasting and to test for future requirements. Compared to later broadcasting developments, the B.B.C. was, in 1922, using very low power transmitters and while the basic predicted range of reception had been calculated at about 100 miles, it was soon found in practice that the real limit of 'quality' reception was about 35 miles with a simple valve receiver and headphones, and only about 12 miles with a crystal set. Greater distances were obtainable at night and in special circumstances of weather and terrain, and for those rich enough to be able to afford multi-valve receivers, reception range was increased to well over 100 miles. Curious freaks of reception did occur of course: readable signals from 2LO were reported to have been received in the Shetland Isles on a 1-valve set, while nearly 200 miles away from London, reception was claimed on a crystal set at Bridlington, Yorkshire.

On Wednesday November 15th, the day after the opening of the first station, the B.B.C.'s second and third stations began broadcasting to listeners in the Midlands. They were Birmingham (call-sign 5IT) on 420 metres, owned by the Western Electric Company, and Manchester (call-sign 2ZY) on 384 metres, owned by Metropolitan-Vickers Electrical Company, each transmitting programmes of concerts and news from about 6pm to 10pm.

Both these companies had strong American connections and like Marconi's had been experimenting with wireless telephony for some time. The Metropolitan-Vickers Electrical Company had earlier in the year been given a licence to begin experimental broadcasts from their station in Manchester, having pooled their patents with those of the Radio Communication Company, who themselves were then operating an experimental broadcasting station from their works in Slough.

Earlier in October, the Western Electric Company, which was part of the Bell Telephone Group of America, had set up a 500 watt transmitting station (call-sign 2WP) in Norfolk Street, London. Later that month, the component parts of 2WP were transferred to Birmingham and installed in the works of the General Electric Company and given a new call-sign, 5IT.

At 6.30pm on December 23rd, the B.B.C.'s new station at Newcastle (call-sign 5NO) opened with an experimental transmission of concert music on 400 metres. By the close of 1922, the B.B.C. had four of its proposed eight main stations in operation, all transmitting within the Broadcast Band to an audience of nearly 36,000 listeners tuning-in on factory-made Broadcast Licence receivers, together with many thousands of amateur experimenters with home-constructed sets.

THE BROADCAST LICENCE

To legally tune to the B.B.C.'s programmes, listeners-in had first to purchase a licence; either the Experimenter's Licence for those building their own equipment at home, or the Broadcast Licence for the less technically minded who wanted a factory-made, 'ready-to-receive' set.

The 10s.0d Broadcast Licence had been introduced along with the B.B.C.'s royalty scheme on November 1st, two weeks before the inception of broadcasting. Although there were no restrictions as to the qualifications, experience or experimental objectives of the applicants, its terms did stipulate that the holder was only allowed to receive B.B.C. broadcasts on British-made equipment which had been manufactured by a member of the B.B.C. and registered and approved by the Post Office. All such equipment could be readily identified by a circular 'BBC/PMG' stamp of approval (see Appendix, fig. 907a) placed either on the cabinet or the panel of the receiver together with an engraved G.P.O. registration number. The stamp however, did not signify any guarantee of the quality of the receiver bearing it.

While the B.B.C. had not actually begun to broadcast until November 14th, this licensing measure was brought into force in advance with the aim of protecting the infant British Wireless Industry from foreign competition, as membership of the B.B.C. was open only to bona-fide British wireless manufacturers. As a contribution towards the expense involved in the erection and maintenance of suitable transmitting stations and studios and the maintenance of regular programmes, the B.B.C. was to receive a moderate royalty on all British factory-built BBC/PMG-stamped receivers, amplifiers and certain accessories sold to the listening public together with a 50 per cent share of the revenue from the Broadcast Licence.

Problems soon arose however, and continued to grow throughout the early part of 1923, as there was an unexpected and overwhelming public interest in the very much cheaper home-constructed type of receiver, whether assembled from odd components and work box 'bits and pieces' or from a commercially-made boxed kit of parts. Both the B.B.C. and the Post Office had miscalculated the appeal of home-construction and soon after official broadcasting began new home-constructors in their thousands applied for the 10s.0d Experimenter's Licence which gave them the legal right to build home-constructed sets which the Broadcast Licence did not. Armed with an Experimenter's Licence, listeners could also legally use non BBC/PMG-stamped factory-made receivers of either domestic or foreign origin. One British company, the Peto Scott Co. Ltd., even sold G.P.O.-registered receivers either with or without the stamp. Their 2-valve Broadcast Major cost an extra 35s.0d in royalties if sold stamped for use with the Broadcast Licence, although listeners could buy it un-stamped at the normal price if they had an Experimenter's Licence, thereby making quite a saving for themselves but otherwise depriving the B.B.C. of its royalty. The B.B.C. therefore were receiving no royalties on sales of un-stamped apparatus or kits of parts (commercially manufactured receivers in kit form were exempt from royalty payment), and no revenue either from the Experimenter's Licence.

In December 1922, in order to curb the rush for Experimenter's Licences, the Post Office re-defined the original terms of that licence by stipulating that it would be granted only for genuine home-made apparatus to bona-fide experimenters who actually *made* their own components. Mr J.W. Wissenden, Head of the Wireless Licence Department of the Post Office defined the term 'home-made' as follows: "Any set which does not contain bought parts such as transformers, inductances, condensers etc., built at home from raw materials by the amateur wireless experimenter constitutes a home-made set. Any major parts of the apparatus that have to be bought for the set (such as valves) have to be stamped with the B.B.C. stamp and therefore have to be of British manufacture. 'Home-made' does not mean sets that have been bought in a kit of parts or made up of wholly manufactured parts which only need a screwdriver or a pair of pliers to assemble them." Therefore, from December 1922, applicants for the

Experimenter's Licence were scrutinised with a lot more attention and an inevitable backlog soon built-up during the early part of 1923.

As well as the BBC/PMG stamp, all sets for use with the Broadcast Licence also bore a G.P.O. registration number, signifying that the circuitry of the set had been tested and passed by the Engineer-In-Chief at the Wireless Section of the General Post Office (North) London as conforming to the technical requirements laid down to prevent interference from oscillation. Before beginning production, a manufacturer had to submit an example of his receiver for testing and if found satisfactory, a registration number would be allotted to it and the set sealed, labelled and returned. All sets in the production run could then bear a BBC/PMG stamp and that particular G.P.O. registration number as long as they were identical to the sealed and registered set, which had to remain sealed and readily available at the factory in case of official inspection. (Post Office officials also had the authority to select sets from the production line and compare them with the standard model they had previously approved).

In December, *Popular Wireless Weekly* sent a reporter down to the Post Office's Wireless Section to see how the registration and approval systems were working. Half a dozen sets were lined up when he arrived and a vast amount of brown wrapping paper and packing provided evidence of how many sets had been there before. He tackled one of the department's officials with the question "Pretty busy?" and received the reply, "This broadcast business is a blessed nuisance!" "And," wrote the reporter, "what more satisfactory indication of the prosperity of the wireless trade could be desired?".

Valve receivers were of the 'tuned radio frequency' ('TRF') type, (also known as the 'straight' type) and used general purpose 'R' valves which could be used either as HF amplifiers, detectors or LF amplifiers. The ubiquitous 'R' valve (fig. 38), with its characteristic bulbous shape and 'top-pip' evacuation seal (a pinch of glass formed at the top of the valve during the air evacuation process in manufacture and common to practically all valves until 1925) dominated the domestic receiver market until towards the mid-1920s. It employed a 'pure' tungsten filament (a tiny trace of thoria was added to improve tensile strength) which required a high temperature to give the necessary electron emission (c.1,050 deg. C. - c.1,200 deg. C.). This consumed a large current from the accumulator and gave rise to the valve's characteristic feature of glowing like an electric light bulb when in use. For this reason it was known familiarly as a 'bright-emitter' and some frivolous people, on occasions when they weren't using their receivers for listening-in, instead merely connected the filaments to the accumulator and turned up the rheostats high enough to provide light to read by or even to light the room. *Wireless World* thought that this practice was extremely foolish and ought to be discouraged at all costs for it considerably shortened the valves' lives. With receivers of this period designed with valves mounted externally on the control panel, the valves' incandescence could prove rather trying on the eyes. To combat this, a device costing 8d placed on the market by a Mr R.F. Gordon of Weymouth provided one remedy. Rather similar in appearance and construction to a well-known family planning product, it consisted of a sleeve of black rubberised material which was rolled snuggly over the valve, and being opaque, effectively shielded the listeners' eyes from the glowing filament. On the upper end of the sleeve was a protective protrusion which prevented the valve's top-pip of glass from damage if accidentally knocked.

In practice the 'R' valve was usually very unstable particularly when used as a HF amplifier due to a small but troublesome anode-grid capacity which could very easily be made to produce excessive feed-back and distortion. To obtain

fig. 38 . 'R' Valve (actual size), by British Thomson-Houston Co. Ltd. Late 1922. A bright-emitter with a nickel-plated base. 4 ¼ in. high. Etched with the BBC/PMG stamp.

a degree of volume, the long-standing favoured method was to employ an adjustable reaction circuit in which part of the amplified energy from the anode of the valve in the aerial circuit was fed back by means of a swinging reaction coil to its grid and therefore further amplified. (The method of 'swinging coil reaction' was very popular until it was displaced by 'capacity controlled reaction' in 1927). The amount of reaction amplification was determined by adjusting the variable reaction control mounted on the panel which would sometimes be labelled 'VOLUME', although with the B.B.C.'s transmitters using very low power and with the relative inefficiency of receiving valves in general, there certainly wasn't much volume to control. Adjustable aerial circuit reaction generally gave better results than other types of circuit but was prone to cause severe oscillations in the receiver's aerial with only the smallest overuse of the reaction control knob by an unsuspecting or novice listener-in. This oscillation would then be radiated locally causing 'howling wails' to be heard in the headphones and loud-speakers of neighbouring receivers tuned-in to the same station for perhaps several miles around, possibly completely drowning out the programme being listened to.

Before the inauguration of the B.B.C., the use of adjustable aerial circuit reaction was universal but under the Broadcast Licence regulations, the use of adjustable reaction in the aerial circuit of all BBC/PMG-stamped valve sets was banned, although fixed reaction could be used in this stage if it was incapable of causing oscillation. Adjustable reaction could be used in a subsequent stage so long as it was not coupled to the aerial tuning circuit. The Post Office therefore only passed manufactured sets which did not oscillate but to produce an efficient receiver under these conditions was extremely difficult. Much to the annoyance of many long established and reputable firms, the home-constructor was virtually given a free hand as to the type of circuit he chose to build and any such amateur-built receiver, no matter how crude, inefficient or liable to cause interference, could cheerfully be used with the Experimenter's Licence without being subject to any kind of Post Office test or approval. Most of these sets had adjustable aerial circuit reaction and therefore most of the problems encountered with oscillation lay squarely with the home-constructor's set. Although the Experimenter's Licence stipulated that home-made sets must not be allowed to cause oscillation, the sheer number of home-constructors made it difficult for Post Office officials to carry out checks. Mr. W.W. Burnham of Burndept Ltd., voiced the opinion that experienced firms such as his were being treated by the Post Office as "schoolboys" by being compelled to submit their sets and this general discontent continued until reaction testing was abolished altogether in October 1923.

Reaction circuit interference from "inexpert amateurs" was very common during the early years of the British Broadcasting Company and was still something of a menace when the Company became a Corporation in 1927. Common too were the sometimes desperate appeals broadcast to listeners-in to control their sets and a black list of defaulting areas was often read out over the air in the hope of "shaming the delinquents". But soon, vast improvements to high frequency amplification with the wide adoption of Neutrodyne circuits in 1925 and the introduction of the screened-grid valve in 1927, led to the development of highly stable TRF receivers which became universal until the mid-1930s when they were finally ousted by the mains superhets.

Local interference from amateur transmitters was also very noticeable within a few weeks of the inauguration of the British Broadcasting Company and their owners were politely requested not to carry out experiments during the broadcasting hours, 5pm to 11pm. The B.B.C. hoped to provide such high grade programmes that all amateurs would be listening-in instead of experimenting during the hours when the broadcasting stations were in operation.

LISTENING-IN

Two basic types of factory-built receiver were available to the public for listening-in to the B.B.C.: the crystal set and the battery-driven valve receiver. There were no plug-in mains receivers at this time and it would be another few years before the first commercial 'mains' wireless receivers began to appear (see 1925).

Crystal Sets

Crystal sets were in general designed for short-range reception of their local medium-wave broadcasting station, and could be used satisfactorily up to about 12 miles from the transmitter. They were by far the most popular type of receiver, due mainly to their sheer simplicity in use, relative cheapness and compact size: most were housed in a small polished wooden box-like cabinet, little bigger than a biscuit tin (fig. 39). They employed a mineral crystal (usually galena) in delicate contact with a tiny coil of wire known as a 'cat's whisker' to detect the transmitted high-frequency currents which were then converted into audio-frequency currents enabling the broadcast programmes to be heard through a pair of headphones. It was not a question of simply turning the set on, for the listener-in first had to carefully search the crystal with his cat's whisker in order to find a spot sensitive enough to produce a good signal in his headphones, (a process called "tickling the cat's whisker"), and this could take some considerable time. Care had to be taken too, once a good contact had been found, not to jog the detector (which was usually protected from dust by being enclosed in a glass tube) as the cat's whisker/crystal arrangement was easily upset: 'permanent detectors', which required no adjustment, were employed by some manufacturers but were never very widely used.

fig. 39. Gecophone Model No.1 Type BC 1002, by General Electric Co. Ltd. 1922. BBC/PMG Stamp, GPO Reg.No.102. Crystal set for headphone use, glass-enclosed cat's whisker/galena detector (open detector version also known), provision for plug-in coils, variometer tuning, ebonite control, nickel-plated fittings, mahogany box with lift-up lid. 6 ¼ in. x 9 in. x 6 in. (closed). £5.10s.0d.

fig. 40 . Exploring the crystal with the cat's whisker in order to get a good signal could prove a time consuming task, leading in some cases to the point of frustration.

For tuning purposes, either a variometer or a cylindrical inductance coil with a slider or tappings was used - the variable condenser (then the 'straight-line capacity type' with semi-circular metal vanes) was at this time quite an expensive component and although fairly common in valve receivers, it was not usually employed to any appreciable extent in crystal sets until 1923 when cheaper examples appeared. While most crystal sets covered the medium-wave Broadcast Band only, a few were provided with interchangeable plug-in or slot-in tuning coils which enabled their basic tuning range to be extended. This was useful for those within reception range who might enjoy listening-in to the ground-to-air conversations from Croydon Aerodrome on 900 metres, or who wished to set their watches or clocks by the Paris time-signals on 2,600 metres.

In the main, the crystal set was for the solitary listener-in even though it was possible to connect up another pair of headphones without too much loss of signal strength. Family listening was generally ruled out as, without the aid of amplification, the output was not strong enough to drive a horn loud-speaker; but it was a fairly common practice to place the headphones in a china fruit bowl or pudding basin which seemed to amplify the signals a little, especially if everyone huddled around.

Unlike valve receivers, crystal sets worked without batteries as all the necessary power came directly from the energy of the transmitted waves picked up by the outdoor receiving aerial. (There were a few rare exceptions to this, with crystal sets using a carborundum crystal and a steel contact, where a small cell of about 1.5 volts was needed to polarize the crystal in order to get it to function properly, fig. 64). The most common form of outdoor receiving aerial was the horizontally mounted 'L' type: a large, cumbersome affair, strung up on poles or fixed to a tree in the garden with the down lead-in wire to the set positioned at one end giving the whole aerial its characteristic 'L' shape. The Broadcast Licence permitted the use of up to 100 ft. of aerial wire and for maximum signal strength this had to be carefully positioned so that it was in a direct line with the nearest broadcasting station.

Given that the crystal set's reception range was not very great, then with a large outdoor aerial, plus a good earth connection and a pair of headphones, plenty of entertainment could be enjoyed for the investment of an average week's wages. As *Popular Wireless Weekly* reported, listening-in soon became "Britain's most favourite hobby - afforded by everyone!"

Valve Receivers

In comparison to crystal sets, battery-driven valve receivers were very expensive. They were capable of greater receiving ranges but were larger and more complicated and generally looked as though they would be far more suitable on a science laboratory bench than in the domestic surroundings of the home. Some, *Wireless World* thought, were of "fearsome appearance" (fig. 41) with their ebonite control panels festooned with an imposing array of protruding bright-emitter valves, plug-in tuning coils for various wave-ranges, knobs, switches and dials. The panels themselves were characteristically either sloping (fig. 65), horizontal (fig. 53) or vertical (fig. 41). Receivers employing from one to as many as eight or more valves were available on the market, and listeners tended to go for the cheaper and basic models like the comparatively short-range 2-valve (DET/LF) receivers rather than the more specialised long-range multi-valve sets which were not very economic due to the heavy filament current consumption and the initial cost of each valve. Valves were not generally included in the price of the receiver and like the other accessories such as batteries, earth wire and an aerial system, they had to be purchased separately.

fig. 41 . 'Cabinet Set', by W.R.H. Tingey. Early 1922. A 5-valve receiver with 3 or 5 valve switching, covering 175 to 28,000 metres in 7 stages, ebonite control panel, ebonised wood case. 16 in. x 18 in. x 7 in. Typical of the "fearsome" type of valve receiver described by *Wireless World*, with its scientific-looking panel bristling with controls.

Valve receivers were of the 'permanently installed' type, and it was not practical to move them once they had been wired-up via panel terminals to the aerial, earth, HT and LT batteries and headphones or, if capable of driving one, a horn loud-speaker. The whole assortment, with trailing wires and accessories spreading out around the receiver, constituted the 'wireless *set*' in its original meaning. If space for an outside aerial system was limited, for example in the case of a flat-dweller, a small indoor directional frame aerial, mounted on a stand or fitting into the top of the receiver's cabinet, was usually found to be adequate for local station reception, although the actual amount of energy it picked up was small.

A good low resistance earth connection was thought essential and there were several methods of obtaining it. The most elaborate was to bury a fan-shaped system of wires under the entire length of the aerial, or the listener could purchase a specially produced copper earth mat which was buried deep in the ground preferably in a damp part of the garden: a 7lb. biscuit tin or an old copper saucepan could give similar results. Most listeners though used a copper tube driven into the earth which they frequently watered. Wiring the receiver's earth terminal to an outside water pipe or an interior gas pipe were other favoured and perhaps more convenient methods, but with the latter, leaded joints in the pipe offered a high resistance which made the connections inefficient. To protect both the receiver and the home from lightning, (an outdoor aerial was an excellent lightning conductor), a throw-over switch was usually employed which disconnected the aerial from the receiver and connected it to the earth wire and thereby directly to earth. But there were apparent hazards with connecting the aerial system directly to a gas pipe being used as the earth which most wireless magazines and books were at pains to point out.

At this time, valve receivers in general were designed for headphone use, although some of the more powerful multi-valve models and those which were used with a separate valve amplifier were capable of driving a horn loud-speaker (a 2-valve DET/LF receiver could also drive a horn loud-speaker if used very close to a transmitter). Loud-speakers with metal, wood or ebonite horns were only being produced in small numbers, and these were usually straight-necked or curved-necked. A few of the more 'modern' swan-necked variety were only just beginning to appear but by the following year these had become the dominant design. Most horns were made of metal (spun aluminium or copper), and these had the annoying property of vibrating at certain specific frequencies especially during passages of loud orchestral music. Some were finished in a crystalline paint which helped to overcome the problem but horns made of ebonite, like those made of wood, were thought of as being comparatively non-resonant.

The sound, intensified by the horn, was reproduced from a drive unit housed in the base of the loud-speaker and the vast majority of these used a magnet system which was very similar to that found in headphones, only with a somewhat larger soft-iron diaphragm. Arrangements were made, via a 'sensitivity control', for altering the distance between the diaphragm and the pole pieces of the magnet so that the drive unit could be adjusted according to the power output of the receiver, a feature which in some cases was used in headphones such as the Brown Type 'A'. Sensitivity controls were also used in moving-iron cone loud-speakers following their introduction in the mid-1920s. During the late autumn of 1922, the first energised moving-coil horn loud-speaker, the Magnavox R2B, was introduced into Britain from America by the Sterling Telephone & Electric Company and this was certainly the most sophisticated horn loud-speaker then on the market (fig.820). In 1926, moving-coil *cone* loud-speakers were introduced which within a few years superseded all other types and became the standard approach to loud-speaker design.

fig. 42 . Straight-necked, curved-necked and swan-necked horn loud-speakers of 1922.

In 1922, wireless receivers, accessories and components were generally bought from the relatively few specialised wireless and electrical retailers established in the cities and towns within the service area of the four B.B.C. stations, or they could be obtained by mail order direct from the manufacturer. (Valves were not generally sent through the post owing to the risk of breakage and were usually purchased locally). Quite unrelated establishments such as cycle shops, newsagents, tobacconists and chemists also sold wireless sets but within a few years, as broadcasting encompassed practically the whole of Britain, a network of specialist wireless retailers was established around the country and the wireless shop, usually with its backroom service engineering department providing repair, battery charging and valve testing facilities, became as common a sight in the High Street as the butchers' or the bakers', and was probably more frequented by men than any other shop in town.

The wireless retailer was the last link in the chain of marketing and his shop was soon to become the showroom of Britain's fastest growing industry, supplying an ever enthusiastic listening public with the latest receivers, headphones, loud-speakers, batteries, components and valves.

In 1922, valves were generally of the 4 volt bright-emitter type and to supply filament current, 6 volt accumulators were required. Known as 'low tension' ('LT') batteries, these comprised three series-connected 2 volt lead-acid cells housed in thick glass containers (fig. 43). Accumulators were very heavy and needed frequent re-charging (the charge lasted from 2 to 3 weeks with average use), and while most battery set users had to put up with the inconvenience of lugging their accumulators down to the nearest wireless retailer or garage who could provide this service, home-charging units had become available during the summer for use in homes connected to a DC mains supply. In September, the Hart Accumulator Company of London inaugurated a motorised re-charging service for the convenience of their customers in outlying districts which was soon to be copied by other battery firms and garages around the country. For 6d a time, the used accumulator would be collected and swapped for a re-charged one, the customer of course having initially to purchase an extra accumulator. Valve receivers also required a 'high tension' ('HT') battery to supply the valves with anode voltage (fig. 44). These were mostly non re-chargeable and would last about 3 to 4 months.

fig. 43 . Lead-acid accumulators, also known as 'LT' (low tension), 'secondary', 'storage' or 'wet' batteries, were re-chargeable 2 volt batteries of varying current capacity, consisting of a thick glass container in which two sets of lead plates were fitted. The plates were made up of lead grids filled with paste: a mixture of red lead, litharge and sulphuric acid for the positive plate, and a mixture of litharge and sulphuric acid for the negative plate, (the sulphuric acid in both mixtures was allowed to dry out before the cell was assembled). The plates, separated by hard wood or ebonite separators, were immersed in an electrolyte comprising a solution of pure sulphuric acid diluted with distilled water to the required specific gravity. Accumulators provided the filament current for the valves and would last about two to three weeks before they needed re-charging, depending upon the number and the type of valves used and the time spent 'listening-in'. In 1922, a 3-cell 6v accumulator of 40 ampere-hour capacity complete in a 7¼ in. x 10 in. x 5½ in. wooden carrying crate cost around £2.10s.0d, and the re-charging service, which usually took about 24 hours, cost around 6d. From the mid-1920s, 'unspillable' accumulators with a 'jelly' electrolyte and accumulators housed in lighter weight 'unbreakable' celluloid containers became popular for use with battery portable receivers. The LT batteries in the photograph date from the late 1920s.

In November at the Olympia Motor Show, Marconi's and Daimler carried out experiments intending to exploit the commercial possibilities of car radio. An experimental receiver was mounted adjacent to the back seat of a limousine to pick up programmes sent from a temporary Marconi transmitter (call-sign 2BP) set up in Olympia for the duration of the show.

However, little came of these experiments and the development programme was subsequently dropped. Over the next ten years, there were various private experiments with car radios (see 1927) but they remained little more than a novelty until the introduction of the first commercially manufactured model in 1932 (see 1932).

In 1922, a few valve sets began to be housed in neat upright wooden cabinets with a battery compartment below and double doors above which were kept closed when not in use to hide the control panel. Known as 'smoker's cabinet sets' because of their resemblance to this article, they became popular with several manufacturers and were the first real attempts to make the wireless fit in with domestic furnishings (fig. 56).

Completely 'all-enclosed' sets with both batteries and a horn loud-speaker contained within the cabinet were rare. One of these, by Wates Bros., was the Cabinet Set which was built into a writing bureau, and Anode Wireless & Scientific Instruments Ltd. offered a Table Model (literally!) with the receiver and all its accessories housed neatly within a rectangular mahogany table so as to "harmonise with the other furniture in the room".

'Unit sets' were very much in evidence too, both in factory-built and home-constructed form (fig. 65). Any number of separate add-on units (e.g. a detector or LF stage) could be purchased as and when required and linked by standard terminal connections to be assembled into anything from a simple crystal set to a multi-valve receiver depending upon the budget or the requirements of the listener-in.

A new type of circuit introduced at about this time was the reflex circuit in which one of the valves served the double purpose of acting simultaneously as an HF and an LF amplifier (fig. 60, Marconiphone Model V2).

Home-construction grew increasingly popular, for with a minimum of technical knowledge, building a receiver on the kitchen table offered a cheaper and to many, a more rewarding way of listening-in, especially if the set worked after it had all been wired together! For the even more technically minded, making some components by hand was comparatively straight forward although there were many sources of cheap ready-made components available to save both time and trouble. There were also many books on the subject and one of the most well known names in this field was that of John Scott-Taggart. A keen experimenter since before the First World War (see 1913), Scott-Taggart founded The Radio Press in 1922 which concentrated on books and magazines (notably *Modern Wireless* and *The Wireless Constructor*) published with the home-constructor's market in mind. He was a prolific writer, with innumerable wireless books and magazine articles to his credit, and amongst wireless collectors, is perhaps best known for his famous series of circuits which bear his initials 'ST' (see 1932).

The problems over the Experimenter's Licence had given the green light to some foreign component manufacturers, who took full advantage of the situation and began to flood Britain with cheap stock. There were plenty of ex-Government components around to experiment with too, as well as surplus World War One wireless receivers, much of it suitable for medium-wave reception. At least one of these receivers, the 1916 Mark III Tuner, was given its own G.P.O. registration number (Reg.No.237) when it emerged in December 1922 in a slightly modified guise as the McMichael Radiomac Crystal Mark III crystal set. This version covered "the entire broadcasting and shipping range, 150/1200 metres" and was described in McMichael's advertisements as "Brand New!", which was probably an accurate statement since the bulk of Mark III Tuners released onto the market straight from Government stores were unissued and had never seen active service.

fig. 44. High tension ('HT') batteries, which were also known as 'primary' batteries, were necessary to provide the valves with anode voltage, and comprised a large number of series-connected 1½ volt dry cells usually arranged neatly in a strong cardboard box and well sealed in with paraffin wax or pitch to form a single unit. Depending on the valves and the type of receiver used, HT batteries in sizes from 45 volts to as much as 180 volts were available, and these were provided with tappings taken from groups of cells at regular intervals so that variations in voltage could be obtained as desired. While being non re-chargeable, a good quality HT battery could, with average use, last for about three to four months and in 1922, one of 60 volts in a 3½ in. x 9 in. x 2¾ in. container cost around £1.0s.0d. HT batteries were sometimes made up of series-connected accumulators, but these were usually used only by listeners who were in a position to do their own re-charging or had a regular collection and re-charging service. The HT batteries in the photograph date from the 1930s.

With valve sets, a good percentage were capable of being adapted to tune outside the medium-wave Broadcast Band by means of interchangeable plug-in coils and this meant from below 200 metres to above 20,000 metres, encompassing both wireless telephony and Morse transmissions. With some models, tuning could be a highly complex process as there were several controls which had to be adjusted and balanced up correctly. The use of a wavemeter to measure the wavelengths of stations in order to calibrate the dials, was useful (fig.179, a later example).

While tuning in both crystal sets and valve receivers was comparatively 'coarse', there was at least one early use of an auxiliary vernier condenser to obtain finer tuning (fig. 62). This was a small unit, comprising one moving and two fixed metal vanes, connected in the circuit of the main tuning variometer making possible fine adjustments in steps of about a tenth of a degree. Although this component first appeared in a crystal set it was not long before vernier condensers were adopted in some valve receivers too and from 1925 they became generally available (see 1925).

As a more accurate indication of station tuning, some listeners-in with valve receivers employed a milliammeter placed in series with the positive HT battery lead and the anode of the output valve, which gave a visual indication of the signals received. The needle would deflect to a maximum point when the required station was fully tuned in, and an accurate reading of the strength of the signal received could then be taken. Visual tuning indicators of this type were occasionally included on the panel of some commercially manufactured valve receivers during the 1920s, but with the advent of automatic volume control and the need for far greater tuning accuracy in the 1930s, various types of visual tuning indicators became widely adopted (see 1932). Another meter sometimes seen on the panels of sets of the 1920s was the ammeter, which was used for measuring filament current.

In general though, the only visual guide to tuning in 1922 was by the two types of dial then in common use. Both had been used in military equipment during World War One and had influenced the design of domestic wireless equipment after. The first type was a rotating, circular dial in Bakelite or ebonite, with white 0-180 degree engraving on the bevelled edge of the dial itself (sometimes 0-100 degrees) and a fixed datum line engraved on the panel so that the reading was always in the most convenient position for the eye (fig. 56). Once broadcasting got under way in November 1922, this latter type of dial was universally adopted and continued practically unmodified for several more years.

The second type of dial was a rotating control knob with an attached pointer to indicate the settings on a semi-circular degree-marked Ivorine scale screwed onto the panel (fig. 53). Less commonly, these scales were also transfer printed or engraved directly onto the panel. Similar, smaller controls were also used to indicate the filament current of bright-emitter valves. Although bright-emitters were universally employed in wireless receivers of this period, they were recognised as being relatively inefficient, for they gave only a tiny power output while their filaments could consume nearly 3 watts. But about this time, interest began to be shown in a new improved class of valve known as the 'dull-emitter', the first commercial example of which, the LT1, had been produced by the M-O. Valve Company in March 1921. The dull-emitter employed a non-incandescent filament made of tungsten coated with thoria which gave the same necessary electron emission as the bright-emitter while operating at a very much cooler temperature (c.600 deg. C. - c.750 deg. C.). It therefore had a very much lower current consumption and required a smaller filament voltage (c.0.8v - 3v).

Initially costing more than an 'R' valve, early thoriated tungsten dull-emitters were too expensive for most listeners-in. But from 1923 with the introduction of the first standard ranges and the lowering of prices, they gradually became popular and soon superseded bright-emitter types, their heyday being from 1925 to about 1927 when they in turn began to be displaced by barium oxide coated types (see 1927).

1923

On May 1st 1923, the British Broadcasting Company moved its 2LO studio to new premises a few hundred yards away at the Institution of Electrical Engineers' building in Savoy Hill, while the original transmitter and aerial were kept in position at the top of Marconi House with a Post Office line connecting the two buildings. This move permitted the gradual construction of several additional studios at Savoy Hill and by the time these had been superseded by the new purpose-built Broadcasting House in May 1932, nine studios were completed, the largest of which (the concert hall) measured 45 ft. x 26 ft.

The first phase of the B.B.C.'s mainland broadcasting scheme was completed on October 17th with the opening of the eighth main station at Bournemouth (call-sign 6BM) on 385 metres. Cardiff (call-sign 5WA) on 353 metres had opened on February 13th, Glasgow (call-sign 5SC) on 415 metres on March 6th and Aberdeen (call-sign 2BD) on 495 metres on October 10th (the Broadcast Band had been extended in October 1923 following recommendations of the Sykes Committee: see THE LICENCE PROBLEM, below).

Each of the eight main stations produced its own separate programme from its own studio which meant that some eight complete programmes had to be produced every night. This proved very expensive and it soon became clear that if broadcasting became very popular and was allowed to expand, it would be essential to increase the potential number of listeners without increasing the number of separate programmes. This

led to the establishment of eleven relay stations around the country by the end of 1924, each with a transmitter output of about 120 watts serving their immediate local area for a radius of about 5 miles.

The first relay station, Sheffield (call-sign 6FL) on 303 metres, was opened on November 16th. The relay station scheme was one of the recommendations of the Sykes Committee following its investigation into broadcasting. The relay stations were to provide a few of their own productions but mainly a simultaneous broadcast programme fed by Post Office telephone lines from London, Glasgow or Cardiff: their own programme costs were therefore very much lower than in the case of the B.B.C.'s main stations.

By the mid-1930s, most of the B.B.C.'s stations were interconnected by long-distance underground cables specially designed for the purpose of simultaneous broadcasting, but when this method was first introduced (Glasgow did the first official 'SB' in the winter of 1923) ordinary Post Office telephone lines were used. By connecting the various broadcasting stations together it was possible for all, or a combination of those stations, to broadcast one single programme simultaneously.

LISTENING-IN

In the winter of 1923, just a year after broadcasting began, there were over 500,000 licensed receivers grouped around the eight main stations and one relay of the British Broadcasting Company. Unless you happened to live close to one of these stations, the type of receiver you could afford to buy did limit your listening. It would be a bad investment to purchase a cheap crystal set if you lived a hundred miles or so away from a transmitter, for the receiving range of this type of set was very limited. Of course, if money was no object, you could buy a long-range multi-valve set and be assured of hearing *something* entertaining practically anywhere in Britain, and there was often the possibility of picking up some really long-distance stations from Europe or even America, especially during long winter evenings when conditions were more favourable.

Fig. 45 . The chance of getting America or other distant stations often kept the really keen listener-in up till the early hours of the morning.

In January there had been a large increase in the purchase price of many valve receivers due to the introduction of the Marconi A1 Licence. A royalty was payable to Marconi's at the rate of 12s.6d per valve holder on receivers covered by Marconi patents and made by member firms of the British Broadcasting Company. (The 'Big Six', under the A2 Licence, paid only 7s.6d per valve holder). During the Marconi Company's existence, it had probably done more original research than any other firm, and this had resulted in an accumulation of patent rights made out in the names of various employees of the firm. Added to this were numerous other patents which had been purchased outright from other companies. Since practically every type of valve set made for broadcast reception was likely to involve the use of various circuits patented by Marconi's, it was usual for manufacturers to work under their patent licences.

In March, Plessey left London and moved to large factory premises at Ilford, Essex and from here it was to grow into one of Britain's foremost manufacturers and suppliers of un-branded chassis, loud-speakers and components to the Wireless Industry. (By 1950, it was the largest manufacturer of radio components in the Commonwealth). On December 29th 1923, the Marconiphone Company Limited was set up by Marconi's to take over from them the responsibility of the sale and distribution of domestic broadcast receivers and accessories and Plessey continued to make Marconiphone receivers for them until 1926. By then, Marconi's had acquired their own domestic wireless manufacturing company, Sterling Telephone & Electric Co. Ltd., who had a factory at Dagenham, Essex, shared office buildings with Marconiphone at Tottenham Court Road and with whom Marconi's had already established a mutual trading relationship. From 1926, orders continued to be received by Plessey from many other wireless companies and soon Plessey branched out into additional fields of production which led to a long association with the Post Office and the Ministry of Defence.

By 1923, the public were getting more used to having the wireless in their homes and as well as hours of entertainment of all kinds, it was providing special services of news, "S.O.S." messages and communiques and weather forecasts, although to some, wireless was still regarded with suspicion. A dealer who ran a battery charging service round the Exmoor farms in his district in the early 1920s recalled a remark made by a farmer's wife whose husband was off hay-making. "He'd better be careful," the dealer told her, "the *wireless* speaks of rain!" "Where did 'ee 'ear that?" she demanded. "Why, on Mrs P.'s set up at Higher House." he replied. The woman sniffed the air disdainfully. "Don'ee take no notice of what that wireless tells 'ee," she said, "'tis only a cheap ol' set!"

The wireless was a distraction and as 'Ariel' reported in the January 20th 1923 issue of *Popular Wireless Weekly*, "the craze for wireless is spreading more rapidly than ever. People are indeed going wireless mad and are forgetting their work. One business man has complained to Marconi House that wireless has been responsible for his wife neglecting her household duties. 'At half-past five each evening,' he wrote, 'instead of my wife preparing the evening meal, she sits down to listen-in'. Perhaps before long, we shall hear of wireless divorces."

On September 28th, the first issue of *The Radio Times* was brought out by the B.B.C. and within a few days over 250,000 copies had been sold. Unlike other publications on wireless, this "Bradshaw of Broadcasting" as the B.B.C.'s Director of Programmes Arthur Burrows described it, did not deal specifically with the technical aspect of the subject but took as its main theme the popular entertainment side of broadcasting, and backed this up by including full programme details of all the B.B.C. stations for the coming week together with news of the Company's activities. Since the inauguration of the B.B.C.'s first station in November 1922, listeners had been able to obtain programme times and details from information published in newspapers and in various wireless magazines such as *Popular Wireless Weekly*. But by early 1923, some newspapers began to fear the competition that this new medium of broadcasting was apparently presenting. This led them to hold a one day boycott of the B.B.C.'s programme listing in February as a protest. However, this incident backfired on them for it was enough to convince the B.B.C. (and Reith in particular) that the Company should bring out its own

independent weekly publication and no longer rely solely on the Press for informing listeners of the details of the B.B.C.'s programmes.

In general, the approximate receiving range using headphones of the various types of factory-built receiver available in 1923 was as follows: Crystal sets (12 miles), 1-valve sets (25/30 miles), 1-valve/crystal sets (45 miles), 2-valve sets, HF/DET (50/80 miles), 3-valve sets, HF/DET/LF (80/120 miles), and 4-valve sets, 2 HF/DET/LF (120/250 miles).

One problem encountered by those equipped with moderate-range valve receivers and living close to their local broadcasting station, was the interference from it. Even though only nine B.B.C. stations occupied the Broadcast Band on the medium-wave, some of their wavelengths were relatively close together, and often when attempting to tune into a more distant station on a wavelength similar to that of their local station, listeners-in would hear both signals together. As a device for eliminating the station causing interference, 'wave-traps' became available for the first time in commercial form. They comprised a unit made up of a coil connected in parallel with a variable condenser, and this was placed between the aerial lead-in wire and the aerial terminal of the set. The unwanted station could then be tuned out by adjusting the variable condenser in the wave-trap although this tended to cause the desired station to diminish in signal strength and meant that the wave-trap usually had to be adjusted again when other stations were required. (With the inauguration of the B.B.C.'s Regional Scheme in the early 1930s, wave-traps were once more back in favour and were employed to combat interference problems encountered particularly by listeners using older types of receiver. See 1930).

THE LICENCE PROBLEM

By the end of April 1923, some 260 British wireless manufacturers had become members of the British Broadcasting Company and the number of various different models of receiver given a G.P.O. registration number had reached 1,450 with some 80,000 BBC/PMG-stamped sets in operation. This figure included all classes of equipment, from crystal sets (still by far the greatest number), valve/crystal sets, 1,2 and 3-valve sets and multi-valve sets and amplifiers. Of the valve sets, those with a 3-valve HF/DET/LF type of circuit were the standard product of many of the top manufacturers and were usually chosen by those prepared to pay a good price for a good quality receiver, while the 2-valve DET/LF type were very popular with the general listening public since they permitted the use of a loud-speaker within short-range of a transmitter.

But there was increasing competition from the home-construction market which threatened the section of the British Wireless Industry which produced ready-made sets and which only now was beginning to grow and to establish itself. The licence problem grew worse, and because the Post Office was looking more closely at new applicants for the Experimenter's Licence, a huge backlog built up during the spring and summer of 1923. Every week more interest continued to be shown in home-construction and a great deal of attention was now being paid by component manufacturers to the design and production of component parts from which the wireless experimenter could build his own wireless apparatus in his own home without too much skill. Kit-receivers, a packaged set of parts complete with a cabinet, were also becoming widely available (fig. 89) and most wireless magazines carried regular articles on circuits and also published plans and blueprints to aid home-construction. In May, details of the new Neutrodyne circuit from America were first published in *Wireless World* who tried to encourage home-constructors to build it since it was a very selective circuit with an HF stage free from causing oscillation interference (see also 1925).

As news of the Post Office backlog spread, more and more home-constructors, either deterred from applying for a licence or just fed up with the long wait, (or even those who had been refused a licence), simply carried on listening-in without a licence of any kind. This serious situation then led to a Parliamentary Committee of Enquiry under the Chairmanship of Sir Frederick Sykes (the Sykes Committee) being assembled in April to help unravel the licence tangle and to review broadcasting as a whole.

Far from being critical of the B.B.C., the Sykes Committee's report, published on October 1st 1923, recommended the extension of the B.B.C.'s licence to broadcast until December 31st 1926, the immediate establishment of various relay stations around the country to further enlarge the broadcasting service and an extension of the present Broadcast Band to cover 300 to 500 metres but excluding 440 metres to 460 metres. (The reason for this exclusion was that the 450 metre wavelength was being used by direction-finding stations, and enough clearance either side of this had to be given to ensure freedom from interference). To substantially reduce the B.B.C.'s partial dependence on the Wireless Industry, the Sykes Committee recommended the abolition of royalties on sets sold by its member firms, and an increase in the B.B.C.'s share of the Broadcast Licence revenue from 50 to 75 per cent.

With regard to the licence problem, the Committee recommended the introduction of a single form of licence. However, this was not introduced until January 1st 1925 (see 1925) when protection of British manufacturers against foreign competitors ceased. At the time of the Committee's report, it was estimated by the Post Office that there were in the region of 200,000 unlicensed receivers in illegal use throughout the country, and so, on October 4th, two new licences were introduced as a counter-measure. They were the Constructor's Licence at 15s.0d for those wishing to construct their apparatus at home using British-made components only, and the Interim Licence also at 15s.0d introduced as an amnesty for all those listening-in on unlicensed equipment which included home-constructed sets made with foreign components and factory-built sets not bearing the BBC/PMG stamp or a registration number. These measures had the desired effect as licence figures for the end of October reveal: Broadcast Licences (128,000), Experimenter's Licences (59,000), Constructor's Licences (29,000) and Interim Licences (200,000).

fig. 46 . Square wires and sloping panels - members of the Hounslow Wireless Society passing a winter's evening in November 1923. Home-construction was very popular, for it offered a cheap alternative to expensive factory-made receivers and was often more of a challenge to the science-minded 'amateur' armed with his 15s.0d Constructor's Licence.

At the beginning of October, the Post Office's requirements for broadcast receivers were revised and out of consideration for manufacturers who were very seriously handicapped by the difficulties experienced in having to design receivers capable

MINIATURE WIRELESS.
VEST POCKET RECEIVING SET.
INSTRUCTIONS FOR USE.
Fix your Aerial to A, your Earth to E,
Connect your Telephones to end marked P,
Then adjust the Cat's Whisker, marked D, on
the crystal until most sensitive position is found.
By placing the two coils together or apart
the maximum signals will be received.
With your existing Aerial and Phones
wonderful results can be obtained.

fig. 47 . Crystal sets came in a variety of shapes and sizes. This unusual miniature receiver, built into an ordinary Bryant & May's matchbox, was provisionally patented by W.J. Hunt and was first shown at a trade exhibition of toys and novelties at the Royal Agricultural Hall in London in July 1923. It was known as the 'Vest Pocket Receiving Set', and was made with only a very short production run by Radiax Ltd. of London W1. The circuit comprises a primative loose-coupled arrangement, made up of two cotton-covered wire coils (the exposed end of one forming a cat's whisker), a galena crystal and boot eyelets for aerial, earth and headphone connections. The detector and coils are extremely difficult to adjust being so small and unstable. Box, ¾ in. x 2¼ in. x 1½ in. Price 2s.6d.
A 'de-luxe' version (for the same price) is known which came with an imitation lizard skin wrap-around label bearing the legend "Miniature Wireless Marvel" in gold lettering together with the distributor's name and address, "Agents - Samuels Ltd., 84 Strand, WC2". Neither version bore a BBC/PMG Stamp nor a G.P.O. registration number.

of non-oscillation, the testing of sets with regard to reaction circuits was abolished with the consequent appearance of Post Office approved receivers with adjustable aerial circuit reaction. Receivers for use under the Broadcast Licence still continued to be approved and stamped, but were now merely tested to see if they were capable of receiving the B.B.C. stations on both a long and a short aerial. While *The Wireless Trader* had given a full account of these test revisions in their November 1923 issue, the facts did not become generally known outside the trade until January 1924, when *Wireless World*, alarmed by the increase in interference naturally brought about by these sets, published a critical account of the Post Office and wondered why the public had not been informed. With the changes, it was inevitable that there should be a great rise in oscillation interference particularly as so many new listeners-in who bought these sets were completely ignorant of the technicalities of wireless. Seeing the BBC/PMG stamp of approval displayed on their receiver they naturally assumed that it was exactly the same as all the other non-oscillating receivers that had gone before and were often blissfully unaware of the problems they were causing.

On the same day as the Post Office's test revisions (October 1st), as a first step towards total abolition, the B.B.C. greatly reduced the royalty payable upon the purchase of factory-built BBC/PMG-stamped apparatus and abolished it entirely on valves, headphones and loud-speakers. Crystal sets benefited well from this for royalties on them dropped from 7s.6d to just 1s.0d and listeners found that those crystal sets which before had only been available in kit form (fig.100), and so had avoided the royalty dues, could now be purchased ready-made for only a shilling extra.

WIRELESS DESIGN

In November further good news came for those listening-in on crystal sets, when S.G. Brown Ltd. of Acton introduced the Crystavox, a combined mechanical amplifier and loud-speaker, which gave them loud-speaker listening for the first time without the use of a separate amplifier (fig.827). The same company also introduced two other mechanical crystal set amplifiers: the Microphone Amplifier Type 'C' (fig.120), which enabled several pairs of headphones to be used with a crystal set and gave "amplification equal to two valves", and the Frenophone, a combined mechanical amplifier and loud-speaker (fig.829).

For valve sets, loud-speakers were becoming more widely used, with the swan-necked metal horn the dominant type of design. This was epitomised in the B.T.H. Model C2 (fig.826), a cheap aluminium horn loud-speaker brought out for the masses in 1923 and in continuous production until about 1930.

During 1923, there was a definite move towards design neatness at the more expensive end of the commercial valve receiver market with an increase in the preference for enclosing the components and batteries in a polished wooden smoker's cabinet. Some of the larger companies produced virtually entirely self-contained receivers: the floor-standing Cabinet De-Luxe by G.E.C. (fig.116) also included an integral horn loud-speaker and needed only external connections to the aerial and earth wires. (Large, floor-standing receivers of this type became very popular in the 1930s when, in mains form, they were known collectively as 'consoles').

In the case of bright-emitter sets, there began a growing tendency to mount the valves inside the cabinet, just behind the control panel. Set into the panel were portholes with metal gauze windows through which the listener-in could inspect the glowing filaments. The panel also supported the controls for the variable condensers and rheostats etc., switches and terminals for HT, LT, the aerial, earth, headphones or loud-speaker. Inside, the valve holders were screwed down onto a flat wooden baseboard chassis which also housed other screwed down components such as resistors, transformers and coils: really, a series of separate components wired together which in the vast majority of cases were bought in from the component manufacturers and not specially designed for the receivers themselves. To inspect the works, there was a lift-up lid and this neat style of receiver was known as an 'American cabinet set' because of its established popularity in the United States. A further American influence first exhibited this year was the use of jack sockets for connecting headphones and loud-speakers (fig. 93). Other types of battery sets with horizontal panels, usually had a hinged top cover which could be closed to protect the controls from dust when not in use (fig.105).

The popular use of variometers and tapped and sliding inductance coils in crystal set circuits continued, although noticeably more manufacturers were now using variable condensers due to the availability of cheaper models. In valve receivers, variable condensers were widely used despite tuning problems increasingly encountered with the semi-circular shape of the metal vanes employed which was found to cause the stations at the lower end of the tuning range to crowd together. Both variable condensers and variometers were usually controlled by rotating black Bakelite or ebonite dials calibrated in degrees. (Fixed Ivorine scales with rotating pointers were by now not so common but were still a definite favourite with B.T.H., fig.109). No receivers of this period were ready-calibrated in wavelengths (let alone station names) and listeners-in had to keep a record of their own set's particular tuning adjustment readings either on a separate card or on one supplied with the set and usually pinned to its lid or, in the case of a smoker's cabinet set (like the B.T.H. receiver referred to above),

on its doors. Each stage in a valve receiver's circuit was controlled by a variable condenser or variometer and there were invariably two or three tuning dials to contend with, together with filament rheostats and perhaps loose-coupled coils and tapped inductance controls, all making the process of tuning-in rather a difficult matter. Like winding the grandfather clock or carving the Sunday joint, the duty of tuning-in the receiver was invariably reserved for the man of the house until the coming of simpler tuning arrangements and dials with station names actually printed on them liberated many women from this 'backseat listening' (see 1931). In October 1923, the first ganged variable tuning condenser was introduced by the Fallon Condenser Co. of London N4. Known as the Duanode, it comprised two identical condensers mounted on the same spindle and enabled two separate tuning circuits to be coupled together and controlled simultaneously by a single dial. Although it made the process of tuning a little simpler, the practice of employing a separate variable condenser and dial for each tuned circuit generally continued until the wide adoption of single dial ganged tuning in the early 1930s.

While the use of bright-emitters was still universal, interest in dull-emitters now began to grow and several examples appeared on the market during the year. Because an extremely high vacuum was required for the efficient operation of thoriated tungsten filaments, a new evacuation process was introduced into dull-emitter manufacture in 1923 in which magnesium was used to clean up residual gas remaining in the sealed bulb. Depending upon the size of the valve, between one and four small pieces of magnesium were placed inside the bulb before it was exhausted and sealed. Usually the magnesium was fixed to an extra plate connected to the anode so that, with the sealing process complete, a high current could be passed through the anode raising its temperature high enough for the magnesium to ignite and burn. At the same time, electron bombardment from induction heating caused residual gas to be given off from the electrodes (a process called 'outgassing') and the combustion from the magnesium absorbed all but a trace of it.

This evacuation process was called 'gettering' and it caused a deposit of magnesium oxide to form on the interior surface of the glass bulb giving the valves a characteristic silver-mirrored appearance. Almost every dull-emitter from 1923 used magnesium as a getter due to its very high efficiency, but occasionally red phosphorus was used in the getter, such valves being identified by the iridescent amber or straw colour of the bulb.

Sometimes, one comes across valves which have a deep blue, red or green coloured bulb, seen particularly on some French valves made by Grammont in the early 1920s. This has nothing to do with a gettering process but was in fact a cosmetic selling point designed to disguise a blackish deposit given off when the manufacturer used impure nickel for the anode. Customers had become suspicious having noticed this deposit on clear glass valves they were offered for they did not want to buy what they thought were used valves, even though they were assured that the deposit had only occurred during the outgassing stage of manufacture. The coloured disguise, however, was quite acceptable. Certain types of American manufactured valves of the mid-1920s had coloured bulbs as a means of brand identification.

Among the dull-emitters produced in 1923, was the first one designed solely for dry cell working: the DE3, made by the M-O. Valve Co. Ltd. (see Appendix). Two of these were supplied by Marconi's in 1923 in their V2 receiver for alternative use as a summer portable or for when difficulty was experienced with accumulator charging as the dry cell supplied with the receiver was capable of lasting about six months. There were not many portables around and Marconi's were then one of the few manufacturers to consider the possibilities of using wireless as an outdoor summer entertainment.

Another valve specially designed for single dry cell working was the Wecovalve (see Appendix), introduced by Mullard as the British-made version of the American Western Electric Company's type 215A 'peanut' valve which had a moulded ebonite base. (Moulded bases were soon to become standard practice with valve manufacturers and the Wecovalve was the first British valve to depart from the metal base). The Wecovalve had a bayonet fitting and its own special socket, or it could be fitted with an adaptor for use in a standard B4 socket, and it remained the world's smallest valve for several years.

'Grid bias', a potential applied to the grid of a valve to bring its working characteristic up to a certain specific point, was first introduced into commercially manufactured valve receivers (fig. 82) although its use had been well known to amateur wireless experimenters for a number of years. An additional small dry cell battery was needed which was inserted between the grid lead return and the negative LT lead. This 'grid bias battery' (fig. 48) was in construction a scaled down version of an HT battery and comprised a set of series-connected 1 ½ volt dry cells and was available in 4 ½ volt to 36 volt sizes (4 ½ volt and 9 volt being standard).

fig. 48. Commercially manufactured grid bias batteries date from 1923, when grid bias was first introduced into the circuits of commercially manufactured valve receivers. Similar to HT batteries, they were non re-chargeable and comprised a set of series-connected 1½ volt dry cells tapped at intervals. They were available from 4½ volt to 36 volt sizes, and in 1923, a standard 9 volt grid bias battery in a 3 in. x 5¾ in. x 1 in. container cost around 2s.0d and lasted about six to eight months or even longer.

ELECTRIC WIRELESS

By 1923, many wireless enthusiasts were experimenting at home with the potential benefits of utilising the current from AC or DC mains for supplying both the anode and filament circuits of their home-constructed valve receivers, thus doing away with batteries and accumulators. It was estimated that the energy from the mains cost between 4d and 6d per 1,000 ampere hours, whereas from batteries, the same energy would cost about 4s.0d. Therefore the running costs of sets would be very much less and the use of mains power would dispense with the bother and expense of having to convey the accumulator to a charging station at regular intervals.

Enthusiasts with a DC supply could, with very little technical know-how, charge their accumulators themselves by connecting them in series with an ordinary domestic lightbulb. On 200v DC, a 100 watt bulb would give a charging rate of 0.5A. Polarity was checked by dipping the bare wires from the DC supply into a glass of watered down vinegar: the negative wire would emit a stream of bubbles enabling the leads to be marked for future use. Those with an AC supply could charge their accumulators with a Tungar Rectifier manufactured by the B.T.H. Co. Ltd.

For listeners whose houses were wired with electricity but had inadequate outdoor space for erecting a suitable aerial or who preferred not to use a frame-aerial, the Dubilier Condenser Company of Hammersmith introduced their Ducon mains aerial device which by means of an integral standard plug, connected directly (and safely) into the house lighting supply.

Until the introduction of indirectly-heated AC mains valves in 1927 (and indirectly-heated DC mains valves in 1931), the idea of 'all-electric' wireless remained very much at the experimental stage and listening-in was often fraught with problems of both interference and safety. When the filaments of valves were directly heated by the raw mains supply, any ripple, interference or fluctuations in that supply showed up in the headphones or loud-speaker as a mains hum which at times could be quite deafening. One easy solution to this was not to dispense with the LT battery, but to just use the mains for supplying the HT. Messing about with high voltage circuits was dangerous for the inexperienced, as metal parts, such as the variable tuning condenser, were often live, and due warnings were usually given at the end of wireless magazine articles describing such circuits.

TELEVISION

During 1923, the first crude experiments in television were being made by John Logie Baird in a house at Hastings in Sussex. He was working on a mechanical scanning system using a spirally perforated rotating disc in both the transmitter and receiver, based on an idea first conceived by the German scientist Paul Nipkow in 1884. By the early spring of the following year, Baird had developed the system sufficiently to be able to transmit a flickering image of a Maltese Cross a distance of a few yards received on a piece of apparatus which he called a 'Televisor'.

1924

The new year opened with the broadcasting of the 12 strokes of midnight from Big Ben, and ever since then with only occasional periods of interruption these chimes have been sent out daily by the B.B.C. as time signals, the exact start of the new hour marked by the first stroke. Another system of time signals, the Greenwich 'dot-seconds' system, was inaugurated on February 5th 1924. Six dot-seconds, popularly known to listeners as 'the pips', from the standard Mean Time clock at Greenwich Observatory were at first superimposed on the broadcast programmes, the last of the dots marking the exact start of the new hour. Later the dots were broadcast alone and from 00.00 hours on January 1st 1972, the sixth and last dot became the now familiar longer dash.

Throughout 1924, the B.B.C. set about completing its relay station programme, and by December 12th ten more had been established. They were as follows: March 28th, Plymouth (call-sign 5PY) on 335 metres, May 1st, Edinburgh (call-sign 2EH) on 325 metres (shortly after it opened, 2EH was found to be incapable of serving the hilly broken country in its neighbourhood, and it became necessary to more than double its aerial power), June 11th, Liverpool (call-sign 6LV) on 318 metres, July 8th, Leeds (call-sign 2LS) on 346 metres and Bradford on 310 metres (Bradford relayed the Leeds service), August 15th, Hull (call-sign 6KH) on 320 metres, September 16th, Nottingham (call-sign 5NG) on 340 metres, October 21st, Stoke-On-Trent (call-sign 6ST) on 306 metres, November 9th, Dundee (call-sign 2DE) on 331 metres, and December 12th, Swansea (call-sign 5SX) on 318 metres.

Several of the larger towns in England, Wales, Scotland and Northern Ireland were now well served (on September 14th the B.B.C.'s ninth main station, Belfast, call-sign 2BE, on 435 metres, had opened to serve Northern Ireland), but many other large cities and towns as well as country districts were not really served at all although there were thousands of enthusiastic listeners in these areas trying to make the best they could of the weak signals that they were able to collect in their aerials.

It was soon realised that it would be impossible to serve the whole of Britain with a large number of low powered stations similar to those the B.B.C. had in operation at the time. And it was not just a question of raising the aerial power of the transmitters in use on the Broadcast Band since doing so would extend the range of acceptable broadcasting to only about 100 miles, at which point signal fading would occur.

It was suggested however, that if a high power station could be operated on a long wavelength, say, above 1,200 metres, fading would be greatly reduced and a very large area of the British Isles could be covered. Several doubts were raised: (1) Would there be interference with other wireless services using long waves? (2) Would existing receivers have to be modified or substituted altogether? (3) Would fading be much less than predicted? In order to settle these questions, an experimental 15 kW long-wave station was erected at the Marconi works in Chelmsford and under the call-sign 5XX began a series of experimental broadcasts on 1,600 metres from July 21st 1924.

The tests were very much of an irregular and unofficial nature and although the opening programme of a concert by Dame Clara Butt was sent out from an improvised studio at the transmitter, all subsequent broadcasts were fed to Chelmsford from the Savoy Hill studios and usually comprised three hour-long 2LO programmes. The other B.B.C. stations around the country would pick up the 1,600 metre signal and re-radiate it locally on their respective medium wavelengths, reverting to their own local programmes once 5XX had finished transmitting.

Practically all valve sets with interchangeable plug-in tuning coils could receive 5XX on the long waveband. Changing wavebands was a simple matter, for all the listener had to do was to select the appropriate coils and plug them in. But some valve sets with no facility for changing coils had to be converted, and most crystal sets could usually cope only with the Broadcast Band on medium waves which ended some 1,100 metres below 5XX. From July, new crystal sets complete with long-wave 'Chelmsford coils' began appearing on the market and listeners could look forward to the greatly increased range that the B.B.C. had promised them with long-wave broadcasting. In fact, 5XX was reported to have been received on a crystal set in Dumfrieshire, 270 miles away. By the winter of 1924, the B.B.C. had assumed a responsibility for providing a complete national broadcasting system accessible to the owner of the cheapest form of set in any part of the country.

LISTENING-IN

In 1924, tuning was improved due to the introduction of 'square law' variable condensers whose specially shaped metal vanes were designed to overcome the tuning problems encountered with the 'straight-line capacity type'. Another type of component introduced for the first time in 1924 was the Marconiphone 'Ideal' LF transformer: the first audio transformer to be designed (and guaranteed) to have an improved frequency response.

There was no doubt that the crystal set, simple and limited as it was, reigned supreme at this time. Figures published in the March 19th issue of *Wireless Weekly* of sales of wireless apparatus in the London area for the month of February make astonishing reading today: 28,831 crystal sets, 346 1-valve/crystal sets, 52 2-valve/crystal sets, 385 1-valve sets, 3,418 2-valve sets, 622 3-valve sets, 1,008 multi-valve sets, 3,879 microphone amplifiers and 4,016 valve amplifiers. These figures are a good indication of the buying habits of the British wireless public throughout the country and are echoed by the percentages in royalty returns received by the B.B.C. from dealers all over the country on BBC/PMG-stamped apparatus sold in March: Crystal sets 65.3 per cent, 1-valve/crystal sets 0.5 per cent, 2-valve/crystal sets 0.3 per cent, 1-valve sets 0.7 per cent, 2-valve sets 12 per cent, 3-valve sets 2.4 per cent, multi-valve sets 3.6 per cent, microphone amplifiers 4 per cent and valve amplifiers 11.2 per cent.

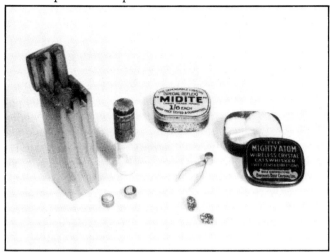

fig. 49. One of the more popular accessories of the crystal set was the spare crystal which was useful for replacement purposes or for when building a crystal set at home. Crystals came in a variety of attractively packaged containers: glass tubes, paper envelopes, pill-boxes and more commonly, in colourful tins which also might contain a spare cat's whisker, a pair of tweezers (to avoid handling) and printed instructions. While there were literally dozens of commercially produced crystals to choose from with exotic and important sounding names such as 'Hertzite', 'Gecosite' and 'Cymosite', most were in fact merely ordinary lumps of galena in natural or synthetic form, although examples of the less commonly used crystals, such as tellurium, were produced. The glass tube in the illustration above houses two of these rarer crystals which the supplier, C.F. Elwell Ltd., marketed as 'Tellite'.

On July 1st, the royalties paid to the B.B.C. from sales of wireless apparatus manufactured by its members were completely abolished and new receivers of all classes were no longer required to be submitted to the Post Office for test and registration. Under new regulations, receivers and valve amplifiers used with the Broadcast Licence could now be bought from *any* British manufacturer and not solely from one who was a member of the B.B.C., although John Reith felt that the public had a "moral obligation" to buy their equipment only from the latter.

Member firms though were still obliged to exhibit the BBC/PMG stamp on their wireless receiving equipment, even though the wording "TYPE APPROVED BY POST MASTER GENERAL" was now redundant. But from September, this was replaced by a second type of stamp which had the letters 'BBC' encircled by the phrase "ENTIRELY BRITISH MANUFACTURE", and examples of this 'BBC/EBM' stamp could still be seen on receivers manufactured as late as 1927 (fig.218). The BBC/EBM stamp was not linked to any royalty payment scheme and its use merely indicated that the apparatus on which it appeared was of British manufacture and was produced by a member of the B.B.C. (such sets could only be used under the Broadcast Licence). It was soon joined by a third, but little-used type of stamp (simply the B.B.C. trademark) which appeared without any peripheral wording (fig.907).

Valve receivers were steadily becoming neater and more compact and there was a notable decline in the unit type of set. Bright-emitter receivers with filament viewing portholes were still in evidence (figs.131,134) as were several 'old fashioned' models still employing externally mounted valves and coils (figs.127,138,150). Dull-emitters were rising in popularity and coming into widespread use and as a bridge between the old and the new technologies, some receivers introduced between 1924 and 1925 included provision for using either bright or dull-emitters (figs.140,143).

Aesthetic improvements to the wireless receiver were not matched in the design of the outdoor aerial system which generally remained large, cumbersome and, in some people's eyes, unsightly. Under the headline ,"THAT UGLY AERIAL", *Wireless World* reported in January, "With a sudden and unaccountable zeal for the beautiful, the Southbourne National Citizens Union has lodged a strong protest with the Town Council against disfigurement of the residential district of Bournemouth by wireless aerials. It appears that the hitherto chaste housetops now bristle with aerial poles, in many cases of the roughest description, while some citizens even desecrate chimneys and trees with suspended wires." There was even a move by various pigeon societies and organisations for the conservation of bird-life to persuade the P.M.G. to bring in legislation enforcing the use of corks on aerials. It was suggested that despite their keenness of vision, birds frequently could not see the wires until too late, and that a cork placed every two yards along the aerial would be quite sufficient.

But a new simpler and more compact type of aerial was introduced which found some popularity for a few years. Known as the Vertex, it was non-directional and looked rather like a large drum-shaped lamp shade and consisted of two horizontal rings spaced about 15 inches apart by vertical rods and held up by a central pole. About 100 ft. of wire was wound in a zig-zag pattern between the two rings and when attached high up on the roof of the house or attached to the chimney stack, fairly good results were obtained.

'Anti-microphonic' valve holders were also introduced for the first time. With the traditional bulbous shape of the glass envelope, the glass was at times found to 'ring' at a particular frequency and the rather flimsy electrode assembly common to early valves could easily be set in vibration by a jar or sharp knock, producing a high-pitched noise in the headphones or loud-speaker which would continue to get louder and louder until the set was switched off and allowed to settle down again. Anti-microphonic valve holders, which were sprung to counter vibration, went some way to curing the problems but it was not until the introduction of the dome shaped valves in the early 1930s that they were eliminated altogether (see 1933).

By 1924, about two and a half million valves were being produced per year and several of the leading manufacturers decided to form an association to safeguard their individual interests. This was the Valve Manufacturers Association, and was formed by B.T.H. Co. Ltd., Burndept Wireless Ltd., A.C. Cossor Ltd., Edison Swan Electric Co. Ltd., Electron Co. Ltd., General Electric Co. Ltd., Marconi's Wireless Telegraph Co. Ltd., Marconiphone Co. Ltd., Mullard Radio Valve Co. Ltd. and Standard Telephones & Cables Ltd.

It was generally accepted that wireless was now progressing beyond the purely experimental stage and this was witnessed among other things by the fact that the "amateur's experimental laboratory" referred to in wireless magazines a few years previously had now become his "wireless den". Within a few years the public had accepted it quite happily into their everyday lives and as the B.B.C.'s Managing Director, John Reith explained at the time, "Wireless itself has made a more vivid appeal to the popular imagination than anything else in our time. Most scientific developments which have had far-reaching consequences have been fully appreciated only by those with the necessary scientific training, but wireless has reached people of every description, whether technically interested in or completely ignorant of scientific matters."

To many people, family life was being strengthened through the common interest of music, literature, drama, wit and humour broadcast every week by the B.B.C., "and", pondered Marconiphone's Christmas 1924 advertisement, "what better way of keeping husband and sons away from the club or public house than by having a wireless in the living room?"

But tragedy could strike at any moment. On May 3rd, *Popular Wireless Weekly* reported, "A man died the other day while listening-in to 2LO. This is the first time anyone has died under such circumstances. He was found lying on the floor with the 'phones still on. The doctor announced that death was due to heart failure accelerated by shock or excitement. The broadcast programmes are *not* responsible."

CIRCUIT DESIGN AND LOUD-SPEAKER DEVELOPMENT

Progress in the design of high-frequency amplification circuits had been relatively slow due mainly to the instability problems encountered with valves used as HF amplifiers. Most valves had been of the general purpose type (one notable exception was the V24, see 1916) but in 1924 several specialist valves began to appear, designed solely for HF and LF work respectively. However, the most significant development was the appearance of the first commercially manufactured multi-valve 'supersonic heterodyne' receiver: the 7-valve Western Electric Model 44002 (fig.128). The practical principle of the supersonic heterodyne receiver (known more familiarly as the 'superhet') was first investigated by Major E.H. Armstrong while serving with the American Expeditionary Force during World War One, who had applied for a patent on December 30th 1918. The high frequency signal picked up in the aerial was changed to a lower fixed frequency by 'beating' it with a signal produced in the circuit by a local oscillator valve. The resulting lower fixed frequency (or 'intermediate frequency') was then amplified by circuits practically insensitive to all others, resulting in a considerable degree of stable amplification and very high selectivity. (The heterodyne circuit from which Armstrong's supersonic heterodyne developed was devised by Fessenden in 1901, the word deriving from the Greek 'heteros' meaning *other* or *external* and 'dynamis' meaning *force*). Although immediately popular in the United States, when these multi-valve receivers first appeared on the market in Britain in the mid-1920s they were far too expensive and technical for the average British listener who just wanted a simple receiver for home-entertainment, and consequently only a handful of models were produced then by some of the larger manufacturers for the 'serious amateur' to experiment with. Eventually though, following a superhet revival in the early 1930s, the superhet in mains form was to become the standard universal approach to circuit design and the most popular type of domestic receiver with both listeners and manufacturers.

At the beginning of May, *Popular Wireless Weekly* began publishing details of a new reaction circuit invented by their technical and assistant technical editors G.V. Dowding and K.D. Rogers. They called it the 'Unidyne' (*one-force*) as it used a single source of power from the LT battery only and completely dispensed with the HT. A new bi-grid space-charge tetrode, the 5-pin Thorpe K4 (see Appendix), was specially produced for use in this circuit by Bower Electric Ltd., of Shaftesbury Avenue, London WC1, who early in June brought out a complete kit of parts priced at six guineas for home-constructors to make a 2-valve Unidyne receiver for loud-speaker reception (fig.152). The K4 was the first British valve to be fitted with a 5-pin base, but its particular size and layout was not adopted by the valve industry as standard when 5-pin 'B5' bases were introduced *en masse* in 1928 (see 1928). Interest in the circuit itself, revolutionary to some, and nonsensical to others (including Marconi and Fleming), soon waned and it had no lasting influence upon the Wireless Industry.

Loud-speaker developments took a significant stride forward with the introduction of the first commercial 'hornless' type: the Sterling Primax (fig.842). The Primax was based on a French patent originally taken out by Lumiere in 1909 (patent number 11,015) and it used a radially-pleated paper diaphragm connected to a moving-iron (magnetic-reed) drive unit, producing near omni-directional sound for the first time. But for something of rather elementary design, it was expensive (seven guineas including a hefty £2 royalty fee), unless of course you happened to have a friend with a boat or an aeroplane who could bring one back for you from France where the price was a mere 35s.0d. Comparing it with a typical horn loud-speaker, *Wireless World* found it "a little insensitive, but with a far better response in the lower register". It came in an alternative statuette version and was also fitted into the Sterling Regina Type 1618 receiver (fig.125), one of the few completely 'all-enclosed' sets then on the market, having both battery compartment and integral loud-speaker. (Almost without exception, valve receivers of this date had to be connected to an external loud-speaker).

Although this type of loud-speaker appeared for only a couple of years and is thought unique to Sterling, its improved bass response and the apparent absence of directional effects experienced with horns did much to establish the hornless type of loud-speaker in public favour. (A wall-mounted pleated diaphragm loud-speaker was announced by George Bowerman Ltd., of London EC4 in September 1926, but it was last heard of held up in the production line by an industrial strike, and it is not known if any examples ever found their way onto the market).

Another significant change in loud-speaker technology was the introduction in September 1924 of the first commercial 'cone' type. This was the Beco, manufactured by the British Electrical Manufacturing Company, Putney, London SW15 (fig.835) which employed a conical diaphragm of aluminium foil connected to a moving-iron drive unit. Its construction was similar in basic design to the Brown reed-type headphone patented in 1910 and, in an enlarged form, used in the Brown H1 horn loud-speaker of the early 1920s (fig.818). Moving-iron cone loud-speakers with paper or taut linen diaphragms appeared early in the following year (see 1925) and rapidly took over from conventional horn loud-speakers, and remained universal until superseded in turn by the moving-coil cone type in the early 1930s.

In the winter, a new type of wire was introduced by the London Electric Wire Company and Smiths Ltd., of London EC1. Known as 'Glazite', it was made of tinned copper wire insulated with a special red, blue, yellow or black heat and damp-proof glazed covering which was guaranteed not to deteriorate with use. Its introduction marked a new era in panel wiring, quickly becoming popular with both home-constructor and manufacturer alike.

1925

On January 1st, the new Receiving Licence was introduced at 10s.0d a year and all previous forms of licence were abolished. The Receiving Licence made no stipulation concerning the country of origin of the receiver to be used, and the lifting of this restriction reflected the growing confidence that the British Wireless Industry had by then established itself and was able to compete fully with foreign imports. Under this new licence, wireless receivers and valve amplifiers could be purchased from any manufacturer, and not solely from one who was a member of the B.B.C. Member firms were no longer required to exhibit a B.B.C. stamp on their equipment, although many continued to do so for patriotic and prestige reasons until as late as 1927.

On January 6th, Chelmsford 5XX began radiating its own long-wave programmes from the Savoy Hill studios every Tuesday, Thursday and Saturday as an alternative to local programmes, and for the first time this officially gave listeners a choice of either their own medium-wave local station programmes or one of a more national character from 5XX.

(On Mondays, Wednesdays, Fridays and Sundays 5XX simultaneously broadcast the same programme as 2LO in London). The idea of giving listeners alternative programmes gained considerable popularity from this time and out of it was to be born the Regional Scheme in its original form with twin high power transmitters sending out two different programmes at equal strength, making the problem of selection as simple as possible. The Regional Scheme was to serve whole regions of the country rather than just single towns or cities as before.

During 1925, a monitoring station at Keston in Kent was opened by the B.B.C. to provide frequency measurement and technical monitoring of their programmes and to facilitate a relay service of programmes broadcast from European capitals. This station was replaced in September 1929 by the Tatsfield receiving station situated on the Kent and Surrey borders.

On April 5th 1925, the 2LO transmitter at Marconi House was closed down and its aerial was removed and re-erected on the roof of Selfridges department store in Oxford Street. From here, a new 2 kW transmitter came into use radiating programmes sent by a Post Office telephone line from the Savoy Hill studios.

The long-wave experiments at Chelmsford had by now proved to be so successful that it was decided to build a new permanent, centrally located 25 kW long-wave transmitter at Borough Hill, Daventry in Northamptonshire. It was here that 5XX was transferred, and on Monday July 27th 1925, the station opened on 1,600 metres, relaying to a very large part of the country a mixture of simultaneously broadcast 2LO programmes from the Savoy Hill studios, together with a small proportion of its own programmes. It was from this date that broadcasting really became a national activity, and the opening of Daventry 5XX marked the experimental beginning of the Regional Scheme, bringing an estimated one million more potential listeners within crystal range.

On November 14th 1925, listeners in some areas of the country began to complain of interference while tuned to the B.B.C.'s Bournemouth station on 386 metres. This was due to the first telephony test broadcasts from Eire's first official national broadcasting station, Dublin 2RN, whose 1½ kW transmitter was using the 390 metre wavelength. Although regarded as a 'foreign' station, 2RN received the support of the B.B.C. who had already lent John Reith to the selection committee for choosing the station's Director and Musical Director. The B.B.C. also co-operated over the relaying of programmes – on Dublin's official inaugural night, January 1st 1926, the formal opening was relayed by all the B.B.C. stations. Dublin's programmes were of a definite Irish character and many were put out in the Gaelic language, and despite earlier protests of interference, the new station was generally welcomed with many English listeners writing to express their appreciation, some even saying that they would like "lots more Irish folk songs".

The word 'listener' was now generally accepted as having replaced the old fashioned 'listener-in' although the latter term was still retained by some sections of the Press. However, *Wireless World* thought that a better, more appropriate word ought to be found, and suggested 'audist', 'inlistor' and 'receptor'. Luckily, none of these words was given serious consideration and 'listener' is still used to describe a member of the radio-listening public to this day.

COMMERCIAL PROGRAMMES

In 1925, the first commercially sponsored English language programme was broadcast to listeners in Britain from a Continental station. Captain Leonard F. Plugge, a staunch advocate of commercial radio, had approached Selfridges Department Store in Oxford Street and persuaded them to sponsor a talk on fashion which was to be transmitted on 1,488 metres from the Eiffel Tower station in Paris. The service area covered a large part of southern England, but when invited to write in and say that they had heard it, only three listeners bothered to do so. Despite this initial lack of interest, the number of Continental broadcasting stations willing to include commercial 'slots' began to increase towards the end of the 1920s, with Radio Hilversum (Holland) on 1,072 metres in 1928, and Radio Paris on 1,740 metres and Radio Toulouse on 529 metres in 1929 putting out sponsored light entertainment programmes in English for several hours a week. (The first British wireless manufacturer to sponsor a programme was Brandes Ltd., whose programmes first went out on Radio Hilversum in the winter of 1928). During the 1930s (see 1930), more stations were added and the commercial broadcasts soon became very popular with listeners in Britain. However, they posed a serious threat to the highly un-commercial B.B.C., by providing alternative and competitive listening, and on certain nights their programmes tempted vast audiences to 'switch over'.

By the spring of 1925, the number of transmitting stations in Europe had grown so rapidly and the consequent interference between them so great that with no proper organisational control this 'ether chaos' began to threaten the very existence of broadcasting itself. There were now about forty stations broadcasting in Europe and the B.B.C. decided to invite representatives from the other European Broadcasting Authorities to London for a conference on the problem and this resulted in the formation of the International Broadcasting Union (I.B.U.) in March.

In 1925, another Committee of Inquiry was set up to investigate the B.B.C.'s broadcasting service. Known as the Crawford Committee, its main recommendation was that the service should be "conducted by a Public Corporation acting as a Trustee for the national interest". This led to the establishment of the British Broadcasting Corporation, created by Royal Charter on January 1st 1927 (see 1927).

LISTENING-IN

It was from about 1925 that with improved circuits of 'modern' valve receivers and the greatly increased power of transmitted signals, the need for listeners to erect large outdoor aerial arrays became less important. Instead, the use of a frame aerial or other smaller type of indoor aerial was found in many instances to be quite sufficient, especially for listening to the local station or when using a multi-valve superhet. While large arrays of outdoor aerial wires and masts continued to be a familiar sight in back gardens around the country for many years, (some even persisting until well after the Second World War), by the end of 1925 their presence was beginning to be seen as indicating the use of an obsolete receiver. During the winter, *The Wireless Trader* advised dealers on their rounds or on their way to work by train to look out for homes with large outdoor aerials as they probably indicated a good prospect for a sales lead. Some parts of the country were more behind the times than others and presumably were better prospects: *Wireless World* reported in December that in Rhoswain, North Wales, "the number of wireless masts has evoked a District Councillor's remark that the suburb looks like a harbour full of ships!"

Although erecting an aerial and connecting it to a wireless receiver and a loud-speaker or pair of headphones was the usual way of listening-in, in January 1925 a local wireless and electrical shop owner in Hythe, Hampshire created an alternative method by wiring up loud-speakers in various houses around the village and relaying them with the B.B.C. from a central receiver on his own premises, charging his 'subscribers' a weekly rental for the service. The idea of 'wireless-relays', only this time using existing telephone lines, quickly spread throughout the country and by the end of the 1920s there were

34 relay exchanges with a total of over 8,500 subscribers. The exchange operators were granted a special licence from the Post Office, and even though subscribers only possessed a loud-speaker and not an actual wireless receiver, each one had to take out a Receiving Licence in the normal way.

RECEIVER DESIGN

While styles from the past were persisting with examples of receivers having exposed valves and coils still appearing on the market in 1925 (fig.166), there was also now a greater attempt at changing the complicated scientific instrument appearance which had characterised the outward form of domestic factory-built valve receivers since the early 1920s. Having passed through the 'experimental laboratory' stage, many more receivers were now being produced purely for the field of home-entertainment. With these, controls were simplified and the components enclosed in polished and highly finished mahogany, oak or walnut cabinets complete with a built-in battery compartment, and the only external connections being made were to the aerial, earth and a separate loud-speaker. Christie & Hodgson Ltd., of Sheffield went further than most by disguising the scientific aspect of the wireless when bringing out their Kudos Model No.7, a very novel 3-valve battery receiver built as a table lamp complete with shade so that it appeared to be an ordinary household object.

One design innovation which made its first significant appearance in 1925 was that of the all-enclosed outdoor battery portable complete with integral loud-speaker and battery compartment and, in most cases, an internal frame aerial: a type of receiver that was eventually to dominate the market until the end of the decade. One of the first of this class was the Pye 555 (fig.184) which was a single station Daventry-only long-wave model complete with a built-in horn loud-speaker.

'Table models' (all-enclosed valve receivers with integral loud-speakers solely designed for indoor use rather than outdoor portability) were not introduced in significant numbers until the late 1920s, but as a step towards them, Rotax brought out the Rotola III which was a 3-valve receiver with a built-in Amplion Radiolux folded horn loud-speaker, and Elwell introduced their Statophone Model S50 and Model S60 with built-in electrostatic loud-speakers. Compact and self-contained, they were designed to be sited on a small table in the living room or drawing room. (The Model S50 was a 3-valve receiver which employed a crystal as the detector, but in general, the practice, popular a few years before, of using a crystal detector in what essentially was a valve receiver, was now beginning to disappear and a detector valve was being used instead).

Crystal sets, for the first time since broadcast began, were beginning to wain in popularity as both listeners and manufacturers began to turn more of their attention to valve receivers. Although reflex circuits, single valve receivers and others designed for headphone use only were in decline, 2-valve (DET/LF) models were still very popular, especially with those listeners satisfied with loud-speaker reception of their local station only. The use of grid bias was now becoming a standard practice with commercial valve receivers designed for loud-speaker use.

At the opposite end of the scale, there was an increasing interest in superhets, with about half a dozen factory-built examples and a few in kit-form (figs.176,181). Superhets employed as many as eight valves: typically three intermediate frequency amplifiers, two optional low frequency amplifiers, a separate local oscillator valve and two detectors, offering a wide tuning range of as much as 175/3,000 metres. They were being discussed by everyone, especially within the pages of the wireless Press but, as *Wireless World* pointed out, they were "only being purchased by the affluent few".

At this time there was a great all-round advance in the quality of high frequency amplification due to the rise in popularity of the Neutrodyne type of circuit used in both home-constructed and factory-built receivers. Patented by Professor Hazeltine in the United States and first introduced into Britain in 1923, it employed a small neutralising condenser mounted on the panel and adjusted so as to neutralise or balance out the anode-grid capacity of the HF valve. The circuit enabled a number of stages of high frequency amplification to be effectively stabilised and allowed the development of highly selective TRF receivers. A characteristic of these early Neutrodyne circuits was the so-called 'magic' or 'sacred' angle (54.7 degrees) at which the tuning coils were supposed to be set in order to prevent interaction.

Neutrodyne receivers required fewer valves than superhets and were very popular until about 1928 when, following the development of the screened-grid valve, there was no longer any need for external neutralisation. Although TRFs became practically universal, the superhet, in its later form as a mains receiver, was revived in 1930 and soon became the staple product of most manufacturers, quickly rising in popularity until within a few years or so it completely displaced the TRF. However, two main manufacturers, Philips and A.C. Cossor, preferred to continue to concentrate their main efforts into producing ranges of large and expensive TRFs in the first half of the 1930s: respectively, the Super-Inductance (see 1931) and the Super-Ferrodyne (see 1934).

Tuning had become easier with the general introduction of three new types of degree-calibrated tuning controls: vernier condenser dials, notably Burndept's Super-Vernier dial (fig.172), the Indigraph range from Igranic (fig.181) and 'slow-motion' dial controls by Ormond and Gecophone (fig.213). As the increasing number of broadcasting stations began to crowd the existing wavebands from the mid-1920s and with the advent of more selective and critically tuned receivers, slow-motion dials began to be imperative. While degree-calibrated tuning dials and scales remained universal right to the end of the 1920s, one of the first receivers calibrated directly in metre wavelengths appeared in 1925: the Marconiphone Type 81 (fig.173).

In 1925, the first commercially manufactured 'HT battery eliminator' appeared: the Tangent AC Model by Gent & Co. Ltd. of Leicester. (HT battery eliminators for use with a DC supply began to be produced in 1926). The Tangent was fitted with step-up and step-down transformers and a simple smoothing circuit, and used an ordinary receiving valve with the grid and anode pins bridged, thereby forming a two-electrode rectifying valve. This method of 'making' a rectifying valve was outlined as far back as April 1921, when, in an article published in *Wireless World*, Professor M. Moye of the University of Montpellier, France, suggested connecting the grid and anode pins of an R-type bright-emitter to make a rectifier for an AC-powered circuit. The introduction of the Tangent HT eliminator enabled listeners with an AC mains supply to obtain HT current directly from the household lighting circuit, thus doing away with HT batteries, although they still had to use an accumulator for the LT supply. This mains and battery combination was a compromise, but it greatly reduced the mains 'hum' experienced if the filaments were connected directly to raw AC.

'MAINS RECEIVERS'

During 1925, several commercially manufactured 'mains' receivers were produced for the first time, each powered by its own matching AC or DC mains unit. In March, Read & Morris Ltd., of 31 East Castle Street, London W1, brought out their 4-valve Mains Four receiver at £47.5s.0d which they claimed to be the "first mains set in the world". Although arguably not a mains receiver in the strictest sense (it comprised an ordinary battery valve circuit powered by a separate matching AC or DC mains unit) it was the first commercially manufactured receiver to derive both HT and LT current directly from the house lighting mains, entirely dispensing with batteries. Other 'mains' designated receivers soon followed including the Simplicity Five at £53.3s.0d (a 2HF/DET/LF receiver, again from Read & Morris Ltd., London W1 - separate matching AC or DC mains unit extra); the Tinol Electric Mains Set at £13.10s.0d (a crystal/2LF receiver with a separate matching DC mains unit from Tutills Ltd., Manchester - it needed an LT battery); a Mains Supply Receiver at £30.0s.0d (a HF/DET/LF receiver with a separate matching DC mains unit from Dynamergy Mains Supply, Staines); and the Baby Grand DC at £17.0s.0d (a DET/LF receiver from Gambrell Bros., London SW1). Like all the receivers above, the Baby Grand used an ordinary battery valve circuit powered by a mains unit. In the circuits of early DC mains receivers, the filaments were connected in series and this pattern was followed by all subsequent DC sets until 1931, when indirectly-heated DC mains valves were introduced (see 1931). Unlike the other mains receivers on the market in 1925, the mains unit of the Baby Grand DC was enclosed within the cabinet and as such, tempted the manufacturers to claim that it was "the first all-enclosed mains receiver on the market", although like the vast majority of all valve receivers of this period, it had no integral loud-speaker and still needed to be connected to one. ('All-enclosed' more accurately defines a receiver with a built-in loud-speaker in addition to an integral power supply).

In the autumn of 1925, the first of an unusual three-filament valve range was introduced by the Nelson Electrical Company Ltd., of Merton Park, London SW19. These were known as 'Multi valves', and any one of their three filaments could be brought into use by the scissor-type switch on the base of the valve which also allowed two to be run in parallel so the valve could be used as a power amplifier (see Appendix).

With advances in valve technology, the first 'pipless' valves appeared in significant numbers as the vacuum seal was now made inside the base instead of at the top of the bulb. One of these valves was the Mullard PM4 (see Appendix), the first in a long line of very low-current 'battery triodes' which, in 2 volt filament versions, were to dominate the outdoor portable wireless scene until the end of the decade. They ranged from the ordinary detector type and later through power, super-power to extra super-power types with 2, 4 or 6 volt filaments. Almost overnight, the famous top-pip type of valve envelope became obsolete and by 1926, few valves exhibited it. (It was revived again in post-war years with the 'B7G' and 'B8A' all-glass miniature valves but until then was only used intermittently, notably with the Hivac range in 1935, see Appendix).

By the end of 1925, few valve receivers solely designed for headphone use were being manufactured and the use of headphones was now slowly diminishing as more listeners employed a loud-speaker. One of the crudest, and certainly ugliest range of horn loud-speakers to come onto the market in 1925 was the 'Scientific' series made in rough-surfaced papier-mache by the Scientific Supply Stores of London SE1. (fig.850). Together with ebonite and wooden horns, papier-mache horns were comparatively non-resonant and unlike metal horns, were not prone to ringing at certain critical note frequencies.

While the traditional horn types remained dominant, they were soon to be challenged and quickly superseded by moving-iron cone loud-speakers which included 'cabinet models' contained in an attractive wooden cabinet to harmonise better with domestic surroundings. (A few horn loud-speakers in cabinets also appeared. Because of the limited internal space the horn was usually folded to squeeze it into the cabinet, fig.846). Following on from the Beco cone loud-speaker introduced in 1924, several more moving-iron cone loud-speakers with simple reed-type or more sophisticated balanced-armature movements appeared during 1925 and these included the Celestion Hornless loud-speaker in February (fig.849), the Edison Bell Cone, the Sterling Mellovox and the B.T.H. Type 'E' in August (fig.883) and the Western Electric Kone on October 1st (fig.855).

In America an energised moving-coil cone loud-speaker designed by Chester Rice and Edward Kellogg of the U.S. General Electric Company was demonstrated at the spring Convention of the American Institute of Electrical Engineers in St. Louis. It was the prototype of the modern moving-coil loud-speaker and in 1926 it first became commercially available in Britain (see 1926) and by the mid-1930s the moving-coil, due simply to its high quality reproduction, had completely superseded all other types of loud-speaker.

fig. 51. The arrangement of the 'Magnetic Bar Microphone' connected to a Brownie No.2 crystal set, an Amplion 'Dragonfly' loud-speaker and two Ever Ready dry cells.

fig. 50 . The 'Magnetic Microphone Bar' amplifier was one of a small number of successful commercially manufactured crystal set amplifiers on the market in the 1920s which increased the weak signals in the crystal set without the use of valves. The volume they produced was sufficiently powerful enough to drive a small loud-speaker and this was considered socially important for it allowed family listening where before usually only the one person with a single pair of headphones was able to hear the programmes.

The 'Magnetic Microphone Bar' was produced in 1925 by the New Wilson Electrical Manufacturing Co. of London W1 and cost £1.18s.0d. An adjustable metal bar (acting as a diaphragm) clamped to an aluminium telephone earpiece and was connected to the headphone circuit of a crystal set. The signals were transformer-coupled to a loud-speaker, the transformer being housed in the black ebonite base of the amplifier, and the power was derived from one or two dry cells: a 4s.0d 3v battery would last over 3 months. Some of these amplifiers were marketed by the Empire Electric Co. of London NW1 from July 1926 and these have the letters 'EEC' moulded into the top of the ebonite base. Height 4 ½ in., base 3 ¾ in. dia.

TELEVISION

During 1925, there had been some new developments with Baird and his system of television. He had moved up to London in August of the previous year and had set up his apparatus on the third floor of 22 Frith Street, Soho. In March 1925,

he met Gordon Selfridge jnr. who was so impressed with his activities that he hired Baird to put on a series of television demonstrations in his Oxford Street department store enabling the general public to see it for the first time. In June, with a capital of £500 subscribed by his mother's family, Baird formed Television Ltd., the first company of its kind in the world. Previously, Baird had been continually hampered in his research by lack of funds, but with this new-found financial security he was able to concentrate wholeheartedly on improving his apparatus. He was now using discs with a spiral of lenses instead of just holes, and having worked during a series of experiments using a ventriloquist's dummy as the televised subject, Baird transmitted his first detailed living image on October 2nd, the face of office boy William Taynton.

1926

Just before midnight on June 28th 1926, a dual-transmitter test broadcast was conducted from the B.B.C.'s Savoy Hill studios using the 2LO transmitter on 365 metres, then in current use at Selfridges in Oxford Street, and the original 2LO transmitter on 460 metres which was still installed at Marconi House in the Strand. The test lasted from 11.15pm until midnight, with each transmitter radiating a different programme of entertainment at approximately the same aerial power to listeners in the London area. The object of the test was to determine whether it was possible to provide two distinct programmes sent out at the same strength on different wavelengths from stations in close proximity to each other.

Throughout the test area, listeners with valve receivers found little difficulty in separating the two transmitters and they were able to tune into each programme quite independently. However, crystal set owners generally discovered that their simple circuits could not separate them and they heard both programmes simultaneously through the headphones. It became immediately obvious to listeners in London that if the B.B.C. pursued this dual programme policy, then the days of the crystal set were numbered and in fact from this time the number of new models manufactured dropped dramatically.

In the summer, work began on building a medium-wave test transmitter at the Daventry site alongside 5XX, in order to develop the best possible circuit for a high power medium-wave transmitter and to test the effect of two transmitters radiating simultaneously from the same station. This new transmitter with its call-sign 5GB was to become known as 'Daventry Experimental' or more familiarly 'Little Daventry' and when built, would provide a local regional medium-wave programme, while 5XX would provide a national programme on long-wave, thus catering for the widely differing tastes of the listening public (see 1927).

On November 14th, the *Geneva Plan* came into operation. It was the first in a series of international wavelength plans brought in by the I.B.U. (see 1925) over the next ten years in an attempt to keep a check on the rapid increase in the number of European broadcasting stations, and to allocate specific wavelengths to each station in order to minimise interference between them. Immediately before the adoption of the Plan, the B.B.C. was using twenty-one different wavelengths, but these were reduced by the Plan to just ten, with nine of the relays on 288.5 metres.

OUTDOOR BATTERY PORTABLES

Interest in outdoor battery portables began to grow, and there were more than fifty different models on offer. In the case of the earliest receivers of this type, the term 'portable' was a very elastic expression indeed. Ideally, a portable should have been light and easily carried, but the average 1926 portable was far from ideal, being rather bulky and very heavy, and designed, according to *Wireless World*, to be carried by the "strong silent type with a jaw of chilled steel".

Most 1926 portables were manufactured without a built-in loud-speaker, but a small and growing number did contain one, these being either the folded metal horn or the more modern moving-iron cone type whose use was increasing all the time. Of the all-enclosed portables on the market, a few were housed in a small leather 'suitcase' with the loud-speaker fitted into the lift-up lid, but most were contained in an upright polished wooden case with a hinged front door entirely covering the front, and which opened to reveal the control panel and the loud-speaker opening. The necessary HT, LT and grid bias batteries were normally housed in the bottom of the case making the whole set weigh as much as 35 lb.

Portables were mainly of the TRF type employing three or four 2 volt battery triodes in a reaction circuit, but there were also a few built with superheterodyne and reflex circuits. The majority had a built-in frame aerial, wound in the lid or on the front or back door, or around the inside of the cabinet. Because this type of aerial had strong directional properties, the portable had to be carefully positioned with the aerial in the plane of the incoming signals. In this position, reception was at its strongest and to make manoeuvering easier, a turntable was usually provided underneath the cabinet.

From 1926, the outdoor battery portable quickly rose to take a leading share of the market and was to stay in that position until the early 1930s. The very characteristic of broadcasting was its omni-directional property, and while a transmitting aerial did not send out waves with equal strength in all directions, reception was generally available anywhere within transmitter range. Broadcasting was therefore highly suitable for outdoor reception with a portable receiver, and those listeners who had become accustomed to the companionship of wireless in their homes during the winter months would, according to a sales brochure from the Halcyon Wireless Supply Company, naturally feel loath to part company with their receivers when the time came for the enjoyment of the open-air life of the summer. "A lazy afternoon or evening on the river, a picnic party, or a dance on the lawn after tennis - all excellent occasions when wireless could be called in to assist". (In some districts, by-laws prohibited the use of wireless in the garden).

Wireless appealed to all classes in Britain. In January, in the House of Lords, Lord Cave extolled its virtues in a comment surely still echoed today: "I know from experience what a pleasure it is to hear good music and speaking, and also what a pleasure it is to be able to turn it off when one has had enough!"; also, following the installation of a wireless receiver in the Narborough Workhouse, a member of the Board of Guardians in a letter to *The Times* deplored the possibility that "the new attraction might lead to an influx of interested inmates".

TUNING CONTROLS

Simplicity of operation was now becoming an important consideration, and an advertisement from a retail wireless shop featured in *The Wireless Trader* summed up progress made: "Your wife does not need to be a mechanic to use her sewing machine. Now *you* do not have to be a wireless engineer to get good results from your modern wireless set."

To this end, four new types of tuning control were introduced. The first was the edgewise-mounted 'drum scale' tuning control introduced by G.E.C. with their eight valve superhet: a method which set a new design trend and which became very popular during the second half of the 1920s (figs.250,271,276,277). Each degree-calibrated scale (usually marked from 0-100 degrees) was marked on a narrow drum which moved through a vertical plane behind a small panel-mounted window and was finger (or thumb) controlled by a milled disc attached to the drum and protruding through a slot next to the window. This method exhibited neatness, originality and a desire to break with the 'scientific instrument' conception of the wireless which still lingered with a few manufacturers. As a compromise to ganging, which was to be adopted within a few years, it was particularly suited to operating a pair of tuning circuits in step: two drum scales were simply mounted side-by-side enabling two separate variable condensers to be moved in unison.

The second new control was Burndept's Ethlog geared dial. It was a slow-motion dial with a replaceable paper dial card mounted behind and around the control knob, which allowed the listener to log the position of stations on the 0-100 degree dial. Although its use was confined solely to factory-built receivers manufactured by Burndept during this period (figs.199,207), Ethlog dials were sold too for the home-constructor's market, and were still in evidence nearly ten years later when they appeared in a home-constructor's set designed by 'Lucifer' of *Wireless World* in 1935 (fig.486).

'Drum-drive' and 'disc-drive' tuning controls also appeared for the first time, their readings being viewed through a small window let into the control panel. With the drum-drive, a narrow degree-marked drum scale was used but was driven by a control knob housed away from it, as opposed to the edgewise-mounted drum scale control which was attached directly to the scale. The first set to employ this method of tuning was the Gecophone Model BC 2740 with its drum scale driven by slow-motion controls (fig.213). With disc-drive (fig.200), a single control knob turned a flat metal disc upon which was printed the tuning scale marked in degrees. The disc was usually turned either by its edge, or by the knob's spindle running through its centre. Among several sets to exhibit disc-drive tuning in 1926 was the All-Clear Type 44 by William Dibben & Sons of Southampton, which was among the few sets whose tuning scales were now being calibrated in metre wavelengths as opposed to degrees. By 1929, the use of degree calibrations was beginning to decline as a growing number of receivers' dials and scales were printed in wavelengths.

Two interesting 'no-dial' receivers which employed pre-selected tuning were introduced for the first time in 1926. The Dual Station receiver by Felcourt Products Ltd. of East Grinstead had press-button tuning for a local station and for Daventry, and the General Electric Company's L & D model (again for a local station and for Daventry) had just a single knob station selection switch visible on the front panel, all the subsidiary pre-set tuning controls being situated inside the cabinet.

DEVELOPMENTS IN THE TRADE

New receivers with externally mounted valves were now quite rare, and only a few models appeared in 1926 showing this obsolete style of design (figs.198,202). For those who could afford to do so, updating with a new receiver every year was becoming the done thing, and everyone began looking forward to the new national wireless exhibition at Olympia - 'Radiolympia' - held for the first time from September 4th to 18th and which immediately became the venue for launching the new models and the traditional beginning of 'the wireless season'. For the next ten years or so, employment within the Wireless Industry was seasonal with extra workers being taken on in August and then fired in the spring when orders fell and when production was wound down. As mass-production techniques developed in the late 1920s, more and more workers were needed on the assembly lines during peak production periods and women were generally employed, preferred because they had nimbler fingers and were cheaper to hire and easier to fire. They were often despised rather than valued, the attitude towards them in some quarters of the trade was summed up by one major firm's seasonal workforce being disparagingly referred to as "the scum of Holloway".

To encourage more reluctant listeners to part with their obsolete sets in favour of up-to-the-minute models, some wireless retailers began to introduce part-exchange schemes although this did not really become an established retail trade practice until the mid-1930s (see 1936). It was such a new idea in 1926 that *The Wireless Trader* made quite a feature of one of its subscribers who had begun such a scheme in December. The problem for the dealer was what to do with old sets brought in for part-exchange. This particular retailer had two main methods of disposal: either he gave the sets a complete overhaul and passed them through an auction room with a guarantee as to their condition, or if the sets had practically no value (a 2-valve battery model was given as an example) he would break them up and save the components. When he had accumulated a sufficient quantity of parts, he would send them for auction in various lots which usually realised between 3d and 1s.0d each.

One of the major disruptions to the wireless trade and indeed to the whole country was the General Strike of May 1926. It had far reaching effects on the public's appreciation of the B.B.C. and broadcasting in general for with no newspapers being printed and no available contact with colleagues at work for exchange of the latest news, the wireless set became the sole means of mass communication. As the strike took hold, more and more people who had never owned a wireless receiver before rushed to buy them up from rapidly depleting stocks, swelling the ranks of confirmed listeners.

This 'mini-boom' in wireless sales created a handsome profit for some manufacturers who were able to keep going and certainly for most retailers, who were often cleared out within a few days. Contemporary notes surviving from the diary of the Stores Manager of the Brownie Wireless Company give a brief but illuminating account of the firm's activities during the strike, when sales of their tube type and their Model No.2 crystal sets ran well into five figures, and as he pointed out, "every set sold to a new listener meant the sale of one more pair of headphones, one more coil of aerial and earth wire, and one more set of accessories". In expectation of the strike, stocks of Brownie crystal sets had been sent in readiness to different parts of the country and seven days before the strike began, staff were increased and a circular publicity campaign was prepared. Here are some extracts from the diary:

"Tuesday May 4th. Commencement of strike. By noon 1,000s of window bills were circulated to all retailers in London and home counties area. Wholesalers were telephoned to be told that stocks were available.

"Wednesday May 5th. Snowed under with orders. Staff working 12 hours a day. First delivery van smashed but other transport arrangements made. Electricity cut off from assembly shops. Evening work carried out by candle-light.

"Thursday May 6th. 10.30am. Van arrived from our Birmingham metal works after travelling all night bringing in a large supply of necessary metal parts. Telephoned some of our Midland dealers and arranged for shipment of goods to them by van returning that night.

"Friday May 7th. Orders on hand entirely exceed expectations. Deliveries effected by private motor cars and by calls from wholesalers and retailers. Special posters displayed all over London area. Moulding works closed down owing to failure of electric power.

"Saturday May 8th. Rush of orders now accepted as ordinary daily routine. Demand entirely outstripping works capacity, floating stock now sadly depleted. Unpacked large quantity of sets which had been ready for export to Australia and other countries on the outbreak of the strike, as it was quite clear these could not be shipped for the time being. Moulding tools removed from our works to another part of London where power was available.

"Monday May 10th. Weekend spent erecting tools and altering new hydraulic presses to accommodate them. Monday morning all arrived expecting slight respite, but on contrary, business greater than ever. 11 o'clock, first moulds arrive from new factory. O.K.'d and work proceeded.

"Tuesday May 11th. No abatement of orders.

"Wednesday May 12th. Last day of strike.

"Saturday May 15th. Contrary to expectations, orders still coming in and showing clearly that no stocks of our apparatus exist anywhere in the country, and everything points to our being busy for some time to come."

ALL-ELECTRIC WIRELESS

In 1926, the *Electricity (Supply) Act, 1926* was introduced which for the first time aimed at producing an effective national co-ordination of the various non-standard supplies around the country. Returns for 1926/27 show that there were 482 electricity generating stations in Britain, of which 156 generated AC only, 223 DC only and 103 both AC and DC.

Of the total of 259 AC supplies, 233 employed the frequency of 50 cycles, but the remaining 26 covered 13 different frequencies. House lighting voltages were chaotic, with 35 different voltages of AC supply and 24 of DC.

The Act created a public corporation, the Central Electricity Board, to concentrate on the generation of electricity in a limited number of selected main stations, and to interconnect these stations, linking up the existing regional system of 1919 into a 'National Grid' by the erection of a high-tension main transmission system (see 1929).

DC was to be phased out over several years, and the Board was required to standardise the frequency of AC throughout the country, so that effective interconnection could be established with the output from the main stations being purchased and re-sold to local undertakings requiring electricity for distribution.

During the year, several HT battery eliminators were brought out for DC mains operation. For AC mains, a few eliminators appeared fitted with newly introduced rectifying valves (see Appendix), which included the Mullard DU 10 (half-wave), the Mullard DU5 (full-wave) and the Osram U5 (full-wave). These valves were also used in a commercial receiver: the Baby Grand AC by Gambrell Bros., London SW8 (fig.206), which was the first AC 'mains' receiver with a built-in mains unit. Like the DC version of 1925, the Baby Grand AC used an ordinary battery valve circuit and this was powered by an AC mains unit housed in the bottom compartment of the cabinet. This built-in unit employed a pair of the new Mullard DU 10 half-wave rectifiers (some versions used a single Mullard DU5 or an Osram U5 full-wave rectifier), supplying not only LT and HT current, but, for the first time, grid bias as well, all directly from the house lighting mains. (In the following year, 'all-battery eliminators' appeared, see 1927).

With regard to other mains equipment, the first indirectly-heated AC mains valve, the KL1, was produced by the M-O.

Valve Company and its introduction heralded the era of true mains receivers. The KL1 was designed as an LF amplifier, and had a normal 4-pin B4 base with an additional terminal mounted on the side which was attached to the cathode, and although its patent was filed in June 1926, it did not appear for sale until January 1927 (see 1927). Anti-microphonic valve holders were now in widespread use and new split-pin valve legs which provided firmer socket location were introduced in April by G.E.C. (Osram).

Another development originating in the United States and now produced in this country for the first time, was the first commercially manufactured mains-energised moving-coil cone loud-speaker: the Rice-Kellogg by B.T.H. It was expensive and was sold in a floor-standing polished mahogany cabinet which also contained a single stage amplifier and a mains unit in either AC or DC versions. By the early 1930s, cheap and compact moving-coil loud-speakers of excellent quality had superseded all other types.

In July 1926, the British Radio Valve Manufacturers Association (BVA) was formed to "promote, encourage, foster, develop and protect the interests of the public, the trade and the manufacturers of British-made thermionic valves". The founder member companies were all those belonging to the VMA (see 1924) plus Cleartron Radio Ltd.

In September, Cleartron produced a wireless receiver in 2 and 3-valve versions (ready-built or for home-construction) based upon the Lodge 'N' Circuit, a curious circuit designed by Sir Oliver Lodge (fig.191). Readers of *Popular Wireless Weekly*, of which Lodge was Scientific Adviser, had for several months been teased by articles promising full constructional details of the "reactionless 'N' circuit" which claimed to give as much volume as a reaction set, without any interference to neighbouring sets and yield "wonderfully pure tone". Details and a circuit diagram for the 2-valve set finally appeared in the issue of September 18th, but like so many wireless inventions heralded at the time as "revolutionary", the 'N' circuit did not change the course of wireless history and soon faded into obscurity.

TELEVISION

The development of television had been slowly progressing. On January 27th, Baird had demonstrated his system to members of the Royal Society who crowded into his Frith Street address to witness the event. With his transmitter in one room and his Televisor in another, the demonstration was successfully carried out, although the general opinion was that the apparatus as it stood was far too crude to be placed on the commercial market. The images (first the ventriloquist's dummy and then a living face) were flickering and distorted with only a very narrow observable field of vision. However, the work continued and Baird moved to a new laboratory and offices at Motograph House in Upper St. Martin's Lane near Leicester Square. Having been able to transmit and receive television images within the confines of his laboratory, Baird was anxious to experiment over a distance. He made contact with H.L. Kirke, the B.B.C.'s Chief Research Engineer, and arranged to conduct a series of experimental transmissions using the B.B.C.'s 2LO transmitter linked via Savoy Hill by Post Office telephone line to Baird's laboratory. Here, the flickering pictures, made up of 30 strips, were received successfully, but the experiments which were very much of an unofficial and secretive nature were soon put a stop to, according to Baird, by "someone up above" in the B.B.C.

But this was a temporary setback, for Television Ltd. then went ahead and applied to the Post Office for a licence to transmit television signals. Subsequently, a licence (2TV) was granted for them to conduct official experiments on 200 metres and a low power transmitting station was hastily erected at

Motograph House with the receiving station set up at Green Gables, a villa in Harrow some 10 miles to the north west.

1927

On January 1st, the British Broadcasting Corporation was created by Royal Charter and, "acting as a Trustee for the national interest", took over from the original British Broadcasting Company. Under this first Charter, the Corporation was to be established for an initial term of ten years until January 1st 1937, and administered by five directors with a Director-General (John Reith) appointed by the Crown as Chief Executive Officer. The shareholders in the old Company were paid off and the Company's trade directors retired, but the Corporation retained the original sources of revenue together with the staff, studios and transmitters previously held by the Company. The general policy, including that of political independence and impartiality, was little affected, for the Company had all along been administering the broadcast service in the spirit of a public trust rather than purely as a commercial concern. In recognition of his past services with the British Broadcasting Company, John Reith received a knighthood and was to remain at his new post of Director-General until June 30th 1938.

fig. 52 . This scene, typical of the kind of studio arrangement that the Corporation inherited from the Company, shows the staff of the Plymouth 5PY relay station in 1927. Left to right: Gwen Goodanew, James Langham (Station Director), Godfrey Adams (Announcer and Assistant Director - later, an announcer with the London Station and after the war, Light Programme Director), Eric Morden (Plymouth Repertory Company), Mrs Winifred Grant (pianist, sitting facing camera) and Mrs Madge Taylor (the B.B.C.'s first lady announcer, engaged at 5PY in July 1925 as 'Auntie Madge' on children's programmes and appointed as an announcer in 1926). The walls and ceiling of the 40 ft. x 20 ft. studio are hidden behind thick draperies "in tasteful hues of blue and grey, preventing the possibilities of echoes reaching the microphone and ensuring a serene and restful atmosphere for the artistes". In the foreground, on castors, is the 'meat safe' microphone, common to all B.B.C. studios in the 1920s. The actual instrument itself, the moving-coil 'Round-Sykes Magnetophone', was mounted in a rubber sling suspended in a mahogany frame. A large perforated metal cover was placed over the microphone to protect it, and it was this that gave the microphone its colloquial name. (At that time, when household refrigerators were rare, meat and other perishables were kept in a perforated metal meat safe which the microphone cover resembled). The whole contraption was mounted on a heavy mahogany trestle the size of a gymnasium horse. In the background, above one of the two studio fireplaces and behind Godfrey Adams' left shoulder is the 'volume control' giving instructions indicated by a warning light for the announcer to "Come Closer" if extra volume was required or "Away" if he was too loud. Only one completely original 'meat safe' microphone is thought to have survived.

On August 27th, the new high power medium-wave transmitter, Daventry Experimental (call-sign 5GB), was brought into service on 491.8 metres for experimental Regional Scheme broadcasts to the Midlands, radiating an entirely different programme from that of Daventry 5XX on the long waveband. Together, 5GB and 5XX made up the world's first twin-wave transmitting station and were the forerunners of the Regional Scheme, the essential feature of which was that each transmitting station had two separate and independent transmitters radiating different and contrasting national and regional programmes. However, the range of Daventry 5XX was not found to be sufficient to cover the whole of Britain, and so a number of National Programme relay stations on the medium waveband were built over the next six years which succeeded in bringing the National Programme to a very large area of the country.

The new service from Daventry 5GB was greeted enthusiastically by those tuning-in on valve receivers, but like the 1926 tests in London, it wreaked havoc among crystal set owners, many of whom found their sets to be incapable of separating 5GB from their own local medium-wave station. However, the crystal set was becoming rather obsolete by now: listeners were looking for something a little better and a little less crude, and only a few manufacturers produced new models in 1927. Among these was the Model No.3 by Brownie Wireless (fig.227), a two-band crystal set brought out in the hope of dealing with Daventry 5GB and 5XX. More and more listeners were going over to up-to-date valve receivers and putting their once beloved crystal sets away in the attic or, more usually, in the dustbin. It was estimated that well over 50 per cent of licensed listeners were now tuning-in on valve receivers, where only three years before the figure was under 25 per cent.

EMPIRE BROADCASTING

On November 11th, the British Broadcasting Corporation began sending test transmissions to the British Empire from an experimental short-wave station (call-sign G5SW) sited at Marconi's Chelmsford works and coinciding with this opening, several short-wave only receivers appeared on the market including the Burndept Mk.IV. (fig.226). The broadcasts were on 25.53 metres at a power of approximately 16 kW, and they were conducted to see whether there was a demand in the British Colonies and Dominions for the reception of a regular broadcast service from England, and to find the best technical means of meeting it. Some five years later, on December 19th 1932 (see 1932), these experiments resulted in the inauguration of the B.B.C.'s Empire Service.

However, before G5SW opened, Gerald Marcuse, a 'radio ham' from Caterham in Surrey, began his own private 32 metres short-wave Empire Service to Australia under a special licence granted to him by the Post Master General. Marcuse was authorised to transmit speech and music using a transmitter with an input power of not more than 1 kW (he did in fact use 1 ½ kW) on condition that he omitted news, current affairs and advertisements. Under the call-sign G2NM, the service was inaugurated on September 11th 1927 and continued almost daily until August 1928, during which time the programmes included gramophone music and live concerts as well as items re-broadcast from 2LO.

Running parallel to their short-wave broadcasting activities, Marconi's Wireless Telegraph Company was also involved in setting up the Imperial Telegraph Service: a chain of short-wave wireless stations established for commercial telegram traffic on behalf of the British Post Office and the Dominion Governments. A plan for linking the Empire in a network of long-wave wireless telegraphy stations had first been mooted by Marconi in 1906, but it was not until towards the end of 1927 that the chain was at last inaugurated, with

short-wave transmitters chosen instead. During the 1920s, Marconi had become increasingly interested in experimenting with long-distance directional short-wave communication using wavelengths of between about 10 to around 90 metres. In 1923, he had begun experimental reception tests from a 12 kW short-wave transmitter coupled to a parabolic beam reflector set up on a 325 feet high mast at Poldhu. The beam was directed towards the South Atlantic where Marconi was cruising in his steam yacht *Elettra*, which he had bought in 1920 to serve as a floating wireless laboratory.

Off the island of St. Vincent in the Cape Verde group, some 2,300 nautical miles south south west of Poldhu, Marconi found that the signals he picked up from the experimental beam transmitter at Poldhu were considerably stronger than those from the long-wave Post Office arc transmitter at Leafield, despite this station being some twenty times more powerful. The effectiveness of short-wave beam transmission for long-distance communication was confirmed by further tests conducted on board the *Elettra* and Marconi eventually succeeded in persuading the British Government to adopt this system for the Imperial Telegraph Service, despite them having been practically committed to long-wave stations as early as 1912.

By the end of 1927, short-wave beam stations were opened in England for the transmission and reception of telegrams to and from Canada, South Africa, Australia and India with reciprocal stations in each country. Marconi's also built their own beam stations for telegram traffic to and from Argentina, Brazil, U.S., Egypt and Japan using wavelengths of between 15 and 37 metres.

The combination of Marconi's beam system and the Imperial Telegraph Service was an outstanding success. But this had unforeseen consequences, for so great was the threat posed to the Empire's long-established cable companies that at the insistence of the British and Dominion Governments, Cable & Wireless Limited was formed in 1929 to take over and combine the licences, patent and commercial traffic rights and investments of Marconi's Wireless Telegraph Company, the Eastern Cable Companies and various other cable interests.

By the 1930s, commercial wireless communication from England to the rest of the world was in the hands of two main bodies: the British Post Office (long-distance subscriber telephone services, wireless telegraphy services to Europe, and shore-to-ship wireless telephony and telegraphy traffic) and Cable & Wireless Limited (long-distance wireless telegraphy services).

OUTDOOR PORTABLE RECEIVERS

By 1927, the number of outdoor battery portables was increasing rapidly, the majority being two-band TRF models covering the B.B.C.'s medium-wave stations and Daventry on long-wave. A typical portable used five 2 volt battery triodes with one 2 volt accumulator to supply filament current. Although this meant a slight saving in weight, (a 2 volt accumulator was one third the size of one of 6 volts) the portable was still comparatively heavy, weighing on average some 25 lb. Built-in frame aerials were now universal, wound around the inside of the case or sometimes within the hinged back door which opened to allow access to the components. Most portables of 1927 were now fitted with an integral loud-speaker: about 75 per cent of the moving-iron cone type and about 25 per cent of the old folded horn type, and the loud-speaker opening was usually embellished with an artistically decorated fretwork grille (fig.231). The controls were either mounted above the loud-speaker (fig.230) or on the side and were sometimes hidden by a hinged flap (fig.231). The hinged door, covering the whole of the front, which had been a popular feature of the previous year's models had now largely disappeared, while suitcase portables, with the loud-speaker housed in the lift-up lid, were becoming firmly established.

WIRELESS IN THE HOME

In general, the domestic battery wireless receiver exhibited an increasing trend towards neatness, simplicity of control and ease of maintenance, and was more widely being accepted into the home as a piece of furniture instead of being regarded as a scientific instrument at odds with its surroundings. The set was now more compact since the inclusion of battery compartments, hiding the batteries within the cabinet, had become standard practice. Although a small number of indoor receivers were appearing with a built-in loud-speaker (fig.223) plus a frame-aerial (fig.220) - features then practically standard in outdoor battery portables - the majority were still the permanently-installed type, sited near the feed-in wire of the outdoor aerial system and connected to a separate loud-speaker placed on top of the receiver or nearby. Separate loud-speakers had become widely available in a variety of guises, the most popular of which were wooden cabinet types housing a moving-iron cone behind a decorative grille (fig.875) and new novelty loud-speakers disguised as ornaments and employing horn drive units (fig.871). Not until the 1930s did mass-produced, simple-to-use 'all-enclosed' domestic mains receivers emerge to displace battery sets and dominate the market in console, table and transportable forms which simply plugged in to a handy light-socket.

The method of waveband changing employing the familiar 2-pin plug-in tuning coils was becoming obsolete. Instead of inserting the appropriate coil for the chosen waveband, coils wound on cylindrical formers were now starting to become permanently fixed in the circuit and waveband changing was achieved by single-knob switching.

CAR RADIO

In 1927, a domestic battery receiver installed in his Standard Park Lane saloon car caused Captain L. Plugge to be fined 20s.0d at Bow Street court for obstruction. This was probably the first time that a wireless had been built into a private motor car in Great Britain, and wherever he stopped, the novelty caused crowds to surround his car to admire it. The receiver was a 7-valve superhet plus a 2-valve amplifier manufactured by Western Electric and this was concealed behind the dashboard to the left of the steering column, with a Sterling Primax loud-speaker facing downwards from the roof. The volume control knob was operated from its position on the steering wheel and there was another for passengers at the back of the car. A frame aerial, encased in celluloid for protection against the weather, was mounted on the off-side wing and the power for the set, which weighed something in the region of 100 lb., came from a row of batteries slung in cradles beneath the chassis. But despite the interest, it would be another five years before the first commercially manufactured model was introduced (see 1932) and eight years before the first car radio was fitted as standard (see 1935).

VALVE DEVELOPMENTS

In January, the M-O. Valve Company introduced the KL1 AC mains valve onto the market. Designed by C.W. Stropford in 1926, it had an amplification factor of 7.5, and was used as a low-frequency amplifier. It was soon followed by the general purpose version, the KH1.

The 'K' series AC valves used a conventional 4-pin B4 base on the side of which was a terminal connected to the cathode, a nickel cylinder about one eighth of an inch in diameter, air-spaced around a bright-emitting hairpin filament heater. But they were not at all successful, due mainly to their long warm-up time (about one minute), short heater life and unsatisfactory electrical characteristics. They were quickly overshadowed by

the revolutionary Cosmos AC/G (Green Spot) and AC/R (Red Spot) indirectly-heated AC mains valves manufactured by Metro-Vick Supplies Ltd. and released in September.

It is not thought that any commercially manufactured AC mains receiver of 1927 was ever designed solely around the 'K' series M-O. valves. But when, later in the same year, Marconiphone brought out their Model 22, Type 51 and Type 32 Universal Feed Receivers (fig.217), provision was made by means of multi-way supply cables for obtaining HT, LT and grid bias voltage from separate AC or DC supply units (known as 'all-battery eliminators', see below) as an alternative to using batteries, and when sold for AC mains operation, 'K' series valves were supplied.

The Marconiphone Company also brought out an instruction book and a full-size wiring plan for the Model K1 home-constructor's receiver in February. Assembled with Marconiphone and Sterling branded components, this used three KL1's and a U5 rectifier and was intended for those keen on experimenting with the new valves at home.

Home-construction was still rising in popularity and at the 1927 Radiolympia, held between September 24th and October 1st, kit-sets and components were exhibited in profusion. Ormond introduced their large (3 ¾ in.) dual-indicator slow-motion dial, a type which, in both large and smaller versions (fig.243) was for many years to feature on the control panels of thousands of home-constructed receivers including the Melody Maker manufactured by the valve company A.C. Cossor. This was the first in their famous series of home-constructors' receivers, and it originally made its appearance at the 1927 Radiolympia in the form of a chart giving constructional details and a list of parts needed which naturally specified Cossor valves. The home-constructor could take his list along to a local wireless dealer who would make up a set of components and supply a wooden cabinet and baseboard, an ebonite panel engraved "Cossor Melody Maker" and two of the new Ormond dials. A year later the Melody Maker appeared for the first time as a complete kit of parts marketed in an attractive carton (see 1928).

Another set for home-constructors was the Cosmos Mains Kit Set from Metro-Vick Supplies Ltd. which used the new Cosmos indirectly-heated AC mains valves shown to both trade and public for the first time in 1927. Apart from the latest models of receiver, Radiolympia usually gave the first showing of the new season's valves which meant that receiver manufacturers often held back production in case any startling advances in valve technology should appear. Some firms however did not employ new types of valves for at least twelve months, preferring to let others have the teething troubles.

The Cosmos AC/G (see Appendix) was used as a detector and the AC/R as an LF power valve and both possessed a unique cathode heater design, whereby the filament was 'slip-coated' by being dipped in liquid porcelain clay and then fired in a kiln. This produced a very hard and microscopically thin insulation, and the coated filament was then inserted into a tubular cathode a mere millimetre in diameter. This insulation and construction method was patented by E. Yeoman Robinson: filed on July 7th, less than two weeks after Stropford had filed his. It was completely successful from the very start, exhibiting a rapid warm-up time, lower heater temperature and a high efficiency which would not be equalled by any other valve of its type for another five years. It revolutionised the valve industry, and eventually, by about 1933, superseded all other methods and became universally adopted by AC valve manufacturers throughout the world.

The Cosmos AC valves at first appeared with a peculiar 5-pin base (three normal sized pins and two short pins) which fitted into a special holder. Because the pins were not common to other valve bases of the time, Metro-Vick Supplies Ltd.

produced a special adaptor-disc. When fitted to the valve base, this enabled the valve to be plugged into standard 4-pin valve holders so that battery set owners could very simply convert their sets to mains use without altering the original wiring.

From about this time, a method of coating the filaments of battery valves and the cathodes of mains valves with a compound of barium and other metal oxides was beginning to be generally employed by valve manufacturers and by the end of the 1920s, this had become standard practice.

During 1927, the first 'all-battery eliminators' were introduced in which separate plug-in units could be connected to the battery terminals of ordinary battery receivers (or to sets like the Marconiphone Universal Feed receivers referred to above), to enable them to be fed HT, LT and grid bias voltage direct from the mains. Among the handful of units newly available during the year were an AC version from Burndept and a DC version from E.K. Cole Ltd., who also brought out their All-From-The-Mains DC receiver with their new eliminator housed within the cabinet. Until the introduction of the indirectly-heated DC mains valves in 1931 which resulted in true DC mains receivers, DC 'mains' receivers continued to employ directly-heated battery valves.

During 1927, 'capacity controlled reaction' was introduced which, providing greater stability and smoother reaction control, quickly displaced the swinging coil method which had been in widespread use since the early 1920s. In a further attempt at overcoming the instability often experienced with reaction circuits of this period, the M-O. Valve Company introduced the S625 screened-grid valve in the spring. Designed by H.J. Round, the S625 was a horizontally-mounted double-ended tetrode with three pins at one end and two at the other (see Appendix). It had a very small anode-grid capacity, with a second grid placed between these two electrodes called a 'screen grid' or 'control grid'. This was kept at a positive bias, but at a lower potential than the anode thereby acting as a screen and preventing uncontrollable feed-back between the anode and grid. Its introduction did away with the need for externally neutralized circuits and enabled the development of better quality circuits with highly stable, high amplification HF stages and marked the first successful departure from the ubiquitous triode (see also 1928). Before the introduction of the screened-grid, valve receivers were frequently assembled without much thought being given to the placing of the wiring. But when the screened-grid came into use, it became necessary to take the greatest care in planning the wiring layout especially in each of the HF stages, as these had to be carefully screened from one another and from the rest of the receiver. And so, from this time, the building of a wireless receiver began to be a neater and a more precise exercise.

Among the first commercially manufactured receivers to employ the screened-grid in 1927 was the Marconiphone Round Six and the British Radio Corporation's Radio Exchange: a receiver ahead of its time having eight pre-set wavelengths with eight corresponding station names showing up when selected on an illuminated disc. There was no tuning dial as the stations were selected at the flick of a switch and each of the twenty-four tuned circuits (eight sets of three) had to be carefully adjusted by B.R.C.'s agents when a set was sold to a customer.

Although it was not the first receiver to have pre-set tuning (see 1926) it was the first to show a selection of station names and the first to illuminate them. But as their advertisements said, "A set of the future", for at the time European wavelength allocations were in a continual state of change and the main objection to the introduction of the Radio Exchange was that the services of B.R.C.'s agents would constantly be called upon to alter the pre-set tuning until, at some future time, wavelength allocations reached more of a state of permanancy. (See 1931, STATIONS ON THE DIAL).

TELEVISION

In April, the Baird Television Development Company Ltd. was formed as a public company with an authorised capital of £125,000 while Television Ltd. remained as the parent company. Despite this massive investment, Baird's system had still not reached a very advanced stage of development, as was confirmed by the audience of the British Association meeting at Leeds to whom Baird gave a demonstration on September 7th. However, directly as a result of this meeting, the Television Society was formed whose sole interest "would be the study and development of problems associated with television and allied subjects". Earlier in the year, the American Telephone and Telegraph Company had staged the first public demonstration of television outside this country using both telephone land-line and wireless transmission, and with world-wide interest in the subject now being shown, the pressure on Baird to produce a practical and reliable system began to increase. At the end of the year Baird moved to bigger premises, occupying the first and second floors of 133 Long Acre in Covent Garden where his laboratory and a purpose-built television studio were installed.

1928

By 1928, it had long been realised that the B.B.C.'s Savoy Hill site had been developed to its limit which was clearly insufficient for the production of the large number of programmes needed for the proposed Regional Scheme. Plans were therefore finalised for the erection of a new purpose-built B.B.C. headquarters in London to be known as Broadcasting House (see 1932).

The B.B.C. by the beginning of the year had nearly two and a half million licensed listeners and in the summer, outdoor listening on a suitcase portable became such a national activity that 1928 was dubbed by the wireless Press as the "Year Of The Suitcase Portable". This type of receiver had become more popular than any other in its class. It came complete with a frame aerial and a moving-iron cone loud-speaker neatly housed in the lift-up lid while the control panel, chassis and batteries were contained in the main compartment (fig.240). The majority employed a two waveband, 5-valve (2 HF/DET/2 LF) triode circuit which was capable of good quality reception of up to about 70 miles from the nearest local station as well as five or six other stations at good loud-speaker strength, although listeners in the Nottingham area lost the 5NG relay, which broadcast for the last time on November 25th.

Portables appealed to people from all walks of life, as Wireless World reported in May, "A party of debutantes awaiting admission to Buckingham Palace last week killed time with a portable wireless set". But in the summer months, portables really came into their own for the first time as an essential addition to outdoor leisure, and as they grew in popularity, sales of aerial wire were reported by The Wireless Trader as showing "a remarkable decrease" and with flat dwellers too employing frame aerials in increasing numbers, the demise of the large array of wires and poles was being recognised by everyone.

In general though, despite the popular attraction of the portable, and by now the growing interest in AC mains and to a lesser extent DC mains receivers, the staple product of the British Wireless Industry continued to be the permanently installed type of indoor battery powered TRF receiver with a two-band (medium and long-wave) 3-valve circuit connected by wires to a separate loud-speaker and an outdoor aerial and earth system (fig.244): interest in superhets had for the moment completely disappeared.

While the vast majority of battery valve receivers covered medium and long waves, there were a few more expensive models with short-wave also; and at the lower end of the market, some with the medium waveband only (fig.239). Some battery valve receivers began to be provided with two aerial inputs: one for local and one for distant station reception (fig.241). In general, the procedure for changing wavebands by means of a single switch was now widely adopted and had largely taken the place of the 2-pin plug-in coil method, although with short-wave only sets, the practice of using separate plug-in coils for the various wave ranges of the short waveband was to continue. To tune-in to the required stations with medium and long-wave sets, edgewise-mounted drum scale controls were used more and more on new models and the calibration of tuning scales directly in metre wavelengths slowly increased (fig.240).

For the growing market of home-construction, there was an expanding range of specially manufactured components and kits. The Cossor Melody Maker (fig.248) appeared for the first time in a kit form and came complete with an ornamental steel cabinet and, unlike the 1927 'chart' version, used a screened-grid valve: the Cossor SG 220 with a conventional 4-pin B4 base and top terminal. Thanks to the full instructions and really simplified and easy-to-follow diagrams, the 1928 Melody Maker could be built and operated by those with little technical knowledge and, according to Cossor's advertisement, "something less than the average amount of dexterity". Released towards the end of the year, it was an ideal project for the Christmas holidays: "you can spend the first part assembling it and the second part listening to it!". Everything was included in the carton down to the last nut and bolt; even a screwdriver was supplied, and for the flat dweller, and those others who were unable to use an outdoor aerial, Cossor also provided a matching Melody Maker Frame Aerial kit for 17s.6d. The Melody Maker series really helped to put kit sets on the map and within four years, over 350,000 had been constructed, and the name was still being used on Cossor's factory-built receivers right up to the early 1950s.

Cabinets were now becoming an important part of the home-constructor's market and there were now several firms specialising in wireless cabinet making. The Carrington Manufacturing Company set up their Camco Works in South Croydon, and began producing neat wooden 'Camco' cabinets for both home-constructors and manufacturers, and one of their first major commercial production commissions was to supply the wooden cabinets for Cossor's 1930 Melody Maker kit brought out in 1929. 'Kabilok' wooden cabinets, made by W. & T. Lock of Bath, were similarly available (fig.239).

By the middle of 1928, several manufacturers were offering high quality moving-coil loud-speakers, but being cumbersome affairs with large diameter cones and massive field magnets energised directly from the mains, these needed a very strong signal to drive them and were not available to the mass of listeners who had relatively small power battery operated receivers. Only the more affluent members of the "LS5 brigade", as *Wireless World* called them, with access to a mains supply could afford to run them. (The LS5 was an expensive, high power output valve first introduced by the M-O. Valve Company in 1923, see Appendix). But in 1928, the first permanent magnet moving-coil loud-speakers appeared, using standard horseshoe or bar magnets. Although the earliest examples were relatively inefficient and expensive, they were soon improved upon and by the early 1930s these high quality loud-speakers were in widespread use in battery receivers and later superseded the energised type in mains receivers.

The quality of another branch of home entertainment was also improved in 1928 with the introduction of electric pickups and electric radiograms, which were exhibited for the first time at Radiolympia in September, and provided greatly improved record reproduction. By the following year, many wireless manufacturers were providing terminals on the backs of their receivers so that the low frequency section of the circuit could be used as an auxiliary amplifier for connection to an ordinary wind-up gramophone fitted with a new electric pick-up.

TELEVISION

One of the Radiolympia stands which drew a lot of interest was that belonging to the Baird Television Development Company. For the first time in public they were exhibiting commercially manufactured 30-line disc Televisors in mahogany cabinets, although at this stage of development only a handful had been made. The display comprised Model 'A' at £20, a basic portable vision-only instrument which could be worked from an ordinary valve receiver; Model 'B' at £90, a table model Televisor with an integral moving-coil loud-speaker which worked from two ordinary valve receivers (one for tuning to the sound signals and the other to the vision signals); and Model 'C' at £150, as Model 'B', but in a floor-standing cabinet, the lower half of which contained two separate valve receivers, a frame aerial, a rotary converter and a 12 volt accumulator. Because no actual transmitting demonstrations were allowed in the Radiolympia building the display itself was a static exhibit but Baird hired premises nearby and was able to put on a working exhibition during which various celebrities were televised.

As early as February 1928, following work on the standardization of Baird's transmitting and receiving equipment by Commander W.W. Jacomb, during which the heavy-lensed discs were replaced by light aluminium ones with a spiral of small holes around the periphery, the company had been sufficiently confident to begin advertising their television receivers. A campaign of Press advertisements during the summer announcing "TELEVISION IN THE HOME" gave rise to public speculation that a regular television service was about to begin, but to the B.B.C. and the Post Office, these advertisements were misleading. The B.B.C. had a monopoly of broadcasting in this country and wanted to see definite scientific experiments conducted. Only then, if proving that Baird's invention had practical possibilities, would they consider allowing experimental broadcasts from one of their transmitters, and while the B.B.C. remained unco-operative, Baird suggested to the Press that he might go ahead and apply for a licence to set up a high power television transmitting station independent of the Corporation.

The Post Office's attitude was a little more positive and they asked Baird to conduct a special demonstration for them. This took place on September 18th with the transmitter set up at the Baird studios in Long Acre and a Televisor at the Engineers Club several hundred yards away. They were quite impressed with the result and urged the B.B.C. to reconsider its position but the Corporation's Chief Engineer, P.P. Eckersley, was not satisfied with the Post Office's report on the proceedings and insisted on an independent demonstration conducted in their presence. This was arranged for October 9th but again, the B.B.C. felt that the images shown did not justify a trial through one of their transmitters. As a result, the Baird Television Development Company went ahead and formally applied to the Post Office for a licence.

Meanwhile, during 1928, Baird had been carrying out other experiments from his Long Acre studio into the various uses of television and these he generally conducted after 11.30 at night. In the early hours of February 9th, Baird succeeded in transmitting television images across the Atlantic. In front of a small party made up of Press representatives and a few personal guests assembled in the Long Acre studio, the demonstration began at midnight. The televised signals, which included the images of his ventiloquist's doll and a Mrs Howe, the wife of an American journalist, were sent via a Post Office telephone line to Baird's private experimental wireless station at Coulsdon, Surrey, (call-sign 2KZ) and were sent across the Atlantic using an aerial power of 2 kW and a wavelength of 45 metres. The signals were received on a Televisor taken to America by two Baird representatives and installed in an amateur receiving station at Hartsdale, a few miles from New York City. A month later, while the Televisor was being brought back to England on the Cunard liner *Berengaria*, the experiments were again repeated in the early hours of March 7th while the ship was in mid-Atlantic. As a result of the success of these experiments, Vowlers, the stockbroking firm, arranged in June to underwrite a third company, Baird International Television Ltd. with an authorised capital of £700,000.

Baird continued to explore television from other angles during experiments from Long Acre. While since his earliest investigations Baird had always relied on artificial light, in June he gave the first demonstration of daylight television. Having made improvements to the light-sensitivity of his scanning equipment, he was able to televise his subjects as they sat out on the roof above his laboratory. On July 3rd, he demonstrated a colour television picture of a kind and was already experimenting with stereoscopic television, although without any great success. The activities of Baird were now being well covered by a new monthly publication called *Television* which was the world's first television journal and also the official organ of the Television Society. The proprietors of the magazine, Television Press Ltd. made arrangements with the owners of the world patent rights to the Baird television system to issue free 'sub-licences' to their readers "for the limited purpose of the construction of one set of apparatus for television, if erected and operated by the sub-licensee purely as an amateur". The magazine gave regular constructional details of Baird receivers and if made without a sub-licence, the home-constructor was liable for prosecution for infringements of Baird patents. Such was the interest among home-constructors, who were already weaned by wireless, that by April 1st 1928, over 500 sub-licences had been issued.

From December 4th 1928, regular transmission of television in conjunction with music, singing and speech began twice weekly on Tuesday and Saturday nights between the hours of midnight and 1am with vision on 200 metres and sound on 250 metres.

While the B.B.C. were being negative about Baird's television system, they had already committed themselves to another branch of television in which still pictures would be transmitted in a series of experiments by the Fultograph process from the long-wave Daventry transmitter during certain afternoons of the week. This process had been invented by Otto Fulton and the Fultograph receiver was first publicly shown at the 1928 Radiolympia by its manufacturers, Wireless Pictures (1928) Ltd. The receiver cost £22.15s.0d in an oak case and £24.15s.0d in mahogany, and in the following year came out in kit form at £15 for the benefit of the home-constructor. The receiving mechanism (resembling an Edison phonograph) was mounted in the case and comprised a rotating clockwork-driven metal drum to which was fixed a blank sheet of sensitive paper. When the transmitted signal was received, the drum automatically began to revolve and a stylus travelled along the drum building up an image on the paper. The Fultograph printed a still picture 4 in. x 5 in. and could be used by anyone who possessed a wireless set able to receive Daventry on the long waveband: it was simply connected to the set in place of the loud-speaker. The B.B.C.'s series of experimental Fultograph long-wave transmissions which initially ran until October 31st 1929 and then after a pause continued on 261.3 metres until June 21st 1932, began on October 30th 1928

although they were not billed in *The Radio Times* until the following February. By then, topical news pictures, cartoons and fashion plates etc. were being broadcast by the Fultograph process from several continental stations as well.

Television magazine was not amused by the B.B.C's co-operation in the Fultograph venture believing that the broadcasting of still pictures was a hindrance rather than a help to the development of television. The caption to a cartoon in their December 1928 issue showing a blind-folded John Bull character addressing the B.B.C., sums up their attitude.

"Take from my eyes,
These shades of doubt,
Of Fulton photos
I will have nowt.
I want to see
Before me spread,
The Empire living - not dead"

VALVE DEVELOPMENT

With valve receiver design, the most up-to-date type of battery model was one which employed a screened-grid HF/DET/ Pentode LF circuit. The Pentode (see Appendix) was an entirely new type of valve and was designed as a screened high efficiency power output valve. The first on the market was the Mullard PM24 and soon advertisements were urging everyone to "try a Pentode!". And it was easy, for the new valve fitted the conventional 4-pin B4 socket without wiring alterations, the side terminal which was connected to the screened-grid electrode being simply connected to the HT battery.

In some more elaborate circuits, push-pull amplification was being experimented with as a method of obtaining a large undistorted output from the last stage of the receiver. Since being patented before World War One, it had occasionally created interest over the years and now in its modern use, two ordinary power triodes could be made to give results equivalent to one of the extra super-power types (see also 1933, quiescent push-pull).

Following the introduction of AC mains valves, AC mains TRF receivers (some using newly introduced Westinghouse metal rectifiers) steadily gained ground and from this time, until the mid-1930s, many of them employed directly-heated pentodes as power output valves, tolerating the amount of inevitable mains hum: even when indirectly-heated pentodes first appeared in May 1930, it was a good five years before directly-heated types went out of general use. DC 'mains' receivers too showed an increase and in 1931, true DC mains receivers appeared with the introduction of DC mains valves. However, because of the foreseen demise of the DC supply system, the number of new models was to remain relatively small until with the wide introduction of 'universal' AC/DC receivers towards the mid-1930s, DC-only models were phased out altogether (see 1934).

In 1928, the M-O. Valve Company introduced the 'Point-eight' series of directly-heated AC valves which had a filament consumption of 0.8 amps at 0.8 volts, hence the name. These used a short, very thick filament, the thermal inertia of which avoided mains hum, and were designed for connection to the raw AC lighting supply and dispensing with the necessity of rectifying and smoothing circuits. The Point-eight series included various classes of triodes, screened-grids and pentodes, but they were not successful, and were very soon superseded by indirectly-heated types with slip-coated filaments.

In 1928, the first Cosmos indirectly-heated screened-grid valve appeared, the AC/S. The success of the Cosmos indirectly-heated slip-coated AC valves had become so great that early in the year the M-O. Valve Company abandoned the original (and inferior) construction of their own 'K' series indirectly-heated mains valves and contracted Metro-Vick Supplies Ltd. to manufacture KL1 and KH1 valves with AC/R and AC/G slip-coated filament construction. These valves can easily be identified as their glass envelopes are etched with the words, e.g., "MARCONI TYPE KL1. AC/R. Made by Metro-Vick Supplies Ltd." and the M-O. Valve Company boxes they were supplied in were overstamped "MADE BY METRO-VICK SUPPLIES". They had ordinary 4-pin B4 bases with a screw terminal on the side of the base connected to the cathode: the same base layout as the original 1927 'K' series. (Both examples of the Metro-Vick 1928 'K' series valves were used in the Marconiphone Type 23 Universal Feed receiver, fig.238).

Later that year, the side terminal connection of these valves was taken to an extra pin on the base, creating the new 5-pin 'B5' base and this was soon adopted by mains triode valves in general (see Appendix) including the Cosmos AC/R and AC/G valves which abandoned their unique base configuration.

The M-O. screened-grid S625 also changed form in 1928. By the summer it had evolved from its original horizontal double-ended form into a conventional 4-pin B4-based valve with its control grid now connected to a threaded terminal on top of the glass envelope. It was now re-designated as the M-O. S215 and was first used in the Marconiphone Type 44 receiver. Nearly all other valve manufacturers in Great Britain produced B4-based screened-grid valves from 1928, but chose instead to bring the anode out to the top screw terminal, a practice which remained standard throughout the screened-grid's lifetime of production.

With the growing use of the HF screened-grid valve, a neater design sense and a more professional attitude to receiver construction was exhibited by the Wireless Industry. Receivers began to use metal partition screening in which (preferably) the input and output stages were carefully wired and arranged on opposite sides of the same partition, with the envelope of the screened-grid valve extending part of the way through, thus greatly reducing interstage interference (fig.236). Instead of the traditional wooden baseboard supporting an assembly of components and wires, metal (sheet steel or aluminium) was now beginning to be used for the chassis, neatly screening the wiring and components beneath from the valves and tuning components housed on top. In some cases where extra screening was thought necessary, metal was even used for the cabinet (figs.248,251). The G.E.C. Victor 3 (fig.250) was housed in a metal case. Inside, the only immediately visible components were the valves and the two tuning condensers mounted on a insulating paxolin plate. The rest of the components were boxed in, connected together in a very novel way by hard-rolled copper strips making it a not too distant relative of the printed circuit of the 1950s. Most of the components were specially designed and made for the receiver by G.E.C. itself and not just bought in 'off the peg' from component manufacturers, a trend which was soon adopted by other receiver manufacturers.

Several other developments within the valve industry took place in 1928. One of the most noteworthy was the establishment in Britain of a factory by the Hungarian valve and lamp manufacturers Tungsram, who began marketing 2 volt battery triodes principally for the outdoor portable market. Three years later, they became the only British-based company to branch out into making a full range of American-type AC mains valves for supplying imported American-made receivers which had then begun their rise in popularity in this country (see 1931). Also in 1928, Associated Electrical Industries was formed by the British Thomson-Houston Co. Ltd. (B.T.H.), Edison-Swan Electric Co. Ltd. (Ediswan) and Metro-Vick Supplies Ltd. (Cosmos), with B.T.H. dropping its own name and producing valves under the 'Mazda' trademark.

During 1928, there occurred the biggest and most important patents action in the Wireless Industry's history. The case involved the Brownie Wireless Company's legal fight against Marconi's in a challenge to the validity of the Marconi Patents, under which most wireless receivers were manufactured. After many months, the case resulted in Brownie being granted a compulsory licence to manufacture valve sets on a royalty basis of 10 per cent of the wholesale selling price of a set, subject to a minimum of 5s.0d for the first and 2s.6d for each subsequent valve holder. The R.M.A. took the lead in trying to clarify the position of other firms holding Marconi Licences, and there were protracted discussions as to whether the compulsory licence was valid or not. The year ended without a final settlement, as Marconi's had decided to appeal.

1929

On Janaury 13th, listeners throughout Britain were unpleasantly surprised by the putting into operation of the I.B.U.'s *Brussels Plan* in a further attempt to sort out the growing 'ether chaos' caused by interference between the expanding number of broadcasting stations around Europe. With thirteen B.B.C. stations changing their wavelengths at once under the new Plan (the rest followed in the months after), listeners were once again put to the inconvenience of having to re-calibrate their dials and to get used to the new station settings. They were not heartened either by the additional news that from July 7th yet another Plan and another re-allocation of wavelengths would come into force. This was the *Prague Plan* which for the first time allocated wavelengths not to individual stations but to countries, with each country being free to distribute its own particular group of wavelengths as it saw fit. Among the changes during the year, two of the B.B.C.'s original main stations, Bournemouth and Newcastle, were both relegated to relays, on January 13th and November 3rd respectively.

TELEVISION

Under pressure from the Post Office, the B.B.C. arranged with Baird for a further demonstration of his television system and this took place on March 5th. In consequence, the Corporation at last agreed to allow one of their transmitters to be used by the Baird Television Development Company for experimental 30-line ('low-definition') television transmissions outside the normal broadcasting hours. These began on September 30th and were radiated daily (except Saturdays and Sundays) between 11am and 11.30am on 356.3 metres using the 2LO transmitter at Selfridges, the programmes being relayed via a Post Office landline from the Baird studios in Long Acre. Of those few viewers equipped with Televisors, those with the vision-only Model 'A' or with similar vision-only home-constructed sets first had to tune in the 356.3 metres wavelength on an ordinary wireless receiver which acted as a separate tuner and amplifier. The receiver's loud-speaker was then disconnected and replaced by the Televisor which was fed television signals via the loud-speaker terminals. Because only one wavelength was available, vision and sound could not be broadcast at the same time, and in the main, the experiments were conducted in vision only. However, on the inauguration day, vision and sound were transmitted one after the other in two minute sequences. The first guest to appear was Sir Ambrose Fleming, the President of the Television Society who was televised in silence from 11.08am to 11.10am. Immediately after this he gave the same speech in sound only, and viewers with vision-only Televisors had to hurriedly re-connect the loud-speaker to their wireless sets in order to hear the speech. This disjointed performance was repeated by other guests and performers until 11.30am. Wireless listeners without Televisors could tune into the experiments as well, but during the televised sections all they would hear would be a characteristic low-frequency throb superimposed on a high-pitched whistle.

A few weeks later, on October 21st, part of the B.B.C.'s new high power twin medium-wave transmitting station opened at Brookmans Park in Hertfordshire, linked by four Post Office cable circuits to the studios at Savoy Hill, 16 miles to the south. As a result, the old 2LO transmitter at Selfridges in Oxford Street was closed down after just four years service. At first only the Regional Programme transmitter was brought into service, radiating 2LO London on 356.3 metres to listeners in London and the Home Counties and taking over the 30-line experimental television transmissions. The partial opening of the station was to allow time for wireless receiver circuits to be modified before the second transmitter (broadcasting the National Programme on 261.3 metres) was brought into service in March 1930. This also meant that for the first time, with two wavelengths available, the 30-line television experiments could be transmitted in synchronised sound and vision, and the increased power would make the signals available to prospective viewers in a very much enlarged area (see 1930).

CHANGES IN WIRELESS DESIGN

Crystal sets with their inefficient and unselective circuits were obsolete by now and the B.B.C. actually took positive steps to discourage the use of those still in the hands of stalwart listeners by publishing a pamphlet pointing out the greater benefits of valve receivers. With the continual growth of high power transmitting stations both in this country and in Europe, the need had arisen for greater selectivity in order to prevent interference from stations broadcasting on adjacent wavelengths. Improvements to selectivity had usually meant a loss in reception quality, and the use of wave-traps, while useful for cutting out an unwanted station, inevitably meant a reduction in signal strength. But a new method of tuning was developed which helped to solve these problems. Known as 'band-pass tuning', it employed a pair of tuned circuits, with the variable condensers ganged together for simplicity of control. As the name implies, the band-pass system passed a selected band of frequencies while rejecting all others. The adoption in 1929 of two stages of screened-grid HF amplification in the circuits of the more sophisticated and expensively designed type of receivers had greatly improved matters, but band-pass tuning was to lead to a greater all-round improvement in selectivity, reception range, sound quality and reliability, although it was not used commercially to any great extent until towards the end of 1930, after Brookmans Park had fully opened.

Amongst all classes of receiver, the 2-band TRF was the dominating type and although within a year or so superhets were to begin their rise to supremacy, interest in them for the present had completely subsided.

There now began a slow increase in the number of all-enclosed indoor battery receivers: the battery 'transportable' class, designed to be compact and light enough to be easily and conveniently carried to wherever the broadcast programmes were needed in the home, and the battery 'table model' class. However, the number of new indoor battery models of the permanently installed type wired to an outdoor aerial system and separate loud-speaker remained steady and with the exception of the outdoor battery portable, the inclusion of a loud-speaker within the cabinet was still far from being standard practice. Few horn loud-speakers were now being offered for sale, having been generally replaced by the moving-iron cone type, housed in a wooden cabinet. But one or two early examples still clung on, notably the B.T.H. Model C2 and Amplion's Dragon, the latter being (unbelievably) "as popular as ever and increasing in demand" according to advertisements in May 1929. An advance in permanent-magnet

moving-coil loud-speaker design took place with the introduction of the four-claw cast-steel magnet, a type which held the field until 1932.

There was still a lot of interest in outdoor battery portables, which was especially keen with the approach of summer. In many areas of the country, they were also still very much of a novelty, as the *Birmingham Post* reported to its readers in October, "A portable owner who switched on his set in a Birmingham street has been fined ten shillings for drawing a crowd which caused obstruction".

Popular too, was the habit amongst some listeners of seeing how many distant foreign stations they could tune-in and identify, although with Britain just entering the Depression following the collapse of the New York Stock Exchange, foreign station listening was seen in some quarters as unpatriotic. To help the long-distance listener (or 'knob-twiddler' or 'ether hog' as he was sometimes scornfully described), and to supplement information already obtainable in *World Radio* (the B.B.C.'s foreign station equivalent of *The Radio Times*), *Wireless World* offered a station identification service to readers who were puzzled as to which European station they had been listening to. The queries from them were often quite ludicrous, eg., "Last night at 9.30pm I heard some music, and later a ticking noise like a clock. I do not know the wavelength but my condensers pointed to 63 and 75. What station was that?".

Mains operated receivers were still in the minority, constituting only about 17 per cent of the new models released in the autumn. Yet it was recognised that within the next few years, mains receivers would rise to dominate the market, particularly as work on the National Grid Scheme had begun that year and millions of homes would soon experience the benefits of mains electricity for the first time.

New AC mains receivers outnumbered DC models by about 3:1, with metal rectifiers being used in just under 50 per cent of them. Like indoor battery models, most receivers still required a separate loud-speaker, but 1929 marked the first significant appearance of the all-enclosed mains table model, a type which, in superhet form, quickly rose to become the staple part of the Wireless Industry and remained so until the coming of the transistor portables towards the late 1950s. The first mains table model with a built-in loud-speaker to be manufactured was the Pye Model 275 AC (fig.262), and it was closely followed by the first example of an all-enclosed mains transportable: the Selector All-Electric Transportable, heavily priced at £57.15s.0d.

In all classes of receiver, polished wood (walnut, mahogany and to a lesser extent, oak) was still being used as the main cabinet material and was seen as particularly desirable for domestic table models (fig.262) which had to harmonise as furniture with the decor of the home. But other materials, such as metal (fig.276) and particularly plastics (fig.256) were also used. Moulded Bakelite cabinets, which from the 1930s were to rival wooden cabinets, began to appear around 1929.

On the control panel, adjustable reaction control knobs were still very much in evidence. Tone control knobs and, at the backs of the chassis, electric gramophone pick-up terminals were seen on several up-to-the-minute receivers for the first time.

All-metal chassis construction and the use of metal screening compartments (and screening cans for tuning coils in at least one early example, fig.253) were methods now widely adopted. Aluminium was the most popular material for internal screening, followed by nickel-plated brass, copper, brass and tin-plate. Chassis of factory-built receivers were now designed as complete units bolted into an attractive wooden cabinet. This replaced the former system of somewhat randomly screwing components to a wooden baseboard, although this method continued to be the norm with home-constructed receivers until well into the 1930s.

Speaking of the 'complicated' components that all went together to make a wireless receiver, Miss Evelyn Spilsbury (a 1929 Radiolympia 'Mullard-Girl') gave her impressions of the modern receivers on show to *The Wireless & Gramophone Trader*. "I should like to say how well manufacturers assemble these many parts into an attractive whole. Today, even the cheapest set looks like a small carved cabinet and the untidy home of the wireless enthusiast has no longer any justification." This statement represented the "feminine view of modern wireless equipment. A question to which the progressive trader pays ever increasing attention." (And it seems that they took *The Wireless & Gramophone Trader's* advice, for in 1929, only 15 per cent of visitors to Radiolympia were women whereas three years later, the figure had risen to 50 per cent).

Listeners were generally satisfied with the ubiquitous two waveband type of receiver giving plenty of entertainment and news from the B.B.C. and European stations on the medium and long wavebands. But for those who wanted to tune-in to the far corners of the globe on short waves as well (and could afford to do so) there were comparatively few commercial 'all-wave' receivers being manufactured in 1929 (fig.260, Burndept's Universal Screened Five). For the less well off, short-wave converters, introduced in add-on unit form enabled any ordinary two waveband receiver to be converted into an efficient short-wave receiver with no change of internal wiring (see later examples figs.327,397).

As a means of changing wavebands, single-knob waveband switching was now universal. In medium and long waveband receivers, the use of 2-pin plug-in tuning coils had practically disappeared although on retailers' shelves there were still a few left-over models from the past being sold which employed this obsolete method (fig.198). In short-wave sets, the use of plug-in coils continued. Capacity controlled reaction (see 1927) had completely displaced the swinging coil method, but with continually improving HF amplification the use of reaction in circuits slowly began to diminish.

For selecting the required station, the old circular bevelled Bakelite and ebonite dials were rapidly dying out, but edgewise-mounted drum scale tuning controls were now at the height of their popularity (figs.269,276,277). With many two-band receivers employing ganged tuning condensers, the simple single knob tuning control with a drum-drive scale or a disc-drive dial, a small portion of which was visible through a small escutcheon window above the knob, was becoming popular (figs.253,255,273).

There was now an increasing number of receivers with tuning scales calibrated directly in metre wavelengths rather than degrees (figs.253,259,263,276) and in October, the International Consultative Committee of the Radio Electrical Conference meeting in the Hague, Holland, re-classified the waveband terms used in wireless broadcasting. Throughout the 1920s, the term 'Short' had been extensively used both on the control panel of domestic broadcast receivers and in wireless literature for describing the band between about 200 and 500 metres, with 'Long' standing for anything above about 700 metres. But from about 1929, the 200/500 metres band was generally referred to as the 'Medium Waveband' with anything below this as 'Short' and then 'Ultra Short'. That is why, with many receivers produced up to the end of the 1920s and even into the 1930s, confusion can arise due to the panel being marked 'Short' and 'Long' where in today's terms, it would be 'Medium' and 'Long'. The definitions decided by the Consultative Committee were as follows, and although they were not universally adopted, the spirit of the re-classification was:

LONG: 3,000 metres and above. MEDIUM: 200/3,000 metres. INTERMEDIATE: 50/200 metres. SHORT: 10/50 metres. ULTRA SHORT: 10 metres and below.

On August 12th, it was announced that all A.E.I. Group valves then being manufactured by Edison-Swan Electric Co. Ltd., British Thomson-Houston Co. Ltd. and Metro-Vick Supplies Ltd., (under the trademarks Ediswan, Mazda and Cosmos respectively), would in future be marketed entirely by the Edison-Swan Company under the Mazda trademark. 'Mazda' grew to be one of the foremost names on the British valve market during the 1930s with Mazda valves being selected by many leading receiver manufacturers.

In December, The Gramophone Company at Hayes in Middlesex took over the control of the Marconiphone Company which from 1930, carried on the production of Marconiphone receivers from their new Hayes address. During that year, The Gramophone Company produced their first offering to the Wireless Industry in the form of the Model 174 cabinet loud-speaker (fig.898), and in 1931 first entered the field of wireless manufacture when they began making receivers under the H.M.V. ('Little Nipper') trade-mark (fig.316). In the same year, The Gramophone Company merged with the Columbia Graphophone Company to form Electric and Musical Industries Ltd. (E.M.I.).

Throughout 1929, the Brownie and Marconi's patents litigation had held the stage. Marconi's had appealed and the hearing ended in May. When the reserve judgement was given by Mr Justice Luxmore in June, Marconi's were successful and the Controller General's orders were discharged leaving the fixing of Marconi royalties in Marconi's hands. Shortly afterwards, negotiations opened between the company and the R.M.A. to determine the future situation, and Marconi's offered a new agreement until 1933, based on a 5s.0d per valve holder royalty payment. The final terms were issued in November and a year later, the new licence, the A3 Licence, came into force (see 1930).

fig. 53 . Ericsson 'Two Valve Receiver', by British L.M. Ericsson Manufacturing Co. Ltd. 1922. BBC/PMG stamp, GPO Reg.No.2013. 2-v Batt, for headphone use, 0-180 deg, brass fittings, brown ebonite control panel, walnut case. 7 ½ in. x 12 ½ in. x 9 ½ in. Semi-circular degree-marked Ivorine scales with rotating pointers to indicate settings.

fig. 54 . Fellophone 'Two Valve Receiver', by Fellows Magneto Co. Ltd. 1922. BBC/PMG stamp but no GPO Reg.No. 2-v Batt, for headphone use, 0-100 deg MW, brass fittings, ebonite control panel, oak case with instructions in lift-up lid. 8 ¾ in. x 10 in. x 7 ½ in. The company's first wireless receiver. Uses P1 valves by A.C. Cossor Ltd. HT battery housed inside case.

fig. 55 . H.P.R. 'Simplex No.493', des: H. Powell Rees. 1922. BBC/PMG stamp, GPO Reg.No.1008. 1-v Batt for headphone use, black ebonite panel, mahogany case. 2 ½ in. x 5 in. x 9 in.

fig. 56 . Gecophone Model BC 2001, HF/DET, by General Electric Co. Ltd. November 1922. BBC/PMG stamp, GPO Reg.No.2000. 2-v HF/DET Batt, for headphone use, MW (300/500m) 0-180 deg, variometer and variable condenser tuning controls, black ebonite control panel, battery compartment, mahogany 'smoker's cabinet'. 17 in. x 11 ½ in. x 9 in. £25.0s.0d inc valves, headphones and HT and LT batteries. Rotating circular Bakelite dials calibrated in degrees with the fixed datum line engraved on the panel. Socket provided for additional tuning coils. Printed instruction cards pinned to the double doors which close to hide the control panel when the set is not in use.

The BC 2001 was first shown at the All-British Wireless Exhibition in September 1922 when it appeared with a tapped A.T.I. (aerial tuning inductance) control knob on the bottom right of the panel. This was several weeks before the British Broadcasting Company was set up and receivers from this early production run do not bare either a BBC/PMG stamp or a G.P.O. Registration Number. The BC 2001 is of similar appearance to the later Model BC 3200, DET/LF (BBC/PMG stamp, GPO Reg.No.5394) which came out in early 1924.

fig. 56a . In the illustration, the BC 2001 is shown sitting on its matching 'Two-Stage LF Amplifier' Gecophone Model BC 2580 (BBC/PMG stamp, GPO Reg.No.3360), making a 4-valve combination set. The two units were connected together by means of three short cords and plugs at the back of the instruments and could be bought together as the Model BC 3400 for £32.5s.0d.

fig. 57 . A 3-valve receiver for headphone use by the Marconi Scientific Instrument Co. Ltd. 1922. No BBC/PMG stamp but GPO Reg.No.0270. Employs a QX (detector) and two V24 valves in a reflex circuit (des: H.J.Round). Loose-coupled tuning, brass fittings, dark oak cabinet. 17 in. x 22 in. x 9 in.

fig. 58 . 'All Wave Receiver F.B.', by Clemens & Taylor. 1922 (pre-B.B.C.). 2-v Batt, for headphone use, swinging reaction coils inside, (externally mounted plug-in tuning coils for various wave ranges extra), brass fittings, ebonite control panel, mahogany case. 6 in. x 12 in. x 9 in.

fig. 59 . R.I. Type V.I.M., by Radio Instruments Ltd. Winter 1922. BBC/PMG stamp, GPO Reg.No.3001. 1-v Batt LF Amplifier, brass fittings, ebonite panel, mahogany case. 6 in. x 6 ¼ in. x 5 ½ in.

fig. 60 . Marconiphone Model V2, by Marconi's Wireless Telegraph Co. Ltd. (Chassis made by Plessey, Holloway). November 1922. BBC/PMG stamp, GPO Reg.No.2001. 2-v Batt, for headphone use, reflex circuit, 185/3,200m, plug-in regenerator unit, slot-in range blocks, spade tuning controls, mahogany cabinet. 10 ½ in. x 13 in. x 8 in. (front panel removed). £25.0s.0d. Capable of tuning in steps from 185 to 3,200 metres by selecting one of 11 slot-in range blocks in conjunction with the appropriate plug-in regenerator unit. The circuit incorporates 'spade tuning' in which a pair of flat metal 'spades' were moved over the selected range block by means of metal rods terminating in two spherical nickel-plated knobs at either side of the cabinet. Notches on the rods indicated the tuning settings. A matching 2-valve amplifier (using bright-emitters), Type NB2, enabled the V2 to be used with a loud-speaker. A dull-emitter version of this amplifier, Type A2 (fig.142) was brought out in 1924.

The V2 was first produced in the summer of 1922 without a plug-in regenerator unit and with 'R' valves or LT1 and LT3 dull-emitters as standard. From November 1922, it then appeared with a plug-in regenerator unit and was given the GPO Reg.No.2001 and bore the BBC/PMG stamp of approval. In the spring of 1923, it appeared as the 'V2A, Long Range Model', with a BBC/PMG stamp and the new GPO Reg.No.0175, although the circuit after very close examination appears to be identical to the 2001. DER valves were now used as standard and two dry battery versions (using DE3's) also came out at this time for those who experienced difficulty in getting their accumulators charged, and, with a canvas and leather carrying case and with the cabinet interior adapted for accomodating HT and LT batteries, for those who wanted a portable.

After the summer of 1924 when Post Office registration regulations had ceased and some six months after a new company (the Marconiphone Co. Ltd.) had taken over the marketing of 'Marconiphone' receivers, the V2A appeared without a GPO Reg.No. although it continued to bear the BBC/PMG stamp. Finally, in 1925, surplus V2 receivers left over from 1922, and still bearing their original BBC/PMG stamp and the GPO Reg.No.2001 (fig.170), were updated with

the rotary micrometer tuning device which was first used on the Marconiphone Model V3 in 1923 (fig. 82). Several slight variations in cabinet construction have been noted.

fig.60a. 1922 Marconiphone Model V2 with front panel replaced and lid closed. Note the portholes for inspecting the valves' filaments.

fig. 61 . Radieco 'Simplex', by Radio Equipment Co. 1922. BBC/PMG stamp, GPO Reg.No.1020. 1-v batt, MW 0-180 deg, for headphone use, black ebonite panel, oak cabinet. 9 ¼ in. x 10 ½ in. x 8 in. £5.17s.6d.

fig. 62 . General Type GRC4, by General Radio Co. Ltd. Winter 1922. BBC/PMG stamp, GPO Reg.No.132. Crystal Set for headphone use, cat's whisker/galena detector, variable and vernier tuning controls, 0-180 deg, brass fittings, black ebonite control panel, mahogany case. 6 in. x 11 in. x 6 in. Small window for illuminating the detector and another for inspecting it. Terminals for connecting to an amplifier.

fig. 63 . Siemens Type CV, by Siemens Bros. & Co. Ltd. 1922. 1-v/crystal set for headphone use, open Perikon detector, LF 'R' valve, filament viewing lens set into ebonite control panel, slot-in tuning coil, nickel-plated fittings, mahogany case. 8 ½ in. x 9 ½ in. x 5 ½ in. £6.10s.0d inc B.B.C. royalties, headphones, batteries, LF valve and a medium-wave coil. This receiver could be used in three modes: as a crystal set, as a 1-valve set or as a crystal set with a 1-valve amplifier.

fig. 64 . Marconiphone 'Crystal A' Type RB3 M2, by Marconi's Wireless Telegraph Co. Ltd. (Chassis made by Plessey, Holloway). November 1922. BBC/PMG stamp, GPO Reg.No.101. (Earliest examples, devoid of both BBC/PMG stamp and GPO Reg.No., were released between August and October 1922). Crystal Set for headphone use, carborundum/steel detector (polarized by a 1.5v cell) plus open cat's whisker/galena detector, slot-in range blocks for various wave ranges, spade tuning controls, nickel-plated fittings, black ebonite control panel, ivorine badge with the initials 'MWT' (Marconi's Wireless Telegraph Co. Ltd.) set into a recess in the top of the rexine-covered wood case. 5 ¼ in. x 11 ½ in. x 6 ¼ in. (closed). £9.10s.0d inc headphones, aerial and earth wires. Spare crystals, a range block and instructions are housed in the lid. A smaller version, the 'Crystal Junior', appeared at the same time (fig. 68). The case and many of the components of the 'Crystal A' were later used with the Marconiphone Type RB10 valve/crystal receiver (fig.112).

In November 1925, a parcel of 15,300 'Crystal A' and 'Crystal Junior' crystal sets were acquired by J.M. Millet & Sons of Southampton who simply pasted on their own labels and instructions and sold them to retailers as the 'Millet A' and the 'Millet Junior', price 17s.6d and 12s.6d respectively, less 33 ⅓ per cent for lots of 100.

fig. 65 . Home-constructed unit-type rceiver, c.1922. 4-v Batt, no integral loud-speaker, plug-in coils, 0-180 deg, variable condenser and loose-coupled tuning controls, brass fittings, sloping ebonite control panels, mahogany cabinet. 10 in. x 35 ½ in. x 11 ½ in.

fig. 66 . Elwell 'Panel No.11', by C.F. Elwell Ltd. Winter 1922. BBC/PMG stamp, GPO Reg.No.104. Crystal set for headphone use, open Perikon detector with zincite and 'tellite' (tellurium) crystals, variable condenser and tapped inductance tuning, MW, headphone socket, nickel-plated fittings, black ebonite control panel, mahogany case. 7 ¾ in. x 4 ½ in. x 7 in.

fig. 67 . 'Duo Coupling Receiver', by Nirvanax Ltd. 1922. BBC/PMG stamp, GPO Reg.No.225. Crystal set for headphone use, open cat's whisker/galena detector, variometer and variable condenser tuning, terminals for LF amplifier, black ebonite control panel, mahogany cabinet. 6 in. x 10 in. x 5 ½ in. (closed).

fig. 68 . Marconiphone 'Crystal Junior' Type RB2, by Marconi's Wireless Telegraph Co. Ltd. (Chassis made by Plessey, Holloway). November 1922. BBC/PMG stamp, GPO Reg.No.100. (Earliest examples, devoid of both BBC/PMG stamp and GPO Reg.No., were released between August and October 1922). Crystal Set for headphone use, open cat's whisker/galena detector, slot-in range blocks for various wave ranges, spade tuning controls, nickel-plated fittings, black ebonite control panel, rexine-covered wood case. 5 ¼ in. x 8 in. x 5 ¾ in. (closed). £5.15s.0d inc headphones, aerial and earth wires. Spare crystals, a range block and instructions are housed in the lid. Alternative carborundum/ steel detector (polarized by a 1.5v cell) provided.

fig. 69 . Model IEC, by International Electric Co. Ltd. Winter 1922. BBC/PMG stamp, GPO Reg.No.160. Crystal set for headphone use, glass-enclosed Perikon detector, variometer tuning, MW, brass fittings, ebonite control panel, mahogany case. 6 in. x 7 in. x 7 in.

fig. 70 . Western Electric Model 44001, by Western Electric Co. Ltd. Winter 1922. BBC/PMG stamp, GPO Reg.No.134. Crystal set for headphone use, open Perikon detector, variometer tuning, MW, nickel-plated fittings, black painted wood control panel, mahogany cabinet with headphone compartment and lift-up lid containing instructions. 7 in. x 8 ½ in. x 7 ¼ in. (closed). Very similar to 'Aeriola Junior' by Aeolian Co. Ltd. and 'Cosmos Radiophone' by Metropolitan Vickers Electrical Co. Ltd.

In 1923, Western Electric brought out a matching 2-valve 'Weconomy' LF amplifying unit (fig. 84) which fitted into the headphone compartment of the Model 44001 and enabled it to drive a horn loud-speaker.

fig. 71 . 'Fellocryst Super', by Fellows Magneto Co. Ltd. Winter 1922. BBC/PMG stamp, GPO Reg.No.177. Crystal set for headphone use, open cat's whisker/galena detector, variable condenser and tapped inductance tuning, MW + provision for LW coil, brass fittings, black Bakelite control panel, oak cabinet with lift-up lid housing instructions. 6 ¼ in. x 8 ¼ in. x 8 ¼ in. £4.15s.6d inc headphones and aerial equipment + 7s.6d B.B.C. royalty. Long-wave plug-in tuning coil for receiving the Paris Time Signals on 2,600 metres, price 6s.0d extra.

fig. 72 . Butler No.111, by H.D. Butler & Co. Winter 1922. BBC/PMG stamp, GPO Reg.No.118. Crystal set for headphone use, open cat's whisker/galena detector, variable condenser and double slide coil tuning, brass fittings, ebonite control panel, mahogany cabinet with lift-up lid and flap-down front. 5 ¾ in. x 6 ¾ in. x 6 ¾ in. £2.10s.0d + 7s.6d B.B.C. royalty.

fig. 73 . Ethophone No.1, by Burndept Ltd. Winter 1922. BBC/PMG stamp, GPO Reg.No.114. Crystal set for headphone use, open cat's whisker/galena detector, MW + plug-in tuning coil for Paris Time Signals on 2,600 metres, fine and coarse tapped inductance tuning (one position marked 'PARIS'), brass fittings, black ebonite control panel, walnut cabinet with lift-up lid containing instructions. 6 ¼ in. x 8 ¼ in. x 8 ¼ in. An extra tuning coil, price 7s.0d, could be provided for the reception of telephony from the Croydon Aerodrome on 900 metres. Identical to Sterling No.1 by Sterling Telephone & Electric Co. Ltd. which has GPO Reg.No.130, although both share the same Reg.Des.No.690578.

fig. 74 . B.T.H. Type 'C', Form 'A', by British Thomson-Houston Co. Ltd. Winter 1922. BBC/PMG stamp, GPO Reg.No.106. Crystal set for headphone use, twin celluloid-enclosed cat's whisker/galena detectors, variometer tuning, MW 300/600m + provision for LW tuning coil, nickel-plated fittings, brown ebonite control panel, brown ebonite knobs (receivers from the earliest production run have the raised letters 'BTH' moulded in the knobs), metal carrying handle, walnut cabinet with lift-up lid housing instructions. 8 ½ in. x 11 ¼ in. x 5 ¼ in. (closed). £1.15s.0d + 7s.6d B.B.C. royalty. Two detectors were provided so that the crystal found to be giving the better results could be selected by means of the 'CHANGE CRYSTAL' switch. A long-wave tuning coil for the Paris Time Signals on 2,600 metres was available price 3s.6d extra and this was fitted to the two terminals on the left of the control panel. In the summer of 1924, a '5XX' tuning coil was introduced for receiving the B.B.C.'s new 1,600 metre experimental long-wave station at Chelmsford. (The B.T.H. Type 'C', Form 'A' was made until around 1925, and the date of production is found printed in the corner of the instructions. The name 'Radiola' appears on later models).

fig. 75 . 'Cee Bee' Model No.3, by City Battery & Wireless Co. Winter 1922. BBC/PMG stamp, GPO Reg.No.249. Crystal set for headphone use, open cat's whisker/galena detector and Perikon detector, tapped inductance tuning, brass fittings, black ebonite control panel, mahogany cabinet with lift-up lid housing instructions. 4 in. x

5 ¼ in. x 4 in. (closed). This model is very similar to the 'Ceebee' Model No.3, by Fowler & Brigden, London NW1, which has the same GPO Reg.No. but only the Perikon detector.

fig. 76 . Gecophone No.2, Type BC 1501, by General Electric Co. Ltd. Winter 1922. BBC/PMG stamp, GPO Reg.No.103. Crystal set for headphone use, open cat's whisker/galena detector (with buzzer for testing sensitivity), variometer and condenser tuning with stepped tuning for aerial circuit, provision for plug-in tuning coils for various wave ranges, nickel-plated fittings, black ebonite control panel, mahogany cabinet with lift-up lid housing spare crystals and instructions. 6 ¾ in. x 12 ¾ in. x 9 ½ in. (closed). £9.15s.0d inc headphones and aerial equipment. The No.2 was originally shown at the first All British Wireless Exhibition, held in London from September 30th to October 7th 1922, and being manufactured before the inauguration of the Post Office's registration scheme and before the formation of the B.B.C., receivers from this early production run are devoid of both the BBC/PMG stamp and a GPO Reg.No.

fig. 77 . R.I. Model No1, by Radio Instruments Ltd. Winter 1922. BBC/PMG stamp, GPO Reg.No.122. Crystal set for headphone use, glass-enclosed cat's whisker/galena detector, variometer tuning, brass fittings, ebonite panel, mahogany cabinet with lift-up lid. 7 ½ in. x 5 ½ in. x 5 ½ in.

fig. 78 . 'Oracle', by Bassett Lowke Ltd. Winter 1922. BBC/PMG stamp, GPO Reg.No. 270. Crystal set for headphone use, open cat's whisker/galena detector, twin tapped inductance tuning (coarse and fine), oak base. ¾ in. x 4 in. x 6 ½ in.

fig. 79 . Headphone/Crystal Set. 1923. BBC/PMG stamp, GPO Reg.No.4145. The right hand earpiece, marked 'Tuner', contains a tapped inductance tuning coil calibrated from 1 to 20. The left hand earpiece contains an 18 ft. length of fine copper aerial wire woven into a ribbon. When required, this pulls out from a slot and is wound back in again by the handle. A Perikon detector is contained in the centre of the handle. Additional aerial, earth and headphone terminals are provided. Brown moulded ebonite earpieces, 2 ¼ in. diameter. Manufacturer unknown.

fig. 79a . The adjustable leather headbands enable the Headphone/Crystal Set to rest comfortably on the head.

fig. 80 . Ericsson 'Super Three Valve', by British L.M. Ericsson Manufacturing Co. Ltd. 1923. BBC/PMG stamp, GPO Reg.No.0327. 3-v Batt, plug-in tuning coils for various wave ranges, no integral loud-speaker, 2 or 3-valve switching for headphone or loud-speaker use, sloping ebonite control panel, walnut case. 12 ½ in. x 15 in. x 10 ¼ in. 18.15s.0d inc tuning coils. Valves extra. The actual model illustrated in the photograph was originally owned by Paul Schofield (who then was the Managing Director of Ericsson's) and differs slightly from the standard commercial version.

fig. 81 . Sterling 'Threeflex' Model R1590, by Sterling Telephone & Electric Co. Ltd. 1923. 3-v Batt + Crystal Detector, reflex circuit, plug-in coils for various wave ranges, valve portholes, black metal control panel, walnut cabinet. 18 in. x 13 ½ in. x 10 ½ in. £35.10s.0d inc frame aerial, headphones, HT, LT & grid bias batteries and all leads. DE3 valves extra (list price in December 1923 advertisement, 30s.0d each). A compass is set into the top of the cabinet for correct positioning of the aerial which is rotated by a control knob on the panel.

fig. 82 . Marconiphone Model V3, by Marconi's Wireless Telegraph Co. Ltd. 1923. BBC/PMG stamp, GPO Reg.No.0556. 3-v Batt, for headphone use, reflex circuit, plug-in regenerator unit, slot-in range blocks for various wavelengths, spade tuning controls, ebonite control panel, nickel-plated carrying handles, mahogany cabinet. 17 ½ in. x 15 ½ in. x 11 ½ in. One of the first broadcast receivers with grid bias. Capable of tuning in steps from 185 to 3,200 metres by selecting one of 11 slot-in range blocks in conjunction with the appropriate plug-in regenerator unit. Like the V2, the V3 employed 'spade tuning', but this was now controlled by a rotary micrometer tuning device which used a differential screw to move the spades in and out over the range blocks, with small pointers attached to the spades running over Ivorine scales to indicate the settings. (This device was later used to update surplus V2 receivers in 1925, fig.170).

fig. 83 . Ericsson 'Four Valve Receiver', by British L.M. Ericsson Manufacturing Co. Ltd. 1923. BBC/PMG stamp, GPO Reg.No.0398. 4-v Batt, 0-180 deg, swinging coil and variable condenser tuning, 300/500m range, no integral loud-speaker, black ebonite top and front panel, mahogany case. 12 ½ in. x 17 ½ in. x 10 ¼ in. 2-v/4-v switch for use with headphones/loud-speaker.

fig. 84 . 'Weconomy' LF Amplifying Unit, by Western Electric Co. Ltd. 1923. BBC/PMG stamp, GPO Reg.No.3415. A 2-valve dry cell operated amplifier designed to enable the 1922 Western Electric Model 44001 crystal set to operate a horn loud-speaker. It employs two miniature 'Wecovalves'. Nickel-plated fittings, black ebonite control panel, mahogany frame. 4 ½ in. x 3 in. x 6 ½ in.

fig. 85 . The 'Weconomy' LF Amplifying Unit housed neatly in the headphone compartment of the Model 44001 crystal set.

fig. 86 . Master 'Junior', by Master Radio Manufacturing Co. October 1923. BBC/PMG stamp, GPO Reg.No.899. Crystal set for headphone use, open cat's whisker/galena detector, swinging slide coil tuning, brass fittings, mahogany control panel and base. 2 ¾ in. x 5 ½ in. x 4 in. 7s.6d + 1s.0d B.B.C. royalty.

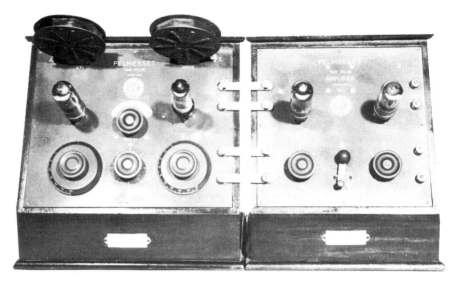

fig. 87 . Left: 'Pelmerset', by Fellows Magneto Co. Ltd. for Peronet Ltd., London WC1 (Mail order/HP only). 1923. BBC/PMG stamp, GPO Reg.No.2126. 2-v Batt, plug-in coils, no integral loud-speaker, brass fittings, sloping ebonite control panel, mahogany cabinet. 12 in. x 12 in. x 9 in. £9.0s.0d + B.B.C. and Marconi royalties and valves. Right: Matching 2-v Batt amplifier, BBC/PMG stamp, GPO Reg.No.3026. 12 in. x 10 ½ in. x 9 in. £5.10s.0d. The complete set was available on HP for 20s.0d deposit plus monthly payments totalling £15.9s.0d. Identical to the 'Fellophone Super 2' receiver and the 'Fellophone 2-Valve Amplifier' (same Reg.Nos.). The receiver later appeared in 1924 as the 'Tonyphone Super Two', which was sold by British Engineering Products Ltd., London SW1 on HP and Mail Order only.

fig. 88 . Sterling Type R1588, by Sterling Telephone & Electric Co. Ltd. 1923. BBC/PMG stamp, GPO Reg.No.2184, 2-v Batt, HF/DET, for headphone use, variometer tuning, black painted metal control panel, portholes for inspecting the valves' filaments, Chinese lacquered cabinet (a de-luxe extra, the standard cabinet was in polished walnut). 19 in. x 14 in. x 9 ½ in.

fig. 89 . Model 24P, by Radiax Ltd. 1923. 2-v Batt Kit, for headphone use, black ebonite control panel, lift-up lid, mahogany cabinet. 4 ½ in. x 12 ½ in. x 10 in. £6.5s.0d. Supplied complete with the cabinet as a kit of parts for the home-constructor.

fig. 90 . Western Electric 'Loud Speaking Amplifier', by Western Electric Co. Ltd. 1923. BBC/PMG stamp only (GPO/Reg.No. unknown). 2-v Batt LF Amplifier, mahogany cabinet with lift-up lid and flap-down front. 5 in. x 5 ¼ in. x 10 in. £24.0s.0d. Note the valve portholes for viewing the filaments.

fig. 91 . Cosmos 'Radiophone' Type VR2, by Metropolitan Vickers Electrical Co. Ltd. 1923. BBC/PMG stamp, GPO Reg.No.0722. 2-v Batt for headphone use, variometer, ebonite control panel, mahogany case. 6 in. x 13 in. x 6 ½ in. £25.5s.0d inc valves, headphones, HT & LT Batteries and aerial equipment.

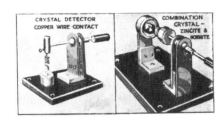

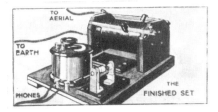

fig. 94 . 'Mecophone', by Mann, Egerton & Co. Ltd. 1923. BBC/PMG stamp, GPO Reg.No.4050. 1-v Batt, for headphone use, MW only, sloping black ebonite control panel, mahogany case. 8 ½ in. x 9 ½ in. x 7 ¾ in. £8.15s.0d + £4.10s.0d for valve, batteries and headphones, plus 10s.0d B.B.C. royalty. Advertisement claimed that it was "better than the best B.B.C. two-valver on the market".

fig. 96 . 'A1 Radio'. Winter 1923. BBC/ PMG stamp, GPO Reg.No.4216. Crystal set for headphone use, glass-enclosed cat's whisker/galena detector, ebonite base and top, nickel-plated fittings, MW 250/700m, variometer tuning, outer coil wound around hollow cardboard body. 3 in. diameter. 7s.6d + 1s.0d B.B.C. royalty. Manufacturer unknown, but the 'A1 Radio' has the same GPO Reg.No. as the 'Bijouphone' by Wates Bros.Ltd., produced in the winter 1923, and also the 'Bébéphone' crystal set by Rooke Bros. produced in June 1924. All three sets are of practically identical appearance.

fig. 92 . A home-constructed crystal set for headphone use. Open cat's whisker/galena detector (or alternative Perikon or carborundum/steel detectors), MW/LW 0-180 deg, double sliding inductance, variable condenser, wood baseboard 12 in. x 8 in. Made by Eric Westman using instructions from a series of 25 cigarette cards entitled "HOW TO MAKE YOUR OWN WIRELESS SET", issued in 1923 by Godfrey Phillips Cigarettes. The receiver could pick up Broadcast Band stations within a radius of about 25 miles and also the Paris time signals on 2,600 metres.

fig. 95 . 'Clydelco', by Clyde Electrical Co. 1923. BBC/PMG stamp, GPO Reg.No.0871. Crystal set for headphone use, double glass-enclosed cat's whisker/galena detectors, variometer tuning, telephone condenser, brass fittings, tubular celluloid body, black ebonite control panel and base. 7 ½ in. high x 5 in. diameter.

fig. 97 . Edison Bell Type 'B', by Edison Bell Ltd. 1923. BBC/PMG stamp, GPO Reg.No.615. Crystal set for headphone use, double glass-enclosed cat's whisker/galena detector with crystal selection switch, plug-in tuning coils for various wave ranges, black ebonite control panel, oak cabinet with lift-up lid. 7 ¼ in. x 8 ¾ in. x 5 ¾ in. The crystal detector is illuminated from below by a bulb powered by a battery which fits into the sliding drawer contained within the cabinet.

fig. 93 . (Left): Model G.R.C.16, by General Radio Co. Ltd. 1923. No BBC/PMG stamp, but GPO Reg.No.2030. 2-v Batt for headphone use, MW/LW 0-180 deg, variometer tuning control, headphone socket, valve portholes, ebonite control panel, mahogany cabinet. 6 ½ in. x 15 ½ in. x 7 in. £13.7s.6d inc B.B.C. royalty.

Medium waveband marked 'Short'. (Right): Matching amplifier Model G.R.C.13, audio amplifier. No BBC/PMG stamp, but GPO Reg.No.3012. 2-v Batt, headphone socket, valve portholes, ebonite control panel, mahogany cabinet. 6 ½ in. x 11 ¾ in. x 7 in.

fig. 98 . 'Abbiphone' Type CRO, by Abbey Industries Ltd. 1923. (Photo, actual size). BBC/PMG stamp, GPO Reg.No.492. Miniature crystal set for headphone use, open cat's whisker/galena detector, rotary stud tuning control, brass fittings, brown ebonite panel, mahogany case. 1 in. x 1 ½ in. x 2 in. £1.1s.0d. Advertisements claimed that it was the "smallest set approved by P.M.G.".

fig. 99 . 'Brownie Wireless' (des: James William Barber), by J.W.B. Wireless Co. October 1923. BBC/PMG stamp, GPO Reg.No.4155. Crystal Set for headphone use, open cat's whisker/galena detector, MW, slide coil tuning, black ebonite control panel, nickel-plated fittings, black enamelled tuning coil wound around hollow cardboard body. 6 ½ in. high x 3 ¼ in. diameter (body only). 7s.6d + 1s.0d B.B.C. royalty. Several forms of this tube type crystal set came out. (1) Originally as a kit of parts from January 1923 (fig.100) with detachable cardboard cap to which a rectangular ebonite panel with detector and terminals was screwed; no BBC/PMG stamp or GPO Reg.No. (2) As a kit of parts from May 1923, now with a moulded circular ebonite cap upon which the detector and terminals were mounted; no BBC/PMG stamp or GPO Reg.No. (3) Ready-assembled from October 1923 (as illustrated), now with BBC/PMG stamp and GPO Reg.No.4155. (4) As a hybrid in early 1924, price 12s.6d + 1s.0d B.B.C. royalty, by the Western Union Wireless Co. who simply substituted the original detector with their

own 'Permion' permanent detector and housed it within the 'Brownie Wireless' body; still with BBC/PMG stamp and GPO Reg.No.4155. (5) In the early autumn of 1924, a new version of the original 'Brownie Wireless' appeared (fig.136) fitted with a sloping glass–enclosed cat's whisker/galena detector (Brownie 'D.L.5') and a loading bridge provided to accomodate tuning coils for Chelmsford 5XX and other long-wave stations. BBC/EBM stamp but no GPO Reg.No. Price, 7s.6d. It also had an optional detachable moulded ebonite base, price 1s.6d extra. (6) In March 1925, the J.W.B. Wireless Co. produced their 'Brownie Wireless Ideal Home Outfit' to coincide with the *Daily Mail* Ideal Home Exhibition at Olympia. This consisted of the glass–enclosed sloping detector crystal set, aerial and earth wires, a tuning coil for Chelmsford 5XX, a pair of headphones, and an ebonite base: all individually boxed and contained in an attractive presentation carton for 24s.0d. (7) By late autumn of 1925, when the original company had changed its name to the Brownie Wireless Company (of Gt. Britain) Ltd., the ebonite base had become a standard fitting and was included in the basic price of the receiver (7s.6d).

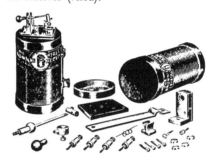

fig.100. The 'Brownie Wireless' in kit form, January 1923.

fig.101. 'Revophone', by Cable Accessories Co. Ltd. Spring 1923. BBC/PMG stamp, GPO Reg.No.349. Crystal set for headphone use, open cat's whisker/galena detector, fine and coarse tapped inductance tuning (fine & coarse), MW, nickel-plated fittings, black ebonite control panel, mahogany cabinet with headphone compartment and lift-up lid containing instructions. 7 in. x 10 ½ in. x 7 in. £2.10s.0d + 7s.6d B.B.C. royalty.

fig.102. 'Rexophone', by Morch Bros. Ltd. October 1923. BBC/PMG stamp, GPO Reg.No.792. Crystal set for headphone use, twin glass enclosed cat's whisker/galena detectors ("the one not in use is held in reserve for emergency"), tapped inductance tuning, nickel-plated fittings, Xylonite control panel and knobs in simulated marble, mahogany cabinet with lift-up lid housing instructions. 6 in. x 8 ½ in. x 5 in. £2.5s.0d + 1s.0d B.B.C. royalty. Came supplied with a plug-in long-wave tuning coil for receiving the Paris Time Signals on 2,600 metres. The control panel and knobs were also available in a variety of other moulded plastic finishes: red, blue, slate, brown, grey, purple, tortoiseshell, onyx and black. The nickel-plated fittings were standard, but for 5s.0d extra, you could get them gold-plated.

fig.103. Model No.1, by C.T. Ltd. Spring 1923. BBC/PMG stamp, GPO Reg.No.419. Crystal set for headphone use, open cat's whisker/galena detector, brass fittings, ebonite control panel, wooden base, slide coil tuning, black enamelled tuning coil wound around hollow cardboard body. 6 ¼ in. high x 4 in. diameter. 12s.6d + 7s.6d B.B.C. royalty, or complete with headphones, aerial and earth wires, price £2.0s.0d. Also came unassembled as a kit of parts, price 10s.0d. (Kits were exempt from the B.B.C. royalty).

fig.108. B.T.H. 'Bijou', by British Thomson-Houston Co. Ltd. 1923. BBC/PMG stamp, GPO Reg.No.861. Crystal set for headphone use, open cat's whisker/galena detector, variometer tuning, MW, brown ebonite knobs and control panel, walnut cabinet with lift-up lid housing instructions. 7 in. x 5 ¼ in. x 5 ¼ in. £1.0s.0d + 1s.0d B.B.C. royalty. Illustrated with B.T.H. headphones and leaflet. A later MW/LW version, 'Bijou, Form BB', came out in 1925.

fig.104. Fellophone 'Portable Three', by Fellows Magneto Co. Ltd. 1923. BBC/PMG stamp, GPO Reg.No.0753. 3-v Batt Suitcase Portable, for headphone use (or if tuned-in close to a transmitter, a separate loud-speaker could be employed), frame aerial in front door, battery compartment, black ebonite control panel, cow hide covered wood case with mahogany interior. 15 ½ in. x 21 in. x 7 in. £15.15s.0d + £1 B.B.C. royalty and £1.17s.6d Marconi royalty. Valves extra. Plain mahogany case version, price £14.0s.0d. A very early example of a compact portable receiver, "for use indoors, on the river, when motoring, or equally well to while away the time on a long train journey".

fig.109. B.T.H. Model VR2, by British Thomson-Houston Ltd. 1923. 2-v Batt, for headphone use, 0-100 deg, plug-in coils, headphone compartment, inlaid and cross-banded walnut cabinet. 18 in. x 13 in. x 10 in. £21.0s.0d inc valves, headphones LT/HT batteries. B.B.C. royalties extra. Engraved Ivorine scales with rotating pointers. Printed instructions pinned to doors.

fig.105. R.I. Type V3A, by Radio Instruments Ltd. Dated 12/3/23. BBC/PMG stamp, GPO Reg.No.0476. 3-v Batt for headphone use, 0-100 deg, variometer and tapped inductance tuning control, ebonite control panel, lift-up lid, mahogany cabinet. 5 ½ in. x 15 ½ in. x 9 in. (base).

fig.106. 'Wemco No.1 Valve/Crystal Receiver', by Walters Electrical Manufacturing Co. 1923. 1-v Batt, for headphone use, glass enclosed Perikon crystal detector, black ebonite control panel, mahogany case. 4 in. x 11 in. x 5 ½ in. This set originally came out in 1922 in separate units: the 'Wemco' 1-valve amplifier panel, BBC/PMG stamp, GPO Reg.No.2002, and the 'Wemco No.1' crystal set, BBC/PMG stamp, GPO Reg.No.124. The combined valve/crystal receiver (illustrated) appeared in 1923 with the two GPO registration numbers left engraved but unfilled. A new number, GPO Reg.No.0281, was given to this set as its circuit had been modified: an LF transformer, an HF choke and a grid coupling condenser were added to use the valve as an HF/LF reflex amplifier.

◄ fig.107. Sterling 'R1533', by Sterling Telephone & Electric Co. Ltd. 1923. BBC/PMG stamp, GPO Reg.No.3185. 1-v Batt LF Amplifier, black enamelled cast metal case, wood base. 3 ½ in. x 4 ½ in. x 6 ½ in. A version with an integral horn drive-unit was also produced in 1923 by Sterling.

fig.110. R.I. Model V2A, by Radio Instruments Ltd. 1923. BBC/PMG stamp, GPO Reg.No.2100. 2-v (HF/DET) Batt, tuning range 300/4,000 (no provision for plug-in coils), 0-90 deg, black ebonite control panel, mahogany case. 11 ½ in. x 12 ½ in. x 9 in.

fig.111. B.T.H. 'Radiola 1' Type VC Form 'B', by British Thomson-Houston Co. Ltd. 1923. BBC/PMG stamp, GPO Reg.No.0373, 1-v Batt/crystal set for headphone use, twin enclosed cat's whisker/ galena detectors either of which could be selected by means of a switch, degree-calibrated Ivorine tuning scales with moving pointers, variometer tuning control for 300/ 600m plus plug-in tuning coil for Paris long-wave station, brown ebonite control panel, walnut cabinet with back door for access to HF valve. 8 ¾ in. x 11 ½ in. x 10 ½ in. £11.0s.0d inc HT battery, headphones and valve. Printed instructions housed in lid. Combined valve/crystal receiver version of B.T.H. Type 'C' Form 'A' crystal set (fig. 74).

fig.112. Marconiphone Type RB10, by Marconi's Wireless Telegraph Co. Ltd. (Chassis made by Plessey, Holloway). February 1923. 1-v/Crystal Set for headphone use, carborundum/steel detector (polarized by a 1.5v cell), DEV valve, reflex circuit, slot-in range blocks, spade tuning controls, nickel-plated fittings, black ebonite control panel, black rexine-covered wood case. 5 ¼ in. x 11 ½ in. x 6 ¼ in. (closed). A valve adaptor was available so that an ordinary 4-pin valve could be used in place of the DEV which had side and end contacts. The RB10 was sold with a matching black rexine-covered battery box and was first exhibited at the *Daily Mail* Ideal Home Exhibition from March 1st to 24th 1923. It used the same case and many of the components of the 1922 Marconiphone

'Crystal A' Type RB3 M2 crystal set, fig. 64 . The carrying handle shown in the photograph was not originally part of the case, but is thought to have been added soon after the set was bought. In January 1930, surplus RB10 receivers were off-loaded at 17s.6d by Electradix Radios, Upper Thames Street, London EC.

The GPO registration number of the RB10 is unknown. All the surviving examples that have been examined are devoid of both the number and a BBC/PMG stamp, and have a black rexine patch glued on the top of the case. When peeled off, the patch reveals a small circular ivorine badge housed in a recess. This shows a plain face, but on its reverse, it bears the initials 'MWT' (Marconi's Wireless Telegraph Co. Ltd.). This badge originally appeared face-up and in full view on the case of the 'Crystal A'. It is thought that these un-stamped, un-registered and 'patched' RB10s were sold after the summer of 1924, that is, after the marketing of Marconi's domestic broadcast receivers had been taken over by the Marconiphone Company on December 29th 1923 and after the end of the G.P.O. registration scheme on July 1st 1924. An RB10 with a BBC/PMG stamp and GPO Reg.No. has yet to be found.

fig.113. Home-constructed valve/crystal receiver. 1923. 1-v Batt, for headphone use, LF valve, Perikon and enclosed cat's whisker/ galena detectors, plug-in tuning coils for various wave ranges, 0-100 deg, black ebonite control panel, clear glass sides, mahogany base. 6 in. x 13 in. x 11 in.

fig.114. 'Faeritone', by Mechanical Utilities Co. Spring 1923. BBC/PMG stamp, GPO Reg No.393. Crystal set for headphone use, open cat's whisker/galena detector, tapped inductance tuning, brass fittings, ebonite control panel, mahogany cabinet with lift-up lid. 7 in. x 7 in. x 6 ¾ in. 17s.6d + 7s.6d B.B.C. royalty. Wireless retailers could also buy this receiver as a kit direct from the manufacturers, price 13s.0d. With the blueprint provided, they could then assemble it themselves and sell it in the normal way, with, if they chose, their own labelling.

fig.115. Siemens Type 125, by Siemens Bros. & Co. Ltd. Summer 1923. BBC/PMG stamp, GPO Reg.No.599. Crystal set for headphone use, Perikon and glass-enclosed cat's whisker detectors, slot-in slab coil with swinging disc tuning, mahogany cabinet with lift-up lid. 5 in. x 7 ½ in. x 7 in. (closed). £1.15s.0d + 7s.6d B.B.C. royalty.

◄ fig.116. Gecophone 'Cabinet de-Luxe' Model BC 2010, by General Electric Co. Ltd. 1923. BBC/PMG stamp, GPO Reg.No.0720. 4-v Batt, plug-in coils, internal horn loud-speaker, mahogany cabinet. 48 in. x 30 in. x 21 in. £115.0s.0d + royalties. An early example of an 'all-enclosed' receiver. Compartment in bottom of cabinet houses a complete set of tuning coils.

fig.117. Marconiphone 'Baby', by Marconiphone Co. Ltd. Winter 1923. BBC/PMG stamp (moulded), GPO Reg.No.4215. Crystal set for headphone use, glass-enclosed cat's whisker/galena detector, swinging coil tuning, MW, nickel-plated fittings, moulded black ebonite oval base. 5 ½ in. wide x 1 ½ in. high. Two similar models appeared later in the summer of 1924 to coincide with the opening of the B.B.C.'s experimental long-wave station at Chelmsford: the MW/LW 'Universal Baby', and the LW-only 'Chelmsford Baby'.

fig.119. Fellophone 'One Valve Receiver', by Fellows Magneto Co. Ltd. 1923. BBC/PMG stamp, GPO Reg.No.1195. 1-v Batt, for headphone use, swinging coil tuning, (plug-in coils for various waveranges housed inside), 0-100 deg, black ebonite control panel leatherette covered wood cabinet. 5 ½ in. x 5 ½ in. x 8 ¾ in.

fig.123. 'OTB' Type 'A', by Harding, Holland & Fry Ltd. Autumn 1923. BBC/PMG stamp, GPO Reg.No.745. Crystal set for headphone use, open cat's whisker/galena detector, variometer tuning, MW, nickel-plated fittings, black ebonite control panel, turned mahogany lidded box (lid not shown). 2 ¼ in. high x 5 in. diameter. £1.15s.0d + 1s.0d B.B.C. royalty. Type 'B' (price £1.10s.0d + 1s.0d B.B.C. royalty) is similar, but has an internal lightning arrester and plug-in terminals on the sides so that the lid may be closed down without removing the aerial, earth or headphone connections.

fig.118. 'Astrophone', by Amplifiers Ltd. Spring 1923. BBC/PMG stamp, GPO Reg.No.410. Crystal Set for headphone use, open cat's whisker/galena detector, diamond cross-sectioned MW coil with swinging slide coil tuning, LW plug-in tuning coil for receiving the Paris Time Signals on 2,600m, circular ebonite control panel mounted on 4 wooden legs. 6 in. diameter. A 'De Luxe' model was also available, mounted in a black rexine covered box and padded with royal blue watered silk.

fig.120. Brown 'Microphone Amplifier' Type 'C', by S.G. Brown Ltd. 1923. A 1-stage microphone amplifier designed to enable several pair of headphones to be used from a single crystal set. The output from the set is fed to a moving-iron unit coupled to a carbon microphone button energised by a 6v battery. Mahogany case, 4 ¼ in. x 6 ¼ in. x 3 ½ in. A similar model, Type 'V', was also produced in 1923 for operating a loud-speaker from a 1-valve receiver. A 2-stage version of the Type 'C', the 'Crystal Amplifier', appeared in 1926, (fig.209).

fig.124. Gamage's 'Crystal Receiver', sold by A.W. Gamage Ltd. 1923. BBC/PMG stamp, GPO Reg.No.765. Crystal set for headphone use, glass-enclosed cat's whisker/galena detector, slide coil tuning, 180/950 metres, nickel-plated fittings, black ebonite panel mounted on a mahogany base. 6 ¼ in. x 4 ¾ in. x 5 ¾ in.

◄ fig.121. Ashley 'L.F. Amplifier', by Ashley Wireless Telephone Co. Ltd. 1923. BBC/PMG stamp, GPO Reg.No.3070. 2-v Batt LF Amplifier, brass fittings, ebonite control panel, mahogany cabinet with lift-up lid. 8 ¾ in. x 8 ½ in. x 8 ¼ in.

fig.122. Pye Model 530, by W.G. Pye & Co. ► 1923. BBC/PMG stamp, GPO Reg.No.0568. 3-v Batt for headphone use, 4 wave ranges: 300/570m, 550/1,000m, 1,000/1,900m, 1,800/3,400m, mahogany cabinet. 11 in. x 19 in. x 15 in. £24.13s.9d inc royalties, valves, batteries and headphones.

fig.125. Sterling 'Regina' Type 1618, by Sterling Telephone & Electric Co. Ltd. 1924. 4-v Batt, 0-100 deg, plug-in coils for various wave ranges, pleated Lumiere cone loud-speaker, Jacobean oak cabinet. 43 in. x 23 in. x 19 in. (closed). £63.0s.0d + royalties. (Also mahogany version).

fig.126. Gecophone Model BC 3250, by General Electric Co. Ltd. 1924. BBC/PMG stamp, GPO Reg.No.5448. 2-v Batt, DET/LF, plug-in tuning coils for various wave ranges (loading bridges shown in place), black ebonite control panel, mahogany base. 5 ½ in. x 12 ¾ in. x 9 ½ in. £9.12s.0d with DER valves. Horizontal cabinet version of 'smoker's cabinet' Model BC 3200.

fig.127. Sterling 'Anodion', Type 1592, by Sterling Telephone & Electric Co. Ltd. Summer 1924. BBC/PMG stamp, but no GPO Reg.No. 4-v Batt, Broadcast Band + 1400/3000m, 0-180 deg, plug-in coils, no integral loud-speaker, ebonite control panel, walnut cabinet. 6 ½ in. x 16 in. x 11 in.

fig.128. Western Electric Model 44002, by Western Electric Co. Ltd. 1924. BBC/PMG stamp, GPO Reg.No.5318. 7-v Batt SHet, for headphone use, MW/LW (300/3000m) 0-100 deg, variable condenser tuning control, ebonite control panel, mahogany cabinet.

fig.129. 'Delaphone No.2', by T.W. Thompson. Spring 1924. BBC/PMG stamp, GPO Reg.No.4371. Crystal set for headphone use, open cat's whisker/galena detector, varible condenser tuning, plug-in tuning coils for various wave ranges, brass fittings, ebonite control panel, mahogany cabinet with lift-up lid. 7 in. x 8 ½ in. x 5 ½ in.

fig.130. 'Revo Little Gem', by Cable Accessories Co. Ltd. Summer 1924. Crystal set for headphone use, open cat's whisker/galena detector, nickel-plated fittings, MW tuning coil wound around turned pearwood body. 2 ½ in. high x 3 ½ in. diameter. 5s.6d.

8 ¾ in. x 24 ¾ in. x 6 ¼ in. £75.0s.0d inc frame aerial, battery box and headphones. Volume is affected by means of three switches which control successive stages of amplification.

fig.131. 'Bligh'. 1924. 4-v Batt, various wave ranges, fixed aerial coil with tapped inductance tuning, variable condenser tuning, plug-in anode and reaction coils, valve portholes, no integral loud-speaker, woodgrained ebonite control panels, mahogany cabinet with battery compartment. 24 in. x 17 in. x 12 in. The receiver comprises two units: the Bligh 'Radio/2 MkV' 2-valve tuner, BBC/PMG stamp, GPO Reg.No.2176, and the Bligh 'Audio/2 MKVII' 2-valve amplifier, BBC/PMG stamp, GPO Reg.No.4410. Manufacturer unknown.

fig.132. Radionette 'Popular Model', by Peter Curtis Ltd. Late summer 1924. Crystal set for headphone use, open cat's whisker/galena detector, variometer tuning, LW, nickel-plated fittings, ebonite panel, oak case. 6 in. x 6 ½ in. x 6 ½ in. £1.0s.0d. Designed to receive the B.B.C.'s new experimental long-wave station at Chelmsford.

fig.133. 'Bijou Radio Card', printed in Germany. 1924. A novelty crystal set in the form of a postcard, cat's whisker/galena detector, flat curved tuning coil housed within the cardboard body, swinging slide coil tuning, MW, boot eyelets for aerial, earth and headphone connections. 5 ½ in. x 3 ½ in. The card was sent through the post in a matching envelope which was printed with the instructions. Crystal set postcards were produced by only a few manufacturers and have various pictorial fronts either connected or unconnected with wireless. Manufacturer unknown.

fig.134. Efescaphone 'Rodney', by Falk, Stadelmann & Co. Ltd. Autumn 1924. 3-v Batt for headphone use, MW/LW 0-180 deg, tapped inductance and variometer tuning controls, mahogany cabinet. 14 in. x 12 ¼ in. x 9 ¾ in. £22.0s.0d. Identical to the 1923 'Rodney' (BBC/PMG stamp, GPO Reg.No.0276), but as an improvment to selectivity and range of reception, 1924 models incorporate variable reaction, the control being found on the right hand side of the cabinet.

fig.135. 'Uncle Tom'. July 1924. A crystal set in the form of a clear glazed china figure with brown, red and black enamel decoration. Designed by John P. Gowland and made at the Grafton China Works of A.B. Jones & Sons Ltd. Open cat's whisker/galena detector (cat's whisker attached to the 'bow tie', and the crystal, as a 'diamond stud', attached to the 'waistcoat'), slide coil tuning, black enamelled coil wound around the 'top hat'. 9 in. high. 17s.6d. (Wireless retailers could obtain a sample for 12s.6d).

fig.136. 'Brownie Wireless', (des: James William Barber), by J.W.B. Wireless Co. Early autumn 1924. BBC/EBM stamp. Crystal set for headphone use, sloping glass-enclosed cat's whisker/galena detector (Brownie 'D.L.5'), MW, slide coil tuning, loading bridge provided to accomodate tuning coils for Chelmsford 5XX and other long-wave stations, ebonite control panel, nickel-plated fittings, black enamelled tuning coil wound around hollow cardboard body. 5 in. high x 3 ¼ in. diameter (body only). 7s.6d. Optional detachable moulded ebonite base (not illustrated), price 1s.6d extra. Note: the illustration on the side of the body shows the original 1923 'Brownie Wireless' with its open horizontal detector.

fig.137. 'Weconomy Tuner', by Western Electric Co. Ltd. 1924. BBC/PMG stamp, GPO Reg.No.2217. 2-v (HF/DET) Batt, for headphone use, MW plus plug-in tuning coils for wave ranges up to 3,000 metres, 0-180 deg, mahogany case. 11 in. x 5 in. x 10 in. £15.2s.0d inc valves. Used 2 miniature 'Wecovalves' which worked from 2 dry cells and needed an anode current of 45 volts.

fig.138. Burndept 'Ethophone Duplex', by Burndept Ltd. 1924. 2-v Batt, 0-100 deg, plug-in coils for various wave ranges, no integral loud-speaker, black moulded ebonite case. 3 ½ in. x 9 in. x 8 ½ in. £5.5s.0d + Marconi royalty. Designed for loud-speaker reception of the local station.

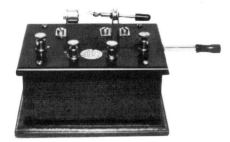

fig.139. Ediswan Model 1924B, by Edison Swan Electric Co. Ltd. Summer 1924. BBC/PMG stamp, GPO Reg.No.4385. Crystal set for headphone use, open cat's whisker/galena detector, slide coil tuning (medium-wave coil housed within body wound on rectangular former, tuned by pulling out the slider on the right), nickel-plated fittings, black ebonite control panel, mahogany base. 2 ½ in. x 5 ¼ in. x 3 ¼ in. £1.17s.9d inc headphones, aerial and earth equipment. Model 1924P, for receiving the B.B.C.'s new experimental long-wave station at Chelmsford, came with a long-wave coil which fitted into a socket provided in the back of the set.

fig.140. 'Broadcast Receiver', by W.J. Henderson & Co. Ltd. 1924. BBC/PMG stamp, GPO Reg.No.03278 (sic). 5-v Batt, plug-in coils, loose-coupled tuning control, no integral loud-speaker, walnut cabinet. 14 ½ in. x 22 ½ in. x 9 ¼ in. Double filament resistors for using either bright or dull-emitters. Two-position switch for listening-in using 3 valves (for headphones) or 5 valves (for loud-speaker). Based on a circuit designed by Percy W. Harris, Assistant Editor of *Modern Wireless*, and published in that magazine as the 'Transatlantic Five' with a blue-print for the home-constructor. The same circuit was also copied by Peto Scott Ltd. who placed the valves out of sight behind the panel (then a more 'modern' idea), and marketed it as the 'Transatlantic V'.

fig.141. Marconiphone Type B2, by Marconiphone Co. Ltd. 1924. BBC/PMG stamp only. 2-v Batt LF Amplifier, switch for 1 or 2 valves, 2 'Ideal' transformers (introduced in 1924), black ebonite control panel, mahogany cabinet with double front doors. 9 in. x 11 in. x 9 in. £27.2s.0d inc valves batteries and royalties.

fig.142. Marconiphone Type A2, by Marconiphone Co. Ltd. 1924. 2-v Batt LF Amplifier, 2 'Ideal' transformers (introduced in 1924), mahogany cabinet with lift-up lid and removeable front panel. 10 ½ in. x 13 in. x 8 in. £16.12s.0d inc DE6 and DER valves, batteries and royalties. (DE5 valves could also be used). The Type A2 is the dull-emitter version of the Marconiphone Type NB2 which used bright-emitters (2 'R' valves originally, and then an 'R' valve plus an LS3 in 1923). The Type NB2 was first introduced in 1922 as a matching accessory to the Marconiphone V2 receiver (fig. 60) to enable it drive a horn loud-speaker. The later Type A2 is of very similar appearance and was built into the same cabinet. It therefore bears a BBC/PMG stamp and the Type NB2's original GPO Reg.No.3104, and also has valve portholes even though dull-emitters are used.

fig.143. Cosmos 'Radiophone', by Metro-Vick Supplies Ltd. 1924. 2-v Batt receiver unit Type VR3, BBC/PMG stamp, GPO Reg.No.5146, with 3-v Batt amplifying unit Type A5, BBC/PMG stamp, GPO Reg.No.5147. Plug-in range blocks for large wave-range fitting beneath ebonite panel, 0-10 deg, solid oak floor standing cabinet with lift-up lid. 30 in. x 22 in. x 19 in. (lid closed). £36.15s.0d. (£38.15s.0d for mahogany model). Filament rheostat controls for both dull and bright-emitter type valves.

fig.144. Efescaphone 'Nelson Grand', by Falk, Stadelmann & Co. Ltd. Autumn 1924. 3-v Batt for headphone use, MW/LW (150/4000m) 0-180 deg, tapped inductance and variometer tuning controls, sloping ebonite control panel, valve portholes, battery and headphone compartments, mahogany cabinet. 22 in. x 15 ¼ in. x 13 in. £27.10s.0d. The cabinet has a roll front which pushes up clear of controls. An identical circuit was also used in the 'Nelson' model, with a walnut cabinet of smaller proportions, and the 'Rodney' model, in a walnut cabinet with no battery or headphone compartments. These three models first came out in 1923 and all bore a BBC/PMG stamp, and the GPO Reg.No.0276, but as an improvment to selectivity and range of reception, 1924 models incorporated variable reaction, the control being found on the right hand side of the cabinet (illustrated).

fig.145. Pye Model 547, by W.G. Pye & Co. 1924. 4-v Batt, 4 wave ranges: 300/520m, 500/900m, 900/1800m, 1,700/3,400m, sprung anti-microphonic valve holders, no integral loud-speaker, terminal outputs for either loud-speaker or headphones, walnut cabinet. 15½ in. x 20 in. x 18 in. The Model 547 first came out in 1923 but because of its low sensitivity it did not sell well. The circuit was changed and the improved version (illustrated) was introduced in 1924.

fig.146. 'Sparta', by Fullers United Electric Works Ltd. July 1924. BBC/PMG stamp only (no GPO Reg.No. as this set was made just after the abolition of the registration scheme). Crystal set for headphone use, open cat's whisker/galena detector, swinging coil tuning, MW 300/500m + miniature LW plug-in coil, nickel-plated fittings, black ebonite control panel, black rexine covered wood case (grey rexine version also known). 3 in. x 6 ½ in. x 4 ¾ in. (closed). £1.1s.0d. Coil for the B.B.C.'s experimental long-wave station at Chelmsford, price 2s.9d extra (standard receiver provided with a loading bridge). The aerial terminal is fitted with a removeable plug for connection to the removeable socket of the earth terminal. This feature afforded "complete protection against lightning when shutting down the set at the conclusion of the evening's concert".

fig.149. Gent 'Four Valve Receiver', by Gent & Co. 1924. BBC/PMG stamp, but no GPO Reg.No. 4-v Batt, for headphone use, swinging coil tuning, plug-in coils for various wave ranges, black ebonite chassis and sloping front panel on solid oak frame. 7 in. x 25 in. x 8 in. £25.5s.0d. Sockets for headphones on 2, 3 or 4-valve operation. A calibration chart (missing in photograph) fitted into the two runners on the right hand side of the control panel.

fig.147. 'Aristophone' Type 160, by C.F. Elwell Ltd. 1924. BBC trademark stamp, 4-v Batt, 300/800m, 700/1,400m, 1,300/3,000m, variometer and tapped inductance for coarse tuning, variable vernier condenser for fine tuning, no integral loud-speaker, brown ebonite control panel, mahogany cabinet. 9 in. x 20 ½ in. x 12 in. (Earlier version first appeared in 1923).

fig.150. 'Paddon' Model 1, by M. Paddon & Son. Autumn 1924. (Built by the son, A.J. Paddon). 4-v Batt, plug-in coils for various wave ranges, variable condenser and loose-coupled tuning controls, no integral loud-speaker, black ebonite sloping control panel, mahogany cabinet. 14 in. x 17 ½ in. x 10 ½ in. Typical of a small manufacturer set, produced for the local community.

fig.152. 'Unidyne', a home-constructor's receiver based on a circuit published in *Popular Wireless* on June 7th 1924. 2-v Batt for headphone use, plug-in coils, ebonite control panel, oak cabinet. 9 in. x 12 in. x 9 in. Uses two Thorpe 5-pin K4 tetrodes and an LT battery only, and dispenses with an HT supply. Also available as a kit from Bower Electric Ltd., 15 Grape Street, London WC2, price £6.6s.0d.

fig.148. 'Dainty', by Radio Equipment Co. Autumn 1924. Crystal set for headphone use, open cat's whisker/galena detector, MW, slide coil tuning, nickel-plated fittings, moulded black ebonite base. ½ in. x 5 in. x 2 ½ in. 12s.6d. A 'long-range' version with provision for a long-wave plug-in tuning coil was also available.

fig.151. Gecophone Model BC 2050, by General Electric Co Ltd. 1924. BBC/PMG stamp, GPO Reg.No.4177. 5-v Batt, 0-180 deg, variometer, plug-in coils, no integral loud-speaker, mahogany cabinet. 13 in. x 21 ½ in. x 13 ½ in. £36.10s.0d inc valves.

fig.153. Hamley's 'Crystal Receiver', sold by Hamley Bros. Ltd. July 1924. BBC/PMG stamp only (no GPO Reg.No. as this set was made just after the abolition of the registration scheme). Wall mounted crystal set for headphone use, glass-enclosed cat's whisker/galena detector, double slide coil tuning, brass fittings, ebonite sub-panels, mahogany baseboard. 13 ½ in. x 15 ½ in.

fig.154. 'Omniaphone', by Omniaphone Radio Co. Spring 1924. BBC/PMG stamp, GPO Reg.No.4961. Crystal set for headphone use, swinging slide coil tuning, MW, black ebonite control panel, oak case. 2 ½ in. x 6 ¾ in. x 4 ¾ in. 10s.6d + 1s.0d B.B.C. royalty. A 'De Luxe' version was produced in an oak cabinet with lift-up lid, price 17s.6d + 1s.0d B.B.C. royalty.

fig.155. 'Triood Radiophone'. Summer 1924. BBC/PMG stamp only (no GPO Reg.No. as this set was made just after the abolition of the registration scheme). Crystal set for headphone use, open cat's whisker/galena detector, swinging slide coil tuning, black ebonite control panel, mahogany cabinet with lift-up lid housing instructions. 5 in. x 7 in. x 4 ½ in. (closed). Manufacturer unknown.

fig.156. 'Lissen', by Lissen Ltd. Autumn 1924. Crystal Set for headphone use, glass-enclosed cat's whisker/galena detector, swinging disc tuning, plug-in coils for various wave ranges, nickel-plated fittings, moulded black ebonite base. ¾ in. x 5 in. x 4 ¼ in. 10s.0d, extra tuning coils from 4s.10d.

fig.157. Sterling 'One Anodion' Type R1586, by Sterling Telephone & Electric Co. Ltd. 1924. BBC/PMG stamp but no GPO Reg.No. 1-v Batt, 0-180 deg, 275/7,600m, for headphone use, black ebonite control panel, walnut case. 7 in. x 9 in. x 11 in. £7.7s.0d.

fig.158. 'PAL'. Summer 1924. Miniature crystal set for headphone use. Open sprung steel/galena detector, swinging slide coil tuning, tuning coil wound on a rectangular cross-sectioned former, nickel-plated fittings mounted on a black impregrated card panel, black rexine covered wood box. 1 ½ in. x 3 ¾ in. x 2 ¼ in. (closed).

fig.159. Radionette 'Junior', by Peter Curtis Ltd. Late summer 1924. Crystal set for headphone use, open Perikon detector, variometer tuning, MW, nickel-plated fittings, ebonite panel, oak case. 5 in. x 4 in. x 4 in. 15s.0d. Designed for short-range reception of the B.B.C.'s medium-wave stations.

fig.160. 'A.T.E.' by Parkside Electric & Radio Supplies. Winter 1924. Crystal set for headphone use, open cat's whisker/galena detector on ebonite sub-panel, variable condenser tuning, pink plastic control panel, chromium-plated central band, ebonised wood base. 2 ¼ in. high x 6 in. diameter.

fig.161. Home-Constructed Receiver. 1924. Crystal set for headphone use, glass-enclosed cat's whisker/galena detector, variable condenser tuning, externally mounted plug-in coils for various wave ranges, black ebonite control panel, imitation snakeskin covered wood cabinet with lift-up lid. 5 ¼ in. x 7 in. x 5 in.

fig.162. 'New Type Crystal Set', by Western Manufacturing Co. July 1924. BBC/PMG stamp only (no GPO Reg.No. as this set was made just after the abolition of the registration scheme). Crystal set for headphone use, open cat's whisker/galena detector, MW + plug-in tuning coil for Chelmsford 5XX, nickel-plated fittings, black ebonite control panel, mahogany case. 6 in. x 3 ¾ in. x 6 in. (This company went bankrupt in October 1925).

fig.163. T.M.C. Model No.2, by Telephone Manufacturing Co. Ltd. Summer 1924. (Panel engraved "GPO Reg.No.183", see below). Crystal set for headphone use, open cat's whisker/galena detector, slide coil tuning, MW/LW, (continuous tuning: no extra plug-in coil needed for changing to LW), black ebonite control panel, oak cabinet with lift-up lid housing instructions. 5 ½ in. x 5 ½ in. x 5 in. This model originally appeared as a medium-wave only receiver in the winter of 1922 when it was given the GPO Reg.No.183. The MW/LW version illustrated, used practically the same components including the engraved panel but was modified in the summer of 1924 to receive the B.B.C.'s experimental long-wave station at Chelmsford.

fig.164. Gecophone Model BC 3300, by General Electric Co. Ltd. 1924. BBC/PMG stamp, GPO Reg.No.5464. 3-v Batt, provision for plug-in tuning and reaction coils, 0-180 deg calibrations on dial controls, no integral loud-speaker, solid mahogany cabinet with battery drawer, lift-up lid revealing components and opening front doors revealing ebonite control panel. 15 in. x 15 in. x 11 in. £28.0s.0d inc valves, batteries and headphones. (Also Model BC 3350, version without battery drawer and front doors).

fig.165. Marconiphone Model V1, by Marconiphone Co. Ltd. 1924. 1-v Batt, for headphone use, slot-in range blocks containing both aerial and reaction coils for tuning from 300m to 4,600m in six steps, brown ebonite control panel, mahogany cabinet with lift-up lid. 7 ½ in. x 8 ¾ in. x 6 ¾ in. £6.5s.0d inc Marconi royalty, DER valve, and standard medium-wave range block (additional range blocks, price 15s.0d).

fig.166. A.J.S. Type F6, by A.J. Stevens (1914) Ltd. 1925. 4-v Batt, HF/DET/2LF, plug-in coils for various wave ranges, no integral loud-speaker, ebonite control panel, walnut cabinet. 13 ½ in. x 17 in. x 10 in. £26.15s.0d. (Also available in mahogany). Sloping panel version of fig.186.

fig.167. 'Goltone Super', by Ward & Goldstone. 1925. Crystal set for headphone use, glass-enclosed cat's whisker/galena detector, 'Archimedian' slide coil tuning (by turning the control knob, the slider is automatically moved up or down the coil), MW/LW 150/1860m, moulded red ebonite base and cap. 6 in. high x 4 in. diameter base. 7s.6d. Medium-wave 'Broadcast Band' model appeared in 1924.

fig.168. Gecophone 'Junior', by General Electric Co. Ltd. 1925. BBC/EBM stamp. Crystal set for headphone use, glass-enclosed cat's whisker/galena detector, variable condenser tuning, MW 300/500m + provision for LW tuning coil, nickel-plated fittings, mahogany control panel and base. 3 in. x 5 ¾ in. x 8 in. 16s.0d. 1,600 metre tuning coil for 5XX, 7s.6d extra.

fig.169. Fellophone 'Little Giant Four', by Fellows Magneto Co. Ltd. 1925. BBC/EBM stamp, 4-v batt, provision for plug-in tuning coils (loading bridge shown in place), 0-100 deg, no integral loud-speaker, black ebonite control panel, brown rexine covered wood case. 5 ½ in. x 14 in. x 8 ½ in.

fig.170. Marconiphone Model V2, with rotary micrometer tuning device. In 1925, surplus V2 receivers left over from 1922 and still bearing their original BBC/PMG stamp and the GPO Reg.No.2001, were updated with a rotary micrometer tuning device first used on the V3 in 1923 (fig. 82). This attachment could also be bought separately for 2s.0d. For details of the original Model V2, see fig. 60 .

fig.173. Marconiphone 'Straight 8' Type 81, by Marconiphone Co. Ltd. 1925. 8-v Batt, 300/500m with optional plug-in tuning coils and condensers for higher wave ranges. Ivorine scales engraved in metre wavelengths on which additional notes of positions of stations could be added in pencil as desired. 5 neutralised independently tuned HF stages, 1 detector and 2 transformer-coupled LF stages, showing an early attempt at minimising the distortion and interference common to domestic receivers of the day. Black ebonite control panel, mahogany cabinet with lift-down lockable front cover, battery compartment, no integral loud-speaker. 17 in. x 26 in. x 13 ½ in. £67.16s.0d

inc Marconi royalty, valves and all necessary batteries. Contrary to a popular rumour about the extreme rarity of this set reinforced by profound statements like that in *The Times* (issue dated Saturday 5th October 1985) that "only eight were made", the Type 81 did in fact appear in quantity production and was widely advertised. While it is not known the exact numbers involved in the original production run, certainly a large batch of surplus Type 81 receivers complete in original packing cases with valves and batteries was being off-loaded in 1930 at £9.0s.0d by the wholesalers V. Zeitlin & Sons Ltd. of London WC1.

fig.171. A.J.S. Model 'Z', by A.J. Stevens & Co. (1914) Ltd. 1925. 2-v Batt, plug-in coils for various wave ranges, 0-180 deg, slow-motion drive, no integral loud-speaker, black ebonite control panel, mahogany cabinet with lift-up lid. 11 in. x 14 in. x 9 in. £8.2s.6d, or £13.18s.6d complete with all accessories and horn loud-speaker.

fig.174. 'Cosmos Radiophone' Type C4, by Metropolitan Vickers Electrical Co. Ltd. 1925. BBC/PMG stamp only which is moulded on the tuning knob (no GPO Reg.No. as this set was made after the abolition of the registration scheme). Crystal set for headphone use, glass-enclosed cat's whisker/galena detector, variable condenser tuning, plug-in tuning coils for various wave ranges (these were fitted beneath the receiver), nickel-plated fittings, moulded ebonite body. 6 ½ in. diameter (base). £1.5s.0d inc 'BBC' coil for 300/700m. Also available, a '5XX' tuning coil for 1,300/ 3,000 metres, price 4s.6d extra. The Type C4 could be supplied with a Cosmos 'Permtector' permanent detector in place of the glass-enclosed detector. By means of a cord loop attached to the body, the set could be hung up on the wall if desired: the instruction leaflet which came with the set felt that "an ideal position for it is by the fireside".

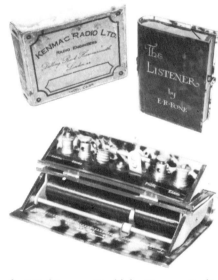

fig.175. 'Kenmac Book', by Kenmac Radio Ltd. 1925. Crystal Set for headphone use, open cat's whisker/galena detector, MW 0-100 deg, slide-coil tuning control, brass fittings, 'tortoiseshell' plastic case in the form of a book. 4 ¾ in. x 3 ½ in. x 1 in. £2.2s.0d. (Also versions in a red, blue or green leather-covered wooden case, price £1.1s.0d). Provision was made on the side of the case for inserting a tuning coil for the B.B.C.'s long-wave station, Daventry 5XX, which opened in July 1925. The 'Kenmac Book' bears the inscription "The Listener by E.R.Fone". Reviewing the set in their September 5th 1925 issue, *Popular Wireless & Wireless Review* found the craftsmanship good, but disliked the wording on the 'cover'.

fig.172. Burndept 'Ethophone V' Mark V, by Burndept Wireless Ltd. 1925. 4-v Batt, plug-in coils for various wave ranges, 0-180 deg, no integral loud-speaker, ebonite control panel, mahogany cabinet with double front doors. 11 in. x 22 in. x 13 in. £37.10s.0d inc coils for 300/500m. The Mark V receiver includes two new Burndept 'Super Vernier' dials which were introduced in 1925.

However, for a small charge, the purchaser could have any lettering he wanted, and with Christmas approaching, the reviewer thought that there would be quite a demand for lettering such as "From Uncle To George" etc. On test, the 'Kenmac Book' gave "splendid results....as good as we have heard".

fig.176. McMichael 'Autodyne', by L. McMichael Ltd. 1925. 7-v Batt SHet Kit, plug-in coils, no integral loud-speaker, black ebonite control panel, walnut cabinet. 8 in. x 18 ½ in. x 10 in. The 'M.H.' symbol found on McMichael sets and components from 1920 to 1932 stood for McMichael-Hesketh (Ben Hesketh was the firm's designer).

fig.177. Burndept 'Ethophone III' Mark III, by Burndept Wireless Ltd. 1925. 3-v Batt for headphone use, MW/LW 0-100 deg ('Super-Vernier' dial), ebonite control panel, lift-up lid, mahogany cabinet. 11 ½ in. x 13 ½ in. x 11 in. Very similar to 1924 'Ethophone III' which used conventional dials.

fig.178. Marconiphone Type 31, by Marconiphone Co. Ltd. 1925. 3-v DET/2LF Batt, switch for 1 or 2 LF stages, provision for plug-in tuning coils for various wave ranges from 300 to 3,200 metres, no integral loud-speaker, black ebonite control panel, mahogany cabinet. 9 ½ in. x 14 ½ in. x 10 in. £21.15s.6d inc Marconi royalty, all necessary batteries and a medium-wave coil.

fig.179. Gecophone Model BC 1385, by General Electric Co. Ltd. 1925. BBC/EMB stamp. Wavemeter in mahogany case, 6 ¼ in. x 9 in. x 6 in., with variometer (0-180 deg), buzzer and dry cell compartment.

fig.180. B.T.H. Type VA1 Form AB, by British Thomson-Houston Co. Ltd. 1925. BBC/EBM stamp. 1-v Batt LF Amplifier, control for using either a bright or a dull-emitter, moulded brown ebonite top panel, walnut case. 5 in. x 5 in. x 7 in. £3.18s.6d inc Marconi royalty.

fig.182. 'Flinderphone', by Flinders (Wholesale) Ltd. 1925. Crystal set for headphone use, glass-enclosed cat's whisker/galena detector, variometer tuning, tubular brown ebonite body. 5 in. high x 4 ½ in. diameter. £1.7s.6d.

fig.183. B.T.H. Type VR2 Form BA, by British Thomson-Houston Co. Ltd. 1925. BBC/EBM stamp, 2-v Batt, for headphone use, plug-in tuning unit, control for using either bright or dull-emitters, moulded brown ebonite top panel, walnut case. 7 in. x 10 in. x 7 ½ in. £7.5s.0d inc Marconi royalty. Optional extras: tuning units for various wave ranges, price 18s.0d, 1-v amplifier Type VA1, price £3.18s.6d (fig.180) and 2-v amplifier Type VA2, price £7.10s.0d for loud-speaker use.

fig.181. Western Electric Co. 'Superhet Kit' made using Igranic components from Igranic Electric Ltd. EC4. 1925. 6-v Batt SHet Kit, 0-100 deg, Indigraph tuning dial, plug-in coils, no integral loud-speaker, mahogany cabinet. 13 ½ in. x 30 ½ in. x 16 ½ in. £15.15s.0d (chassis only) + £5.5s.0d royalty.

fig.184. Pye Model 555, by W.G. Pye Ltd. 1925. 5-v Batt Portable, closely pre-set to the Daventry 5XX 1,600 metre wavelength only, vernier tuning control, internal horn loud-speaker, internal frame aerial, mahogany cabinet. 18 in. x 16 ¾ in. x 7 ¼ in. £30.12s.6d. Fitted with Amplion 'Radiolux' horn loud-speaker. (Later Model 555, which came out in 1927, had a modified cabinet and loud-speaker grille and was fitted with a moving-iron cone loud-speaker).

fig.185. Cosmos Type VR4, by Metro-Vick Supplies Ltd. 1925. BBC/EBM stamp. A 3-valve battery powered 'local and Daventry' receiver of unconventional design, in black moulded ebonite with a brown ebonite cover "resembling in form a railway waiting-room sandwich container". Cover 9 ½ in. diameter x 9 in. high. £15.5s.3d inc B.B.C. coil, valves, batteries, aerial and earth equipment, Amplion loud-speaker and royalties.

The base contains the coupling resistances, condensers and grid leaks together with the greater part of the wiring. The top of the base carries three valve holders, a tuning unit, a filament rheostat and switch (for use with either bright or dull-emitters), an aerial condenser switch and terminals for connecting to the aerial and earth wires and to a loud-speaker. All the tuning controls are mounted on a separate ebonite platform raised from the base on metal rods. Separate tuning coils are provided for the long-wave Daventry 5XX station and for stations on the Broadcast Band.

Originally designed as a 3-valve/crystal set, a few of the earliest contemporary advertisements show a crystal detector mounted next to the tuning unit and directly above the filament rheostat. However, it is believed that with minor adjustments, the set was found to work just as well without the detector and all but the initial production run were produced as a 3-valve receiver while still retaining the connections leading to where the detector was originally meant to go.

fig.186. A.J.S. Type F6, Model TM2, by A.J. Stevens & Co. (1914) Ltd. 1925. 4-v Batt, loose-coupled plug-in coils, no integral loud-speaker, mahogany cabinet. 13 ¼ in. x 21 ¼ in. x 19 ½ in. (closed). £30.10s.0d. The model illustrated is fitted with slightly later valves. (Also sloping panel version).

fig.187. 'Excelophone' Type 4C, by Excelsior Motor Co. Ltd. 1925. 4-v Batt, plug-in coils for various wave ranges, no integral loud-speaker, battery compartment, lift-up lid, oak cabinet. 18 ½ in. x 18 ½ in. x 12 in. £30.0s.0d inc valves, batteries, headphones and aerial wires. The 'Excelophone' was a curious mixture of the old and the new, for while it retained the old fashioned and practically obsolete idea of filament viewing portholes, it did included in its circuit the new Mullard PM4 valve. This was one of a new breed of ultra modern 'pipless' valves whose new glass envelope design brought about a new era in valve technology.

fig.188. Brownie No.2, by Brownie Wireless Co. (of Gt.Britain) Ltd. September 1st 1925. Crystal Set for headphone use, glass-enclosed cat's whisker/galena detector (Brownie 'D.L.5'), MW, swinging-arm slide-coil tuning control plus Daventry 5XX long-wave plug-in coil, nickel-plated fittings, black moulded ebonite case. 4 ¼ in. x 6 in. x 5 ¾ in. 10s.6d. A matching 2-valve amplifier ('Note Magnifier') came out in 1926 (fig.195).

fig.189. 'Polar Twin', by Radio Communication Co. Ltd. 1925. 2-v Batt, for headphone use, 0-100 deg, plug-in tuning coils for various wave ranges, black crystalline painted metal panels on a diecast metal frame, black ebonite top panel. 5 ¾ in. x 5 ½ in. x 4 ½ in. £6.15s.0d. (Also oak case version, price £8.2s.6d).

fig.190. 'Everyman Four', a home-constructed receiver from a circuit published

in *Wireless World*. 1926. (des: W. James). 4-v Batt, MW (circuit later modified for receiving Daventry 5XX long-wave), new Burndept 'Etholog' dials, no integral loud-speaker, engine-turned aluminium control panel, mahogany cabinet. 9 ½ in. x 27 in. x 11 ½ in. This was the first receiver to obtain really effective HF amplification from a single neutralised RF stage and was equal to many of the early screened-grid circuits. The Eagle Engineering Company of Warwick brought out two simplified versions of the 'Everyman Four' later on in the autumn of 1927: a factory-built model, price £24.10s.0d including royalties, and a kit set for home-constructors, price £8.19s.0d, cabinet and royalties extra. In the same year, Stratton & Company of Birmingham introduced the Eddystone 'Scientific Four' (fig.224) which followed very closely the circuit design of the 'Everyman Four'.

fig.191. Cleartron Sir Oliver Lodge 'N' Circuit Receiver, by Cleartron Radio Ltd. 1926. 2-v Batt, MW/LW 0-100 deg, plug-in coils for 200/500m and Daventry, no integral loud-speaker, Honduras mahogany cabinet. 10 ½ in. x 18 in. x 17 in. £15.15s.0d (or £1 deposit, followed by 15 monthly payments of £1.1s.0d). Came complete with all accessories, loud-speaker, royalties, free installation with free monthly inspections. (Also 3-valve model, price £19.19s.0d).

fig.192. B.S.A. Model 5010, by B.S.A. Radio Ltd. 1926. BBC/EBM stamp. 3-v Batt, MW/LW, plug-in tuning coils for various wave ranges, no integral loud-speaker, brass sheet front panel, dark mahogany cabinet. 12 in. x 12 in. x 8 in. £36.15s.0d inc Marconi royalty, valves, coils and batteries. The first wireless receiver from the proprietors, Birmingham Small Arms. Uses three miniature valves: one BSA-Standard P425A, and two Wecovalves. Also available in oak and as a 'fireside' model with a small cupboard housed beneath the panel.

fig.193. Loewe Model OE 333, by Loewe Radio A.G., Berlin, Germany, distributed in Gt. Britain by Loewe Radio Co. Ltd. 1926. 1-v Batt, plug-in tuning coils for various wave ranges, no integral loud-speaker, plywood control panel, solid oak base. 2 in. x 5 ½ in. x 7 ¼ in. (base only). A British-made version was introduced in 1928. The receiver uses a '3NF' valve which was a multiple valve consisting of three tetrodes, two anode resistors, two grid resistors and two coupling capacitors, all contained within a single glass envelope. It was used for detection and for LF amplification. The rest of the set literally only comprised four other components: an on/off switch, a variable condenser and two tuning coils. Model RO 433, with a black moulded plastic base and coils, came out in 1929.

fig.194. General Type 15, by General Radio Co. Ltd. 1926. 2-v Batt, MW 0-100 deg, no integral loud-speaker, black crystalline painted metal front panel, walnut cabinet. 8 ½ in. x 11 ½ in. x 8 ¾ in. £6.15s.0d without valves, or £13.5s.0d including valves, batteries, loud-speaker, headphones and aerial wire. The panel is hinged and lifts down to reveal the components for ready access. Primarily designed for loud-speaker reception of the local station.

fig.195. Brownie 'Two Stage Note Magnifier', by Brownie Wireless Co. (of Gt. Britain) Ltd. 1926. 2-v Batt (dull or bright-emitters), black moulded ebonite case. 3 ¾ in. x 12 in. x 8 ½ in. £3.3s.0d. On top of the case are indentations to house the Brownie No.2 crystal set (fig.188). The amplifier came in a variety of sprayed finishes: gold, silver, bronze and anodised metal and its basic mould was later used for the 1927 Brownie 2-valve battery receiver, (fig.221).

fig.196. Brownie 'Two Stage Note Magnifier' with the No.2 crystal set in place.

fig.197. Graves 'Vulcan', by J.G. Graves Ltd. 1926. 2-v Batt, MW/LW 0-180 deg, no integral loud-speaker, black moulded ebonite front panel, oak cabinet. 9 in. x 10 in. x 8 ½ in. Switch for waveband selection, medium waveband marked 'short'. Sold as part of a complete outfit which included aerial wire, HT and LT batteries and Graves horn loud-speaker (fig.863). Similar appearance to earlier 1925 version which had plug/socket waveband selection, with the long-wave socket marked 'Daventry'.

fig.198. 'Bijou', by Edison Bell Ltd. 1926. BBC/EBM stamp. 2-v Batt, 0-100 deg, loose-coupled tuning control, plug-in coils, no integral loud-speaker, black ebonite control panel, oak plinth, hinged oak cover with celluloid viewing window. 10 ¾ in. x 12 ½ in. x 10 ½ in. (cover closed). £3.15s.0d excluding valves, batteries and Marconi royalty. Similar to 1925 'Bijou' (with reaction coil attached to left hand side of hinged oak cover: no window) and 1925 'Gem' (with plinth only: no cover or window).

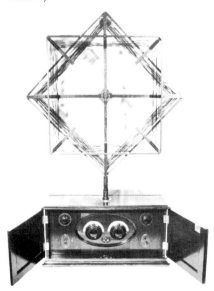

fig.199. Burndept 'Ethodyne', by Burndept Wireless Ltd. 1926. 7-v Batt SHet, MW/LW 0-100 deg, Etholog tuning dial, no integral loud-speaker, mahogany cabinet. 12 in. x 25 ½ in. x 14 in. With Burndept Frame Aerial No.979 for 1000/2000 metres. £80.12s.6d inc valves and medium-wave and long-wave

frame aerials. A compass set into the top of the receiver's cabinet was used to position the frame aerial. Less than a year later, in November 1927, these receivers were being off-loaded to wireless retailers at £19.10s.0d by Chas. Rodwell Ltd., London Bridge, London SE1.

fig.200. A.J.S. 'Symphony Two', by A.J. Stevens & Co. (1914) Ltd. 1926. 2-v Batt, MW/LW 0-100 deg, plug-in coils, disc-drive dial, no integral loud-speaker, mahogany cabinet. 11 in. x 22 in. x 14 ½ in. £17.10s.0d inc valves, batteries, horn loud-speaker, frame aerial and Marconi royalty. Employed the new disc-drive dial. (Similar to the A.J.S. 'Symphony Three').

fig.201. B.S.A. Model 4V, by B.S.A. Radio Ltd. 1926. BBC/EBM stamp. 4-v Batt, MW/LW 0-180 deg, no integral loud-speaker, socket for loud-speaker or headphones, 'figured walnut' ebonite control panel, oak cabinet with double doors. 17 ½ in. x 12 in. x 13 in. The circuit employs 3 Wecovalves and 1 Western Electric Co. '4101 DL' output valve, overstamped 'BSA PA4'.

fig.202. Chakophone Model No.1B, by Eagle Engineering Co. Ltd. 1926. 3-v Batt, MW/LW 0-100 deg, no integral loud-speaker, oak 'smoker's cabinet'. 17 in. x 11 ½ in. x 10 in. £11.17s.0d. One of the few sets then still being produced with externally mounted valves.

fig.203. 'Abbon-Daventry', by R.R. & Co. Autumn 1926. Crystal set for headphone use, Brownie 'Permion' permanent detector (introduced in the autumn 1926), MW with plug-in LW coil for Daventry 5XX, brass fittings, black ebonite control panel, oak veneered plywood case. 6 ¼ in. x 5 in. x 4 ¾ in.

fig.204. Home-Constructed Receiver. 1926. 4-v Batt, Indigraph tuning dials, 0-100 deg, plug-in coils for various wave ranges, no integral loud-speaker, ebonite control panel, mahogany cabinet. 11 in. x 24 in. x 14 in.

fig.205. Gecophone Model BC 2820, by General Electric Co. Ltd. November 1926. BBC/EBM stamp. 2-v Batt, MW 0-100 deg, no integral loud-speaker, mahogany cabinet. 9 ¼ in. x 11 ½ in. x 8 ½ in. £13.9s.3d inc royalty, valves, batteries and Gecophone Type 'C' loud-speaker. Plug-in hinged reaction coils (first introduced in 1925): the angle between the hinged and fixed coil controlled the amount of reaction.

fig.206. Gambrell 'Baby Grand, AC Mains Model', by Gambrell Bros. Ltd. August 1926. 2-v + 2R, AC, MW/LW 0-180 deg, plug-in coils, filament viewing portholes at back of cabinet, no integral loud-speaker, mahogany cabinet. 15 in. x 13 in. x 9 in. £21.0s.0d. This was the first receiver to be produced in Britain with an enclosed AC mains unit providing HT, LT and grid bias all from the alternating current mains, thereby entirely dispensing with batteries. Circuit (des: Robert Annan) uses a B.T.H. B5 detector (1924) and a B.T.H. B7 LF amplifier (1925) in what essentially is an ordinary 2-valve battery circuit, with a pair of Mullard DU 10 half-wave rectifiers (1926) in the mains unit: some versions used a single Osram U5 full-wave rectifier (1926). Fitted with a lethal looking metal ON/OFF switch, the set is rumoured to have probably killed more people than given pleasure to! (Also 3 and 4-valve AC models, plus earlier 2-valve DC model).

fig.207. Burndept 'Ethophone III', by Burndept Wireless Ltd. 1926. 3-v Batt, MW/LW 0-100 deg, Etholog tuning dial, no integral loud-speaker, mahogany cabinet. 10 ½ in. x 12 ¾ in. x 10 ½ in. £18.0s.0d plus 37s.6d Marconi royalty. Switches for selecting 2 or 3 valves, and the local or Daventry station.

fig.208. 'Abbonphone', by R.R. & Co. Ltd. 1926. 2-v Batt for headphone use, MW + Daventry 5XX, 0-180 deg, battery compartment behind left hand door, oak cabinet. 11 in. x 14 in. x 8 ½ in. 'Local & Daventry' switch.

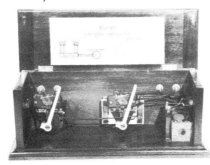

fig.209. Brown 'Crystal Amplifier', by S.G. Brown Ltd. 1926. A 2-stage version of the Brown 'Microphone Amplifier' Type 'C' of 1923 (fig.120), designed to enable a crystal set to work a loud-speaker, mahogany cabinet with lift-up lid housing instructions. 5 in. x 13 in. x 5 in. £3.10s.0d. Range: 15 miles from the local station, or 150 miles from the high-power long-wave station at Daventry.

fig.210. McMichael Superhet, by L. McMichael Ltd. 1926. 7-v Batt SHet, 0-180 deg, plug-in 'Dimic' coils (introduced 1926) for various wave ranges from 300m to 4,500m, coil No.1a (illustrated) for 450/950m, no integral loud-speaker, black ebonite control panel, mahogany cabinet. 10 in. x 23 in. x 13 in.

fig.211. Gamage's 'Two Valve Receiver', by A.W. Gamage Ltd. 1926. 2-v Batt, MW only, 0-100 deg, 4 tapped inductance tuning studs, no integral loud-speaker, black ebonite control panel, oak cabinet. 8 in. x 14 in. x 11 in.

fig.212. Omniaphone 'The Homeplayer', by Clarke Bros. (Leicester) Ltd. 1926. 2-v Batt, MW/LW 0-180 deg, no integral loud-speaker, 'Mahoganite' (imitation wood) front panel, solid mahogany cabinet with flap-down side revealing the two valves. 6 ¾ in. x 13 ¼ in. x 10 ¼ in. £6.6s.0d plus £1.5s.0d Marconi royalty.

fig.213. Gecophone Model BC 2740, General Electric Co. Ltd. 1926. BBC/EBM stamp. 4-v Batt, MW/LW 0-100 deg, drum-drive scale, no integral loud-speaker, woodgrain painted aluminium control panel, lift-up lid, mahogany cabinet. 11 ½ in. x 22 ½ in. x 10 in. This was the first use of a drum-drive scale, and this was operated by means of a slow motion control knob. The cabinet (with practically the same control layout) emerged again in the winter of 1928 when it housed the Gecophone 'All-Electric 3', Model BC 2935 AC mains receiver.

fig.214. Pye Model 222, by W.G. Pye & Co. 1926. 2-v Batt, 0-100 deg, plug-in coils with porcelain holders, no integral loud-speaker, black crystalline painted aluminium front and sides, ebonite sheet back panel, oak base and top. 7 in. x 10 ¾ in. x 7 in. £6.18s.0d inc royalties and valves. Designed for the new Mullard PM1 and PM2 battery triodes. Space for GB battery beneath the base.

fig.215. Pye Model 750, by W.G. Pye & Co. 1927. 5-v Batt, plug-in coils for various wave ranges, no integral loud-speaker, black

ebonite control panel, walnut cabinet with storage space for batteries. 12 in. x 31 ½ in. x 15 in. £32.10s.0d inc 200/600m coils. Marconi royalty, batteries and valves extra. Set of coils for 1,000/3,000m range, £2.5s.0d extra.

fig.216. Igranic 'Neutrosonic Seven', by Igranic Electric Co. Ltd. 1927. 7-v Batt SHet, plug-in tuning units for various wave ranges, 0-180 deg, no integral loud-speaker, lift-up lid housing tuning units and leads etc., black leatherette covered wood case (front cover removed in photograph). 13 ¾ in x 14 ¾ in. x 9 in. £40.0s.0d inc valves + spare long-wave tuning unit. Royalties extra. Optional accessory (not shown): battery box which came complete with batteries, frame aerial and cone loud-speaker, price £21.0s.0d. (Frame aerial could be incorporated within the receiver).

fig.217. Marconiphone 'Universal Feed Receiver' Type 32, by Marconiphone Co. Ltd. 1927. 3-v Batt, MW/LW 0-100 deg, disc-drive dial, plug-in coils, anodised bronze escutcheon, no integral loud-speaker, mahogany cabinet. 11 ½ in. x 17 ½ in. x 13 in. £13.7s.6d inc Marconi royalty and long-wave Daventry coil. Medium waveband marked 'Short'. HT, LT and grid bias could also be provided from AC or DC mains units in conjunction with the appropriate pattern of multi-way supply cable. With AC, the set (using 'K' series AC mains valves) came with a Marconiphone AC1 mains unit, price £9.7s.6d extra, while for use with DC, a Model DC1 mains unit was supplied, price £6.10s.0d extra. (Also Marconiphone 'Cabinet 32A', an upright floor-standing version with built-in cone loudspeaker, price £25.15s.0d).

fig.218. Gecophone Model BC 7000, by General Electric Co. Ltd. 1927. BBC/EBM stamp (late use). 7-v Batt Shet Portable, MW/LW 0-100 deg, internal horn loud-speaker, internal aerial in hinged back door, oak cabinet. 15 in. x 21 in. x 9 ¾ in. £50.0s.0d inc £5.12s.6d Marconi royalty. Weighed 60lb with a full load of batteries. Came with a detachable leather carrying strap (not shown - probably fell off with the weight).

fig.219. Brown 'Junior Wireless Set', by S.G. Brown Ltd. February 1927. A combined crystal set and 1-stage microphone amplifier for driving a loud-speaker, open Perikon detector, variometer tuning, MW + provision for LW coil, mahogany cabinet with lift-up lid containing instructions (mahogany panel covering the tuning and amplifying units not shown in the illustration). 5 in. x 13 in. x 5 in. £15.0s.0d inc Brown Type 'E' horn loud-speaker, and small battery box supporting a frame aerial. First shown at the British Industries Fair at the White City in London from February 21st to March 4th 1927. The cabinet of the 'Junior' is identical to the one used by the Brown 2-stage 'Crystal Amplifier' of 1926 (fig.209).

fig.220. 'Climax', by Climax Radio Electric Ltd. 1927. 3-v Batt, MW 0-100 deg, internal frame aerial, cone loud-speaker, mahogany cabinet. 16 in. x 22 in. x 7 in. One of the few indoor battery receivers with a built-in aerial and a loud-speaker (although no space for batteries).

fig.221. Brownie 'Two-Valve Receiver', by Brownie Wireless Co. (of Gt.Britain) Ltd. 1927. 2-v Batt, fixed 0-100 deg (the pointer moves around the scale), loose-coupled tuning control, plug-in coils, no integral loud-speaker, black moulded ebonite case. 3 ¾ in. x 12 in. x 8 ½ in. £2.10s.0d plus £1.5s.0d Marconi royalty. (The set illustrated is not fitted with Brownie plug-in coils). Styled "a valve set for the million", this cheap and basic receiver represented a dying breed of design with its externally-mounted valves and coils. It used the same basic mould as the 1926 Brownie 'Two Stage Note Magnifier' (fig.195) and the body is therefore marked with the provisional patent suffix '/26' although the 'Two-Valve Receiver' was designed a year later than this.

fig.222. B.T.H. Type VR3 Form 'A', by British Thomson-Houston Co. Ltd. 1927. 3-v Batt, MW/LW 0-100 deg, no integral loud-speaker, brown ebonite control panel and knobs, mahogany cabinet. 9 ¾ in. x 14 ¼ in. x 10 in.

fig.223. General Model 3V, by General Radio Co. Ltd. 1927. 3-v Batt, MW/LW 0-100 + 0-200 deg, drum scale, variometer and variable condenser, Beco moving-iron aluminium foil cone loud-speaker (see fig.835), wire mesh grille, steel chassis, anodised copper escutcheon, metal knobs, battery compartment, mahogany cabinet. 12 ½ in. x 13 ½ in. x 14 ½ in. One of the few self-contained receivers for indoor use.

fig.224. Eddystone 'Scientific Four', by Stratton & Co. Ltd. 1927. 4-v Batt, MW/LW 0-180 deg, plug-in coils for various wave ranges, no integral loud-speaker, black ebonite control panel, mahogany cabinet. 9 in. x 23 in. x 9 ½ in. The circuit of this receiver followed closely that of the 1926 'Everyman Four', fig.190.

fig.225. Fellows 'Little Giant Three', by Fellows Manufacturing Co. Ltd. c.1927. 3-v Batt, 0-180 deg, no integral loud-speaker, solid oak cabinet and legs. 30 in. x 15 ½ in. x 15 ½ in.

fig.226. Burndept 'Short Wave Receiver Mk.IV', by Burndept Wireless Ltd. 1927. 3-v Batt, SW 0-100 deg, plug-in coils for 12/ 100m range, no integral loud-speaker, Etholog dials, red mahogany cabinet with drawer for storage of 8 plug-in coils in base. 12 in. x 17 in. x 9 ½ in. £35.0s.0d inc royalties. Designed to pick-up American and Australian short-wave stations, but was also brought out in readiness for the inauguration in November of the B.B.C.'s experimental Empire short-wave station, call-sign G5SW, sited at Marconi's Chelmsford works.

fig.227. Brownie No.3, by Brownie Wireless Co. (of Gt.Britain) Ltd. 1927. Crystal Set for headphone use, glass-enclosed cat's whisker/ galena detector (Brownie 'D.L.5'), MW/ LW, swinging-arm slide-coil tuning control, black moulded ebonite case. 4 ¼ in. x 6 in. x 5 ¾ in. 12s.6d. Wave-range switch: no extra plug-in tuning coil needed to receive Daventry 5XX or other long-wave stations. The No.3 used the same basic mould as the 1925 Brownie No.2 (fig.188) and is therefore marked '/25' although it was first manufactured in 1927 to coincide with the opening of the B.B.C.'s new high-power medium-wave station, Daventry 5GB. It was still being sold in the autumn of 1933 by All British Products Ltd. from their stand at Radiolympia which was emblazoned "GOODS THAT ARE NEVER OBSOLETE!"

fig.228. Chakophone 'Junior Three', by Eagle Engineering Co. Ltd. 1927. 3-v Batt, switch for 2 or 3 valve use, switch for selecting '5XX' (long-wave) or 'B.B.C.' (medium-wave), 0-100 deg, no integral loud-speaker, oak front panel and cabinet. 7 in. x 15 ½ in. x 7 ½ in. £5.17s.6d.

fig.229. Ensign Model 'C', by Ensign Radio Co. 1927. Crystal set for headphone use, open Perikon detector (made by A. Hinderlich, London NW2), MW, nickel-plated fittings, ebonite panel, ebonised wood box with removeable front. 2 ½ in. x 5 ½ in. x 4 ½ in.

fig.230. Rees-Mace 'Super Four', by Rees-Mace Manufacturing Co. Ltd. 1927. 4-v Batt Portable, MW/LW 0-100 deg, cone loud-speaker, internal frame aerial, leather carrying handle, mahogany case. 16 ½ in. x 17 ½ in. x 8 in. £29.8s.0d. Key switch for filaments preventing unauthorised persons from using the set. Pre-tuned to Daventry, 1600 metres long-wave. (Also oak, walnut and leather-covered versions).

fig.231. Pye Model 25, by W.G. Pye 1927. 5-v Batt Portable, MW/LW 0-100 deg, cone loud-speaker, internal frame aerial in hinged back door, leather carrying handle, mahogany case. 16 in. x 16 in. x 8 in. £30.12s.6d. (Also walnut case version). Controls housed in side, behind small door. Earliest production run has a small gold 'Rising Sun' transfer in the middle of the fretwork sun.

fig.232. 'Met-Vick 5', by Metro-Vick Supplies Ltd. 1927. 5-v Batt, plug-in coils for various wave ranges, no integral loud-speaker, compartments for batteries and HT/LT battery eliminators (for alternative AC or DC mains operation), oak cabinet supplied by Waring & Gillow. 14 in. x 32 in. x 15 in.

fig.233. Home-Constructed Receiver. 1927. 5-v Batt, plug-in coils for various wave ranges, no integral loud-speaker, ebonite control panel, mahogany 'Kabilok' cabinet. 11 in. x 23 ½ in. x 11 in.

fig.234. Chakophone 'Junior 2, MkII', by Eagle Engineering Co. Ltd. 1927. 2-v Batt, MW/LW 0-100 deg, oak cabinet. 7 in. x 13 in. x 8 in. £3.15s.0d + Marconi royalty. Medium waveband marked 'Short'.

fig.235. Marconiphone 'Short Wave Receiver' Model 34, by Marconiphone Co. Ltd. 1928. 3-v Batt, SW 0-100 deg, plug-in coils for 16/52m range plus a coil adapter for receiving the 'Broadcast Band' on medium-waves, no integral loud-speaker, mahogany cabinet. 11 in. x 17 in. x 13 in. £23.17s.6d inc Marconi royalty, 16/52m coil, medium waveband coil adapter, plugs and connecting cable.

fig.236. Gecophone 'World-Wide Screened Grid Four', Model BC 2940, by General Electric Co. Ltd. 1928. 4-v Batt, MW/LW, 0-100 deg, no integral loud-speaker, dark brown crystalline-painted metal case. 9 ½ in. x 11 ¾ in. x 11 ¾ in. £23.10s.0d inc Marconi royalty. Uses two double-ended S625 S.G. valves together with aluminium partitioning, and was the first set to use ganged variable tuning condensers. A frame aerial can be screwed into the chassis when the lid has been removed. (Also Model BC 2945, floor standing mahogany cabinet version, price £34.7s.6d inc Marconi royalty).

fig.236a. Gecophone Model BC 2940 with lid removed showing partitioning and position of screened-grid valves.

fig.237. Halcyon Battery Portable, by Halcyon Wireless Supply Co. Ltd. 1928. 3-v Batt Suitcase Portable, MW/LW 0-100 deg, frame aerial and cone loud-speaker housed in lid, hide covered wood case. 9 in. x 13 in. x 13 ½ in. (closed).

fig.238. Marconiphone 'Universal Feed Receiver' Type 23, by Marconiphone Co. Ltd. 1928. 2-v Batt, MW/LW 0-100 deg, disc-drive dial, 1-piece tuning control, no integral loud-speaker, anodised escutcheon, brown Bakelite sloping control panel, mahogany cabinet. 10 in. x 13 in. x 9 ½ in. £13.17s.6d. Using multi-way supply cables, the Type 23 could also be operated from either AC or DC mains via an appropriate supply unit. (The Marconiphone AC4, illustrated, right, was used when the Type 23 was fitted with Metro-Vick 'K' series AC mains valves: the unit, one of the early 'all-battery eliminators', providing HT, LT and grid bias).

fig.239. 'Allscott', by James Scott & Co. Ltd. 1928. 3-v Batt, MW 0-100 deg, Indigraph tuning dial, no integral loud-speaker, figured ebonite control panel, mahogany cabinet. 9 in. x 13 in. x 10 in. Housed in 'Kabilok' cabinet made by W. & T. Lock Ltd., St. Peters Works, Bath.

fig.240. Burndept 'Screened Suitcase Portable', by Burndept Wireless (1928) Ltd. Late 1928. 4-v Batt Suitcase Portable, MW/LW Mtrs, Etholog tuning dials, cone loud-speaker and internal frame aerial in lift-up lid, crocodile-grained hide-covered wood case. 9 in. x 15 in. x 15 in. (closed). £25.12s.6d. (Also blue Morocco-covered wood case, price £30.0s.0d and mahogany case versions).

fig.241. B.T.H. Type VR2, Form C/A, by British Thomson-Houston Co. Ltd. 1928. 1-v Batt, MW/LW 0-100 deg, no integral loud-speaker, brown Bakelite case. 8 ½ in. x 6 ½ in. x 9 ¼ in. Described as a 'Two Stage Valve Receiver', the VR2 used a single B.T.H. two-in-one valve with two independent sections and a common filament. Two aerial inputs were provided, one for local and one for distant station reception.

fig.241a. Type VR2 with cover removed.

fig.242. Home-Constructed Receiver. 1928. 5-v Batt, plug-in tuning coils for various wave ranges, variable condensers with worm drive, 0-100 deg, no integral loud-speaker, mahogany framed cabinet with plate glass panels. 9 in. x 26 in. x 10 ½ in.

fig.243. Home-Constructed Receiver. 1928. 3-v Batt, MW/LW, 0-180 deg, no integral loud-speaker, lift-up lid, oak cabinet. 8 ½ in. x 19 in. x 10 ½ in. Uses two small Ormond dual-indicator slow-motion dials introduced in 1928 (larger versions of the dial were introduced the previous year).

fig.244. Burndept 'Screened Ethophone', by Burndept Wireless (1928) Ltd. 1928. 3-v Batt, MW/LW 0-100 deg, no integral loud-speaker, leathercloth-covered metal control panel, hinged front flap, mahogany cabinet. 10 ½ in. x 17 in. x 9 ¼ in. £12.7s.0d inc Marconi royalty. (Also version without hinged front flap).

fig.245. Marconiphone Type 53, by Marconiphone Co. Ltd. 1928. 5-v Batt Portable, MW/LW 0-100 deg, drum scale, edgewise tuning control, cone loud-speaker, internal frame aerial, walnut cabinet. 16 ½ in. x 18 in. x 8 in. £29.8s.0d inc Marconi royalty. This receiver won the *Wireless World* 1928 Readers' Radiolympia Ballot in the 5-valve class.

fig.246. Selector 'Super' Model U32, by Selectors Ltd. 1928. 7-v Batt Portable, MW/LW 0-100 deg, sockets on inside panel for charging accumulator from mains supply, ammeter for measuring state of accumulator, magnetic-reed cone loud-speaker, socket for extension loud-speaker, internal frame aerial, turntable, leather carrying handle, mahogany cabinet. 18 ¼ in. x 18 in. x 8 in. £54.12s.0d.

fig.247. Philips Model 2514, by Philips Lamps Ltd. November 1st 1928. 3-v + R, AC TRF, MW/LW 0-180 deg, drum-drive scales, no integral loud-speaker, moulded 'Philite' ends, dark blue rexine covered metal cabinet. 8 in. x 14 ½ in. x 5 in. Three wave-ranges: 200/400m, 300/800m and 1,000/2,000m. Identical cabinet to Model 2502 (AC, DC or battery) and Model 2501 (LT from AC mains, HT from separate AC mains unit).

fig.248. Cossor 'Melody Maker', by A.C. Cossor Ltd. 1928. 3-v Batt Kit, MW/LW 0-100 deg, plug-in coils, no integral loud-speaker, black crystalline-painted steel cabinet. 9 in. x 17 ½ in. x 10 in. £7.15s.0d. Used 4-pin plus top terminal S.G. valve. (Also marketed in 1928 in factory-built or kit form as the 'Harlie Melody Maker' by Harlie Bros. Ltd., Balham Rd, London N9). In spring 1929, Cossor's cabinet was being offered in a choice of ten coloured finishes.

fig.249. 'The Europhone', by Europhone Radio Co. Ltd. 1928. 2-v Batt, MW 0-100 deg, variometer and variable condenser tuning controls, no integral loud-speaker, wood chassis, black crystalline-painted tinplate case. 11 in. x 10 ½ in. x 4 ½ in. Mantle-clock case: as the central tuning control knob is turned, it trips a small counter which mimics the second hand of the clock. (Also 3-v version).

fig.250. Gecophone 'Victor 3' Model BC 2930, by General Electric Co. Ltd. 1928. 3-v Batt, 2MW/LW 0-10 deg, drum scale, edgewise tuning control, no integral loud-speaker, black-painted wood base and top, brown crystalline-painted metal case. 8 in. x 9 in. x 5 in. £6.17s.0d inc Marconi royalty. Components are mounted on a Paxolin chassis and connected not by wire, but by copper strips. (The 'Victor 3' is identical to the 1927 'Arcolette' by the German Company, Telefunken).

fig.251. Philips Type 2515, by Philips Lamps Ltd. December 1928. 2-v +R, AC TRF, MW/LW 0-180 deg, no integral loud-speaker, brown crackle finish painted steel case. 7 ¼ in. x 6 ¾ in. x 10 ½ in. £12.10s.0d. Primarily a 'local station' receiver, but designed also to receive the B.B.C.'s high-power Daventry station on 1,600 metres.

fig.252. Burndept 'Screened Four', by Burndept Wireless Ltd. January 1928. 4-v Batt, MW/LW Mtrs, no integral loud-

speaker, mahogany cabinet. 11 ½ in. x 18 in. x 13 in. £26.10s.0d. Used the new S625 horizontally mounted double-ended screened-grid valve together with aluminium plates as screening inside the cabinet. Wavebands changed by means of a 3-position switch (Med/Off/Long) and not by changing plug-in coils: a method which was fast becoming obsolete. (Also 'Empire Screened Four', late 1928 SW/MW version for B.B.C.'s experimental short-wave service, see 1927).

fig.253. R.I 'All-Electric Transportable, Model AC, Madrigal', by Radio Instruments Ltd. 1929. 3-v +R, AC TRF Transportable, MW/LW Mtrs, disc-drive dial, no integral loud-speaker, mahogany cabinet. 15 ½ in. x 17 in. x 13 in. £30.0s.0d inc Marconi royalty. (Also DC version).

fig.253a. R.I. 'All-Electric Transportable, Model AC, Madrigal' with matching moving-coil loud-speaker unit, AC model, in a mahogany cabinet. 30 in. x 18 ½ in. x 14 ½ in. £18.18s.0d. (Also DC model).

fig.254. A home-constructed 2-valve receiver for headphone use. MW/LW, 0-180 deg, Ormond slow-motion dial, oak cabinet, 7 in. x 14 in. x 8 in. Made by Norman Jackson based on instructions from a series of 25 cigarette cards entitled 'HOW TO BUILD A TWO VALVE SET', issued by Godfrey Phillips Cigarettes in 1929.

fig.255. Gecophone Model BC 3032R, by General Electric Co. Ltd. 1929. 3-v Batt, MW/LW, Mtrs + 0-100 deg, drum-drive scale, no integral loud-speaker, mahogany cabinet. 15 in. x 14 ½ in. x 11 in.

fig.256. Pye Model 232, by Pye Radio Ltd. 1929. 2-v Batt, MW/LW Mtrs, no integral loud-speaker, brown Bakelite cabinet. 7 in. x 9 ½ in. x 8 in. £6.0s.0d inc valves and Marconi royalty. The moulded cabinet was made by Birkbys Ltd., Liversedge, Yorkshire, who called their particular type of Bakelite material 'Elo'.

fig.257. Pye Model 25C, by Pye Radio Ltd. 1929. 5-v Batt Portable, MW/LW Mtrs, drum scale, edgewise tuning control, internal frame aerial, carrying handle, turntable, solid mahogany cabinet. 15 in. x 15 ½ in. x 7 ½ in. £23.10s.0d inc valves, batteries and Marconi royalty. Very similar cabinet to Pye 'Screened Four'.

fig.258. Beethoven 'Screen Grid Four' Model SG 2730, by Montague Radio Invention & Development Co. Ltd. 1929. 4-v Batt Portable, MW/LW 0-100 deg, cone loud-speaker, internal frame aerial, brown ebonite control panel with ebonite mouldings, mahogany and walnut cabinet. 19 ¼ in. x 14 ½ in. x 9 in. 26.5s.0d inc royalty.

fig.259. Pye Model 460, by Pye Radio Ltd. 1929. 4-v Batt, MW/LW Mtrs, celluloid drum scale, edgewise tuning control, no integral loud-speaker, battery compartment, walnut cabinet. 17 in. x 18 in. x 14 ½ in. £19.10s.0d inc royalties. (Also AC version, Model 350).

fig.260. Burndept 'Universal Screened Five', by Burndept (1928) Ltd. 1929. 5-v +R (+MetR for grid bias), cone loud-speaker, AC TRF, SW/MW/LW Mtrs, hinged front flap, walnut cabinet. 40 in. x 24 in. x 15 in. 16/2000m without coil changing. Used newly introduced indirectly-heated AC screened-grid valve.

fig.261. McMichael 'Super-Screened Portable Four', by L. McMichael Ltd. 1929. 4-v Batt Portable, MW/LW 0-100 deg, single dial ganged tuning, moving-iron cone loud-speaker, leather carrying handle, brown figured ebonite control panel and knobs, walnut cabinet. 18 ¼ in. x 16 in. x 8 in. The two tuning condensers are controlled by a single tuning knob divided into two discs, the outer one of which drives both condensers through worm gears. This disc is provided with finger holes in the front and is part of the dial normally used when searching for stations. When a station is picked up, the next step is to place the fingers on the outer knurled edges of both discs and rotate them together. This automatically stops one condenser and rotates the other, bringing the two tuned circuits into exact resonance and providing fine tuning. "Having once mastered the principle," says the McMichael brochure, "the control is delightfully simple to operate".

fig.262. Pye 'Presentation Two', All-Electric Model 275 AC, by Pye Radio Ltd. March 1929. 2-v +MetR, AC TRF Table Model, MW/LW 0-100 deg, cone loud-speaker, brown Bakelite knobs, solid walnut cabinet. 14 ¾ in. x 13 ¼ in. x 8 in. £17.10s.0d. The first all-enclosed mains table model to appear on the British market. Early 1929 production run used Cosmos 5-pin bases, late 1929 run used standard British 5-pin 'B5' bases and a veneered walnut cabinet. (Cabinet identical to 1928 Pye 'Presentation Two', Battery Model 275).

fig.263. Philips 'All-Electric' Type 2511, by Philips Lamps Ltd. 1929. 4-v +R, AC TRF, MW/LW Mtrs, drum-drive scale, no integral loud-speaker, lockable lift-up lid, cabinet comprising 'Arbolite' panels fitted onto a steel frame. 11 in. x 19 ½ in. x 9 in. £37.10s.0d. Used with Philips Type 2013 floor standing moving-coil loud-speaker (fig.893). 'Arbolite' was the trade name used by Philips for a thin plastic laminated board employed as a cabinet material on certain of their wireless receivers. It came in a variety of coloured patterned finishes, from flecked oxblood to different woodgrain imitations and was of similar construction to Paxolin. Phenolic (Bakelite) green resins were used to impregnate layers of thin paper to which were added a patterned paper and then a sheet of cellulose paper. The patterned paper gave the 'Arbolite' its colour or woodgrain effect, and the cellulose overlay its protective glossy surface. Strong heat and pressure fused the layers together into a solid panel or they could be placed into steel moulds for shaping.

fig.264. Selector 'Cabinet Portable', by Selectors Ltd. March 16th 1929. 4-v Batt Portable, MW/LW 0-100 deg, turntable, frame aerial, ebonite control panel in woodgrain finish, mahogany cabinet. 17 in. x 15 in. x 8 in. £33.12s.0d. Station names and corresponding dial settings were written on cards (missing in photograph) which were attached to the double front doors. Jack-socket provided for home-charging, with a meter fitted on the back panel to indicate the state of the accumulator. (Also available as a suitcase portable, and in an AC mains version).

fig.266. Gecophone 'Portable Screened 4' Model BC 3047R, by General Electric Co. Ltd. 1929. 4-v Batt Suitcase Portable, MW/LW 0-100 deg, turntable, internal frame aerial, cone loud-speaker housed in lift-up lid, brown leathercloth covered wood case. 10 ¾ in. x 15 ½ in. x 16 in. £24.3s.0d.

fig.269. Columbia Model 303a, by Columbia Graphophone Co. Ltd. 1929. 5-v Batt Portable, 0-100 deg, drum scale, edgewise tuning control, cone loud-speaker, frame aerial in hinged back door, turntable, anodised metal fittings, oak cabinet. 15 ½ in. x 13 ½ in. x 8 in. £17.17s.0d. (Also Model 303b in blue 'crocodile' leathercloth, price £19.19s.0d).

fig.267. Marconiphone Type 39, by Marconiphone Co. Ltd. 1929. 3-v Batt, MW/LW 0-100 deg, drum-drive scales, no integral loud-speaker, gramophone input, mahogany cabinet. 14 in. x 13 in. x 10 in. £15.15s.0d. Could also be used with an optional Marconiphone AC7 or DC7 mains unit for alternative AC or DC supply operation. Complete with AC equipment, price £21.0s.0d or with DC equipment, price £17.15s.0d.

fig.265. Marconiphone Model 55, by Marconiphone Co. Ltd. 1929. 5-v Batt Portable, MW/LW Mtrs, drum scale, edgewise tuning control, cone loud-speaker, floral tracery grille, internal frame aerial, anodised bronze metal control panel, hinged back door, oak cabinet. 14 ½ in. x 14 ½ in. x 8 in. £18.18s.0d. The first receiver to be sold with an instruction booklet providing a price list of spare parts, from the door hinges to the silk loud-speaker cloth, in an attempt to encourage Model 55 owners to effect simple minor repairs themselves rather than go to the service department of their local wireless shop.

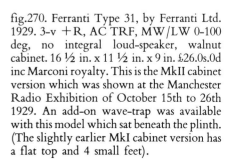

fig.268. Graves 'Regional', by J.G. Graves Ltd. 1929. 3-v Batt, MW/LW 0-180 deg, no integral loud-speaker, black Bakelite front panel, oak cabinet with lift-up lid. 9 ½ in. x 17 in. x 8 in.

fig.270. Ferranti Type 31, by Ferranti Ltd. 1929. 3-v +R, AC TRF, MW/LW 0-100 deg, no integral loud-speaker, walnut cabinet. 16 ½ in. x 11 ½ in. x 9 in. £26.0s.0d inc Marconi royalty. This is the MkII cabinet version which was shown at the Manchester Radio Exhibition of October 15th to 26th 1929. An add-on wave-trap was available with this model which sat beneath the plinth. (The slightly earlier MkI cabinet version has a flat top and 4 small feet).

fig.271. K.B. Model 169, by Kolster-Brandes Ltd. 1929. 3-v +R, AC TRF, MW/LW 0-100 deg, edgewise tuning controls, no integral loud-speaker, silver oxidised metal escutcheon, oak cabinet. 16 ½ in. x 17 in. x 7 ¾ in. £17.10s.0d.

fig.276. Marconiphone Model 47, by Marconiphone Co. Ltd. 1929. 4-v +R, AC TRF, MW/LW Mtrs, drum scale, edgewise tuning control, no integral loud-speaker, metal case painted in woodgrain finish "to harmonise with furniture in the home". 8 ½ in. x 15 ½ in. x 9 ½ in. £24.0s.0d.

fig.272. Chakophone 'Junior Four', by Eagle Engineering Co. Ltd. 1929. 4-v Batt Suitcase Portable, MW/LW 0-100 deg, drum-drive scale, frame aerial, moving-iron cone loud-speaker and tuning controls housed in lift-up lid, leather carrying handle, walnut cabinet. 9 in. x 15 in. x 12 in. (closed). £13.13s.0d.

fig.274. Cossor 'All-In', by A.C. Cossor Ltd. 1929. 2-v +R, AC TRF Table Model, MW/LW 0-100 deg, cone loud-speaker, blue leathercloth-covered metal control panel beneath lift-up lid, solid oak cabinet. 17 ½ in. x 16 in. x 9 in. £14.14s.0d. A.C. Cossor's first factory-built set. (Also metal cabinet version with no integral loud-speaker).

fig.277. K.B. 'Brandeset IIIA', by Kolster-Brandes Ltd. January 1929. 3-v DET/2LF Batt, MW/LW 0-100 deg, drum scales, edgewise tuning controls, no integral loud-speaker, silver oxidised metal fittings and escutcheon, tin-plate chassis, fumed oak cabinet. 9 ½ in. x 17 in. x 8 ½ in. £7.5s.0d. Volume controlled by switching in 1 or 2 LF valves. First introduced in 1927 with different shaped escutcheon. (K.B. Model 102, 1929 screened-grid battery receiver is of similar appearance).

fig.273. Ekco 'Ekcolectric' Model SGP3, by E.K. Cole Ltd. 1929. 3-v +MetR, AC TRF, MW/LW 0-100 deg, drum-drive scale, no integral loud-speaker, metal escutcheon, walnut cabinet. 9 in. x 17 in. x 9 ½ in. £21.0s.0d. (Also 2-valve AC model, Model P2).

fig.275. Danipad 'Popular Regional Three', by Danipad Rubber Co. Ltd. 1929. 3-v Batt, MW 0-100 deg, no integral loud-speaker, black crystalline painted metal case with wood base. 6 ½ in. x 7 in. x 4 in. £4.4s.0d. Also in bronze and gilt painted finishes. First advertised in the summer of 1929 in readiness for the inauguration of the B.B.C.'s Regional Programme transmitter at Brookmans Park, this receiver was still being shown at the 1931 Radiolympia.

fig.278. Burton 'Empire 3', by C.F. & H. Burton Ltd. 1929. 3-v Batt, MW/LW 0-180 deg, no integral loud-speaker, black ebonite panel, oak cabinet. 10 ¼ in. x 18 ¾ in. x 9 ¼ in. £5.10s.0d, royalty and valves extra. Burton's first wireless receiver. (Also AC mains version, price £14.15s.0d inc valves. Royalty extra).

2 The 1930s

1930

On March 9th, the B.B.C.'s second high power medium-wave transmitter was brought into service at Brookmans Park, radiating London National on 261.3 metres, while 2LO London on 356.3 metres became officially known as London Regional. On the same day, Daventry 5XX on 1554.4 metres became Daventry National and Daventry 5GB on 479.2 metres became Midland Regional. The inauguration of the B.B.C.'s London National transmitter now meant that Baird's 30-line television experiments could be transmitted for the first time with synchronised sound and vision, on 356.3 metres and 261.3 metres respectively. These 'dual' transmissions began on March 31st (although for some reason they did not appear billed in *The Radio Times* until two weeks later on April 14th). Half hour television programmes were sent out on five mornings and two nights each week, fed from the Long Acre studio along two Post Office telephone lines to the control room at Savoy Hill and then on to the transmitting station at Brookmans Park. By this time, the first quantity production of the new vision-only 'Baird Televisor' in a pressed aluminium case had been brought out price £26.5s.0d (or £16.16s.0d for the kit of parts) and this was later followed by the companion Baird 'All-Mains' sound receiver. In June, the Baird Television Development Company and Baird International Television Ltd. amalgamated to form Baird Television Ltd. and in September, Baird's original company Television Ltd. was liquidated.

With the full opening of the Regional Scheme for London and the Home Counties area, many listeners were surprised to find that their older valve receivers were neither able to separate the two transmissions nor to prevent interference between the Brookmans Park station and others on the Broadcast Band, despite well publicised warnings from the B.B.C. and the wireless Press that many thousands of sets would be rendered obsolete overnight unless their circuits were modified. The re-introduction of separate wave-traps helped to provide an answer to the problem and many different models appeared on the market from 1930 under the grander description of 'station rejectors'. From this time too, some manufacturers provided their new mains receivers with two aerial input sockets at the backs of the chassis (fig.297): one for maximum range and the other for 'Regional listening', where maximum selectivity was required, a feature which had first been incorporated in battery receivers in 1928. Several receivers had now begun to include a volume control in addition to, and in some cases in place of, the reaction control, while there were a small but growing number of receivers which were now being designed without reaction.

In March, the International Broadcasting Company (I.B.C.) was registered, and under the directorship of Captain L.F. Plugge, began selling unused air-time on existing Continental broadcasting stations to British firms willing to sponsor light entertainment and variety programmes which would be radiated to listeners in this country. These were mainly consumer companies manufacturing gramophone records, food products (notably the biscuit firm Huntley & Palmer), toothpaste and cigarettes. During the 1930s, nearly a dozen I.B.C. Continental stations (plus one in Eire: Radio Athlone) were to put out commercially sponsored programmes in English, the more important ones being Radio Normandie, also known as Fécamp (from October 1931), Radio Luxembourg (from spring 1933), Poste Parisienne (from November 1933) and Radio Lyon (from 1936). Radio Luxembourg differed from the other stations because it had been set up with the main object of broadcasting advertising programmes to neighbouring countries which did not allow

advertising on their own national programmes. The other stations were already established and only used sponsored programmes in English as a small addition to programmes in their own language. Needless to say, these 'light' commercial programmes soon attracted a large following in Britain and provided a welcome break from the sometimes 'stuffy' content of those sent out by the B.B.C.

In October, the B.B.C.'s new Symphony Orchestra gave its first concert on the air. Because Savoy Hill was too small to accommodate the full orchestra of 119 players, it had been necessary to find alternative accommodation at a separate studio. This was known as Studio No.10, and was housed in a disused warehouse near Waterloo Bridge on the south bank of the river. It was in use until 1934 when Studio No.1 at Maida Vale replaced it.

From wireless manufacturers, there was now a tremendous increase in the number of new mains receivers being produced, in particular AC table and transportable models, which prompted *Wireless World* to hail the 1930 Radiolympia exhibition in September as "the beginning of the All-Electric Season". While sets needing a separate loud-speaker continued to be in the majority, several all-enclosed receivers appeared including the first AC mains superhet (the Melva by Rialton Radio Ltd., London W1), whose introduction marks the beginning of the superhet revival. Another notable mains receiver was the McMichael Mains Three (fig.296) which was the first to employ an illuminated 'full-vision' horizontal scale and a tuning control with a cord-driven cursor (pointer), a method which quickly became standard practice and is still very much in use today. *Wireless World* said at the time, "the single tuning control which moves a pointer across an illuminated scale calibrated in wavelengths is fascinating to see and is likely to set a new fashion".

In permanent-magnet moving-coil loud-speakers, enclosed pot and built-up magnets with laminated poles had a short vogue in the winter of 1930/31 and in the moving-iron class, a very much improved type of loud-speaker was introduced. This was the Inductor Dynamic which was designed for use with good quality multi-valve receivers and gave (for the first time) reasonably faithful reproduction of the bass register (fig.897).

By now, valve rectifiers were showing a marked lead over the metal type since they were capable of handling higher HT currents, were relatively indifferent to heat and took up much less space on the chassis. The problem of mains hum encountered with AC receivers which employed directly-heated pentodes as output valves was dispensed with by the Mazda AC/PEN, the first indirectly-heated AC mains output pentode, introduced by the Edison-Swan Electric Company in May (see also 1928).

Just under 30 per cent of homes in England, Wales and Scotland had access to electricity and AC and DC supplies were now distributed about 1:1, compared with about 4:5 three years before. On April 30th the first part of the National Grid Scheme, in Central Scotland, was officially inaugurated by the Minister of Transport. In the remaining 75 per cent of non-electrified homes, people who wanted to listen-in still had to use batteries to power their receivers, but given the choice, those with a mains supply usually chose to run a mains receiver. If their houses had recently been supplied, people having battery receivers who did not wish to go to the expense of buying a new mains model, could purchase a relatively cheap battery eliminator and use it to run their receiver directly from an electric light socket.

Kolster–Brandes 'Rejectostat' AC table model receiver in a walnut cabinet designed by Betty Joel, 1933. (See fig.415).

Of the various classes of receiver newly introduced that year, about 45 per cent were AC, 15 per cent DC and about 40 per cent battery. Several manufacturers were beginning to bring out both AC and DC versions of particular models but as the National Grid scheme progressed and DC supplies declined, so DC-only sets declined too. While new battery models were for the first time being overshadowed, those already in existence far outnumbered the mains type of receiver and they would continue to do so until many more homes in mainland Britain became electrified. Interest in the 5-valve suitcase battery portable, so popular a few years before (see 1928) had drastically waned, and only a handful of new models were shown at Radiolympia. But despite the general decline in battery models, new mass-production techniques coupled with the benefits brought about by a stabilisation of the Marconi patent position (see 1928), led to the mass introduction of very low-priced simple 2 and 3-valve battery receivers principally aimed at the working man (figs.294,308). A 'three-power pact' was announced between Marconi's, The Gramophone Company and Standard Telephones, which enabled a single combined manufacturing licence to be issued. Known as the A3 Licence, it became available in November with terms at 5s.0d per valve holder, and with its introduction, patents ceased to be a major source of unsettlement in the Industry.

Factory-built receivers of all classes adopted a new form of assembly as new mass-production techniques spread throughout the Wireless Industry. The simple wooden baseboard with screwed-down components of the pioneering 1920s had been left behind forever and in its place came the modern type of receiver with coils and valves housed under cylindrical metal cans for effective screening. Modern chassis design now favoured a pre-formed metal box, enclosing the decoupling and distributive components with the valves and tuned circuits mounted on top, an arrangement which provided effective screening and straightforward concealed wiring. The design was more suitable to mass-production methods for it allowed manufacturing operations to be split into separate sections with each semi-skilled worker on the assembly line being responsible for assembling a single section rather than having to build an entire receiver from start to finish.

In cabinet construction, 80 per cent of new models had wooden cabinets (with walnut being used as the stock cabinet material throughout the 1930s); 12.5 per cent were in the form of a suitcase, 4 per cent were in metal and 3.5 per cent (and rising) were in moulded Bakelite or similar plastics with a great increase in the use of moulding in component manufacture. There was also a great increase in ganged waveband switching and ganged tuning operated by a single control. Edgewise-mounted drum scale tuning controls were starting to decline as they were overtaken by the single-knob disc-drive or drum-drive method coupled to a ganged condenser and this was adopted by at least 60 per cent of the new receivers appearing on the market. By the end of 1930, direct calibration in metre wavelengths was beginning to be more generally employed but despite the recommendations of the International Consultative Committee (see 1929), some new two-band receivers (covering the medium and long wavebands) still appeared marked 'Short' and 'Long' (figs.292,297).

Although the crystal set was now well passed its heyday, one new model (the Magnum, fig.309) was introduced in 1930 specially designed for use by blind listeners. A neglected section of the listening public for several years, they were first given a little independence in 1926 when the B.B.C. began issuing braille editions of *The Radio Times*, but it was not until Christmas 1929 that in a broadcast appeal by Winston Churchill, the British Wireless For The Blind Fund was officially launched with the object of raising money for the purchase of receivers specifically for blind and visually handicapped listeners.

Despite the Depression, the response from the public was overwhelming and within a few months the Magnum became the first in a long line of braille receivers. It was made Burne-Jones & Co. Ltd, London SE1 and was cleverly thought out to give the easiest possible handling for the blind listener. The usual problem of a delicate and easily upset cat's whisker/crystal arrangement was overcome by having the detector arm spring-loaded so that if accidentally knocked from the side the contact remained undisturbed. The tuning dials, marked in braille, were very large and to avoid confusing the terminals, the aerial and earth were set far apart, while the headphone terminals were close together.

RADIO RENTALS

While outright purchasing had always been the usual method of acquiring a wireless, various hire purchase and rental schemes had been tried out over the years in order to attract business by making payment easier, particularly for those with limited incomes. As early as 1923, sets could be bought with 'easy payments' (fig. 87) and towards the end of the 1920s, at a time when Britain was facing the growing economic crisis, several rental firms such as Rentertainments Ltd. of Hainault became established around the country, renting wireless receivers to the public for relatively small monthly payments. In August 1930, a new firm with offices in Brighton was set up by P. Perring-Thoms. It was called Radio Rentals, which was to grow into the largest rental company in Britain with over 280,000 radio subscribers by the time it celebrated its Silver Jubilee in 1955. For the first four years of its existence, Radio Rentals used standard Ekco receivers: Model 313 in 1930 (their first rental set, fig.304), Model RS2 in 1931, Model M23 in 1932 (fig.318) and Model AC 74 in 1933 (fig.413). But in 1934 an agreement was entered into with E.K. Cole Ltd. for them to supply receivers designed exclusively for Radio Rentals (see 1934) in addition to standard sets, and this practice was followed later by other suppliers, including Kolster-Brandes in the late 1930s and Mains Radio & Gramophones Ltd. after the Second World War, until receiver rental ceased altogether in 1965 and Radio Rentals concentrated on the rental of television sets.

1931

On March 23rd, the second phase of the Regional Scheme got under way with the beginning of North Regional reception tests from the new North of England high power twin medium-wave transmitting station at Moorside Edge near Huddersfield. On May 17th, the North Regional transmitter became fully operational. At the same time the old British Broadcasting Company's 1922 low power Manchester station (call-sign 2ZY), and the Bradford, Hull, Liverpool, Sheffield and Stoke relays were closed down: Aberdeen was relegated to a relay on May 31st. A week later, on June 8th, the North National transmitter began reception tests and on July 12th, both transmitters began a full twin-wave broadcast service to the densely populated industrial North. The range of North National (301.5 metres) was not as great as North Regional (479.2 metres) but as Daventry 5XX was sending out the same National Programme on long waves, listeners in poor reception areas could re-tune to Daventry.

A lot of interference problems were encountered with the Moorside Edge station just as there had been with Brookmans Park (see 1930) and for many listeners, especially those with rather unselective receivers living close to the transmitter, the signals from it often drowned out other stations on the Broadcast Band. One firm though, the enterprising Northampton Plating Company, brought out the Regional Unit, which when connected between the aerial and the receiver was designed to overcome "the enormous interference caused by the new

Regional stations". Acting as a station rejector, the unit could tune-out the interfering signals and comprised a small black wooden box containing one adjustable and one fixed condenser mounted in the centre of a coil - not a great deal for 7s.9d (fig.279).

fig.279. The Northampton Plating Company's 'Regional Unit', 1931. A 'station rejector' which could tune-out interference to other stations caused by the B.B.C.'s new Moorside Edge transmitter. Black-painted wooden case, 4½ in. x 3½ in. x 2 in. Price 7s.9d.

FOREIGN COMMERCIAL STATIONS

In June, a concession originally obtained by the French company, Société Luxembourgeoise d'Etudes Radiophoniques in the previous September, was re-sold to another French company, Compagnie Luxembourgeoise de Rediffusion to build a high power station of at least 100 kW in Luxembourg and broadcast commercial programmes under the direction of a Commission appointed by the Luxembourg Government. The B.B.C. had a legal monopoly of broadcasting in Great Britain and were staunchly against the idea of commercial broadcasting but until now had not taken steps to interfere with the occasional commercial broadcasts picked up from stations on the Continent. However, Radio Luxembourg was being set up with the expressed intention of broadcasting full advertising programmes to Britain and neighbouring countries and if built, would be one of the most powerful stations in Europe and able to threaten the B.B.C.'s monopoly without being subject to British Law. Also, it was seeking a long-wave allocation at a time when the long-wave 'ether' was already heavily congested, and the B.B.C. expressed these worries in its first official protest.

From October, the I.B.C. arranged sponsored programmes with Radio Normandie, a 10 kW station on 223 metres near Fecamp on the northern coast of France which was soon to grow into one of the I.B.C.'s most popular stations with British listeners. Initially on Sunday nights, having waited patiently for the B.B.C. to close down, the station put out a programme of hit records sponsored by the American wireless manufacturers, Philco, which the disapproving B.B.C. described as being in the "blatant American manner". But the programme times were soon cheekily extended to include the early part of Sunday afternoons as well since the B.B.C.'s own schedule did not begin until later at around 3pm.

WIRELESS-RELAYS

By the end of 1931, wireless-relays had become very popular and there were now 132 exchanges with a total of nearly 44,000 subscribers throughout the country. One of the biggest

exchange companies was Rediffusion Ltd. who had managed to persuade the B.B.C.'s ex-Chief Engineer, P.P. Eckersley, to join them (Eckersley was forced to resign from the B.B.C. in the autumn of 1929 over a divorce). Unlike most of his technical colleagues at the B.B.C., Eckersley was a staunch advocate of 'wire-broadcasting' and predicted (incorrectly as it turned out) the complete development of such a system in place of conventional *wireless* broadcasting.

In subscribing to one of the exchange companies, there were several advantages for those listeners who wished to dispense with the fuss and bother of running and maintaining their own wireless sets. Firstly, there was only a loud-speaker to contend with, and with just a switch for on/off/volume and station selection, operations were kept to a minimum. As well as the B.B.C. stations, the exchange companies could usually offer foreign programmes (including those arranged by the I.B.C.) and reception of these was usually better than that obtained by many higher-priced wireless sets due to the quality of the companies' master sets and the special aerial arrays erected at the exchanges.

TELEVISION

During the year, the B.B.C.'s attitude to Baird's low-definition television system had modified and the Corporation now felt that in the foreseeable future, it could develop into both a practical and a commercial proposition. Interest in television was growing and while the total number of Televisors sold by the beginning of the year was less than one thousand, Baird estimated that those people who had constructed their own television receivers from his plans could run into many times this figure. In August, the B.B.C. for the first time gave permission for one of their own studios (Studio No.10 near Waterloo Bridge) to be used by Baird for producing his experimental low-definition television programmes which had previously been relayed from the Baird Studios at 133 Long Acre. In place of the conventional disc-scanner, Baird now began experimenting with an improved portable transmitter employing a 'mirror-drum' which scanned in 30 vertical strips and gave larger and brighter images; in June of the following year, Baird Television Ltd. adopted the mirror-drum in their Televisors, and the picture size was increased to 9 in. high by 4 in. wide, and this form of receiver became the standard type until the termination of the low-definition broadcasting service in September 1935.

WIRELESS DESIGN

In the Wireless Industry, AC mains superhets were slowly growing in number and although very expensive and regarded as luxury items, especially during this time of economic depression, they were nevertheless creating a lot of interest both with the public and with the trade. But 1931 saw the appearance of the first in a range of high-performance TRF 'Superinductance' receivers by Philips: Model 720A and its version with an integral loud-speaker, the 730A. The essential feature of these receivers was the quality of the tuning coils which effectively made reaction unnecessary and simplified operation. In 1930, Philips had decided to pursue high quality TRF receivers rather than superhets and continued to produce their Superinductance range until, by 1934, it was obvious that the superhet had become cheaper and better than even the best TRF. The first Philips AC mains superhet, Model 588A, was launched in the autumn of that year at Radiolympia, with the last of the Superinductance range, Model 577A, bowing out a year later in 1935.

Amongst all classes of receiver, compact table-model mains and battery sets in upright wooden cabinets complete with built-in loud-speakers fitted behind decorative grilles were for the first time in the majority. Many mains receivers also had provision for connecting an external loud-speaker which meant that an 'extension speaker' could be wired up and the programmes conveniently piped from the main receiver to any part of the house, the garage or garden shed or wherever they were needed. Although a large outside aerial was still recommended for long-range reception, over a comparatively short range, most new receivers were sensitive enough to operate satisfactorily with only a short indoor aerial. On some mains receivers, provision was made for using the mains supply wiring for the aerial.

Having fully shaken off the 'experimental laboratory' look of the 1920s, the wireless had, by 1931, been generally accepted into the home as an ultra-modern item of domestic equipment. The more innovative manufacturers quickly realised that if they were to continue to attract sales, then the hithertoo rather overlooked cabinet would have to be made more decorative and appealing in order for it to remain in complete harmony with the changing styles of its domestic surroundings. Professional artistic help was sought by many manufacturers, and cabinets began to appear from the drawing-board design ideas of leading artists, furniture designers and even architects - many reflecting the Art Deco movement popular throughout this decade (figs.333,347).

Among the furniture designers who became involved in the Wireless Industry was R.D. Russell, who between 1931 and the late 1940s designed most of Murphy Radio's wooden cabinets. They were made by Gordon Russell Ltd. at Broadway in Worcestershire and, from 1935, at their new factory premises at Park Royal in West London, opened to meet the growing demand for high quality wireless cabinets.

R.D. Russell's range of cabinet designs, with their crisp lines and forms devoid of much detail, appeared rather severe and austere in a market dominated in the early 1930s by highly stylised and well-decorated cabinets. The public were at first slow to approve of them and Murphy Radio dealers and sales representatives initially loathed them, dubbing Russell's first offering, (the Model A3, fig.338), the 'Dartmoor Super' or 'the Prison Set' because of the bars across the front of the loud-speaker opening. But within a few years, the public and the trade began to accept them and soon several receiver manufacturers were imitating Russell's design ideas. By the end of the 1930s (according to N. Pevsner writing in *Architectural Review* in May 1940), Russell's cabinets represented "Britain's most significant contribution to international radio design, and one of Britain's most noteworthy contributions to contemporary industrial art.....". (See also the comments about the Murphy Model A24 of 1934, fig.439).

While there were many manufacturers like Murphy Radio Ltd. who were content to treat the wireless as a piece of furniture and produced only polished wooden cabinets, there were others who attempted to treat the wireless as an object in its own right and to depart from the established 'furniture-style' concept. While some had been experimenting with Bakelite since the late 1920s, E.K. Cole Ltd. (named after the firm's founder and Managing Director, Eric Kirkham Cole) was the first British company to explore fully the unique moulding properties of this material by making a startlingly different and attractive series of cabinets throughout the 1930s, beginning with their first all-enclosed Bakelite mains table model, the M23 (fig.318), designed by a young Cambridge graduate, J.K. White.

With receivers in general, the loud-speaker grille was now becoming a prominent part of modern cabinet design, serving to protect the loud-speaker and to decorate the opening. By far the most popular grille design of 1931 was executed in 'floral tracery' in which the grille was cut in flowing lines resembling petals or stems (figs.315,342). Next came the geometric grille (figs.324,350) which was soon to become highly fashionable as the influence of Art Deco spread, and then the pictorial grille

designs associated with one particular manufacturer: e.g. Pye's 'Sunrise' (fig.332), Philips' 'Star' symbol (fig.321) and Ekco's 'Willows By A Riverbank' (fig.314).

Glued behind the grille was the loud-speaker cloth which was often made of silk or rayon. Usually plain or with a simple pattern, it protected the loud-speaker from dirt and dust, but was vulnerable to attack from a careless duster or playful cat. Damaged loud-speaker cloths are the bane of wireless collectors today as they are notoriously difficult to match with modern fabrics. (Another bane, although more easily remedied, is the common occurrence of paint spots. Why didn't people ever seem to cover up their wireless sets while decorating?).

fig.280. HT battery eliminators were popular with listeners with battery sets whose houses had a mains supply. The one illustrated, made by E.K. Cole in the early 1930s, provided an HT output of between 60 and 150 volts from the AC mains and had facilities for charging a 2v accumulator. Brown Bakelite case. 5 in. x 9 in. x 5 in.

STATIONS ON THE DIAL

One of the major innovations of 1931 was the first British receiver to have a full range of station names printed on the dial. This was the Ekco RS3 Consolette (fig.314) in a moulded Bakelite cabinet, which like the M23, was designed by J.K. White. ('Consolette' was the name of a new breed of all-enclosed mains receiver, larger than a table model but smaller than a console). The uncertainty over the allocation of European wavelengths was by now not as great as it had been, and Ekco felt confident that the dial of the RS3 would be accurate for at least a few more years to come. Having station names printed on the dial made the process of tuning-in very much easier of course; the dial was ingeniously placed around the loud-speaker and a single pointer travelled around the edge and merely pointed to the name of the station being received. At the outset of broadcasting in 1922, tuning had been a comparatively complicated matter and the idea had been fostered that it was one of those duties best left to the man of the house. Tearful children wanting to listen to the 'Children's Hour' were accustomed to hearing statements like "You will have to wait till *father* gets home". But now, according to Ivee Smith, Publicity Supervisor for E.K. Cole at Radiolympia 1931, the new Ekco station dial showed women in particular just how simple station-finding really could be. Speaking to *The Wireless & Gramophone Trader* she said, "What pleased me most was the interest which women took in the station dial. The idea of being able to tune-in by name captured their imagination. Instead of having to submit to the humiliation of watching the competent skill with which 'John', 'George' or 'Bill' tuned in foreign stations for their gratification, these women had visions of being able to do the job themselves and of proving it by showing the name of the station to which the receiver is tuned. I think that Ekco is the first firm to produce a receiver which really appeals to women as well as men."

While most new receivers in 1931 were now directly calibrated in metre wavelengths, identifying a station (particularly a *foreign* station), still remained a puzzle to many listeners. To help matters, *Wireless World* published a foreign broadcast guide listing the daily programme content of each station together details of its wavelength. Also in the same year, the *Daily Mail* produced the first of their 'Radio-at-a-Glance' card disc calculators with which the listener could 'dial' any one of 76 British and European stations and show 9 important facts about each one: its wavelength, closing down sign and aerial power etc. (In 1933, an improved version was brought out with ten important facts).

In the increasing number of receivers whose tuning dials were made of translucent celluloid, many employed a small bulb behind the dial to illuminate the reading (fig.321). Edgewise-mounted drum scale tuning controls were out-dated and had almost entirely disappeared with two notable exceptions. Burton Products' Empire Speaker Three (fig.347) employed this obsolete tuning control technology but was contained within an ultra-modern 'Egyptian Temple' style Art Deco cabinet, and A.C. Cossor's Model 732 (fig.345) exhibited the 'missing link' by having the same single drum scale worked by two alternative types of control: the listener could either use the old-style edgewise-mounted control or the up-to-date drum-drive control mounted on the side of the cabinet. While drum-drive scales and disc-drive dials (fig.346) viewed through small metal or Bakelite escutcheons were now widely employed, driving ganged condensers with a single-knob control, fixed full-vision dials and scales with moving cursors were gaining in popularity and would soon sweep them aside (fig.324).

Ganged tuning had become a standard feature of all but the cheapest types of receiver and during construction each condenser had to be matched with the others in the ganging to ensure accurate tuning. To achieve this the practice of fitting segmented end-vanes to each set of condenser rotors was introduced in the autumn, allowing minor divergencies in condenser capacities to be corrected at various rotor settings by bending the segments during production at the factory.

'Local-distance' switches also appeared for the first time on several receivers (figs.325,338). Living in the shadow of a local transmitting station could cause a lot of problems to those listeners who wanted to hear other stations on the same waveband. Foreign-listening was still very popular, but often signals from abroad were comparatively weak or were swamped by the local transmitter. To help solve this problem, some manufacturers fitted a small series-condenser in the aerial input lead controlled by a switch mounted at the back of the receiver and generally labelled 'LOCAL-DISTANCE'. In the 'off' position, the switch would bring the condenser into operation making the receiver more selective and more sensitive to weaker signals. In the 'on' position the switch would short-circuit the condenser and bring in the local station at its normal strength.

There were soon various accessories and devices which listeners could buy to improve selectivity. 'Pix' was a commercially packaged aerial condenser which was fitted into the aerial lead and for 2s.0d had much the same effect as the local-distance switch. "Cut out the local and get Algiers and other foreign stations," said their advertisement, "No more dual programmes. Enjoy foreign concerts while your local station is working or when being swamped or interfered with by a powerful station. Just fix a PIX in your aerial!"

An alternative method chosen by a few receiver manufacturers was to fit a variable resistance and a variable condenser aerial coupler but since this required a certain amount of skill in using and therefore might be a little too 'technical' for some listeners, it did not find general favour.

During 1931, there were three important valve developments. Indirectly-heated DC mains valves were produced by Mazda which led to the introduction of the first true DC mains receivers, and although these were technically as good as AC models, the phasing-out of DC supplies meant that the valves were used only in a minority of receivers.

In December, 'metallised' valves appeared for the first time (see Appendix). A fine dull-grey coating of zinc was sprayed onto the glass bulb and earthed to the chassis via one of the pins. This prevented stray coupling, particularly between HF stages, and assisted the stability of the receiver as it was able to make the valve withstand high amplification without oscillating. The first valve to be metallised was the Cossor 220VSG, a variable-mu HF screened-grid valve, the battery version of the first AC mains variable-mu screened-grid (the Osram VMS4) introduced in the summer. (In 1933, the rather drab colour of zinc-sprayed metallised valves was brightened up when Philips' Golden Range and Mullard valves with a gold-coloured metallised spray finish were first introduced).

The first receiver to employ the VMS4 in 1931 was the Amplion Six (fig.323), a receiver which exhibited all the latest features of the modern wireless set: two variable-mu screened-grid HF stages; grid detector; push-pull output; power rectifier; band-pass input filter; ganged tuning control; illuminated tuning scale; built-in capacity aerial; local-distance switch and an integral mains-energised moving-coil loud-speaker.

Moving-iron cone loud-speakers were now usually used only where cheapness was the main consideration. Improved production methods and new materials had brought about a considerable reduction in size and cost and a vast improvement to power and efficiency in both the mains-energised and the permanent-magnet type of moving-coil loud-speaker. The compact all-enclosed mains receiver had brought about a demand for small mains-energised loud-speakers which could work well at much lower levels of volume. With some of these loud-speakers, power could now be derived from the HT supply of the receiver rather than directly from the mains as previously, and the term 'mains-energised' although continuing in use, became in these cases, a misnomer. While the electro-magnetic type of moving-coil loud-speaker was in widespread use in mains receivers throughout the 1930s, the permanent-magnet type, then principally used in battery receivers, eventually superseded all others.

In factory-built receivers, many leading wireless manufacturers began for the first time to produce radiogram versions of their principal receiver chassis. Chassis construction generally continued along mass-production lines and more and more cheap and simplified receivers were, in their tens of thousands, being brought out especially for the masses (fig.350). Kit sets for the first time widely adopted pre-formed metal chassis methods and were now very much simplified, with the finished result in many cases as attractive and as well finished as factory-built receivers. Component parts for the home-constructor were a major part of the Wireless Industry's output and interest in home-construction, especially from plans and blueprints published in wireless magazines, continued unabaited.

FOREIGN COMPETITION

From across the Atlantic, several different models of midget AC mains receivers began to arrive in Britain (fig.320). These were a lot smaller and more compact than our own which were produced for the first time that year (fig.330). Within the British Wireless Industry, fears had already been expressed of an invasion of cheap American-made receivers (mainly resulting from surplus production in 1930). This was first brought about by an advertisement sent to many British retailers early in January 1931 offering them a 6-valve AC American midget receiver through a Belgian agency at only £6.15s.0d. This was certainly a competitive price (a typical British midget cost around £16) and was seen as an indication of the potential damage to the stability of U.K. trade, particularly as Britain was at the height of economic depression with unemployment peaking at just over 21 per cent. Besides, to buy foreign merchandise was regarded by many people in this country as unpatriotic, just as tuning-in to foreign stations (especially to those of the commercial network) was to loyal B.B.C. listeners. Ralph Stranger, in his book *Reproduction of Wireless Signals* (Newnes, 1931) broke off from a discourse on the merits of the moving-coil loud-speaker to appeal to his readers to "Buy British" for he felt that buying "cheap foreign junk" would do "some poor devil of a Briton out of his Sunday joint". (The official Buy British Campaign, which included products from the British Empire, was inaugurated on the National Programme by the Prince of Wales on November 16th).

To some extent, the British Wireless Industry was protected from foreign competition by laws and import duties but this led to a number of foreign manufacturers setting up subsidiary factories in Britain during the 1930s, the most notable of whom were Belmont, Philco, Pilot and Majestic.

From the early 1930s until the end of World War Two, general public interest in American-made receivers of all types began to grow, and although the numbers imported never really developed into the predicted invasion, by the end of the 1930s tens of thousands of such receivers were in use throughout the country, with the midget type being the most popular (see also 1943). Because of the small size of midget receivers, there was not usually enough room in the cabinet for a conventional mains dropper or a transformer to cut down the mains voltage for the valves. In America, it was common practice to use a 'line-cord' resistor, which was a flexible resistance wire wound on asbestos and contained within, or taped to, the twin-wire mains lead. The length was cut to suit the voltage needs of the particular valve heaters in use. In America, with receivers designed to work off 110/120 volts the line-cord was just a few feet long, but for use in this country on our greater 200/240 volt supply, the line-cords had to be considerably lengthened to drop the voltage to the required level. Because of the substantial heat generated by the resistance wire in the cord, there was always the risk of fire, particularly if the asbestos insulation received damage. As an alternative, an external mains dropper in a protective sheath or a small mains transformer was sometimes fixed to the back of the receiver or connected as a separate unit between the receiver and the mains plug.

In 1931, to cater for the growing interest in American-made receivers, Tungsram Electric Lamp Works (Gt. Britain) Ltd. became the first British-based company to begin making a full range of American-type AC valves. These came with 'UX' 4-pin and 'UY' 5-pin bases: the 'UX' base being identified by the two thicker heater pins which allowed for positive location in the socket, while the pins of the 'UY' base were all the same diameter.

1932

In planning a system of broadcasting for this country, the B.B.C. had always been faced with various geographical difficulties which included irregular coastline, mountainous and hilly countryside coupled with great variations in the density of the population. The Scottish Regional Scheme met all these problems on a grand scale, but so successful was the B.B.C.'s broadcast planning for this area that when the scheme was inaugurated towards the end of 1932, just over 80 per cent of Scotland's population was able to receive the service without difficulty.

A new high power twin medium-wave transmitting station was built at Westerglen near Falkirk and tests began on May 2nd using its Regional transmitter. A month later, on June 12th, the Scottish Regional Programme on 376.4 metres took over the whole service from the low power transmitters at Dundee, Edinburgh and Glasgow.

The Nat. transmitter began tests on August 22nd and began broadcasting the Scottish National Programme on 288.5 metres on September 25th, joining Scottish Regional and inaugurating the full twin medium-wave service, with both transmitters being fed programmes live by landline from the B.B.C.'s Edinburgh studios.

BROADCASTING HOUSE

Meanwhile in London, the B.B.C.'s new headquarters at Broadcasting House had been completed, although it was recognised that conditions would be cramped and that additional premises would have to be acquired in order to accomodate all the staff and all the programme productions. The new building, designed by the architect Lieut.-Col. G. Val Myer, was brought into partial service on May 2nd and on the 14th, the old studios at Savoy Hill were locked up for the last time after just over nine years service. Broadcasting House now took over completely, except for Studio No.10 near Waterloo Bridge which continued to be used by the B.B.C. Symphony Orchestra for many of their concerts until 1934. Purpose-built for broadcasting and described by the architect Lord Gerald Wellesley as having the "most important example of untraditional interior decoration yet completed in this country", the building contained some twenty-two studios, the largest of which, the concert hall, measured 106 ft. x 42 ft. There was also something unofficially called "Studio 10a", although this was not a real studio, but a felt-lined box containing the interval signal clock. The interval signal had been brought into use by the B.B.C. in December 1930 and was transmitted in the event of unforeseen delays between programmes or when a breakdown had occurred. A microphone in the box picked up the tick from the second hand of an electric clock and this was broadcast to fill in the intervals where an otherwise sudden silence might lead the listener to believe that his set had developed a fault.

It is interesting to note that two leading architects who both designed studios for Broadcasting House also produced Bakelite wireless cabinet designs for E.K. Cole in the 1930s (figs.413,448). E.K. Cole had committed themselves to the production of Bakelite cabinets for their receivers and in the spring of 1932 had begun work on a plant for the production of Bakelite mouldings at their Southend works. Three 1,000 ton hydraulic high-speed presses were employed, then the largest in use in Britain. The architects were Wells Coates, who designed the News Studios 4a and 4b and the Dramatic Effects Studio 6D, and Serge Chermayeff who designed Studio 8A at the top of the building, used for orchestras and bands, and the two Talks Studios, 3b and 8b.

This grand and imposing building indicated the degree by which the stature of broadcasting had risen in just ten years since 2LO had first been in temporary occupation of a single studio on the top floor of Marconi House in the Strand. The B.B.C. now had almost five million licensed listeners, with Bournemouth claiming to be the most 'radio minded' town in Britain: out of 22,459 homes, 21,039 had wireless receivers.

Broadcasting House though was not everybody's cup of tea. To some, it looked like a beached ocean liner and quite out of place amongst the more refined and classical architecture of Portland Place. *Wireless World* was not too keen on the name either and felt that "from the beginning, the B.B.C.

has shown absurd modesty in regard to their new building". The very name 'Broadcasting House' was, they believed, "evolved by an imaginative work foreman in need of a second postal address!" (No, I didn't understand that bit either). They let their readers in on the 'secret' that the 25 ft. high aerial masts seen on top of the building were purely ornamental since no actual transmission took place from the building and their object was "to give the place an *air* in order to distinguish itself from a hostelry or a treacle factory". (In reality, these masts did for a time carry receiving aerials for testing the reception quality of programmes).

fig.281. A view of the newly built Broadcasting House in 1932.

In May 1932, the Post Office joined the B.B.C. in condemning commercial broadcasting stations when it protested about Radio Luxembourg's recent seizure of the 1,250 metre wavelength for experimental broadcasting, since it interfered with British aircraft wireless services. Luxembourg's request for a long-wave allocation had been turned down by the I.B.U. who could not sympathise with any type of programme which was entirely based on the idea of commercial advertising, although by now considerable interest was being shown by various British firms in commercial broadcasting, indicated by the fact that by December 1932, over twenty British firms were sponsoring programmes from Continental stations.

On Sunday June 5th, the B.B.C. took the first positive action against the commercial stations which were taking full advantage of the time outside the Corporation's schedule and filling it with their own programmes. The B.B.C.'s Sunday

afternoon service on the National Programme was lengthened and now made a start at 12.30pm instead of 3pm, but only the times were changed, not the character of the programmes which continued to be 'restrained', leaving variety shows and dance band entertainment to stations like Radio Paris and Radio Normandie. The B.B.C.'s first 'Sunday Dinner Programme' was described by *Wireless World* who welcomed the programmes as being "one of the most popular innovations of the year....from 12.30 to 1pm, Mr G.D. Cunningham will accompany the *hors d'oeuvres* with an organ recital from the Queen's Hall. And then, while we assail the baron of beef Reginald King's orchestra will fortify us with selections from Rose Marie, The Moonbeams Dance and Love Come Back To Me."

TELEVISION

Following the B.B.C.'s change of attitude to Baird and his 30-line low-definition television system, the Corporation now took over the production of his experimental programmes, and made an agreement to provide a limited service from a studio in Broadcasting House until March 31st 1934. This began on August 22nd from Studio BB which had previously been occupied by dance bands, and programmes were put out on four weekday evenings a week from 11pm to 11.30pm, with vision on 261.3 metres (the London National wavelength) and sound on 398.9 metres (the Midland Regional wavelength).

While Baird had been pursuing the development of his mechanical system, progress had already been made by other British companies, not only with mechanical systems, but also in another branch of television using non-mechanical, electronic scanners and cathode ray tube receivers. E.M.I. had been working on an electronic system based upon methods used in the United States since the mid-1920s by V.K. Zworykin who was to develop the Ionoscope electronic television camera in 1933 which E.M.I. modified into the Emitron camera. In November 1932, E.M.I. first approached the B.B.C. to witness a demonstration of their high-definition very high frequency television. The E.M.I. system differed widely from Baird's, and the definition of the picture was far better with a greater number of lines and little sign of flicker, although so far, the system had only been developed for the transmission of film and not living subjects.

THE EMPIRE SERVICE

On December 19th, the B.B.C.'s new Empire broadcasting station was inaugurated at Daventry, sending out a regular short-wave service to all the British Dominions and Colonies scattered around the world. At Reith's insistence, this new 'Empire Service', like that of the B.B.C.'s domestic broadcasting service, was both politically independent and impartial and had been established using funds from the B.B.C.'s licence revenue following the Government's unwillingness to finance the project. Even when the Foreign Office took over the funding with the start of the first foreign language broadcasts in January 1938, Reith had fiercely fought (and won) for the B.B.C.'s right to total editorial freedom, a right which is still claimed today.

The inauguration of the Empire Service was of the first importance to British subjects living overseas, who were in many cases situated thousands of miles from their nearest broadcasting station, and on Christmas Day it enabled King George V to speak for the first time directly to all his people in the far corners of the Empire.

The Empire was divided up into five reception zones, each served by its own directional beam transmission aerial array and these were used to send out programmes on various wavelengths from about 14 to 48 metres. The five zones were

(1) Australia, (2) India, (3) South Africa, (4) West Africa and (5) Canada, although the area covered many other smaller countries situated around these five main areas. Many listeners in Great Britain were also very interested in short-wave reception and in readiness for the opening of the Empire Service a few manufacturers like Kolster-Brandes began to bring out the first 'all-wave' mains superhets (fig.373) - three waveband models which included short waves - although this class of receiver did not appear in significant numbers until 1935 (see 1935).

While electrification of homes under the National Grid Scheme continued, it had nevertheless progressed slowly and only about one third of the estimated eleven million homes in Britain were connected to an electricity supply. It was therefore inevitable that throughout the country, the number of listeners with battery sets was still far greater than those with mains receivers. But amongst listeners with a mains supply, the popularity of mains superhets had grown rapidly since they were first introduced in 1930 and there were comparatively few manufacturers in 1932 who were not producing at least one current model while there were even some who had entirely abandoned the TRF in favour of the superhet. In general though, battery table models and portables, and to a lesser extent, mains TRFs still held the field with the typical 4-valve receiver (variable-mu screened-grid, triode detector, output pentode plus rectifier) the backbone of the Wireless Industry. DC variable-mu valves had become available during 1932, and variable-mu valves in general were by now widely adopted and had almost entirely superseded the original form of screened-grid HF valve.

Some manufacturers, instead of producing both AC and DC versions of the same model, now produced 'AC/DC' (or 'universal') mains receivers for operation on either type of supply: the Decee-Acee model by A. Wade & Co. being the first such British receiver on the market (fig.372). AC/DC receivers can be immediately recognised by the presence of a large upright wire-wound resistance (known as a 'mains dropper') formed on a tube of ceramic material and mounted on the chassis. Metal bands around the resistance provided tappings for the required heater voltages. Sometimes found in place of the mains dropper in AC/DC sets of the early 1930s was a 'barretter' (see Appendix). Although in appearance it resembled a valve, it was really a special kind of electric lamp connected in series with the valves' heaters which protected them from any sudden surges in the mains supply voltage. The barretter's filament resistance changed in response to fluctuations in the mains supply in such a way that the current it passed always remained constant over a wide range of applied voltages.

New receivers produced without an integral loud-speaker were now rare. The fitting of small moving-coil loud-speakers of the electro and permanent-magnet variety in new mains and battery receivers was now standard practice and new permanent magnet types with chrome steel and forged magnets were introduced giving excellent results but at a much lower production cost than cast-steel permanent magnet types which had been in widespread use since 1929. New 'all-range' moving-coil loud-speaker units were also first introduced at about £6.0s.0d, promising "for the very first time, sound produced naturally". These employed a treble and a bass speaker mounted together as one unit, with each speaker designed to respond to its own particular band of frequencies. The loud-speaker grille continued to be a decorative feature of cabinets with geometric designs now becoming more popular. In a design innovation which in 1934 became standard throughout the Wireless Industry, a few receivers appeared with the loud-speaker opening completely plain and uncluttered with decorative fretwork or horizontal or vertical bars (fig.383) and

just cloth between loud-speaker and listener.

Tuning scales of new mains models were almost invariably both illuminated and calibrated in metre wavelengths, and an increasing number now also included station names popularly arranged on a long horizontally mounted fixed full-vision scale with a moving cursor (fig.383). 'One-piece' tuning controls appeared in great numbers (figs.353,372) and these had the control knob surround and the escutcheon window linked in one continuous moulding or pressing. Although examples can be found much earlier (figs.238,317), these were very much in vogue for the first time in 1932. Apart from rare and isolated instances (fig.375), edgewise-mounted drum scale tuning controls had all but disappeared and the use of canned coils and simple-to-use ganged tuning condensers was universal, even in cheap receivers.

One exception to simple tuning in a receiver was the ST 400, made from plans published in *The Wireless Constructor* and one of the famous 'ST' series of home-constructor's sets designed by John Scott-Taggart during the 1920s and 1930s and bearing his initials (fig.355). Unlike the simple control of the switch-on, tune-in receiver, 'ST' sets were for the man who liked plenty of knobs to turn; anything in the circuit that could be hand-controlled *was* hand-controlled. In the six weeks before the ST 400 was officially launched in the pages of *The Wireless Constructor*, Scott-Taggart went to extraordinary lengths to field test it, flying a prototype of his new receiver to readers' homes all over the country as far as Scotland, piloting his own aeroplane and often landing it in a convenient field and parking it in a corner for the night. You can imagine the startled looks of listeners when answering a knock on their door to find John Scott-Taggart standing there in his leather flying helmet asking to use their aerial to check the reception and performance of his new circuit. This enthusiasm and attention to detail was typical of Scott-Taggart whose name, in the two decades before the Second World War was one of the most widely known in the world of wireless home-construction.

In a move to combat the problem of fading experienced with tuning-in to distant foreign stations, Murphy Radio introduced automatic volume control ('AVC') in their Model A8 superhet which was the first all-enclosed mains receiver to be produced in this country in a horizontal cabinet (fig.367). Another receiver to embody AVC was the Zetavox AC mains model. Described as "the set of the future", it was tuned by a push-button arrangement with each button pre-tuned to one of nine selected stations. The Multi-Programme Automatic Ethatrope brought out by M.P.A. Wireless (1930) Ltd. in the same year could have twelve pre-tuned stations selected at will by a single knob, but pre-selected tuning, especially push-button tuning did not become reliable or popular until 1938 (see 1938).

The interest in purchasing new outdoor portables remained slight and it was now becoming fashionable to hire a portable for a special countryside motoring excursion or garden party rather than to go to the expense of buying one that was only going to be used for a few weeks a year. For example, for 3s.6d daily or 15s.0d weekly you could hire the latest McMichael Type 'S' (fig.368).

To help solve the problem of boredom on long car journeys, interest in car radio was once again revived with the introduction in the autumn of the first commercially produced British car radio, the 5-valve Philco Transitone superhet complete with the new AVC circuit. Priced at £34.13s.0d, the receiver was housed in a cabinet below the left hand side of the dashboard with the loud-speaker and tone control on the right, above the accelerator (fig.282). The tuning dial and volume control knob were housed on a remote control unit attached to the steering column and the whole set was powered by a 135 volt HT battery bolted beneath the floor. Five years earlier, in 1927, the original Transitone was brought out by the Philadelphia Storage Battery Company in America and was the first commercially manufactured car radio to be produced in the world. By the time the British version of the Transitone was released, an estimated 100,000 car radios were in use in the United States.

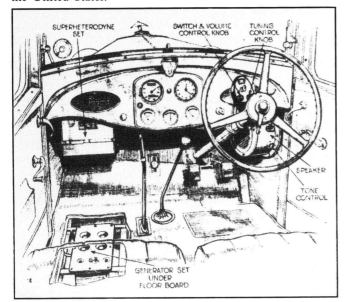

fig.282. The Philco 'Transitone' car radio installed in a 1932 Vauxhall.

1933

A new high power twin medium-wave transmitting station was built at Washford Cross near Watchet, Somerset and on April 24th its West Regional transmitter began experimental test broadcasts to the West of England and to South Wales. Some three months later on July 17th, its West National transmitter began testing and within a month, a full dual-wave service was in operation. The inauguration took place on August 13th with West Regional on 309.9 metres and West National on 261.6 metres and it completed the final part of the B.B.C.'s original Regional Scheme. On the same day, the low power transmitters at Cardiff and Swansea closed down, but the broadcasting studios at Cardiff remained to produce West Regional programmes jointly with new studios built at Bristol.

There were now four twin medium-wave transmitting stations: London Regional, North Regional, Scottish Regional and West Regional, and one twin medium and long-wave station at Daventry, all sending out a dual-wave service. Of the original eight main transmitting stations, Aberdeen, Bournemouth and Newcastle had been reduced to relays. The five others had been dismantled, and of the original eleven relay transmitters, only that at Plymouth was retained since it was needed to deal with the special reception difficulties encountered in Devon and Cornwall. It continued in service until June 14th 1939 when a new transmitter was opened 25 miles away at Start Point. Well before then, the regular production of programmes from the B.B.C.'s original Plymouth 5PY studios had all but ceased: from January 15th 1934 only the occasional programme was put out from here until, in the early years of the war, new headquarters were found away from the bomb damaged city centre.

By 1933, the B.B.C. had recognised that the Daventry transmitting station (or as *Wireless World* had put it, "that old crock amongst European broadcasting transmitters") had become obsolete and so it was decided to construct a new high power station at a different location in order to increase the power and range and to bring the quality up to modern standards. The station would house a new high power long-wave National Programme transmitter covering practically the whole country, and a new high power medium-wave Midland Regional transmitter serving the immediate area. The site chosen was 3 miles north east of Droitwich (see 1934).

In the spring, in defiance of the B.B.C., the Post Office and the I.B.U., the commercial Radio Luxembourg station began regular transmissions of sponsored programmes in English arranged by the I.B.C. on the pirated long wavelength of 1,250 metres. At first, these were put out on Sundays only but were later extended to other days of the week as the station became more popular. In retaliation, the B.B.C. banned publication of Radio Luxembourg's programme details in *World Radio* from its April 7th issue but there was little more the Corporation could do to stop this or any other of the commercial stations from beaming their transmissions into this country.

During 1933, Baird transferred his headquarters from Long Acre to the top of the South Tower at the Crystal Palace, where tragically three years later on November 30th 1936, a great deal of his equipment was destroyed by a devastating blaze which razed the Palace. Baird had already become alarmed over the various developments in electronic television and soon began to experiment in this field himself, using a 120-line high-definition cathode ray system licensed from the Farnsworth Television Laboratory of Philadelphia, although he never really had much success here. While in his low-definition experiments Baird continued to use mirror-drum scanners, he was now concentrating his main efforts on two high-definition electro-mechanical processes. In the first, which was especially suitable for outdoor subjects, both the scene and the sound were recorded together by a special cine camera and in less than 30 seconds the film was developed, fixed and washed. It was then mechanically scanned while still wet by a 120-hole disc. This 'intermediate film' method resulted in a short time delay between the filming of the subject and its transmission, leading it to be known also as 'delayed television'. The other method, for studio work, involved the use of a high-intensity beam of light which rapidly scanned the subject and reflected the light from it to a bank of photo-electric cells. In February and April, the E.M.I. electronic system had been given very favourable reports when it had been demonstrated to the Post Office and the B.B.C. and it was generally felt that compared to Baird's, the E.M.I. system was "immeasurably superior".

WIRELESS DESIGN

In 1933, listeners who wanted an ordinary new domestic wireless receiver would find one which covered the medium and long wavebands with which it was possible to use just a short length of aerial wire hanging down from the back of the chassis. Over the years, the output power of broadcasting stations had greatly increased and this, combined with the development of modern efficient circuit designs, meant that large arrays of masts and aerial systems strung up in gardens were fast disappearing and were usually only seen where households still clung on to their old and obsolete receivers. "The garden is no longer desecrated with an ugly pole. The modern home has no unsightly wires!" announced an advertisement in *Practical Wireless* for the Pix Invisible Indoor Aerial, a length of self-adhesive wire which could be tidily placed out of sight above the picture rail.

Reasonably priced AC mains superhets were now leading the mains wireless field and were no longer regarded as luxury receivers. They had completely taken over from the larger class of TRF, although for the listener who was primarily interested in the reception of his local station, simple and inexpensive TRFs consisting of a reacting detector followed by one or two stages of LF amplification offered a wider choice of models. AC/DC receivers were still in the process of development and the numbers released were small. However, there was good news for all mains receiver owners in general when A.F. Bulgin & Co. of Barking introduced their new comprehensive range of "definitely shockproof" (!) wall-mounted plugs and sockets. Mains receivers up till then were plugged into the electric light socket which in some cases was the only available source of supply in the room. But in many newly-built or newly-wired homes, wall-mounted power points freed the electric light socket for its original purpose and meant that wires could be better hidden and were no longer seen trailing in an unsightly fashion from the back of the receiver up to the ceiling rose.

The use of automatic volume control continued and with its general adoption, 'visual tuning indicators' began to be included as a standard feature on some receivers. With a circuit employing AVC, difficulty was often experienced in tuning in a station accurately by ear and some sort of visual indicator was found necessary. One of the preferred methods among manufacturers in the early 1930s was a small coloured bulb set into the cabinet just above the tuning dial which grew steadily brighter as the station was tuned in. Climax Radio Electric sold one in an add-on unit for those whose receivers were not already fitted with a tuning indicator.

There were other problems associated with AVC. During tuning (ie. between stations) an AVC receiver was often very noisy. Sensitivity was always at its maximum, and atmospherics and any local interference were automatically reproduced at great volume. A lot of this local interference was caused by man-made static from electrical machinery: from refrigerators, electric fans, lifts, flashing signs, trams and traffic signals etc., and it was often the bugbear of salesmen trying to convince a doubting customer that the terrible sparking noises coming from the receiver he was demonstrating were caused by the refrigerator in the butcher's shop next door and not a fault in the receiver's circuit.

To help overcome this problem, quiet automatic volume control ('QAVC') was introduced in some receivers, mainly those at the higher priced end of the market (fig.414). This was a system of inter-station noise suppression in which the loud-speaker was automatically faded out of the circuit so long as the signal fell below a certain strength. When a station was reached, the signal began to rise again and the loud-speaker was faded back in. An alternative method, used by many receivers having AVC but not QAVC, was the use of a 'static (or noise) supression switch', usually fitted to the chassis at the back of the receiver or, more usefully, incorporated into one of the control knobs (fig.430). The switch was kept closed during tuning so that most signals were kept at quite a low volume, and when the desired station had been found, the switch was opened for normal strength reception.

To further help listeners troubled by local electrical interference, a new type of receiving aerial was introduced around this time. It comprised a metal rod of about 12 to 18 feet, which was vertically mounted on a bracket high up on the side of the house or chimney stack. Vertically polarised aerials were least susceptible to picking up induced interference, and the rod-type, being non-directional, could be more easily positioned than other types of outside aerial.

VALVE DEVELOPMENTS

Since the gradual spread of the National Grid Scheme across the country together with the introduction of the mains superhet in 1930, interest in table model battery receivers had shown a slow decline. However, during 1933, there was a marked increase over previous years in the number of new battery table models and portables placed on the market due to the introduction of Class 'B' valves and quiescent push-pull ('QPP') amplification which greatly economised battery current consumption. In QPP, the arrangement of the circuit was much

the same as with push-pull (see 1928), except that two pentodes were used in place of two triodes as this was found to give still greater efficiency. Class 'B' valves developed from the push-pull arrangement and were really two triode valves combined within one glass envelope (two anodes, two grids and two filaments). The special merit of Class 'B' valves was that when used in a suitable battery receiver circuit, a large power output could be obtained without distortion and with only a minimal drain on the HT battery. A typical Class 'B' valve, such as the Cossor 240 B introduced in March, gave an output volume of about twelve times that of an ordinary power output valve, yet the current it drew was less. In consequence Class 'B' amplification became practically universal in new battery receivers during 1933, and by December nearly 400,000 models incorporating this feature had been sold (fig.392).

With the introduction of the Class 'B' valve came the seven-pin 'B7' valve base which was to be used on many new multiple-electrode valves produced around this period: the mains double-diode triode, the mains double-diode pentode, the mains heptode, the battery variable-mu HF pentode (all 1933), the battery QPP double-pentode, the mains triode-hexode and the mains triple-diode-triode (all 1934).

In 1933, the bulbous shaped glass envelope of the valve which had been standard for nearly two decades gave way to a new stepped dome shaped design which effectively divided the valve into two sections and overcame the microphonic tendencies experienced with earlier valves (see 1924). Inside the new envelope, was a rigid electrode support structure consisting of a mica retaining disc of such a size that it created a tight fit with the inner walls of the glass at a point where the dome (or 'shoulder') was formed. This prevented the electrode assembly from vibrating or moving in any direction even if the receiver was shaken, and the special shape of the glass prevented it from ringing.

In May 1933, the release of the world's first metal-enveloped valves was announced, the M-O. 'Catkin' series. An exposed copper anode formed the metal envelope of the valve and this was fused to a lower section of glass and the whole surrounded with a hexagonal perforated cadmium-plated brass screening which also served to prevent accidental contact being made with the otherwise exposed anode. The Catkin valves represented the first complete break with the tradition of glass envelope valve manufacture.

Another unconventional 'valve' released in the same year was the Westector Cold Valve manufactured by the Westinghouse Brake and Saxby Signalling Company. Although listed for many years in Wireless World's valve data charts it was nevertheless a solid-state device and, consisting essentially of copper/cuprous oxide contacts with a diameter of about one thirty-secondth of an inch, bore no relation to the conventional idea of a valve. Two types were made, a half or a full-wave version for use as a detector or rectifier and they required no filament or anode current. They were chiefly employed in some superhet receivers (fig.399) as the second detector, replacing the double-diode, and were about the same size as a grid-leak or metallised resistance. (See Appendix for illustrations of the valves mentioned).

THE LUCERNE PLAN

In May and June 1933, an International Conference of the I.B.U. took place in Lucerne to allocate channels on the medium and long wavebands in European countries in such a way that each might be assured of good reception by listeners in the service areas of each particular broadcasting station. A plan was agreed, and it was decided to introduce the new wavelengths on January 15th 1934 (see 1934). From late summer 1933, many manufacturers began equipping their new receivers with interchangeable tuning dials which, when the changes came into effect, could be substituted at a small cost with a replacement showing the new *Lucerne Plan* wavelengths (figs.413,416). This would prove useful too, for if at any time in the future further wavelength changes occurred the receiver's dial could very easily be brought up to date, and interchangeable dials continued to be generally employed by manufacturers until at least the 1935/6 season (fig.501), and there were even a few isolated examples as late as the early 1950s (fig.732).

There was now an increase in the use of full-vision dials and scales with moving cord-driven cursors, but a dramatic decline in the number of new models employing drum scales. Small escutcheoned window dials (mainly calibrated in metres) and larger horizontal or vertical full-vision scales (calibrated either in station names and metres, or metres only) were fairly evenly mixed. During 1933, large semi-circular full-vision dials appeared for the first time in large numbers (fig.410) and these were mainly calibrated in both station names and metres (fig.425), although there were many in metres only (fig.392) and even a few in 0-100 degrees and metres (fig.423).

For those with receivers calibrated in metres only, station identification continued to be a problem especially as with improved circuits the number of stations able to be tuned-in was increasing all the time. To help solve the problem, *Wireless World* published instructions for building their Station Finder, which was essentially a simple and accurate form of wavemeter complete with a two shilling Ivorine tuning scale showing 88 British and foreign station names thus enabling easy identification.

fig.283. An Ekco Model AC 74 emerging from a soak test at the factory of E.K. Cole Ltd., Southend-on-Sea in 1933. Is that a hand emerging too?

Horizontal rectangular wooden cabinets in open and simple designs became very popular with manufacturers in 1933. The horizontal shape of the cabinet enabled the loud-speaker to be placed to one side, with the chassis at the other, and in many cases a larger loud-speaker could be used since more space was available. The grille often reflected the clean design of the cabinet with simple geometric Art Deco fretwork (figs.418,419) and in an increasing number of cases, manufacturers were supplying simple stands as an optional extra, thus enabling a table model to be easily and quickly converted into a 'pedestal model'.

Extension speakers had now become fashionable as more and more people wanted to have the convenience of being able to listen-in to the wireless in more than one room at a time, and a good percentage of new receivers were now fitted with extension speaker sockets to facilitate this. In loud-speaker design, the composite cobalt and tungsten steel permanent magnet was introduced and at the same time, mass-production methods resulted in the standardisation of all classes of moving-coil loud-speaker, not only of their mechanical design but also of their quality of reproduction.

One curious development in wireless receiver design in 1933

was the introduction by the Multitone Electric Company of their Wireless Set For The Deaf. This comprised a combined receiver and hearing aid and enable the hard-of-hearing either to listen to the broadcasts or to join in the general conversation around them: the sound being greatly amplified through headphones, a miniature earpiece or a bone-conductor.

General interest in crystal sets had lain dormant for several years, indeed out of the many hundreds of receivers on show at the 1933 Radiolympia, there was only one example of a crystal set, and for those who still wanted to buy one over the counter there seemed to be a very great shortage in wireless shops. 'Free Grid', writing in *Wireless World* in August, had himself spent two days tramping the streets of London in a heatwave trying to get hold of one. As he told his readers: "I started off by visiting the lordly emporiums of the West End, and after a vain and perspiring search, I gradually descended in social scale until I found myself in the Caledonian Market. Strange to relate, although I was offered two coherers and an old Marconi Magnetic Detector, I unearthed only one crystal receiver, and this of very ancient vintage. The grasping owner, taking advantage of their scarcity, had the nerve to ask me five guineas for his wretched contraption. I speedily told him where he got off, and departed in high dudgeon."

But in a couple of years, with public awareness of the need for an efficient stand-by or emergency receiver in case of a battery shortage, a mains failure or even a future blackout if war came, interest would once again be revived, especially as with a modern circuit and high power transmitters, crystal sets could be reasonably efficient.

Although the unemployment figures had fallen slightly from their 1931 peak, Britain was still suffering from the economic crisis in 1933, yet the Wireless Industry remained in a relatively stable and profitable position and was able to give employment to well over 75,000 people. The average price of a mains receiver in 1929 was £24 but by 1933 it had fallen to £15 and despite the finacial gloom, over 500,000 new mains receivers were bought between January and December: altogether, nearly a million new wireless receivers of all types were sold during this period which represented a total retail value of about £14,000,000.

Listening to the wireless had become very much a leisuretime activity, and to help listeners enjoy their programmes even more, *Wireless World* published a list of helpful suggestions to prevent even the finest broadcast "falling on inattentive ears or ears which for a variety of reasons, are unable to do justice to what was offered them". There were seven basic rules:

"(1) The room should be of fair size with plenty of rugs, curtains, books etc. and with few unbroken wall spaces. (2) Listeners should sit directly in front of the loud-speaker, usually at a distance of 5 to 10 feet. (3) The receiver should be adjusted to moderate volume; if the announcer's words are intelligible in the far corners of the room the volume is usually about right. (4) Avoid interruptions and discontinuities - once the volume and tuning controls are adjusted they should be left alone during the programme. (Undue meddling with the controls is a common complaint of many domestic 'experts' and is irritating and distracting to the rest of the household). (5) Keep quiet - shut windows on noisy streets etc. and avoid conversation..... (6) The room should be dimly lit.....even dark.....dim illumination undoubtedly helps the listener to create his own imaginative background to the heard broadcast. (7) Choose a comfortable chair and wear comfortable clothes."

The writer thought that some kinds of clothing caused discomfort and would therefore distract from the act of listening-in but he left it up to the listener to decide whether or not to indulge in special 'broadcast wear' for the occasion.

Another piece of advice given to the listener, often by the B.B.C. itself, was to switch the wireless on well before the desired programme began "to let it warm up", since the heaters of some valves could take quite a time to reach their required working temperature: time in some cases, from the initial switching on of the receiver, to go and make a cup of tea before the loud-speaker spluttered into life.

Interest in car radio began to increase although it was still being seen as somewhat of a luxurious novelty as it had been since the 1920s. Despite there being no separate display of car radios at the annual Olympia Motor Show several firms were fitting them into their cars and these included an Ekco superhet in the Austin Sixteen, a Philco in the M.G. Magnette and a Majestic in the Terraplane Big Six and a number of cars had aerials included as standard.

While few people would object to the reception of soothing music while driving, it was rumoured that the Ministry of Transport might prohibit the use of the car radio while the car was actually in motion and there was alarm amongst some car radio manufacturers who thought that the public was unlikely to spend their money on something that might be banned at a future date. There were objections that the driver would take his eyes off the road when tuning-in, for the tuning controls and dial were usually mounted well below eye-level either on the dash or bolted to the steering column. Also, the driver could well be distracted by listening too attentively to a classical concert or to a debate from the Talks Studio, putting himself, pedestrians or other motorists in peril. *Practical Wireless* thought that it might be advisable to prepare special programmes for the motorist consisting of tom-tom music or slow fox-trots as these would require the minimum amount of concentration. All these problems proved to be unfounded and by the end of 1938 the car radio was taking its place as an officially recognised car accessory and was being fitted as standard in many cars.

1934

On January 15th, the *Lucerne Plan* came into operation, marking the last major change in wavelength allocation by the I.B.U. that was to take place in Great Britain before the war. One of the new sets showing the Lucerne wavelengths was the Radio Rentals Model 157 (fig.433) which was the first receiver designed exclusively for them by E.K. Cole Ltd. It was offered upon receipt of a refundable deposit of £1 at the favourable rental of 12s.6d per month during the first year and reducing in steps to 2s.6d after the fifth and subsequent years. The person renting the receiver retained the option to purchase it outright at any time at the price of £13.17s.6d less any monthly instalments that might have already been paid. The scheme also provided for free servicing and replacement of faulty components or even another receiver (damage by ill use excepted), and where Radio Rentals were unable to repair a faulty set efficiently the rentee could buy it for the nominal sum of just 1s.0d.

During January, further demonstrations of the E.M.I. television system, now using the perfected Emitron camera and cathode ray tube receivers, were given and with reports once again extremely favourable it was recognised that Baird's system would probably not be adopted if and when a television service was undertaken by the B.B.C. However, although both Baird and E.M.I. agreed that a 30-line system was now obsolete and that the future development of television lay with much higher definition, the B.B.C. did not immediately abandon the experimental 30-line transmissions when their agreement with Baird expired on March 31st, and the Corporation in fact decided to continue with at least two programmes a week for the benefit of those pioneer viewers with Baird Televisors.

In March, Marconi's joined E.M.I. to form the Marconi-E.M.I. Television Company. This was formidable opposition for Baird, for the new company combined Marconi's long-proven expertise in transmitter and aerial design with E.M.I.'s extensive research experience and comprehensive laboratory facilities at Hayes, manned by a team of scientists under the direction of Isaac Shoenberg. In order to compare the work of Baird and Marconi-E.M.I., and to discuss the relative merits of other systems being developed, including those by A.C. Cossor Ltd. and Scophony Ltd., representatives of the Post Office and the B.B.C. met at St. Martins le Grand on April 5th. They agreed that a Government-appointed Committee should be set up to advise the Post Master General and on June 7th, under the chairmanship of Lord Selsdon, the Selsdon Committee began to consider the rival television systems and the organisation of a public television service.

Towards the end of the year on October 7th, the new high power long-wave transmitter on 1,500 metres opened at Droitwich, superseding Daventry 5XX as the National Programme transmitter. Its greater service area extended to practically the whole country and for those listeners living within its shadow, 'Droitwich swamp filters' were included in the circuits of some new receivers to cut down the overpowering effect of the station. These can readily be identified by an extra aerial input socket, usually marked 'D', on the back of the chassis. Daventry continued to put out the Midland Regional Programme on the medium-wave until February 1935, when its new transmitter at the Droitwich site took over, inaugurating the full twin-wave service (see 1935).

Soon after the *Lucerne Plan* had come into force earlier in January, Radio Luxembourg had seized the 1,304 metre wavelength on the long waveband which had been allotted to Warsaw but had not been taken up. With British listeners, Radio Luxembourg was now one of the most popular commercial broadcasting stations of the I.B.C. network and this situation had been greatly assisted by the various exchange companies who during the 1930s were among its biggest patrons. Already alarmed by the threat from commercial stations, the B.B.C. also feared the growth of wireless-relays and their involvement in the supply of sponsored programmes picked up from the Continent. In October 1931, the B.B.C. had reached an agreement with two of the largest exchange companies, Radio Central Exchanges Ltd. and Standard Relay Services Ltd., for them to relay only B.B.C. programmes. This agreement broke down in the following year since it needed the approval of the Post Office who, although against the idea of Continental stations beaming sponsored advertising programmes into this country, refused in this case to reinforce the B.B.C.'s monopoly. The Post Office argued that listening restrictions on wireless-relay subscribers were not imposed on the private owners of ordinary wireless sets who, while having the same Receiving Licence as the wireless-relay subscribers, were free to listen-in to anything they chose.

By 1934, Radio Luxembourg was already managing to poach many of the B.B.C.'s leading artists. Among those who were to appear on sponsored programmes before the Second World War were George Formby, Tommy Handley, Jack Warner, Vic Oliver, Bebe Daniels, Webster Booth, Charlie Kunz, Tessie O'Shea and Christopher Stone. Christopher Stone had been the B.B.C.'s very first professional 'disc-jockey', and had presented programmes of gramophone record recitals for them since July 1927. When he began regular broadcasts from the Continent however, he found that the B.B.C. had retaliated and had terminated their contract with him. Many of the sponsored programmes of the I.B.C. stations, especially the variety shows, were recorded on disc in front of 'live' studio audiences here in this country. They were taken out to the various stations for transmission since the Post Office had refused to let any of their landlines be used by commercial stations, although as mentioned above, they were perfectly willing to let the exchange companies use their lines to relay these programmes to their subscribers.

fig.284. The Broadcaster and the Listener. The B.B.C.'s Chief Announcer Stuart Hibberd at the microphone on February 22nd 1934. (Photo: B.B.C. Copyright). Hibberd joined the B.B.C. in November 1924 and soon became their Chief Announcer, a post he held until 1949 when he retired after 25 memorable years. His was one of the most famous and best loved voices on vintage B.B.C. radio. He had a dependable, old-fashioned courtesy and his style added dignity to even the most dignified of occasions. At the end of the day his closing announcements, which always ended with a sincere "Goodnight Everybody.... Goodnight", gave the impression that he was speaking personally to those listening-in at home, and this was a great comfort especially to those living alone - the pause, he explained, was designed to give listeners a chance to say "Goodnight" back to him.

During the year, the B.B.C. opened five additional studios at premises in Maida Vale, part of which had once been a skating-rink. This now became the B.B.C.'s largest studio and was named Studio No.1. It measured 110 ft. x 72 ft. and was used to produce many of the B.B.C.'s concerts as it could accommodate the full B.B.C. Symphony Orchestra of 119 players. Studio No.1 replaced Studio No.10 near Waterloo Bridge from which the Orchestra had broadcast on many occasions since their first appearance in October 1930. The opening of the Maida Vale studios helped to alleviate the rather cramped conditions at Broadcasting House which had been somewhat eased in October of the previous year when the 'B.B.C. Theatre' in Langham Place opened and began producing mainly variety programmes.

For listeners who wanted a new receiver in 1934, there was a notable decline in the number of new TRF models, although as a challenge to superhets A.C. Cossor introduced their new range of Super-Ferrodyne TRF receivers. These used highly selective iron-cored Ferrocart coils, which boosted their sales figures so much that they claimed that 1 in 7 receivers bought was a Cossor. But AC superhets greatly increased their lead

in the mains wireless field and even Philips, who had stuck with mains TRFs throughout the early 1930s brought out their first superhet, Model 588A. At Radiolympia, the majority of manufacturers were staging a 4-valve plus rectifier, two-band AC superhet as their principal exhibit and many of these were provided with the additional facility of a variable tone control for the first time. QAVC was beginning to be used more in the circuits of expensive multi-valve receivers, while the more ordinary type of receiver used AVC. There was an increased number of three-band AC receivers and those covering the short waveband only, and AVC systems were widely used here, specially designed to overcome the high-speed fading of distant stations.

AC/DC superhets including midgets from both Britain (fig.438) and America (fig.447) were now more widely available. Although several DC-only models were still being manufactured, they were soon to be phased out, and in 1934 there was a definite tendency for them to be displaced by the AC/DC receiver due to the fear of the purchaser that his DC supply could be changed to AC within a short period, thus rendering his DC receiver useless. As the National Grid Scheme had progressed, manufacturers, while continuing to pander to the seasonal interest in battery portables, had directed less of their attention towards table model battery receivers and although many up-to-date models were being shown at Radiolympia, the Wireless Industry was preparing for the inevitable supremacy of the AC mains superhet.

On new models, horizontally-mounted full-vision tuning scales with cord-driven cursors were now the most popular (fig.444), followed some way behind by semi-circular full-vision dials with pivoted cursors (fig.433) and vertical full-vision scales (fig.440) with only a few of the early type small escutcheoned window dials still in evidence (fig.435). In general, the vast majority of new receivers, whether battery or mains, TRF or superhet, were now calibrated in both station names and metre wavelengths.

One of the most striking new tuning dial designs produced in the 1930s was the 'clock-face', introduced and named first by Ultra Electric Ltd., in their Model 44 and 22 receivers (fig.441) and which was quickly imitated by other manufacturers including Aerodyne, Burgoyne, K.B. and Ormond. As its name suggests, the dial was laid out like a clock-face with the wavelength numerals only circling a centrally pivoted pointer. A pull-out tray housed beneath the cabinet of the set illustrated contained a station-finding chart, detailing the names and their corresponding wavelengths.

Another new type of dial introduced in 1934 was the 'aeroplane' dial, found on several receivers of that year including the K.B. Model 381 (fig.442). Aeroplane dials were round and initially were of modest dimentions with a double-ended pointer pivoted at the centre indicating both station names and wavelengths and would certainly not have looked out of place on a pilot's instrument panel. Soon though, they grew in size and popularity, particularly with the rise of the all-wave superhets from 1935, which, with their dials straining to accommodate station names and wavelengths from three or more wavebands, expanded the definition of the term to indicate any very large round or oval dial (figs.530,555,568).

Completely unconnected with the aeroplane dial, the word 'AIRCRAFT' first appeared opposite the 900 metre calibration on some receivers (fig.417). This wavelength was used for communication between aircraft in flight and the London Airport control tower at Croydon, and tuning into it could provide an interesting diversion from the normal evening's entertainment on the B.B.C.

Several different types of neon visual tuning indicator had become available by the end of 1934 and these were being employed in an increasing number of new receivers. They included Fluid Light Tuning by Marconiphone (fig.440), Neon Lamp Tuning by Cossor and Bush (fig.470), and to a lesser extent, Neon Searchlight Tuning by Hacker. To modern eyes, the layout of the tuning controls of sets and the design of the actual knobs themselves made in the 1930s seems generally straightforward and sensible. However early in 1934, *Wireless World* was conducting a campaign "for more comfortable tuning", since it felt that some manufacturers were neglecting the physical side of tuning a receiver for the artistic side, and often the listener had to be a contortionist to tune the set. However in February, the magazine reported that The Gramophone Company at Hayes had called in anatomical experts to advise their research engineers on the best type and position of the tuning knobs for the new H.M.V. Superhet Four-Forty. Mr Richard Haigh, Manager of the company, confided that they considered the new knobs to be "practically crampless", a statement *Wireless World* was very gratified to hear.

In receiver circuits, several new types of valve base were introduced in 1934 (see Appendix). They were the 9-pin 'B9' base, and the Mullard 'Universal' or 'Continental' side-contact bases: the 8-sided 'P' base and the 5-sided 'V' base. In the winter, a miniature triode known as the Acorn first appeared on the market. Originally developed in America, the Acorn triode was intended for experimental ultra short-wave work (0.5 metres) and was not generally employed in ordinary domestic receivers. It was an 'all-glass' valve with a filament rating of 6.3 volts, only 1 in. high by ¾ in. diameter with no base as such, the electrode pins being set around the periphery of a glass ring.

S.T.C. introduced their comprehensive 'BRIMAR' range of American-type mains valves with either British-type bases or American-type 'UY' 5-pin or 'UX' 4, 6 or 7-pin bases. 'BRIMAR' stood for the BRItish Made American Range and this was introduced for use in imported receivers (fig.447) and receivers made in British-based American factories like Philco. American receivers were growing in popularity and in a few years time there would be 1,500,000 sets with American-type valves in use in Great Britain.

In cabinet design, plain loud-speaker openings completely devoid of a decorative fretwork grille were becoming fashionable in new models (fig.437). Even Pye Radio's famous Art Deco sunrise fretwork symbol used since 1927 was temporarily abandoned in favour of a plain loud-speaker opening in their S/Q and SP/B models. In a complete break with tradition, E.K. Cole brought out the first completely circular receiver, the AD 65, which had been designed by the architect Wells Coates in 1932 (fig.448). It was housed in a moulded Bakelite case and its simple rounded form was echoed by the centrally positioned loud-speaker opening and semi-circular celluloid dial which had some 58 station names marked on it, indicating the huge choice of listening available in 1934.

In fact the number of broadcasting stations in Europe was now over 200, (Newnes' *Wireless Constructor's Encyclopaedia* listed 218), and the British Isles lay within the service area of a very large number of them. While most new receivers showed the names of the British stations and several foreign ones on their dials, there were of course hundreds of thousands of older receivers in use throughout the country calibrated in metres or degrees only, making station identification for many, a matter of guesswork.

This had always been somewhat of a problem and various aids and guides to station identification had been published at various times over the years. But in 1934, John Scott-Taggart produced his definitive guide to European station identification in his *Book Of Practical Radio*, which was based on listening to the intonation of the broadcast voice or the content of the programme. Radio Normandie (Fécamp), frequently transmitted programmes in English while the announcer made "occasional announcements in French to keep the French population happy". The station could be identified by the fact that they "talk a great deal about the I.B.C., stockings, cosmetics, old gold etc.". (Radio Normandie was a commercial station and belonged to the International Broadcasting Company). According to Scott-Taggart, the intonation of the language of various stations was an extremely useful aid to identification. For example, Czechoslovakian stations could be identified by the fact that the language was like "a rather angry man speaking demonstratively with a hot prickly potato in his mouth, and introducing the syllable *vitch* extremely frequently".

Stations usually ended the day's broadcast with their own particular closing message. Barcelona closed down with "*Hasta mañana, si Dios quiere*" ("until tomorrow if God so wills it"). Barcelona obviously did not have much confidence in its own broadcasting arrangements.

1935

There was a change to the wavelengths of several British broadcasting stations in the early part of 1935. On January 6th, Belfast was re-named Northern Ireland and on February 17th changed its wavelength from 267.4 metres to 307.1 metres. On the same day, the Midland Regional transmitter at Daventry closed down and the Midland Regional Programme was now broadcast from its new transmitter at Droitwich inaugurating the full twin-wave service from this station. North National changed its wavelength to that of London National and West National (261.1 metres) and thereafter all three stations appeared on the dial grouped together as 'Nationals': Scottish National continued on its own wavelength of 285.7 metres until 1937 (see 1937). Other wavelength changes were made to Newcastle, Scottish Regional and West Regional.

From January 1st, the National Grid system was in full commercial operation in the greater part of mainland Britain and by now most newly-built houses, especially those in the rapidly growing town suburbs, were wired for AC as a matter of course. The number of new battery models continued to fall and AC mains superhets now completely dominated the market, or as *Wireless World* put it, "reigned supreme!". Among these, all-wave superhets covering short, medium and long-waves were greatly increasing in popularity (although receivers with the short waveband-only drastically declined). AC/DC superhets followed behind but DC-only receivers had all but disappeared with only a handful of new models being produced. TRFs were noticeably few in number and these fell either into the cheapest class or the highly specialised type.

In battery receivers, 'miniature' portable models for headphone use were produced for the first time due to the introduction of Hivac 2-volt midget valves manufactured by the High Vacuum Valve Company of London EC1, and although they were originally intended for hearing-aid use, their introduction meant that truly portable receivers could now be made small enough and light enough to be carried anywhere. Three types of Hivac valve were made; a triode and a screened-grid with a 4-pin base and an output tetrode with a 5-pin base, although they also came in a bayonet fitting with soldered stumps instead of pins and these fitted into their own special valve holder (see Appendix). Among the first receivers to be manufactured using these valves were the All-Wave International Mite (a 3-valve TRF) and the Empiric Pocket Set (a 4-valve TRF based on a circuit employed by the Brighton police force and weighing just 2 lb.). Several circuit designs were published in various wireless magazines for the benefit of home-constructors keen on experimenting with the new valves and one printed in *Wireless World* developed into a factory-built receiver, 'Grid Leak's' Pocketphone of 1937 (fig.559). Some twenty years later, in 1957, the first transistorised 'pocket sets' appeared which worked either with a miniature built-in loud-speaker or with an earpiece (see 1957).

fig.285. A display at the British Industries Fair of Bakelite mouldings from the Bakelite Plant of E.K. Cole Ltd., Southend-on-Sea, 1935. Among the wireless receivers on show are Models SH 25, AC 74, AD 65, AC 85, ADT 95 and AD 36, exhibited in brown, 'walnut' and black (phenol formaldehyde) and in various non-standard colours such as green marble, white, cream, yellow, amber, red, blue and grey (urea formaldehyde), which were supplied with their own carefully matched silk loud-speaker cloths.

Ekco's non-standard coloured cabinets were only available by special order and because comparatively few were made, they are extremely rare today. They were at the time the latest design innovation in the Wireless Industry, and were part of the "colour in the home" campaign generated by the Art Deco movement which had already brought about the introduction of brighter and more colourful designs used in interior decorating and in domestic furnishings generally.

Suitcase battery portables, like Beethoven's Super Minor (fig.479), were still in evidence although having first appeared on the scene some ten years before, their appearance now seemed rather obsolete.

In general, receivers fitted with QAVC circuits for the first time outnumbered those with AVC and on a few new models, noise suppression switches were still in evidence (fig.491).

The use of large, horizontally-mounted full-vision scales calibrated in both station names and in metre wavelengths and using a moving cursor had now become widespread, closely followed by vertically-mounted full-vision scales and aeroplane dials with pivoted pointers. Interchangeable dials and scales still continued to feature on some models (fig.491) and Thermometer Tuning was introduced by Cossor (figs.498,501). A moving metal rod, linked mechanically to the condenser spindle, simulated the mercury column of the familiar thermometer. It rose or fell as the stations were tuned in and stopped opposite the one selected. Another notable tuning idea was Geographical Tuning introduced by Mullard in their Model MU35 (fig.493) where the stations were laid out on the scale in geographical groups rather than in order of wavelength.

A new system of multi-function single-knob control was introduced by the Decca Gramophone Company in their Model 919 (fig.478). The outer collar of the control adjusted the tuning while the inner knob turned to switch the receiver on and off and vary the volume, and by pulling it out, changed the waveband. It was soon imitated by other manufacturers, most notably by Philips and Mullard (see 1936).

In 1935, Aerodyne Radio Ltd. introduced one of the first remote control tuning devices with their Aeromagic superhet. The receiver could be tuned in the ordinary way like any other, but when connected via a cable to its armchair control unit, the listener could change stations without having to get up. Remote control systems raised all sorts of possibilities. For example, it would be possible for a receiver's chassis to be hidden away, mounted, say, in the loft or in the cellar with only the remote control unit and the loud-speaker in the living-room. But the idea never really took hold; remote control remained somewhat of a novelty and was only very rarely used in commercial wireless receivers.

The quality of circuits and loud-speaker reproduction had so much improved that the term 'high-fidelity' was now for the first time being applied to receivers, with H.M.V. introducing their High-Fidelity range at Radiolympia, including Model 441, and G.E.C. their Fidelity range, including Model AC5.

CRYSTAL SETS

One interesting feature of the Radiolympia exhibition, held from August 14th to 24th, was that crystal sets were to be seen on more than one stand indicating that interest in them was once more about to begin as people and manufacturers realised that so long as allowances were made for their limitations, a crystal set could prove very useful in an emergency and when carefully designed and given a decent aerial and earth, would be capable of bringing in a high power Regional station up to 50 miles away, and the high power Droitwich National station up to about 100 miles.

Public interest was clearly demonstrated by a Mr R.C. Stone, who reading in the *Radio Times* that the long-wave station at Droitwich could be heard on a crystal set, decided to find out by building one himself.

"I wrote to the local paper, thinking that one or two people might be interested to come to my house and try the set. Little did I think what the result of that letter would be.

"On the evening it was published, people started coming at 6.15pm and the last caller came at 9.15pm....at one period during the evening I had to give people chairs on my front lawn whilst others were inside listening to the set....but the *class* of caller interested me as there *was* no class. Rich people in their cars, ladies with their companions, music teachers, retired colonels, retired businessmen, ladies with limited incomes living in rooms and in flats, young fellows of the shop assistant type, representatives from wireless shops, representatives of bed-ridden men and women, but with one exception, a boy of 13, no one under about the age of 25. They all wanted the same thing, the National and Regional stations on a crystal set, nothing more.

"I then offered to send any interested party a circuit diagram of the crystal set I'd made and this was announced by the local paper, and for several days demands for the diagram came in by every post, after which I handed all the correspondence to a radio shop in the town to do what they liked with the matter, as almost all those who called on me had asked me to make them a set.

"If I experienced all this through one letter in the Press and in one town, it is obvious that there is a real demand for a good crystal set – the demand I find is sometimes discouraged, as naturally, there is more profit in a valve set. With a suitable wave-trap, one can have Radio Normandie as well as our local station at quite a good strength. A large number of people, I find, cannot get on with the cat's whisker, some cannot see it, others have not the necessary delicacy of touch; an energised crystal would seem to be indicated."

TELEVISION

With television development, the Selsdon Committee's report appeared in January, recommending the setting up of a Television Advisory Committee with Post Office, B.B.C. and Department of Scientific & Industrial Research representatives. It also recommended that the B.B.C. should provide a television service from an experimental station and that such a service should use very high frequency high-definition apparatus of not less that 240-lines from both the Baird and Marconi-E.M.I. companies which would be used alternately for a trial period. By then, Baird had developed a 240-line system at Crystal Palace based on the intermediate film method and while he was also still experimenting with electronic scanning based on the Farnsworth system, he found more success with using mechanical scanners in his transmitters, although he had now entirely gone over to cathode ray tube receivers. Marconi-E.M.I. on the other hand had developed a standard 405-line all-electronic system and compared to this, Baird's apparatus was crude and inferior.

The Television Advisory Committee first met on February 5th and soon the B.B.C.'s first Director of Television (Gerald Cock) was appointed. On June 1st, the B.B.C. acquired the lease for the south-east corner of Alexandra Palace in North London next to the derelict branch terminus of the London & North Eastern Railway, and soon work began on the installation of the new television station. With the planned opening of the high-definition service, the B.B.C. finally closed down the 30-line experimental broadcasts in September.

1936

More changes to the B.B.C.'s transmitter network occurred during 1936. In March, the low power transmitter at Belfast was replaced by a modern high power station at Lisnargarvey, some 9 miles away, which extended the Northern Ireland Regional Programme service to almost the whole of that country. In October, in order to reinforce the B.B.C.'s Scottish Regional Programme service to Scotland, a new additional high power transmitter opened at Burghead transmitting on the same wavelength (391.1 metres) as the Scottish Regional Programme transmitter at Westerglen.

In March, the publication of the Ullswater Committee's report on the future of broadcasting proposed that the B.B.C.'s second Charter (to come into force on January 1st 1937) should remain substantially unaltered and, like the first Charter, should be granted for a period of ten years. With regard to Empire broadcasting, it authorised the B.B.C. to carry on the service "for the benefit of Our dominions beyond the seas and territories under Our protection", and it also entrusted the Corporation with setting up a high-definition Television Service, which began from Alexandra Palace in North London on November 2nd 1936 (see below).

All-wave AC superhets were greatly increasing in numbers and they now became a standard production of the British Wireless Industry. Some began to include the Trawler Band (about 60 to 188 metres) used by fishing vessels to communicate with each other. In October, *Wireless World* listed 177 different all-wave AC mains receivers manufactured by 66 different companies, and of these a mere 32 were TRFs, while the rest were superhets with the exception of a highly unorthodox hybrid TRF/superhet by A.C. Cossor (their all-wave Model 348) which worked as a superhet on short-wave only and a TRF on the medium and the long waveband.

The term 'all-wave' was seen by many in the wireless retail trade as a misnomer, likely to mislead the non-technical public, for receivers so designated merely covered a *part* of the short, medium and long wavebands (typically 15/60, 200/570 and 1,000/2,000 metres) whereas wireless transmissions spanned anything from below 10 metres to above 20,000 metres. In fact, the U.S. Federal Trade Commission had in 1935 prohibited American manufacturers from using the term 'all-wave' in connection with wireless receivers, stipulating that they should be known as 'three-band', 'four-band' etc. But despite protests in the retail trade and in the wireless Press, the label stuck in this country and manufacturers continued to use the term with wild abandon.

Renewed interest in crystal sets had continued during the year and correspondence columns of wireless magazines began to feature regular demands for an efficient set. In February, *Wireless World* had been the first to comply when they published circuit and constructional details of their selective two-band By-Request perikon detector crystal set.

In valve design, Philips' red 'E' series side-contact valves which were of greatly reduced physical size were introduced and were easily identified by their red metallic coating (see Appendix). A new type of cathode ray tuning indicator was introduced for the first time in some British-made receivers. Popularly known as the 'Magic-Eye' (see Appendix), it was more sensitive and accurate than other types of indicator and comprised a miniature cathode ray tube combined with a triode amplifier all contained within its single glass envelope. On its screen, viewed at the end of the bulb through an aperture set into the cabinet, could be seen a cast shadow in the shape of a wide segment. When a signal was being tuned in, the shadow closed up until when fully tuned in the shadow segment became very narrow. It was also known as the Mystic-Eye, Tune-Ray and Tuning Beacon and sometimes had a hood, rather like an eye-lid, to shield the light and make viewing easier (fig.539).

Following Decca's introduction of the multi-function single knob control in 1935 (see 1935), Mono-knob (or Joy-Stick) controls were included on the Philips 795A (fig.543) and the Mullard MAS5 and MUS5, all three having the same basic chassis. The single central knob was moved vertically for adjusting the volume, horizontally for tone and axially for tuning, and the outer chrome collar controlled on/off and waveband switching.

THE B.B.C.'S TELEVISION SERVICE

On the dial, the word 'TELEVISION' began to appear for the first time on some all-wave wireless receivers due to the introduction of the world's first regular high-definition television service from Alexandra Palace in North London. Television sound was radiated on 7.23 metres and this meant that listeners without a television set could at least hear the new programmes provided that their wireless receivers had a suitable short-wave band. The B.B.C. installed both the 240-line Baird system and the 405-line Marconi-E.M.I. system and used them for alternate transmissions. Consequently, television sets manufactured for the first few months from the inauguration of the service were dual standard models and had a switch (usually marked 'BAIRD/EMI') for selecting the appropriate system. Baird's vision transmitter operated on 6.67 metres and employed a spotlight scanner for close-ups and small groups in the studio, intermediate film equipment for televising large scenes within 30 seconds of the scene being filmed, and a Telecine unit for transmitting standard 35mm film. An electron camera based on the Farnsworth system was also used but was not very successful. The Marconi-E.M.I. vision system (also operating on 6.67 metres) produced a 405-line picture and was based on the Emitron electronic camera which could be used indoors or outdoors under ordinary lighting conditions. Television sound was radiated by a 3 kW transmitter manufactured by Marconi's Wireless Telegraph Company who also made the sound and vision aerial systems which were mounted on a 300 ft. mast perched above the Palace.

The service was inaugurated on November 2nd by the Post Master General following a period of twice daily experimental transmissions for the benefit of Radiolympia visitors conducted for the duration of the exhibition from August 26th until September 5th. While received with great interest by members of the public, some wireless manufacturers viewed television with hostility and suspicion, seeing it as the 'Big Bad Wolf' of the Wireless Industry. However, several companies who had traditionally made wireless receivers now began to turn their attention to the new television set market and by the end of the year the very first commercially produced television sets designed for the new service were either in the process of production or had been released by the following companies at prices between 85 and 120 guineas: Bush Radio (who made television sets under the Bush-Baird trade name), A.C. Cossor, E.K. Cole, Ferranti, G.E.C., The Gramophone Company, Halcyon Radio, Marconiphone, Murphy Radio, Philips Lamps, and Pye Radio.

The introduction of the television service unfortunately brought with it a problem of interference. Those viewers settling down to proudly watch their new sets were oblivious to the fact that oscillations, emitted from the line time-base circuits, were being radiated to the immediate surrounding area and potentially were a nuisance to neighbours listening-in to wireless programmes on the medium or long wavebands. These oscillations, although delighting the Post Office in post-war years because they could be very easily picked up by a 'detector van' and used to bag an unlicensed viewer, were very annoying to neighbouring listeners for they came over the loud-speaker as a continuous high-pitched whistle. Over the years, the Post Office received tens of thousands of letters of protest: in a sample year, radiation from television line time-base circuits resulted in 5,697 recorded complaints in the twelve months ending January 15th 1953 (figures from *Practical Wireless*). Metal screening of the line output stage somewhat eased the problem, but even today with current circuit practice and modern semiconductor technology, medium and long-wave listening can still be ruined by line time-base interference, some 50 years after it was first noticed.

The decline in the number of new battery table model wireless receivers continued to reflect the rise in popularity of AC mains receivers. By 1936, over 500,000 homes a year were being changed from DC to AC with the same number of newly built homes being ready supplied with AC. Figures for 1936 published in *The Broadcaster Trade Annual, 1937*, show that out of nearly 8,000 town and district supply undertakings, there were now less than 1,400 supplies of DC electricity. They estimated that there were 11,382,212 homes in mainland Britain, and out of these, 4,784,169 were still unwired, while 5,607,639 had AC and 990,404 had DC. (One would have thought that by today, nearly 60 years after the scheme got under way in 1929, all communities in Britain would have been connected to the National Grid. However, in January 1986, 21 homes on the northern side of the village of Bolventor on Bodmin Moor, Cornwall were still without mains electricity and were still relying on running their own generators, and Bolventor is possibly the last village in Britain yet to be fully connected to the National Grid).

In 1936, in DC districts where the changeover date was uncertain, local wireless retailers took the opportunity of creating some new business and sent out circulars urging people to buy AC/DC receivers: "Now! A DC set may be useless in a week or so: an AC set may be no good for months yet....So you can have a brand new set now and laugh at the electricity supply people's antics!". Although there would still be a good market for AC/DC receivers for many years to come, there were notably fewer models available in 1936, and a mere ten DC-only models were shown at Radiolympia. Also at the show,

woven metal loud-speaker grilles were introduced for the first time on several new receivers (figs. 522, 527) along with 'Expamet', a pierced and expanded metal grille material which became so popular with wireless manufacturers that it was heavily employed for the next twenty years or so (figs. 703, 718).

1937

During 1937, the B.B.C.'s network of transmitting stations was substantially extended. On January 31st, a new medium power transmitter was opened at Penmon on the north eastern tip of Anglesey, North Wales. At first, it put out the West Regional Programme for the benefit of listeners in North Wales, using the same wavelength as the West of England Regional transmitter at Washford Cross (373.1 metres). From July 4th, both these transmitters radiated the new Welsh Regional Programme, and the other transmitter at Washford Cross, which until then had been sending out the West National Programme, began transmitting West Regional on 285.5 metres. The Scottish National transmitter, which had previously occupied this wavelength, now shared the common wavelength of 261.1 metres with the London and North National transmitters, and from this date, these three stations appeared on the dial grouped together as 'Nationals'.

On October 19th, a new high power transmitter at Stagshaw in Northumberland opened, giving a much improved North Regional Programme service to listeners in Cumberland and Westmorland (today absorbed into Cumbria), Durham and Northumberland. Its inauguration caused the closure on the same day of Newcastle, the last of the original main B.B.C. transmitting stations.

Traditionally, the beginning of the 'wireless season' was marked by the Radiolympia exhibition where new lines in receivers and accessories would be shown to the public and trade for the first time. The season would usually end soon after Christmas whereupon there was a dearth of new models until the following autumn. But in 1937, the policy of releasing all new models solely around the time of the Radiolympia exhibition went through a change as some manufacturers started to aim for year-round production. This was revealed by the fact that in the months from January to April 1937, over one hundred and twenty new receiver models were brought onto the market which meant that employment in the Wireless Industry became less of a seasonal affair (see also 1926) and stability within the workforce was retained.

But Radiolympia still continued to be the focal point of the wireless calendar. At the 1937 exhibition, all-wave AC superhets with two or more short-wave bands led the field and had become firmly established as the mainstay of the Wireless Industry, while TRFs were very much overshadowed. *Wireless World* reported: "When the 1937 Radiolympia comes to be summed up in a word or two in future lists of historical dates, it will probably be known as the show at which the All-Wave Superhet first became really popular". These receivers offered entertainment on a global scale and since the average person could never hope to afford a holiday abroad, by being able to tune to stations around the world he was able to capture at least a flavour of a foreign country. Manufacturers promised just about everything with the 'Modern Magic Carpet', the all-wave superhet: "You can listen to liners talking to the shore; you can hear amateurs speaking to Australia, and aerodromes instructing aeroplanes. Trawlers in the North Sea will reveal their secrets to you. Then, in a flash, you can skip round the globe, listening to broadcast programmes from such romantic-sounding places as Klipkeuval, Bankok, Tokio, San Domingo, La Paz."

One of the carrots dangled in front of a prospective customer coming into the wireless shop with the thought of buying a brand new modern receiver, was to offer him part-exchange terms on his old model. This had now been a common practice for a couple of years and in fact it was first tried out in about 1926 (see 1926). But there was a great diversity of opinion as to the part-exchange value of each particular obsolete model, and so in April 1937, the National Association of Radio Retailers published what they considered was a fair allowance price guide in the hope that retailers would adopt the values recommended. The figures, on average about 8 to 10 per cent of the original price, represented the maximum which it was considered a retailer could afford to allow so that a second hand receiver could be overhauled and sold at a reasonable margin to cover overheads and profit.

While the subject of remote control was largely ignored by manufacturers, it continued to be a recurring topic of discussion within the wireless Press and was of great interest to the home-constructor. Two basic types were being experimented with. The more favoured system employed a remotely controlled electric motor which was used to drive the tuning condenser. In fact, a year later, motor-driven tuning, (not remotely controlled, but operated by push-buttons on the receiver), was incorporated by several manufacturers on their more expensive receivers (see 1938). The other system involved fitting the tuning condenser itself into the remote control unit, but in either case, a trailing wire had to be contended with and this was not to everybody's liking (see also 1956).

In the spring of 1937, the M-O. Valve Company introduced their G-type 'International octal' range of 8-pin valves, so named because their particular base configuration and their working characteristics were already a standard internationally, both on the Continent and in America. G-type octals were originally developed in the United States by Sylvania in 1935 and most International octals adopted their 6.3v, 0.3A heater rating and followed closely their physical design: they had the same self-locating base and being generally interchangeable with American-made equivalents, were therefore also known as 'American' octals. The pins, varying in number from 5 to the full set of 8 depending on the valve type, were arranged in a circle around a central keyed spigot which fitted easily into a key-way in the socket. This not only provided positive location, but also helped identify the pin numbers. Other British valve manufacturers, including S.T.C. (Brimar) who were already heavily committed to the production of American-type valves, soon followed the M-O. Valve Company's lead and from 1937, G-type International octals were widely employed in receiver circuits until they were superseded just after the Second World War by the GT-type (see 1946).

In 1937, tuning dials were larger, clearer and easier to read than before, some were as large as 14 in. wide, and many more magic-eye tuning indicators were in evidence. Murphy Radio Ltd. introduced 'alphabetical' tuning (fig.566) in which the list of stations was printed in alphabetical order on a stationary glass scale while a drum with various markings revolved behind it as the receiver was tuned. G.E.C. showed off their Chromoscopic Scale (fig.585): "light from an unseen source penetrates the interior of the glass scale so that individual station names stand out, edge-illuminated, making a vivid coloured contrast on the black background, while wavebands are indicated by distinctive colours".

TELEVISION AND RADAR

In February, following a decision taken by the Television Advisory Committee, Baird's 240-line system of television transmission from Alexandra Palace was dropped and the Marconi-E.M.I. 405-line system was adopted by the B.B.C. as standard. The dual-standard switches on new television sets now entirely disappeared. Television was no longer regarded with suspicion by most members of the Wireless Industry and with several old-established wireless manufacturers now going into serious production, the foundations of a modern television manufacturing industry were laid. Although television sales were at first slow to get off the mark with under 400 sold at the beginning of the year, by December, 2,000 television sets had been installed in homes in and around London, and with interest growing all the time, (this was especially noticeable at the 1937 Radiolympia exhibition) wireless receivers with a short waveband now invariably included the television sound wavelength on their dials.

The foundation of a television industry also hid a more serious side. In 1935, Robert Watson-Watt had demonstrated to the Air Ministry how radio-waves could be used to detect flying aircraft and this led, in 1937, to contracts being placed by the Government for the secret production of a chain of 'radiolocation' (radar) stations. Initially, the transmitters were made by Metro-Vick and the receivers by A.C. Cossor with both companies, save one representative from each, working without the knowledge of the other's role. The manufacture of radar screens involved the production of cathode ray tubes, and at Cossor's in 1937 the additional numbers needed were able to be hidden amongst those made for television without inviting attention.

MARCONI

On July 20th, the death had been announced of Guglielmo Marconi and on the following day a two-minutes' silence was observed on all transmitters of the B.B.C. A tribute was broadcast by Professor E.V. Appleton, who said: "For over forty years Marconi has worked as a radio experimenter, with unflagging energy and enthusiasm. He has never been content to rest. For with him we were always at the beginning of things.... If difficulties seemed to be ahead he tackled them with the zeal of a young experimenter beginning his first research. He was like this to the end.... Great as his scientific and technical achievements have been, the man has been as great as his work."

1938

In January, Mazda produced their first range of 'British Octal' valves (see Appendix). Their base design was very close to that of the International octal introduced the year before, but the British Octal's heater pins were set slightly further apart to avoid confusion. The central keyed spigot was also slightly larger and since it accommodated the exhaust tube, smaller valves could be designed with shorter internal leads. Made until well into the 1950s, British Octals were exclusive to Mazda and were not interchangeable with conventional International-type octals. The call for valve standardization had been heard for some years and with the introduction of the British Octal, many writers in the wireless Press believed that it was just another example of "valve lunacy", adding to the 1,000 or so different types of mains and battery valves already available to the "confused public".

Another new type of valve introduced in 1938 was the 'Loctal' (see Appendix). Similar to octals, the loctal base formed part of the glass envelope with the pins formed out of the wires leading through the glass. A metal shield fitted over the base and bore a central metal spigot. This had a bulbous end which acted as a locking device, and firmly held the valve in its socket. The metal shield and centre spigot were earthed and the grid and the anode pins were diagonally opposite each other with the spigot acting as a shield between them.

PUSH-BUTTON TUNING

Even though it was only available in the London area, television continued to attract wide interest at the 1938 Radiolympia exhibition (August 24th to September 3rd), although there was much criticism that the 'standard' 8 in. x 10 in. picture size, aimed at reducing the price, was too small. In wireless design, the outstanding new feature of many of the models on show was push-button and automatic selective tuning, and this even included a few receivers with no dials at all, just a row of buttons for selecting the desired programme (e.g. the Bush Model PB50, All-Button Receiver, fig.595).

Three main methods were used: (1) Mechanical rotation of the main tuning condenser. This was employed in the Cossor Teledial Model 397 in which ten settings were provided by a telephone-type dial giving a choice of eleven stations, since Radio Luxembourg on long-wave and London Regional on medium-wave were arranged to coincide. The settings of these two stations, along with Droitwich and the Nationals were adjusted at the Cossor works and the remaining settings were left to the dealer or his customer to choose. To select the desired station, the listener merely 'dialled' the appropriate setting. (2) Electro-mechanical rotation of the main tuning condenser. A small motor controlled the movement of the tuning condenser and was activated by pressing the appropriate pre-set station button. 'Motor-cruising' was also employed whereby the pointer could be swept around the dial in either direction by the press of a button, stopping at the desired station when the button was released. (3) Separate pre-tuning. Simply, a set of pre-tuned circuits (each tuned to its own particular station) and each switched in by pushing a button.

There were a few technical problems with some of the push-button mechanisms, particularly on some of the cheaper sets, but in general they were well liked by the public and soon became *the* type of set to buy. Push-button tuning had already found its way into car radios to which it was ideally suited for it obviated the need for the driver to take his eyes off the road while selecting a station. Several new car radios incorporating this facility were shown at the Earls Court Motor Show and for the first time, the car radio took its place as an officially recognised motoring accessory.

WAR PREPARATIONS

Despite efforts at securing peace, preparations continued for war. At the beginning of September, the Air Ministry announced its decision to form a Civilian Wireless Reserve consisting largely of amateur experimenters, who would, if the need arose, provide a reserve of personnel experienced in the operating procedure of the R.A.F. Behind the scenes, a new VHF system of fighter control was being rapidly developed and during the year, three hundred pieces of equipment for use in aircraft were hand-made by G.E.C.

At the end of September, Prime Minister Chamberlain signed the Munich Agreement with Hitler which was "symbolic of the desire of our two peoples never to go to war with one another again". The B.B.C. covered Chamberlain's arrival back at Heston Aerodrome, and while many listeners were relieved to hear him proclaiming that it was "peace for our time", others correctly foresaw that Britain was heading for war.

For most of the decade, the B.B.C. and the Post Office had been protesting against European commercial stations and against Radio Luxembourg in particular. Earlier in the year, at the World Telecommunications Conference held in Cairo, the Post Office had sought to have a resolution adopted in which "no wave....may be used by a country in this (European) region for transmissions in the nature of commercial publicity sent in any other language but the national language or languages of that country". The resolution was defeated, Britain being supported by only eight European delegations out of twenty-seven, indicating that attitudes to commercial broadcasting stations were changing. In fact, with Europe's 'ether' beginning to be dominated by Nazi propaganda, the British Government thought that it might be better to make use of Radio Luxembourg's powerful transmitter rather than

seek to destroy it. In a change of direction, prompted by a specific request from the Prime Minister and the Foreign Office, the B.B.C. actually helped Radio Luxembourg by providing it with special recordings of Chamberlain's speech following the Munich meeting and in the months before the war gave further help on a few more politically important occasions. This, however, did not divert Radio Luxembourg from its role as a popular commercial station and it continued defiantly on the air until September 21st 1939 when its own Government forced it to close down.

1939

In February, there began a general distribution of two million corrugated steel Anderson air-raid shelters which were soon to become a familiar sight in the back gardens of houses up and down the country, while provision for gas attack was made with the production of 38,000,000 gas masks complete with carrying cases. On March 15th, German forces had invaded and occupied the whole of Czechoslovakia and in July, the *Civil Defence Act* completed initial preparations for protecting the British population during total war.

During the spring, developments in the domestic Wireless Industry had continued optimistically despite the shadow of grave international events. Following the introduction of the Red 'E' series of side-contact valves in 1936, Mullard were the first British firm to introduce the Red E30 series, similar to the 'E' series but with International octal bases (see Appendix). Mullard also introduced their first series of 'all-glass' valves which included the EC52 for short-wave work, and the EF50, a metallised valve originally intended for use in television circuits. Unfortunately, the outbreak of war called a halt to this, but they were nevertheless put to good use in radar receivers. The EF50 had a 9-pin base which was made out of machine-pressed glass into which the pins were set. It was designed on the bayonet-lock principle, the pin ends being L-shaped and by applying a slight pressure followed by a twist, the valve could be firmly locked into its socket and only a twist in the opposite direction could release it. A central locating metal spigot ensured correct insertion into the base. Within a very short time however, the metallising of the glass bulb was replaced by a separate metal jacket, and the L-shaped pins were dropped in favour of more conventional straight pins due to the inherent danger of the glass cracking around the pins (see Appendix).

Towards the summer, seasonal interest in outdoor battery portables was shown once more and *The Wireless & Electrical Trader* thought that air-raid shelter owners would certainly make the best prospects for sales. It published a list of other 'portable prospects' as a helpful guide to retailers and this included A.R.P. officials, boat and yacht owners, businessmen, camping enthusiasts, commercial travellers, elderly ladies, farmers, flat dwellers, hotel guests, households without electricity, invalids and nurses, nursing homes, wealthy folk who could use several receivers, and week-enders with seaside cottages or country bungalows.

The new season's sets on show at Radiolympia had been well received when it opened on August 23rd, and the Wireless Industry was looking forward as usual to an expected autumn sales boom. Television exhibits continued to hold the public's interest and the design tendency now was towards the use of bigger tubes and therefore bigger screens. In wireless circuits, developments were thought to have reached a state of near perfection, especially with regard to the quality of sound reproduction and it was difficult to see where improvements could occur next. Push-button receivers were once again shown in great numbers and the teething troubles of some of the pre-set mechanisms shown at last year's exhibition had now been ironed out and greatly improved. New all-dry battery portables provided one of the most practical technical developments. 1.4 volt all-dry valves had been introduced whose LT current was derived from a dry cell, thus dispensing with an accumulator and the need for recharging. In some cases, the LT cell was combined into a single unit with the HT battery.

A new plan for the allocation of broadcast wavelengths, the *Montreux Plan*, was due to come into force on March 4th 1940, and this created something of a problem as manufacturers had to decide whether or not to fit their new season's receivers with Montreux-calibrated dials. But it was decided by the R.M.A. that this would not be done until after January 1st 1940 and until then, the old type of dial markings would continue to be fitted. In the event, with the outbreak of war, the Plan was abandoned.

One new feature of the 1939 Radiolympia was the emphasis on the export market, an area which *Wireless World* thought had long been neglected. It said that it was more often the case that *British* broadcasting was being received in *British* Dominions and Crown Colonies through the intermediary of *foreign* sets - a "disgraceful situation" - but it was gratified to record that this year a considerable number of manufacturers had gone to the trouble of producing 'overseas models'.

THE B.B.C.'s HOME SERVICE

On Friday September 1st, Germany invaded Poland and in Britain black-out regulations were enforced and civilian evacuation plans got under way. The worsening world political crisis brought Radiolympia to a premature close at mid-day, while at Alexandra Palace, the infant high-definition 405-line television service was abruptly suspended. On the same day, the B.B.C. made lightning changes to its wavelength and service structure and at 8.15 in the evening, a single national programme was introduced on the medium waveband. It was called the Home Service, and it replaced the Regional Scheme on medium waves and Droitwich on long waves, with the various transmitters being divided into two geographical groups; those in the North on 391.1 metres (the old Scottish Regional wavelength) and those in the South on 449.1 metres (the old North Regional wavelength). The old long-wave transmitter at Daventry which had been taken out of service in 1934 was converted for operation on the 391.1 metre wavelength, but reverted back to the long waveband two years later when it was used by the European Service (see below).

The synchronization of the B.B.C.'s transmitters was designed to prevent enemy aircraft from using them as navigation beacons. If such aircraft came within a range of about 25 miles, that particular transmitter would close down but listeners would still continue to hear the programme, albeit with a weaker signal, from one of the other transmitters on the same wavelength. (Droitwich was forced to close because it was then the B.B.C.'s only long-wave transmitting station in service and synchronization was therefore impossible. However, it was soon converted for medium-wave operation with an increased power output and on October 7th 1939, joined the Brookman's Park, Moorside Edge and Westerglen transmitters which were by then putting out European Service broadcasts after the hours of darkness on a synchronized wavelength of 261.1 metres. In November 1941, Droitwich was converted back to long-waves and along with other long-wave transmitters at Brookmans Park and Daventry, it carried out synchronized transmissions to Europe for the B.B.C.'s European Service until in February 1943. During this month a very high power station, designed to radiate up to four programmes simultaneously on long and medium wavelengths and with a maximum power of 800 kilowatts, was inaugurated at Ottringham near Hull).

Following the introduction of the Home Service on September 1st 1939, there was immediate chaos as many listeners

had missed the B.B.C.'s technical announcements of the wavelength changes. Many of those who were unaware of them had jumped to the conclusion that their receivers had suddenly developed faults, and for days dealers in several areas were inundated with service calls. One genuine problem encountered with the introduction of the Home Service was with the popular push-button only receivers since many were not pre-set to the two wavelengths being used, although those pre-set to Scottish Regional and North Regional were of course unaffected.

Almost as soon as the Home Service was inaugurated, listeners in several areas of the country began complaining that they were experiencing very poor reception on the two wavelengths used. However, no improvements were forthcoming until December when the B.B.C. advised them to re-tune to the Home Service on 342.1 metres after 6pm to see if reception was any better. This wavelength was that of the old London Regional Programme and from December 19th it was used for experimental reception tests for the proposed Forces Programme (see 1940).

THE SECOND WORLD WAR

Two days after the invasion of Poland, at 11.15am on Sunday September 3rd, millions of listeners heard Prime Minister Chamberlain's grave announcement that a state of war existed between this country and Germany. Within months, the production of domestic wireless receivers and components would be seriously curtailed as one by one, manufacturers were compelled to re-tool and concentrate on the production of communications equipment for the Armed Forces.

There would not be a single firm, large or small, with wireless manufacturing experience that would not produce for the war effort, while hundreds of other firms, normally engaged in other industries, turned their factories over to the manufacture of Military communications equipment. As a result, the wartime Wireless Industry eventually grew to five times its pre-war size. Entire cotton mills, stocking, perfume and patent medicine factories turned over to valve production while makers of toys, artificial flowers, church organs and stained glass, made receivers and accessories. The call-up of men and women for the Armed Forces increased as the conflict wore on, and demands were to grow for civilian workers, especially female labour, in all industrial areas of Britain. In December 1941, war work for unmarried women aged between 19 and 30 became compulsory, although for married women it remained voluntary. Within a few years, in congested and highly industrialised centres where all the available labour was absorbed and demands for additional labour were unsatisfied, 'outworking' was found to be a suitable expedient. The scheme involved the establishment of auxiliary factories in outlying areas perhaps miles away from the mother factory, using vacant buildings, village halls and even people's front rooms to set up make-shift production lines. To man them, the Ministry of Production recruited a workforce of women (usually housewives) from the local community who on the whole were only too pleased to have a part in the war especially as most had husbands away fighting in the Forces. Even the country houses of the rich became involved in this scheme, and, as one example of the tremendous contribution outworking made to the war effort, in a small building in the grounds of Queen Mary's wartime home at Badminton, over 665,000 Westinghouse rectifiers were assembled by a few dozen outworkers during the war.

As well as the stress on production, the war gave a new impetus to electronics research and for the first time ideas could be shared freely between scientists, the Military and the Wireless Industry on which, Government spending rose from £5,000,000 to £24,000,000 a year. Such were the rapid advances that by the end of the war, a parallel Electronics Industry had become firmly established.

The term 'electronics' encompassed the employment of thermionic valve circuits (and much later, semi-conductor technology with transistors and integrated circuits) in non radio-communications areas, the greatest wartime application of which was to be in radar. In 1939, electronics was a relatively new and still small subsidiary of the domestic Wireless Industry. But even by then, electronic engineering, particularly with regard to electronically controlled machinery in factories, had already come to the attention of the man-in-the-street, so much so that in October of that year, *Television And Short-wave Review* felt it necessary to change its title to *Electronic And Television & Short-wave Review* to encompass the modern expanded use of valve circuits. Whereas before, the magazine always concentrated on television and short-wave reception, its first three wartime issues also dealt with electronic apparatus for measuring brain activity (October), high-frequency heating and photo-electric incendiary bomb detectors (November) and burglar alarms, lift and automatic door controls, height gauges and automatically controlled machinery (December).

While Chamberlain was broadcasting his historic declaration, the British Expeditionary Force began to leave for France and the carefully planned evacuation of over one and a half million children, mothers and teachers away from 'danger areas' which had begun on September 1st, was now practically complete. During the first weeks following the outbreak of war, the public's demand for receivers became unprecedented and shelves and storerooms of wireless shops around the country soon began to empty as panic buying set in. Manufacturers cleared out storerooms of old and forgotten stock. C.F. & H. Burton Ltd., of Walsall still had 500 new/boxed Empire Two battery receivers that they had originally made in 1930 (fig.294) and these were all sold within an hour and a half of being put out on display in a local wireless retailer's shop window. There was a spectacular rush for battery portables for use as stand-by receivers in case of a mains failure or for use in air-raid shelters to help while away the time. The newly introduced all-dry battery portables established themselves overnight and were soon being turned out by manufacturers as fast as they could. Batteries of all types, (as well as small home battery-charging units) were in heavy demand especially in rural districts where 50 per cent of houses were still without electricity, compared with only 26 per cent in urban areas. There was also a rush for the smaller type of mains receiver for use in case the 'house' set developed a fault. The King and Queen, according to *The Wireless & Electrical Trader*, set "a good example" by immediately purchasing additional receivers for the royal household: "Pilot receivers from Harrods, Ltd."

While it was not illegal to own and use an ordinary wireless receiver, the *Emergency Powers (Defence) Act, 1939*, controlled the possession, use and sale of transmitting apparatus and other specified equipment including some short-wave coils and valves capable of an anode dissipation exceeding 10 watts. Permits would now be necessary for the purchase of these valves or receivers containing them, and much paperwork was generated trying to extricate valves like replacement PX4 power triodes, required, for example, for many H.M.V. and Marconiphone receivers of this period.

Since the B.B.C.'s television service had closed down, the wireless set had began to play an even more indispensable role as a provider of morale boosting entertainment and, more importantly, as a purveyor of news. On the B.B.C., *The News*, normally the 9pm bulletin, quickly became an institution in most households, almost as sacrosanct as family prayers had once been in Victorian times. News from the B.B.C. was heavily supplemented by regular news broadcasts in English from over 60 foreign short-wave stations, and by December, domestic wireless manufacturers were beginning to dispense with the long waveband and concentrate on the production of two-band, short and medium-wave receivers to satisfy the increasingly 'short-wave conscious' public.

Interest in long-wave reception was minimal. Since the outbreak of the war, there had been no long-wave broadcasting in this country and only five long-wave stations abroad were providing programmes in English. In Luxembourg, the commercial long-wave radio station had been closed down on September 21st at the insistence of its Government in the interest of the country's neutrality. The only surviving pre-war commercial station was Radio Normandie (Fécamp) which continued to operate for a few more months on 212 metres, producing programmes specially for the British Expeditionary Force which was now stationed in France. But early in the new year, it was closed down on the orders of the French Command on grounds of security: its wavelength was not synchronised and there was speculation about the nature of some of its broadcasts in German. (It was following the closure of this station, that the B.B.C. had the good fortune to attract one of Radio's legendary figures, Roy Plomley. Plomley had been with Radio Normandie since 1936 and after joining the B.B.C. in 1940 thought up what was to turn out to be one of the Corporation's most popular and longest running radio programmes, *Desert Island Discs*, which Plomley was to present for more than 40 years until his death in 1985).

The B.B.C. also sent out programmes in German, and this was just one in a growing number of its foreign language services. These had begun on January 3rd 1938 with the inauguration of the Arabic Service to the Middle East and this had been followed on March 14th by the Latin-American Service in Spanish and in Portuguese. Later on in that year, on September 27th, services to European countries began with the start of the French, German and Italian Services and by the end of 1939, a European Service with eleven foreign language programmes had become fully established. By then, the short-wave Empire Service had increased its output of programmes in English to British Dominion and Colonial audiences and with the addition of foreign language programmes to countries outside Europe, had grown into the Overseas Service.

German radio too was putting out programmes in English and a great many listeners in Britain were becoming interested in the broadcasts of an American-born fascist, William Joyce, whose opening words to each programme, "Germany calling, Germany calling, Germany calling", delivered in his idiosyncratic accent soon became a popular catchphrase. Joyce, a self-declared British subject of Anglo-Irish parentage, was hired by Walter Kamm, head of the German Overseas Service, to broadcast socially subversive propaganda to listeners in Britain, much to the annoyance of this country's Ministry of Information. He had joined Reichs-Rundfunk on September 11th 1939, and soon after started broadcasting from the Hamburg and Bremen stations on the medium waveband. Because of the peculiar way he spoke, he became known to listeners in Britain as 'Lord Haw Haw', a nickname given to him by Jonah Barrington, the radio critic of the *Daily Express*. With almost any set in Britain able to pick him up, he gathered quite an audience intrigued with the novelty of tuning into the enemy, and for many, listening to him on the wireless during the black-out added a little colour to what was to be for several months an otherwise fairly dull war. But by the summer of 1940, this 'phoney war' had come to an abrupt end, and with the evacuation of the British Expeditionary Force from Dunkirk and the fall of France in June, the start of the Battle of Britain in August and the Blitz in September 1940, people increasingly began to ask whether it was right to invite a traitor into one's home every night, and soon Lord Haw-Haw's audience rapidly dwindled.

fig.286. Burndept 'De Luxe Model 1851', by Burndept Wireless (1928) Ltd. 1930. 3-v +R, AC TRF, MW/LW 0-100 deg, drum scales, edgewise tuning controls, cone loud-speaker, Bakelite knobs and control panel in woodgrain finish, mahogany cabinet. 39 in. x 23 in. x 10 in. (Model 1850 is oak cabinet version).

fig.287. Gecophone 'All Electric Three Valve Receiver' Model BC 3130, by General Electric Co. Ltd. 1930. 3-v +R, AC TRF, MW/LW 0-100 deg, no integral loud-speaker, steel chassis, gilded metal escutcheon, black and gold sprayed wood cabinet with lift-up lid housing the instructions. 10 ½ in. x 16 in. x 10 in. £18.0s.0d. (Available on hire purchase: £1.16s.0d deposit followed by 12 monthly payments of £1.8s.4d).

fig.288. Ultra Model DC3, by Ultra Electric Ltd. 1930. 3-v DC-only TRF, MW/LW 0-180 deg, no integral loud-speaker, copper front panel, solid mahogany cabinet. 8 ½ in. x 14 in. x 10 in. (Also AC version).

fig.289. Adey 'Cigar Box Portable', by Adey Radio Co. Ltd. 1930. 1-v Batt Portable, for headphone use, MW only, variable tuning condenser marked 0-7, gramophone pick-up socket, frame aerial wound around body, built into a 'genuine' wooden cigar box edged with decorative paper border and branded with the words 'dial', 'earth', 'phones' etc. 8 in. x 4 ½ in. x 2 ½ in. £2.15s.0d inc valve and batteries. Headphones, price 12s.6d extra. A 3-function jack-plug 'key' (on the top, to the right of the tuning knob) provided (1) on/off by inserting/extracting the key, (2) fine tuning by turning the key on its axis, and (3) variable reaction (volume) control by means of a multi-positioned switch. A similar receiver was developed for Police work in conjunction with a loud-speaker fitted into a Policeman's helmet.

fig.290. Gecophone 'Osram 4 Music Magnet', by General Electric Co. Ltd. 1930. 4-v Batt Kit, MW/LW Mtrs/0-100 deg, drum-drive scale, no integral loud-speaker, aluminium screening cans, brown painted aluminium front panel, oak cabinet with lift-up lid. 8 ½ in. x 17 ½ in. x 11 ½ in. (The 'Music Magnet' first appeared in the winter of 1928 with two slow motion dials mounted on the front panel).

fig.291. Marconiphone Type 220, by Marconiphone Co. Ltd. 1930. 2-v +R, AC TRF, MW/LW 0-100 deg, drum scale, edgewise tuning control, no integral loud-speaker, solid oak cabinet. 5 ½ in. x 14 in. x 11 in.

fig.292. Ferranti Model 32, by Ferranti Ltd. 1930. 3-v +R, AC TRF Table Model, MW/LW Mtrs, brown rexine-covered metal cabinet. 20 in. x 12 ½ in. x 9 in. Medium waveband marked 'Short'. (Also console and wood cabinet versions in 1931, see figs.340 and 343).

fig.293. Cossor 'Silvertone', by A.C. Cossor Ltd. 1930. 2-v Batt, MW/LW 0-180 deg, cone loud-speaker, oak cabinet. 12 ½ in. x 12 ½ in. x 6 in. Given away as a 'free gift' with cigarette coupons. It was also marketed in 1930 as the 'Servis Junior', by Harris, Williams (Manufacturers) Ltd., Barbican, London EC1, which was identical to the 'Silvertone' except for the loud-speaker fret which had a cut out petal design with the word 'SERVIS' running through it.

fig.294. Burton 'Empire Two' by C.F. & H. Burton Ltd. 1930. 2-v Batt, MW/LW 0-100 deg, edgewise tuning control, no integral loud-speaker, walnut Bakelite cabinet. 6 ½ in. x 9 ¾ in. x 4 ¾ in. £2.17s.6d (valves extra).

fig.295. Pye 'Twin-Triple Portable' Type B4D by Pye Radio Ltd.1930. 4-v Batt Portable, MW/LW Mtrs, drum-drive scale, cone loud-speaker, internal frame aerial, turntable, carrying strap, solid walnut cabinet. 18 in. x 15 in. x 9 in. £23.2s.0d. (Also Type DC4D, DC version, and Type AC4D, AC transportable version, see fig.305).

fig.296. McMichael 'Mains Three', by L. McMichael Ltd. 1930. 3-v +MetR, AC TRF, MW/LW Mtrs, illuminated full-vision tuning scale, cord-driven cursor, no integral loud-speaker, walnut cabinet. 15 in. x 13 in. x 9 ½ in. £21.0s.0d. This was the first mains receiver to employ a cord-driven cursor to indicate scale readings. (Also battery version, 'Battery 3', price £14.14s.0d).

fig.297. Amplion 'Two Valve All-Mains', by Graham Amplion Ltd. 1930. 2-v +MetR, AC TRF, MW/LW 0-100 deg, edgewise tuning control, drum scale, no integral loud-speaker, solid and veneered walnut cabinet. 8 in. x 18 in. x 10 ½ in. An "up-to-the-minute set for Regional conditions". Medium waveband is marked 'Short'.

fig.298. K.B. 'Masterpiece', by Kolster-Brandes Ltd. 1930. 2-v Batt TRF (French-made 'Fotos' valves), MW/LW 0-100 deg, cone loud-speaker, 'walnut' Bakelite case. 7 ¼ in. x 7 ¼ in. x 7 ¼ in. (closed). The entire production run of these receivers was secured by the cigarette manufacturers Godfrey Phillips Ltd. of Commercial Street, London E1, who gave them away as a 'free gift' in return for 500 coupons from their BVD cigarettes - ('BDV' stood for Best Dark Virginia). One coupon was included in every 6d packet of ten cigarettes and so it was necessary to buy some 500 packets (total outlay £12.10s.0d) in order to have enough coupons. A 3-valve K.B. receiver in a wooden cabinet, also called the 'Masterpiece', was given away by Godfrey Phillips Ltd. in 1931 (see fig.346).

fig.299. Lumophon Model AC3, by British Lumophon Ltd. 1930. 3-v +R, AC TRF, MW/LW 0-100 deg, disc-drive dial marked 'Short' and 'Long', wood control panel, metal cabinet in walnut painted finish. 8 ¼ in. x 15 ¼ in. x 7 ½ in. £12.12s.0d inc valves and royalties. (Also DC version).

fig.300. Umello 'Five Valve Receiver', by Umello Ltd. 1930. 5-v Batt, MW/LW 0-100 deg, drum scales (one for each waveband), edgewise mounted controls, cone loud-speaker, veneered and solid walnut cabinet. 14 ½ in. x 14 ¾ in. x 8 ¼ in.

fig.301. Columbia 'Twin Station Receiver' Model 309 0C, by Columbia Graphophone Co. Ltd. 1930. 2-v + MetR, AC TRF Table Model with GB Battery, pre-set tuning only, plug-in coils, oak cabinet. 15 in. x 14 in. x 8 in. £12.12s.0d. Designed for local reception of the London National and Regional stations, or for the Daventry National and Midland Regional stations, these wavelengths being set to the customer's requirements by his local wireless retailer. (Also DC version).

fig.302. Philips Model 2531, by Philips Lamps Ltd. 1930. 3-v +R, AC TRF, MW/LW 0-180 deg, drum-drive scale, no integral loud-speaker, brown moulded 'Philite' cabinet. 7 in. x 13 ½ in. x 8 in. 'Philite' was Philips' trade name for a Bakelite type of moulding material.

fig.303. Ekco Model 312, by E.K. Cole Ltd. 1930. 2-v +MetR, AC TRF, MW/LW 0-100 deg, drum-drive scale, no integral loud-speaker, dark 'mahogany' Bakelite cabinet. 8 in. x 12 ½ in.x 8 in. (Also DC version, and Bakelite cabinets in 'oak' and dark jade). Below the receiver is a matching Ekco moving-iron cone loud-speaker, 'Ekcone' Model LS1, in a dark 'mahogany' Bakelite cabinet (also in 'oak' and dark jade). 15 ½ in. x 14 ½ in. x 9 ½ in.

fig.304. Ekco 'All Electric' Model 313, by E.K. Cole Ltd. July 1930. 3-v +MetR, AC TRF, MW/LW Mtrs, drum-drive scale, no integral loud-speaker, dark 'mahogany' Bakelite cabinet. 8 in. x 17 in. x 9 in. £22.10s.0d. (Also DC version, and cabinets in 'oak' and dark jade). On top of the receiver is a matching Ekco moving-coil loud-speaker, 'Ekcoil' Model LS2, in a dark 'mahogany' Bakelite cabinet (also in 'oak' and dark jade cabinets). 16 ½ in. x 14 ½ in. x 8 in.

fig.305. Pye 'Twin-Triple Transportable' Type AC4D, by Pye Radio Ltd. 1930. 3-v +R, AC TRF Transportable, MW/LW Mtrs, drum-drive scale, cone loud-speaker, internal frame aerial, turntable, solid walnut cabinet with walnut wings and headpiece (also version with black-painted wings and headpiece). 19 ¾ in. x 17 ¼ in. x 9 in. (Also Type DC4D, DC version, and Type B4D, battery portable without wings and headpiece, see fig.295).

fig.306. Decca 'Radio Model', by Decca Gramophone Co. Ltd. 1930. 5-v Batt Portable, MW/LW 0-100 deg, (Medium waveband marked 'Short'), moving-iron cone loud-speaker, internal frame aerial, brown ebonite control panel, light oak cabinet. 15 ½ in. x 16 in. x 8 ½ in.

fig.307. Cossor Model MR 133, by A.C. Cossor Ltd. 1930. 2-v +R, AC TRF, MW/LW 0-100 deg, no integral loud-speaker, light oak cabinet. 10 in. x 15 in. x 11 in. £11.10s.0d. (Model MR 331 is 3-v +R version, price £15.0s.0d).

fig.308. 'Red Star', by Red Star Radio Ltd. 1930. 3-v Batt, MW/LW 0-100 deg, drum scale, edgewise tuning control, no integral loud-speaker, anodised escutcheon, painted tinplate and oak cabinet. 10½ in. x 16 in. x 8 in. £4.4s.0d. Advertised as "a set for the working classes who can only be reached by a very keen price appeal". Lotus components. (Also a 2-valve version, price £3.3s.0d).

fig.309. 'Magnum Crystal Set', by Burne-Jones & Co. Ltd. 1930. Crystal Set designed for blind listeners. Headphone use only, spring-loaded cat's whisker/galena detector, loose-coupled plug-in coils, variable condenser, braille calibrated tuning controls, black Bakelite control panel and knobs, mahogany base. 3 ½ in. x 9 in. x 9 in. Donated through the "British Wireless For The Blind Fund".

fig.310. Cossor 'Silvertone', by A.C. Cossor Ltd. 1930. 3-v Batt Table Model Kit, MW/LW 0-100 deg, moving-iron cone loud-speaker, oak veneered plywood cabinet. 18 ½ in. x 13 in. x 7 in.

fig.311. McMichael 'Colonial Receiver', by L. McMichael Ltd. 1931. 4-v Batt SHet, 3SW/MW 0-100 deg, 14/30m, 25/55m, 50/95m, 250/500m, no integral loud-speaker, black painted aluminium control panel, insect proof teak cabinet. 9 in. x 14 ½ in. x 9 in. £15.0s.0d. A short-wave receiver with provision for the medium-wave broadcast range designed primarily for use in the British Colonies. An 'autodyne' type of superheterodyne circuit was employed in which the detector was used in an oscillating condition, a suitable beat frequency resulting from the amount of coupling between the windings of the grid and anode circuits.

fig.312. The tuning unit of the McMichael 'Colonial Receiver'. Normally with short-wave receivers, a collection of plug-in coils was needed, but with the McMichael 'Colonial Receiver' a novel plug-in tuning unit (or 'coil box') was employed in which all the necessary coils for reaction and grid circuit input tuning were assembled within a rectangular case, the four faces of which carried the engraved wavelength scales. The tuning unit was pressed into a recess with the required wave range facing the front and contacts on the side of the unit engaged four spring blade contacts within the recess.

fig.313. K.B. 'Kobra Junior', by Kolster-Brandes Ltd. 1931. 3-v Batt, MW/LW 0-100 deg, disc-drive dial, no integral loud-speaker, light oak cabinet. 10 ½ in. x 12 ½ in. x 9 in.

fig.314. Ekco 'All Electric Consolette' Model RS3, by E.K. Cole Ltd. August 17th 1931. 4-v +R, AC TRF Consolette, MW/LW Mtrs/StN, celluloid tuning dial, cord-driven cursor, anodised copper grille, 'mahogany' Bakelite cabinet (des: J.K. White). 18 in. x 17 ½ in. x 10 in. £25.4s.0d. (Also 'walnut' Bakelite version). This was the first British receiver with a full range of station names printed on the dial (indicated by a single travelling cursor). The later Ekco Model SH 25, 5-v +R, AC/DC SHet of 1932, is of similar appearance and the two are often confused (the SH 25 has a *double* travelling cursor).

fig.315. Marconiphone Model 42 AC, by Marconiphone Co. Ltd. 1931. 3-v +R, AC TRF Table Model, MW/LW Mtrs, disc-drive dial, floral tracery grille design, wood knobs, solid walnut cabinet. 17 ¼ in. x 20 in. x 10 ¾ in.

fig.316. H.M.V. '3 Valve Radio Receiver' Model 435, by The Gramophone Co. Ltd. 1931. 3-v +R, AC TRF Table Model, MW/LW Mtrs, mahogany cabinet. 16 in. x 16 ¾ in. x 12 ¼ in. £23.2s.0d. The Gramophone Company's first broadcast receiver.

fig.317. Marconiphone 'Super Power II' Type 246, by Marconiphone Co. Ltd. 1931. 2-v +R, AC TRF, MW/LW 0-100 deg, disc-drive dial, 1-piece tuning control, no integral loud-speaker, brown Bakelite escutcheon, wood knobs, oak cabinet. 5 ½ in. x 14 ¾ in. x 10 ½ in.

fig.318. Ekco Model M23, by E.K. Cole Ltd. 1931. 3-v +MetR, AC TRF Table Model, MW/LW Mtrs, moving-coil loud-speaker, dark brown Bakelite cabinet (des: J.K. White). 16 in. x 14 in. x 9 ¼ in. £17.17s.0d. (Also DC version). Cabinet identical to 1931 Model RS2 AC with balanced armature cone loud-speaker and Model RS2 DC with moving-iron cone loud-speaker.

fig.319 Philips 'Radioplayer, All-Electric' Type 2634, by Philips Lamps Ltd. 1931. 3-v +R, AC TRF Table Model, MW/LW 0-180 deg, 200/450m, 400/950m, 900/2100m, balanced armature cone loud-speaker, oxydised bronze grille, cadmium-plated bent iron frame chassis, mottled brown Bakelite cabinet. 19 in. x 15 in. x 9 in. £25.0s.0d.

fig.320. 'Peter Pan', imported from U.S. and distributed in Britain by Jackson-Bell Distributors Ltd. Hammersmith. 1931. 3-v +R, AC SHet Table Model 'midget', MW/LW 0-100 deg, walnut cabinet. 11 in. x 10 in. x 7 in. Fitted with a 240v transformer.

fig.321. Philips 'Local Station Receiver' Model 930A, by Philips Lamps Ltd. 1931. 3-v +R, AC TRF Table Model, MW/LW 0-100 deg, illuminated celluloid disc-drive dial, balanced armature cone loud-speaker, 'Arbolite' cabinet in rosewood finish, 18 ½ in. x 15 ¾ in. x 6 in. £13.15s.0d. (Also Model 930C, DC version and Model 930B, wood cabinet version).

fig.322. G.E.C. 'All Electric AC' Model BC 3235, by General Electric Co. Ltd. 1931. 3-v +R, AC Table Model, MW/LW 0-100 deg, brown Bakelite grille, solid walnut cabinet. 18 in. x 16 ¼ in. x 10 ½ in.

fig.323. Amplion 'Six', by Graham Amplion Ltd. 1931. 5-v +R, AC Table Model, MW/LW Mtrs, illuminated tuning scale, local-distance switch, walnut cabinet. 22 in. x 15 ½ in. x 10 in. £21.0s.0d. The first receiver to use a variable-mu S.G. valve. (Also console version).

fig.324. McMichael 'Moving Coil Mains Receiver', by L. McMichael Ltd. 1931. 3-v +MetR, AC TRF Table Model, MW/LW Mtrs/Kcs, full-vision tuning scale, cord-driven cursor, geometric grille, ebonite trim, walnut cabinet. 18 in. x 17 in. x 9 ½ in. £25.4s.0d.

fig.325. Gecophone 'Table Four, All-Electric Screen-Grid Receiver', Model BC3240, by General Electric Co. Ltd. 1931. 4-v +R, AC TRF Table Model, MW/LW Mtrs, drum-drive scale, no integral loud-speaker, local-distance switch, Bakelite escutcheon, walnut cabinet. 11 in. x 18 in. x 12 in. One of the the first British receivers to employ a 'local-distance' switch.

fig.326. Adey 'De Luxe', by Adey Radio Co. Ltd. 1931. 4-v Batt Portable, MW/LW 0-100 deg, internal frame aerial, turntable, red and gold Chinese lacquered wood cabinet. 10 ¾ in. x 10 in. x 7 in. A 3-function jack-plug 'key' (on the top, to the left of the carrying handle) provided (1) HT/LT on/off by inserting/extracting the key, (2) variable reaction (volume) control by means of a multi-positioned switch, and (3) fine tuning by rotating the key around its verticle axis. The waveband selection control is on the front of the cabinet, and a coarse tuning knob is on top, to the right of the carrying handle.

fig.327. Eelex 'Short-Wave Converter', by J.J. Eastick & Sons. 1931. 1-v Batt, SW 16/190 Mtrs, no integral loud-speaker, brown lizard-covered wood case, anodised copper edging. 8 ¾ in. x 8 in. x 7 in. £3.0s.0d. "Will add 70 extra stations to the log of most receivers". (Also 1-v and 2-v AC versions).

fig.328. Cossor 'All Electric Melody Maker', by A.C. Cossor Ltd. 1931. 3-v +R, AC TRF Kit, MW/LW 0-100 deg, no integral loud-speaker, brown crystalline finished metal front, oak cabinet. 8 in. x 17 in. x 13 in. £9.19s.6d.

fig.329. Philips Model 2607, by Philips Lamps Ltd. 1931. 4-v +R, AC TRF Console, MW/LW 0-180 deg, walnut finished 'Arbolite' panels on painted steel frame. 32in. x 21 in. x 11 in. (Very similar to Model 2601 of 1930).

fig.330. Ultra 'Tiger Three', by Ultra Electric Ltd. 1931. 3-v +R, AC TRF Table Model 'Midget', MW/LW Mtrs, disc-drive dial, walnut veneered plywood cabinet. 17 ½ in. x 16 in. x 9 ½ in. £15.15s.0d.

fig.331. Radiophone 'Straight Two', by British Radiophone Ltd. 1931. 2-v Batt Table Model, MW/LW 0-100 deg, (Medium waveband marked 'Short'), moving-iron cone loud-speaker, dark oak cabinet. 12 in. x 12 in. x 5 ½ in.

fig.332. Pye Model MM, by Pye Radio Ltd. 1931. 3-v + MetR, AC TRF Transportable, MW/LW Mtrs, walnut veneered plywood cabinet. 18 ½ in. x 16 in. x 9 ½ in. £17.17s.0d.

fig.333. Lissen 'Two Valve AC Receiver', by Lissen Ltd. 1931. 2-v +R, AC TRF Table Model, MW 0-100 deg, illuminated celluloid cord-driven drum scale, balanced armature loud-speaker, brown Bakelite cabinet. 14 in. x 12 ½ in. x 5 in. £7.7s.0d. (Also DC version). Primarily for local station reception. Art Deco 'Egyptian Temple' style cabinet.

fig.334. Marconiphone Model 66, by Marconiphone Co. Ltd. 1931. 4-v Batt Portable, MW/LW Mtrs, internal frame aerial, turntable, mahogany veneered plywood cabinet. 17 ¾ in. x 15 ¾ in. x 9 in.

fig.335. 'The Carlton' Model SG4, by Fred Bulmer. 1931. 4-v Batt Table Model, MW/LW 0-100 deg, moving-iron cone loud-speaker, internal frame aerial, oak cabinet. 20 in. x 15 in. x 8 in.

fig.336. Home-Constructed Receiver, c.1931. 3-v Batt, MW/LW 0-100 deg, components by Telsen, Ormond, Lissen and Pye, oak cabinet. 18 in. x 12 in. 10 in.

fig.337. Hampton Table Model, by Hampton Radio Ltd. 1931. 4-v DC TRF Table Model, MW/LW 0-180 deg, disc-drive dial, internal frame aerial, turntable, mahogany cabinet. 20 ¼ in. x 15 ¾ in. x 9 ¾ in. (Also AC version).

fig.338. Murphy Model A3, by Murphy Radio Ltd. 1931. 3–v +R, AC TRF Table Model, MW/LW Mtrs, illuminated drum-drive scale, local-distance switch, cadmium-plated steel chassis, solid walnut cabinet (des: R.D. Russell). 18 ½ in. x 16 in. x 10 in. £19.19s.0d. 15,000 were sold. The 1932 version, Model A3A, price £17.17s.0d, is very similar but is housed in a wider cabinet made of walnut veneered plywood which has no back. The Model A3A was sold with a detachable wooden stand to turn it into a pedestal model.

fig.339. 'Lumophon', by British Lumophon Ltd. 1931. 4–v +R, AC Table Model, MW/LW Mtrs, drum-drive scale, solid and veneered mahogany cabinet. 19 in. x 15 in. x 10 in. £19.19s.0d.

fig.340. Ferranti Model 32, by Ferranti Ltd. 1931. 3–v +R, AC TRF Console, MW/LW Mtrs, solid and veneered walnut cabinet. 40 in. x 17 in. x 12 ½ in.

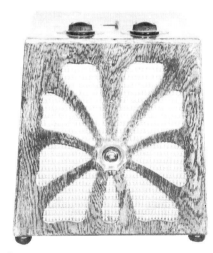

fig.341. K.B. 'Pup', by Kolster-Brandes Ltd. 1931. 2–v Batt Table Model, MW/LW 0-180 deg, cone loud-speaker, controls on top of cabinet, imitation tortoiseshell dials, oak cabinet. 12 in. x 11 ½ in. x 8 ½ in. £4.10s.0d. (Also AC model, price £7.10s.0d). The 'Pup' first came out in 1930 in a slightly different cabinet. This was square and upright with a sloping and overlapping top, and had a plinth surround at the bottom.

◄ fig.342. Lotus '3 Valve All Electric', by Lotus Radio Ltd. 1931. 3–v +R, AC TRF Table Model, MW/LW Mtrs, drum-drive scale, bronze escutcheon, mahogany cabinet. 20 in. x 14 ½ in. x 10 in. £15.15s.0d. (Also walnut version, and battery version, price £9.9s.0d).

fig.343. Ferranti Model 32, by Ferranti Ltd. ►
1931. 3–v +R, AC TRF Table Model, MW/LW Mtrs, fleur-de-lis grille, mahogany stained birch plywood cabinet. 21 in. x 13 ½ in. x 9 in.

fig.344. K.B. 'Kobra' Model 305, by Kolster-Brandes Ltd. 1931. 3–v +R, AC TRF Table Model, MW/LW 0-90 deg, disc-drive dial, oak cabinet. 17 in. x 13 in. x 9 ½ in. £11.18s.6d. Also battery version, price £8.10s.0d.

fig.345. Cossor Model 732, by A.C. Cossor Ltd. 1931. 4–v Batt Table Model, MW/LW Mtrs, drum-drive scale and edgewise tuning control, oak cabinet. 18 in. x 14 ½ in. x 10 in. £12.15s.0d.

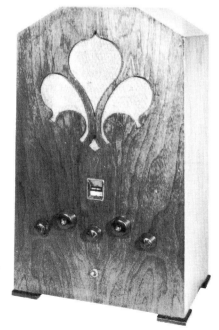

fig.346. K.B. 'Masterpiece', by Kolster-Brandes Ltd. 1931. 3-v Batt TRF, MW/LW 0-100 deg, disc-drive dial, cone loud-speaker, oak cabinet with rosewood inlay. 16 ¼ in. x 13 ½ in. x 9 ½ in. Like its 2-valve namesake in a Bakelite cabinet (see fig.298), the 3-valve 'Masterpiece' was given away as a 'free gift' by the cigarette manufacturers Godfrey Phillips Ltd. in return for their BDV cigarette coupons.

fig.347. Burton 'Empire Speaker Three', by Burton Products Ltd. 1931. 3-v Batt, Table Model, MW/LW 0-100 deg, drum scale, edgewise tuning control, cone loud-speaker, oak veneered plywood cabinet. 15 in. x 12 in. x 9 ½ in. £7.15s.0d. (Also walnut veneered plywood cabinet, price £8.0s.0d). Art Deco 'Egyptian Temple' style cabinet. Medium waveband marked 'Short'.

fig.348. Climax 'All Mains Four', by Climax Radio Electric Ltd. 1931. 3-v +R, AC TRF Table Model, MW/LW Mtrs, mahogany veneered plywood cabinet. 16 in. x 12 ¾ in. x 9 in. £15.15s.0d.

fig.349. Pye Model 'Q', by Pye Radio Ltd. 1931. 4-v Batt Portable, MW/LW Mtrs, drum scale, edgewise tuning control, internal frame aerial, turntable, carrying handle, solid walnut cabinet (also known with grained fabric-covered cabinet). 17 ½ in x 16 in. x 9 ½ in. £14.14s.0d. Two versions of the Model 'Q' were made: the 'P' series and the 'Q' series. Only slight circuit modifications were evident in both series, the last letter of the serial number denoted which series the set belonged to, e.g. 'FFP 2251' is from the 'P' series and 'FFQ 2251' is from the 'Q' series.

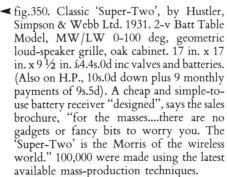

◄ fig.350. Classic 'Super-Two', by Hustler, Simpson & Webb Ltd. 1931. 2-v Batt Table Model, MW/LW 0-100 deg, geometric loud-speaker grille, oak cabinet. 17 in. x 17 in. x 9 ½ in. £4.4s.0d inc valves and batteries. (Also on H.P., 10s.0d down plus 9 monthly payments of 9s.5d). A cheap and simple-to-use battery receiver "designed", says the sales brochure, "for the masses....there are no gadgets or fancy bits to worry you. The 'Super-Two' is the Morris of the wireless world." 100,000 were made using the latest available mass-production techniques.

fig.351. Monarch 'Cadet', by William Dibben & Sons Ltd. 1931. 2-v +R, AC TRF Table Model, MW/LW Mtrs, cone loud-speaker, oak cabinet. 13 ½ in. x 12 in. x 10 in.

fig.352. Viking Model 810, by Viking Sales Ltd. 1932. 3-v +MetR, AC TRF Table Model, MW/LW Mtrs, brown Bakelite escutcheon and knobs, black painted feet, walnut veneered plywood cabinet. 16 ½ in. x 15 in. x 10 ½ in. The same basic cabinet, with a different fret design, was used by the Wade 'Decee-Acee', fig.372.

fig.353. Telsen 'MacNamara - The Golden Voice', by Telsen Electric Co. Ltd. 1932. 3-v +R, AC TRF Table Model, MW/LW Mtrs, drum-drive scale, 1-piece tuning control, walnut veneered plywood cabinet. 19 ¼ in. x 15 ½ in. x 8 ½ in. (Named after A.W. MacNamara, the Managing Director of Telsen).

fig.354. 'Umello', by Umello Ltd. 1932. 3-v +R, AC Table Model, MW/LW Mtrs, loud-speaker opening facing upwards in top of cabinet, 'figured walnut' Bakelite tuning escutcheon and knobs, walnut veneered plywood cabinet. 13 in. x 11 in. x 10 ½ in. A very compact and tightly packed receiver. Socket adjustments for tone control, marked 'Brilliant', 'Bright', 'Mellow' and 'Deep'.

fig.355. Model ST 400, (des: John Scott-Taggart). November 1932. 4-v Batt, MW/LW 0-100 deg, no integral loud-speaker, oak veneered plywood cab. 7 in. x 16 in. x 11 in. A home-constructed receiver made from a blueprint published in *The Wireless Constructor*.

fig.355a. Interior of Model ST 400.

fig.356. Ferranti Kit Receiver, by Ferranti Ltd. 1932. 4-v +R, AC, MW/LW Mtrs, drum-drive scale, no integral loud-speaker, walnut stained plywood cabinet. 12 in. x 20 in. x 13 in. Safety mains switch operated by raising the lid.

fig.357. Philips 'Superinductance' Model 630A, by Philips Lamps Ltd. 1932. 5-v +R, AC TRF Table Model, MW/LW Mtrs, illuminated dial, brown Bakelite loud-speaker and dial surround, walnut veneered plywood cabinet. 21 ¼ in. x 17 in. x 10 ½ in. £24.3s.0d.

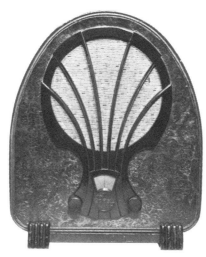

fig.358. Philips 'Superinductance' Model 830A, by Philips Lamps Ltd. 1932. 4-v +R, AC TRF Table Model, MW/LW Mtrs, illuminated dial, brown Bakelite loud-speaker and dial surround, 'Arbolite' case in simulated walnut finish. 19 ¼ in. x 16 ¼ in. x 8 in. £16.16s.0d.

fig.359. Decca Model 222, by Decca Gramophone Co. Ltd. 1932. 4-v +R, AC SHet Table Model, MW/LW Mtrs, illuminated dial, walnut veneered cabinet. 18 ½ in. x 16 ½ in. x 11 ¼ in.

fig.360. Bush Model AC3, by Bush Radio Ltd. 1932. 3-v +R, AC TRF Table Model, MW/LW Mtrs, 2 aerial inputs and an internal plate aerial ("an ideal device for flat dwellers"), gramophone pick-up terminals, moulded imitation wood fret, 'Cathedral' (or 'Gothic') style walnut veneered plywood cabinet (supplied without back): a type highly popular in America from the late 1920s to the early 1930s. 18 in. x 13 ½ in. x 9 in. £17.17s.0d. Bush's first receiver. With the receiver having such an ecclesiastical shape, it is not surprising to learn that the particular model illustrated originally belonged in the 1930s to the brother of the then Archbishop of Canterbury, Archbishop Lang. He sold it in 1936 to a Reverend Wilson and it was in continuous use by him until 1980.

fig.361. Cossor 'Melody Maker' Model 334, by A.C.Cossor Ltd. 1932. 3-v Batt, MW/LW 0-100 deg, two tuning dials, no integral l/s, walnut cabinet. 10 in. x 14 in. x 10 in. (Model 335 with l/s).

fig.362. Graves Model B3, by J.G.Graves. 1932. 3-v Batt, MW/LW 0-100 deg, disc-drive dial, anodised metal control panel, oak cabinet. 11 in. x 14 in. x 11 in. £9.15s.6d. Terminals at the back of this set were used to connect a separate loud-speaker.

fig.363. 'Adey 4', by Adey Radio Co. Ltd. 1932. 4–v Batt Portable, MW/LW 0-100 deg, internal frame aerial, turntable, lockable back, walnut cabinet. 10 in. x 8 ½ in. x 7 in. A 4-function jack-plug 'key' (on the top, to the right of the carrying handle) provided (1) HT/LT on/off by inserting/extracting the key, (2) waveband switching, (3) variable reaction (volume) control by means of a multi-positioned switch, and (4) fine tuning by rotating the key around its verticle axis. The first three stages in the circuit employ Adey self-coupling valves (Type C210), each with an integral HF choke wound around their base. An 'all-wave' version came out in 1935, the last of the Adey line.

fig.364. Ultra 'Blue Fox', by Ultra Electric Ltd .1932. 2–v +R, AC TRF Table Model, MW Mtrs, walnut veneered plywood cabinet. 17 in. x 14 ¾ in. x 7 ¾ in. £10.10s.0d.

fig.365. Murphy Model B4, by Murphy Radio Ltd. 1932. (des: E.J. Power). 4–v Batt TRF Transportable, MW/LW Mtrs/StN, internal frame aerial, mahogany cabinet. 17 in. x 15 in. x 9 in. £15.15s.0d. The B4 firs† came out in July 1930 with a mirrored 'M' grille design and with the dial calibrated in metres only, and this version was Murphy Radio's first receiver.

fig.366. Lissen 'Skyscraper', by Lissen Ltd. 1932. 3–v Batt Kit, MW/LW 0-100 deg, no integral loud-speaker, metal chassis and painted metal control panel, brown Bakelite control knobs and escutcheon, mahogany cabinet. 9 ½ in. x 16 ½ in. x 9 ½ in. (Lissen 'Skyscraper 3' kit receiver is version with enclosed loud-speaker).

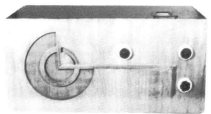

fig.367. Murphy Model A8, by Murphy Radio Ltd. 1932. 8–v +R, AC SHet Table/Pedestal Model, MW/LW Mtrs, illuminated tuning dial, black Bakelite knobs and aluminium surround, walnut veneered plywood cabinet (des: R.D. Russell). 12 in. x 24 in. x 13 in. £24.0s.0d. The first receiver to employ AVC. Also came with an optional wooden stand (price £31.10s.0d complete), which had a shelf for holding a copy of *The Radio Times*.

◀ fig.368. McMichael 'Duplex Four' Type 'S', by L. McMichael Ltd. 1932. 4–v Batt Suitcase Portable, MW/LW Mtrs, loud-speaker and internal frame aerial housed in lift-up lid, brown Bakelite grille, anodised aluminium valve cover, brown woodgrain control panel, black leathercloth–covered wood case. 9 ½ in. x 15 ½ in. x 15 in. £17.17s.0d inc batteries.

fig.369. Pye Model 'G', by Pye Radio Ltd. 1932. 3-v + MetR, AC Table Model, MW/LW Mtrs/StN, drum-drive scale, walnut veneered plywood cabinet. 20 in. 16 ½ in. x 9 in. £18.18s.0d. (Note: 4-valve battery version of Model 'G', Type G/B, is in identical cabinet to Pye Model 'S').

fig.370. Pye Model 'K', by Pye Radio Ltd. 1932. 2-v +MetR, AC TRF Table Model, MW/LW Mtrs, solid walnut cabinet. 15 ½ in. x 16 in. x 7 ½ in.

fig.371. Pye Model 'S', by Pye Radio Ltd. 1932. 6-v +MetR, AC SHet Table Model, MW/LW Mtrs/StN, drum-drive scale, brown Bakelite knobs, walnut veneered cabinet. 20 in. x 15 in. x 9 in. (Note: Pye Model 'S' is in identical cabinet to Pye Model 'G', Type G/B).

fig.372. Wade 'Decee-Acee', by A. Wade & Co. (Burnley) Ltd. May 1932. 3-v + MetR, AC/DC TRF Table Model, MW/LW Mtrs, disc-drive dial, one-piece tuning control, metal escutcheon, brown Bakelite knobs, black painted feet, walnut veneered plywood cabinet. 16 ½ in. x 15 in. x 10 ½ in. £18.18s.0d. This was the first self-contained AC/DC receiver introduced in Great Britain.

fig.374. 'Beethoven Transportable', by Montague Radio Inventions & Development Co. Ltd. 1932. 3-v + R, AC Transportable, MW/LW Mtrs, internal frame aerial, illuminated dial, walnut veneered plywood cabinet. 19 ¾ in. x 15 ¼ in. x 10 ½ in.

fig.378. Marconiphone Model 282, by Marconiphone Co. Ltd. 1932. 3-v Batt Table Model, MW/LW Mtrs, walnut veneered plywood cabinet. 19 in. x 14 in. x 9 ½ in.

fig.373. K.B. Model 321, by Kolster-Brandes Ltd. 1932. 3-v +R AC Table Model, MW/LW Mtrs, illuminated drum-drive scale, brown Bakelite knobs, walnut cab. 16 in. x 15 in. x 8 in. £14.17s.6d. (Short-wave tuning was made possible by the connection of a SW coil, price 6s.6d. extra).

fig.375. Lotus 'Bud', by Lotus Radio Ltd. 1932. 2-v + MetR, AC TRF Table Model, MW/LW 0-100 deg, drum scale, edgewise tuning control, metal escutcheon, walnut veneered plywood. 16 ½ in. x 13 in. x 7 in. Described as a "simple home model, not the set for those who want to go touring around Europe every night".

fig.379. G.E.C. 'Osram Thirty-Three, New Music Magnet', by General Electric Co. Ltd. 1932. 3-v Batt Table Model Kit, MW/LW Mtrs, moving-iron cone loud-speaker, brown Bakelite cabinet. 18 ¾ in. x 15 ¾ in. x 9 ½ in. £9.9s.0d. The valve panel was assembled, wired and tested by the manufacturers before despatch.

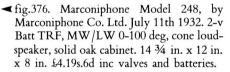

◄ fig.376. Marconiphone Model 248, by Marconiphone Co. Ltd. July 11th 1932. 2-v Batt TRF, MW/LW 0-100 deg, cone loud-speaker, solid oak cabinet. 14 ¾ in. x 12 in. x 8 in. £4.19s.6d inc valves and batteries.

fig.377. Majestic 'Screen-Grid Superhet' ► Model 15, by Majestic Electric Co. Ltd. 1932. 4-v + R, AC SHet Table Model, MW/LW Mtrs, wood knobs, antiqued bronze fittings, walnut veneered cabinet. 15 ¼ in. x 13 in. x 9 ¾ in. Originally made by the Grigsby-Grunow Company in Chicago as the 'Havenwood Model 151', a single band, medium-wave receiver. It was imported and distributed in Britain by the Majestic Electric Company who fitted a voltage dropper and also a 2-waveband converter controlled by an extra knob on the left hand side.

fig.380. McMichael 'Duplex Mains Four Transportable', by L. McMichael Ltd. 1932. 4-v +MetR, AC TRF Transportable, MW/LW Mtrs, internal frame aerial, turntable, walnut veneered plywood cabinet. 19 ¼ in. x 16 ½ in. x 10 in.

fig.383. Gecophone 'New Viking IV', by General Electric Co. Ltd. 1932. 4-v +R, AC TRF Table Model, MW/LW Mtrs/StN, full-vision tuning scale, cord-driven cursor, walnut cabinet. 20 in. x 16 in. x 12 in.

fig.386. Portadyne 'Challenger', by Portadyne Radio Ltd. 1932. 4-v Batt Transportable, MW/LW Mtrs/StN, internal frame aerial, turntable, controls and dial housed under lift-up lid, solid and veneered walnut cabinet. 16 ¼ in. x 16 ¼ in. x 9 ½ in. £12.17s.0d.

fig.381. McMichael 'Duplex Four' Type C, by McMichael Radio Ltd. 1932. 4-v Batt Transportable, MW/LW Mtrs, internal frame aerial, turntable, brown figured ebonite panel, walnut veneered plywood cabinet. 18 ¼ in. x 17 in. x 8 ½ in. £17.17s.0d.

fig.384. Ferranti Model A1, by Ferranti Ltd. 1932. 6-v +R, AC SHet Table Model, MW/LW Mtrs/StN, brown Bakelite knobs, walnut veneered plywood cabinet (supplied without back). 19 ½ in. x 17 in. x 10 ¾ in.

fig.387. Westminster 'President' Model SG3, by Belcher Ltd. 1932. 3-v +R, AC TRF Table Model, MW/LW Mtrs, walnut veneered plywood cabinet. 21 in. x 17 in. x 9 in.

fig.382. Ultra 'Tiger', by Ultra Electric Ltd. 1932. 4-v +MetR, AC Table Model, MW/LW Mtrs, illuminated dial, walnut veneered plywood cabinet. 20 in. x 16 in. x 9 in. (Also AC/DC version, and 1933 Class 'B' battery version).

fig.385. Consolidated 'AC Receiver', by Consolidated Radio Co. Ltd. 1932. 3-v +R, AC Table Model, MW/LW Mtrs, veneered and solid walnut cabinet. 17 in. x 16 in. x 9 ½ in. (Also DC model).

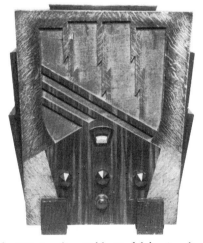

fig.388. Amplion Table Model, by Amplion (1932) Ltd. 1932. 3-v +MetR, AC TRF Table Model, MW/LW Mtrs, oak and rosewood veneered plywood cabinet. 19 ½ in. x 16 ¾ in. x 13 ½ in.

fig.389. Majestic Model 49C, by Majestic Electric Co. Ltd. 1933. 4-v +R, AC SHet 'Midget', SW/MW Mtrs, cut aluminium grille, birch plywood cabinet with black painted decoration. 11 ¼ in. x 8 ¼ in. x 5 in. Originally made by the Grigsby-Grunow Company in Chicago, it was imported, modified and distributed in Britain by the Majestic Electric Company.

fig.390. Ferranti 'Gloria', by Ferranti Ltd. 1933. 6-v +R, AC SHet Table Model, MW/LW Mtrs/StN, clock in front of loud-speaker opening, brown Bakelite knobs, walnut veneered plywood cabinet (supplied without back). 19 in. x 16 ½ in. x 10 ½ in. £25.4s.0d. Also 1933 version without clock which has zig-zag fret design instead.

fig.391. Philco 'Baby Grand' Model 1260, by Philco Radio & Television Corporation of Great Britain Ltd. 1933. 4-v +R plus Shadow Tuning Indicator, AC SHet, MW/LW Mtrs, walnut veneered plywood cabinet. 12 ¼ in. x 23 ½ in. x 11 in. £14.14s.0d. Model 260 is identical, but without Shadow Tuning Indicator.

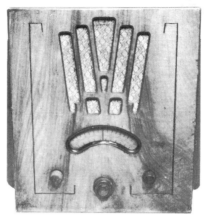

fig.392. Portadyne Model PB5, by Portadyne Radio Ltd. 1933. 5-v Batt Transportable, MW/LW Mtrs, full-vision tuning dial, internal frame aerial, turntable, walnut veneered plywood cabinet. 16 ½ in. x 16 ¼ in. x 9 ½ in. £13.13s.0d. The first battery receiver to incorporate Class 'B' amplification.

fig.393. Lissen 'Skyscraper 4', by Lissen Ltd. 1933. 4-v Batt Kit, 2SW/MW/LW, no integral loud-speaker, no cabinet. A kit set for the home-constructor covering 12/2,100m, chassis components only, packaged in a cardboard box. 3 ½ in. x 14 in. x 24 in. £5.12s.6d.

fig.394. Ferranti 'Lancastria Magna', by Ferranti Ltd. 1933. 4-v +R, AC SHet Table Model, MW/LW Mtrs, bulls-eye magnifying lens over tuning dial, mahogany and walnut veneered plywood cabinet. 17 ½ in. x 13 ½ in. x 8 ½ £15.15s.0d.

fig.395. Philips 'Superinductance' Model 634A, by Philips Lamps Ltd. 1933. 4-v +R, AC TRF Table Model, MW/LW Mtrs/0-180 deg, brown Bakelite loud-speaker and dial surround, solid and veneered mahogany cabinet. 19 in. x 16 in. x 10 ½ in. £16.16s.0d. Beneath the set is housed a pull-out station and wavelength chart. It acquired the name of 'the Ovaltiney Set' following its appearance in the Ovaltine advertisements on television in the early 1980s.

fig.396. McMichael 'Duplex Super Five', by McMichael Radio Ltd. 1933. 5-v Batt Transportable, MW/LW Mtrs, internal frame aerial, turntable, walnut veneered plywood cabinet. 19 ½ in. x 15 ½ in. x 9 ¼ in. £16.16s.0d.

fig.397. Eddystone 'Short-Wave Converter', by Stratton & Co. Ltd. 1933. 2-v +R, AC, SW 0-180 deg, brown Bakelite tuning dial, escutcheon & knobs, no integral loud-speaker, walnut veneered plywood case. 9 ½ in. x 12 in. x 6 in.

fig.398. McMichael 'Duplex Four, Type CMC', by McMichael Radio Ltd. 1933. 4-v Batt Transportable, MW/LW Mtrs, internal frame aerial, turntable, walnut veneered plywood cabinet. 18 in. x 17 in. x 8 ½ in.

fig.399. Pye Model 'P', by Pye Radio Ltd. 1933. 5-v +MetR +West, AC SHet Transportable, MW/LW Mtrs/StN, disc-drive dial, internal frame aerial, turntable, solid and veneered walnut cabinet. 18 ½ in. x 15 ¾ in. x 10 in. £15.15s.0d. (Also Model 'P', Type P/B, battery version price £14.14s.0d. Westector used as a 2nd detector to provide delayed AVC).

fig.400. 'Britannia', by Britannia Batteries Ltd. 1933. 3-v Batt Table Model, MW/LW Mtrs, walnut veneered plywood cabinet. 18 ½ in. x 20 in. x 10 in. (Also, AC 3-v +R version).

fig.401. Pye Model 'E', Type E/AC, by Pye Radio Ltd. 1933. 5-v +MetR, AC SHet Table Model, MW/LW Mtrs/StN, drum-drive scale, solid mahogany cabinet. 20 in. x 15 in. x 9 in. £15.15s.0d. (Also Type E/B, battery version).

fig.402. Philips 'Superinductance' Model 834A, by Philips Lamps Ltd. 1933. 4-v +R, AC TRF Table Model, MW/LW Mtrs, brown 'Philite' front with 'Arbolite' sides. 17 ¾ in. x 15 ¾ in. x 8 ½ in. £11.11s.0d. (DC-only version, Model 834C).

fig.403. Orr Model D3, by Orr Radio Ltd. 1933. 3-v Batt Table Model, MW/LW 0-100 deg, instructions and station/wavelength chart on inside of slide-up back panel, black Bakelite knobs, walnut veneered plywood cabinet. 16 in. x 12 ¼ in. x 9 in.

fig.404. Philips 'Superinductance' Model 636A, by Philips Lamps Ltd. 1933. 7-v +R, AC TRF Table Model, MW/LW Mtrs, brown Bakelite loud-speaker and dial surround, walnut veneered plywood cabinet. 23 ½ in. x 16 ¾ in. x 10 ¾ in. £24.3s.0d.

fig.405. K.B. Model 333, by Kolster–Brandes Ltd. 1933. 3-v Batt Table Model, MW/LW, Mtrs/StN, walnut veneered plywood cabinet. 17 ½ in. x 13 ¾ in. x 9 ½ in.

fig.406. Pye Model 'O', Type O/B2, by Pye Radio Ltd. 1933. 4-v Batt Portable, MW/LW Mtrs/StN, disc-drive dial, internal frame aerial, turntable, solid dark oak cabinet. 16 in. x 16 in. x 8 ½ in. £10.10s.0d.

fig.407. G.E.C. 'Overseas Model', by General Electric Co. Ltd. 1933. 4-v +R, AC SHet, SW/MW 13/30m, 30/80m, 200/560m, interchangeable plug-in coils, no integral loud-speaker, teak cabinet with moisture and insect proof insulation. 12 in. x 18 ½ in. x 12 ¼ in. £25.4s.0d. (Chassis only, price £23.0s.0d). Presentation plaque below tuning knob added later. Although designed as an export model for Colonial use, this set was also popular in Britain for listening to the B.B.C.'s short-wave Empire Service.

fig.408. Murphy Model A4, by Murphy Radio Ltd. 1933. 4-v +R AC SHet Table Model, MW/LW Mtrs, black Bakelite tuning surround & knobs, mahogany veneered and birch plywood cabinet. 18 in. x 15 in. x 10 in. £14.10s.0d. (Also available, were Model D4, a DC superhet, and Model B5, a battery version).

fig.409. Marconiphone Model 283, by Marconiphone Co. Ltd. 1933. 3-v Batt Table Model, MW/LW Mtrs, local-distance switch, walnut stained plywood cabinet. 19 in. x 14 ¼ in. x 9 ½ in. £8.15s.0d.

fig.410. Cromwell 'Universal', by William Dibben & Sons. 1933. 3-v +Bar, AC/DC TRF Table Model, MW/LW Mtrs, brown Bakelite escutcheon and knobs, rosewood and walnut veneered plywood cabinet. 12 in. x 23 in. x 8 in.

fig.411. Lotus 'Double Pentode Universal Receiver' Type 33, by Lotus Radio (1933) Ltd. 1933. 2-v (pentode detector + output pentode) +R +Bar, AC/DC TRF Table Model, MW/LW 0-100 deg, walnut veneered plywood cabinet. 12 ½ in. x 11 ¼ in. x 8 in. Designed primarily for high quality reception of local stations, with a 'selectivity control' for separating the twin London stations at Brookmans Park. The set took at least 1 ½ minutes to 'warm up'. With its live chassis and exposed mains 'safety' fuse at the back, it was a potential hazard to the unwary listener.

fig.412. Philco 'Five Star Baby Grand', by Philco Radio & Television Corporation of Great Britain Ltd. 1933. 4-v +R, AC SHet Table Model, MW/LW Mtrs, illuminated dial, automatic volume control, walnut veneered plywood cabinet. 17 ¾ in. x 14 ½ in. x 10 ¼ in. £15.15s.0d. Chassis made in Canada, cabinet made in England by Carrington Manufacturing Co. Ltd.

fig.413. Ekco Model AC 74, by E.K. Cole Ltd. 1933. 4-v +R plus Light Beam and Shadow Tuning Indicator, AC Shet Table Model, MW/LW Mtrs plus celluloid tuning scale printed with station names, local-distance switch, interchangeable silk loud-speaker cloth, walnut Bakelite cabinet (des: Serge Chermayeff). 18 in. x 15 in. x 10 in. £13.10s.0d. (Also black/chrome version, and battery version). A separate removable transparent celluloid tuning scale engraved in station names was included with the receiver, which could be fixed by studs over the permanent metre scale thereby giving station/metre readings. If new wavelength allocations were made in the future, up-to-the-minute station scales could be provided by the manufacturer.

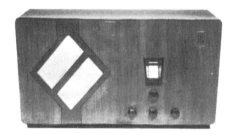

fig.414. K.B. 'Rejectostat' Model 666, by Kolster Brandes Ltd. 1933. 5-v +R, AC Shet Table Model, MW/LW Mtrs, walnut veneered plywood cabinet. 14 ½ in. x 25 in. x 10 ½ in. £16.16s.0d. Available with stand. Circuit employs a system of rejecting man-made static.

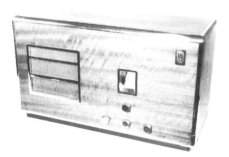

fig.415. K.B. 'Rejectostat', by Kolster-Brandes Ltd. 1933. 5-v +R, AC SHet Table Model, MW/LW (plus provision for a plug-in short-wave converter), Mtrs, drum-drive scale, chromium-plated edging, knobs and trim, Queensland walnut veneered plywood cabinet (des: Betty Joel). 14 ½ in. x 24 ½ in. x 10 ½ in.

fig.416. Ekco Model AC 64, by E.K. Cole Ltd. 1933. 4-v + R, AC SHet Table Model, MW/LW Mtrs/StN, interchangeable tuning scale, brown Bakelite cabinet. 16 in. x 13 ½ in. x 9 in. £11.11s.0d. (Also DC version, Model DC 64, price £11.11.0d, and battery version, Model B54, price £10.10s.0d).

fig.417. K.B. 'Rejectostat' Model 888, by Kolster-Brandes Ltd. 1933. 7-v + R, AC SHet Console, MW/LW Mtrs, drum-drive scale, chromium-plated edging, knobs and trim, Queensland walnut veneered plywood cabinet (des: Betty Joel). 43 in. x 22 in. x 12 in. £26.5s.0d. Single bookshelf at bottom of cabinet. It came out again in 1934 with station names, including 'AIRCRAFT' on 900 metres.

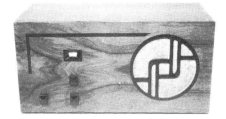

fig.418. Burgoyne 'Class B.3', by Burgoyne Wireless (1930) Ltd. 1933. 3-v Batt Table Model, MW/LW Mtrs, black Bakelite escutcheon and knobs, black-painted detail, walnut cabinet. 11 in. x 21 ¾ in. x 10 in. £6.10s.0d.

fig.419. Lissen Model 8039, by Lissen Ltd. 1933. 3-v + R, AC SHet Table Model, MW/LW Mtrs, disc-drive dial, walnut veneered and black-painted plywood cabinet. 10 ½ in. x 22 in. x 9 in. Geometric Art Deco cabinet.

fig.420. Graves 'National', by J.G. Graves Ltd. 1933. 3-v Batt TRF Table Model, MW/LW Mtrs, disc-drive dial, walnut veneered plywood cabinet. 10 in. x 17 in. x 9 in.

fig.421. Portadyne Model 'S', by Portadyne Radio Ltd. 1933. 4-v + R, AC SHet Table Model, MW/LW Mtrs/StN, local-distance switch, walnut cabinet. 14 ¾ in. x 17 ¾ in. x 10 ¾ in. £15.15s.0d. According to the instruction booklet, the Model 'S' had one of the quickest warm-up times for a mains set of this period: "wait for 20 seconds while the valves warm up".

fig.422. McMichael 'Twin Supervox RV8', by McMichael Radio Ltd. 1933. 4-v + MetR, AC TRF Table Model, MW/LW Mtrs, twin moving-coil loud-speakers, walnut veneered plywood cabinet. 11 in. x 25 in. x 12 in. £18.18s.0d.

fig.423. Alba 'Band Pass Four' Model 52, by A.J. Balcombe Ltd. 1933. 3-v + Bar, DC TRF Table Model, MW/LW 0-100 deg + Mtrs, full-vision tuning dial, walnut veneered plywood cabinet. 17 in. x 14 ½ in. x 10 in. £11.0s.0d. (Also AC version, price £9.19s.6d).

fig.424. Ultra 'Lynx', by Ultra Electric Ltd. 1933. 3-v +R, AC Table Model, MW/LW Mtrs/StN, walnut veneered plywood cabinet. 18 in. x 14 in. x 7 in.

fig.425. G.E.C. 'Superhet 5', by General Electric Co. Ltd. 1933. 4-v + Bar, DC SHet Table Model, MW/LW Mtrs/StN, full-vision tuning dial, bronze trim, walnut veneered plywood cabinet. 16 ¼ in. x 14 in. x 8 in. £14.14s.0d. (Also AC, battery, console and radiogram versions).

fig.426. Ferranti 'Lancastria', by Ferranti Ltd. 1933. 4-v + R, AC SHet Table Model, MW/LW Mtrs, walnut veneered plywood cabinet. 15 in. x 10 ½ in. x 9 in. The first in the 'Lancastria' series (it was later put into larger cabinet as the 'Lancastria Magna', fig.394) and the first superhet in Britain to employ a heptode frequency changer. For second series model, see fig.465.

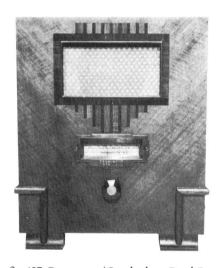

fig.427. Regentone 'Quadradyne Band-Pass Four', by Regentone Ltd. 1933. 3-v + R, AC SHet Table Model, MW/LW Mtrs/StN, tuning control only on front of cabinet, walnut veneered plywood cabinet with rosewood inlay. 20 ¼ in. x 16 ¾ in. x 10 ½ in. £10.10s.0d. (Also DC version).

fig.428. Cossor 'Melody Maker' Model 342, by A.C. Cossor Ltd. 1933. 3-v Batt TRF Table Model, MW/LW Mtrs walnut veneered plywood cabinet. 13½ in. x 18 ½ in. x 10¼ in.

fig.429. Telsen Model 474, by Telsen Electric Co. Ltd. 1933. 3-v + R, AC TRF Table Model, MW/LW Mtrs, walnut cabinet with black line inlay. 14 ½ in. x 11 ¾ in. x 8 ½ in.

fig.430. Marconiphone Model 276, by Marconiphone Co. Ltd. 1933. 6-v + R, AC SHet Table Model, MW/LW Mtrs, drum-drive scale, static suppressor switch, brown Bakelite trim, mahogany cabinet. 18 ½ in. x 16 ½ in. x 11 ½ in. £23.2s.0d. Marconiphone's first superhet. The static suppressor was activated by the push-pull action of the volume control knob: "If the next door refrigerator starts a machine gun obligato, just switch in the Static Suppressor and peace will reign once more".

fig.431. Ekco Model AC 85, by E.K. Cole Ltd. 1934. 5-v + R, AC SHet Table Model, MW/LW Mtrs/StN, chrome-centred black Bakelite knobs, chromium-plated trim, black Bakelite cabinet. 12 ½ in. x 21 in. x 9 ½ in. £13.13s.0d. (Also brown Bakelite version and Model B85, battery version price £13.2s.6d). Optional wooden stand, £1.9s.6d extra.

fig.432. Ferranti 'Gloria', by Ferranti Ltd. 1934. 5-v + R, AC SHet, MW/LW Mtrs/StN, electric clock, black Bakelite knobs with chromium-plated inserts, simulated mother-of-pearl tuning scale with chromium-plated surround, walnut veneered plywood cabinet. 24 in. x 15 in. x 9 in. £25.4s.0d. The electric clock is marked in both the 12 hour and the 24 hour systems "for the convenience of those who listen to foreign programmes".

fig.433. Radio Rentals Model 157, by E.K. Cole Ltd. 1934. 4-v + R, AC/DC SHet Table Model, MW/LW Mtrs plus interchangeable celluloid tuning scale printed with station names, local-distance switch, brown Bakelite cabinet. 16 in. x 13 ½ in. x 9 in. E.K. Cole Ltd.'s first set designed exclusively for Radio Rentals.

fig.434. Clarke's 'Atlas' Model 7-5-8, by H. Clarke & Co. (Manchester) Ltd. 1934. 4-v + R, AC SHet Table Model, MW/LW Mtrs, chromium-plated and brown Bakelite trim, simulated mother-of-pearl tuning scale (tilting for easy reading), mahogany veneered plywood cabinet. 11 in. x 22 ¼ in. x 11 ½ in. £14.14s.0d. Note diagonally positioned loud-speaker.

fig.435. G.E.C. 'Universal Mains Three', by General Electric Co. Ltd. 1934. 2-v +R +Bar, AC/DC TRF Table Model, MW/LW 0-100 deg, brown Bakelite cabinet. 13 ¼ in. x 13 ¼ in. x 6 ¼ in. £7.15s.0d.

fig.436. G.E.C. 'Compact Three', by General Electric Co. Ltd. 1934. 3-v Batt Table Model, MW/LW 0-100 deg, brown Bakelite cabinet. 12 ½ in. x 15 ¾ in. x 8 ¼ in. £5.10s.0d.

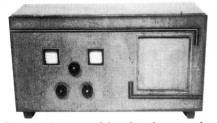

fig.437. Climax Model S5, by Climax Radio Electric Ltd. 1934. 4-v +R, SHet Table Model, MW/LW Mtrs, black and white painted detail, oak veneered plywood cabinet. 13 in. x 22 in. x 9 ½ in. £10.10s.0d. (Also produced in vertical cabinet).

fig.438. Sunbeam Model 22, by Sunbeam Electric Ltd. 1934. 3-v +R, AC/DC Table Model Midget, MW/LW Mtrs, walnut veneered plywood cabinet. 8 ¼ in. x 11 in. x 6 in. £9.9s.0d.

fig.439. Murphy Model A24, by Murphy Radio Ltd. March 1st 1934. 4-v +R, AC SHet Table Model, MW/LW Mtrs, plywood cabinet (des: R.D. Russell) with walnut veneers, an 'apron' veneered in bird's-eye maple, and beech cross bars over the loud-speaker cloth. 17 ¼ in. x 16 in. x 10 ¼ in. £14.10s.0d. Veneered plywood cabinets were lighter and were stronger compared with solid wood, and veneers could be made in expensive woods like bird's-eye maple which would otherwise prove too costly to use in the solid form. In common with his earlier cabinet designs, Russell's Model A24 was greeted at first with cries of protest. But this particular design caused more controversy amongst Murphy dealers than any other Murphy set, and Russell confessed to feeling "like Public Enemy No.1" every time he opened his post. However, Frank Murphy championed the A24 with large advertisements in the wireless and national Press showing him gazing at the set with the caption, "I don't know anything about design, but I know what *I LIKE* and ..... the longer you look at it, the more you like it!". In fact the listening public *did* like it. A dealer in Bournemouth reported that a lady customer thought the A24 clashed badly with the decor of her sitting room, but she liked the set so much she decided to have the entire room re-papered and re-painted to match it (report in *Murphy News*, March 10th 1934).

fig.440. Marconiphone Model 296 AC, by Marconiphone Co. Ltd. 1934. 4-v +R plus Fluid Light Tuning Indicator, AC SHet Table Model, MW/LW Mtrs/StN, illuminated full-vision tuning scale, brown Bakelite trim, walnut cabinet. 16 in. x 18 in. x 10 ¾ in. £14.3s.6d. The tuning indicator showed a rising column of light as the station was tuned in.

fig.441. Ultra Model 22 , by Ultra Electric Ltd. 1934. 3-v +R, AC SHet Table Model, MW/LW Mtrs, tone control, new 'clock-face' tuning dial in simulated mother-of-pearl, chromium-plated escutcheon and knobs, walnut cabinet. 19 in. x 15 ½ in. x 10 in. £12.12s.0d. A drawer beneath the cabinet contained a chart of the new *Lucerne Plan* wavelengths.

fig.442. K.B. 'Rejectostat Universal' Model 381, by Kolster-Brandes Ltd. 1934. 4-v +R, AC/DC SHet Table Model, MW/LW Mtrs/StN, aeroplane dial, brown Bakelite trim, walnut cabinet. 14 in. x 14 in. x 9 in. £10.10s.0d.

fig.443. H.M.V. 'Greenwich Superhet Five' Model 468, by The Gramophone Co. Ltd. 1934. 4-v +R, AC SHet Table Model, MW/LW Mtrs/StN, clockwork clock in front of moving-coil loud-speaker, mahogany and walnut cabinet with rosewood inlay. 19 ¼ in. x 17 in. x 11 ½ in. £19.19s.0d. (H.M.V. Model 467, without clock).

fig.444. McMichael 'AC Superhet', by McMichael Radio Ltd. 1934. 4-v +MetR, AC SHet Table Model, MW/LW Mtrs, full-vision tuning scale, cord-driven cursor, brown Bakelite trim, walnut veneered plywood cabinet. 20 in. x 15 in. x 10 in. £14.14s.0d.

fig.445. Sunbeam 'Universal' Model 57, by Sunbeam Electric Ltd. 1934. 4-v +R, AC/DC SHet Table Model, MW/LW Mtrs/StN, interchangeable 'aeroplane' dial, walnut and mahogany veneered plywood cabinet. 18 in. x 14 in. x 7 ½ in. A strip of light projected onto the celluloid dial from behind is used to indicate the station settings. ('Universal' Model 55 has tuning control knob in centre of dial, otherwise the cabinet is identical).

fig.446. Pye Type SE/U, by Pye Radio Ltd. 1934. 4-v +MetR, AC/DC SHet Table Model, MW/LW Mtrs/StN, walnut veneered plywood cabinet. 12 ½ in. x 19 ½ in. x 12 ¼ in. £16.16s.0d.

fig.447. 'Penthouse', by R.K. Radio Laboratories. 1934. 3-v +R, AC/DC SHet Table Model 'Midget', MW/LW 0-100 deg, line-cord, chromium plated grille and tuning dial, solid and veneered walnut cabinet. 8 ½ in. x 14 in. x 6 in. A combined radio/drinks cabinet made in the U.S.A. for the British market. It used Brimar valves with UX bases. The left hand hinged wing opens to reveal 6 miniature glasses with silver banding while the right hand hinged wing holds 3 small glass bottles marked 'Rye', 'Bourbon' and 'Scotch'.

fig.448. Ekco Model AD 65, by E.K. Cole Ltd. 1934. 3-v +R, AC/DC SHet Table Model, MW/LW Mtrs/StN, chrome-centred knobs, chromium-plated trim, black Bakelite cabinet (des: Wells Coates, 1932). 15 in. dia x 8 in. deep. £11.11s.0d. (Also plain brown Bakelite version. Various non-standard colours such as imitation green marble were also available for this and other Ekco receivers by special order from the Ekco Bakelite Plant of E.K. Cole Ltd., see fig.285).

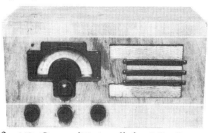

fig.449. Graves 'National', by J.G. Graves. 1934. 3-v +R, AC SHet Table Model, MW/LW Mtrs/StN, brown Bakelite trim, walnut veneered plywood cabinet. 10 in. x 18 in. x 10 in.

fig.450. R.I. 'Ritz Airflo', by Radio Instruments Ltd. 1934. 4-v +R, AC SHet Table Model, MW/LW Mtrs/StN, drum-drive tuning scale, controls are fitted into a sunken panel at the side, walnut veneered bent plywood cabinet. 19 ½ in. x 16 ¾ in. x 10 ½ in. £16.16s.0d. This receiver appeared again in 1947 with SW/MW/LW and a full-vision dial.

fig.451. Radio Rentals Model RR 484, by E.K. Cole Ltd. 1934. 3-v +R, AC/DC SHet Table Model, MW/LW Mtrs/StN, interchangeable station dial, brown Bakelite cabinet. 17 ¼ in. x 14 ¼ in. x 9 ¾ in.

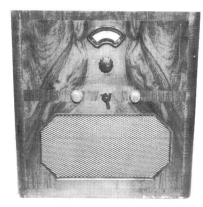

fig.452. McMichael 'Twin Speaker Superhet', by McMichael Radio Ltd. 1934. 4-v +R, AC SHet Table Model, MW/LW Mtrs, noise-suppressor switch, twin moving-coil loud-speakers, walnut veneered plywood cabinet. 20 in. x 19 ¼ in. x 10 in.

fig.453. Philips 'Superinductance' Model 274A, by Philips Lamps Ltd. 1934. 4-v + R, AC TRF Table Model, MW/LW Mtrs, walnut veneered plywood cabinet. 16 in. x 13 ½ in. x 8 ½ in. £9.9s.0d.

fig.454. McMichael 'Duplex Transportable', by McMichael Radio Ltd. 1934. 5-v Batt TRF Transportable, MW/LW Mtrs, internal frame aerial, turntable, walnut veneered plywood cabinet. 19 ½ in. x 15 ½ in. x 9 in. £14.14s.0d.

fig.455. McMichael 'Superhet Mains Transportable', by McMichael Radio Ltd. 1934. 4-v + R, AC SHet Transportable, MW/LW Mtrs, internal frame aerial, turntable, walnut veneered plywood cabinet. 20 in. x 15 in. x 10 in. £16.16s.0d.

fig.456. Beethoven 'Major' Model S.G.4, by Beethoven Radio Ltd. 1934. 4-v Batt Suitcase Portable, MW/LW Mtrs with station names and *Lucerne Plan* wavelengths on a separate card, black painted wooden loud-speaker fret with chromium-plated trim, Bakelite tuning control panel, blue 'lizard' cloth covered wood case, with walnut and mahogany veneers. 10 in. x 13 in. x 14 in. (lid closed). £10.10s.0d.

fig.457. Philco Table Model, by Philco Radio & Television Corporation of Great Britain Ltd. 1934. 3-v + R, AC SHet Table Model, MW/LW Mtrs/StN, walnut veneered plywood cabinet. 15 ¾ in. x 12 ¾ in. x 8in.

fig.458. G.E.C. 'Superhet Five' Model DC5, by General Electric Co. Ltd. 1934. 4-v + Bar, DC SHet Table Model, MW/LW Mtrs/StN, walnut veneered plywood cabinet. 12 ¼ in. x 21 ¼ in. x 8 ½ £13.13s.0d. (Model AC5 is AC version).

fig.459. Pegasus 'Table Model', by Pegasus Ltd. 1934. 4-v + R, AC SHet Table Model, MW/LW Mtrs/StN, chromium-plated loud-speaker and dial surrounds, walnut veneered plywood cabinet. 19 in. x 16 in. x 9 ½ in.

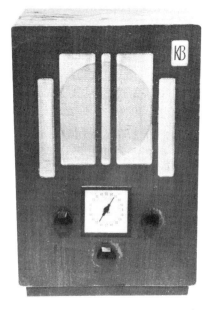

fig.460. K.B. 'New Pup' Model 362, by Kolster-Brandes Ltd. 1934. 3-v Batt Table Model, MW/LW 0-90 deg/StN, new 'clock-face' tuning dial, walnut grained plywood cabinet. 16 in. x 10 ¾ in. x 8 ¾ in. £5.15s.0d. (2-v + R, AC version is Model 397).

fig.461. Vidor Model CN 213, by Vidor Ltd. 1934. 3-v + R + Bar, AC/DC TRF Table Model, MW/LW Mtrs, walnut veneered plywood cabinet. 12 ½ in. x 15 in. x 8 in.

fig.462. H.M.V. Model 463, by The Gramophone Co. Ltd. 1934. 5-v +R, AC SHet Transportable, MW/LW Mtrs/StN, illuminated drum scale, frame aerial in hinged back door, turntable, black Bakelite knobs and escutcheon, walnut veneered plywood cabinet. 18 in. x 15 in. x 9 in. £16.16s.0d.

fig.463. Ferranti 'Arcadia' Model T1/AC, by Ferranti Ltd. 1934. 4-v +R, AC SHet Table Model, MW/LW Mtrs/StN, simulated mother-of-pearl tuning scale, chromium-plated escutcheon, black Bakelite loud-speaker surround, black Bakelite knobs with chromium-plated inserts, plywood cabinet veneered in quilted maple, figured walnut and Macassar Ebony. 20 ½ in. x 15 ½ in. x 9 ¼ in. £15.15s.0d. (Model T2/AC is later version, with slightly modified circuit).

fig.464. Philips 'Superindictance' Model 372B, by Philips Lamps Ltd. 1934. 6-v Batt TRF Table Model, MW/LW Mtrs, walnut veneered plywood cabinet. 15 ¼ in. x 17 in. x 9 in. £11.11s.0d.

fig.465. Ferranti 'Lancastria' (2nd Series), by Ferranti Ltd. 1934. 3-v +R, AC SHet Table Model, MW/LW Mtrs/StN, simulated mother-of-pearl tuning scale with chromium-plated surround, black Bakelite knobs with chromium-plated inserts, bird's-eye maple, walnut and rosewood veneered plywood cabinet. 20 in. x 14 ½ in. x 9 in. £12.12s.0d.

fig.466. Regentone Model B/35, by Regentone Ltd. 1934. 3-v Batt Table Model, MW/LW Mtrs/StN, stamped metal escutcheon, brown Bakelite knobs and control panel, walnut veneered plywood cabinet. 18 in. x 13 ½ in. x 10 in. £7.15s.0d.

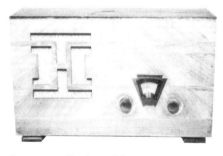

fig.467. Mullard Model MB3, by Mullard Wireless Service Co. Ltd. 1934. 3-v TRF Batt Table Model, MW/LW Mtrs, 'Droitwich swamp filter', walnut veneered plywood cabinet. 13 ½ in. x 21 ¼ in. x 8 ¾ in. £8.8s.0d. Mullard's first complete factory-built receiver. (Model MB3A in upright cabinet introduced in 1935).

fig.468. Ekco Model ADT 95, by E.K. Cole Ltd. 1934. 5-v +R, AC/DC SHet Transportable, MW/LW Mtrs/StN, internal frame aerial, turntable, brown Bakelite knobs and cabinet. 18 in. x 15 in. x 10 in. £15.15s.0d. (Battery version, Model BT 95).

fig.469. Philips Model 588, by Philips Lamps Ltd. 1934. 5-v +R, AC SHet Table Model, MW/LW Mtrs, walnut veneered plywood cabinet. 16 ¼ in. x 13 ¾ in. x 8 ½ in. £12.0s.0d.

fig.470. Bush Model SAC5, by Bush Radio Ltd. 1934. 4-v +R +West plus Neon Lamp Tuning Indicator, AC SHet Table Model, MW/LW Mtrs, tone control, chromium-plated grille and trim, walnut veneered plywood cabinet. 18 in. x 15 in. x 9 in. £13.13s.0d. As the station was tuned in, the light from the tuning indicator lamp grew brighter.

fig.471. Philips 'Superinductance' Model 472A, by Philips Lamps Ltd. 1934. 5-v +R, AC TRF Table Model, MW/LW Mtrs/StN, interchangeable station dial cards, brown Bakelite knobs and dial surround, walnut veneered plywood cabinet. 18 ½ in. x 14 ¾ in. x 8 ½ in. £15.15s.0d. Supplied with two dial cards: one giving a selection of the principal European transmitters and the other closely calibrated with the name of every station likely to be received.

fig.472. Philips 'Superinductance' Model 838U, by Philips Lamps Ltd. 1934. 3-v +R +Bar, AC/DC TRF Table Model, MW/LW Mtrs/StN, brown Bakelite knobs and tuning scale surround, walnut veneered plywood cabinet. 17 in. x 14 ½ in. x 9 in. £9.19s.6d.

fig.473. Ekco Model AC 86, by E.K. Cole Ltd. 1935. 5-v +R, AC SHet Table Model, MW/LW Mtrs/StN, chromium-plated trim, black Bakelite cabinet. 12 in. x 22 in. x 8 ½ in. £13.13s.0d. Cabinet also in 'walnut' Bakelite. (Model SW 86 is SW/MW/LW export version, and Model B86 is MW/LW battery version).

fig.474. McMichael Model 135, by McMichael Radio Ltd. 1935. 4-v +R, AC SHet, MW/LW Mtrs/StN, interchangeable station and wavelength card, twin moving-coil loud-speakers, walnut stand, walnut veneered plywood cabinet. 14 in. x 22 ½ in. x 13 ½ in. (without stand).

fig.475. Philips Model 587U, by Philips Lamps Ltd. 1935. 6-v +R +Bar plus Fluid Light Tuning Indicator, AC/DC SHet Console, MW/LW Mtrs/StN, brown Bakelite scale surround, walnut veneered plywood cabinet. 33 ½ in. x 18 ½ in. x 13 ½ in. Interchangeable celluloid station card.

fig.476. Philips Model 940A, by Philips Lamps Ltd. 1935. 2-v +R, AC Table Model, MW Mtrs, local-distance switch, brown Bakelite cabinet. 10 in. x 12 ½ in. x 6 ¾ in. £6.16s.6d. Designed as a 'local station' receiver.

fig.477. Ekco Model AD 76, by E.K. Cole Ltd. 1935. 4-v +R, AC/DC SHet Table Model, MW/LW Mtrs/StN, chrome-centred black Bakelite knobs, chromium-plated trim, black Bakelite cabinet. 15 ¾ in. diameter x 7 ¾ in. deep. £12.1s.6d. (Also AC-only version, Model AC 76, price £11.11s.0d and alternative brown 'walnut' Bakelite cabinet).

fig.477a. Ekco Model AD 76 on optional matching wooden stand. 26 ½ in. high, price £1.5s.0d.

fig.478. Decca Model 919, by Decca Gramophone Co. Ltd. 1935. 3-v +R, AC SHet Table Model, MW/LW Mtrs/StN, rosewood veneered plywood cabinet. 14 in. x 18 in. x 8 ½ in. Single-knob control for wave-change, station tuning and volume. (Also 'Home & Car' mains/battery version, also AC/DC version).

fig.479. Beethoven 'Super Minor', by Beethoven Radio Ltd. 1935. 4-v Batt Suitcase Portable, MW/LW Mtrs/StN, loud-speaker and internal frame aerial in lift-up lid, chromium-plated trim, mahogany and walnut veneered panels, celluloid control panel, blue lizard-covered wood case. 8 ½ in. x 11 in. x 12 in. £10.10s.0d.

fig.480. Marconiphone Model 235, by Marconiphone Co. Ltd. 1935. 3-v +R, AC TRF Table Model, MW/LW Mtrs/StN, chromium-plated knobs, grille and dial surround, black rexine covered wood cabinet. 10 in. x 16 in. x 9 in. £8.18s.6d. (Model 238 is walnut veneered plywood cabinet version).

fig.481. Defiant Model M900, produced by the Co-operative Wholesale Society Ltd. 1935. 3-v +R, AC Table Model, MW/LW Mtrs, brown Bakelite cabinet. 12 ½ in. x 13 in. x 7 ¾ in. Chassis made by Plessey. In the early 1930s, signatories of the Radio Wholesale Trading Agreement refused to supply the Co-op with receivers because the 'dividend' they offered was seen as unfair price-cutting. In response to this, the Co-op defiantly organised the manufacture of their own brand of receivers (hence the name) which they produced from the end of 1933 until well after the Second World War.

fig.482. Clarion 'Old Lager', made in America for the British market. 1935. 3-v +R, AC TRF, MW 0-100 deg, line-cord resistor, beer-barrel shaped oak cabinet with copper bands. 7 in. diameter x 10 ¼ in. long. Principally sold by Selfridges in Oxford Street, London. This was one of several 'barrel' receivers produced from the mid-1930s to the late 1950s in both America and in Britain. Some of these were: 'Radiokeg', by R.K. Radio Laboratories, Chicago. 1935. 4-v +R, AC SHet, MW Mtrs, line-cord resistor, oak barrel with copper bands. 10 ½ in. x 9 ½ in. x 12 in.; 'Unique Beer-Barrel', by Unique Radio Ltd., Chadwell Heath, Essex. November 1954. 4-v +R, AC/DC SHet, MW Mtrs/StN, 4 station switching by means of the 'beer tap', volume/on/off operated by the bung, oak barrel with a choice of brass, copper, chrome or black bands. £25.0s.0d inc PT; 'Rum Barrel Novelty Radio', by Whitley & Holroyd Ltd., Bradford. February 1958. 4-v +R, AC/DC SHet, MW Mtrs, oak 'rum barrel' cabinet in an oak cradle, copper bands. £21.8s.0d + PT.

fig.483. 'International', by Radio Accoustic Products Ltd. 1935. 4-v +R, AC SHet Table Model, SW/MW/LW Mtrs/StN, walnut veneered plywood cabinet. 13 ¾ in. x 17 ¾ in. x 8 ½ in.

fig.484. Beethoven Model 77, by Beethoven Radio Ltd. 1935. 4-v +R, AC SHet Table Model, MW/LW Mtrs + 0-100 deg, walnut cabinet with chromium-plated trim. 19 in. x 14 in. x 12 in. £11.11s.6d. Hidden in the two front feet are lists of station names and their wavelengths printed on pull-out cards.

fig.485. Ekco Model AD 36, by E.K. Cole Ltd. 1935. 3-v +R, AC/DC TRF Table Model, MW/LW Mtrs/StN, chrome-centred black Bakelite knobs, chromium-plated grille bars, black Bakelite cabinet. 14½ in. diameter. £8.18s.6d. (Also 'walnut' Bakelite version with plain brown Bakelite knobs price £8.8s.0d. Various non-standard colours such as yellow and blue were also available for this and other Ekco receivers by special order from the Ekco Bakelite Plant of E.K. Cole Ltd., see fig.285).

fig.486. 'Three In One', a home-constructor's set designed by 'Lucifer' of *Wireless World*. Plans published in September 13th 1935 issue. 3-v Batt Portable for headphone use, 'Etholog' tuning dial, 0-100 deg, internal frame aerial, leather strap, headphone compartment, oak cabinet. 11 ¼ in. x 13 in. x 4 3/4 in.

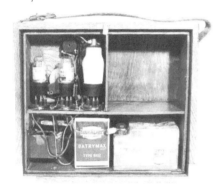

fig.486a. The back of the 'Three In One' with panel removed.

fig.487. Ferranti 'Arcadia Console', by Ferranti Ltd. 1935. 4-v + R, AC SHet Console, MW/LW Mtrs/StN, simulated mother-of-pearl tuning scale, black Bakelite knobs with chromium-plated inserts, mahogany, walnut and rosewood veneered plywood cabinet. 32 ½ in. x 17 in. x 10 ½ in. £18.18s.0d.

fig.488. Ekco Model ACT 96, by E.K. Cole Ltd. 1935. 6-v + R, AC SHet Transportable, MW/LW Mtrs/StN, internal frame aerial, turntable, chromium-plated trim, black Bakelite cabinet. 18 in. x 14 ½ in. x 9 ½ in. £15.15s.0d. ('Walnut' Bakelite version, price £15.4s.6d).

fig.489. Ferranti 'Nova Consolette', by Ferranti Ltd. 1935. 3-v + R, AC SHet Table Model, MW/LW Mtrs/StN, simulated mother-of-pearl scale, brown Bakelite cabinet. 18 in. x 13 in. x 9 in. £11.11s.0d.

fig.490. AC Table Model, by F.C. Heayberd & Co. 1935. 4-v + R, AC SHet Table Model, MW/LW Mtrs/StN, lift-up lid revealing dial and controls, walnut veneered plywood cabinet. 12 in. x 17 in. x 10 ¼ in.

fig.491. Philips Model 585U, by Philips Lamps Ltd. 1935. 5-v + R plus Fluid Light Tuning Indicator, AC/DC SHet Table Model, MW/LW Mtrs/StN, interchangeable tuning scale, tone control, noise suppression switch, walnut veneered plywood cabinet. 19 in. x 15 in. x 9 ½ in. £14.14s.0d.

fig.492. Philips Model 580A, by Philips Lamps Ltd. 1935. 5-v + R, AC SHet Table Model, MW/LW Mtrs, walnut veneered plywood cabinet. 11 ½ in. x 16 in. x 7 ¾ in. £12.12s.0d.

fig.493. Mullard Model MU 35, by Mullard Wireless Service Co. Ltd. 1935. 5-v + R + Bar, AC/DC SHet Table Model, MW/LW Mtrs/StN, tone control, walnut veneered plywood cabinet. 17 ¼ in. x 13 ½ in. x 8 in. £12.12s.0d. Mullard's first mains receiver. 'Geographical tuning', with station names grouped geographically on the scale.

fig.494. G.E.C. 'AC Mains Four', by General Electric Co. Ltd. 1935. 3-v +R, AC Table Model, MW/LW Mtrs, chromium-plated grille bars, chrome-centred brown Bakelite knobs, brown Bakelite cabinet. 16 ¼ in. x 14 in. x 8 ½ in. £9.15s.0d.

fig.497. Pegasus 'Table Model', by Pegasus Ltd. 1935. 4-v +R, AC SHet Table Model, MW/LW Kcs/StN, tone control, static suppressor knob, chromium-plated loud-speaker and dial surrounds, walnut veneered plywood cabinet. 20 in. x 17 ½ in. x 9 in.

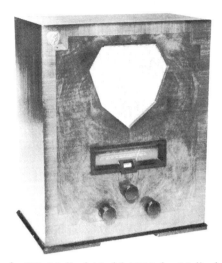

fig.500. Mullard Model MB4, by Mullard Wireless Service Co. Ltd. 1935. 4-v Batt Table Model, MW/LW Mtrs, brown Bakelite trim, walnut veneered plywood cabinet. 17 ¾ in. x 14 ½ in. x 9 in. £9.12s.6d.

fig.495. Pye Model T/M, by Pye Radio Ltd. 1935. 3-v +R, AC SHet Table Model, MW/LW Mtrs/StN, walnut veneered plywood cabinet. 18 ¾ in. x 14 ½ in. x 9 ¾ in.

fig.498. Cossor Model 364, by A.C. Cossor Ltd. 1935. 4-v +R, AC SHet Table Model, SW/MW/LW Mtrs/StN, interchangeable tuning scale, thermometer tuning, chromium-plated trim, brown Bakelite knobs, walnut veneered plywood cabinet. 16 in. x 14 ½ in. x 10 ½ in. £11.11s.0d. (Also Model 366A, battery version).

fig.501. Cossor 'All Electric' Model 367, by A.C. Cossor Ltd. 1935. 3-v +R, AC TRF Table Model, MW/LW Mtrs/StN, interchangeable tuning scale, thermometer tuning, brown Bakelite trim, walnut veneered plywood cabinet. 16 in. x 14 ½ in. x 10 ½ in. £9.19s.6d.

fig.496. Ultra Model 66, by Ultra Electric Ltd, 1935. 3-v +R, AC/DC SHet Table Model, MW/LW Mtrs/StN, clock-face dial in simulated mother-of-pearl, chromium-plated trim, walnut veneered plywood cabinet. 18 ¼ in. x 14 ¾ in. x 8 ¾ in. £9.9s.0d.

fig.499. Burndept 'Mobile Radio', by Burndept Ltd. 1935. 4-v +R +Bar, AC/DC Transportable, MW/LW Mtrs/StN, walnut veneered plywood cabinet. 16 ½ in. x 15 in. x 10 ¼ in.

fig.502. Murphy Model A26, by Murphy Radio Ltd. 1935. 4-v +R, AC SHet Table Model, MW/LW Mtrs, Australian walnut veneered plywood cabinet (des: R.D. Russell). 17 in. x 16 in. x 9 ¾ in. £11.0s.0d.

fig.503. Alba Model 880, by A.J. Balcombe Ltd. 1935. 5-v + R plus Neon Lamp Tuning Indicator, AC SHet Table Model, SW/ MW/LW Mtrs, walnut veneered plywood cabinet. 19 ½ in. x 15 ½ in. x 12 in. £16.16s.0d.

fig.504. Bush Model SAC 25, by Bush Radio Ltd. 1935. 4-v + R, AC SHet Table Model, MW/LW Mtrs/StN, mahogany veneered plywood cabinet. 21 in. x 16 in. x 10 in. £14.3s.6d.

fig.505. Ormond Model 608, by Ormond Engineering Co. Ltd. 1935. 4-v + R, AC SHet Table Model, SW/MW/LW Mtrs/ StN, walnut veneered plywood cabinet. 19 in. x 16 in. x 10 ¾ in.

fig.506. Philips 'Superinductance' Model 577A, by Philips Lamps Ltd. 1935. 5-v +R, AC TRF Table Model, MW/LW Mtrs/StN, interchangeable station cards, brown Bakelite knobs & dial surround, walnut veneered plywood cabinet. 19 in. x 15 in. x 9 in. £13.13s.0d.

fig.507. McMichael Model 435, by McMichael Radio Ltd. 1935. 5-v + R, AC SHet Transportable, MW/LW Mtrs/StN, internal frame aerial, turntable, chromium-plated trim, walnut veneered plywood cabinet. 20 in. x 15 in. x 10 ½ in. £16.16s.0d. (Also battery version in same cabinet).

fig.508. K.B. Model 433, by Kolster-Brandes Ltd. 1935. 2-v + R, AC Table Model, 0-90 deg/StN, walnut veneered plywood cabinet. 14 ½ in. x 14 ¾ in. x 9 in. £9.17s.6d.

fig.509. K.B. 'Rejectostat' Model 430, by Kolster-Brandes Ltd. 1935. 3-v + R, AC/ DC SHet Table Model, MW/LW Mtrs/ StN, brown Bakelite trim, walnut veneered plywood cabinet. 16 in. x 13 ¾ in. x 9 in. £8.18s.6d.

fig.510. K.B. Model 428, by Kolster-Brandes Ltd. 1935. 4-v + R AC SHet Table Model, MW/LW Mtrs/StN, Bakelite trim, walnut veneered plywood cabinet. 19 ¼ in. x 16 in. x 10 ¼ in. £14.14s.0d. This receiver employed a 'Fototune' dial which showed one station at a time through a window as each station was tuned in.

fig.511. G.E.C. Model BC 635, by General Electric Co. Ltd. 1935. 4-v Batt Table Model, SW/MW/LW Mtrs/StN, aerial wire wound on back of set, chromium-plated trim, walnut veneered plywood cabinet. 17 ½ in. x 14 ½ in. x 10 in.

fig.512. Derwent 'International Five', by Central Equipment Ltd. 1935. 4-v + R, AC SHet Table Model, MW/LW Mtrs/StN, walnut veneered plywood cabinet. 15 in. x 18 in. x 9 in.

fig.513. Cossor 'Super-Ferrodyne' Model 368, by A.C. Cossor Ltd. 1935. 3-v + R, AC TRF Table Model, MW/LW Mtrs/StN, interchangeable tuning scale, brown Bakelite knobs and trim, mahogany stained plywood cabinet. 13 ½ in. x 20 in. x 10 in. £8.18s.6d.

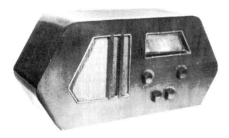

fig.514. McMichael Model 235, by McMichael Radio Ltd. 1935. 3-v + R, MW/LW Mtrs/StN, chromium-plated trim, walnut veneered plywood cabinet. 12 in. x 24 ½ in. x 9 in. £12.12s.0d. (AC/DC version, Model 535U, in same cabinet).

fig.515. Aerodyne 'Nightingale', by Aerodyne Radio Ltd. 1935. 3-v Batt Table Model, MW/LW Mtrs/StN, chromium-plated bars over grille, walnut veneered plywood cabinet with rosewood inlay. 13 in. x 18 in. x 10 in. £7.17s.6d.

fig.516. Ferranti 'Lancastria', by Ferranti Ltd. 1935. 3-v + R, AC SHet Table Model, MW/LW Mtrs/StN, simulated mother-of-pearl tuning scale, black Bakelite knobs with chromium-plated inserts, bird's-eye maple, walnut and rosewood veneered plywood cabinet. 18 in. x 14 in. x 9 in. £12.12s.0d.

fig.517. 'Transatlantic', by Radio Accoustic Products Ltd. 1935. 4-v + R, AC SHet Table Model, SW/MW/LW Mtrs/StN, walnut veneered plywood cabinet. 13 ¼ in. x 19 ¾ in. x 9 in.

fig.518. H.M.V. Model 360, by The Gramophone Co. Ltd. 1935. 3-v + R, AC TRF Table Model, MW/LW Mtrs/StN, walnut cabinet. 11 in. x 17 ¼ in. x 9 in. £9.9s.0d. (Identical chassis used in Marconiphone Model 240 and Columbia Model 359).

fig.519. 'Good Listening' Table Model. 1935. 4-v + R, AC SHet Table Model, SW/MW/LW Mtrs/StN, walnut veneered plywood cabinet. 12 in. x 20 ¼ in. x 9 in.

fig.520. Ferranti 'Parva', by Ferranti Ltd. 1936. 3-v Batt TRF Table Model, MW/LW Mtrs/StN, brown Bakelite knobs with chromium-plated inserts, brown Bakelite cabinet. 17 ¾ in. x 13 in. x 9 in. £6.15s.0d.

fig.521. Ultra Model 101, by Ultra Electric Ltd. 1936. 3-v + R, AC SHet Table Model, MW/LW Mtrs/StN, chromium-plated trim, mahogany veneered plywood cabinet. 18 ¼ in. x 14 ¾ in. x 10 ¼ in. £9.19s.6d. (Also AC/DC version, Model 102, price £11.0s.6d, and battery version, Model 103).

fig.522. Marconiphone Model 219, by Marconiphone Co. Ltd. 1936. 5-v +R, AC SHet Table Model, MW/LW Mtrs/StN, gold coloured woven metal grille (newly introduced that year), brown Bakelite trim, walnut veneered plywood cabinet. 17 in. x 18 in. x 11 in. £13.2s.6d.

fig.523. Philco 'People's Set' Model 269, by Philco Radio & Television Corporation of Great Britain Ltd. August 1936. 3-v +R, AC SHet Table Model, MW/LW Mtrs/ StN/Kcs, walnut and mahogany veneered plywood cabinet. 18 in. x 14 ½ in. x 9 ½ in. £9.9s.0d. (Model 444 is Bakelite cabinet version, fig.535). The Philco 269 was the first model released in the 'People's Set' series of comparatively cheap and fairly basic receivers. They were designed to be affordable by the masses and were produced "that no one in Great Britain need be without the benefits of radio, and.....to ensure that the enjoyment of good radio be universally attained".

fig.524. Mullard Model MAS4, by Mullard Wireless Service Co. Ltd. 1936. 4-v +R, AC SHet Table Model, SW/MW/LW Mtrs/ StN, tuning meter, brown Bakelite and bronze trim, walnut veneered plywood cabinet. 18 in. x 19 ½ in. x 11 in. £14.14s.0d.

fig.525. Ace Model BS4, by Ace Radio. 1936. 5-v +R, AC SHet Table Model, SW/MW/ LW Mtrs/StN, walnut veneered plywood cabinet. 16 in. x 23 ½ in. x 10 in.

fig.526. Philco 'People's Set' Model 333, by Philco Radio & Television Corporation of Great Britain Ltd. September 1936. 3-v Batt Table Model, MW/LW Mtrs/StN/Kcs, black Bakelite cabinet. 16 ½ in. x 13 ½ in. x 11 in. £5.5s.0d. (AC version, Model 444, fig.535).

fig.527. R.G.D. Model 625, by Radio Gramophone Development Co. Ltd. 1936. 5-v +R plus Neon Lamp Tuning Indicator, AC SHet Table Model, 2SW/MW/LW Mtrs/StN, aeroplane dial, woven metal grille, walnut veneered plywood cabinet. 22 in. x 17 in. x 13 in.

fig.528. Philips Model V5A, by Philips Lamps Ltd. 1936. 4-v +R, AC SHet Table Model, SW/MW/LW Mtrs/StN, brown Bakelite cabinet. 13 ½ in. x 16 ¾ in. x 7 ½ in. No separate chassis, the components were fixed to lugs mounted on the inside of the cabinet encircling the loud-speaker.

fig.529. Ultra Model 48, by Ultra Electric Ltd. 1936. 4-v +R, AC SHet Table Model, SW/MW/LW Mtrs/StN, walnut veneered plywood cabinet. 17 ¼ in. x 20 ¾ in. x 11 ½ in. £13.13s.0d.

fig.530. Pilot Model U650, by Pilot Radio Ltd. 1936. 5-v +R plus Magic-Eye Tuning Indicator, AC SHet Table Model, 2SW/MW/LW Mtrs/StN, aeroplane dial, bronze trim, walnut and rosewood veneered cabinet. 20 in. x 15 in. x 11 in. £16.16s.0d. One of the first receivers with a Magic-Eye.

fig.531. H.M.V. Model 425, by The Gramophone Co. Ltd. 1936. 5-v +R, AC SHet Table Model, MW/LW Mtrs/StN, expanded metal grille, brown Bakelite trim, walnut veneered plywood cabinet. 18 in. x 15 ½ in. x 10 ¾ in. £11.11s.0d.

fig.532. Milnes 'Diamond' Type 'D', by Milnes Radio Co. Ltd. 1936. 7-v Batt SHet Table Model, SW/MW/LW Mtrs/StN, chromium-plated trim, walnut veneered plywood cabinet. 22 ¾ in. x 15 in. x 11 ½ in. £16.16s.0d. 'Florentine bronze' trim optional extra. (Also three other models in identical cabinet: 'Pearl', 5-v +R AC SHet, price £17.17s.0d, 'Emerald', 6-v Batt SHet, price £11.11s.0d, and 'Ruby', 6-v +R AC SHet, price £13.13s.0d).

fig.533. Ekco 'All Electric' Model AC 97, by E.K. Cole Ltd. 1936. 4-v +R plus 'Mystic-Eye' Tuning Indicator, AC SHet Table Model, MW/LW Mtrs/StN, 'fidelity control', ivory coloured knobs and trim, black Bakelite cabinet. 21 in. x 12 ¾ in. x 8 ½ in. £13.13s.0d. Also in 'walnut' Bakelite cabinet, price £13.2s.6d.

fig.534. 'Transatlantic', by Radio Accoustic Products Ltd. 1936. 3-v +R, AC SHet Table Model, SW/MW/LW Mtrs/StN, walnut veneered plywood cabinet. 13 ¼ in. x 17 ¾ in. x 9 ½ in.

fig.535. Philco 'People's Set' Model 444, by Philco Radio & Television Corporation of Great Britain Ltd. September 1936. 3-v +R, AC SHet Table Model, MW/LW Mtrs/StN/Kcs, black Bakelite cabinet. 16 in. x 12 ½ in. x 9 ½ in. £6.6s.0d. (Model 269 is upright wooden cabinet version, fig.523, and Model 333 is battery version in Bakelite cabinet, fig.526). Several other versions of the People's Set appeared later in 1937: Model U427, 3-v +R +Bar, AC/DC SHet, MW/LW, price £7.7s.0d; Model A527, 4-v +R, AC SHet, MW/LW, price £7.7s.0d; Model U527, 4-v +R +Bar, AC/DC SHet, MW/LW, price £7.17s.6d; Model P527, 5-v Batt SHet, MW/LW, price £8.8s.0d; Model B537, 4-v +R, AC SHet, SW/MW/LW, price £9.9s.0d; Model V537, 4-v +R +Bar, AC/DC SHet, price £9.15s.0d (fig.562).

fig.536. McMichael Model 362, by McMichael Radio Ltd. 1936. 4-v +R, AC SHet Console, SW/MW/LW Mtrs/StN, walnut veneered plywood cabinet. 33 in. x 18 in. x 13 ½ in. £18.7s.6d. (Table Model, price £16.5s.6d).

fig.537. Roberts Model M4B, by Roberts Radio Co.Ltd. 1936. 4-v battery suitcase portable, MW/LW Mtrs (a card was supplied giving a list of all the principal European stations), internal frame aerial in lid, interior mahogany facing, plywood case covered in black leatherette (also in blue). 8 in. x 12 in. x 12 in. £9.9s.0d. The manufacturers claimed that it was the smallest portable then on the market.

fig.538. McMichael Model 367, by McMichael Radio Ltd. 1936. 4-v Batt Suitcase Portable, MW/LW Mtrs/StN, internal frame aerial, blue rexine-covered plywood case, walnut panels. 7 ¾ in. x 13 ¼ in. x 13 in. £8.18s.6d inc batteries.

fig.539. Belmont Model 746, by British Belmont Radio Ltd. 1936. 6-v +R plus Magic-Eye Tuning Indicator, AC SHet Table Model, SW/MW/LW Mtrs/StN, aeroplane dial, anodised bronze trim, wood knobs, walnut veneered plywood cabinet. 11 in. x 18 in. x 9 in. £13.2s.6d.

fig.540. McMichael Model 362, by McMichael Radio Ltd. 1936. 4-v +R, AC Table Model, SW/MW/LW Mtrs/StN, walnut veneered plywood cabinet. 21 in. x 16 ¼ in. x 11 ½ in. £16.5s.6d.

fig.543. Philips Model 795A, by Philips Lamps Ltd. 1936. 4-v +R plus Magic-Eye Tuning Indicator, AC SHet Table Model, SW/MW/LW Mtrs/StN, mono-knob tuning control, brown Bakelite escutcheon, chromium-plated trim, walnut cabinet. 17 ½ in. x 22 in. x 11 in. £18.18s.0d. Hinged tuning scale lifts forward when in use. (Same chassis as 1936 Mullard Models MAS5 and MUS5).

fig.546. Ultra Model 26, by Ultra Electric Ltd. 1936. 3-v +R, AC SHet, MW/LW Mtrs/StN, walnut veneered plywood cabinet. 19 ¼ in. x 15 ½ in. x 10 in.

fig.541. G.E.C. Model AC 37, by General Electric Co. Ltd. 1936. 3-v +R, AC Table Model, MW/LW Mtrs/StN, chromium-plated grille bars, brown Bakelite cabinet. 17 ½ in. x 14 ½ in. x 8 ¾ in. £8.18s.6d. The circuit employs a 'Droitwich rejector' on the long waveband.

fig.544. Vidor Model 254, by Vidor Ltd. 1936. 3-v +R, AC/DC TRF Table Model, 2SW/MW/LW Mtrs/StN, walnut veneered plywood cabinet. 17 ¾ in. x 13 ¾ in. x 9 ¾ in. £9.9s.0d. (Same chassis used in 1936 Burndept Model 252).

fig.547. Ferguson Model 366, by Universal Radio Distributers Ltd. 1936. 4-v +R +Bar, AC/DC SHet Table Model, 16/2,000m Mtrs/StN, walnut veneered plywood cabinet. 17 ½ in. x 12 ¾ in. x 9 ½ in. £10.10s.0d.

fig.542. Murphy Model A30, by Murphy Radio Ltd. 1936. 3-v +R, AC SHet Table Model, MW/LW Mtrs, mahogany and rosewood veneered plywood cabinet (des: R.D. Russell). 18 in. x 16 ½ in. x 8 ½ in. £9.17s.6d.

fig.545. McMichael Model 368, by McMichael Radio Ltd. 1936. 4-v Batt Table Model, MW/LW Mtrs/StN, simulated mother-of-pearl dial, walnut veneered plywood cabinet. 20 ½ in. x 15 ¾ in. x 10 ¼ in. £12.12s.0d.

fig.548. Ferranti 'Arcadia' by Ferranti Ltd. 1936. 4-v +R, AC SHet Table Model, SW/MW/LW Mtrs/StN, simulated mother-of-pearl tuning scale, walnut and rosewood veneered plywood cabinet. 18 in. x 16 in. x 9 ¼ in. £15.15s.0d.

fig.549. Alba Model AC 870, by A.J. Balcombe Ltd. 1936. 4-v +R, AC SHet Table Model, SW/MW/LW Mtrs/StN, walnut veneered plywood cabinet with rosewood inlay. 18 ½ in. x 17 ½ in. x 10 ½ in.

fig.550. Lissen Model 8214, by Lissen Ltd. 1936. 3-v +R, AC SHet Table Model, MW/LW Mtrs/StN, walnut veneered plywood cabinet. 18 ½ in. x 14 ¾ in. x 8 ½ in. £9.10s.0d.

fig.551. McMichael Model 361, by McMichael Radio Ltd. June 1936. 3-v +R, AC SHet Table Model, MW/LW Mtrs/StN, walnut veneered plywood cabinet. 18 ½ in. x 15 ¾ in. x 9 ¾ in.£11.7s.6d. Twin dial tuning with separate scales for stations and wavelengths.

fig.552. Wayfarer 'Major', by London Electric Appliances Ltd. 1936. 4-v Batt Portable, MW/LW Mtrs/StN, turntable, spring-open lid, ivory painted grille detail, blue Rexine covered wood case. 12 ½ in. x 8 ½ in. x 6 ½ in. £7.7s.0d.

fig.553. Benson Model 420, made in the United States for the British market. 1936. 4-v +R, AC/DC SHet Table Model, MW/LW Mtrs/StN, line-cord resistor, black Bakelite knobs, walnut veneered plywood cabinet. 7½ in. x 11 in. x 5½ in.

fig.554. Philips Model 745A, by Philips Lamps Ltd. 1936. 4-v +R, AC SHet Table Model, SW/MW/LW Mtrs/StN, brown Bakelite scale surround, walnut veneered plywood cabinet. 15 ¼ in. x 18 ½ in. x 10 ½ in. £12.12s.0d. Dial can be tilted forward and back. (Also AC/DC version, Model 745U).

fig.555. Decca Model 66, by Decca Gramophone Co. Ltd. c.1937. 4-v +R +Bar, AC/DC SHet Table Model, SW/MW/LW Mtrs/StN, aeroplane dial, anodised escutcheon, walnut and rosewood veneered plywood cabinet. 19 in. x 15 in. x 8 in. £10.10s.0d.

fig.556. Decca 'Triple Range All-Wave Universal Five-Five' Model 55, by Decca Gramophone Co. Ltd. 1937. 4-v +R +Bar, AC/DC SHet Transportable, SW/MW/LW Mtrs/StN, internal frame aerial, blue leathercloth covered wood case. 10 ½ in. x 13 ½ in. x 7 ½ in. £9.9s.0d. (Also black or maroon versions).

fig.557. McMichael Model 374, by McMichael Radio Ltd. 1937. 5-v +R plus Magic-Eye Tuning Indicator, AC Transportable, SW/MW/LW Mtrs StN, internal frame aerial, turntable, walnut veneered plywood cabinet. 23 in. x 17 in. x 11 ¾ in.

fig.558. Murphy Model AD 32, by Murphy Radio Ltd. 1937. 3-v +R, AC/DC SHet Table Model, MW/LW Mtrs/StN, walnut veneered plywood cabinet (des: R.D. Russell). 13 in. x 21 in. x 9 ½ in. £8.5s.0d. One of R.D. Russell's most successful cabinet designs, the first in which he used the potential of bent plywood to the full: the top and front are made from one continuous sheet of bent walnut veneered plywood.

fig.559. 'Grid Leak's Pocketphone', Type DB/P, by A. Reid Manufacturing Co. Ltd. 1937. 3-v Batt 'Midget' Portable for headphone use, internal frame aerial, black leathercloth-covered wood case. 1 ¾ in. x 7 ¼ in. x 5 ½ in. (closed). Uses 3 Hivac miniature valves in a circuit which first appeared in *Wireless World* on October 25th 1935. The 'Pocketphone' was designed for truely portable use "at the office, in the train, in the car, cycling, hiking - wherever you are, it will pick up at least one B.B.C. station up to 50 miles away". Brought out too with the 1937 Coronation in mind, to use on the processional route while listening to the B.B.C.'s commentary. (Also kit version for home-constructors).

fig.560. Magnum Model 3V, by Burne-Jones & Co. c.1937. 3-v +MetR, AC TRF Table Model, SW/MW/LW, Braille calibrated tuning dial, black Bakelite knobs, oak cabinet. 9 ¼ in. x 15 ½ in. x 8 in. Donated through the British Wireless For The Blind Fund.

fig.561. Philco Model U647, by Philco Radio & Television Corporation of Great Britain Ltd. 1937. 5-v +R +Bar, AC/DC SHet Table Model, 2SW/MW/LW Mtrs/StN/Kcs/Mcs, walnut veneered plywood cabinet. 20 ¼ in. x 17 ½ in. x 9 ½ in. £19.19s.0d.

fig.562. Philco 'People's Set' Model V537, by Philco Radio & Television Corporation Ltd. 1937. 4-v +R +Bar, AC/DC SHet Table Model, SW/MW/LW Mtrs/StN, brown Bakelite cabinet. 16 in. x 12 ¼ in. x 9 ½ in. £9.15s.0d.

fig.563. Bruton, made in the United States for the British market. 1937. 5-v +R plus Magic-Eye Tuning Indicator, AC/DC SHet Table Model, SW/MW/LW Mtrs/StN, moving-coil loud-speaker on top of cabinet pointing upwards, walnut veneered plywood cabinet. 13 in. x 12 in. x 10 in.

fig.564. Pye 'Baby Q', by Pye Ltd. 1937. 4-v Batt Portable, MW/LW Mtrs/StN, internal frame aerial, headphone socket on side, blue leathercloth-covered wood case. 10 in. x 11 ½ in. x 7 in. £8.8s.0d inc. batteries. Cabinet identical to 1938 Baby QU, AC/DC mains transportable of which few survived because they were prone to severe overheating and many went up in flames.

fig.565. Ekco Model UAW 78, by E.K. Cole Ltd. 1937. 4-v +R, AC/DC SHet Table Model, SW/MW/LW Mtrs/StN, 'walnut' Bakelite cabinet (des: Misha Black). 20 in. x 13 ½ in. x 9 in. £11.0s.6d. (Also battery version, Model BAW 78, and a "No HT Receiver", Model BV 78 which used a vibratory HT generator operated by a 4-volt accumulator).

fig.566. Murphy A34, by Murphy Radio Ltd. 1937. 3-v +R plus Magic-Eye Tuning Indicator, AC SHet Table Model, MW/LW Mtrs/StN, walnut veneered plywood cabinet (des: R.D. Russell). 16 in. x 21 in. x 9 ½ in. £11.10s.0d. New 'Alphabetical' tuning scale.

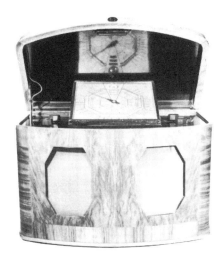

fig.567. McMichael Model 137, by McMichael Radio Ltd. 1937. 4-v +R plus Magic-Eye Tuning Indicator, AC SHet Table Model, SW/MW/LW Mtrs/StN, twin moving-coil loud-speakers, walnut veneered plywood cabinet. 15 in. x 23 in. x 13 in. £17.17s.0d. (AC/DC Model, price £18.7s.6d). Optional stand extra. 'Aeroplane' type dial lifts forward as the lid is raised.

fig.568. Pilot Model U385, by Pilot Radio Ltd. 1937. 6-v +R plus Magic-Eye Tuning Indicator, AC SHet Table Model, SW/MW/LW Mtrs/StN, aeroplane dial, brown Bakelite trim, walnut veneered plywood cabinet. 14 in. x 24 in. x 11 in. £15.15s.0d.

fig.569. Ekco Model B38, by E.K. Cole Ltd. 1937. 3-v Batt TRF Table Model, MW/LW Mtrs/StN, combined reaction control and local-distance switch, 'walnut' Bakelite cabinet. 17 in. x 13 in. x 9 in. £6.19s.6d. Also in black and chrome, price £7.4s.6d. (Model AD 38, AC/DC version).

fig.570. Ultra Model 122, by Ultra Electric Ltd. 1937. 3-v +R, AC/DC SHet Table Model, SW/MW/LW Mtrs/StN, solid and veneered walnut cabinet. 13 in. x 20 in. x 10 ½ in. £13.2s.6d.

fig.571. Philips Model 787 AX, by Philips Lamps Ltd. 1937. 6-v +R plus Magic-eye Tuning Indicator, AC SHet Table Model, MW/LW Mtrs/StN, multi-function 'mono knob' control, fold-down tuning scale, walnut veneered plywood cabinet. 15 ½ in. x 23 ½ in. x 10 ½ in. £20.9s.6d.

fig.572. Pye Model QAC3, by Pye Radio Ltd. 1937. 3-v +R plus Magic-Eye Tuning Indicator, AC SHet Table Model, Mtrs/StN, walnut veneered plywood cabinet. 13 ¼ in. x 20 in. x 10 in. £14.3s.6d.

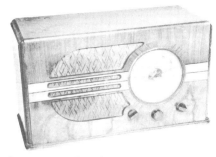

fig.573. Decca 'Triple Range AC' Model 77, by Decca Gramophone Co. Ltd. 1937. 4-v +R, AC SHet Table Model, SW/MW/LW Mtrs/StN, walnut veneered plywood cabinet. 11 in. x 19 ½ in. x 8 in. £9.19s.6d.

fig.574. Ferranti Model 837, by Ferranti Ltd. 1937. 3-v +R, AC SHet Table Model, SW/MW/LW Mtrs/StN, brown Bakelite knobs, brown Bakelite cabinet. 17 ½ in. x 13 in. x 9 in. £9.9s.0d.

fig.575. Brunswick Model BPU/1, by Brunswick Ltd. 1937. 5-v +R, AC SHet Table Model, SW/MW/LW Mtrs/StN, walnut veneered plywood cabinet. 17 ¾ in. x 17 in. x 9 ½ in.

fig.576. Marconiphone Model 562, by Marconiphone Co. Ltd. 1937. 6-v Batt SHet Transportable, MW/LW Mtrs/StN, illuminated tuning scale (exhibiting an extravagant use of battery current), internal frame aerial, walnut cabinet with side carrying handles. 20 ¾ in. x 17 in. x 9 ½ in. £16.5s.6d including batteries.

fig.577. Ferranti Model 1737, by Ferranti Ltd. 1937. 4-v +R plus Magic-Eye Tuning Indicator, AC SHet Table Model, walnut veneered plywood cabinet. 17 ½ in. x 19 ½ in. x 9 ½ in. £17.17s.0d.

fig.580. Ferranti Model 1037, by Ferranti Ltd. 1937. 3-v +R, AC SHet Table Model, SW/MW/LW Mtrs/StN, walnut veneered plywood cabinet. 17 in. x 16 in. x 9 ½ in.

fig.583. Marconiphone Model 537, by Marconiphone Co. Ltd. 1937. 6-v +R plus Magic-Eye Tuning Indicator, AC SHet Table Model, SW/MW/LW Mtrs/StN, gold coloured expanded metal grille, walnut veneered plywood cabinet. 18 in. x 19 in. x 11 in. £16.16s.0d.

fig.578. Pye Model QAC5, by Pye Radio Ltd. 1937. 5-v +R, AC SHet Table Model, 3SW/MW/LW Mtrs/StN/Mcs, walnut veneered plywood cabinet. £18.18s.0d.

fig.581. Graves 'Aerial AC Superhet', by J.G. Graves Ltd. 1937. 4-v +R, AC SHet Table Model, SW/MW/LW Mtrs/StN, brown Bakelite knobs and escutcheon, walnut veneered plywood cabinet. 17 in. x 12 in. x 9 ½ in.

fig.584. Ferranti Model 1137, by Ferranti Ltd. 1937. 3-v +R, AC SHet, SW/MW/LW Mtrs/StN, maple inlay with black banding, walnut veneered plywood cabinet. 19 in. x 19 in. x 10 ½ in. £12.12s.0d.

fig.579. Cossor Model 484, by A.C. Cossor Ltd. 1937. 3-v +R, AC SHet Table Model, SW/MW/LW Mtrs/StN, brown Bakelite knobs and trim, controls at sides, walnut stained plywood cabinet. 20 in. x 15 in. x 11 ½ in. £9.19s.6d.

fig.582. Ultra Model 115, by Ultra Electric Ltd. 3-v +R, AC SHet Table Model, SW/MW/LW Mtrs/StN, brown Bakelite trim, walnut veneered plywood cabinet. 17 ½ in. x 17 ½ in. x 10 ¼ in. £11.0s.6d. (Console version, Model 125).

fig.585. G.E.C. 'All-Wave Super-Six', by General Electic Co. Ltd. 1937. 5-v +R plus Magic-Eye Tuning Indicator, AC/DC SHet Table Model, SW/MW/LW Mtrs/StN, walnut veneered plywood cabinet. 17 in. x 17 ¾ in. x 11 ¼ in. £14.14s.0d. New 'chromoscopic' scale.

fig.586. Model ST 900, (des: John Scott-Taggart). October 1937. 5-v Batt, 4SW/MW Mtrs/StN, plug-in coils, no integral loud-speaker, birch plywood cabinet (no back). 12 in. x 16 in. x 8 in. A home-constructed receiver made from a blueprint published in *Popular Wireless*. Uses six pairs of tuning coils plus an extra pair for TV sound.

fig.587. McMichael Model 808, by McMichael Radio Ltd. 1938. 4-v +R, AC Transportable, MW/LW Mtrs/StN, internal frame aerial, Bakelite escutcheon and handle, walnut veneered plywood cabinet. 11 ¼ in. x 14 in. x 7 in. This set employed a unique method of tuning control called 'rotabar tuning'. Separate scales were provided for the medium and long wavebands and were arranged on each side of the loud-speaker aperture, running horizontally across the front of which was a bar with a thumb-grip. To tune the set, this bar was simply moved up or down in an arc of a circle, moving the ganged tuning condenser and scale pointers. Earlier production run produced in blue or maroon leatherette-covered plywood case. ('Bijou Portable' was battery version in leatherette-covered case only).

fig.588. Ultra 'Teledial' Model 400, by Ultra Electric Ltd. April 1938. 4-v +R plus Magic-Eye Tuning Indicator, AC SHet Table Model, SW/MW/LW Mtrs/StN, manual and mechanical auto-tuning (up to 8 stations could be 'dialled' automatically), brown Bakelite dial surround, walnut veneered plywood cabinet. 20 ½ in. x 17 in. x 10 ½ in.

fig.589. McMichael Model 380, by McMichael Radio Ltd. 1938. 4-v +R, AC SHet Table Model, SW/MW/LW Mtrs/StN, three separate tuning scales, mahogany and walnut veneered plywood cabinet. 15 in. x 14 ½ in. x 9 ½ in. £9.19s.6d. (Also battery version, Model 389).

fig.590. Murphy Model A50, by Murphy Radio Ltd. 1938. 5-v +R plus Magic-Eye Tuning Indicator, AC SHet Table Model, SW/MW/LW Mtrs/StN, 'alphabetical' tuning scale, mirrored smokey-blue glass control panel, mahogany veneered plywood cabinet. 18 in. x 23 in. x 12 in. Noise-suppressor switch "for use in districts where interference is bad".

fig.591. Ekco Model PB 189, by E.K. Cole Ltd. 1938. 6-v +R, AC SHet Table Model, SW/MW/LW Mtrs/StN, push-button motorised and manual tuning, brown Bakelite knobs and trim, walnut veneered plywood cabinet. 15 in. x 23 in. x 11 in. (Console version, Model C389).

fig.592. Murphy Model A52, by Murphy Radio Ltd. 1938. 8-v +R plus Magic-Eye Tuning Indicator, AC SHet Table Model, SW/MW/LW Mtrs/StN, manual and push-button motorised tuning, walnut veneered plywood cabinet. 17 in. x 21 ½ in. x 12 in. £18.10s.0d.

fig.593. Marconiphone Model 855, by Marconiphone Co. Ltd. 1938. 4-v +R, AC SHet Table Model, SW/MW/LW Mtrs/StN, push-button and manual tuning, eliptical moving-coil loud-speaker, walnut veneered plywood cabinet. 15 in. x 24 in. x 9 ½ in. Spare station names and blank labels provided for the listener to choose his own push-button selection.

fig.594. Pye Model 811, by Pye Ltd. 1938. 4-v +R, AC SHet Table Model, MW/LW Mtrs/StN, walnut veneered plywood cabinet with beech grille bars and surround. 13 ¼ in. x 20 in. x 10 in.

fig.595. Bush Model PB 50, 'All-Button Receiver', by Bush Radio Ltd. 1938. 4-v +R, AC SHet Table Model, MW/LW Mtrs/StN, pre-set push-button tuning only (no manual tuning control), two internal frame aerials, walnut veneered plywood cabinet. 14 ½ in. x 16 ½ in. x 9 ¾ in.

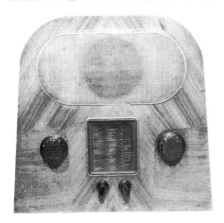

fig.596. Murphy Model A46, by Murphy Radio Ltd. 1938. 4-v +R, AC SHet Table Model, SW/MW/LW Mtrs/StN, walnut veneered plywood cabinet (des: R.D. Russell and Eden Minns). 17 in x 18 in. x 9 in.

fig.597. Midwest 'New Imperial', by Midwest Radio (Manufacturing) Co. Ltd. 1938. 14-v +R, AC SHet Console, 6 wavebands covering 4 ½ to 2,400 metres, chromium-plated chassis, simulated mother-of-pearl dial, walnut veneered cabinet. 47 in. x 26 in. x 14 in.

fig.598. Ultra Model 201, by Ultra Electric Ltd. 1938. 4-v +R, AC SHet Table Model, SW/MW/LW Mtrs/StN, brown Bakelite escutcheon, walnut veneered plywood cabinet. 18 ¾ in. x 16 in. x 9 in.

fig.599. Ekco Model AW 119, by E.K. Cole Ltd. June 1938. 4-v +R, AC SHet Table Model, SW/MW/LW + TV sound, Mtrs/StN, edgewise tuning control moves cursor across horizontal scale, walnut veneered plywood cabinet. 18 in. x 16 ¼ in. x 9 ½ in. £11.11s.0d.

fig.600. Philco Model 600, by Philco Radio & Television Corporation of Great Britain Ltd. 1938. 7-v +R, AC SHet Table Model, 2SW/MW/LW Mtrs/StN, walnut veneered plywood cabinet. 20 in. x 15 ½ in. x 10 ¾ in.

fig.601. Beethoven Model AD 770, by Beethoven Electric Equipment Ltd. 1938. 4-v +R, AC/DC SHet Transportable, SW/MW/LW Mtrs/StN, chromium-plated loud-speaker bars, dark blue rexine covered wood cabinet, lift-up lid revealing controls. 11 in. x 10 in. x 6 ½ in.

fig.602. Regentone 'Transportable 5', by Regentone Products Ltd. 1938. 4-v +R, AC SHet Transportable, SW/MW/LW Mtrs/StN, internal frame aerial, walnut veneered plywood cabinet. 14 ¾ in. x 14 in. x 9 ½ in.

fig.603. Murphy Model A48, by Murphy Radio Ltd. 1938. 4-v +R, AC SHet Table Model, SW/MW/LW Mtrs/StN, walnut veneered plywood cabinet (des: R.D. Russell). 19 ½ in. x 18 ½ in. x 11 ¼ in. £12.0s.0d.

fig.604. 'Deutscher Kleinempfanger' ('German Small Receiver'). 1938. Twin Triode +R, AC TRF Table Model, MW/LW 0-100 deg, balanced armature loudspeaker (the later production run of these receivers produced from the end of 1938 has a twin-tetrode and a moving-coil loudspeaker), black Bakelite cabinet. 9 ¼ in. x 9 ¼ in. x 4 ¾ in. Also brown Bakelite version and battery version in same cabinet. The 'Kleinempfanger' was one in a series of cheap and basic German 'People's Sets' ('Volkesempfanger') produced by the combined efforts of the German wireless manufacturing industry between 1933 and 1939 under the direction of the German Ministry of Propaganda to keep the population informed of Nazi policies and to enable them to listen to Hitler's speeches. Some 3 million in the series were sold, and because of their small size and souvenir appeal, many 'Kleinempfangers' were brought back to England by British soldiers returning after World War Two. The model illustrated was made by Siemens.

fig.605. Philips Model 470A, by Philips Lamps Ltd. 1938. 3-v +R, AC SHet Table Model, SW/MW/LW Mtrs/StN, brown Bakelite cabinet. 11 ¾ in. x 19 in. x 8 ½ in.

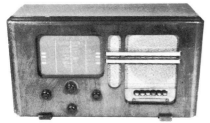

fig.606. McMichael Model 381, by McMichael Radio Ltd. 1938. 4-v +R, AC SHet Table Model, SW/MW/LW Mtrs/StN, push-button and manual tuning, brown Bakelite knobs, copper plated loud-speaker bars, walnut veneered plywood cabinet. 13 ½ in. x 26 in. x 9 in. (Battery version, Model 388, in same cabinet).

fig.607. Philco 'Empire Automatic' Model D521, by Philco Radio & Television Corporation of Great Britain Ltd. May 16th 1938. 4-v +R, AC SHet Table Model, MW/LW Mtrs/StN, push-button tuning, black Bakelite cabinet. 17 in. x 13 in. x 9 ½ in. When sent out from the factory, the D521 was already adjusted for Radio Normandie, London National, London Regional, Cologne and Athlone, with Droitwich and Welsh Regional together on one button, and Luxembourg and West Regional on another. These settings could be changed by the listener to suit his own requirements, and extra station-name tabs were supplied for insertion into the appropriate buttons when needed. (Three other models were released during the year in the same cabinet: Model D531, AC SHet, SW/MW/LW on June 15th, Model X521, AC/DC SHet on July 1st, and Model S521, Batt SHet on August 1st).

fig.608. Tempovox 'Grandmother Clock Radio', by British Tempovox Ltd. 1938. 4-v +R +Bar, AC/DC SHet, MW/LW Mtrs/StN, black painted and walnut veneered plywood cabinet. 57 in. x 14 in. x 7 in. £15.15s.0d. A combined receiver and electric grandmother clock, designed for the small modern house where space set a limit on the number of pieces of furniture that could be accommodated in any one room.

fig.609. Bush Model PB 51, by Bush Radio Ltd. 1938. 4-v +R, AC SHet Table Model, SW/MW/LW Mtrs/StN, push-button and manual tuning, walnut veneered plywood cabinet. 14 in. x 18 ½ in. x 11 in.

fig.610. Pilot Model BT 530, by Pilot Radio Ltd. 1938. 4-v +R, AC SHet Table Model, SW/MW/LW Mtrs/StN, manual and push-button tuning, walnut veneered plywood cabinet. 19 ¾ in. x 16 in. x 10 ½ in.

fig.611. H.M.V. Model 456, by The Gramophone Co. Ltd. 1938. 5-v +R plus Magic-Eye Tuning Indicator, AC/DC SHet Table Model, SW/MW/LW Mtrs/StN, eliptical moving-coil loud-speaker, brown Bakelite knobs and escutcheon, solid and veneered walnut cabinet. 19 ½ in. x 17 ¾ in. x 11 in.

fig.612. H.M.V. Model 654, by The Gramophone Co. Ltd. 1938. 4–v +R, AC/DC SHet Table Model, SW/MW/LW Mtrs/StN, walnut veneered plywood cabinet. 19 in. x 17 ½ in. x 9 ¾ in.

fig.613. Cossor Model 77B, by A.C. Cossor Ltd. 1939. 3–v + 2–v power unit on separate chassis, AC SHet Table Model, SW/MW/LW Mtrs/StN, brown Bakelite cabinet. 18 ½ in. x 14 ½ in. x 10 in. (Also wood cabinet version, Model 77).

fig.614. Ekco Model AW 70, by E.K. Cole Ltd. 1939. 3–v +R, AC SHet Table Model, SW/MW/LW Mtrs/StN, brown Bakelite cabinet. 19 ½ in. x 15 in. x 9 ½ in. £8.8s.0d. (Model BAW 71, battery version).

fig.615. Ultra Model 309, by Ultra Electric Ltd. August 1939. 3–v +R, AC SHet Table Model, SW/MW/LW Mtrs/StN, manual and push-button tuning, brown Bakelite trim, walnut veneered plywood cabinet. 17 ¼ in. x 17 in. x 8 ¼ in. (Console version, Model 310).

fig.616. Murphy Model A72, by Murphy Radio Ltd. 1939. 4–v +R plus Magic-Eye Tuning Indicator, AC SHet Table Model, SW/MW/LW Mtrs/StN, walnut veneered plywood cabinet (des: R.D. Russell). 22 ¾ in. x 18 in. x 9 ¼ in. £12.10s.0d. Optional remote control push-button unit extra.

fig.617. Murphy Model A76, by Murphy Radio Ltd. 1939. 5–v +R plus Magic-Eye Tuning Indicator, AC SHet Table Model, SW/MW/LW Mtrs/StN, mahogany veneered plywood cabinet (des: R.D. Russell and Eden Minns). 19 ½ in. x 23 ¼ in. x 9 ¾ in. £16.10s.0d. Optional extras: push-button unit (illustrated), price £1.15s.0d and remote control unit, price £3.10s.0d.

fig.618. Ferranti Model 139, by Ferranti Ltd. July 1939. 4–v +R, AC SHet Table Model, SW/MW/LW Mtrs/StN, brown Bakelite cabinet. 12 in. x 22 ½ in. x 9 in. Cabinet similar to Ferranti 'Prestune' push-button model of 1938. Chassis used in wood cabinet Model 239, fig.620.

fig.619. G.E.C. Model BC 4040, by General Electric Co. Ltd. 1939. 4–v +R, AC SHet Table Model, MW/LW Mtrs/StN, push-button and manual tuning, brown Bakelite cabinet. 11 in. x 18 ½ in. x 9 in. £9.9s.0d. 'Thermometer' type tuning: employs a red and cream coloured fabric which rises and falls to indicate the stations. (Battery version, Model BC 4046).

fig.620. Ferranti Model 239, by Ferranti Ltd. August 1939. 4–v +R, AC SHet Table Model, SW/MW/LW Mtrs/StN, walnut veneered plywood cabinet. 13 in. x 21 ½ in. x 9 in. Uses the same chassis as Bakelite cabinet Model 139, fig.618.

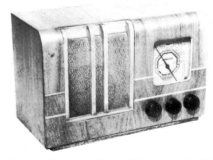

fig.621. Ferguson 'Mains Minor' Model 909, by Universal Radio Distributors Ltd. 1939. 4–v +R AC/DC SHet Table Model, SW/MW Mtrs/StN, walnut ply. cabinet 8 in. x 13 in. x 7 in.

fig. 622 . Murphy Model A70, by Murphy Radio Ltd. 1939. 4-v +R, AC SHet Table Model, SW/MW/LW Mtrs StN, walnut veneered plywood cabinet (des: R.D. Russell). 19 ¼ in. x 18 in. x 9 ¼ in. Optional extras: push-button unit, price £1.15s.0d, and remote control unit, price £3.10s.0d.

fig.625. Ekco Model PB 510, by E.K. Cole Ltd. 1939. 4-v +R, AC SHet Table Model, SW/MW/LW Mtrs StN, manual tuning and motorised 'Radio-Brain' tuning control with 'cruising' facility, walnut veneered plywood cabinet. 17¾ in. x 22 in. x 12 in.

fig.628. Mullard Model MAS 90, by Mullard Wireless Service Co. Ltd. August 1939. 3-v +R, AC SHet Table Model, SW/MW/LW Mtrs/StN, brown Bakelite cabinet. 12 ¾ in. x 17 ½ in. x 8 ½ in.

fig.623. Ever Ready Model 5218, by Ever Ready Co. (Great Britain) Ltd. 1939. 4-v Batt Table Model, MW/LW Mtrs/StN, internal frame aerial, walnut veneered plywood cabinet. 17 ½ in. x 14 in. x 9 ½ in.

fig.626. Amplion 'Alternative', by Amplion (1932) Ltd. 1939. 3-v +R, AC M/Batt Portable, MW/LW Mtrs/StN, internal frame aerial, wood case finished in red crackle paint. 10 ¼ in. x 14 ½ in. x 7 ½ in. Battery only version, Model ADP2, produced later in December 1946.

fig.629. Pye 'New Baby Q', by Pye Ltd. 1939. 4-v Batt Portable, MW/LW Mtrs/StN, blue leathercloth-covered wood case. 12 in. x 11 ½ in. x 7 ½ in.

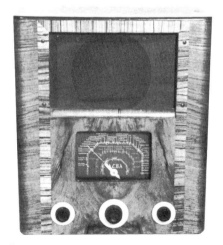

fig.624. Alba Model AC 810, by A.J. Balcombe Ltd. April 1939. 3-v +R, AC SHet Table Model, SW/MW/LW Mtrs/StN, walnut veneered plywood cabinet with rosewood inlay. 17 ½ in. x 16 in. x 9 ¼ in.

fig.627. Pilot 'Little Maestro', by Pilot Radio Ltd. February 1939. 4-v +R, AC/DC SHet Table Model, MW/LW Mtrs/StN, walnut veneered plywood cabinet. 7 ¾ in. x 11 ¾ in. x 5 ½ in. (Also light grained oak and blue leatherette-covered wood cabinets. A Bakelite cabinet version was released in 1940, fig.640).

fig.630. McMichael Model 394, by McMichael Radio Ltd. August 1939. 4-v +R, AC SHet Table Model, SW/MW/LW Mtrs/StN, push-button and manual tuning, walnut veneered plywood cabinet. 19 ½ in. x 16 ½ in. x 12 in.

fig.631. Marconiphone Model 878, by Marconiphone Co. Ltd. March 1939. 4-v + R, AC SHet Table Model, SW/MW/LW Mtrs/StN, manual and push-button tuning (11 pre-set stations + on/off), gold coloured expanded metal grille, brown Bakelite trim, walnut veneered plywood cabinet. 20 in. x 17 ½ in. x 10 in.

3 The 1940s

1940

On January 7th, an experimental alternative programme designed to appeal to the British Expeditionary Forces in France began from the B.B.C. at 6pm on 342.1 metres (during the day, this wavelength carried the Home Service). It consisted mainly of dance band and light music, variety and sporting items, and as it became popular it was expanded on February 18th into a full daily programme from 11am to 11pm, put out during the day on 373.1 metres and during the evening on 342.1 metres. It was now known officially as the Forces Programme, and to make sure the B.E.F. continued to tune-in, over 1,500 Ever Ready all-dry battery portables bought from a fund of £15,000 given by Lord Nuffield, were shipped across to the troops. From March 17th, the B.B.C.'s Overseas Service was additionally allocated the old London National 261.1 metre wavelength on the medium waveband, and its programmes were also put out on the 373.1 metre wavelength of the Forces Programme after 10pm each evening.

To improve the quality, and to ensure the continuity of the B.B.C.'s Home Service around the country, a large network of 60 low power medium-wave relay transmitters was erected and brought into service in large areas of population between November 3rd 1940 and December 1941. They were all synchronised on a wavelength of 203.5 metres, had a range of less than 10 miles, and collectively were known as the 'H-Group'. Their other, more sinister purpose, only disclosed after the war, was that they were to be used to keep the public informed in the event of an invasion (a real possibility in 1940) or if broadcasting from the ordinary B.B.C. transmitters discontinued. In these cases, the sites chosen would be worked by B.B.C. engineers in co-operation with local men whose voices were known to the public.

On the 'Home Front', identity cards and food rationing had been introduced in January. By then, three out of every four evacuees had gone back home: lack of air-raids, home sickness and the Government's demand for a small parental contribution to the support of evacuated children all contributed to the mass return.

WIRELESS SHORTAGES

Although a total of over four hundred different models of wireless receiver were shown in the 1939/40 catalogues of nearly forty principal manufacturers, demand increasingly outweighed supply. Each week, more and more manufacturers were compelled to turn their efforts away from the home market and towards Armed Forces requirements. Military valve production demands were enormous and revolutionary changes in valve design had introduced over 600 new types. The development of radar was to call for the additional production of an average of 360,000 cathode ray tubes per year, and in 1940 the demand for them was so great that each day's production was usually flown straight from the factory to the new radar stations.

The shortage of new domestic receivers and accessories began to get more apparent as the year progressed and old receivers, long ago put away at the back of a cupboard or up in the attic, were now being dug out and put to good use. As one soldier reported to *Wireless World*, "The manageress of my billet has achieved the reputation of being able to produce anything from a soldering iron to a bathing hut. Not even the remark that it would be a good idea to have a wireless receiver in our sitting room was beyond her, for she invited me to look in the attic for relics. Sure enough, there was a set - an ancient 4-valve battery affair with a loud-speaker that was a far cry from being a Rice-Kellog achievement. But who was caring

for that, when the set had an earth in a flowerpot with a knife sprouting out and a terminal neatly screwed on to the handle?"

Those who wanted to look after their receivers and keep them in good condition could send them in to their local wireless shop for a 7s.6d overhaul, a service which was very popular during the early part of the war. This service usually comprised: (1) Collecting the set , (2) Testing valves and adjusting valve contacts, (3) Cleaning and re-centring the loud-speaker, (4) Cleaning the wave-change switch, (5) Cleaning the volume control, (6) Re-sealing the electrolytic condensers, (7) Testing all the components for insulation, resistance and capacity, (8) Cleaning and polishing the cabinet, (9) Delivering the set, connecting it up and reporting on the aerial and earth systems.

Single valve receivers, which since the mid-1920s had been a rarity, were once more receiving a lot of attention in the wireless Press, and due to their compactness and low construction and running costs, were seen as the ideal home-contructed set for emergency use. Interest also recurred in Hivac miniature valves and several very small battery receivers based on them were produced including the Denco Pocket-Two, a 'personal' set built into a 4 inch long tinned metal box and designed for those on active service or for use as a stand-by receiver in the home. *Practical Wireless* published details of their Gas Mask Handy Two Valve Midget Portable which could be built into an empty gas mask carrying case, reflecting the fact that by now, not having experienced any gas attacks, most people had stopped carrying their gas masks around with them. A new development in commercial circuit design was the battery economy switch which was fitted to several new battery portables in 1940 to reduce the power used when listening to a strong local station (fig.632).

Definite trends in wartime domestic receiver design were emerging. The number of different models quickly reduced as the year wore on and there was a general simplification of chassis design and an all-round saving in materials. In January, the R.M.A. had taken steps to control all materials required for the production of domestic broadcast receivers, components and replacement parts by wireless manufacturers, whether members of the R.M.A. or not. There was an urgent need for collective action, for as the war progressed, it was inevitable that the raw material situation would become more difficult and the availability or lack of materials for manufacture and maintenance of wireless sets would ultimately affect everyone in the manufacturing and selling chain.

With cabinets, supplies of wood were soon restricted and had become very expensive, especially walnut which in the first six months of the war had been supplanted by mahogany as the standard wireless cabinet material. There was a rapid decline in the number of consoles whose cabinets needed a lot of wood which could otherwise be more usefully employed, and all unnecessary wooden decorative effects tended to be eliminated. Some manufacturers went over to Bakelite as an alternative (fig.633).

Supplies of paper and cardboard were also being restricted and there was a shortage of cartons in which wireless receivers were despatched to dealers. To encourage the re-use of cartons, H.M.V., Marconiphone and Murphy Radio were among the first manufacturers to offer an allowance to retailers for the return of 'empties' in good condition, and this ranged from 9d for a table-model carton to 10s.0d for a console carton.

On March 25th, prohibition of the importation of all foreign wireless apparatus, valves and components was introduced,

Murphy Model AD 94, AC/DC table model
receiver in a black Bakelite cabinet designed
by Eden Minns, 1940. (See fig.633).

although this did not apply to receivers bought for re-export as the wartime export trade was seen as vitally necessary to the British economy.

On May 10th, Germany invaded the Low Countries and that same evening, Winston Churchill became Prime Minister. Certainly, no other voice was to rally the British people quite as much as his, nor demonstrate the power of the wireless as a means of mass communication, and throughout the war his inspirational broadcasts, particularly at times of crisis, brought hope and encouragement to those listening-in at home and in occupied countries. During the year, the B.B.C.'s news announcers became 'personalities' since for the first time they gave their name at the beginning of each bulletin as a security measure to reassure listeners that it really was them reading the news and not an enemy announcer impersonating them. This limelight lasted until May 4th 1945, when they once more reverted to anonymity when reading the news.

fig.632. H.M.V. Model 1406, by The Gramophone Co. Ltd. July 1940. A 5-valve battery portable covering the medium and long wavebands (scale marked in both metres and station names). It has 4 push-buttons and a battery economy switch. Black Bakelite control panel, blue rexine-covered plywood case, 11 in. x 15 in. x 7 in. Price £11.11s.0d. Identical to Marconiphone Model 895.

At the end of May 1940, the Post Master General cancelled the ordinary Receiving Licence for the "installation and working of wireless apparatus in road vehicles". All motorists who had car radios and aerials installed in their motor car or other road vehicle (caravans, as long as they did not have an engine, were exempt), had until June 2nd to take steps to remove them. Some 50,000 car radios were impounded by the police in the first week although many escaped the net and were usefully converted for domestic use with the help of circuits published in the wireless Press following hundreds of urgent requests from ex-motoring listeners. Such was the demand for converting car radios, that Philco even introduced a suitable transformer unit which enabled a very low AC voltage supply to be obtained from the house mains.

Some police forces were a little over zealous with enforcing this law. In the autumn, at the Norwich Bench, a man was fined 2s.6d for "installing a wireless receiving apparatus in his car". He had apparently carried his faulty domestic receiver to a dealer to be repaired but had gone to collect it by car. A couple of police officers had spotted him loading his receiver onto the back seat and interpreted the law to mean that it was illegal to transport a wireless set by car from house to house,

or to take it by car to be repaired. The Bench however, took a very dim view of the attitude of the police and imposed a very small fine, stating that the law had been "designed against the Germans and Fifth Columnists, not against British citizens".

In June, the Ministry of Home Security announced that "all Germans living in this country, irrespective of age or grade, must immediately dispose of their wireless receiving sets". 'Thermion', writing in the June 22nd issue of *Practical Wireless* on the day France capitulated, urged his readers to tell the police immediately if they knew of any German who owned a wireless set. It did not matter if they had been resident in this country for even sixty years, for he felt they could still be anti-British: "one should not be misled by the spoken hatred of Hitler, for once a German, always a German at heart".

Profiteering was also seen as anti-British, and some unscrupulous dealers were cashing in on the general shortage of wireless receivers and demanding heavily inflated prices. From June 1st, the *Prices of Goods Act* made it illegal to sell receivers, radiograms and related component parts and accessories at a price higher than that prevailing on August 21st 1939, while allowing only justifiable wartime increases to be taken into consideration. Unfortunately, these regulations do not seem to have applied to vintage receivers sold at auction, and these invariably changed hands at enormous prices, whereas in pre-war days, dealers would have been loath to part with a few shillings in part-exchange for them.

On October 21st, Purchase Tax was introduced under Section 18 of the *Finance (No.2) Act, 1940*, and continued in force for over thirty years until April 1st 1973 when it was replaced by Value Added Tax (VAT). Being chargeable at 33 ⅓ per cent of the wholesale value of wireless receivers, radiograms, batteries, accumulators and valves, Purchase Tax put an additional burden on both the listening public and the wireless retailer. A few weeks earlier, the Blitz had begun, and apart from the threat of having their business premises blown to pieces overnight, wireless retailers had to get used to the public's new buying habits brought about by the bombing.

fig.633. Murphy Model AD 94, by Murphy Radio Ltd. 1940. A 4-valve plus rectifier, AC/DC table model superhet, covering the short and long wavebands (scale marked in both metres and station names). Black Bakelite cabinet (des: Eden Minns), 13½ in. x 12½ in. x 7 in. Price £9.10s.0d. This was Murphy Radio Ltd.'s first all-Bakelite cabinet and it was later used to house the 1945 Model SAD 94S and Model SAD 94L (see 1945).

There was a marked tendency to shop early in the day and to buy from a local dealer rather than visit the town's central shopping area. Casual window-shopping expeditions came to an end, and people now had a definite objective in mind when they went out to buy. Every business was curtailed, especially in the dark winter months with longer black-out hours.

One bright note though, for workers in the factories at least, was the introduction on June 23rd of the *Music While You Work* programme which became an instant success and a popular remedy for reducing assembly-line fatigue. While aimed primarily at the factory work force, its twice daily broadcasts reached a wide audience as it was transmitted not only on the Home Service but also on the Forces Programme. During the war, several morale boosting factory and military-based variety programmes were introduced including *Ack-Ack, Beer-Beer* designed in May 1940 for men and women of the anti-aircraft, balloon barrage and search-light units and *Workers Playtime*, a show which was broadcast from factory canteens around the country.

1941

Wartime expansion had led the B.B.C.'s European Service to leave Broadcasting House and find new accommodation at Bush House in Aldwych, London. Bush House, sandwiched between the Australian and Indian High Commissions, had originally been intended as an international trade centre by the American entrepreneur, Irving T. Bush, but the B.B.C. put it to good use and by the end of the war, broadcasts in forty different foreign languages were being put out, not just to Europe, but to many distant parts of the world. In June 1941, initiated by the Belgian Service, the first of the European Service's most famous series of broadcasts began - the 'V For Victory' campaign. Today, Bush House is still the London Headquarters of the B.B.C.'s External Services, the collective title first given in 1948 to the B.B.C.'s broadcast services "directed to people in other lands".

Throughout 1941, there was a vast and unprecedented increase in the demands upon the expanding Wireless Industry for all types of communications equipment, electronic apparatus and components for the Armed Forces. Towards the end of the year, this even included receivers made in England for Russian soldiers with the instructions printed in their own language. The increase was quickly felt by the general public as it soon led to an even greater scarcity of new receivers, HT batteries, valves and other components for the maintenance of domestic sets, and the Government's plan for a large expansion of export business had to be abandoned because of the "essential work".

The number of retailers' service engineers was dwindling as more were called up or stepped forward to volunteer for the Armed Forces. Those who stayed on behind the counter were often out on more urgent calls, servicing the intricate circuits of radiolocation gear, and Army, Navy and R.A.F. equipment, and the servicing of domestic wireless sets, of course, had to come last.

VALVE SHORTAGES

Since the outbreak of war there had been a growing shortage of new valves available for domestic use as production had progressively been geared up to supplying the Military. For the past two years, stocks of pre-war valves had increasingly been used for the maintainance of domestic receivers but by May 1941 these were running low and the situation was causing concern among retailers. While fully appreciating the needs of the Armed Forces, the National Council of the Wireless Retailers' Association voiced the general feeling that more valves should be available to the public. They saw it as palpably necessary for the population to have receivers in working order,

not merely for the purpose of entertainment, but to ensure that official news was widely heard.

But so urgent were the needs of the Armed Forces, that severe restrictions were now imposed on the manufacture of valves both as replacements and for use in new domestic receivers. Consequently, those receivers in the course of production had to be withheld from the market because there were simply no valves for them. It was estimated that about 125,000 sets were 'in progress' and it was hoped that they would be equipped with valves and other necessary components and put on the market in the following year. This did not in fact happen until 1943, (see 1943).

On March 11th, at a time when the United States was still neutral, President Roosevelt signed the *Lend-Lease Act* which permitted the American Government to sell, lend or lease services and materials to Great Britain or any other country whose defence was considered of supreme importance to the United States. The Act provided aid for British purchases of war and other essential equipment and saved this country from the imminent bankruptcy we were facing under the heavy financial strain of conducting the war. In the following year some of the Act's benefits were being felt by our domestic Wireless Industry (see 1942). In December, following the Japanese attack on Pearl Harbour, America entered the war and a month later her troops began to arrive in Britain.

1942

In January, the Radio Manufacturers' Association announced a plan to retain sufficient skilled and semi-skilled radio service personnel and to train school leavers to provide the public with minimum service facilities for the duration of the war. The Ministry of Labour agreed to suspend temporarily the call-up of radio servicemen in order to help the repair situation but in September it decided that retail service departments of wireless shops were "not essential works" and the call-up continued as before.

By the middle of 1942, it was estimated by the British Institution of Public Opinion that out of the total number of wireless sets in people's homes, something like one tenth were silent because of defects of one kind or another, and that amounted to about one million sets. The situation was going to get worse as the Wireless Industry had now completed the changeover from peace to war production, and the output of domestic receivers and related components and accessories had all but ceased.

Since the spring, retailers' stocks of batteries and valves (other than those of the run-of-the-mill variety) had generally run out and even the humble galena crystal was so scarce that it was proving almost impossible to build even a very simple emergency crystal set. In an advertisement appearing in *Wireless World*, the Edison Swan Electric Company explained that Mazda valves were "a little difficult to obtain" because every time the R.A.F. attacked in great strength, over 250,000 valves were 'on ops' in the aircraft and at the ground bases. In the winter, the enemy's own valve supply was hard hit when the German-controlled Philips factory at Eindhoven in Holland was attacked in a low level daylight raid by nearly 100 R.A.F. bombers. The target was considered an important one since it was the largest valve manufacturing plant in occupied Europe and the whole of its production went straight to Germany.

Difficulty in obtaining replacement rectifiers for commercial battery chargers used by wireless dealers added to listeners problems by making accumulator re-charging impossible in some areas. By August, the valve shortage had become no better although everything possible was being done to release valves of British manufacture and to obtain supplies from the United States. In late autumn, it was announced that imports of various types of American valves were to be allowed. These would be used to replace British-made octals and loctals etc. interchangeable with American equivalents, and would also act as replacements in the tens of thousands of American-made receivers imported into this country before the war. Some valves were released on a rather disappointing scale in December 1942 under the American *Lend-Lease Act* (which had been revised in February 1942), and to prevent profiteering, an Order was issued by the Board of Trade controlling the prices charged by official selling agents of all valves imported under the Lend-Lease provisions.

On November 8th, in the largest combined operation so far attempted in the war, a force of four American and British divisions was put ashore in French North Africa. Known as 'Operation Torch', this landing heralded the beginning of the North Africa Campaign and for the benefit of British and Commonwealth troops fighting here and in the neighbouring Middle East, the B.B.C introduced a special short-wave programme service, which in just over twelve months would develop into the General Overseas Service (see 1943).

1943

On January 10th, the North Africa and Middle Eastern short-wave services for British and Commonwealth Forces fighting in those areas was named the Overseas Forces Programme and on June 13th it was extended to cover listeners from the Burmese frontier with India to the West Coast of Africa. On November 21st it was further extended to cover the South Atlantic shipping lanes, South America and the United States and Canada and afterwards became known as the General Overseas Service. It now provided a world-link with Britain and her English-speaking Dominion and Colonial audiences as well as with British and Commonwealth Forces stationed around the world.

By the end of 1943, the Overseas Service of the B.B.C. had also expanded and in addition to programmes in English to the Empire and the United States, was sending out programmes in 21 world-wide foreign languages including Afrikaans, Bengali, Cantonese, Malay, Tamil, and Turkish. The European Service now included programmes in 23 European languages in addition to English, plus a Morse code service of news which had begun in March 1942 for the benefit of the Resistance.

At home, the servicing and maintenance of civilian broadcast receivers had become an extremely serious problem and the short-staffed service departments of wireless shops, many of whom had been forced to 'call-up' retired service engineers to help out, were now having to resort to cannibalizing other equipment or even making up components themselves in order to patch up faulty receivers. Major circuit faults, such as a burnt out mains transformer, had of course, to be attended to by professional service engineers and where there were no supplies or stocks of the correct replacement components or no one qualified to do the work, nothing could be done. But in many cases, it was well within the average listeners' capabilities to remedy minor problems themselves, even though they may have never peered into the back of a set. To help and advise in this matter, Murphy Radio Ltd. brought out a simple sixpenny booklet entitled *Keep It Going*. It was designed to show the owner of any set (not just a Murphy set), how to find and remedy simple faults, and with a bit of luck, to keep it working throughout the war without imposing upon or wasting the precious time of skilled service engineers.

During January, the release of more American Lend-Lease valves was announced, but as *The Wireless & Electrical Trader* reported, "it seems to be taking a long time for them to filter through to the wireless shops, very few of them are about yet. Far too many sets are out of action either because spares are

unobtainable or because what radio servicemen are left cannot cope with the work thrown upon their depleted ranks." But by the late summer, the situation had somewhat improved when a large number of U.S. Lend-Lease valves became available.

Battery shortages continued. For several months, an exceptionally heavy demand by the Armed Services for batteries had been created as a result of the North Africa Campaign, and despite a limited importation for domestic use of a small quantity of Lend-Lease HT batteries from the United States in the spring of 1943, customers in certain areas were having to wait up to three months for a delivery. *Wireless World* felt that "those dependent upon batteries for news and general wartime information deserved special consideration. Broadly speaking, these were country dwellers living in areas which were still not yet supplied with electricity, and who represented the most isolated section of the listening community. Naturally wishing to conserve the current of their batteries as much as possible, they were not able to afford the luxury of an all-day stream of broadcasting like those living in towns listening-in on mains fed receivers could".

By April, the component situation had begun to ease and the President of the Board of Trade announced that plans had been made for the immediate supply of components, including the valves needed for the completion of the 125,000 domestic receivers whose production had been held up for about 18 months (fig.634). Although by July, only about 14,000 of these sets had been completed and marketed, the rest were released by the middle of the following year.

Plans were also afoot for the importation of Lend-Lease receivers from the United States at an early date. This turned out to be October, when about 10,000 U.S. receivers of various types arrived at the docks but because these all required grading, testing and pricing before release and most had to be converted to suit our supply voltage, a further frustrating delay occurred.

fig.634. Rees-Mace Type RMC, by Rees-Mace Manufacturing Co. Ltd. April 1943. A 4-valve battery table model, covering the short and medium wavebands (scale marked in both metres and station names). Black rexine-covered plywood cabinet. 11 in. x 16½ in. x 8 in. One of the 125,000 domestic receivers which had previously been held up in the production line due to component shortages.

THE MODERN RADIO INDUSTRY

Co-ordination of all the various manufacturers' efforts in the production of communications equipment became imperative to meet the ever increasing requirements of the Armed Services. In conjunction with the War Cabinet's new Radio Board, an organisation known as the Radio Production Executive was formed. Such was the sophisticated technological level reached by the Wireless Industry since the beginning of the war, that it had by now earned the modern title of the *Radio* Industry

- the word 'wireless', in official and professional quarters at least, was thought of as being rather archaic and not at all appropriate. The R.P.E. had executive powers over the Ministry of Supply's own radio production departments without belonging to them and the Radio Industry in effect submitted to voluntary control under the R.P.E. which was concerned primarily with valves, components and complete equipment, and was responsible for ensuring the success of hundreds of exceptionally urgent 'crash' production programmes.

In October 1943, the Radio Industry Council was formed with the amalgamation of the Radio Manufacturers' Association, the British Radio Valve Manufacturers' Association and the Radio Component Manufacturers' Federation with the object of unifying the radio trade: (a fourth member, the Radio Communications & Electronic Engineering Association joined in the spring of 1944).

The Government now decided to plan for the mass-production of a single new type of receiver specifically for the domestic market, made to a simple standard design. It was officially called the Wartime Civilian Receiver and by November, a design had been agreed upon and deliveries of raw materials and components had been planned. But it was well into 1944 before this new type of receiver was ready for the eagerly waiting market.

1944

While new British receivers would remain in very short supply until the summer, a few small businesses specialising in component supply put together kits which the home-constructor could buy for around £10. One of these firms was the appropriately named Austerity Radio Limited of High Holborn in London who advertised a 3-valve battery kit and a 4-valve mains kit in January, although their advertisement added "regret no cabinets".

On February 27th, the Forces Programme was scrapped and the General Overseas Service became the General Forces Programme on 296.1 and 342.1 metres and on short-wave. It took over from the Forces Programme as *the* alternative programme for listeners at home and became a world-wide general programme in English for all British Forces serving overseas, thereby securing "a community of spirit between them and their homes".

On March 6th, a statement issued by the R.M.A. said that it was expected that the work of testing the first 10,000 U.S. imported receivers and adapting them to the British voltage supply would shortly be completed and distribution to the retail trade outlets would begin towards the end of the month. An additional 26,000 U.S. sets had recently been imported and there were about 7,000 more on their way; it was hoped that all of them would be made available in the early summer. This would be followed by the release of the new Wartime Civilian Receivers whose manufacture had begun in February, and whose numbers when released were hoped to ease significantly the great shortage of new receivers.

During March, good news came for car radio owners, when it was announced that the ban imposed in May 1940 (see 1940) on the installation of receivers in motor vehicles was being lifted and owners of impounded car radios had to apply to their local police station for their sets' return.

In June, in the month that saw the invasion of Normandy on D-Day and the beginning of the Allied advance into Europe, the first of the Wartime Civilian Receivers were released although they did not appear in any significant numbers until later in the summer. They were designed to tune to the medium waveband only and there were two versions: an AC mains set in an upright wooden cabinet, and a battery set in a horizontal wooden cabinet, each having a dial marked in metres and the

B.B.C.'s Home Service and General Forces Programmes only (see Appendix). *Wireless World* commented, "These sets cover only the medium waveband, but that is of no great moment today for there is nothing on the long waves likely to attract the average listener. But prices do seem to be rather high for a single waverange mains or battery receiver." (£12.3s.4d and £10.19s.0d respectively).

The unadorned appearance of their pinewood cabinets caused much comment too and soon they were widely being referred to as 'Utility Sets'. A Member of Parliament stated in the House of Commons, "whilst the components of the new Utility Sets are very good and efficient, the outside appearance is cheap and nasty". Within the trade, they were also known as the 'Industry Set', reflecting the fact that they had been made with the co-operative effort of over 40 different manufacturers.

For the benefit of the British, American and Canadian forces who, following D-Day, found themselves fighting side by side in France, the Allied Expeditionary Forces Programme was introduced by the B.B.C. on June 7th on 285.7 metres, the old West Regional medium wavelength. The A.E.F. Programme was the brain-child of General Eisenhower, who had been appointed Supreme Commander of the Allied Forces in the run-up to D-Day. He had conceived the idea with the intention of eliminating nationalistic rivalries between the three Allies and fostering a "genuine team spirit". The programmes, which included the latest news from the Allies' respective countries as well as from all war fronts, were mainly drawn from the existing output of the B.B.C., the American Forces Network and the Canadian Broadcasting Corporation but also included programmes exclusive to the A.E.F., with the number of programmes allocated to each of the Allies being directly proportional to their invading forces: 50 per cent U.S., 35 per cent British and 15 per cent Canadian. The A.E.F. Programme was transmitted every day for the next fourteen months from 5.55am to 11pm, and was sent out from Broadcasting House (where the Americans demanded, and got, a whole floor to themselves). As well as news, it also provided relaxation and entertainment with top-line dance bands and star-studded variety and comedy shows which, when space at Broadcasting House was at a premium, were put on in theatres, clubs and cinemas around the West End.

By mid-September, American Forces had crossed into Luxembourg and had found to their surprise that the powerful transmitter belonging to the Radio Luxembourg station had been left relatively undamaged, despite last-minute German attempts to dynamite it. From September 22nd, it was back in full operation again and during the latter stages of the war, under the direction of the American Psychological Warfare Division, it was employed for 'black' broadcasting during early morning hours in the guise of a German-language station (station 'Twelve Twelve') in order to create confusion in Germany while the Allied Forces advanced. After the war, Radio Luxembourg reverted to its role as a commercial English-language station: the last surviving member of the pre-war I.B.C. Continental network (see 1946).

In a final mass aerial attack on Britain which was to cost the lives of thousands of civilians in southern England, especially in the London area, the Germans launched the first V1 flying-bombs in June and the first V2 rockets in September. Hundreds of people left the target areas, and many important factories, including those involved in the manufacture of communications equipment, were forced to move out and set up emergency premises in South Wales, the North and in Scotland. But despite this, the main danger of air-raids by German aircraft was thought to have passed and on September 17th, the Government announced substantial modifications to the black-out regulations and a 'dim-out' was introduced whereby ordinary curtains and blinds were allowed once more.

1945

With the new year, the likelihood of peace was daily becoming more certain. Although it would be several months before the war finally came to an end, people were optimistic about the future and were looking forward to a fresh beginning. On April 23rd, all dim-out regulations were removed, except for a 5 mile belt around the coast, and just over a week later Britain's air-raid warning system was discontinued. Within the radio Press there was much discussion about how the Radio Industry would get back to normal after the war. The Board of Trade announced that it was setting up a regional organisation to assist manufacturers in the changeover from war to peacetime production in order to avoid 'Whitehall bottlenecks'. The organisation would deal with the problems of factory de-requisition, allocation of surplus Government factories, reconversion of industry, decentralisation and the release of labour and materials. Radio manufacturers whose once household names had been out of the public's eye for several years now began to advertise themselves again and remind both the public and trade that they were still around and would still be around to serve after the war. Under the headline 'THE SLEEPER AWAKES', E.K. Cole Ltd. explained the situation. "The Radio Industry has been tied down as far as supplying the public is concerned. But now, there is the Industry Set in the shops for those who must have a new radio. We at Ekco have been far from asleep during these years and we're looking forward to proving how wide awake we are!"

THE END OF THE WAR

On May 8th, Germany unconditionally surrendered to the Allies in Berlin and on August 15th, with the defeat of Japan, the Second World War was over. Slowly, the story of the great contribution made by the Radio Industry during the war began to emerge and the public now began to realise just what was meant when they had been told that radio manufacturers and service engineers "were on essential work". Stories of the importance of the humble 'wireless' also came to light, not only from Britain where the public were free to listen-in to morale boosting talks and entertainment, but from occupied countries, where being found in possession of a receiver was almost invariably punishable by imprisonment or the firing squad. E.K. Cole Ltd. received a letter from a listener in the Channel Islands describing the difficulties of listening to the B.B.C. whilst under German occupation.

"Now that we in the Channel Isles are able to write again to England after nearly five years of German occupation, for three of which it has been forbidden under heavy penalty to have a radio of any sort, I feel I should like to send you my appreciation of your 1939 model 7-valve Ekco radio which I have retained and used throughout the war. We, my wife, young son and self, live in the centre of a group of three houses, the other two have been occupied by German soldiers throughout this time.

"I had the set carefully hidden and we have listened to the B.B.C. news regularly, using myself as the aerial by putting my finger on the aerial socket. We used to take it in turns to listen while the others kept a look out. Many times we have received warnings that the Gestapo were in the district searching, but every time I was fortunate enough to get the set away in a sack on my bicycle. The bicycle had solid tyres for years, so you may realise that the set has had a severe shaking each time it was moved. It has also been buried in the garden for a few days and hidden under a stack of wood in a damp shed. All this time it was out of its cabinet to reduce its size. I feel it is up to me to let you know how faithfully and well your Ekco radio has served us under treatment which no one would think of inflicting on it in ordinary circumstances. It was our only means of hearing the real true news and it served to keep our morale up throughout these long years."

THE POST-WAR YEARS

On May 31st, not long after the war in Europe had ended, the B.B.C. announced that as from the end of July, they would changeover from wartime to peacetime programmes. The first stage of their post-war home broadcasting plans was put into operation on July 29th with the inauguration of a regionally-based Home Service Programme on nine medium wavelengths, and for national coverage, the new Light Programme on both the long and medium wavebands. On the day before, the Allied Expeditionary Forces Programme came to an end, and the General Forces Programme lost its two medium waveband wavelengths but continued (from July 30th) on short-wave as a round-the-clock programme in English for listeners in the Pacific, S.E. Asia, Middle East, Central Mediterranean, West Africa, West Indies and Latin America.

The Home Service was divided up into seven regions with each region having its own Programme Director and transmitting a certain amount of regional material. In general, dial markings on pre-war sets remained correct, with only West Regional and Northern Ireland now on new wavelengths. North Regional had an extra wavelength which it shared with Northern Ireland and for several months until June 2nd 1946, the latter station had to take the North Regional Home Service Programme. Dials of some post-war sets though, continued to be marked 'National' instead of 'Light', and a few models released as late as 1946 even used pre-war calibrated dials (fig.635).

The Light Programme went out primarily from the Droitwich long-wave transmitter on 1,500 metres with hoped-for national coverage, but it was supplemented on 261.1 metres (one of the wartime medium wavelengths used by the Overseas Service) by three synchronised medium-wave transmitters at Brookmans Park, Moorside Edge and Westerglen, to improve reception in the London, Northern and Scottish areas. Outside these areas, the Light Programme's medium-wave signal was generally described as "very poor" and was prone to fading, and in certain parts of the Midlands and South Wales, it could not be picked up at all. In these areas, with the Light Programme being satisfactorily received only on the long waveband, listeners with single band medium-wave receivers were unable to receive it. Such sets included the Wartime Civilian Receiver, and a lot of unrest was created because tens of thousands of listeners had, only a few months before, gone to the expense of buying one.

At least one manufacturer brought out a two waveband (MW/LW) Wartime Civilian Receiver soon after the war (see Appendix), but the only solution for those with the original single-band version was to connect a long-wave adaptor to extend the tuning range to cover the Light Programme on 1,500 metres. However, commercially-made supplies of these did not become available until November, and until then approaches had to be made to friendly service engineers who might undertake to design and make one up.

Complaints about the poor quality of the Light Programme on the medium-wave even influenced one major manufacturer, Murphy Radio Ltd., to modify their SAD94S medium and short-wave model (introduced in September 1945) and instead, make it into a medium and long-wave model, and this came out from November as the SAD94L.

Despite the teething troubles with the Light Programme, W.J. Haley, the Director General of the B.B.C., thought that both it and the Home Service were making a beginning towards what ought to be the picture of peacetime broadcasting in this country, but in order to do the job properly, listeners should be given the choice of *three* programmes. It was hoped to introduce such a programme (the Third Programme) in the following year to give a wider and more comprehensive service than in any other country in the world. The proposed Third Programme (which was also known as the 'C' programme before its inauguration) was described as "cultural" and would be used for the broadcasting of plays, complete orchestral concerts, symphonies and other 'serious' material.

THE PEACETIME RADIO INDUSTRY

The structure of the Radio Industry, its technology and its production methods had changed dramatically since 1939. It had entered the war mainly concentrating on its traditional role of manufacturing relatively simple wireless receivers for people's homes, but had emerged now fully skilled in a variety of radio communications and having developed a parallel industry equipped in the modern and intricate technology of electronic engineering.

With the coming of peace, some firms decided to continue pursuing the new Government defence market created during the war for specialised electronic equipment, while others went back to serving the home consumer. The end of the war had certainly not seen the beginning of a consumer boom, in fact goods and materials of all kinds were in very short supply in the shops. A large percentage of Britian's potential labour force had not yet returned from abroad and the factories they would man were still winding down from wartime production. Rationing was still in force and was later even extended, and life continued to be lived on austere lines for several more years to come. To make matters worse, President Truman had, without any prior warning, announced on August 21st that arrangements under the *Lend-Lease Act* (see 1941) were immediately terminated, and this put Britain into a very serious financial position. However, a mutual settlement was reached in early December which included the United States Government agreeing to cancel almost $25,000,000,000 as non-repayable, and giving Britain a further loan of $650,000,000 to cover 'goods in the pipeline'.

But with Britain in serious debt it was seen that she would have to trade her way out of trouble in order to recover and the Government now launched a campaign for industrial production to create exports and turn these into foreign currency. However, for a few years problems arose as the Pound was too high against the Dollar making British goods difficult to sell abroad. The Government's production drive meant that of the new goods that were produced a large percentage were made solely for export and not for domestic consumption. The inevitable shortage of new receivers in the shops created a seller's market, and even though the Radio Industry bravely agreed to the Government's production target of around 1,000,000 sets in twelve months, with about 400,000 of these going for export, demands by the public for new receivers were not adequately satisfied until well towards the end of the 1940s.

In 1945, the Radio Industry Council was acting as the co-ordinating body for four associations of manufacturers which represented all sections of the Radio Industry. These were the British Radio Equipment Manufacturers' Association, the Radio Communication & Electronic Engineering Association, the British Radio Valve Manufacturers' Association and the Radio Component Manufacturers' Association. In August, a statement issued by the R.I.C. made it clear that the next few months would see the gradual release of limited supplies of new branded domestic receivers as the Radio Industry gradually began to get back to peacetime production. The first announcements of planned new ranges were soon made by Ambassador, Ferranti, G.E.C., Ultra and Vidor, and in September, Ferranti's Model 145 (fig.643) became the first post-war set to make an appearance on the market. Other manufacturers also announced their new releases: Bush and Murphy (in September), Alba, Cameo, Ekco, Ferguson and

Ultra (in October), Ace, Aerodyne, Invicta, Philco, Pilot and Pye (in November) and Sobell (in December). The increased cost and shortage of both labour and materials, plus the added Purchase Tax, inevitably made post-war receiver prices high although arrangements made with the Board of Trade resulted in about 50 per cent of the initial production for the home market being of sets retailing at a reasonable £15 or less plus Purchase Tax.

The outward appearance of many of the first post-war sets was similar to pre-war ranges. There was nothing overwhelmingly different about the styling of the cabinets, for with regard to radio, the war had mainly influenced the development of science, not art, and the cabinet designers seemed to have merely picked up again where they had left off. In pre-war years, it was common practice particularly in the 1930s for the cabinet designers all to echo whatever particular design trend was in vogue at the time: geometric grilles would be 'in' one year, plain grilles the next, and so on. But after the initial post-war production runs, and for several more years until well into the 1950s, this uniformity was dropped and once things began to get back to normal, manufacturers in general began to pursue their own individual styles and designs. Many continued to use polished veneered wood for their cabinets but a great many others, because of natural material shortages, began to use plastics, and this type of cabinet material was now used by more manufacturers than ever before.

With the expiration and cancellation of war contracts, reasonable but not adequate supplies of new component parts were now starting to filter through from the manufacturers although the supplies of timber for cabinets and raw materials in general were restricted and usually only obtainable under licence.

GOVERNMENT SURPLUS MARKET

At the end of the year, the disposal by the Government of surplus radio equipment and components produced during the war became a problem of major concern to the Radio Industry whose firms were anxious to see a return of any parts which would be useful in peacetime manufacture. Thousands of complete pieces of equipment and millions of components were in store and were in the process of being declared surplus to Service requirements. This included about 3,000,000 valves, but like the rest of the stock, it was not all suitable for use in domestic receivers. Much of it operated on strange high frequencies or required unusual supply voltages which were not easily provided for home use. Although the surplus equipment was of advanced design and constructed to very high standards, for the listener who wanted a radio receiver for the broadcast bands it was practically useless, and converting it was not economically viable. The Radio Industry and the component manufacturers especially were uneasy about this surplus being suddenly released and swamping the market and wary too of some of it falling into the hands of unscrupulous dealers who might unload completely unsuitable 'bargain' equipment on an unsuspecting public in a repeat of the way certain ex-Government equipment was dealt with after the First World War (see 1920). This applied particularly to returning ex-Servicemen who were warned to exercise the greatest care before rushing in and committing themselves to the purchase of new retail business premises and to beware of attempts at exploitation. In one case, *The Wireless & Electrical Trader* strongly advised its readers not to be tempted to buy unused out-of-date electrolytic condensers as these could be liable to explode when a current was passed through them. The same also applied to electrolytic condensers already fitted into the circuits of 'idle' radios, and the magazine showed a photograph of the cabinet of an Ekco Model AD 37 which had been in store since 1940. Having returned home from the Services five years later, the owner brought the set down from the loft where it had been kept wrapped up throughout the war. When he switched it on, one of the electrolytic condensers exploded with such force that its cap flew off and blew a hole nearly two inches in diameter in the top of the Bakelite cabinet.

However, the great attraction of all this surplus was the fact that it was incredibly cheap and very useful for stripping down for simple components such as resistors etc., which could possibly then be used to repair receivers. Much of the surplus equipment was cannibalized in this way by service engineers who were then able to patch-up (albeit crudely in many cases) their customers' pre-war receivers without having to wait for the new component situation to return to normal. Surplus American valves imported under the Lease-Lend arrangements were also released and some found their way into the chassis of pre-war British receivers, substituted for dud British-based valves by means of ingenious adaptors, and when fitted with modified feed supplies, the sets were given a new lease of life. Many more radio shops, particularly those in the Soho, Tottenham Court Road and Holborn areas of London which specialised in components, now began making up and selling their own chassis and kits, to fill in the gap before the large-scale factories began producing sets again. Small firms such as Lasky's Radio of Paddington who even during the middle of the war could boast a stock of 5,000 American and British valves, and Alfred Imhof Ltd. of New Oxford Street who now started to specialise in the design of metal cases for radios, amplifiers, power packs and electronic equipment, began to build up reputations by which they are still known today. While many individual retailers carried on with single premises, the post-war years saw a great expansion of retail chains with firms like J. & M. Stone (fig.723) and Civic Radio Services, who merged in the mid-1950s into a chain of over 100 branches spread around the country.

As the troops began to arrive home after the war, a few German radios came with them. The most collectable of these was the small black or brown Bakelite *Kleinempfanger* - the German People's Set - which had been produced in the late 1930s. It had a Swastika moulded into the front of the Bakelite cabinet and was an obvious souvenir for the homecoming Tommy, fitting easily into his kit-bag. It also had the advantage of working on British 200 to 240 volt supplies (fig.604).

1946

In February, the first post-war trade exhibition of radio components took place at Grosvenor House in London, with a general trend being shown in a reduction of component size and improved standardization. Although it represented 80 per cent of the industry, the show was on fairly austere lines due mainly to problems encountered with the shortage of raw materials and labour, and reconstruction and re-tooling following war work.

The Radio Industry continued to negotiate with the Government over the return of useful surplus stock and while a lot of it was re-purchased on the open market, later in the year came unconfirmed reports that tens of thousands of pounds worth of brand new ex-Government radio equipment had been dumped in the Irish sea, and vast quantities of components had been crushed, buried and concreted over. In some cases where Government contracts were not immediately cancelled but were allowed to run out, production continued after the war and some of this stock was rumoured to have been taken directly from the factory and simply driven to disused coal mines for dumping. While *The Wireless & Electrical Trader* was critical of the destruction of standard manufactured parts which could be useful to the industry, it felt that certain surplus electronic units, like the H2S aerial radar or the Oboe blind-bombing radar systems, while "delighting those who worked on them

or with them", had no value for use in peacetime and so should be dumped or perhaps saved for a museum or as a souvenir. In fact, a lot of radar equipment and plans were sold by the Government and were made good use of by several firms including Marconi's, who now began to develop it for civilian navigational use in various parts of the world.

TELEVISION

The re-opening of the B.B.C.'s 405-line television service from the Alexandra Palace transmitter on June 7th heralded a succession of new transmitters that were to bring B.B.C. television on Band I (41-68 Mc/s) to a large part of the country within a matter of years, and its inauguration brought new life to that part of the industry which had been stifled with the outbreak of war. At the beginning of the month, a combined Radio and Television Licence had been introduced at £2 a year while the Receiving Licence fee for radio only was increased to £1 and re-named the Broadcast Receiving Licence. Within nine months, over 14,500 people had taken out combined Radio and Television licences and such was the rapid growth in interest that a mere five years later, the figure had reached nearly 1,500,000 with the television service within reach of about 80 per cent of the population. In the face of this growing competition, the radio set gradually lost its supremacy in the home as the centre of entertainment and in a little more than ten years, there were more viewers than listeners (see 1958).

THE RADIO INDUSTRY

Despite a continuing shortage of new receivers in the shops throughout 1946, the Radio Industry was already looking towards new avenues of development. The 'second set' market was virtually untapped even though the idea of having a small compact second set of the mains transportable class for use around the home in the bedroom, kitchen, study or playroom had first been mooted in the late 1930s. With about 80 per cent of British homes already owning one radio set, a market readily existed for this type of receiver, and several such models began to appear from this time (fig.660). These receivers did the job of an extension speaker by providing radio entertainment away from the 'house' set, but in addition, of course, gave an alternative choice of programme listening and from about this time, the idea of having an extension speaker began to wain.

Another avenue, although still a long way off, was the B.B.C.'s proposed introduction of a high power VHF broadcasting service using either frequency modulation (FM) or amplitude modulation (AM) in the hope of providing high quality interference-free reception. In the United States, FM had been successfully developed by E.H. Armstrong who took out four patents dealing with frequency modulation in 1933. From the early 1940s, the FM system had been widely adopted by U.S. commercial stations and in June 1945, the B.B.C. began to conduct its first VHF experiments using both FM and AM in order to determine the relative merits of each system. But there would be a lot of work and consultation with the Radio Industry to do before VHF broadcasting became a practicable proposition and nearly another ten years before the service (using FM) was fully inaugurated (see 1955).

BROADCASTING

The Radio Luxembourg station, which in 1944 had been recaptured from the Germans and had been put into service by the Americans as a 'black' broadcasting station, recommenced its role as an English language commercial station on July 1st and continued to represent the alternative approach to broadcasting by putting out sponsored programmes. It managed to attract sponsorship from large companies including Horlicks,

Rowntrees and Lever Brothers, and the number of British listeners captured from the B.B.C. continued to increase, especially those living in Southern England where Radio Luxembourg's long-wave signal on 1,293 metres was strongest.

On September 29th, the B.B.C.'s new Third Programme was introduced on the medium waveband "for the alert and receptive listener", and appeared on the dial marked 'THIRD', although in some cases it was marked 'BBC III'. For the benefit of the Midlands area, it was radiated on 514.6 metres by the Droitwich transmitter, while listeners in other parts of the country were served by several low power transmitters synchronised on 203.5 metres. These were at Aberdeen, Belfast, Bournemouth, Brighton, Bristol, Cardiff, Dundee, Edinburgh, Glasgow, Huddersfield, Leeds, Liverpool, London, Manchester, Middlesborough, Newcastle, Plymouth, Portsmouth, Preston, Sheffield and Southampton, and more were planned for the future.

BRITAIN CAN MAKE IT EXHIBITION

The most significant radio event of 1946 was the Council of Industrial Design's Britain Can Make It exhibition which was opened by King George VI at the Victoria & Albert Museum in South Kensington on September 24th. The exhibition featured the latest in consumer items from all sections of British industry and with factories having been diverted to the war effort for six years, it was seen as being "a symbol of the changeover in production from war to peace". It was also designed to cheer the public up who, after years of drab wartime austerity and standardization, were at last given something to look forward to: "a dream of the future", according to one of the exhibition's designers, James Gardner.

The exhibits covered radio, television, heating, lighting, cooking and other domestic equipment, as well as clothing, furniture, glass, pottery, toys, cameras, watches, clocks, pens, stationery, leather and travel goods, musical instruments, packaging, printing and transport. The exhibition, which by the time it closed on October 31st had attracted an average of over 20,000 visitors a day, was primarily concerned with "design from the outward form", although technical and constructional requirements were all taken into consideration by the members of the Selection Committee who, for the radio section, were H.J. Dyer (Philips), G.J. Freshwater (E.M.I.), A. Middleton (Ferranti) and G.P. Wickham-Legg (Bush).

Out of 130 items submitted from the Radio and Television Industries, 25 were chosen as representative. Bush Radio Ltd. showed their newly introduced Bakelite Model DAC 90 (fig.652), which, along with its 1950 successor, the DAC 90A (fig.729), became probably the most successful and popular of all post-war receivers. Murphy Radio Ltd. had on display their Model A104 Baffle Receiver (fig.651) which was a complete breakaway from the traditional rectangular wooden box type of radio which had dominated the scene since the early 1930s. The components were housed on a basic chassis member which comprised a narrow steel shelf running behind the length of the baffle cabinet. It was the first in a series of Murphy baffle sets and the novel chassis arrangement gave better access to components, both for assembly and servicing, and the baffle, according to the Murphy brochure, "an improved, high-fidelity sound". It could also hang on the wall, although the Marquis of Donegal, reviewing the exhibition for *Practical Wireless*, could not possibly conceive why anyone would want it to.

Cossor's exhibit was "a very nice grey table model", but on closer inspection it was found to be nothing more than a dummy. While a few of the exhibits had already been on the market since the autumn of 1945, many were still in the early stages of production or like the Cossor, still at the design stage,

and prospective buyers were warned that they would have to wait some time before goods reached the shops in anything other than small quantities.

One really eye-catching set on display at the exhibition was the black and chrome Romac midget battery portable (fig.659). It resembled in form a small folding camera case and was designed to be carried about by means of a PVC shoulder strap which cleverly concealed the aerial. The Romac drew a lot of interest not only because of its novelty but also because it employed four very small American 7-pin all-glass valves, and was the first set in this country to do so: the British version of these miniature valves, designated 'B7G', was not produced until the following year, but its arrival heralded a true general reduction in size of radio receivers of all classes and along with its later 9-pin companion, the 'B9A' of 1951, quickly became an industry standard (see 1947).

Another valve receiving much attention during 1946 was a new type of octal. Since being widely introduced in 1937, the G-type octal briefly continued in production after the war but in 1946 a development of this class housed in a much smaller and slender glass envelope was first announced by the M-O. Valve Company. Known as GT-type octals, ('GT' stood for 'glass tubular') they superseded the earlier form in the following year and like the G-type were based upon valves originally developed in the United States. (The first GT-type American octals were introduced by Hytron of Massachusetts in 1938).

Perhaps the most un-traditional and unique receiver design to be introduced in 1946 (although not shown at the Britain Can Make It exhibition) was the Emor Globe (fig.678). Its 3-waveband chassis was contained within a metal globe (available in chrome, 'gold' or a variety of painted pastel shades) supported by an adjustable stand. It was initially made for export but from 1947 it was released for the home market and began to find its way into the sitting-rooms of the more adventurous members of the British listening public.

1947

On January 1st, the B.B.C.'s third Charter was granted, and the Corporation was authorised to provide broadcasting services for reception "in other countries and places" outside the British Commonwealth, reflecting the fact that the B.B.C.'s Empire Service in English, founded in 1932, had now developed into a world service which included in addition to English, broadcasts in a great many foreign languages. On the same day, the General Forces Programme on the short waveband was re-named the General Overseas Service, and broadcast continuous, round-the-clock programmes in English to audiences in the British Empire, to British Forces and to British communities overseas, with much of its entertainment material selected from the B.B.C.'s domestic services. (The General Overseas Service was later re-named the World Service in 1965).

RADIOLYMPIA

On October 1st, the 1947 National Radio Exhibition opened at Olympia and now organised by the Radio Industry Council, the show did much to re-establish in the eyes of the world the prestige of the British Radio Industry. When it closed on October 11th, the attendance figures had beaten all previous records, for not only had the public been starved of a Radiolympia since 1939, there were also several other new and exciting categories of radio development for them to look at on the stands of more than 170 principal exhibitors. For the first time, the exhibition was extended to include a large display of electronic equipment which included radar navigational aids, radio-frequency heaters for use both in industry and in medicine, and industrial machinery controlled by valve circuits. Also prominently on show were communications receivers (for 'serious' short-wave reception), and VHF radio-telephone equipment. Several public and commercial services were then turning to low power VHF to provide local channels of communication and these included the police, fire brigades, harbour boards and taxi-hire services.

Many people also went specially to Radiolympia to see the latest developments in television or had come along with a view to replacing radio receivers which had done them good service throughout the war years, although supplies of new models in the shops were still far from adequate. The Radio Industry was still concentrating a large percentage of its output in the export field, and in September, an export target of £1,000,000 per month had been set which was regarded as "tough, but not impossible". The attendance figures at Radiolympia had been further boosted because thousands more men and women had become interested for the first time in some branch of radio through their wartime service, just as their counterparts had done during the First World War (see 1915).

The typical domestic radio receiver of 1947 was a 4-valve plus rectifier table model superhet with 'fly-wheel' tuning. Although a few examples had been on the market since about 1932, 1947 saw a huge rise in the popularity of fly-wheel tuning systems with over 50 per cent of sets on show at Radiolympia employing it (fig.690). A heavy fly-wheel was fitted to the shaft of the tuning control knob and if this was spun, the inertia of the fly-wheel then carried it on. Its use therefore made it easier and quicker to pass from one end of the tuning range to the other and it also improved the 'feel' of the control although the fashion disappeared almost as quickly as it had appeared.

Wartime research had accelerated the development of smaller valves and circuits needed for use in compact and lightweight Military communications equipment, and in peacetime this soon began to influence the circuit designs of radios used in the home. In 1947, a year after their American forerunners appeared in Britain, the first British 7-pin 'B7G' (button base) all-glass miniature valves were introduced and were soon in widespread use leading to a general reduction in size of table models, battery portables (figs.683,685) and amplifiers. In the same year, British 8-pin 'B8A' miniature 'Rimlock' valves were put on the market by Mazda and Mullard. They had a metal base shell with a protruding nipple which located and locked into its valve holder and prevented it from springing out. Later, from about 1953, the metal shell was dispensed with by Mullard who increased the width of the lower portion of the glass bulb to compensate for the change. Although Rimlocks were intended to be the post-war industry standard, they were never widely accepted and by the second half of the 1950s they had been superseded by the B7G and 9-pin 'B9A' (noval base) miniature valves, the latter type first introduced by Mullard in 1951 (see Appendix).

Magic-eye tuning indicators, so popular just before the war, were only included in a few new models, and another popular feature of the immediate pre-war years, push-button tuning, had also largely been abandoned. This was mainly due to economic reasons and while push-button tuning was retained in a few of the more expensive sets, the pre-war lavishness of using up to a dozen or more buttons had become restrained and a mere four to six were usually used now (fig.692). Several new 'second set' models appeared incorporating an electric clock which could be arranged to switch the set on or off at a pre-determined time, or used as an alternative to a bed-side alarm clock (fig.682).

As another result of wartime design developments, chassis were now generally more accessible and easier to remove from the cabinet for servicing. However, during the autumn and for many months afterwards, there were several reports in the radio Press of a deterioration in the standard of workmanship found in many new receiver circuits and a glut of premature faults developing, especially with regard to faulty wiring, condenser leakages, valve failure and badly soldered joints. These faults, put down to "post-war sloppiness", were usually discovered by the retailer during a shop demonstration or after a few weeks use by the customer and this naturally caused a lot of ill-feeling amongst those concerned, some retailers experiencing the return for repair of 30 per cent of new sets sold in the space of a single month.

Soon after Radiolympia had closed, rumours began to spread that Purchase Tax was about to be increased from 33 ⅓ per cent to 100 per cent, and panic buying set in in many areas of the country. However, when the new rates were announced on November 13th, the Tax had risen to 50 per cent although it was still large enough to cause a loud protest.

1947 had been a difficult year for Britain's industries. Towards the end of January, the worst winter weather experienced since 1895 brought near industrial breakdown and much needed exports were lost during the freeze-up which continued for many weeks. By February, the Government had reduced coal allocation and had ordered power cuts and over two million people were sent home as thousands of vital factories were forced to close down. Among these were those belonging to the majority of the country's radio, television and electrical goods manufacturers and the production of sets and component parts therefore dried up. Coal was Britain's major energy source and was vital to her economic recovery. Having experience a reduction in coal allocation during the freeze-up, Britain's factories were later faced with another shortage during the miner's strike in August which lasted 5 weeks.

With electricity used in the home, a new development had taken place in July when the specification for the modern 'square pin' fused plug was first issued (B.S.1363). The pins of the plugs were rectangular to distinguish them from the existing non-fused round pin plugs and together with the shuttered rectangular socket outlets introduced at the same time, are exactly the same as those in standard use in homes throughout the country today. On October 1st, the domestic supply voltage which had been standardized on all existing 50 c/s systems for a year, was now made mandatory for all new systems brought into use on or after that date.

1948

EXPERIMENTAL PRINTED CIRCUITS

In 1948, serious attempts at producing a wire-*less* radio began with the first developments of inlaid and printed circuit techniques. In January, John Sargrove Ltd. of Walton-On-Thames announced the production of the first complete receiver to be mass-produced by electronic circuit-making equipment, a development of a prototype first reviewed in *Wireless World* in April 1947 and first publicly shown at the 1947 Radiolympia. It was a 2-valve AC/DC local station receiver made especially for the Indian market. The 'wiring' and some of the components were produced automatically by spraying molten metal into narrow grooves and depressions moulded into a sand-blasted Bakelite circuit board. After the initial spraying, the board's surface was milled with diamond cutters to skim off the surplus metal, varnished, dried and electronically tested. In the narrow grooves, the metal deposit formed coils and connections between the various parts of the circuit. Small components were soldered in place and the larger ones, such as the electrolytic smoothing condenser and the loud-speaker were eyeletted in and hollow rivets were inserted to form valve holders. In the depressions (moulded into both sides of the panel), the metal formed the plates of the capacitors, and the resistors were produced by spraying a graphite compound through a mask. By this process, chassis containing completed circuits could be produced at the rate of three per minute. The finished product was housed in a Bakelite cabinet which apart from having a speaker grille in place of a tuning dial, was identical to the one later used by the Hale Electric Company for their 1950 Midgetronic receiver (fig.727).

While Sargrove were developing their sprayed circuit techniques, various other companies were experimenting with resistance ink. This was of the same consistency as normal printing ink, but contained colloidal silver, which, when applied to any insulated surface and allowed to dry, produced an excellent conductive coating. *Wireless World* felt that if resistance ink could be developed, "it may shortly be possible to print working circuits of radio receivers.... When this happens there's more than a possibility that even the most complicated communication receivers, or televisors, or even radar sets, could be built up at small cost from numbers of individually printed panels.... An astonishing prospect!". The magazine also successfully predicted that radio and television servicing would become extremely simple: "having tracked down your fault to one particular panel, you pull it out, throw it into the dustbin and replace it with a new one costing about fourpence!" (see 1958).

One of these resistance inks was made by the industrial chemists Ward, Blenkinsop & Co. Ltd., 6 Henrietta Place, London W1. It was available as a liquid, paste or powder and was applied by printing, brushing or spraying. But in those early experimental days there were many problems to be overcome, especially to obtain permanent adhesion of the metal to the plastic base and to avoid melting the base when soldering on components.

THE RADIO INDUSTRY

In February, the R.I.C. decided that the usual Radiolympia Exhibition would not be held that year so that the Radio Industry might have time and space to concentrate without distractions on the achievements of its export target (set at around £12,000,000) and to enable more time to be set aside for research and the development and production of new sets for the home market. When the total 1948 export figures became known the following year, exports of British radio equipment, navigational aids and industrial electronic apparatus had doubled.

The disposal of Government surplus components built up during the war had resulted in the establishment of several firms dealing in spares and a renewed interest in kit sets and home construction. The Premier Radio Company of London EC4 put together their famous Midget Radio kit (fig.709) which contained a complete set of parts necessary for building a 4-valve medium and long-wave TRF receiver. The cabinet (purchased separately) was identical to the one used for the Bakelite version of the Pilot Little Maestro in 1940 (fig.640) and from the late 1940s right up to the early 1960s, the same basic cabinet moulding was used by many other firms for various kit sets.

Home-constructed crystal sets also experienced a minor revival caused mainly by power cuts which were being experienced with increasing regularity as the decade wore on. A new type of highly stable silicon crystal rectifier (type CS7A), developed during the war and used in most centimetric radar and communications receivers, was released for general use in the early spring by B.T.H. Known popularly as the 'crystal valve', it comprised a silicon-tungsten junction sealed in a cartridge and for those who wanted to build a 'modern' crystal set, it was obtainable from Webbs Radio, 14 Soho Street, London W1, priced 7s.6d. (The term 'crystal valve' was not new: it had first been used in the early 1920s to describe a

particular crystal detector of the Perikon type).

In the field of valve development, Mullard introduced a series of 25 mA sub-miniature all-glass valves which reflected a growing preoccupation within the industry with the miniaturization of radio and electronic equipment. They were produced primarily for use in National Health Service hearing-aids but also found experimental use in miniature portable receivers.

In April, the Purchase Tax on radio and television sets was increased to 66 ⅔ per cent and as a result, demand for receivers fell considerably, causing a glut for the first time for nearly a decade as thousands of sets remained unsold on the shelves of radio shops throughout the country. There were widespread protests as many firms were forced to lay off staff, and a deputation led by the R.I.C. Chairman J.W. Ridgeway was sent to the Treasury. As a result, on June 16th, the Tax was amended to the original 1940 figure of 33 ⅓ per cent on both radios and television sets.

During 1948, the European Broadcasting Conference was held in Copenhagen with delegates from thirty-two nations debating the serious problem of the re-allocation of wavelengths used by some 340 European stations and synchronised networks congesting the long and medium wavebands. After discussions lasting ten weeks, agreement with the *Copenhagen Plan* was finally reached in October, with the Plan coming into operation on March 15th 1950 (see 1950).

It was hoped that the Plan would last for a period of five years and provide an interim answer to the problem of mutual interference between so many stations. But to provide a long term solution and to search for higher quality broadcasting, the B.B.C. had already begun to look towards two systems of VHF transmission: amplitude modulation (AM), by which the ordinary short, medium and long wavebands were already transmitted, and frequency modulation (FM). In March, they had begun building a VHF station at Wrotham Hill in Kent in order to field test the two systems.

THE FIRST TRANSISTORS

The first component point-contact transistor (an abbreviation of 'transfer resistor') was developed by John Bardeen and Walter Brattain working at Bell Telephone Laboratories in America in December 1947, and was first publicly announced on July 1st 1948. Describing it as an "amplifying crystal", *Wireless World* thought that "the Transistor could usefully take the place of valves". After five years of research during which William Shockley developed the more reliable junction transistor, component transistors began to be mass-produced and a revolution in the miniaturization of radio and electronics began, although it was not until 1956 that the first British all-transistor radio was produced (see 1956). From the second half of the 1950s, transistors began to be employed in every field of electronics and opened up many new ones, and in radio, the valve, which had reigned supreme in circuits for over fifty years, soon began to be displaced. The transistor introduced an era of true miniaturization, high reliability and low power consumption, all of which had been long-desired goals of the Radio Industry.

1949

In April, the Radio Component Manufacturers' Association changed its name to the Radio & Electronic Component Manufacturers' Federation in order to conform to the wider scope of its modern-day activities which encompassed components both for electronic engineering and for the manufacture of domestic radio and television receivers. With the term 'wireless' now widely regarded as out-dated, except among the diehard members of the listening public, *Wireless World* pointed out (with somewhat unconscious irony) that

"*Radio* is the word that is used by all up-to-date people when they are referring to communications of any kind made by means of electro-magnetic waves".

The National Radio Exhibition was held as usual at Olympia in the autumn, but this was the last time that the show would be put on at this venue, and consequently the last time it would be known as 'Radiolympia'. For the first time, television dominated the exhibition and radio took second place. While the London area still had the only television service in the country, the building of a second B.B.C. Band I television transmitter at Sutton Coldfield near Birmingham was nearing completion and it would only be a matter of a few months before a prosperous new market for television sales would open up in the Midlands. There was vast publicity at Radiolympia for this new station and prospective viewers could cast their eyes over television displays from nearly 40 manufacturers. For those interested in the more technical aspect, the B.B.C. had constructed a full working television studio similar to those in use at Alexandra Palace, with facilities for viewing both the transmitted scene and the received picture. It had long been realised that the Alexandra Palace site in North London would be completely inadequate for the proper expansion and development of television and in March the Corporation had secured a 13 ½ acre site at Wood Lane near the White City in West London for the proposed construction of a purpose-built Television Centre. Since this project would take several years to complete, the B.B.C. had to find provisional accommodation meanwhile, and in November they were able to acquire five studios at the Rank Film Studios just half a mile to the south of the Wood Lane site at Lime Grove, Shepherds Bush. In May of the following year, the first one (Studio 'D') opened for children's television: the last programme from the Alexandra Palace studios, *Thank You, Ally Pally*, was broadcast on March 19th 1954.

Despite the focus of attention at the 1949 Radiolympia being on television, manufacturers emphasised the continuing need for the possession of an ordinary radio receiver and tried to dispel the mistaken idea that broadcasting without vision was now out-of-date. Television was complementary to, rather than a substitute for the radio. Forty-seven out of the 56 manufacturers in the broadcast section in the Grand Hall were exhibiting radio receivers "catering for every shade of taste" from the small bed-side 'second set' at under £10 (fig.714) to the multi-band receiver for world-wide reception at around £50 including Purchase Tax (fig.717) which reflected the feeling that the years of austerity, if not completely over, were perhaps at last departing. The radio supply situation in the shops was now easing considerable but Britain's goods were still difficult to sell abroad as the Pound continued high against the Dollar. However, in September 1949, the Pound was devalued and the price of British imports in the United States was cut in the shops by as much as 20 per cent and this paved the way to a reduction in the Dollar Debt.

Since the 1947 Radiolympia, the number of manufacturers offering battery portables had trebled (fig.722) although the backbone of all the radio exhibits continued to be the table model 4-valve plus rectifier superhet (fig.718). The electronics section at the 1949 Radiolympia had taken over practically the whole of the National Hall and developments in this field had been so rapid that *Wireless World* felt that "the layman....can hardly be expected to know what it can (or cannot) do for him". The areas here covered scientific, industrial, and medical apparatus, and airborne and marine radar.

By the spring of 1949, so many taxi hire-services, newspaper offices, and haulage companies etc. had installed mobile and home-based low power VHF radio-telephones to provide a network of local communication, that in order to enforce some form of control the Business Radio Licence had been introduced at £5 plus £5 for each additional transmitter-receiver. At the Radiolympia exhibition, several major firms including Marconi's, Ekco, G.E.C. and Pye put on quite extensive displays of equipment to cater for this growing market.

fig.635. Ekco Model AD 75, by E.K. Cole Ltd. January 1940. 3-v +R, AC/DC SHet Table Model, MW/LW Mtrs/StN, on/off control combined with volume knob, brown Bakelite case. 14 in. diameter x 6 ½ in. deep. £7.7s.0d. Designed to meet wartime needs: "By exercising economy in design, the rising costs of the components have been offset, but no attempt has been made to cheapen either the materials or the finish". Re-released in October 1946, price £11.11s.0d plus £2.9s.8d PT, with ON/OFF switch mounted on the side of the cabinet and with slight chassis divergencies: the dial, however, in both versions, shows *pre*-war station names.

fig.636. Pilot 'Major Maestro', by Pilot Radio Ltd. March 1940. 4-v +R, AC/DC SHet Table Model, SW/MW Mtrs/StN, brown Bakelite cabinet. 9 in. x 15 in. x 6 ¾ in. (SW/MW/LW version released in November 1946).

fig.637. Murphy Model A90, by Murphy Radio Ltd. 1940. 5-v +R AC SHet Table Model, SW/MW/LW Mtrs/StN, push-button waveband selection, mahogany veneered plywood cabinet with black Bakelite panel and knobs. 17 ½ in. x 16 ¼ in. x 9 ¾ in. £11.0s.0d.

fig.638. Murphy Type B93, by Murphy Radio Ltd. 1940. 5-v Batt, SW/MW Mtrs/StN, internal frame aerial, turntable, black leatherette covered plywood cabinet. 14 in. x 13 ½ in. 8 in.

fig.639. Marconiphone Model 911, by Marconiphone Co. Ltd. August 1940. 4-v +R, AC SHet Table Model, SW/MW/LW Mtrs/StN, internal frame aerial, chassis mounted upside down, brown Bakelite cabinet. 10 ½ in. x 15 in. x 8 in.

fig.640. Pilot 'Little Maestro', by Pilot Radio Ltd. 1940. 4-v +R, AC/DC SHet Table Model, MW/LW Mtrs/StN, brown Bakelite cabinet. 6 ¾ in. x 11 ¼ in. x 6 in. £12.5s.0d. This is the Bakelite cabinet version of the 1939 wooden 'Little Maestro' (fig.627). It was released after the war too with post-war dial markings, and in the Autumn of 1947, in a choice of powder blue, pastel green or peach coloured Bakelite cabinets. The basic cabinet moulding of the 'Little Maestro' enjoyed a very long production life, and was used by many other firms from the late 1940s to house various kit sets for the home-constructor. Beginning with the Premier receiver of 1948 (fig.709), the cabinet was supplied with over a dozen kit sets until at least the early 1960s including the 'Occasional 4' by Precision Electronic Equipment Co. in 1951, the 'Atomic' and the 'Meteor III' by Norman H. Field in 1954, and the 'Ocean Hopper' by Concord Electronics in 1959.

fig.641. Murphy Model A92, by Murphy Radio Ltd. April 1940. 5-v +R, AC SHet Table Model, 6SW/MW/LW, push-button and manual tuning, black stained oak cabinet with black moulded Bakelite front. 20 ¼ in. x 20 in. x 10 ¼ in. £15.15s.0d. On medium and long-waves, a 4-v +R circuit was employed, but on short-waves, an additional RF amplifying stage was introduced.

fig.642. Philco Model A9 BG, by Philco Radio & Television Corporation of Great Britain Ltd. 1940. 4-v +R, AC SHet Table Model, SW/MW/LW Mtrs/StN, walnut veneered plywood cabinet. 17 in. x 20 in. x 8 in.

fig.643. Ferranti Model 145, by Ferranti Ltd. September 1945. 4-v +R, AC Shet Table Model, SW/MW/LW Mtrs/StN, expanded metal grille, brown Bakelite cabinet. 18 in. x 13 in. x 9 in. £15.0s.0d + PT.

fig.644. Ekco Model A22, by E.K. Cole Ltd. 1945. 3-v +R, AC SHet Table Model, SW/MW/LW Mtrs/StN, Perspex tuning scale, 'florentine bronze' loud-speaker surround, 'walnut' Bakelite cabinet. 14 ½ in. x 13 in. x 7 ½ in. £14.14s.0d + £3.3s.3d PT. Also black Bakelite cabinet version with chromium-plated trim. In 1946, the A22 was shown in a moulded green cabinet, a one-off non-standard colour produced specially for the Britain Can Make It Exhibition.

fig.645. Sobell Model 615, by Sobell Industries Ltd. December 1945. 5-v +R, AC SHet Table Model, 2SW/MW/LW Mtrs/StN, walnut and maple veneered plywood cabinet. 16 in. x 21 ½ in. x 13 in. £19.19s.0d + PT.

fig.646. Murphy Model B97, by Murphy Radio Ltd. 1945. SW/MW/LW Mtrs/StN, push-buttons for wave change, black Bakelite cabinet. 17 in. x 15 ½ in. x 9 ½ in. £15.17s.6d + PT. Cabinet identical to Model A96, SW/MW AC SHet of 1943.

fig.647. Portadyne Table Model, by Portadyne Radio Ltd. 1945. 4-v +R, AC/DC SHet Table Model, SW/MW/LW Mtrs/StN, walnut and maple veneered plywood cabinet. 10 ½ in. x 16 in. x 8 in.

fig.648. Pye Model 15A, by Pye Ltd. 1945. 3-v +R, AC SHet Table Model, SW/MW/LW Mtrs/StN, 'fly-wheel' tuning control, walnut veneered plywood cabinet. 13 in. x 18 in. x 9 in. £15.0s.0d + PT. Pye's first post-war domestic receiver. 'Quick release' chassis held on by just two small screws - the result of wartime improvements in receiver design.

fig.649. Ultra Model T406, by Ultra Electric Ltd. November 1945. 3-v +R, AC SHet Table Model, SW/MW/LW Mtrs/StN, brown Bakelite knobs, maple trim, walnut veneered plywood cabinet. 13 in. x 19 in. x 8 in.

fig.650. Aerodyne Model 302, by Aerodyne Ltd. December 1945. 4-v +R, AC/DC SHet Table Model, SW/MW/LW Mtrs/StN, line-cord, walnut veneered plywood cabinet. 8 ½ in. x 4 ¾ in. x 5 ¾ in. £13.0s.0d. + £2.15s.11d PT.

fig.651. Murphy Model A104, by Murphy Radio Ltd. 1946. 4-v +R, AC SHet Table Model, SW/MW/LW Mtrs/StN, mahogany 'baffle' cabinet. 23 ¾ in. x 18 in. x 5 ½ in. £25.0s.0d + PT. First shown at the Britain Can Make It Exhibition.

fig.652. Bush Model DAC 90, by Bush Radio Ltd. April 1946. 4-v +R, AC/DC SHet Table Model, MW/LW Mtrs/StN, cloth grille, internal frame aerial, 'walnut' Bakelite cabinet. 9 ¼ in. x 11 ¾ in. x 7 in. £11.11s.0d + PT. Also black Bakelite or cream Bakelite (urea formaldehyde) cabinets. (Later cabinet version, c.1948, with expanded metal grille). Similar to Bush Model DAC 90A of 1950 (fig.729).

fig.653. Ever Ready Model 'C', by Ever Ready Co. (Great Britain) Ltd. November 1946. 4-v all-dry Batt SHet Portable, MW/LW Mtrs/StN, cream painted plywood sides, cream perspex front. 12 ¾ in. x 10 in. x 8 in. £11.11s.0d + £2.13s.9d PT. (Similar to Model C/A, 1947, and C/E, 1948).

fig.654. McMichael Model 451, by McMichael Radio Ltd. 1946. 3-v +R, AC SHet Table Model, SW/MW/LW Mtrs/StN, walnut veneered cabinet. 17 in. x 16 in. x 8 ½ in.

fig.655. Ekco Model A28, by E.K. Cole Ltd. August 1946. 4-v +R plus Magic-Eye Tuning Indicator, AC SHet Table Model, 7SW/MW/LW plus TV Sound Channel Mtrs/StN, push-button and manual tuning, brown Bakelite panel and knobs, walnut veneered plywood cabinet. 15 in. x 25 in. x 10 in. £29.8s.0d + £6.6s.5d PT. Shown at the Britain Can Make It Exhibition.

fig.656. Ferranti Model 146, by Ferranti Ltd. 1946. 4-v +R, AC SHet Table Model, SW/MW/LW Mtrs/StN, black Bakelite cabinet with white front. 12 in. x 20 in. x 9 in. £18.18s.0d + PT. (Battery version, Model 615, released in 1951).

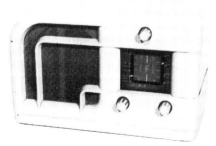

fig.657. Ferranti Model 546, by Ferranti Ltd. 1946. 4-v +R, AC/DC SHet Table Model, MW/LW Mtrs/StN, cream plastic cabinet. 7 in. x 11 ½ in. x 6 in. £15.15s.7d inc £2.15s.7d PT.

fig.658. G.E.C. Model BC 4650, by General Electric Co. Ltd. January 1946. 4-v +R, AC SHet Table Model, SW/MW/LW Mtrs/StN, push-buttons for on/off and wavechange, brown Bakelite cabinet. 14 in. x 15 in. x 8 in. £14.14s.0d + PT. (Model BC 4655 is AC/DC version).

fig.659. Romac Model 106, by Romac Radio Corporation Ltd. August 1946. 4-v Batt Portable, MW Mtrs/StN, PVC shoulder-strap containing aerial, chromium plated trim, black-painted metal case, 5 ¼ in. x 9 ½ in. x 2 in. £14.14s.0d + PT. This was the first receiver in Britain to use U.S. 7-pin miniature all-glass valves. Also five later variations: Model 126 (June 1947); Model 136L (MW/LW, July 1948); Model 136S (SW/MW, August 1948); Models 236L and 236S, (these were 136 models adapted in 1949 to operate also with mains power unit).

fig.660. Ultra Model T401, by Ultra Electric Ltd. February 1946. 3-v +R; AC SHet Table Model, SW/MW/LW Mtrs/StN, aerial wire wound on a 'tidy' on the back, cream Bakelite front and knobs, brown Bakelite cabinet. 7 ¾ in. x 12 in. x 6 ½ in. £13.17s.6d + PT. A small, compact receiver aimed at the 'second set' market. Other cabinet colours released in December 1946: Cuban Red, Ivory Cream and April Green, price £15.15s.0d + PT.

fig.661. Braidio Model 21, by E.K. Cole Ltd. for Rentertainments Ltd. 1946. 4-v +R, AC SHet Table Model, MW/LW, Mtrs/StN, interchangeable tuning dial, cloth grille, brown Bakelite cabinet. 10 in. x 16 ½ in. x 9 in.

fig.662. Cossor Model 464, by A.C. Cossor Ltd. 1946. 4-v +R, AC SHet Table Model, SW/MW/LW Mtrs/StN, black Bakelite cabinet. 9 in. x 13 ½ in. x 6 ¾ in. £18.0s.0d inc PT. (Cabinets also available in green or ivory sprayed finish).

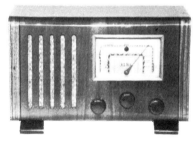

fig.663. Alba Model 472, by A.J. Balcombe Ltd. December 1946. 4-v +R, AC SHet Table Model, SW/MW/LW Mtrs/StN, walnut veneered plywood cabinet with rosewood inlay. 8 ¾ in. x 14 in. x 5 ¼ in.

fig.664. Vidor 'Chanson' Model CN 349, by Vidor Ltd. 1946. 4-v +R plus Magic-Eye Tuning Indicator, AC SHet Table Model, 2SW/MW/LW Mtrs/StN, walnut veneered plywood cabinet. 11 in. x 19 in. x 9 ½ in. £16.10s.0d + £3.11s.0d PT.

fig.665. Murphy Model A100, by Murphy Radio Ltd. 1946. (des: A.F. Thwaites). 4–v +R, AC SHet Transportable, MW/LW Mtrs/StN, dark red Bakelite case. 7 ½ in. x 9 ¼ in. x 4 ¾ in. £12.0s.0d + PT. Shown at the Britain Can Make It Exhibition. (Model A100F has internal frame aerial).

fig.666. McMichael Model 463, by McMichael Radio Ltd. 1946. 4–v Batt Portable, MW/LW Mtrs/StN, leather strap handle, internal frame aerial, turntable, brown/yellow crackle finished plywood cabinet. 11 ½ in. x 11 in. x 6 in. £13.0s.0d + £2.15s.11d PT.

fig.667. Masteradio Model D110, by Masteradio Ltd. 1946. 4–v +R, AC/DC SHet Table Model, MW/LW Mtrs, 'walnut' Bakelite cabinet. 7 in. x 10 ½ in. x 6 in. £14.3s.6d + PT. Also available in white, green or blue plastic cabinets. Masteradio 'Sandown Star' came out in 1951 in an identical cabinet but with a built-in aerial and a larger loud-speaker.

fig.668. Bush Model AC 91, by Bush Radio Ltd. 1946. 4–v +R, AC SHet Table Model, SW/MW/LW Mtrs/StN, white plastic grille, 'walnut' Bakelite knobs and cabinet. 9 ½ in. x 11 ½ in. x 7 in.

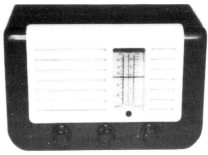

fig.669. Ekco Model U29X, by E.K. Cole Ltd. June 1946. 4–v +R, AC/DC Table Model SHet, SW/MW/LW Mtrs, internal frame aerial, white plastics front, brown Bakelite cabinet. 7 ¾ in. x 12 in. x 7 in. £13.13s.0d. + £2.18s.8d PT. (Model U29 is MW/LW Mtrs/StN version).

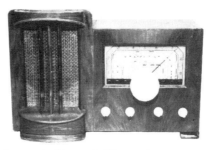

fig.670. 'Table Model' by Radio Accoustic Products Ltd. 1946. 4–v +R, AC SHet Table Model, 3SW/MW/LW Mtrs/StN, chromium-plated chassis, plate glass back, walnut veneered plywood cabinet. 13 ½ in. x 18 in. x 9 ¼ in.

fig.671. Ekco Model A23, by E.K. Cole Ltd. August 1946. 4–v +R, AC SHet Table Model, SW/MW/LW plus TV Sound Channel Mtrs/StN, push-button and manual tuning, brown Bakelite knobs and cabinet. 13 in. x 22 in. x 10 in. £19.19s.0d + PT. (Model U49 is 1947 AC/DC version, price £23.2s.0d + PT).

fig.672. Bush Model BP 90, by Bush Radio Ltd. November 1946. 4–v all-dry Batt Portable, MW/LW, Mtrs/StN, internal frame aerial, blue leathercloth covered plywood cabinet. 9 in. x 12 in. x 8 ½ in. £14.14s.0d + PT.

fig.673. Ever Ready Battery Table Model, by Ever Ready Co. (Great Britain) Ltd. 1946. 4–v Batt Table Model, MW/LW Mtrs/StN, brown Bakelite cabinet. 12 in. x 12 ½ in. x 8 in.

fig.674. Peto Scott Type H52, by Peto Scott Co. Ltd. April 1946. 4–v +R, AC SHet Table Model, SW/MW/LW Mtrs/StN, walnut veneered plywood cabinet, part-stained to simulate rosewood. 16 ½ in. x 19 in. x 10 in. £19.19s.0d + £4.5s.10d PT. (Model H51 is 2SW/MW version).

fig.675. Philips Model 186A, by Philips Electrical Ltd. 1946. 4-v +R plus Magic-Eye Tuning Indicator, AC SHet Table Model, SW/MW/LW Mtrs/StN, slotted glass tuning scale, walnut and mahogany veneered plywood cabinet. 13 in. x 22 in. x 9 in.

fig.676. Sobell Model 516, by Sobell Industries Ltd. November 1946. 4-v +R, AC Table Model SHet, SW/MW/LW Mtrs/StN, walnut veneered plywood cabinet with gold painted loud-speaker grille inset. 15 in. x 19 in. x 11 in. £20.0s.0d + PT.

fig.677. Pye Type L75B, by Pye Ltd. 1946. 4-v Batt Portable, SW/MW/LW Mtrs/StN, internal frame aerial, cream plastic tuning scale surround, blue rexine covered plywood case. 12 in. x 13 in. x 7 in. £13.10s.0d + £2.18s.1d PT.

fig.678. Emor 'Globe', by Emor Radio Ltd. April 1946 (for export), 1947 (for domestic market). 4-v +R, AC Shet, SW/MW/LW Mtrs/StN, chromium-plated metal globe and stand. 11 ½ in. dia x 42 ½ in. high. £14.14s.0d. Tuning is affected by rotating the globe; wave-change and volume controls are concentrically mounted on supporting stand. (Also came in various pastel shades and 'gold'). Other version on stand 54 in. high, adjustable to 72 in. high.

fig.679. Radio Rentals Model RR 57, by Mains Radio Gramophones Ltd. (A subsidiary of Radio Rentals). 1947. 4-v +R, AC SHet Table Model, SW/MW/LW Mtrs/StN, internal frame aerial, ivory moulded plastic front, 'walnut' Bakelite cabinet. 11 ½ in. x 20 in. x 9 ½ in.

fig.680. Table Model by Radio Accoustic Products Ltd. 1947. 3-v +R, AC SHet Table Model, SW/MW/LW Mtrs/StN, walnut veneered plywood cabinet. 12 ¾ in. x 20 ½ in. x 9 in.

fig.681. Amplion 'Delegate' Model HU 610, by Amplion (1932) Ltd. 1947. 4-v +R +Bar, AC/DC SHet Table Model, SW/MW/LW Mtrs/StN, walnut veneered plywood cabinet. 8 in. x 13 in. x 6 ½ in. £15.15s.0d + PT.

fig.682. Goblin 'Time-Spot' Model CR, by British Vacuum Cleaner & Engineering Co. Ltd. 1947. 4-v +R, AC SHet Table Model, SW/MW/LW Mtrs/StN, mahogany veneered plywood cabinet. 13 ½ in. x 17 ½ in. x 9 in. £24.0s.0d + PT. The set incorporates a synchronous clock with an automatic pre-set on/off time switch.

fig.683. Hermes 'Radio Tourist', by Hermes, Brooke & Co. November 1947. 4-v (uses new 'B7G' all-glass miniature valves) Batt Portable, MW 55-140 deg, screwed-on information plate showing station names and corresponding degree readings, frame aerial built into sliding back panel, green mottled tinplate case in the form of a book. 8 ½ in. x 6 in. x 2 ¾ in. £13.13s.0d + PT. "For the hiker and holidaymaker", the 'Radio Tourist' came complete with a shoulder sling and a waterproof carrying case in a wide choice of colours (not shown).

fig.684. Decca 'Double Decca', by Decca Record Co. Ltd. 1947. (des: H.G. Hammond). 3-v AC/DC M/Batt Portable, SW/MW/LW Mtrs/StN, internal frame aerial, white sprayed aluminium front panel, cream 'Air Travel' fabric covered wood case. 9 ½ in. x 12 ½ in. x 7in. £15.0s.0d + PT. The LT battery received a trickle charge when the set was being used on the mains. (MW/LW version 1946, SW/MW version 1949).

fig.685. Cossor Model 469, by A.C. Cossor Ltd. October 1947. 4-v (uses new 'B7G' miniature all-glass valves) Batt Portable, MW/LW Mtrs/StN, internal frame aerial, Perspex panel sprayed deep maroon, clear Perspex dial window, cream plastic knobs and carrying handle, expanded metal grille, green fabric covered wood case. 13 in. x 10 in. x 7 ½ in. £13.15s.0d + PT.

fig.686. Dulci Model MSU4, by Dulci Radio Ltd. 1947. 3-v +R, AC/DC Table Model, MW/LW Mtrs/StN, white plastic knobs, red plastic cabinet. 6 in. x 8 in. x 6 in. £13.13s.0d + PT.

fig.687. Magnum 'Hampshire', by Burne Jones & Co. January 1947. 3-v +R, AC SHet Table Model, MW/LW Mtrs and braille markings, solid oak front and solid mahogany sides. 16 in. x 11 ¾ in. x 9 ¾ in. Donated through the Hampshire Association For The Care Of The Blind, Winchester and the British Wireless For The Blind Fund.

fig.688. Fidelity Model 2546, by Fidelity Radio Ltd. May 1947. 4-v +R, AC/DC SHet, SW/MW Mtrs/StN, green plastic knobs, red-brown 'Tufnol' cabinet (also available in a number of shades). 8 in. x 13 in. x 6 in. £14.14s.0d + PT. 'Tufnol' was the trade name of a shellac impregnated fibre material made by Ellison Insulations Ltd., Perry Bar, Birmingham. Model 2546 was Fidelity Radio's first receiver and its unusual shape gave it the title of the 'caravan set'.

fig.689. Murphy Model A122, by Murphy Radio Ltd. June 1947. 4-v +R, AC SHet Table Model, SW/MW/LW Mtrs/StN, birch plywood cabinet. 19 ½ in. x 22 in. x 8 in. £22.0s.0d + PT. One in the baffle board series of Murphy radios. (Also Model A122C, console version, price £27.10s.0d + PT).

fig.690. Murphy Model A122C, by Murphy Radio Ltd. July 1947. 4-v +R, AC SHet Console (optional legs extra), SW/MW/LW Mtrs/StN, flywheel tuning control, scale mounted on top of cabinet, mahogany control panel, black painted plywood cabinet. 20 ½ in. x 25 ½ in. x 9 in. £27.10s.0d + PT. (Console version of Model A122 baffle receiver, fig.689).

fig.691. Champion 'Venus', by Champion Electric Corporation Ltd. 1947. 4-v +R, AC/DC SHet Table Model, MW Mtrs/StN, internal frame aerial, moving-coil loudspeaker housed in top facing upwards, chromium-plated base, clear Perspex twist decoration, eau-de-nil Perspex case. 11 ½ in. high x 8 ½ in. diameter. £15.15s.0d + PT. Also available in a variety of pastel colours. For use abroad, export customers could choose a combination of short, medium or long wavebands to suit their requirements.

fig.692. G.E.C. Model BC 4750, by General Electric Co. Ltd. October 1947. 4-v +R, AC SHet Table Model, SW/MW/LW Mtrs/StN, 5 push-buttons, 'Hi-Fi' moving-coil loud-speaker, mahogany veneered plywood cabinet. 13 ¾ in. x 22 ½ in. x 9 ¼ in. £23.12.6d + PT.

fig.693. Ferranti Model 347, by Ferranti Ltd. 1947. 4-v +R, AC SHet Console, SW/MW/LW Mtrs/StN, black Bakelite knobs, walnut veneered plywood cabinet. 36 in. x 21 ½ in. x 12 in. Has two pre-set stations operated by wave change knob.

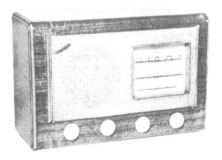

fig.694. Beethoven Model U3038, by Beethoven Electric Equipment Ltd. October 1947. 3-v +R, AC/DC SHet Table Model, SW/MW/LW Mtrs/StN, mahogany veneered plywood cabinet. 12 in. x 18 in. x 7 in. £17.17s.0d + PT.

fig.695. Philips Model 462A, by Philips Electrical Ltd. March 1947. 3-v +R, AC SHet Table Model, SW/MW/LW, Mtrs/StN, plate glass tuning scale, internal plate aerial, brown Bakelite cabinet. 13 ¼ in. x 16 ¾ in. x 8 in. £18.18s.0d + £4.1.4d PT.

fig.696. Alba Model C112, by A.J. Balcombe Ltd. 1947. 4-v +R, AC/DC Table Model 'Midget', SW/MW/LW Mtrs/StN, aerial wound on 'tidy' on back, white plastic cabinet with blue decoration on knobs. 5 in. x 8 in. x 4 ½ in. £13.13s.0d + PT. In 1949, the cabinet also became available in ivory, pink, green, blue, 'walnut' and black.

fig.697. 'Strad' Model 471, by R.M. Electric Ltd. September 1947. 4-v +R, AC SHet Table Model, SW/MW/LW Mtrs/StN, brown plastic knobs, matt walnut veneered plywood cabinet. 10 ½ in. x 16 ½ in. x 8 ¼ in.

fig.698. G.E.C. Model BC 4835R, by General Electric Co. Ltd. 1947. 5-v +R, AC/DC SHet Table Model, SW/MW/LW, Mtrs/StN, 'walnut' Bakelite cabinet with white moulded plastic knobs and grille. 8 in. x 11 in. x 6 ½ in. £14.14s.0d + PT.

fig.699. Ferranti Model 547, by Ferranti Ltd. 1947. 4-v +R, AC/DC SHet Table Model, MW/LW Mtrs/StN, internal plate aerial, cream plastic cabinet with gold painted front. 8 in. x 12 in. x 6 ½ in. £14.14s.0d + PT.

fig.700. Marconiphone Model P17B, by Marconiphone Co. Ltd. 1947. 4-v (uses new 'B7G' all-glass miniature valves) Batt 'Personal' Miniature Portable, MW Mtrs, frame aerial housed in lid, chromium plated control panel, black plastic case. 2 ½ in. x 9 ¼ in. x 5 in. (lid closed). £13.2s.6d + PT. The set switches on and off when the lid is raised and lowered. Identicle circuit and components to Ever Ready Model 'B'. *The Wireless & Electrical Trader* considered the P17B to be a very superior model: "This set proves irrisistible to those in the higher income group for holidays, picnics and garden use. Well worth a direct mailing to your better class customers."

fig.701. Cossor Model 470 AC, by A.C. Cossor Ltd. 1947. 4-v +R, AC SHet Table Model, SW/MW/LW Mtrs/StN, walnut veneered plywood cabinet. 13 ½ in. x 15 in. x 9 in. £21.11s.6d + PT.

fig.702. Marconiphone 'Companion' Model T15 DA, by Marconiphone Co. Ltd. 1947. 4-v +R, AC/DC 'Midget' Transportable, MW/LW Mtrs/StN, internal frame aerial, red plastic knobs and handle, brown Bakelite cabinet. 8 ½ in. x 9 ¼ in. x 7 in. £15.4s.6d. (Red or cream cabinet versions too).

fig.703. Ambassador Type 548, by R.N. Fitton Ltd. 1948. 4-v +R, AC/DC Radio/ Bookcase, SW/MW/LW Mtrs/StN, gold coloured expanded metal grille, mahogany veneered plywood case with solid walnut shelves. 33 ¼ in. x 24 in. x 10 in. £32.14s.2d inc PT. (Very similar to Ambassador 4756 series of 1947).

fig.704. Marconiphone Model P20B, by Marconiphone Co. Ltd. December 1948. 4-v Batt 'Personal' Miniature Portable, MW/ LW Mtrs, 'snakeskin' covered cast metal body with cream plastic base and lift-up lid (latter housing a frame aerial). 3 in. x 7 in. x 5 in. (lid closed). £11.19s.6d + PT. The set switches on and off when the lid is raised and lowered.

fig.705. Pye Model 47X, by Pye Ltd. March 1948. 3-v +R, AC/DC SHet Table Model, MW/LW Mtrs/StN, white plastic knobs, brown moulded Bakelite cabinet. 6 ½ in. x 13 in. x 5 ¾ in. (Identical to 1948 Invicta Model 200).

fig.706. G.E.C. Model BC 4941, by General Electric Co. Ltd. April 1948. 4-v Batt Portable, MW/LW Mtrs/StN, internal frame aerial, black Bakelite case. 12 ¾ in. x 13 in. x 6 in. £15.15s.0d + PT.

fig.707. Philips Model 474B, by Philips Electrical Ltd. July 1948. 6-v Batt Table Model, SW/MW/LW Mtrs/StN, brown Bakelite cabinet. 13 ¼ in. x 18 ¼ in. x 9 ½ in. £18.18s.0d + PT.

fig.708. Ferranti Model 248, by Ferranti Ltd. 1948. 5-v +R, AC SHet Table Model, SW/ MW/LW Mtrs/StN, mahogany veneered plywood cabinet. 15 in. x 22 in. x 10 in. £31.11s.3d inc PT.

fig.709. Premier 'Midget Radio Kit', by Premier Radio Co. Ltd. 1948. 3-v +R, AC/ DC TRF Table Model Kit, MW/LW Mtrs/ StN, cream Bakelite cabinet. 6 ¾ in. x 11 ¼ in. x 6 in. £8.0s.11d, cabinet extra: cream, price 29s.4d, brown, price 27s.4d.

fig.710. Westminster Model ZA 818, sold by Curry's Ltd. 1948. 6-v +R plus Magic-Eye Tuning Indicator, AC SHet Table Model, SW/MW/LW Mtrs/StN, brown Bakelite cabinet. 10 in. x 19 ½ in. x 10 ¾ in.

fig.711. Ekco 'Consort' Model U76, by E.K. Cole Ltd. October 1948. 4-v +R, AC/DC SHet Table Model, SW/MW/LW Mtrs StN, internal frame aerial, pilot light, ivory plastics grille, black Bakelite case. 9 in. x 14 in. x 7 in. £14.13s.5d + PT. (Also in 'dark walnut' Bakelite).

fig.712. Pye Model M78F, by Pye Ltd. 1948. 4-v Batt Portable, MW/LW Mtrs/StN, black and cream Perspex case. 7 ¼ in. x 5 ¾ in. x 3 ¼ in. £12.12s.0d + PT. (Also eau-de-nil Perspex case). For the first time since its introduction in 1927, Pye's famous sunrise fret motif was used without clouds. This unfortunately caused it to resemble too closely the national flag of Japan, then Britain's recent hated enemy. There was an immediate public outcry and accusations of "bad taste", and the sets were withdrawn. It is thought that out of the original run of around 1,000 delivered to retailers' shops, as many as 800 remained unsold and these were quickly recalled and a bonfire made of them at the Pye works.

fig.713. Murphy Model A188C, by Murphy Radio Ltd. 1949. 5-v +R plus Magic-Eye Tuning Indicator, AC SHet Console, MW/LW Mtrs/StN, walnut veneered plywood, baffle type cabinet. 34 in. x 27 in. x 7 in.

fig.714. Sobell 'Sobellette' Model 439, by Sobell Industries Ltd. 1949. 3-v +R, AC/DC Transportable Midget, MW/LW Mtrs/StN, brown Bakelite case. 8 ½ in. x 9 in. x 7 in. £7.7s.10d + PT. (Painted cabinet finish also available in light green, metallic green, beige and cream).

fig.715. Ever Ready Model 'H', by Ever Ready Co. (Great Britain) Ltd. 1949. 2-v all-dry Batt Table Model, MW/LW, cream painted tin cabinet. 10 ½ in. x 11 ½ in. x 7 in. £6.17s.11d + PT. Designed "for use in cottage homes, for old people and others to whom economy is of prime importance".

fig.716. Cossor 'Melody Maker' Model 494, by A.C. Cossor Ltd. July 1st 1949. 4-v +R, AC SHet Table Model, SW/MW/LW Mtrs/StN/Mcs, cream painted scale and loud-speaker surround, 'walnut' Bakelite cabinet. 10 in. x 16 in. x 8 in. £12.19s.6d + PT. (The wood cabinet version, Model 500, came out in 1950).

fig.717. H.M.V. Model 5201, by The Gramophone Co. Ltd. 1949. 4-v +R plus Magic-Eye Tuning Indicator, 6SW/MW/LW Mtrs/StN, walnut veneered plywood cabinet. 15 ¾ in. x 22 ¼ in. x 11 ¾ in. £37.16s.0d + PT.

fig.718. McMichael 'Supervox' Model 498, by McMichael Radio Ltd. 1949. 4-v +R, AC/DC SHet Table Model, MW/LW Mtrs/StN, twin moving-coil loud-speakers, gold coloured expanded metal grille, cream plastic knobs, walnut veneered plywood cabinet. 8 ¼ in. x 17 ¼ in. x 7 ½ in.

fig.719. Pam Model 607, by Pamphonic Reproducers Ltd. 1949. 3-v +R, AC SHet Table Model, SW/MW/LW Mtrs/StN, bow-fronted walnut cabinet with double doors. 19 in. x 17 in. x 12 in.

fig.720. Ever Ready 'Saucepan Special', by Ever Ready Co. (Great Britain) Ltd. September 1949. 4-v Batt, SW (25/90m) Mtrs/StN (Lusaka, Accra, Brazzaville etc., plus B.B.C. SW stations), principally designed for the Central African market, tropicalised insect-proof aluminium cabinet sprayed blue, (research had shown that Africans were superstitious about almost every other colour). 9 in. diameter. Also had limited sales in Britain for short-wave listening, price £5.0s.0d + £1.5s.0d for a 300 hour battery: the receiver sat on this as the battery was too big to go inside. The cabinet was made at a North London saucepan factory.

fig.721. Philips Type 291 U/15, by Philips Electrical Ltd. 1949. 3-v +R, AC SHet Table Model, MW/LW Mtrs/StN, brown Bakelite cabinet. 8 in. x 11 in. x 7 in. £10.10s.0d + PT.

fig.722. Roberts 'Junior', by Roberts Radio Co. Ltd. 1949. 4-v Batt Portable, MW/LW Mtrs/StN, red plastic knobs, red leathercloth covered case, cream plastic detail. £14.14s.0d + PT. It came with a separate waterproof carrying bag with sling handles and zip fastener which protected the receiver from dust and afforded "an attractive disguise for travelling".

4 The 1950s

1950

The B.B.C.'s high power VHF transmitting station at Wrotham Hill in Kent opened for experimental broadcasts in the spring, and began radiating AM on 93.8 Mc/s (3.20 metres) and FM on 91.4 Mc/s (3.28 metres). Apart from the B.B.C.'s own staff of test engineers, few members of the listening public had equipment suitable for picking up the station, but in the autumn, Pye Radio Ltd. introduced a VHF/AM adaptor which allowed anyone in the service area with a standard radio set to receive the tests put out by the experimental AM transmitter. (Pye Radio considered AM to be the best method of VHF transmission, although following the Wrotham tests, the B.B.C. eventually opted for FM when their VHF service was inaugurated in 1955).

Since coming back on the air in 1946, the long-wave commercial Radio Luxembourg station had once more built up a considerable audience in Great Britain, especially on Sunday afternoons, due mainly to the popularity and quality of the stars and bands engaged on its programmes and the high standard of its transmissions. But planning their Radio Luxembourg entertainment had always been a problem for listeners as the station's programmes were not generally publicised in the British Press. However, from their January 27th 1950 issue, the music paper *Melody Maker* began to carry complete programme details every week, and the wealth of entertainment shown in the first listing for Sunday afternoon February 5th indicates why the B.B.C. feared competition from this foreign commercial station. Among the programmes were, at 1.45pm *Carroll Gibbons & His Orchestra*, 2.30pm *The Stanley Holloway Show*, 3.00pm *Hollywood Calling*, 3.15pm *Charlie Kunz at the Piano*, 3.30pm *Treasure Hunt*, 4.30pm *Opportunity Knocks* (Hughie Green's very popular talent-spotting programme which had been resurrected by Radio Luxembourg with sponsorship by Horlicks after being taken off the B.B.C. in the autumn of 1949) and at 5.15pm *Vera Lynn*. At 11.05pm that evening was a short programme called *Top Three* which featured recordings of the three best selling records for that week. Like *Melody Maker*, Radio Luxembourg was closely in touch with the latest trends in popular music. On Sunday April 2nd, *Top Three* turned into the hour-long *Top Twenty* programme which was to become the station's peak programme, reflecting the rise in interest in popular music which towards the mid-1950s with the 'Rock 'n Roll Revolution' was to sweep the country. On Saturday October 6th 1951, Radio Luxembourg was broadcast on 208 metres on the medium waveband having been carried on this wavelength together with 1293 metres since early summer. With the station's gradual preoccupation with popular music from the early 1950s onwards, 208 metres eventually became known as the 'pop wavelength'.

On March 15th 1950, when the *Copenhagen Plan* came into force, the following bands of wavelengths were allocated to broadcasting in Britain : 1,176-1,875 metres (long-wave), 187-571 metres (medium-wave) and 75, 49, 41, 31, 25, 19, 16, 13 and 11 metres (short-wave). For a nominal charge, buyers of the 1949/1950 season's receivers could up-date them by purchasing a replacement tuning scale printed with the new wavelengths. But many older receivers were not designed to tune below 200 metres and with one of the new Third Programme wavelengths on 194 metres, listeners out of range of Droitwich which transmitted the Third Programme's other wavelength of 464 metres, were unable to tune into that programme.

Earlier, in January, the R.I.C. announced that the National Radio Exhibition would not be held at Olympia, its traditional London venue, but would instead be staged at the B.I.F. Buildings, Castle Bromwich in Birmingham. Television was again to be the main feature, and the decision to move had been taken in view of the expected sales of television sets in the Midlands area following the recent opening of the B.B.C.'s second television transmitter at Sutton Coldfield on December 17th 1949. An estimated 40,000 television sets had already been sold in this area alone during December and with 'H' and 'X' television aerials starting to go up on roofs and chimney stacks all over the country, complaints began to be received by the Post Office and the B.B.C. that television was disfiguring the landscape just as wireless had done with its own aerials in the 1920s (see 1926). A report in the August 1950 issue of *Practical Wireless* stated that local authorities in some areas were banning the erection of television aerials.

With more emphasis now being given to television than ever before, *The Wireless & Electrical Trader* warned its subscribers not to ignore the importance of radio sales, and published an article from a Scottish retailer on the subject of "Maintaining Radio Sales After The Advent of Television".

"Utilize the fact that television will attract people into the showroom. Ensure that the customers have to pass a lane of radio sets leading to the television displays. Judicious grading of radio sets along the lane is important and emphasize the fact that the price of radio compared to television is relatively low.

"Alongside the television being demonstrated, a small 'take-about' set (e.g. the Ekco U122) should be switched on deliberately when the demonstration is over. The television salesman should be instructed to make quite clear the need for both television and radio."

The Ekco U122 was one of a large number of small 'second set' mains transportable receivers on show at the National Radio Exhibition which opened in Birmingham on September 6th. The growing use of miniature all-glass valves had led to an all-round reduction in the size of receiver chassis, and a corresponding reduction in the size of cabinets (fig.725). However on some of the stands, *Wireless World* had spotted that local modifications to cabinet lines had been made in the interests of ventilation which suggested to them that some designers had overlooked the fact that the valve makers, for all their skill, had not yet succeeded in miniaturizing the watt! Battery portables, which had been very popular the year before, had now been overtaken by the AC/DC/battery set and in mains receivers, magic-eye tuning indicators were once more seeing a revival.

One significant influence on the radiogram side of the Radio Industry was the introduction in September of the first long-playing records made by the Decca Record Co. Ltd. which led to the appearance at the Exhibition of new pick-ups, record changers and radiograms able to play at 33⅓ rpm. On the electronics side, there were only a few exhibits of scientific, industrial and medical apparatus and the Exhibition seemed to be turning away from the heavy engineering side of the Radio Industry and beginning to concentrate once more on equipment for the domestic consumer.

Among the components on show were G.E.C.'s new germanium crystal diodes whose development had first been announced in May although experimental work on germanium diodes had begun at the start of the Second World War. Their introduction led to a minor resurgence of crystal sets which lasted throughout the 1950s and several manufacturers began to bring out miniature plastic-cased crystal sets now aimed principally at the schoolboy and novelty market (fig.726). In other fields by the autumn of 1952, G.E.C.'s germanium diodes

Bush Model TR82, all-transistor outdoor portable of 1959.
(*See fig.800, page 197, also page 249*).

were even finding their way into television circuits and were available in a range of twelve different types.

Although by 1950, the radio supply situation in the shops had reached a state of near normality, the years of austerity were still not yet completely over and any strengthening of the economy that might have been gained received a set-back when Britain with the United Nations became involved in the Korean War. Although Britain did not play a major role, the country undertook massive rearmament and contributed a large naval force, and once again the Radio Industry was called upon to fulfil Government contracts and to secure improved exports.

1951

In February, Ward, Blenkinsop & Co. Ltd., working in conjunction with A.H. Hunt Ltd., made significant advances in printed circuit techniques when they overcame the earlier problems encountered with the adhesion of metal to a plastic base and also by the development of special miniature low-wattage soldering irons to prevent the base from melting. In another development, a new circuit production technique was announced by the Ministry of Supply. Circuits were broken down into small assemblies of components together with their associated wiring, and these were then hermetically sealed into clear plastic blocks with pins protruding from the bottom which fitted into corresponding holes in a circuit board. They were designed to be used primarily in Military radio and radar equipment and although exhibiting a novel approach to circuit design, were short-lived in the light of the subsequent development of transistorised printed circuit assemblies.

The National Radio Exhibition, held at Earls Court between August 29th and September 8th, broke the London tradition which Radiolympia had held for many years. The loss of the familiar title of the exhibition, although thought unfortunate, did introduce an air of novelty into an event which was becoming a little stereotyped. Although television once again stole the show at the National Radio Exhibition, the radio was still the focal point in the majority of homes around the country. In fact, during 1951, the Radio Industry attained its highest production in history with over 2,000,000 receivers and radiograms being produced, despite Purchase Tax on radio (and television sets too) being raised from 33 ⅓ per cent to 66 ⅔ per cent on April 10th which for a time had quite an effect on sales and led to a minor recession.

In general, the standard product of the Radio Industry continued to be the 4-valve plus rectifier table model superhet in a polished veneered wooden cabinet (fig.737), while there was now quite an increase in the number of mains/battery receivers and all-dry portables. With the latter, sets reminiscent of the 1920s suitcase models were popular although with progress in circuit miniaturization, these receivers were now more correctly described as 'briefcase models' (fig.741). A relatively new feature of the National Radio Exhibition was the inclusion of tape recorders by a growing number of manufacturers. During the 1950s, there were to be great advances in sound recording and hi-fi equipment and a tremendous growth of public interest in the subject. This eventually resulted in the late 1960s in a rise in popularity of Audio Fairs which encompassed the whole spectrum of home sound entertainment and included hi-fi tuners and amplifiers, record players, tape recorders, and loud-speakers, and not just radios. By then, practically the only traditional class of radio being produced in any number was the battery portable, in its new updated transistorised form, and the demand for an ordinary mains table model radio had practically ceased and very few manufacturers were producing them. In their place were tuners bought as part of hi-fi systems by a public in search of better sound quality.

fig.723. A crowded corner of the Swindon showrooms of J. & M. Stone, the radio, television and electrical retailers, 1952.

Meanwhile, at the 1951 Earls Court Exhibition, G.E.C. introduced an experimental germanium crystal triode (a point-contact transistor) receiver which had four radio frequency stages, a detector and push-pull output and within two years, component transistors from G.E.C. and other British manufacturers were made generally available and were soon finding application in various fields of low-power electronics.

The planned opening on October 12th of the B.B.C.'s third television station at Holme Moss on the Pennines 9 miles west of Huddersfield, attracted many visitors from the North who crowded into Earls Court to view studio television programmes, television demonstrations, and historic exhibits from the Baird Museum. An estimated 11,000,000 people would be within the service area of this station and since the early summer, interest in the building's progress had been eagerly watched by thousands of sightseers whose numbers had persuaded nearby farms to open up for teas and had attracted a little community of ice cream and mineral water vendors who had set up their stalls on the summit.

At the Exhibition, the other features were radio-controlled model ships, Military equipment, radar navigational aids and other electronic items. For the first time at a National Radio Exhibition, receivers were shown being assembled, soldered and tested: the demonstration taking place on the Ersin Multicore Solder stand by staff of E.K. Cole Ltd.

In the autumn 1951 issue of *B.B.C. Quarterly*, the B.B.C.'s proposals for high power VHF broadcasting were outlined. The plan was for a chain of FM stations in Band II (87.5-100 Mc/s) giving practically complete national coverage with three programmes. The Corporation had decided to opt for FM rather than AM primarily because FM resulted in a considerable reduction in both receiver hiss and in impulse interference. The VHF system was seen as a considerable reinforcement rather than a replacement of the medium and long-wave networks and close co-operation now began with the Radio Industry to ensure development and production of VHF/FM receivers in time for the planned inauguration of the scheme in 1955 (see 1955).

1952

In January, in an effort to help the economy which was suffering following the outbreak of the Korean War in 1950, emergency financial measures were introduced by the Government. These included limiting the production of radio, television and electrical apparatus for the domestic market to two thirds of the 1951 level and restricting hire purchase agreements by imposing a minimum initial deposit of 33 ⅓ per cent and a maximum period of repayment of 18 months. Heralded by *The Wireless & Electrical Trader* as "Austerity measures again!", they were nevertheless short-lived and within a few years the economy was expanding and the Radio Industry was experiencing one of its biggest ever sales booms (see 1954).

The B.B.C.'s television network continued to grow. On March 14th, the Scottish television station opened at Kirk O'Shotts about ten miles south of Falkirk and was followed on August 15th by the Wenvoe station near Cardiff which opened to serve Wales and the West of England. While the B.B.C. remained the main instrument of broadcasting in Britain, the Government felt that with the expanding field of television, provision should be made to permit "some element of competition". And so, when the Corporation's fourth Charter was granted on July 1st for a period of ten years (later extended a further two years to July 29th 1964) it was made, for the first time, non-exclusive. Subsequently, a Broadcasting Licence, for television only, was given to the Independent Television Authority which was set up in August 1954, and a year later opened the first of a series of independent commercial television transmitters in Band III, 174-216 Mc/s (see 1955). While one-channel viewing was to come to an end with the beginning of commercial television, there were to be no British independent commercial radio stations until 1964 when Radio Caroline, the first of the 'Pop Pirates' came on the air (see 1964).

The National Radio Exhibition opened at Earls Court from August 27th to September 6th and the public's interest in television was sustained with over 80 new television receivers on show. In households where the television set had taken over as the centrepiece, mains/battery portables were very popular as the sound-only receiver and there were about 40 models newly available to choose from. These were closely followed by compact mains transportable receivers like the Champion Model 784 (fig.746) whose small size and restrained pastel coloured moulded case reflected the trend which had grown with the gradual introduction of miniature valves soon after the Second World War, away from the great dark monolith type of receivers which had demanded attention during the 1930s. Not that large receivers were completely out of fashion, for where the best possible quality of reproduction was demanded, especially at the lower frequencies, cabinets with a large baffle area were still thought essential.

Manufacturers and some wireless retailers were now reported to be showing a tendency to refuse to repair any sets made before 1939, often insisting that a new model be acquired instead. 'Thermion' writing in the March issue of *Practical Wireless* thought that this was a scandalous situation and told of attempts by a friend of his to have a set repaired which needed a new transformer and a new switch: "He had tried everywhere to get the set repaired, including the manufacturers who sent him a snooty letter implying that he had had his money's worth out of it, and that he should scrap it and buy another". In a few years however, it became generally recognised on both sides of the shop counter that the cost of servicing and repair of obsolete sets could in a growing number of instances far outweigh the actual value of the set and that buying a modern replacement would be a wiser course of action (see 1958).

1953

The National Radio Exhibition was held once again at Earls Court in London and opened from September 2nd to 12th. The pre-occupation with television continued and there were

heavily featured displays too of electronics "in the air, at sea, in industry, in business and in medicine". But there was also an unexpected increase of public interest in the ordinary domestic radio and many stands reported a tremendous rise in the number of enquiries for replacement receivers, and by the end of the year nearly 1,000,000 new models had been sold. Since the Second World War, manufacturers, wholesalers and retailers had all laid great emphasis on the establishment of television on the domestic market which quickly resulted in the public's acceptance of television as an essential part of home entertainment and, with help from outside broadcasts of great spectacles like the Coronation, as a window on world events. The Coronation Day broadcast on June 2nd was then the biggest operation in the B.B.C.'s history and there had been an unprecedented demand for television sets (over 1,400,000 were sold during 1953) especially for halls, clubs and restaurants, with about 2,750,000 television sets in use on the day and an estimated 22,000,000 viewers looking-in around the country.

All this emphasis on television had inevitably led to some neglect of the ordinary radio receiver market. The public's sudden revival of interest therefore came as rather a surprise but this was explained by one popular theory that television sets, with their excellent sound reproduction, were showing up the poor quality of obsolete radios and leading their owners to do something about buying new models. This, coupled with the lowering of Purchase Tax in April from 66 ⅔ per cent to 50 per cent and the relaxation in hire purchase allowing "no deposit terms", had given them some incentive to buy. There were still about 10,500,000 sound-only licences in existence and it was estimated that a very high proportion of these must be for obsolete radios giving a performance much below what was possible with modern radio receivers.

Since the early 1920s, home-construction had been very popular, and even in the early 1950s interest continued and, helped by the new branch of television, was even on the increase. *Practical Wireless* in their August issue estimated that from the quantity of blue-prints they had sold over the years, there must be something like 1,500,000 home-constructed radio receivers in operation and something like 300,000 home-constructed television sets too, with firms who had remained faithful to supplying this market reporting an ever-increasing turnover.

One interesting development among the receivers on display at Earls Court was the fitting of sub-miniature aerials in some of the portables (fig.754). Aerial windings were mounted on a pencil-like rod of ferromagnetic material with the medium-wave coil at one end and the long-wave coil at the other, and these new 'ferrite rod' aerials soon began to appear in many classes of receiver and were to become the standard type of aerial used in transistor circuits. Component transistors were now being made in this country by G.E.C., Mullard and S.T.C. At this stage of development, research into transistors had most successfully been directed towards the production of low frequency and low power types, which were only really suitable for hearing-aids or at best, for low power audio amplifiers: but it would only be a matter of a few years before they appeared in the first British all-transistor radio (see 1956).

A new market for portables now began to be created as manufacturers turned their attention to the female of the household and from the beginning of the 1953/54 season started to produce sets like the Ever Ready Sky Queen (fig.752) and the later Vidor Lady Margaret (fig.755) which was made "in feminine colours, and no larger than a lady's handbag" (see also 1957).

The standard table model mains superhet with a 4-valve plus rectifier circuit remained undisturbed by any startling new developments although a minor trend began with the increased use of elliptical loud-speaker diaphragms, favoured by H.M.V. since the late 1930s (fig.611) and now used by several firms to help solve a variety of layout problems where space was limited.

1954

In July, the Winter Trading Co. Ltd. of Harrow Road, London W2 began distributing two small 'personal' valve portables manufactured by Braun of Frankfurt, West Germany: the 100B/54 and the Exporter. The Exporter was at the time the smallest set on the market and measured 4 ½ in. x 7 in. x 2 in. with a built-in miniature 2 ¼ in. diameter loud-speaker. It came with an optional AC mains unit so that it could be used either as an outdoor battery portable or as an indoor mains set: mains/battery portables were at the height of their popularity around the mid-1950s.

Towards the end of the year, printed circuit techniques began to be increasingly employed in the manufacture of more compact British-made valve receivers, many of which were shown for the first time at the National Radio Exhibition held at Earls Court from August 25th to September 4th. During 1954, a new printed circuit process was developed by the Telegraph Condenser Company in which chemical etching was used to form a wiring pattern on an insulated baseboard. The Company had first commercially used the process in part of the manufacture of Truvox tape recorders but had quickly seen its potential application in the field of radio and television receivers, and by November had developed it sufficiently to offer "a printed circuit service to the electronics industry". The method involved drawing a large scale plan of the wiring, the marks for the valve pins and the terminations for all the other component connections onto a sheet of paper on the drawing board and producing a reduced silk screen image of this photographically. The resulting pattern was then inked through the silk screen onto a copper film one and a half thousandths of an inch thick firmly bonded onto a sheet of Bakelite. This was immersed in a chemical etching bath to remove all the un-inked copper, leaving behind the wiring pattern on the Bakelite panel which was then cleaned of all traces of ink.

The printed panel was then drilled in pre-determined spots, and through these holes all the components' leads, tags and valve holder sockets were firmly threaded. The treated side of the panel was then dipped into a bath of molten solder in which in a single operation all the copper film became coated and all the components automatically soldered into place. There were no dry joints or wiring errors and all the surplus solder was simply shaken off. This technique enabled circuit production to be greatly speeded up while at the same time eliminating expensive chassis operations and ensuring a consistent performance and greater compactness.

Shown at the National Radio Exhibition was an experimental portable transistor radio designed by G.E.C. In August, considerable extensions had been made at the Company's factory at Wembley to house new sections undertaking research into transistors and other forms of semi-conductors. The techniques developed, from the production of pure germanium and various semi-conductor alloys, to electronic equipment in which diodes and transistors could be used, gave the impression that the industry was on the threshold of the biggest revolution in certain aspects of electronics since the thermionic valve was developed at the beginning of the century.

The opening of the National Radio Exhibition marked its coming of age, for it was the twenty-first to be held since 1926. There was a record attendance of 315,970 visitors and from the amount of business being done on all the stands, manufacturers prepared themselves for the biggest rush for both television and radio receivers since the end of the Second World War. By the end of the year, in radio sales alone, over 1,500,000 new sets had been bought in the U.K. By 1954, the economy was expanding and people generally began to enjoy a far higher standard of living following the period of post-war austerity which had been prolonged somewhat by Britain's involvement in the Korean War (the Armistice had been signed in July 1953). In this new 'Age of Affluence' which was to last until well into the 1960s, a great many more people found themselves with money to spend and something to spend it on. A lot of it of course was 'borrowed': in 1954 the Chancellor had abolished the restrictions on hire purchase imposed a few years earlier and hire purchase agreements became a great source of business for retailers in both television and radio sales. Sales assistants were often able to tag a radio set onto a hefty television hire purchase agreement "for just a few shillings a week extra" in a subtle way of persuading a customer to buy a second or even third radio set for the household.

In preparation for the introduction of the B.B.C.'s new high power VHF/FM radio service in the following year, some manufacturers at the National Radio Exhibition introduced receivers which included the new VHF band and whose dials were marked in the new Band II wavelengths accordingly (figs.763,766). From this time, receivers with long, medium or short waveband circuits which also included the VHF band were called 'AM/FM sets': AM referring to amplitude modulation which was the usual method by which broadcasting on the long, medium and short wavebands was transmitted. For converting existing receivers to VHF, several FM adaptors were brought out which plugged straight into the pick-up socket at the back of the set, while a few FM tuner units also appeared and these were intended for operation with existing high quality audio amplifiers.

The interest in television continued to grow and the Exhibition staged the world's largest demonstration of television sets up to that time. In January it had been announced that the new commercial television channel planned for 1955 would use Band III (174-216 Mc/s) and manufacturers busied themselves designing Band I and III televisions and also converters for modifying existing Band I sets for the additional I.T.A. service. The B.B.C.'s own television service was expanding all the time and on June 1st the combined Radio and Television Licence fee was raised to £3 to enable the B.B.C. to use the extra revenue to continue with its development programme.

1955

THE B.B.C.'s VHF/FM SERVICE

On May 2nd, the first of the B.B.C.'s nine proposed high power VHF/FM radio broadcasting stations was brought into regular service at Wrotham Hill in Kent, transmitting with a range of about 50 miles to London and the Home Counties area on 89.1 Mc/s (Light Programme), 91.3 Mc/s (Third Programme) and 93.5 Mc/s (Home Service). The other eight stations, sited at existing and projected television transmitters around the country, were planned to be completed by the end of 1956 with each station having six transmitters: two in parallel for each of the three programmes to be radiated. When this stage had been completed, it was estimated that 83 per cent of the United Kingdom would be covered by the VHF/FM service. Wrotham had been in operation experimentally since 1950, but two months before it was fully inaugurated it had closed down from March 5th for nearly five weeks to allow its Home Service transmitter to be installed. However, in response to a request from the British Radio Equipment Manufacturers' Association, the B.B.C. began radiating a daily low power VHF/FM test transmission from Alexandra Palace on 93.8 Mc/s so that retailers in the London area would still be able to demonstrate FM receivers to their customers until the Wrotham station was back on the air.

The new VHF/FM service naturally created a great deal of public interest and at the National Radio Exhibition held at Earls Court between August 26th and September 3rd (it opened two days late because of a labour dispute), over 50 new mains AM/FM valve table models were introduced together with several FM tuner units and receivers covering VHF/FM only. Battery AM/FM valve portables were slow off the mark and never appeared in anything but very small numbers. Many manufacturers provided their VHF/FM receivers with an internal VHF/FM dipole aerial for use in areas where reception of the new service was good. The aerial was usually in the form of a paper-backed foil glued underneath the top and on the sides or on the back of the receiver. In fringe areas where reception was fair to poor, outdoor multi-element arrays were usually recommended.

In September, some 60,000 AM/FM radios were sold, adding to the 120,000 already in use mainly around the Wrotham area, and by the end of the year with two more VHF/FM stations having opened at Pontop Pike near Newcastle and at Wenvoe near Cardiff (Light and Third Programme only), the figure had risen to over 500,000. Television sets combined with an integral VHF/FM radio tuner ('TV/FM sets') were a new development and several models now appeared.

COMMERCIAL TELEVISION

The other main attraction at the National Radio Exhibition was the imminent introduction of the I.T.A.'s commercial television service on Band III which began from their Croydon transmitter on September 22nd 1955 and now gave viewers an alternative choice of channels. This created not only a spectacular rush for new television sets but also an enormous demand on service engineers to convert older Band I models.

Despite a decline in defence contracts, the closing of some overseas markets and the latest harassing of the domestic receiver side of the industry by hire purchase and Purchase Tax changes (the former had been free of restrictions until February and the latter had gone up to 60 per cent in October) the British Radio and Television Industries had a record year in 1955 with sales being greatly boosted by the introduction of VHF/FM radio and commercial television. Sales of radios and television sets were now running practically neck-and-neck and each accounted for about £1,500,000 in business. On the electronics side, due to the ever expanding use of electronics in science, navigation and industry generally, the demand for equipment, components and valves began to increase greatly and in factory production lines there were now signs of the general beginning of automation which was largely dependent upon electronically controlled machinery.

For the first time since the Second World War, a definite common style in radio cabinet design and detail now began to be copied by several manufacturers. With the more sophisticated mains table model receivers, a 'Continental' influence began to be felt with the use of attractive woods with a high gloss piano finish relieved by gilded brass trim. Waveband switching was almost invariably performed by 'piano key' press buttons with the quality of reproduction improved by the inclusion of elaborate tone controls and several loud-speakers: the Grundig Hastings incorporated all these up-to-the-minute features (fig.767). Specialist manufacturers such as Framestyles Ltd. of Nottingham were beginning to be established, supplying the trade with decorative brasswork trims, discs and rings for knobs and cabinet detailing. Oversized circular dial controls in clear Perspex were first introduced in a few receivers (fig.776) and control knobs decorated with gilded centres or outer rings now became generally fashionable although they had been used

sporadically by a few manufacturers since the early 1950s (fig.743) and as early as 1934, Ekco used chrome-centred knobs on their black Model AD 65 (fig.448) and Model AC 85 (fig.431).

On September 1st, new regulations came into force which controlled radio and television interference emanating from refrigerators and other domestic electrical apparatus driven by small electric motors. From that date, it became an offence to cause such interference to the reception of B.B.C. Home, Light and Third Programme stations on the medium and long wavebands and B.B.C. television transmissions on Band I, although the regulations did not apply to interference caused to either the Band II VHF/FM services or to I.T.A.'s Band III television transmissions.

1956

On March 28th, the B.B.C.'s original television transmitting station at Alexandra Palace closed down and the London area service was taken over by a new station at Crystal Palace. The B.B.C. had by now over a dozen television transmitters around the country and I.T.A. would have a total of four by the end of the year covering the London, Midland and Northern Regions. During the year, both organisations conducted a series of colour television experiments in order to test that reception was clear both in monochrome as well as in colour so that viewers who did not have the means to buy costly new sets for receiving colour television could nevertheless receive the same programmes on their ordinary sets in black and white. The tests were made in conjunction with the Television Advisory Committee and the Radio Industry Council who were to eventually advise the Post Master General on the best colour system for Britain. They were conducted on 405-lines, but it was thought at the time that higher definition using 625-lines would be needed: a standard which was already in use on the Continent.

TRANSISTOR RADIOS

In March, the first British all-transistor radio was announced by Pam (Radio & Television) Ltd., a subsidiary of Pye Radio Ltd. Known as Model 710 (fig.724), it was a portable and employed eight Pye transistors in a printed circuit with variable tuning on the medium waveband and fixed tuning for the Light Programme on 1,500 metres long-wave. At £22.14s.10d plus £8.15s.3d Purchase Tax it was an expensive investment and cost about twice the price of an average battery-powered valve portable. Although the Model 710 heralded the rapid demise of the valve receiver, at this stage of development the component transistor was still generally incapable of equalling valve performance, especially at high frequencies and was only really suitable for handling relatively low powers. Because of this, many transistor radios (including many of those used in cars) which appeared around this time were in fact hybrids, with valves in the HF and the IF stages, and transistors used only in the output stages, which economised on battery consumption (fig.786). But rapid developments were taking place all the time, and research soon led to the introduction of transistors capable of handling higher frequencies and much higher powers, and within a few years reliable component transistors for every stage of the circuit were being mass-produced in Britain and abroad and the challenge to the valve in most fields of radio and electronics would become serious. The first class of radio to be completely ousted by the transistor was the valve portable, which by the early 1960s had all but disappeared. Television sets though were to lag behind, and it was not until the late 1960s that all-valve television circuits had given way to transistor/valve hybrids and not until towards the mid-1970s that all-transistor television sets (monochrome at first, and then colour) were generally available.

fig.724. The first British all-transistor radio, Pam Model 710 of March 1956. Although designed at Pye Ltd.'s own research laboratories, the 710 was actually released through their subsidiary, Pam (Radio & Television) Ltd. — being rather uncertain of the transistor's viability, the parent company was unwilling to risk its own established reputation on such a new and uncertain innovation. (*For the full Pam 710 story, see pages 288 to 291*).

A new exhibition centre opened in London's Haymarket in April 1956. Called the Design Centre, it became a permanent showcase for selected British products and at its inauguration some twenty firms showed examples of their latest radio and television sets, among which was the first portable (the Jester) from Berec Radio Ltd., a newly formed subsidiary of Ever Ready.

From August 21st to September 1st, the twenty-third National Radio Exhibition was held as usual at Earls Court, and because of the introduction of the transistor in portable radios and the rapid developments in miniaturized components, miniature loud-speakers, light-weight chassis and printed circuits, it was heralded as the "Milestone Radio Show". Printed circuits had now emerged from the experimental stage and were being used by many more manufacturers who either produced them in their own factories or had them made up by specialist firms such as A.C. Cossor Ltd. who began offering a printed circuit service to the Radio, Television and Electronics Industries in July. Cossor's first printed circuit set, Model 543, was released in the same month (fig.781).

Helped by the few all-transistor radios on show at the Exhibition, interest in the radio had once more become very great and disproved those who had forecast that the introduction of television would mean the end of sound radio. The swing over by manufacturers to mains AM/FM table models which had begun the previous year with the introduction of the B.B.C.'s VHF/FM service had now, in 1956, become a landslide and the industry was going for an all-out replacement of old receivers with new VHF/FM types. By the end of the year five more of the B.B.C.'s VHF/FM stations had opened at Divis (Belfast), Holme Moss (Manchester), Meldrum (Aberdeen), North Hessary Tor (South Devon) and Tacolneston (Norwich). The last of the nine stations in the first phase of the VHF/FM coverage opened at Sutton Coldfield on April 30th 1957. However, this new service was not to everyone's liking, especially many older people whose ears had been trained to years of listening to the mellow tones produced by the conventional 'wireless', and to whom the crisp sounds produced

by VHF/FM sets sounded harsh and tinny. Furthermore, with VHF/FM-only sets, listeners were limited to hearing just three stations whereas with an AM radio they could hear the same three stations plus maybe a dozen or so foreign stations all on the same waveband.

Combined TV/FM sets continued to be popular. The most notable one was the Ekco Model TMB 272 which was the first mains/battery portable television to be produced in this country. Placed on the market in June, it worked from either AC mains or from a 12 volt car battery and had a multi-position switch for selecting the television channels plus Home, Light and Third FM broadcasting. With the increasing popularity of television as a form of home entertainment, a need had arisen for a 'second set' for occasional use in the bedroom, kitchen or, like the Ekco mains/portable, in caravans or on picnics etc., although bright daylight made outdoor viewing of the screen difficult.

As transistorised radios were now starting to be introduced, *The Wireless & Electrical Trader* thought that it would not be long before they would begin to come into the workshop for servicing and there was therefore a need for the service engineer to familiarize himself with their circuits. To help in this matter, the magazine began publishing a detailed series on "Servicing Transistor Equipment" from September, although there was understandably some opposition to this new technology from older engineers steeped in the tradition of valve circuits which were both easier to handle and easier to see.

1957

Since about 1953, when Ever Ready introduced their Sky Queen portable (fig.752), manufacturers had been designing small valve portables with a feminine flavour in 'handbag' forms and in various pastel shades, polka dot designs, imitation snakeskin and woven fabric coverings reflecting the art and fashion of the 1950s. This reached a peak in the summer of 1957 when over 45 different models were brought out aimed specifically at the female market with one, the Jewel (fig.785), available in 25 colour combinations "so that She can make her mind up". The Ever Ready Sky Casket (fig.783) was a further priceless example: "Styled like a vanity case....appealing to her fancy".

Another design trend in small valve portables which began in 1957 and continued for the next few years was the use of an integral leather case into which was built the chassis and control panel (fig.788), combined to produce one unit. Oversized circular dial controls in clear Perspex introduced in 1955 became popular for the first time with the travelling pointer either printed on them (fig.784) or fixed to the spindle (see a later example, fig.800). Through this control the station names and wavelengths could be read and these were printed onto a metal plate fixed to the main body of the radio or embossed on the case.

Retailers were also fast becoming design conscious and for the last few years, a tremendous change in shopfront and counter design had been taking place around the country as old fashioned pre-war ideas were swept away by facades reflecting the modern mood of the 1950s. However, not every manufacturer followed the latest design trends as Period High Fidelity Ltd. of London W1 demonstrated when they began marketing high quality, high-fidelity radios and gramophones in 'craftsman-built' reproduction period furniture.

At the end of March, E.K. Cole Ltd. took over the marketing of all domestic radio and television sets made under the 'Ferranti' trademark and formed a subsidiary, Ferranti Radio & Television Ltd. In the following month, Ferguson and H.M.V. (the radio and television interests of Thorn Electrical Industries and E.M.I. respectively) joined together as the British Radio Corporation

Ltd., and this new company became responsible for the design and marketing of all receivers under the Ferguson, H.M.V. and Marconiphone trademarks.

On August 1st, the combined Radio and Television Licence was increased to £4 and for the first time since the introduction of a regular television service in 1936, the number of viewers had caught up with the number of listeners, the respective licence figures now being roughly equal. At the end of the month, from August 28th to September 7th, the 24th National Radio Exhibition took place at Earls Court. The new AM/FM sets on show (mainly mains table models, but a few battery valve portables as well) were generally as cheap as an ordinary AM receiver: the B.B.C.'s first phase of nine VHF/FM stations had been completed and was further supplemented during 1957 by stations at Blaenplwyf near Aberystwyth (April 29th), Rowridge on the Isle of Wight (June 4th) and Kirk o'Shotts (November 30th) bringing millions more listeners within the service areas.

'POCKET' RADIOS

Printed circuits were now generally being used in valve portables and were a standard feature of the increasing number of handbag-sized transistor portables on show at the Exhibition. For the first time, 'pocket' transistor portables with miniature built-in loud-speakers and a few with an extra provision for an earpiece (for 'personal' listening) appeared on the market and were shown by several firms including Cossor, Perdio and Peto-Scott, but in common with many innovations, they were very expensive: the five transistor Perdio model, just 5 ¾ in. long x 3 ¼ in. high x 1 in. deep, retailed at £23.2s.0d.

All the transistor models on show at the National Radio Exhibition were AM models with the cheaper ones covering the medium-waveband only and the more expensive ones, the medium and long wavebands. It would be another three years before quality VHF/FM circuitry was added to the design of transistor radios (see 1960). Since the early 1950s, germanium diode crystal sets had appeared from time to time, and now in order to give these sets loud-speaker performance, Warrens Radio of Luton introduced their single-stage transistorised amplifier.

Developments in component transistors, in particular the more reliable junction type, had been rapid and whereas at one time transistors were only available for low power amplification at audio frequencies, they were now generally branching out in two directions: towards higher power and higher frequencies. In May, a major new company called Semiconductors Ltd. was formed by the Plessey Company of Ilford and the Philco Corporation of America specifically to concentrate on the mass-production of component transistors and other semi-conductors.

From October 23rd to 26th, the first ever Radio Hobbies Exhibition took place at the Royal Horticultural Old Hall, Vincent Square, London SW1 which was announced in *Practical Wireless* with the words "Constructors! At last a show for you!". Organised by the Radio Society of Great Britain, the eager home-constructor, anxious to learn the fundamentals of radio and television design by the practical instruction which set-building provided, was able to see kits of parts for building receivers, transmitters, television test gear, hi-fi amplifiers, Band III converters, transistorised equipment, tape recorders and aerials etc. Far from going out of fashion, the large attendances at the exhibition proved that home-construction was still thriving, a fact echoed by the ever increasing sales of *Practical Wireless* and her sister home-constructors' magazine *Practical Television*.

1958

Late at night on Monday January 13th, the B.B.C. transmitted the first of a number of occasional unscheduled experimental radio programmes in stereo which were broadcast with the object of finding out whether a satisfactory stereophonic effect could be obtained. Tuning-in at home, listeners had to use two radios: one for the left and one for the right-hand channel (a Band I television set could be used instead of a radio for the left-hand channel). Each of the channels was radiated by two transmitters so that four transmitters were used altogether, these being Television Sound on Band I from Crystal Palace and the medium waveband Third Programme for the left-hand channel, and the Home Service from the medium-wave and VHF/FM transmitters for the right-hand channel. The programmes comprised three parts of five minutes each: firstly, two different sustained notes to identify the position of each channel with the note from the left channel being lower than the one from the right; secondly, simultaneous non-stereo transmissions of speech on both channels to assist in obtaining a good balance between the two; and thirdly, a stereophonic tape-recording of orchestral music.

Following the inaugural experiment, the B.B.C. announced that more could be expected in the future, although they stated quite definitely that there was "no intention to introduce a public stereophonic service", for, quite apart from the investment, a great number of technical and practical difficulties were presented. However, a good 10 per cent of listeners who participated in the January experiment were impressed and enthusiastically reported that they had had a clear impression of the orchestra actually being in the room with them, and they were naturally very keen to hear more.

They did not have to wait too long, for during Radio Record Week (May 11th to 17th) two more experimental stereo radio programmes of tape-recorded music were put out. This was principally in acknowledgement of the recent developments which had taken place within the record industry with the introduction at the beginning of May of the first stereo discs under the Pye-Nixa label (Decca followed later at the end of August). Again, two radio receivers (or a radio plus a Band I television) were needed, placed at the recommended distance of between 6 and 12 feet from the listener and the same distance from each other, thus forming an equilateral triangle: "an ideal of geometric listening". The programmes were broadcast on Sunday May 11th from 10.30am to 11am, with the left-hand channel from all the medium-wave and VHF/FM Home Service transmitters and the right-hand channel from all the medium-wave and VHF/FM Third Programme transmitters plus all the Television Sound transmitters. They were repeated again on Saturday May 17th from 11am to 11.30am, this time with the long, medium-wave and VHF/FM Light Programme transmitters on the left-hand channel, and the medium-wave and VHF Third Programme transmitters plus all the Television Sound transmitters on the right-hand channel. For fifteen minutes before the start of the tests special announcements giving instructions on how to listen-in were broadcast by the Third Programme and the Television Sound transmitters, and a caption card describing the programmes was shown on the television screens.

The month of May also marked the beginning of a series of experimental UHF television transmissions by the B.B.C. on Band V (614-854 Mc/s). Lasting three months, they were transmitted from Crystal Palace using the European 625-line standard with vision on 654.25 Mc/s and sound on 659.75 Mc/s. A number of experimental television receivers were used by the B.B.C., I.T.A., the Post Office and the Radio and Television Industries to monitor the broadcasts.

During the year, six more VHF/FM transmitters were opened around the country. These were at Douglas, Isle of Man (March 9th), Sandale, Carlisle (August 18th), Rosemarkie, Moray Firth (October 12th), Llanddona, Anglesey (December

20th), Llangollen, N.E/.Wales (December 20th), and Orkney (December 22nd).

At the National Radio Exhibition, held at Earls Court from August 27th to September 6th, there was a separate audio section called the Hall of Sound, which comprised 38 stands catering for the rapidly expanding public interest in tape recording, hi-fi sound equipment and loud-speaker 'enclosures' housing tweeters, bass and mid-range units. New manufacturing firms were entering this expanding market all the time and since the beginning of 1958, interest in it had become such that in their January 18th issue, *The Wireless & Electrical Trader* had introduced a new regular feature called "Audiotopics", which was concerned with all the latest aspects of quality hi-fi reproduction of sound whether from records, tape or VHF/FM radio.

With the inauguration of occasional experimental stereo radio broadcasts and following the introduction of stereo records by Pye and Decca, the 1958 Exhibition was heralded as "the start of the Stereo Season". While new stereo pickups and record players were produced for the first time, joining stereo tape recorders which were already on the market, twin-channel stereo radios only appeared on the scene in the early 1960s following the commencement of the B.B.C.'s first regular series of experimental 'Multiplex' stereo transmissions in August 1962 in which both channels were sent out on the same carrier-wave (see 1962). Meanwhile, the B.B.C's occasional unscheduled test broadcasts continued. At fortnightly intervals from October 18th, hour-long programmes of music were broadcast from the medium-wave and VHF/FM Third Programme transmitters (left-hand channel) and from the various Television Sound transmitters (right-hand channel), and on November 15th, the first B.B.C. drama in stereo was broadcast: excerpts from Conan Doyle's *Sherlock Holmes*.

Earlier in the same month, the B.B.C. had put out further colour television test transmissions from the Crystal Palace transmitter with thirty minutes of colour films on Tuesdays and Thursdays and a still colour picture from Monday to Friday. For the first time, the number of people with combined Television & Radio Licences had passed those listeners licensed for radio only as interest in viewing continued its upward growth. There had been a credit squeeze since February 1955 but at the end of October 1958, all Government restrictions on hire purchase agreements were removed and this created a welcome new spurt in radio and television trade. Combined TV/FM receivers had now reached a pinnacle of popularity and in television receiver design in general, (as predicted by *Wireless World* ten years before, see 1948), circuits were now beginning to be made up of separate printed circuit panels which could be simply discarded when any component in them developed a fault and a replacement panel, instead of a replacement component, simply slipped in place. It was thought that this production method could soon be finding its way into radios.

The VHF/FM service had now been widely accepted and many competitively priced AM/FM and FM-only valve table models were available on the market and valve portables with a VHF/FM band were now beginning to appear in small numbers as well. Printed circuits were now practically standard in both valve portables and mains valve table models and in this latter category, a new futuristic design trend, initiated by Ferguson's Futura I and Philco's Model 100 (fig.792), began with the introduction of chassis housed in long, horizontal cabinets on little legs: the 'long, low look'.

In transistor portables, a larger than ever selection of pocket-sized sets was available on the market with the lowest priced model at around 13 guineas, although generally, they were still a very expensive novelty. Since their introduction in 1956, all transistor radios had been designed as portables and no attempt

had been made seriously to develop table model versions (either mains or battery operated) solely for indoors. Late in 1958, however, J. & A. Margolin Ltd. and Pam [Radio & TV] Ltd. released the first two British battery-operated transistorised table model radios, the Dansette RT60 and Pam 365 respectively, although quantity production of these did not get under way until 1959. By the end of that year, a few other manufacturers had joined them and for the first time the battery table model transistor was established as a class of receiver (albeit a fairly small class). Within three years, mains/battery transistor radios were being developed (see 1962) followed in 1964 by mains-only transistor table models (*eg.* the B.&O. 900K).

Two new design ideas had found their way over from America during 1958. In May, new style 'bubble packing' was introduced by Belling-Lee in which components etc. were contained in a clear plastic bubble secured to a printed card surround. This enabled the contents of the packet to be clearly seen and identified and instead of being stored on a shelf, the containers could be put out on display, hung by hooks on a special rack.

In June, a British company registered as Daystrom Limited was formed to manufacture electronic kits which had already been established in America where they were known as Heathkits. In America, the Heathkit catalogue included complete kits for building a whole range of sound equipment including AM/FM receivers, tape decks and hi-fi loud-speaker systems, and in December, Daystrom Ltd. were able to introduce their first four Heathkits onto the British market. Home-construction continued in popularity and thirty years after the introduction of their first complete constructor's kit, (the Melody Maker, see 1928), Cossor brought out the first of a series of do-it-yourself audio kits: Model 562K, a 3 watt twin-loud-speaker valve amplifier for use with a radio, a tape recorder, a microphone or a gramophone.

Back in 1952, *Practical Wireless* had reported with some contempt that manufacturers and some wireless retailers were showing a tendency to be unwilling to repair any sets made before 1939, often insisting that a new model should be acquired instead. By 1958, the magazine had itself come round to the opinion that such receivers were not worth repairing, and, asking the question "Is A Pre-War Set Worth Servicing?" in the issue of June 1958, 'Serviceman' argued that on the whole, it was not. He wrote that wherever possible, radio retailers now generally tried to persuade their customers to invest in a new radio rather than have their old one repaired, for it was now often found that the cost of servicing, including the replacement of components and valves, could often be more than the set itself was worth. With pre-war receivers already having given at least 20 years service, it was likely that even if professionally serviced, the set could still break down within a short space of time and it was therefore not reasonable to expect a guarantee to be given. Old AC/DC sets should be viewed "with great suspicion" as the heat radiated inside their cabinets was often very great and this caused a severe deterioration of the components. Sets using side-contact valves should also be rejected as that type of valve, first introduced in 1934, was now proving almost impossible to obtain, as were B5-based mains triodes from the late 1920s. Almost invariably, electrolytic condensers, rectifiers, by-pass condensers, mains droppers and line-cords would all need replacing and unless it was done as a personal favour, or the owner did not mind the cost, then 'Serviceman' thought it inadvisable for the work to be undertaken.

1959

On January 24th, the first experimental live stereo broadcast was made during the Light Programme's *Saturday Club*, which was introduced by Brian Matthew. It featured The Squadcats, although for such an historic occasion, the performance lasted for less than 10 minutes. The left-hand channel was supplied from the medium-wave and VHF/FM Third Programme transmitters and the right-hand channel from the Television Sound transmitters.

During February, major changes in the organization of the Radio Industry were announced. The Electronic Engineering Association (formerly the Radio Communication & Electronic Engineering Association) ceased its membership of the Radio Industry Council, which since 1945 had acted as the co-ordinating body for four associations of manufacturers which represented all sections of the Radio Industry. "We have come to recognise", said R.I.C. Chairman Mr G. Darnley Smith, "that ours is a two-fold industry: one side dealing with broadcasting techniques and equipment and the other with electronics for other purposes". The E.E.A. which covered communications equipment, navigational aids, electronics, transmitters and computers etc. would now pursue its own policies and objectives but would continue to co-operate with the R.I.C. through inter-association committees. There would be no change in the function of the R.I.C. as a co-ordinating body for the remaining associations: the British Radio Equipment Manufacturers' Association, the British Radio Valve Manufacturers' Association and the Radio Component Manufacturers' Association.

Responsibility for organising the National Radio Exhibition and other shows primarily concerned with domestic radio and television products would be transferred to the British Radio Equipment Manufacturers' Association and a new company would be formed called Radio Industry Exhibitions Limited to handle the promotion of all such exhibitions.

The 1959 National Radio Exhibition was held at Earls Court from August 26th to September 5th, and once again the Hall of Sound was included but on a much larger scale than in the previous year, with stereo record players and stereo tape recorders the main attractions in this section. Among the mains valve table models on show, the 'long, low look' introduced in 1958 continued to be popular and many more new models appeared whose cabinets were influenced by this trend. There was also a marked increase in the number of transistor sets, especially in pocket portables (fig.799), but now for the first time a few transistorised battery table models were being shown. With mass-production, component transistors were getting cheaper and several suppliers were able to reduce their prices substantially. The overall trend with valve portables and handbag-sized transistor portables was the inclusion of a car radio aerial socket (fig.800), while with pocket transistors, the extra provision for using an earpiece was now generally being made. This not only gave privacy (for the benefit of the listener as well as those within earshot), but was also useful for battery economy since inserting the earpiece plug usually cut out the high power output stage of the circuit.

The B.B.C. announced an expanded coverage of their VHF/FM service with ten more stations planned over the next three years. During the year, the Home Service transmitter at Wenvoe had been brought into service on March 1st, and on October 5th, a new station had opened at Peterborough, bringing the total number of VHF/FM transmitting stations to nineteen. Correspondingly, the number of mains valve table model AM/FM receivers continued to grow and those sets without a VHF/FM band were now generally relegated to battery valve portables and the low-priced mains valve class.

In the autumn, Britain was riding on a wave of prosperity. Back in April, the Chancellor of the Exchequer had cut Purchase Tax from 60 per cent to 50 per cent and with unemployment the lowest on record, many more people were taking home bigger wage packets.

A new development now took place in electronics with the arrival of the integrated circuit. Although a contract had been placed with Plessey in April 1957 for the development of a semi-conductor integrated circuit, the first real research project was not begun by them until May 1959, by which time Texas Instruments in America had beaten them to it.

fig.725. K.B. Model FB 10, by Kolster-Brandes Ltd. September 1950. 4-v + R, AC SHet Table Model 'Midget', MW/LW Mtrs/StN, cream painted Bakelite case. 7 in. x 10 in. x 6 ¾ in. £8.17s.1d + PT. (An FM-only version, Model FB10 FM, was released in September 1955 price £10.16s.8d in identical case).

fig.726. Ivalek 'De Luxe', by Ivory Electric Ltd. 1950s. Crystal Set for headphone use, germanium diode, MW/LW, white plastic case. 3 ½ in. x 4 ¾ in. x 2 in.

fig.727. Midgetronic Model EMU 4214, by Hale Electric Ltd. 1950. 3-v + R, AC/DC SHet Table Model Midget, MW/LW Mtrs/StN, woven plastic grille, cream plastic knobs, tuning dial and pointer, maroon Bakelite cabinet. 9 in. x 7 in. x 4 ¼ in. £7.17s.6d + PT. Cabinet also available in eau-de-nil and ivory. (In 1953, the cabinet, knobs and dial were sold together, price 12s.6d, by V.E.S. Wholesale Services Ltd. of London W3 to enable home-constructors to fit their own made-up chassis).

fig.728. Electradix Crystal Set, by Leslie Dixon & Co. c.1950. Germanium diode, MW, for headphone use. Uses ex-Government parts and is built into a brown Bakelite clock case. 5 in. x 6 in. x 2 ½ in.

fig.729. Bush Model DAC 90A, by Bush Radio Ltd. January 1950. 4-v + R, AC/DC SHet Table Model, MW/LW Mtrs/StN, 'walnut' Bakelite cabinet. 9 ½ in. x 11 ½ in. x 7 in. £12.1s.8d. + PT. (Cream Bakelite version, price £12.16s.9d). Often confused with the 1946 Bush DAC 90 (fig.652) which is of similar appearance but has a tuning control on the side of the cabinet - the tuning control of the DAC 90A is on the front.

fig.730. Bush Model DAC 10, by Bush Radio Ltd. January 1950. 4-v + R, AC/DC SHet, MW/LW Mtrs/StN, 5 'tortoiseshell' plastic push-buttons (3 for stations, 2 for wavebands) plus manual tuning, internal aerial wound on circular former, cream plastic tuning scale surround, brown Bakelite cabinet. 9 in. x 13 in. x 8 in. £14.16s.0d + PT. (Also version with white plastic tuning scale surround and buttons). In early versions, the three push-buttons were all for medium-wave stations, but later, one of these buttons was for the Light Programme on long-wave.

fig.731. Raymond Model F55, by Raymond Electric Ltd. 1950. 4-v + R, AC SHet Table Model, SW/MW/LW Mtrs/StN, twin moving-coil loud-speakers, gold coloured expanded metal grille, walnut veneered plywood cabinet. 16 ½ in. x 20 in. x 8 ½ in. £21.13s.9d + PT.

fig.732. Radio Rentals Model 61, by E.K. Cole Ltd. for Radio Rentals Ltd. 1950. 4-v + R, AC SHet Table Model, MW/LW Mtrs/StN, interchangeable tuning dial, expanded metal grille, brown Bakelite cabinet. 10 in. x 16 ½ in. x 9 in. This is the 1950 version (with *Copenhagen Plan* dial markings), of the 1946 'Braidio' Model 21 originally made by E.K. Cole for Rentertainments Ltd. (fig.661).

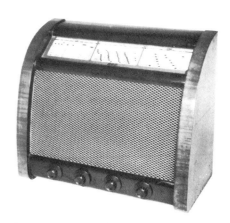

fig.733. G.E.C. Model BC 5639, by General Electric Co. Ltd. August 1950. 4-v + R, AC SHet Table Model, SW/MW/LW Mtrs/StN, internal frame aerial, brown Bakelite cabinet with woodgrain painted ends. 15 ½ in. x 17 ¾ in. x 9 ½ in. £18.3s.3d + PT (Model BC 6638 is AC/DC version, price £19.0s.7d + PT).

fig.734. Ferranti Model 005, by Ferranti Ltd. 1950. 4-v +R, AC SHet Table Model, SW/ MW/LW Mtrs/StN, internal frame aerial, brown crystalline finish metal front, brown Bakelite cabinet. 12 in. x 17 in. x 9 ½ in. £16.1s.3d.

fig.735. Ferranti Model B815, by Ferranti Ltd. 1951. 4-v Batt Portable, MW/LW Mtrs/StN, chromium-plated fittings, blue rexine covered wood attache-style case. 4 ½ in. x 12 ¼ in. x 10 in. On/off switch operates automatically when the lid is raised and lowered.

fig.736. McMichael Model 151, by McMichael Radio Ltd. 1951. 6-v +R, AC SHet Table Model, 2SW/MW/LW Mtrs/ StN, brown Bakelite knobs, gold coloured expanded metal grille, walnut veneered plywood cabinet. 18 ¼ in. x 18 ¼ in. x 10 in. Two indicator bulbs: 'H' lights up when dial pointer reaches Home, and 'L' lights up when dial pointer reaches Light.

fig.737. Ferranti Model 215, by Ferranti Ltd. 1951. 4-v +R, AC SHet Table Model, SW/ MW/LW Mtrs/StN, walnut veneered plywood cabinet. 16 in. x 21 in. x 9 in. £19.5s.2d + PT.

fig.738. Ekco 'Festival' Model A147, by E.K. Cole Ltd. 1951. 4-v +R, AC SHet, MW/ LW, 4 pre-set stations only, cream plastic grille, mahogany veneered plywood cabinet. 12 ½ in. x 16 in. x 6 in. £21.0s.0d inc PT. Brought out to coincide with the Festival of Britain celebrations.

fig.739. 'Stella', by Stella Radio & Television Co. Ltd. June 1951. 4-v +R, AC SHet, SW/ MW/LW Mtrs/StN, clear Perspex knobs, coffee coloured and woodgrain painted Bakelite case. 11 in. x 17 ¾ in. x 7 ¾ in. The first offering by the newly formed Philips subsidiary.

fig.740. Ferranti 'Island' Model 515, by Ferranti Ltd. 1951. 4-v +R, AC/DC SHet Transportable, MW/LW Mtrs/StN, internal frame aerial, brown Bakelite knobs, walnut veneered bent plywood cabinet. 11 in. x 14 ¼ in. x 7 in.

fig.741. Ever Ready Model 'N', by Ever Ready Co. (Great Britain) Ltd. 1951. 4-v Batt Briefcase Portable, MW/LW Mtrs/StN, chromium-plated fittings, cream metal control panel, red and cream rexine-covered wood case. 3 ¼ in. x 14 ½ in. x 9 ¾ in.

fig.742. Ferranti Model 815, by Ferranti Ltd. 1951. 4-v Batt Portable, MW/LW Mtrs, frame aerial in lift-up lid, chromium-plated fittings, green painted control panel, cream lizard skin covered plywood cabinet. 4 ½ in. x 12 in. x 8 in. £11.0s.7d + PT. Batteries extra. Model 915 is mains/battery version.

fig.743. Champion Model 750B, by Champion Electric Corporation Ltd. 1951. 4-v +R, AC SHet Table Model Midget, SW/MW/LW Mtrs/StN, cream grille, internal frame aerial, brown gold-centred Bakelite knobs, brown Bakelite cabinet. 7 ½ in. x 12 ½ in. x 6 ½ in. £13.15s.0d + PT.

fig.744. Philips Model 411A, by Philips Electrical Ltd. 4-v +R plus Magic-Eye Tuning Indicator, AC SHet Table Model, SW/MW/LW Mtrs/StN, walnut and mahogany veneered cabinet. 14 in. x 18 in. x 8 in. £18.7s.6d + PT.

fig.748. H.M.V. Model 1124, by The Gramophone Co. Ltd. 1953. 4-v +R, AC SHet Table Model, 2SW/MW/LW Mtrs/StN, moving-coil loud-speaker positioned behind slatted glass tuning scales (one for each band), cream plastic knobs and tuning scale surround, dark walnut veneered plywood cabinet. 14 in. x 20 ½ in. x 9 in. £31.10s.0d.

fig.751. Pye Type P75A, by Pye Ltd. July 1953. 4-v +R, AC SHet Table Model, SW/MW/LW Mtrs/StN, internal frame aerial, walnut veneered plywood cabinet. 12 in. x 16 in. x 7 ½ in.

fig.745. Philips Model 310A, by Philips Electrical Ltd. 1952. 4-v +R, AC SHet, SW/MW/LW Mtrs/StN, clear Perspex tuning scale/loud-speaker grille, brown Bakelite cabinet. 10 in. x 14 ½ in. x 7 in. £14.6s.9d + PT. Grille lights up in a sunburst effect when the set is on.

fig.749. Pye 'Cambridge International' Model PE 80, by Pye Ltd. 1953. 7-v +R, AC SHet Table Model, 9SW/MW Mtrs/StN, expanded metal grille, walnut veneered plywood cabinet. 17 ½ in. x 23 ½ in. x 10 ½ in.

fig.752. Ever Ready 'Sky Queen', by Ever Ready Co. (Great Britain) Ltd. 1953. 4-v Batt Handbag Portable, MW/LW Mtrs/StN, brass grille, Ivorine trim, perspex carrying handle, cream snakeskin-covered wood case. 9 ½ in. x 12 in. x 6 ½ in. £9.10s.0d + PT. Aimed at the 'female market'.

fig.746. Champion Model TRF 784, by Champion Electric Corporation Ltd. 1952. 3-v +R, AC TRF Table Model, MW/LW Mtrs/StN, loud-speaker, line-cord, cream plastic case. 6 in. x 11 in. x 6 in. £9.19s.6d.

fig.750. Ultra 'Coronation Twin' Model R786, by Ultra Electric Ltd. April 1953. 4-v +MetR, M/Batt Portable, AC/DC, internal frame aerial, coat of arms in centre of loud-speaker opening, plum coloured plastic case with cream Perspex front. 8 ½ in. x 12 in. x 6 ½ in. £13.10s.4d + PT. Brought out to mark the Coronation of Queen Elizabeth II. (The de-luxe version, Model R906, was housed in a simulated crocodile skin covered case with sliding front doors).

fig.747. Pye Model PE98U/LW, by Pye Ltd. 1953. 4-v +R, AC/DC SHet Table Model, SW/MW/LW Mtrs/Kcs, cream Perspex front panel and dial pointer, maroon Bakelite cabinet. 6 ½ in. x 11 ½ in. x 5 ½ in.

fig.753. Portadyne 'Princess', by Portadyne Radio Ltd. 1953. 3-v +R, AC SHet Table Model, MW/LW Mtrs/StN, brown Bakelite cabinet. 7 ¾ in. x 11 ½ in. x 6 ½ in. £7.19s.6d inc PT. (Also in cream, blue or green moulded cabinets).

fig.754. Decca 'Deccette', by Decca Gramophone Co. Ltd. 1953. 4-v Batt Portable, MW/LW Mtrs/StN, ferrite rod aerial, black plastic and metal case. 6 ½ in. x 9 in. x 6 ½ in. £12.13s.7d + PT. One of the first British receivers fitted with a ferrite rod aerial. Optional detachable base housing an AC battery eliminator unit, price £5.5s.0d + PT.

fig.755. Vidor 'Lady Margaret' Model CN 429, by Vidor Ltd. 1954. 4-v Handbag Portable, MW/LW Mtrs, plastic carrying handle, scarlet and silver-grey lizard-covered wood case. 4 in. x 8 in. x 8 in. (lid closed). £9.2s.10d + PT. The receiver switches on automatically when the lid is raised.

fig.756. Murphy Type BA 228, by Murphy Radio Ltd. 1954. 6-v +2MetR, M/Batt Transportable, MW/LW Mtrs/StN, hinged black Bakelite panel flap, black leatherette-covered wood case with black Bakelite ends. 10 ¾ in. x 15 ½ in. x 7 in. £17.5s.0d + PT and batteries. (Model BA 229 is battery portable version in identical cabinet).

fig.757. Philips 'Music Maid' Model 342A, by Philips Electrical Ltd. 1954. 4-v +R, AC SHet Clock-Controlled Bedside Table Model, MW/LW, cream plastic knobs and front, brown Bakelite cabinet. 8 ½ in. x 12 ½ in. x 6 in. £17.9s.9d + PT. Four pre-set stations (3 MW, 1 LW), tuned at the back of the set (no manual tuning or dial). The built-in electric clock can be pre-set to (1) switch on the radio, (2) activate an alarm buzzer, and (3) switch on a 5 amp socket housed on the back of the set which can be used either for a bedside lamp or an electric kettle. At night, a 'slumber switch' can be activated to turn the radio off after up to 60 minutes.

fig.758. Philips Model 141U, by Philips Electrical Ltd. April 1954. 4-v +R, AC/DC SHet Transporable, MW/LW Mtrs/StN, clear Perspex tuning scale/loud-speaker grille (lights up when the set is on), clear Perspex knobs with gilded metal centres, red/brown Bakelite cabinet with moulded carrying handle. 8 ½ in. x 12 in. x 6 in. £11.18s.6d + PT.

fig.759. G.E.C. Model 5445, by General Electric Co. Ltd. August 1954. 4-v +R, AC SHet Table Model, SW/MW/LW Mtrs/StN, gold coloured moulded plastic grille, brown Bakelite cabinet with woodgrain painted ends. 12 ½ in. x 15 ½ in. x 8 ½ in. £21.0s.0d inc PT.

fig.760. Ferranti Model 045, by Ferranti Ltd. 1954. 5-v +R plus Magic-Eye Tuning Indicator, AC SHet, AM/FM Table Model, SW/MW/LW/VHF Mtrs/StN/Mcs, walnut veneered plywood cabinet. 16 ½ in. x 23 in. x 9 ½ in. One of the first AM/FM receivers.

fig.761. Ferranti Model 945, by Ferranti Ltd. 1954. 6-v +MetR, AC M/Batt Portable, MW/LW Mtrs/StN, internal frame aerial, cream plastic carrying handle, plywood cabinet covered in imitation lizard skin. 10 ½ in. x 14 in. x 6 ½ in. £15.10s.0d + PT. Batteries extra.

fig.762. H.M.V. Model 1360, by The Gramophone Co. Ltd. September 1954. 5-v +R, AC SHet Table Model, SW/MW/LW Mtrs/StN, beige plastic front, brown Bakelite cabinet. 11 ½ in. x 16 in. x 7 in. £14.8s.11d + PT. (Identical to Sobell Model 515P).

fig.763. Philips Model 543A, by Philips Electrical Ltd. 1954. 6-v +R, AC SHet Table Model, SW/MW/LW/VHF, Mtrs/ StN/Mcs, 6 piano keys, ferrite rod aerial, gold-centred black Bakelite knobs, gold-painted detailing, black Bakelite cabinet. 13 ½ in. x 20 in. x 8 ½ in. £23.1s.0d + PT. One of the first AM/FM receivers.

fig.764. Ferranti Model 245, by Ferranti Ltd. 1954. 4-v +R, AC SHet Table Model, SW/ MW/LW Mtrs/StN, walnut veneered plywood cabinet. 14 ½ in. x 20 in. x 9 in.

fig.765. Ferranti Model 545, by Ferranti Ltd. February 1954. 4-v +R, AC/DC Transportable, MW/LW Mtrs/StN, walnut veneered plywood cabinet. 11 ¼ in. x 14 ½ in. x 6 in. £13.10s.3d + PT.

fig.766. Bush Model VHF 41, by Bush Radio Ltd. November 1954. 6-v +R, AC SHet, AM/FM Table Model, MW/LW/VHF Mtrs/StN/Mcs, walnut veneered plywood cabinet. 13 in. x 16 in. x 8 in. £20.15s.4d.

fig.767. Grundig 'Hastings' Model 2035/ WD/3D, made in West Germany, distributed in U.K. by Grundig (Gt.Britain) Ltd. December 1955. 6-v +MetR plus Magic-Eye Tuning Indicator, AC SHet Table Model, SW/MW/LW/VHF, Mtrs/ StN/Mcs, 7 piano keys, 4 moving-coil loud-speakers, tone controls, gilded metal fittings, 'Continental-style' mahogany veneered plywood cabinet. 14 ½ in. x 21 ½ in. x 9 ¼ in. £57.15s.0d. Employs a 3D loud-speaker system with two treble units (fitted at either side), a 9 in. bass unit and an electrostatic tweeter. Came with optional remote volume and tone control unit, the Grundig 'Majestic Baton' (below).

fig.768. The Grundig 'Majestic Baton' remote control unit. This has 5 cream celluloid piano keys: (1) '3D' brings into play the two treble loud-speakers at either side of the cabinet giving an all-round sound effect, and (2) 'Voice', (3) 'Orchestra', (4) 'Solo' and (5) 'Jazz' bring different tone control circuits into play, a piano key being selected to match the content of the programme being broadcast. The appropriate illustration lights up when each key is depressed. Brown Perspex case 2 ½ in. x 6 in. x 5 1/4 in.

fig.769. G.E.C. 'AC Compact' Model BC 4644, by General Electric Co. Ltd. 1954. 4-v +MetR, AC SHet Transportable, MW/ LW Mtrs/StN, ferrite rod aerial, cream coloured polystyrene case. 8 ¼ in. x 11 ½ in. x 4 ¼ in. £11.18s.6d + PT. Also available in red coloured case.

fig.770. Ferguson Model 352U, by Ferguson Radio Corporation Ltd. 1955. 3-v + Westalite Contact Cooled Rectifier, AC/ DC SHet Table Model, MW/LW Mtrs/ StN, cream painted grille, cream plastic tuning control with gilded metal centre and clear Perspex surround, black Bakelite cabinet. 9½ in. x 12 in. x 5½ in.

fig.771. Ferranti Model 255, by Ferranti Ltd. 1955. 5-v +R, AC SHet, AM/FM Table Model, MW/LW/VHF Mtrs/StN/Mcs, internal ferrite rod aerial, white plastic knobs, walnut veneered plywood cabinet. 14 ½ in. x 18 in. x 9 in. This was one of the last receivers made by the original Ferranti firm before E.K. Cole Ltd. took over the 'Ferranti' name and formed a subsidiary called Ferranti Radio & Television Ltd.

fig.772. Radio Rentals Model 216, by Radio Rentals Ltd. 1955. 4-v +R, AC/DC SHet Table Model, MW/LW Mtrs/StN, ferrite rod aerial, cream moulded loud-speaker fret and knobs, 'silver walnut' grained Bakelite cabinet. 8 ¾ in. x 13 in. x 5 ½ in. Rental: 10s.6d per month for 9 months reducing with "Free Service, Free Maintenance, Free Valves, Free Replacement and Free Installation".

fig.773. Cossor Model 527/X, by A.C. Cossor Ltd. 1955. 4-v Batt SHet, 2SW/MW Kcs/Mcs, red and ivory painted biscuit tin 'cabinet' made by the Metal Box Company. 6 ¾ in. x 9 ¼ in. x 4 ½ in. Originally produced specifically for the African market, but also sold for use in Britain. Operating instructions are printed on the back of the receiver.

fig.777. Murphy Type A372, by Murphy Radio Ltd. 1955. 5-v +R, AC SHet, AM/FM Table Model, MW/LW/VHF Mtrs/StN/Mcs, clear Perspex tuning scale, maroon Bakelite knobs with gilded metal centres, maroon Bakelite cabinet. 9 ½ in. x 14 ½ in. x 7 in.

fig.780. Ever Ready 'Sky Princess', by Ever Ready Co. (Great Britain) Ltd. July 1956. 4-v Batt Portable, MW/LW Mtrs/StN, ferrite rod aerial, black and cream leatherette covered wood case. 3 ½ in. x 9 in. x 10 in. £10.10s.0d + PT.

fig.774. H.M.V. Model 1127, by The Gramophone Co. Ltd. January 1955. 4-v +R, AC SHet electric alarm clock radio, medium-wave metre settings engraved on side tuning control, brown Bakelite case. 5 ¾ in. x 12 in. x 6 in. £19.19s.0d + PT. The clock can be pre-set to automatically switch on either the radio or the alarm.

fig.775. Ferranti Model M55, by Ferranti Ltd. 1955. 4-v +R, AC/DC SHet Table Model, MW/LW Mtrs/StN, red glass scale, ivory plastic knobs and cabinet. 6 ¾ in. x 12 ¼ in. x 5 ½ in.

fig.778. Pye 'Desk Tuner Unit', by Pye Ltd. 1955. 6-v +R, AC SHet, no integral loudspeaker, walnut veneered plywood cabinet. 8 in. x 9 in. x 6 in.

fig.781. Cossor 'Melody Portable' Model 543, by A.C. Cossor Ltd. 1956. 4-v Batt Handbag Portable, MW/LW Mtrs/StN, printed circuit, ferrite rod aerial, cream leathercloth-covered wood case. 8 in. x 10 in. x 5 ½ in. £8.13s.3d + PT. The set came with a carrying handle and a shower-proof carrying wrapper to afford protection in the rain (not shown).

fig.776. Marconiphone 'Companion' Model T43DA, by Marconiphone Co. Ltd. August 1955. 3-v +R, AC/DC SHet Table Model, MW/LW Mtrs, oversized circular dial control in clear Perspex, cream painted plastic case. 7 ½ in. x 11 in. x 6 in.

fig.779. Ekco Model U243, by E.K. Cole Ltd. April 1955. 5-v +R plus Magic-Eye Tuning Indicator, AC/DC SHet, AM/FM Table Model, MW/LW/VHF Mtrs/StN/Mcs, walnut veneered plywood cabinet. 14 in. x 16 ½ in. x 9 in. £19.16s.2d + PT.

fig.782. Ferguson 'Fleur-de-Lis' Model 383A, by Ferguson Radio Corporation Ltd. August 1956. 5-v +MetR, AC SHet, AM/FM Table Model, MW/LW/VHF Mtrs/StN/Mcs, gilded metal trim on knobs and front of cabinet, directional ferrite rod aerial, mahogany and walnut veneered plywood cabinet. 13 ½ in. x 18 in. x 7 in. £18.19s.1d + PT.

fig.783. Ever Ready 'Sky Casket', by Ever Ready Co. (Great Britain) Ltd. October 1957. 4-v Batt Handbag Portable, MW/LW Mtrs, gilded fittings, cream leathercloth-covered wood case. 7 in. x 9 in. x 6 in. £13.13s.0d + PT.

fig.784. Cossor Model 565, by A.C. Cossor Ltd. November 1957. 3-v +R, AC/DC SHet, MW/LW Mtrs/StN, bent plywood cabinet. 8 ½ in. x 15 in. x 6 in. £10.19s.0d + PT. Oversized clear Perspex tuning control with pointer printed on it.

fig.785. 'Jewel', by Jewel Radio Ltd. April 1957. 4-v +R, AC M/Batt SHet, SW/MW/LW Mtrs/StN, oval green fabric-covered fibre case. 9 in. x 8 in. x 5 ¼ in. £14.14s.0d. Advertised as "The Twin Purpose Set", the Jewel worked off AC mains or from a car battery: a converter for use in the car cost an extra £5.0s.0d. The pilot-light forms a jewel in the headdress of a girl illustrated on the panel label (not shown) and lights up when the set is on. Twenty-five colour combinations were available.

fig.786. H.M.V. Model 1410G, by The Gramophone Co. Ltd. June 1957. 3-v, 2-Tr Handbag Portable, MW/LW Mtrs, ferrite rod aerial, red controls, gilded and red tuning dial, green plastic carrying handle and case. 5 ¾ in. x 7 ½ in. x 2 ¾ in. £9.16s.5d + PT. A valve/transistor hybrid with a 2-transistor output stage. (Also Model 1410B in a blue plastic case. Identical to 1957 Marconiphone Model P60B).

fig.787. Bush Model VHF 64, by Bush Radio Ltd. 1957. 6-V +R plus Magic-Eye Tuning Indicator, AC AM/FM Table Model SHet, SW/MW/LW/VHF Mtrs/StN/Mcs, push-button and manual tuning, twin moving-coil loud-speakers plus electrostatic loud-speaker, gilt metal trim, walnut veneered plywood cabinet. 15 in. x 22 ½ in. x 9 ½ £35.10s.8d + PT.

fig.788. Roberts Model R77, by Roberts Radio Co. Ltd. 1957. 4-v Batt Portable, MW/LW Mtrs/StN, expanded metal grille, ferrite rod aerial, cream plastic gold-centred knobs, cream plastic control panel, integral coach hide leather case, no 'cabinet' as such. 6 in. x 9 in. x 3 ½ in. £13.4s.7d + PT.

fig.789. Pye 'Slim Six' Model P128B, by Pye Ltd. 1958. 6-Tr, MW + Pre-Set LW, Mtrs, brass tuning dial and pointer, sapele wood and bird's-eye maple case. 6 ¾ in. x 9 ¾ in. x 2 ¼ in. An indoor 'mantle' transistor radio.

fig.790. Ultra 'Transistor Six', by Ultra Electric Ltd. 1958. 6-Tr Batt Handbag Portable, MW/LW Mtrs/StN, ferrite rod aerial, cream plastic front and back, dark brown stained bent plywood surround. 8 in. x 12 in. x 3 ¾ in. Heralded by Ultra as the "first completely self-contained home radio".

fig.791. Pye 'Luxury' Model PU 118, by Pye Ltd. 1958. 4-v +R, AC/DC SHet Table Model, MW/LW Mtrs/StN, oversized clear Perspex dial control, gilded trim, plastic mesh front, walnut veneered plywood cabinet. 8 ½ in. x 15 ½ in. x 6 in. New 'long, low look' cabinet design.

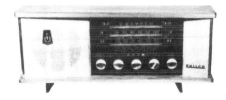

fig.792. Philco Model 100, by Philco (Gt.Britain) Ltd. 1958. 5-v +R, AC/DC SHet Table Model, MW/LW/VHF, Mtrs/StN/Mcs, black plastic gold-centred knobs, black-painted and light mahogany veneered plywood cabinet. 10 in. x 25 in. x 7 ½ in. £19.14s.3d + PT. 'Long, low look' cabinet.

fig.793. Ever Ready 'Sky Emperor', by Ever Ready Co. (Great Britain) Ltd. October 1958. 8-v plus Visual Tuning Indicator, AM/FM Batt Portable, 2SW/MW/LW Mtrs/StN/Mcs, battery economy switch, cream plastic scale surround and gold-centred knobs, fabric covered case with red front and back, and yellow middle. 12 ½ in. x 15 in. x 6 in. £25.0s.4d + PT. This particular model hand-painted by the artist James Butterworth.

fig.794. Bush Model VHF 90A, by Bush Radio Ltd. May 1958. 6-v + MetR, AC/DC SHet, FM Table Model, VHF Mcs, internal frame aerial, oversized clear Perspex tuning control, brown Bakelite cabinet. 9 in. x 13 in. x 6 ½ in. £12.17s.0d + PT.

fig.795. Ever Ready 'Sky Countess', by Ever Ready Co. (Great Britain) Ltd. 1958. 4-v Batt Portable, MW/LW Mtrs, ferrite rod aerial, imitation pig-skin covered wood case. 4 in. x 9 ¾ in. x 9 ¼ in. (closed). £9.1s.11d + PT.

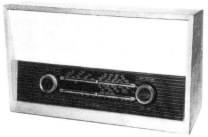

fig.796. Cossor Model 575PC, by A.C. Cossor Ltd. 1958. 5-v + R, AC/DC AM/FM SHet, MW/LW/VHF Mtrs/StN/Mcs, walnut and sycamore veneered plywood cabinet. 11 ¾ in. x 19 in. x 7 in. £16.13s.7d + PT. (Model 579 has tuning indicator).

fig.797. Murphy Model U472, by Murphy Radio Ltd. 1958. 5-v + R, AC SHet, AM/FM Table Model, MW/LW/VHF Mtrs/StN/Mcs, internal frame aerial, clear Perspex grille, brown Bakelite cabinet. 8 ½ in. x 14 in. x 6 ½ in.

fig.798. Ferranti Model PT 1010, by Ferranti Radio & Television Ltd. 1958. 6-Tr Batt Portable, MW/LW Mtrs/StN, frame aerial housed in lift-up lid, red and grey leatherette covered plywood case. 3 ¾ in. x 8 ¾ in. x 7 ¾ in.

fig.799. Pye Model P160 PQ, by Pye Ltd. March 1959. 6-Tr Batt Pocket Portable, MW (+ Pre-Set 1,500m), Mtrs, 3 in. moving-coil loud-speaker, ferrite rod aerial, gilded trim, red and cream plastic case. 3 ½ in. x 6 ¼ in. x 1 ¾ in. £15.15s.0d inc PT.

fig.800. Bush Model TR82, by Bush Radio Ltd. May 1959. 7-Tr + Crystal Diode Batt Portable, MW/LW Mtrs/StN, ferrite rod aerial, push-button wave-change switch, beige leathercloth-covered surround, chromium plated trim, cream plastics carrying handle and case. 11 in. x 13 in. x 4 in. £22.11s.6d. + PT. Car aerial socket. (The moulded case of the TR82 also features on other Bush models, *see page249*).

fig.801. Berec 'Pioneer' Kit, Berec Radio Ltd. 1959. 4-v Batt Kit, SW/MW Mtrs/Mcs, blue sprayed metal case, matt silver sprayed front. 7 ½ in. x 12 in. x 6 in. £4.5.0d. (2SW version, price £4.0s.0d). Ever Ready B103 HT/LT battery, price 18s.6d. Principally sold for home-constructors by Gladstone Radio of Camberley, Surrey by mail order (p&p 2s.6d). Also available ready-made.

fig.802. Perdio 'Continental' Model PR73, by Perdio Radio Ltd. June 1959. 7-Tr Batt Portable, M/LW/Trawler Band (87-197 metres — one of the first transistors to include this band), Mtrs/StN, car aerial socket, gold grille cloth, blue/grey and grey plastic front panels, gold-centred cream plastic knobs (outer knobs laid out like orbiting planets), beige leathercloth covered wood case. 9 in. x 11 in. x 4 in. £14.15s.1d.+ P.T.

5 Postscript, The 1960s

1960

In January, in readiness for the B.B.C.'s planned series of stereophonic tests (see 1962), Mullard announced the development of a stereophonic converter unit, designed by G.D. Browne, which could be added to a VHF/FM stereo radiogram to enable the radio section to receive stereo broadcasts transmitted by the Multiplex system.

In March, the Electronics Industry Council was formed by the Electronic Engineering Association and the Radio & Electronic Component Manufacturers' Association as a complementary body to the Radio Industry Council. It was concerned primarily "with electronic instruments, sound and television transmitters, radio communications, radar and radio navigation aids, computers, industrial electronic control equipment, industrial television and the electronic components used therein". The Radio and Electronics Industries had in reality become two separate industries.

Since the end of the Second World War, the Electronics Industry had been experiencing one of the most spectacular booms the world had ever seen. Electronic apparatus was being developed in many different fields: in factories with the control of production lines, machine tools and HF heating equipment, in farming, transport, hospitals, and schools, in offices with dictating machines and inter-office communications, and in computers and in navigation. With all this modern technology around them, *The Wireless & Electrical Trader* thought that "it would be wise for all radio dealers to look around the wider field of the Electronics Industry and to do everything possible to develop their technical strength".

In June, the first of nine television studios was brought into operation at the B.B.C.'s new Television Centre at Wood Lane, near the White City. In the same month, the Television Advisory Committee recommended the adoption of the European 625-line standard for UHF television transmission and expressed the view that colour television when it was introduced, should be on this standard too. The first public colour television demonstration on 625-lines in this country was given a year later at the 1961 National Radio Exhibition.

JAPANESE TRANSISTORS

Faced with economic difficulties, the Government of the Republic of Ireland had begun offering inducement to overseas industrialists to establish new factories in that country. In March, they announced that companies were to be set up to manufacture Japanese transistor radios, and the first one (the Sony Corporation of Japan) would begin production at Shannon early in the new year. Many British manufacturers, faced with rumours that cheap Japanese radios, televisions and electrical goods would soon be flooding the country from the Far East, and now, from Eire, naturally began to fear this threat of competition but *The Wireless & Electrical Trader* advised its readers not to overrate the danger and reported that a spokesman for the Irish Embassy in London had assured them that efforts would be made to ensure that there would be no unfair undercutting of prices. However, in May the first batch of pocket-sized Japanese-made transistor radios (most covering the medium waveband only and retailing from about £12 upwards) began to arrive from the Far East and in July, a new Anglo-Japanese Trade Agreement was signed which gave the go-ahead for what was soon to become an onslaught.

In Britain, new distribution companies were set up to promote Japanese transistor radios. In November, Tellux Ltd. of London W3 introduced the first Sony model to be imported from Japan: the six transistor Model TR 620, retailing at 18 guineas including Purchase Tax. It measured a mere 3 ½ in. x 2 ⅞ in. x ⅞ in. and, like many of its Japanese counterparts, was a true pocket portable and ideal for carrying around outdoors. With the public, the new Japanese transistors were immediately popular, not only because of their handy size, good performance, styling and comparative cheapness, but also because they exhibited new and attractive packaging ideas and usually came with several accessories individually wrapped in plastic sleeves and all contained in a tempting presentation box. Sony's was typical, for not only did you get the radio, but also a battery, an external aerial, an earpiece for 'personal' listening, a leather case, a silk wrist cord, a cleaning cloth (definitely a new idea) and operating instructions. Sony was a name that would still be at the forefront of electronics over twenty-five years later as would other Japanese companies such as Toshiba, whose first imported transistor radio appeared in December: the six transistor Model 6TP354 distributed by Hall Electric Ltd., London N.W.5 and retailing at 12 guineas including Purchase Tax.

Another threat, principally affecting radio and electrical retailers in many districts appeared in the form of the growing armies of door-to-door salesmen who by 1960 were fast becoming a nuisance by offering radios, televisions, vacuum cleaners and other appliances at very competitive prices. To counteract these activities, the Radio Traders' & Retailers' Association advised its members to publicise widely the fact that only they were able to offer the public fair treatment and give good service, since most of the doorstep salesmen were unable to offer any after-sales service facilities.

At the 1960 National Radio Exhibition, held at Earls Court from August 24th to September 3rd, one rather odd feature was the inclusion of a large piano display. Tom Hicks, Chairman of the Piano Publicity Association explained: "Because of the new interest aroused in music by radio and television, pianos have made a comeback in Britain in recent years and that is one reason that the proper place for a display of pianos is the Radio Show". At the Exhibition, the development was announced of the first British transistorised battery portable television set, some fifteen years before the end of the valve era in television. This was the Ferguson Transvista with a 7 inch tube which first appeared on sale in June of the following year, although it was beaten onto the market by a similar set from Perdio.

In radio design generally, gold-centred knobs and oversized circular dial controls in clear Perspex were still very much in vogue, and with transistorised receivers in particular, battery portables really began to make an impact. The vast majority were handbag-sized models and these had now completely eclipsed portables using valves. Valves were still widely used in mains table models, and with this class, the 'long, low look' in cabinet design continued (fig.803). However, the number of new mains valve table models being produced by manufacturers would soon diminish as the listening public exhibited a growing preference for having a transistorised battery portable for use around the house as well as out of doors.

A year after their first release, several more transistorised battery table models became available during 1960 (fig.804). Released with the intention of rivalling mains valve table models, they were known collectively as 'cordless sets' and although initially popular, they were never to become firmly established and as a class remained comparatively insignificant. While most of them operated on AM only (medium-wave or medium and long-wave, plus a few all-wave models offering 'world coverage'), some transistorised battery table models now included the VHF/FM band for the first time. The first of this class had appeared earlier on June 11th, when the Ferguson Radio Corporation announced the development of the first

British battery transistor circuit able to receive the VHF/FM band. This was marketed in table model receivers made under the H.M.V. and Marconiphone trade marks and the first one to be produced was the H.M.V. Model 1421. It retailed at 28 guineas including purchase tax, and used a MW/LW/VHF circuit containing nine transistors and four crystal diodes.

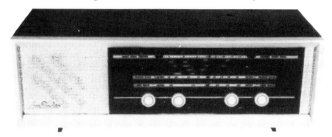

fig.803. Ace Model 357, by Ace Radio Ltd. 1960. A 4-valve plus rectifier AC superhet, covering the short, medium and long wavebands. The black fabric-covered wood cabinet has a cream-painted surround and is designed in the modern 'long, low look' style. 8 in. x 25 in. x 9 in.

fig.804. Bush Model TR 91, by Bush Radio Ltd. September 1960. A 7-transistor battery table model covering the medium and long wavebands, with four push-buttons for OFF/MW/LW/TONE. The tuning scale is in blue-sprayed glass and the 'long, low look' case is in beige plastic with a cream plastic front. 7 in. x 15 in. x 5 in. The TR 91 is an early example of a transistorised battery version of the mains table model, and because of this they were known as 'cordless sets'. Comparatively few models were produced and as a class of receiver they were rather rare, for when choosing a transistor most listeners tended to opt for a portable.

Printed circuits were now widespread amongst all classes of receiver, and in the autumn, Printed Circuits Ltd. announced the opening at Borehamwood of the largest and most modern factory of its type in the world. It was specially designed for the production of all types of printed circuits and used completely automatic electronically controlled circuit board etching techniques in a dust-free atmosphere.

For the first time, Pye Ltd. decided not to exhibit at the National Radio Exhibition but chose instead to hold their own television, radio and electronics exhibition at the Royal Festival Hall a few days before. Along with other companies in the Pye group (Pam, Invicta and T.M.C.) they attracted over 175,000 visitors during the three day show which ran from August 22nd to 24th, and started a trend, soon to be followed by other manufacturers.

In 1960, the first true power transistors were generally introduced and these led to the development of transistorised high-output power amplifiers. For those new to the world of transistors, the Clark-Smith Manufacturing Company brought out the industry's first electronics constructional kit, the Mechtronics outfit, which enabled a large number of experimental circuits to be built. Another new development was the appearance in June of the first outdoor pocket transistor radio which could be converted into a battery table model for home use. This was Grundig's Micro-Boy whose pocket transistor portable, measuring 3 in. x 4 ½ in. x 1 ¼ in., could be fitted back into a slot, set into a long, horizontal cabinet containing a large permanent magnet loud-speaker and extra long-life batteries to form a compact table model. Eumig's Town & Country set and Murphy's Model B385 (fig.807), released later, were similarly designed.

During the year, there was a tremendous increase in the number of transistor portables fitted with car radio aerial sockets so that they could be used when motoring as well as in the home. Car radios too were creating a booming market, and while these generally had to be fitted professionally, Murphy Radio brought out the first do-it-yourself car radio which could be fitted without technical help in about fifteen minutes. Called the Voxson, it had a mirrored front with tuning and volume controls on either side and was stuck to the windscreen by a suction pad, replacing the rear-view mirror. Its separate loud-speaker unit was mounted below the dashboard.

The B.B.C.'s VHF/FM network had now reached the far North of Scotland with the opening of the Thrumster transmitting station near Wick on March 1st. It was estimated that one household in every five owned a receiver capable of tuning to the VHF/FM band and the B.B.C. now began to show an interest in planning a network of low power VHF/FM transmitting stations in cities and in large towns to provide the foundation for the development of local radio. (The Corporation's first local radio station, Radio Leicester, opened on November 8th 1967).

1961

At the National Radio Exhibition, held at Earls Court from August 23rd to September 2nd, a new trade and technical section was featured which was primarily concerned with servicing requirements: components, spares, test equipment, instruments, tools and office and stock record systems were all on display, and particular attention was drawn to the servicing of transistorised equipment. For many older service engineers, steeped in the tradition of valve circuitry all their working lives, this was a completely new field and they were now finding that their concepts and attitudes towards circuit theory and practice had to be drastically revised.

In 1961, the widest application of the transistor in domestic consumer products was in the portable AM receiver which in just a few years had completely changed the nature of the portable radio market and now, with very few exceptions (fig.805), every portable radio was a transistor. (By the early 1960s, 'transistor' was becoming the generic term for a portable radio as well as the component). In its May 6th issue, *The Wireless & Electrical Trader* published the first comprehensive Buyer's Guide to transistor portables, and listed over 160 different models currently available on the market including a few with the VHF/FM band. The overwhelming majority were MW/LW (73 per cent), followed by MW (9 per cent) and SW/MW/LW (6 per cent). The last 12 per cent were made up of a mixture of MW/LW/FM (4.5 per cent), SW/MW (3 per cent), MW/FM (2 per cent), SW/MW/LW/FM (1.5 per cent), SW/MW/FM (0.5 per cent) and FM (0.5 per cent).

The average price for an ordinary small MW/LW transistorised portable was around 18 guineas but you could pay as much as £175.9s.6d for the SW/MW/LW nine transistor Zenith RYL 1000D or as little as £9.19s.6d for the MW/LW six transistor Fidelity Coronet which was the first transistor radio on sale in Great Britain for under £10. The Coronet had a young image and, promoted by the pop idol Cliff Richard (who thought it was "a honey for the money"), was aimed at the very large teenage market and "the young at heart who like to keep up with new ideas".

The models listed in the Buyer's Guide were mainly of British manufacture but the list also contained a fair number of sets imported from the Far East. Competition from the Japanese, who were concentrating on producing pocket-sized transistor radios, was continuing to grow. Sets were being imported into Britain with mounting enthusiasm and prices were falling all the time. The first model by Hitachi (Model TH660) was offered by Lee Products (G.B.) Ltd., of London EC2 and several other British distributors including Denham & Morley Ltd. and Bruce Brent Ltd., now introduced transistor radios from a new source, Hong Kong, where sets, (readily identified by their "Empire Made" labels), were beginning to be mass-produced, assembled from Japanese components. Pocket, and later miniature transistor radios from the Far East were (and still are) calibrated in kilocycles and usually had a thumb-wheel tuning control showing, typically, "5.4, 6, 7.5, 10, 16" markings behind a small cut-out window: this being equivalent to the 540 to 1600 kilocycles range on the medium waveband (approximately 187 to 555 metres).

With electronics now reaching many spheres of life, Minimodels Ltd. (Tri-ang), brought out their Tri-onic Kit 'A', Electronic Construction Set which was aimed at teaching electronics to school children and young people. With it, they could make and use six transistorised circuits using printed circuit boards and plug-in components (fig.806).

Although the VHF/FM band was beginning to be included in more transistorised portable and table model radios, their percentage was still very small, and this band continued to be the domain of the mains valve table model class. During the year, four new VHF/FM stations had opened at Swingate (Dover) on August 8th, Les Platons (Channel Islands) on October 16th, Londonderry (a relay transmitter) on October 23rd, and Llandrindod Wells (another relay) on December 4th.

fig.807. Murphy B385, by Murphy Radio Ltd. This 8-transistor portable receiver was first released in September 1959, but was still being advertised as a current model in 1961 (the actual one illustrated above is stamped "21.2.1961"). Push-buttons for wavechange (medium and longwave) and for ON/OFF, ferrite rod aerial, gold-centred Perspex volume and tuning controls (marked in metres only), beige plastics case 7 in. x 10 in. x 3 in. £22.1s.0d. inc. P.T. Converted into a table model by inserting into the top of a matching 'B1' baffle cabinet containing a larger loudspeaker.

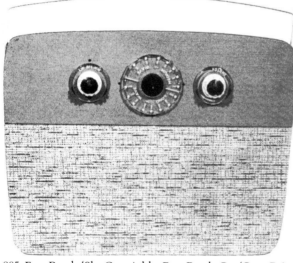

fig.805. Ever Ready 'Sky Captain', by Ever Ready Co. (Great Britain) Ltd. 1961. A 4-valve battery portable covering the medium and long wavebands (dial marked in metres only). Ferrite rod aerial, wood baffle covered in a two-tone check and pink 'Vynair' fabric, moulded plastic back, bent plastic-covered wire carrying handle. 9¾ in. x 12½ in. x 4 in. £7.3s.1d + PT. One of the very last battery valve portables made. (The Berec 'Buccaneer' employs the same chassis and is housed in a similar case).

fig.806. Tri-ang 'Tri-onic, Kit A', by Minimodels Ltd. 1961. An electronic construction set aimed at teaching schoolchildren and young people about electronics. The kit uses six printed circuit boards produced by Mills & Rockleys (Electronics) Ltd., Coventry, from copper clad Bakelite laminate and was supplied with plug-in components for making six different crystal and transistor receivers for headphone use. An add-on kit, 'Tri-onic, Kit A/B', was produced in 1962 to combine with 'Kit A' to make transistor receivers for loud-speaker use, a Morse Code practice set, a microphone and amplifier, and an electronic organ. Box, 3 in. x 12 in. x 14 in.

fig.808. Decca Model TPW 70, by Decca Gramophone Co.Ltd. November 1961. A 6-transistor wall-mounted receiver intended primarily for use in the kitchen or bathroom. Push-buttons for OFF/MW/LW (dial marked in both metres and station names). Gold-centred tuning control and trim, cream and blue plastic case. 10 in. diameter x 2½ in. deep. £13.11s.7d + PT. (Also came in cream and red).

fig.809. 'Maxi-Q Transistor Six', by Denco (Clacton) Ltd. 1961. A 5-transistor battery portable in the form of a book, covering the medium waveband only. Green leathercloth covered case embossed in gold lettering: "SOFT LIGHTS AND SWEET MUSIC BY A TRANSISTOR". The 'pages' are sprayed in gold and the 'cover' opens to reveal a gold sprayed control panel and two cream plastic knobs with gold centres. 7½ in. x 5 in. x 2¼ in. (closed). This is a 'modern' version of the 1925 'Kenmac Book' crystal set (fig.175).

fig.810. Ultra Model TR 80, by Ultra Electric Ltd. 1961. A 6-transistor battery table model ('cordless set'), covering the medium and long wavebands (scale marked in both metres and station names). Painted expanded metal grille, chrome trim, grey plastic knobs and push-buttons (for OFF/MED/LONG), varnished light-mahogany surround. 10 in. x 14½ in x 3¾ in.

fig.811. Perdio Model PR 25, by Perdio Ltd. 1961. A 7-transistor plus diode, medium and long-wave battery portable (dial marked in metres only). Dark and pastel blue polystyrene case of unpleasant texture (resembles the wrinkled skin of a cold rice pudding). 7 in. x 10 in. x 3½ in. £13.19s.6d inc PT. The PR 25 appeared again in 1965 in kit form as the 'Realistic Seven', price £5.19s.6d and was sold by Lasky's Radio of Tottenham Court Road.

1962

On May 5th, *The Wireless & Electrical Trader* published its second comprehensive Buyer's Guide to transistor portables and listed over 200 different models, of which nearly half were imported. The overwhelming majority once again were MW/LW models and with prices ranging from £5.3s.6d for a simple one waveband 2-transistor/crystal diode pocket-set to £171.4s.3d for a 14-transistor/5-crystal diode portable covering the medium and long wavebands, plus seven short wavebands, the magazine felt that "everyone from a child to the connoisseur is catered for".

The number of transistor portables on the market, especially those from the Far East, was growing rapidly and prices showed an overall decrease over the previous year. Generally, transistor radios fell between the two to eight transistor class. The most inexpensive transistor portables were of the pocket-sized medium-wave only class and employed a two or, at most, a three transistor circuit which was capable of driving an earpiece only. In preference to a superhet circuit, TRF circuits were used in an attempt to provide maximum performance with as few components as possible. Where an inexpensive approach to superhet circuitry was needed, four or five transistors could be used. These receivers gave sufficient gain to drive a loud-speaker and provided easier tuning and greater selectivity than TRFs.

Receivers with six transistors generally covered both the medium and long wavebands and invariably introduced the use of a Class 'B' push-pull output stage to drive a loud-speaker which offered the advantage of an increased power output with less distortion, lower power consumption and longer battery life. Adding a seventh transistor introduced the refinement of either an RF amplifier or a separate oscillator-mixer circuit and this improved sensitivity and selectivity. The eight transistor receiver generally incorporated both the RF amplifier and the separate oscillator-mixer circuit.

In July, the distributors Denham & Morley Ltd. announced the "smallest transistor radio in the world": the seven transistor Standard Micronic Ruby, Model SR-G430 (fig.812) manufactured by the Standard Radio Corporation of Japan. It cost £24.3s.0d and measured only 1 ⅞ in. x 1 ⅝ in. x ¾ in. yet still managed to incorporate a loud-speaker behind its gold-plated grille. In the same month, the first transistor radio designed to operate as a mains table model as well as a battery portable was announced by Ekco: the handbag-sized Transistor Twin, Model MBT414. This receiver incorporated a simple low impedance power unit which could also be bought separately to enable any battery transistor set to work off the AC mains. Mains valve table model receivers were generally in decline and the introduction of transistorised versions did not cause a great revival in this class of set. The listening public were now showing an even greater preference for having a transistorised battery portable to use about the house or to take with them outdoors and as the decade wore on, mains radio equipment (mostly transistorised by the end of the 1960s) generally manifested itself in the guise of high quality VHF/FM tuners which formed part of hi-fi systems or were incorporated into radiograms.

At the National Radio Exhibition, held at Earls Court from August 22nd to September 1st, all the television emphasis was directed to the proposed new UHF service on 625-lines. A Government White Paper on the future of broadcasting released earlier in July had announced that the service would begin around mid-July 1964 in the London area and this would be used by a new third television channel (BBC-2). Shortly after the Exhibition closed, the B.B.C. began its UHF transmission tests on Monday September 3rd on Band V, Channel 44 (654-662 Mc/s) from Crystal Palace which lasted until November 1963. Gradually, the 625-line service would be extended across the country and to the other channels on both B.B.C. and I.T.V. and ultimately, although not until early 1985, 405-line transmissions ceased altogether.

Because the UHF television service was not due to be introduced until mid-1964, the company who organised the National Radio Exhibitions at Earls Court (Radio Industry Exhibitions Ltd.) felt that it would be better if television manufacturers kept their new 625-line dual standard models under wraps until after that date, and consequently announced that there would be no Exhibition in 1963. This statement however, did not impress many manufacturers who from about this time went ahead with production and release of new models, converters and aerials in readiness for the inauguration. Whether or not there was a National Radio Exhibition at all did not seem to bother many manufacturers either, for there was now a growing preference, started by the Pye group in 1960, for individual firms or groups to hold their own exhibitions at their own showrooms or at venues such as the Savoy Hotel, Cafe Royal and the Fairfields Hall etc. In this way, individual firms tended to get more publicity in the Press, for they were able to lay on Press previews and provide hospitality for reporters in their own time without having to vie for their attention along with several dozen other firms at the National Exhibition.

The grouping of companies into large organisations had been a notable feature of the post-war years, and an important new group company was announced in November 1962. This was Rank Bush Murphy Ltd., the result of a merger between the Rank Organisation, Bush Radio and Murphy Radio which could now boast five operating divisions: Bush Radio, General Radiological, Murphy Electronics, Murphy Radio and Solus-Schal.

On August 28th, the B.B.C. began the first series of regular once-a-week experimental Multiplex stereo sound transmissions from the Wrotham VHF/FM station which replaced the earlier occasional unscheduled tests. A single carrier-wave from a single transmitter (that for the Third Programme on 91.3 Mc/s) was used to radiate both the left and the right-hand channels and initially the tests were to last for ten weeks in order to enable an engineering assessment of the system to be made under service conditions and to check the extent of the service area (the tests in fact were later extended

until the end of the year). The B.B.C. chose to experiment with the Zenith-G.E.C. Multiplex stereophonic system since it had the advantage of being compatible, enabling the stereo signals to be reproduced monophonically for listeners using conventional mono VHF/FM receivers. The number of VHF transmitters around the country continued to increase. During the year three new relay stations opened: at Redruth on February 26th, Oxford on May 28th and Skye on September 26th.

With a VHF/FM stereo service likely to be introduced in the foreseeable future, several manufacturers now began to produce mains valve stereo tuners and amplifiers, and mains valve table model stereo radios. Among the first of these were Philips' Model 612A at £60.18s.0d and Model 714A at £72.9s.0d, the latter having the added refinement of a reverberation switch.

fig.812. 'Standard Micronic Ruby' Model SR-G430 (actual size), by Standard Radio Corporation, Japan. Distributed in Britain by Denham & Morley Ltd., London W1. 1962. A 7-transistor plus crystal diode miniature portable receiver, tuning from around 540 to 1600 Kc/s on the medium waveband only (dial marked "5.4, 8, 16"). Ferrite rod aerial, 1½ in. loud-speaker, gold-plated grille, red and white plastic case. 1⅞ in. x 1⅝ in. x ¾ in. £24.3s.0d inc PT, silk-lined presentation case, leather carrying pouch, earpiece, carrying strap and mercury-type batteries.

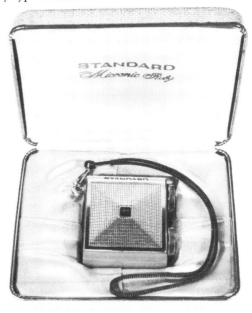

fig.813. The Model SR-G430 in presentation case.

1963

The B.B.C.'s second series of once-a-week stereophonic test transmissions from the VHF/FM station at Wrotham began on January 13th and lasted initially until the end of March. They recommenced from August 20th, when they were increased to three periods a week in order to help manufacturers perfect the design and production of stereophonic radio equipment. Five new VHF/FM relay stations were to be added during the year. These were at Fort William on February 28th, Kinlochleven on April 8th, Oban on June 22nd, Ashkirk (S.E. Scotland) on July 1st and Sheffield on September 2nd.

According to a survey published by the Economist Intelligence Unit Ltd. of London S.W.1, at least 93 per cent of British households owned a radio, ownership being fairly uniform throughout the social classes with the teenage population now providing about 33 per cent of the market for transistor radios and about 40 per cent for record players. The influence of pop music (now given a tremendous boost with the Beatles), was reflected by the fact that many transistor portables were being marketed with reference to Radio Luxembourg: the commercial station which for several years had specialised in playing the latest records from the hit parade. Bandspread coverage of Radio Luxembourg's pop wavelength (208 metres) was featured in many small transistor radios and in December, G.E.C. brought out their Luxembourg Radio pocket receiver aimed specifically at the teenage market.

Transistor radio prices in general had drastically come down by now and this had been helped by the cut in Purchase Tax on January 1st to 25 per cent. The cheapest multi-transistor set on the market was the Japanese six-transistor model 707 distributed by Benkson Ltd. of London W1 which retailed at £5.5s.0d. Although sales of radios of all types were breaking records (4,500,000 were sold in 1963 compared with 1,800,000 in 1959), this was mainly due to the tremendous rise in imports (transistor portables in particular) which accounted for 36 per cent of all sets sold in 1963 compared with a mere 3 per cent in 1959. The future for the British radio manufacturers did not seem bright.

In July, the Post Master General gave the go-ahead for the building of the first eighteen BBC-2 625-line UHF television transmitters over the next three years. From September 30th, the first BBC-2 exhibition was put on at the Design Centre in London and with public interest in the new channel beginning to grow, a major newspaper campaign was then launched from October 28th with the start of Greater London Television & Radio Fortnight with eight supplements published in the *Evening News* and the *Evening Standard* - a "Radio Show in print".

The cancellation of the 1963 National Radio Exhibition caused an unprecedented increase in the number of manufacturers putting on their own 'Showtime Shows': independent shows put on in August and September, the months usually chosen for the National Radio Exhibition. In London and the provinces, 79 firms held exhibitions at their own showrooms, halls or at hotels, (H.M.V., deciding to be different, hired a Thames launch moored to Cadogan Pier off the Chelsea Embankment), while for those members of the trade and public who felt daunted by the weary prospect of trekking around the city to see all the exhibitions, Selfridges in Oxford Street created a temporary Radio & Television Floor enabling the latest models from 25 manufacturers to be conveniently seen under one roof.

1964

From January 1st 1964, the B.B.C. began daily eleven-hour trade test transmissions from their 625-line UHF television transmitter at Crystal Palace using Channel 33 (566-574 Mc/s) on Band IV. Retailers now had the opportunity of getting down to the business of selling new dual standard models, converting older sets and installing UHF aerials in readiness for the start of the new BBC-2 625-line service which was now due to open on April 20th. However, because of a fire at the Battersea Power Station on this date, the BBC-2 studios along with most of the West London area experienced a power black-out, and the new service was forced to open on the following day.

In March it was announced that no decision was to be made on the introduction of a stereophonic radio broadcasting service until 1966. The B.B.C. believed that stereophony could provide worthwhile improvements in sound reproduction, especially of music, and believed that there was a demand for it which, though a minority demand, was substantial. Stereo broadcasting was hoped to further encourage VHF/FM listening and would provide a new market for VHF receivers. By the end of December, the number of VHF/FM stations in Great Britain had risen to thirty-eight, with six more relays opening during the year at Haverfordwest on February 15th, Brougher Mountain (Enniskillen) on February 24th, Bressay (Shetland) on April 15th, Forfar (Angus) on July 13th, Hereford on November 16th and Pitlochry on December 21st.

The B.B.C.'s fifth Charter was granted for a period of twelve years until July 31st 1976, giving the Corporation authority to borrow up to £10,000,000 for temporary banking accommodation and up to £20,000,000 for capital expenditure. Broadcasting Councils for Scotland and Wales were now given powers in television similar to those they already possessed in radio by which they were to decide the content of television programmes designed primarily for their regions. In 1969, a Supplementary Royal Charter was granted to take in the provisions of the *Post Office Act, 1969*, in which the powers in relation to broadcasting formerly exercised by the Post Master General became vested in the Minister of Posts and Telecommunications.

Due to a lack of support from the industry, the 1964 National Radio Exhibition, held between August 26th and September 5th, occupied only the ground floor at Earls Court leaving the entire first floor vacant. Although few people realised it at the time, this would be the last occasion that the National Radio Exhibition would be held. Many of the public visitors felt that they had wasted their 3s.6d entrance fee since they could have seen just as much by taking a walk down their own High Streets. It seemed to be a show for the trade, for while several of the major manufacturers had impressive stands, large portions were found to have been cordoned off "for the trade only" and many of the latest and more interesting developments were displayed within these private enclosures away from public gaze. However, the new BBC-2 625-line television service which dominated the Exhibition was in full view for all to see and the high quality pictures attained impressed all those who crowded into the demonstration rooms. Field trials of UHF colour television had begun on July 6th, although following the failure of European countries to reach agreement on a suitable transmission system for colour television, no plans were being made for its introduction until at least 1967 and the expected demonstrations of colour television at the Exhibition were shelved.

Another prominent feature was made of transistor portables for indoor and outdoor use. A fantasy Transistorland was built, covering 2,000 square feet. In a setting of valleys and hills, 2½ in. gauge railway tracks were laid, along which three engines pulled groups of trucks laden with transistor portables while the 'villages' were made up of other transistor sets. The number of reasonably priced all-wave transistor portables offering 'world coverage' now began to increase as did those with both an AM and a VHF/FM band.

PIRATE RADIO STATIONS

At 12 noon, on Saturday March 28th, a commercial independent pirate pop music station called Radio Caroline, installed on board a Panamanian registered ship moored just over 4 miles off the Suffolk port of Felixstowe began transmitting on 199 metres medium-wave and almost overnight attracted a huge young radio audience, already weaned on Radio Luxembourg's pop programmes and tired of the form of broadcasting that the B.B.C. had followed with little change for over 40 years. Radio Caroline was joined on May 12th by Radio Atlanta on board the *Mi Amigo* anchored off the Essex Coast and later in July, the two stations merged with Caroline South broadcasting from off the East Coast and Caroline North (the old Radio Atlanta) from off the Isle of Man. Earlier, on May 27th, a third independent station called Radio Sutch, initially run by pop singer David 'Lord' Sutch, came on the air and began broadcasting from the gun tower of a disused fort on Shivering Sands, 4 miles off Shoeburyness in Essex. Within a short time, this station was sold and re-named Radio City and in the following months the number of independent stations broadcasting from forts and from vessels anchored off the British coast had grown to more than a dozen. The enormous success they attained was principally due to the attraction of their disc-jockeys' methods of programme presentation which was to have a profound and lasting effect on the style of broadcasting in this country, and to the content of the programmes which perfectly reflected the mood of the 'Swinging Sixties'. While greatly annoying the B.B.C. who objected to their presence on the grounds that they were illegal, Radio Caroline and her sister stations soon began to feature in radio manufacturers' advertisements which assured potential teenage customers that their transistor set "picked up the Pop Pirates".

The importance of teenage listeners continued to grow throughout the decade and one of the most novel British transistor portables aimed at this market on show at the 1964 National Radio Exhibition was G.E.C.'s Transistormatic, Model G822. Described as the "first transistor radio in the world to take a colour photograph", it was in fact a radio combined with a Kodak Instamatic 100 camera and for 19 guineas, which included a colour film, radio and flash batteries, flash bulbs and a carrying strap, you could, according to the brochure, "Twist and Shoot!". But the pocket-sized British transistor radio was generally showing an increasing inability to compete with the price of cheap imports from the Far East, especially those radios made with Japanese components but assembled in Hong Kong where wages were about one fifth of those paid in Britain. Many of these transistor sets were priced from between £2.5s.0d to around £5.0s.0d and this included Purchase Tax, a leather or leatherette carrying case, an earpiece, a battery and a presentation case. Having returned from a fact-finding trip to Japan, Viscount Suirdale, the Chairman and Managing Director of Perdio Ltd. thought that the only possible solution was to design and test small portable transistor radios in Britain but to have them manufactured in Hong Kong.

Echoing the lack of support from manufacturers at the National Radio Exhibition, there was also a big drop in public attendance and with competition from the International Radio & Electrical Trades' Exhibition held at a hotel nearby, an exhibition by distributors of imported radio sets at the Prince of Wales Hotel plus over a dozen individual trade-only shows in and around town, *The Wireless & Electrical Trader* thought that the situation was "chaotic" and did "no good to the corporate image of the industry". Under the headline 'RADIO SHOWS - WHERE DO WE GO FROM HERE?', the magazine felt that the present type of exhibition no longer attracted the public in large enough numbers to make it worthwhile and the 1964 National Radio Exhibition marked a turning point which would force a radical re-thinking of the industry's future exhibition policy.

Towards the end of the year, it was announced that the 1965 National Radio Exhibition would in fact be an international affair and would be taken over by a different company, Industrial & Trade Fairs Ltd. They already had extensive experience in promoting large-scale exhibitions and now planned to promote and organise a series of annual exhibitions at Earls Court with specific attention paid not just

to radio and television but to other forms of home entertainment. These events were seen as the "international successors to the National Radio Exhibitions" which had been held almost continuously since 1926, and it was hoped that the scope and interest of such exhibitions would be considerably widened.

Earlier in June, the first Japanese Floating Fair had been organised which comprised a floating exhibition at Tilbury Docks of Japanese sets promoted by their British distribution companies. The size and the scope of the Japanese radio and electronic industries were impressive and in the face of this threat, many British manufacturers had already given up trying to cope with the competition and were turning away from the production of pocket-sized transistors and instead concentrating on larger transistor portables, valve table models, valve hi-fi and valve television equipment.

fig.814. 'Holiday' 6-transistor pocket radio with imitation black leather carrying case, c.1964. Typical of the "Empire Made" transistor sets mass-produced from the early 1960s in Hong Kong and assembled from Japanese components. Socket for earpiece, thumb-wheel volume and tuning controls, (single waveband dial marked "5.4, 6, 7, 8, 10, 16", visible behind a small cut-out window), cream plastic case. 2½ in. x 4¼ in. x 1¼ in.

1965

In January 1965, Britain, Belgium, Denmark, France, Greece, Luxembourg and Sweden all signed a Council of Europe agreement to ban pirate radio stations. Around Britain, several independent pop music stations were already established on vessels moored offshore, but because they were outside territorial waters their activities were not governed by British law. However, a few stations broadcast from disused forts and these could be prosecuted under the *Wireless Telegraphy Act* which forbade broadcasting without a licence from the Post Master General. The first British summons was issued in September 1966 to Estuary Radio 390, which illegally broadcast from a fort in the Thames estuary. It closed down two months later and ironically, it was not a pop station at all, but rather it concentrated on broadcasting classical and light orchestral music.

In February 1965, details were announced of the planned 1965 International Radio & Television Show at Earls Court, which to give it its ridiculous full title was to be billed as "The '65 International Television, Radio, Record Player, Disc, Tape Recorder, Stereo, Hi-Fi, and Musical Instrument Show". For the first time since 1922, overseas manufacturers would be invited to participate alongside British companies in an attempt to attract the world's leading buyers, giving the British Radio and Television Industries an opportunity to break away with shows of the past and make a fresh start. By March, fifty leading international manufacturers had applied for spaces, but in May, because so many major British companies had held back, the show, planned for August 25th to September 4th, had to be cancelled due to lack of support.

However, while this situation upset the organisers and a few of the radio magazines (*Practical Wireless* said "If we had a flag, it would now be at half mast"), British manufacturers simply carried on as before in the recent past and put on their own exhibitions during the traditional showtime period. Separate exhibitions (several of them for trade-only) had become very popular with manufacturers, especially with the more affluent groups of companies who could afford to choose a luxurious London Hotel where they could exhibit their latest receivers as well as lavishly entertain their clients and pander to the Press. During August, there were twenty-five separate exhibitions in London Hotels and another dozen in firms' showrooms. Seeing all that was on offer involved a mammoth tour of the capital and the consensus of opinion was that while hotel and similar shows might suit manufacturers, they were certainly not popular with either retailers or with the general public who preferred a central exhibition under one roof. In November, in a change of heart, the Pye, Philips, Rank, S.T.C. and Thorn groups all agreed to participate in following year's international, trade-only Television & Radio Show, '66 at Earls Court although G.E.C. decided to stay away. The biggest change was that the show was to be for the trade only and no members of the general public would be admitted.

Among the new transistor portables on show at the various exhibitions around London, a new design (which can still be seen today) had generally become established in which the set was housed in a square-cut rectangular case (either in wood or aluminium) with ends in padded material or in wood (usually teak) while the controls were mounted on the top on a brushed-aluminium panel. The oversized circular dial controls in clear Perspex, popular since the mid-1950s, had now given way to small aluminium tuning knobs and horizontal scales, with spun-aluminium push-buttons for waveband and on/off switching (fig.815).

For the first time, a sun-powered transistor portable was put on show. This was the Sun Charger Royal, Model 555-G by Zenith priced at £41.15s.6d whose nickel-cadmium batteries could be re-charged by sunlight or from the AC mains. At the cheaper end of the scale, the lowest priced British transistor portable on the market was Philips' pocket-sized Popmaster. It retailed at £7.19s.6d, and was designed to combat the increasing sales of small transistor radios from Hong Kong and Japan. Imports from the Far East now accounted for 50 per cent of the total number of all portables on sale in this country although British firms still held their own with regard to valve table models, valve tuners and valve hi-fi amplifiers. The number of transistorised amplifiers was still small and they were generally much more expensive than ordinary valve amplifiers.

On August 20th, *The Wireless & Electrical Trader* decided to bring itself up to date and changed its title to *The Electrical & Electronic Trader*. It doubled its page size and provided readers with "a completely up to date, easier to read journal which would look at future trends in consumer electronics, while dealing, as in the past with all facets of radio, television, audio and electrical apparatus".

fig.815. Ferguson 'Autotwin Mk.II, Model 3140', by Ferguson Radio Corp.Ltd. c.1965. A 9-transistor battery portable/car radio covering the medium and long wavebands (scale marked in both metres and station names). Spun aluminium push-buttons, brushed aluminium panel, black 'square-cut' plastic case with padded ends and carrying handle. 6 in. x 10 in. x 3 in.

Despite the growing sophistication found in the modern world of transistorised electronics, home-construction was still very popular, just as it had been since the pioneering decade of the 1920s. The pages of *Practical Wireless* (the home-constructors' flagship since September 1932) were full of advertisements from firms such as Concord Electronics of Hove, who were offering their San Remo transistor radio kit for a mere 29s.6d, "so tuned that it brings the voices of star entertainers and vocalists dramatically into life - in your home, office etc.". Another kit produced by a British manufacturer was the Micro 6 from Sinclair Radionics Ltd. of Cambridge which was heralded as the "smallest radio set on earth". It measured only 1 ¾ in. x 1 ⅓ in. x ½ in. and the continuing miniaturization of circuits led one commentator in *Practical Wireless* to ask, "What's the point if a piece of equipment is smaller than the knob which is being used to control it?".

You still needed a licence to listen-in on these sets, and at the beginning of August, the Broadcast Receiving Licence fee for radio only was increased to £1.5s.0d while the combined Radio and Television Licence fee was increased to £5.

1966

VHF/FM STEREO SERVICE

On Saturday July 30th, after more than eight years of experiments, the B.B.C.'s first regular VHF/FM stereo service was inaugurated on the Third Programme network radiated from the Wrotham (Kent) and Swingate (Dover) transmitters. The service was broadcast on the Zenith-G.E.C. Multiplex system (also known as the 'Pilot-tone' system), and initially, was confined to just two or three programmes a day (live music, specially recorded concerts and stereo records). However, it was immediately popular and sales of stereo radios, tuner units and amplifiers (a growing number of them now transistorised) in London and the South East greatly increased and manufacturers turned more of their attention towards this new developing market. In 1968, the Third Programme stereo service was extended to the Midlands and the North East region of the country bringing the total number of listeners within the service area to around 33,000,000 and gradually stereo spread to all the other networks and to most areas of Britain.

While 37 new mains valve table models were released in 1966 compared to 23 new mains transistorised table models, the general rise in popularity of the transistor continued at the expense of the valve. This was reflected by the fact that few retailers (in the London area at least) could now offer valve testing facilities and where valve testing equipment was still installed, it was usually done as a favour and not as a service. One correspondent in the July issue of *Practical Wireless* trekked around London in search of a dealer who was willing to take money in exchange for testing some valves. He wrote, "London is littered with radio shops where testers are permanently out of order, not available for use at any time other than those set down by unwritten and ever changing rules, or just not available owing to staff shortage".

Transistor development had now led to the introduction in Britain of the first pocket radio using an integrated circuit. It was manufactured by Sony U.K. and used a tiny single silicon chip incorporating 9 transistors, 4 diodes and 14 resistors. Sinclair Radionics Ltd. introduced the smallest FM receiver yet seen on the market. It was called the Micro FM, measured 2 7/8 in. x 1 3/4 in. x 3/4 in., and comprised a 7 transistor, 2 diode superhet circuit with an output for either an earpiece or for a hi-fi amplifier. Another Sinclair 'first' was their 13 channel, 30 transistor Microvision pocket television receiver which measured 4 in. x 2 1/2 in. x 2 in. Described as "the set that stole The Show", it was first exhibited at the international, trade-only Television & Radio Show '66 held at Earls Court from August 22nd to 26th, but was not planned for limited general release until the following year. The Show's organisers, Industrial & Trade Fairs, Ltd. planned another show for 1967 but in the event, in the year that the B.B.C.'s colour television service would be introduced, it had to be cancelled due to lack of support from the main television manufacturers.

On December 20th, an important Government White Paper on Broadcasting was published. It announced new developments which were planned for the New Year. (1) A new continuous programme of popular music would be introduced called Radio 1, and the other networks would be renamed Radio 2, Radio 3 and Radio 4. (2) Local radio stations would be established at nine centres run by the B.B.C. and Local Radio Councils. (3) Colour television would commence on BBC-2 using the P.A.L. system. (4) There would be no increase in the combined Television & Radio Licence Fee until at least 1968 (although a supplementary fee of £5 was to be charged on colour sets from January 1st 1968).

By December, a change was taking place in Britain in the use of the term 'Hertz' (Hz) in place of the traditional term for units of frequency, 'cycles' (c/s). This was being done to tie in with Continental usage and to honour the name of the German scientist, Heinrich Hertz, who in 1887 first gave the scientific community visual proof of the existence of electro-magnetic waves. By the spring of 1969, the symbol 'Hz' had been universally adopted and 'c/s' was no longer generally used.

1967

COLOUR TELEVISION SERVICE

In 1967, on Saturday July 1st, a limited UHF colour television service was inaugurated on BBC-2 using the P.A.L. system on 625-lines. The opening programme lasted for seven hours and featured a live outside broadcast from the centre court at Wimbledon transmitted during busy shopping hours to enable as many people as possible to see it on demonstration sets placed in retailers windows. David Attenborough, the Controller of BBC-2 thought that seeing colour television would "make monochrome set viewers feel deprived". For the next five months, the service was restricted to only five hours of colour transmissions a week until it 'fully' opened on December 2nd

when this was increased to between fifteen and twenty-five hours per week. Those viewers with new colour televisions wishing to participate in this new service found themselves having to pay a supplementary fee of £5 on combined Radio & Television Licences issued from January 1st of the following year.

Earlier, in August 1967, the first all-transistor colour television, the B.R.C. Thorn 2000, had been introduced and although a few television manufacturers had recently begun producing all-transistor monochrome sets, most televisions at this time were still using all-valve circuits. By 1970 however, virtually all new models were hybrids, with transistors employed in the small-signal circuits and valves in the timebase, video and sometimes audio circuits.

With the cancellation of the planned international Television and Radio Show '67, several trade-only exhibitions were put on in and around London from August 20th to 25th, and now, with a lot more firms concentrating on hi-fi, the display of radios (mostly transistor portables), was generally thought disappointing. In the table model class, already drastically shrinking by this time, the transistor had now almost entirely displaced the valve, and as far as domestic radio receivers in general were concerned, the valve era was finally coming to an end. In transistor portables, the majority offered FM in addition to the normal AM bands and several sets appeared with their tuning scales already marked with the B.B.C.'s new network names (Radio 1, Radio 2 etc.) which were due to come into use at the end of September (see below). However, some tuning scales, instead of showing 'Radio 1' and 'Radio 2' etc., were marked 'BBC1' and 'BBC2' etc., and *Practical Wireless* thought that this was rather puzzling when seen for the first time and added jokingly, "we haven't yet heard of a customer returning a radio because of a poor BBC-2 picture, but we are sure it will happen eventually!".

On August 15th 1967, the activities between 1964 and 1967 of pirate radio stations, financed by advertising and broadcasting pop music from vessels anchored around the coast of Britain were brought to an end by the operation of the *Marine, etc., Broadcasting (Offences) Act*. All these stations ceased broadcasting except Caroline South and Caroline North, whose offices were moved to Amsterdam and arrangements were made to have the vessels supplied from the Netherlands.

RADIO 1

A few weeks later, at 7.00am on Saturday September 30th, the B.B.C.'s new all-pop music network, Radio 1, was inaugurated on 247 metres by disc-jockey Tony Blackburn. Described by *The Radio Times* as "the B.B.C.'s swinging new radio service", it was manned somewhat ironically by many of the old ship-born radio broadcasters whose pirate stations the B.B.C. strongly disapproved of, a fact which certainly says much for the disc-jockeys popularity, influential style of presentation and the programme content. Included among them was Simon Dee, who had been one of the original disc-jockeys on Radio Caroline when it first went on the air in 1964 and by the time Radio 1 opened, Dee had already established himself on B.B.C.tv. with his Saturday evening peak viewing programme *Dee Time*. Radio 1 also attracted disc-jockeys from the B.B.C.'s other long-term commercial antagonist, Radio Luxembourg, including Pete Murray and Jimmy Savile.

On the day that Radio 1 was inaugurated, the B.B.C.'s other networks were given a new image when they were renamed Radio 2 (the old Light Programme), Radio 3 (the old Third Programme) and Radio 4 (the old Home Service). Some weeks later, on November 8th, the first of the B.B.C.'s VHF/FM local radio stations went on the air at Leicester and within a few years, the network had expanded to twenty. Unfortunately, for those listeners with just an ordinary AM receiver, the additional expense of buying a VHF/FM radio in order to listen to the broadcasts was not a very tempting proposition and in order to attract people to the idea of local radio, the B.B.C. were forced to transmit on the medium waveband as well as VHF/FM so that listeners could pick up their local station on any radio.

In the event, following the closing down of the pirate stations, and despite the B.B.C.'s own chain of local radio stations, support for a form of commercial independent local radio service began to grow and by the early 1970s, the pressures were such that on March 29th 1971, a Government White Paper was published proposing the establishment of up to 60 such stations under the control of the I.T.A. This soon led to the passing of the *Sound Broadcasting Act* which altered the structure of the I.T.A., gave it responsibility for sound broadcasting, and changed its name to the Independent Broadcasting Authority. The Act was brought into force on July 12th 1972 and paved the way for the start of independent local radio. In late 1973 the first franchises were awarded to the 'all-news' station of the London Broadcasting Company (L.B.C.) and to Capital Radio in London.

1968

Following one rather indifferent show in 1966, sandwiched between two disastrous cancellations in 1965 and 1967, Industrial & Trade Fairs Ltd. had abandoned any future ideas of holding international Television and Radio shows. In their place in 1968, from August 25th to 29th, manufacturers and distributors carried on with their own trade-only exhibitions at various well-known hotels and other venues in and around London. As regards exhibitions to which the public were welcomed and freely admitted, Audio Fairs had now become very popular although there was not much in the way of radio and television for the visitors to see.

With television receivers, transistor/valve hybrid circuits were now commonplace. Portable valve radios had disappeared at the beginning of the 1960s and while a few valve table model receivers, tuners and amplifiers were still being manufactured in 1968, most new domestic radio and hi-fi equipment was now using fully transistorised circuits. Among the few table models then being produced, Ferguson introduced their first all-transistorised mains radio, the Futura II, which although ultra modern in circuit design, in styling still preserved the 'long, low look' first introduced in 1958 with their Futura I (see 1958). While integrated circuits were coming into more widespread use in electronics generally, Roberts Radio Co. Ltd. announced in the autumn the first British radio to employ an IC, the 2-band Model RIC.1.

Transistorised radio tuners, a great many of them with stereo capability, now vastly outnumbered those employing valves and by the early 1970s, practically no valve tuners were being manufactured. In 1968, the tuner had become an integral part of any domestic hi-fi set up and was being used in preference to an ordinary portable transistor radio where better sound quality was of prime importance. A tuner was basically a "radio set without a built-in power amplifier" and the only tuners considered to be worth getting now were those covering the VHF/FM band since the sole reason for including AM (the ordinary broadcast bands) would be the need for tuning in stations not available on the VHF/FM band. The hi-fi magazines generally agreed that it was better to buy a good VHF/FM tuner and, for the occasional AM broadcast, a cheap portable transistor radio, than to pay a lot more for a combined AM/FM tuner.

The power output capabilities of transistorised stereo hi-fi amplifiers was increasing all the time and many 30 + 30W models were now on the market. Within a year this would be increased to 50 watts per channel. In several quarters though,

the quality of transistorised amplifiers was not thought quite as good as expected, and *Practical Wireless* for one, recommended the use of a lower-priced valve amplifier "while they were still being manufactured". In fact, although the use of the valve in all classes of domestic radio receiver had by the beginning of the 1970s come to an end (lingering on for a few more years in television circuits), the production of valves for certain classes of amplifier never entirely ceased. Valves continue to be used by some manufacturers for high power P.A. and guitar amplification and where 'ultimate quality' is demanded by those hi-fi specialists who insist that they can tell the difference between what they consider the more 'natural' sound produced by the valve and the less than perfect sound produced by a transistor, in hi-fi amplification the valve has to some extent also continued to fight off the transistor. One major manufacturing company, M-O. Valve Company Ltd., has been sufficiently confident of the staying power of the valve to be still (in 1986) producing six different types (including the KT88 output tetrode) which have a current combined yearly run of over 50,000. However, due to economic reasons their valve production is finally being phased out and by about the spring of 1987, production will have come to an end, leaving valve manufacture in the hands of companies in East Germany, Russia and the Far East. This is unfortunate, for within the last five years there have been definite indications that the valve is experiencing a revival in high quality high power amplification equipment, and one specialist firm (Mentmore Industries of London E8) are even managing to sell their specialist hi-fi valve amplifiers to the Japanese. In one corner of Britain's otherwise fully transistorised industry, the valve still manages to live on.

1969

From the late 1960s, just as crystal sets of the 1920s (fig.175) and mains receivers of the 1930s (fig.608) had often been manufactured in disguised forms, many novelty transistor radios, especially those from the Far East, began to appear in various disguises including candlestick telephones, fur poodles, spice racks etc. (fig.816) and similar radio novelties are still being manufactured today.

At the beginning of 1969, on January 1st, the combined Radio and Television Licence fee was increased to £6. For those viewers who were paying an extra £5 for the benefit of receiving BBC-2 in colour, good news came on November 15th, when the 625-line colour service on UHF was extended to both BBC-1 and to I.T.A. in London, the Midlands and the North, and it was expected that by the end of the year about 40 per cent of the population would be within the new service area.

By the end of 1969, virtually all television sets being made in this country were using transistor/valve hybrid circuits, while a small but growing number of fully transistorised monochrome and colour sets were also on the market. Component transistors capable of handling the very high power and pulse voltages of timebases and the large signal swings of the video amplifiers were emerging, but being in the early stages of development were very much more costly than their valve equivalents.

Here then with television, was the last stronghold of the valve in domestic broadcast receiving equipment, (albeit used in a hybrid circuit alongside transistors), and in fact, according to Dr. F.E. Jones, then the Managing Director of Mullard Ltd., in 1970 the number of valves used by the Television Industry numbered 30,000,000. It was not for another five years, towards the end of 1975, that employment of the valve in television circuits practically ceased, an event which finally heralded the end of the valve era in the second of the two main fields of domestic broadcast receiving equipment in Britain.

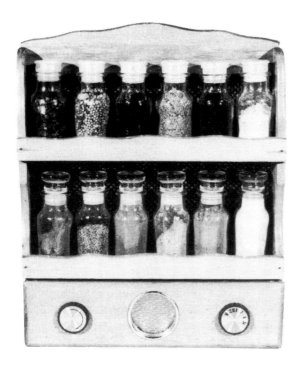

fig.816. 'De-luxe' Transistor Radio/Spice Rack, made in the Far East and sold in England by Shopertunities Ltd., Holborn, London WC1. 1972. A wall-mounted 6-transistor medium-wave battery receiver, tuning from 540 to 1600 Kc/s (dial marked "5.4, 6, 7, 10, 16"), of flimsy birch and plywood construction. 14 in. x 11½ in. x 2½ in. £3.99p inc 12 herb and spice jars plus 76p for box, postage and PP9 battery. (Also Transistor Radio/Spice Cabinet version). These receivers echo the general interest in the use of herbs and spices in cooking which began during the 'hippy' period of the late 1960s. Described as "the ultimate luxury in any kitchen", only 1,000 of each version were put on the market in Britain, and probably most fell off the wall with fatigue after a few weeks.

APPENDICES

The Golden Age of Loud-Speakers, 1922 - 1930

While the outdoor battery portable of the late 1920s was generally designed with an integral loud-speaker, throughout the whole of this decade only a small minority of the indoor 'permanently installed' type of wireless receiver actually contained a loud-speaker within the cabinet. Here, like valves, batteries and the aerial and earth systems, a loud-speaker was not usually included in the basic price of a wireless receiver, and it was necessary therefore to purchase one as a separate item and to connect it up to the terminals provided at the back of the set. During the first half of the 1920s, the use of headphones was gradually superseded by loud-speakers, the earliest of which were the horn types with a straight, curved or swan neck. Apart from the magnetic-reed type moving-iron unit used in the Brown H1, and one early example of a moving-coil unit introduced with the Magnavox R2B in the autumn of 1922, most horn loud-speakers of this period employed a drive unit with an electro-magnet and metal diaphragm, which was little more than an enlarged headphone earpiece whose sound was amplified somewhat by a horn.

In 1924, the first significant general advance in loud-speaker technology and design occurred with the introduction of the first commercial 'hornless' type: the Sterling Primax which had a radially-pleated paper diaphragm driven by a moving-iron unit. In the same year, the first moving-iron 'cone' type appeared. This was the Beco, a small loud-speaker which employed a cone-shaped aluminium foil diaphragm. In the following year, moving-iron cone loud-speakers with paper or taut linen diaphragms were first produced (several housed in stylish wooden cabinets to harmonise better with domestic surroundings), and this type soon took over from conventional horn loud-speakers. At the other end of the 'tasteful' scale in 1925, a crude and unattractive range of horn loud-speakers was brought out by Scientific Supply Stores using papier-mache

horns, and while by 1927, the popularity of horn loud-speakers had drastically wained, brief interest was aroused by new 'novelty' loud-speakers, notably the Andia range, disguised as ornaments and employing horn drive units.

The first moving-coil cone loud-speaker had been introduced by B.T.H. in 1926 and although initially expensive and cumbersome, towards the end of the 1920s, several manufacturers were offering cheap and compact high quality moving-coil cone loud-speakers which by the early 1930s had superseded the moving-iron cone type, and had become an industry standard.

The 1920s was indeed a 'Golden Age' for loud-speakers, for the decade had seen a great many changes in both their technology and style, and as separate units they had been at the height of their popularity. From the early 1930s, loud-speakers were generally enclosed within the wireless cabinet making the wireless set a singular and complete unit and there seemed little need for a separate loud-speaker. However, a demand for having wireless entertainment in other rooms, such as the kitchen, study or playroom, away from where the 'house' set was installed soon gave rise to the loud-speaker's use as an 'extension speaker'. This idea remained generally popular until the 'second set' market got off the ground after 1946, where small compact sets of the mains transportable class did the job of an extension speaker, but provided in addition, a choice of programme listening. By the time cheap mass-produced portable transistor radios appeared in the early 1960s, which could be carried about to anywhere where radio entertainment was needed, the idea of extension speakers had generally gone out of favour. It is a different story today, of course, for as part of sophisticated stereo hi-fi set ups, separate loud-speakers are once again in vogue.

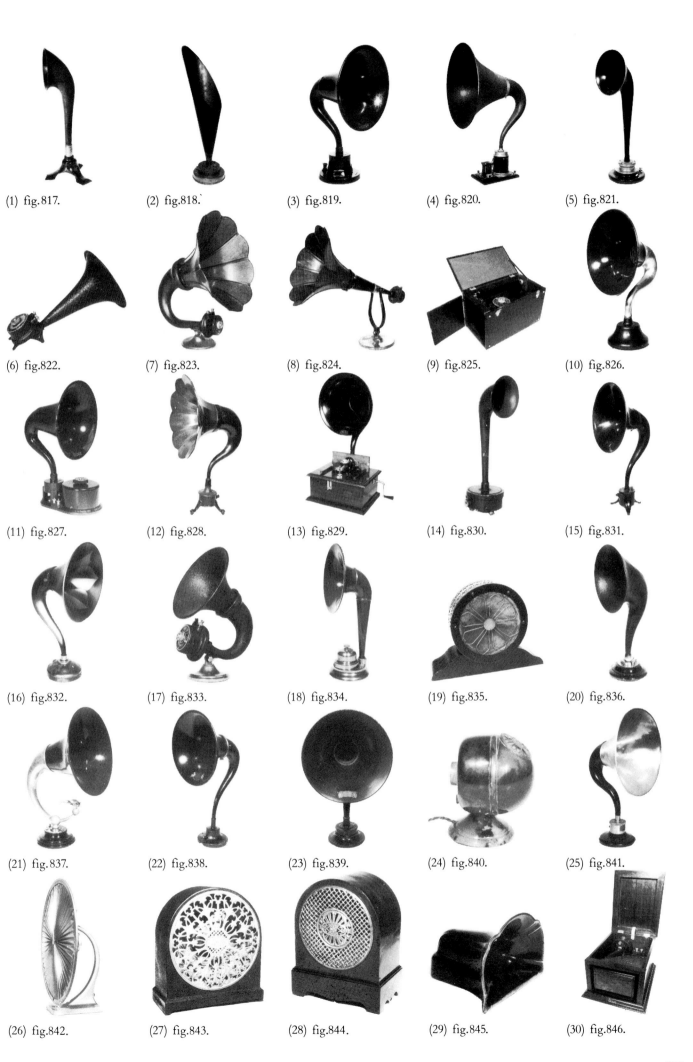

(1) fig.817.　　(2) fig.818.　　(3) fig.819.　　(4) fig.820.　　(5) fig.821.

(6) fig.822.　　(7) fig.823.　　(8) fig.824.　　(9) fig.825.　　(10) fig.826.

(11) fig.827.　　(12) fig.828.　　(13) fig.829.　　(14) fig.830.　　(15) fig.831.

(16) fig.832.　　(17) fig.833.　　(18) fig.834.　　(19) fig.835.　　(20) fig.836.

(21) fig.837.　　(22) fig.838.　　(23) fig.839.　　(24) fig.840.　　(25) fig.841.

(26) fig.842.　　(27) fig.843.　　(28) fig.844.　　(29) fig.845.　　(30) fig.846.

(31) fig.847.　　(32) fig.848.　　(33) fig.849.　　(34) fig.850.　　(35) fig.851.

(36) fig.852.　　(37) fig.853.　　(38) fig.854.　　(39) fig.855.　　(40) fig.856.

(41) fig.857.　　(42) fig.858.　　(43) fig.859.　　(44) fig.860.　　(45) fig.861.

(46) fig.862.　　(47) fig.863.　　(48) fig.864.　　(49) fig.865.　　(50) fig.866.

(51) fig.867.　　(52) fig.868.　　(53) fig.869.　　(54) fig.870.　　(55) fig.871.

(56) fig.872.　　(57) fig.873.　　(58) fig.874.　　(59) fig.875.　　(60) fig.876.

(61) fig.877. (62) fig.878. (63) fig.879. (64) fig.880. (65) fig.881.

(66) fig.882. (67) fig.883. (68) fig.884. (69) fig.885. (70) fig.886.

(71) fig.887. (72) fig.888. (73) fig.889. (74) fig.890. (75) fig.891.

(76) fig.892. (77) fig.893. (78) fig.894. (79) fig.895. (80) fig.896.

(81) fig.897. (82) fig.898. (83) fig.899. (84) fig.900. (85) fig.901.

(86) fig.902. (87) fig.903. (88) fig.904. (89) fig.905. (90) fig.906.

LOUD-SPEAKER CAPTIONS

1922

(1) fig.817. Horn Loud-Speaker by Western Electric Co. Ltd. 1922. Black-enamelled cast metal base, curved-necked 'non-resonant' black ebonite horn. 17½ in. high, 5¼ in. diameter flare.

(2) fig.818. Brown H1, 'Loud-speaking Telephone', by S.G. Brown Ltd. 1922. BBC/PMG stamp of approval. 120 ohm drive unit. Magnetic-reed type moving-iron horn loud-speaker, brass fittings, straight-necked ebonite horn, mahogany and cast metal base. 22 in. high. Could be used free standing, or mounted on the wall. The H1 originally came out in 1920, and one of these early models with its drive unit connected to a gramophone horn, was used on board the passenger liner *Victorian* in July of that year to monitor long-distance telephony broadcasts from Chelmsford (see 1920).

(3) fig.819. Brown H2, by S.G. Brown Ltd. 1922. BBC/PMG stamp of approval. 4,000 ohm drive unit. Black-enamelled metal horn loud-speaker. 12 in. high, 7½ in. diameter flare. £3.2s.6d.

(4) fig.820. Model R2B, by Magnavox, Oakland, California, U.S.A. Autumn 1922. Marketed in Great Britain by Sterling Telephone & Electric Co. Ltd. A moving-coil DC energised horn loud-speaker, mounted on a wooden board with a step-down induction coil. Swan-necked metal horn painted in a crystalline finish to reduce the 'tinny' sound experienced with smooth-painted metal loud-speakers. 31 ½ in. high, 18 in. dia flare.

(5) fig.821. T.M.C. 'Junior', by Telephone Manufacturing Co. 1922. BBC/PMG stamp of approval. Black-enamelled electro-deposited copper horn with curved neck, nickel-plated drive unit, wood base. 18 in. high, 6¼ in. diameter flare. £2.17s.6d.

1923

(6) fig.822. Amplion 'Junior', Type AR 39, by Graham Amplion Ltd. 1923. A table model metal horn loud-speaker with a black crystalline finish. 13 in. long, 8 in. diameter flare. £2.12s.6d.

(7) fig.823. Amplion Type AR 19, 'Standard Dragon', by Graham Amplion Ltd. 1923. Horn loud-speaker with cast metal neck, sectioned oak petal-design flare held together with metal ribs, 2,000 ohm drive unit, nickel-plated weighted brass base. 21 in. high, 14¾ in. diameter flare. £5.5s.0d. Also available with mahogany flare. Type AR 17 has 120 ohm drive unit.

(8) fig.824. Amplion 'Table Model Dragon', by Graham Amplion Ltd. 1923. Horn loud-speaker with metal neck, sectioned oak petal-design flare, black-enamelled stand and nickel-plated brass base. 24 in. long, 14 in. diameter flare.

(9) fig.825. Amplion Type AR 61, by Graham Amplion Ltd. 1923. BBC/PMG stamp of approval. A portable folded horn loud-speaker with wood flare housed in a black rexine-covered wooden case, came complete with folded camera-type tripod stand. 8 in. x 13 in. x 8 in. £6.6s.0d.

(10) fig.826. B.T.H. Type C2, by British Thomson-Houston Co. Ltd. 1923. Aluminium swan-neck, brown-painted aluminium flare, brown Bakelite base and drive unit. 23 in. high, 14 in. diameter flare. £5.5s.0d. Over one million were sold and they were still being advertised in 1930.

(11) fig.827. Brown 'Crystavox', by S.G. Brown Ltd. 1923. Brown-enamelled cast metal neck, spun flare 13 in. dia. £6.15s.0d + 5s.0d B.B.C. royalty. Combined horn loud-speaker and microphone amplifier for crystal set use.

(12) fig.828. Burndept 'Ethovox', Type 750, by Burndept Ltd. 1923. Sectioned mahogany petal-design flare, black-enamelled metal swan-neck, cast metal base and stand. 25 in. high, 14½ in. diameter flare.

(13) fig.829. 'Frenophone', by S.G. Brown Ltd. 1923. Nickel-plated fittings, black-enamelled metal horn, mahogany cabinet. 25 in. x 13¼ in. x 10¼ in. (Cover removed in photograph). A mechanical loud-speaker/amplifier primarily designed for use with crystal sets. The amplifying action depended on the friction between a revolving glass disc (driven by a 70 rpm clockwork gramophone motor) and a thin pad of cork: the pressure of the pad varied through a reed connected to the armature of an S.G. Brown Type 'A' headphone earpiece. The vibrations of the armature were magnified by the power in the friction drive and were applied to a horn-loaded diaphragm connected to the cork pad.

(14) fig.830. Miniature loud-speaker by Telephone Manufacturing Co. 1923. Curved-necked electro-formed copper horn, brass base, brown-enamelled finish. 6¾ in. high. Believed to have been produced as an advertising novelty.

(15) fig.831. Sterling 'Audivox', Type R1284, by Sterling Telephone & Electric Co. Ltd. 1923. BBC/PMG stamp of approval, black-enamelled swan-necked horn loud-speaker. 26½ in. high, 14 in. diameter flare. £3.10s.0d.

(16) fig.832. Sterling 'Baby', by Sterling Telephone & Electric Co. Ltd. 1923. All-metal horn loud-speaker, black enamel with sprayed leaf decoration in antique gold, sensitivity control lever on base. 18 in. high, 14 in. diameter flare. £3.0s.0d. Also came in four other versions: plain brown enamel, plain black enamel (both price £2.15s.0d), brown enamel with sprayed leaf decoration in antique gold (price £2.17s.6d) and matt black with Chinese figures and designs (price £4.15s.0d).

1924

(17) fig.833. Amplion 'Dragonfly', Type AR 102, by Alfred Graham & Co. 1924. Cast metal horn loud-speaker, 2,000 ohm drive unit, spun aluminium flare, black crystalline enamel finish. 9 in. high, 5½ in. diameter flare. £1.5s.0d. Type AR 101 has 120 ohm drive unit.

(18) fig.834. B.T.H. 'Loud Speaking Telephone', Type 'D', Form 'C', by British Thomson-Houston Co. Ltd. 1924. Cast metal base, brown-enamelled metal horn. 18 in. high, 9¼ in. diameter flare. £3.0s.0d.

(19) fig.835. 'Beco', by British Electric Manufacturing Co. Ltd. September 1924. Magnetic-reed type moving-iron loud-speaker, aluminium foil cone, pierced nickel-plated surround, black-painted wooden plinth. 5¼ in. dia x 2 in. deep. (Also anodised silver, copper and gold-plated versions). The first British commercial moving-iron cone loud-speaker. Marketed from the end of January 1925 by British Electrical Sales Organisation, London WC2 and for a short time from April 1925, by E.E. Rosen & Co., 158-160 City Road, London EC as the 'Ultra', minus its black-painted wooden plinth. In January 1926, a new 'Beco-de-Luxe' version appeared enclosed in an oak or mahogany cabinet. The 'Beco' was also used in two commercial all-enclosed battery receivers. In February 1926 it was screwed bodily to the inside lid of the Rolls suitcase portable (which originally came without an integral loud-speaker) and was then sold as an 'all-enclosed' receiver, and in 1927, it was fitted, minus its plinth, into the General Radio 3-valve receiver (fig.223).

(20) fig.836. Brandes 'Table Talker', by Brandes Ltd. 1924. Compressed wood-pulp horn with black crystalline finish, turned wood base. 25 in. high, 12¼ in. diameter base. £2.2s.0d.

(21) fig.837. Brown Type 'Q', by S.G. Brown Ltd. 1924. 4,000 ohm drive unit, mahogany flare and turned mahogany base, aluminium neck, nickel-plated base fitting, silver-plated bird ornament. 23 in. high, 14 in. diameter flare. £15.15s.0d. (Similar Model HQ came out in 1925).

(22) fig.838. Fellows 'Junior', by Fellows Magneto Co. Ltd. 1924. Cast metal base and swan neck, spun aluminium flare, black enamel finish. 18¾ in. high, 9¾ in. diameter flare. £1.17s.6d.

(23) fig.839. Fellows 'Volutone', by Fellows Magneto Co. Ltd. 1924. Cast aluminium base and neck, spun aluminium flare. 20 in. high, 12 diameter flare. £4.10s.0d.

(24) fig.840. 'Magnora', by E. Pack. 1924. Miniature loud-speaker in simulated tortoiseshell case, earphone-type drive unit, brass grille. 3½ in. high, 2½ in. diameter.

(25) fig.841. 'Rola', horn loud-speaker made in U.S.A. but sold on British market. Heavy cast metal base and light aluminium flare. 23 in. high, 14 in. diameter flare.

(26) fig.842. Sterling 'Primax', by Sterling Telephone & Electric Co. Ltd. 1924. Magnetic-reed type, moving-iron loud-speaker, gold-

painted Lumiere paper diaphragm, cast aluminium frame and stand. Licensed by The Gramophone Co. Ltd. £7.7s.0d. (Also bronze-painted 'Statuette' version, price £20.0s.0d, 42 in. high).

1925

(27) fig.843. Amplion 'Radiolux' Model RS1, by Alfred Graham & Co. 1925. Folded metal horn loud-speaker with drive unit screwed under base, black crystalline-finish steel case, gold-enamelled fret. 16¼ in. x 14¾ in. x 6 1/2 in.

(28) fig.844. Amplion 'Radiolux' Model RS2M, by Alfred Graham & Co. 1925. Folded metal horn loud-speaker with drive unit screwed under base, crystalline enamel metal grille finished in antique silver, solid and veneered mahogany case 13¾ in. x 11 in. x 6¾ in. £4.15s.0d.

(29) fig.845. Bristol 'Auditorium, True-Tone Reproducer', by Pountney & Co. 1925. Made in slip-cast black glazed earthenware with gold lustre decoration, Brandes drive unit. Flare, 11 in. wide x 6½ in. high.

(30) fig.846. Brown 'Cabinet Loud Speaker', by S.G. Brown Ltd. 1925. Folded metal horn enclosed in a solid mahogany cabinet with lift-up lid. 8¼ in. x 11¼ in. x 13¼ in. £6.6s.0d.

(31) fig.847. Brown Type H4, by S.G. Brown Ltd. 1925. Cast metal body with spun flare, brown-enamelled finish. 10¼ in. high, 7 in. diameter flare. £1.10s.0d. Similar to larger model, Type H3, produced in same year.

(32) fig.848. 'Bullphone Nightingale', by W. Bullen. 1925. All-metal horn loud-speaker with flare in simulated woodgrain finish, brown Bakelite drive unit case. 21 in. high, 13 3/4 diameter flare. £2.17s.6d.

(33) fig.849. Celestion Model A1, by Electrical Manufacturing & Plating Co. Ltd. February 1925. Moving-iron cone loud-speaker, solid and veneered oak case. 18 in. x 19¼ in. x 8½ in. £6.10s.0d. The paper cone is stiffened on one side by a spiral and on the other by radii of finely split bamboo. (Also mahogany and walnut cabinet versions).

(34) fig.850. 'Gryphon', by Scientific Supplies Stores. 1925. Papier-mache horn with dog's head stand in "roughened old bronze-finish". Purchaser fitted own drive unit. 25 in. high, 12 in. diameter flare.

(35) fig.851. Loud-speaker, c.1925, using a natural conch shell as the horn, decorated with transfers and mounted on a turned wood base, 'Magniphone' drive unit. 13 in. high.

(36) fig.852. 'Puravox', folded horn loud-speaker in solid and veneered mahogany case. 12½ in. x 13¼ in. x 8 in.

(37) fig.853. 'Scientific', by Scientific Supply Stores. 1925. Papier-mache horn loud-speaker with gold highlights. Purchaser fitted own drive unit. 23½ in. high, 14 in. diameter flare.

(38) fig.854. 'Tameside', by Hirst Bros & Co. Ltd. 1925. A combined horn loud-speaker and plant stand. Polished solid oak pedestal, oak horn, Sterling drive unit, metal base. 40 in. high, top 15 in. x 15 in.

(39) fig.855. Western Electric 'Kone', by Western Electric Co. Ltd. October 1st 1925. Balanced armature double cone loud-speaker, cast metal stand, gold-painted paper cone. 17 in. dia. £6.6s.0d. One of the first hornless loud-speakers (Patented on 9/8/24). Double cone produced "non-directional, stereoscopic effects with sound appearing to emanate from various points".

1926

(40) fig.856. Amplion 'Cabinette', Type A114, by Alfred Graham & Co. Ltd. 1926. Horn loud-speaker housed in an oak cabinet, drive unit in Bakelite case. 6 in. x 16½ in. x 6 in. £3.3s.0d. (Also mahogany version price £3.15s.0d).

(41) fig.857. 'Beco Rose Bowl', by British Electric Sales Organisation. 1926. Magnetic reed-type moving-iron loud-speaker, aluminium foil cone, built into an electro-plated nickel-silver rose bowl. 10 in. diameter, 7 in. high. £5.5s.0d. Available in a variety of finishes

including oxydised silver and antique bronze.

(42) fig.858. The 'Beco Rose Bowl' could be filled with water and flowers without harming the loud-speaker.

(43) fig.859. Brandes 'Ellipticon', by Brandes Ltd. 1926. Moving-iron cone loud-speaker, walnut stained birch plywood case. 12½ in. x 10½ in. x 6½ in. £5.10s.0d.

(44) fig.860. 'Donotone', by Donotone (Regd.) Loud-Speakers. 1926. A highly unusual and eccentric loud-speaker in which a moving-iron unit drove a free-edge cone of varnished silk reinforced with cane ribs. Mounted co-axially behind the main cone was a series of smaller cones and in front, around the mouth of the sound chamber, was a series of metal baffles. Between each pair of baffles was fitted a spiral steel spring, free at one end, which was supposed to vibrate in sympathy with the reproduced sound. Mahogany case. 12 in. diameter, 11 in. deep. Baseboard 18 in. x 12½ in. (Also came mounted on an adjustable stand).

(45) fig.861. Gecophone BC 1642, Model 'B', by General Electric Co. Ltd. 1926. Folded horn loud-speaker in oak cabinet. 10 in. x 16 in. x 8½ in. £4.4s.0d.

(46) fig.862. Gecophone BC 1650, by General Electric Co. Ltd. 1926. Metal base and frame with antique coin-bronze finish, directional grain-embossed paper cone. 21 in. high x 16 in. diameter. £6.6s.0d.

(47) fig.863. 'Graves', by J.G. Graves. 1926. Metal horn loud-speaker in dull simulated woodgrain finish. 19 in. high, 13 in. diameter flare. Included in the Graves 'Vulcan' 2-valve receiver outfit (fig.197).

(48) fig.864. 'Priory', Type 'D', by Priory Loudspeaker Co. 1926. Brown moulded ebonite horn loud-speaker. 14 in. diameter flare. £3.15s.0d.

(49) fig.865. 'Radioglobe', by Radiophon Co. 1926. A black painted metal horn loud-speaker with a wood base, made in Germany for the British market and distributed by Anderson's Wireless of London. 26 in. high, 14 in. diameter flare.

(50) fig.866. Revo 'Orchestrian', by Cable Accessories Co. Ltd. 1926. Folded metal horn loud-speaker in mahogany cabinet. 14 in. x 14 in. x 8 in. £5.0s.0d.

1927

(51) fig.867. Blue Spot 'Salon Concert Junior', by F.A. Hughes & Co. Ltd. Grey moulded artificial marble ebonite body ('Marbloid'), black-painted 'non-resonant' plaster horn, Amplion drive unit. 11 in. x 8 in. x 4½ in. £3.15s.0d. (Also 'Senior' Model at £5.10s.0d).

(52) fig.868. Andia 'Chinese Scribe', by Artandia Ltd. 1927. Amplion drive unit, small internal cardboard horn, separate black-painted wooden plinth and feet, painted papier-mache ('Durandia') figure with brown, dark blue, gold and ivory finish. 13 in. high. £6.0s.0d. (Also version with integral papier-mache base, fig.869). Artandia Ltd. also produced several other loud-speakers in Durandia, a papier-mache compound, including 'Mother Hubbard's Cottage', 'Fairy House', 'Coffer' (fig.870) and 'Dresden Figure' (fig.871).

(53) fig.869. Andia 'Chinese Scribe', by Artandia Ltd. 1927. As fig.868, but with integral papier-mache base.

(54) fig.870. 'Andia Coffer', by Artandia Ltd. 1927. Amplion drive unit, small internal cardboard horn, anodised brass carrying handle, bronze-painted papier-mache ('Durandia') cabinet. 9½ in. x 11 in. x 8¼ in. £5.0s.0d.

(55) fig.871. Andia 'Dresden Figure', by Artandia Ltd. 1927. Amplion drive unit, small internal cardboard horn, painted papier-mache ('Durandia') figure. 13½ in. high. £6.0s.0d.

(56) fig.872. Andia 'Miss Muffet', by Artandia Ltd. 1927. Painted papier-mache ('Durandia') figure with an Amplion drive unit. 13 in. high. £4.0s.0d.

(57) fig.873. Andia 'Parrot', by Doulton & Co. for Artandia Ltd. 1927. Torquoise glazed slip-cast white earthenware body on an ormalu plinth, Amplion drive unit. 14½ in. high, base 11½ in. wide. £10.0s.0d. (Also multi-coloured glazed version with integral earthenware base).

(58) fig.874. Andia 'Persian King', by Doulton & Co. for Artandia Ltd. 1927. Green jade glazed slip-cast white earthenware, Amplion

drive unit. 12½ in. high, base 10½ in. wide. (Also coloured table lamp version with the King sitting on a gold and black plinth/table below lampshade).

(59) fig.875. Celestion Model C10, by The Celestion Radio Co. Ltd. 1927. Moving-iron cone loud-speaker, solid and veneered mahogany cabinet. 12 in. x 12 in. x 5¼ in. £5.5s.0d.

(60) fig.876. Gecophone Model BC 1680, by General Electric Co. Ltd. 1927. A moving-iron paper cone loud-speaker in the form of a firescreen, mahogany surround. 33 in. x 24 in. Breadth of feet 9½ in. £6.6s.0d. Plate on back reads "Licensed under Lektophone Patents 16,602 July 14th 1913, 178,862 April 23rd 1921".

(61) fig.877. Marconiphone Model 75, by Marconiphone Co. Ltd. 1927. Moving-iron cone loud-speaker, antique bronze metal grille, walnut veneered baffle, cast metal base. 18 in. diameter. £3.15s.0d. (Baffle version of Model 105).

(62) fig.878. Marconiphone Model 105, by Marconiphone Co. Ltd. 1927. Moving-iron cone loud-speaker, antique bronze metal grille, walnut veneered plywood cabinet. 16 in. x 14½ in. x 5 in. £5.5s.0d. (Cabinet version of Model 75).

(63) fig.879. Mullard 'Pure Music', Model 'E', by Mullard Wireless Service Co. Ltd. 1927. Moving-iron paper cone loud-speaker, brown Bakelite bowl and cast metal base. 19 in. high x 18 in. diameter. £6.6s.0d. Similar to Philips Model 2007 of 1928.

(64) fig.880. 'Sphinx', by S.G. Brown Ltd. 1927. Moving-iron cone loud-speaker housed in a mahogany case. 16½ in. x 17 in. x 6 ½ in. £12.10s.0d.

(65) fig.881. Sterling Model 33, by Sterling Telephone & Electric Co. Ltd. 1927. Simulated woodgrain ebonite horn, cast metal stand. 20 in. high, 12½ in. diameter flare. £5.5s.0d.

(66) fig.882. 'Walbro', by Walker Brothers. 1927. Base, neck and flare made entirely of mahogany, S.G. Brown reed-type drive unit. 20¼ in. high, 13¼ in. diameter flare. £6.6s.0d. (Also 'Senior' Model, with 20 in. diameter flare).

1928

(67) fig.883. B.T.H. Type 'E', Form 'B', by British Thomson-Houston Co. Ltd. 1928. Moving-iron cone loud-speaker, moulded brown Bakelite body. 15 in. high x 13 in. dia. £3.0s.0d. The Type 'E' cone loud-speaker originally appeared in August 1925 with a chromium-plated body.

(68) fig.884. Edison Bell 'Cone', by Edison Bell Ltd. 1928. Moving-iron loud-speaker, black painted double paper cone with Chinese-style floral motifs, nickel-plated bell shaped stand. 17 in. diameter, 14 in. wide.

(69) fig.885. Mullard Type 'H', by Mullard Wireless Service Co. Ltd. 1928. Moving-iron paper cone loud-speaker, brown Bakelite moulding. 17 in. diameter. £6.6s.0d.

(70) fig.886. 'Ormond', by Ormond Engineering Co. Ltd. 1928. Moving-iron paper cone loud-speaker housed in an oak case with sunrise and tree design grille. 12½ in. x 12½ in. x 6 1/2 in.

(71) fig.887. Pye 'Junior', by W.G. Pye & Co. 1928. Moving-iron cone loud-speaker in a solid mahogany cabinet (also in oak or walnut). 14¾ in. x 13½ in. x 9 in. £4.10s.0d. (Also 'Senior' version).

(72) fig.888. 'Teefag' Type 1257, distributed by Telephone Berliner (London) Ltd. 1928. Magnetic-reed type cone loud-speaker made in Germany for the English market, metal base and surround. 17 in. high, 14 in. diameter.

1929

(73) fig.889. 'Beverley' No.3, by Barnstaple Loudspeaker Co. 1929. Moving-iron cone loud-speaker housed in an oak cabinet with tree design grille. 14½ in. x 14½ in. 9 1/2 in.

(74) fig.890. Gecophone Type BC 1792, by General Electric Co. Ltd. 1929. Moving-iron paper cone loud-speaker housed in an oak case with stork design grille. 14 in. x 16 in. x 11 in. £3.15s.0d. (Mahogany version price £4.0s.0d).

(75) fig.891. Marconiphone 'Octagon', Type B1281, by Marconiphone Co. Ltd. 1929. Moving-iron cone loud-speaker, walnut veneered plywood baffle and floral grille on bent-iron

supports, brown ebonite drive unit case. 14½ in. high. £1.19s.6d.

(76) fig.892. Ormond moving-iron paper cone loud-speaker by Ormond Engineering Co. Ltd. 1929. Housed in an oak veneered cabinet with rising sun design grille. 12 in. x 12 in. x 6½ in. £1.9s.6d. (Also mahogany version).

(77) fig.893. Philips Type 2013, by Philips Lamps Ltd. 1929. Floor standing moving-coil loud-speaker housed in a mottled black and gold Bakelite case on a metal stand. 29 in. high. £15.15s.0d. For use with Philips Model 2511 (fig.263). Case also supplied in other mottled colours including red and mauve.

(78) fig.894. Whiteley Model WB, by Whiteley, Boneham & Co. Ltd. 1929. Moving-iron cone loud-speaker in brown moulded Bakelite case. 11½ in. x 12 in. x 3½ in. £2.2s.0d.

1930

(79) fig.895. 'Blue Spot' moving-iron cone loud-speaker by British Blue Spot Co. Ltd. c.1930. Oak plywood cabinet. 13¼ in. x 13 ½ in. x 6 1/2 in.

(80) fig.896. Ferranti permanent magnet moving-coil loud-speaker by Ferranti Ltd. 1930. Solid and veneered walnut cabinet. 18 in. x 18½ in. x 13 1/2 in.

(81) fig.897. Gecophone Type BC 1855, by General Electric Co. Ltd. 1930. An inductor dynamic loud-speaker in a solid and veneered walnut cabinet, with brown Bakelite grille decoration, licensed under the Farrand patent. 15½ in. x 16 in. x 8¼ in. £5.10s.0d.

(82) fig.898. H.M.V. 'Super Power', Model 174, by The Gramophone Co. Ltd. 1930. Moving-coil loud-speaker in a mahogany veneered cabinet. 12¼ in. x 17 1/2 in x 8½ in. This company's first offering to the Wireless Industry.

(83) fig.899. 'Skylark', Type OK, by Sheffield Magnet Co. 1930. Magnetic-reed paper cone loud-speaker housed in a brown Bakelite cabinet. 10¾ in. x 10½ in. x 4 in.

(84) fig.900. Ultra 'Air-Chrome', Model U99, by Ultra Electric Ltd. 1930. Moving-iron linen cone loud-speaker in solid mahogany cabinet. 16 in. x 17 in. x 7 in.

1933

(85) fig.901. Amplion 'Lion', by Amplion (1932) Ltd. 1933. Moving-coil extension loud-speaker housed in a walnut veneered cabinet with multi-impedance tappings. 12½ in. x 16 in. x 7 in.

(86) fig.902. 'Camco' extension loud-speaker cabinet, by Carrington Manufacturing Co. Ltd. 1933. Oak veneered plywood. 14 in. x 13 in. x 7¼ in. Purchaser fitted own moving-coil loud-speaker.

(87) fig.903. Ericsson permanent magnet moving-coil extension loud-speaker, by Ericsson Telephones Ltd. c.1933. Solid walnut cabinet with inlay. 20 in. high, 22½ in. wide. This originally had a grille cloth: the expanded metal grille was added after 1936.

1934

(88) fig.904. 'Fydelitone Minor', by Baker Selhurst Radio Ltd. 1934. Moving-coil extension loud-speaker in brown moulded Bakelite case, cast iron back and chassis. 8 in. x 8¼ in. x 4 in. £1.15s.0d.

1947

(89) fig.905. Vidor Model CN 368, by Vidor Ltd. September 1947. Triangular moving-coil corner extension loud-speaker, birch plywood. 19½ in. high. £4.12s.6d.

1948

(90) fig.906. Truvox Model BX55, by Truvox Engineering Co. Ltd. 1948. Miniature moving-coil extension loud-speaker in a bent birch-ply cabinet, chrome grille-guards. 7½ in. x 8 in. x 5 in. £3.5s.0d.

SUNRISE TO SUNSET

1927 Model 25

1928 Model 275

1929 Model 25C

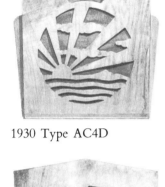

1930 Type AC4D

1930 Type B4D

The rising sun motif was one of the most enduring and evocative of all wireless symbols. Although used by other manufacturers, it was originally adopted by W.G. Pye & Co. of Cambridge from a design their Sales Manager had seen on a colleague's cigarette case and was first introduced as the fret design on Pye loud-speakers and wireless cabinets in 1927. It continued to be widely used by the company until after the Second World War when it made a final, brief and ignominious appearance in 1948. Then, for the first time, with Model M78F, the motif was used without its clouds. Unfortunately, this caused it to resemble too closely the national flag of Japan, then Britain's recent hated enemy, and following a public outcry the set was withdrawn with only a small number having been sold, and the rising sun of the wireless fret set for ever.

1931 Model MM

1931 Model Q

1933 Model O

1932 Model K

1932 Model S

1933 Model E

1932 Model G

1933 Model P

1937 Baby Q

1948 Model M78F

Round Ekcos

Originally designed by the architect Wells Coates, the round Ekco is the most popular wireless cabinet shape of all time. In 1932, Coates won a competition organised by E.K. Cole Ltd. for a new wireless cabinet design using moulded Bakelite, beating those by Serge Chermayeff, Raymond McGrath, Jesse Collins, Misha Black and F.C. Ashwood. Two years later, his winning entry was released in the form of the Model AD 65 and this was the first of five different round Ekco's produced by E.K. Cole Ltd. at their Southend factory between 1934 and 1945 (or 1946 if one counts the post-war re-release of the 1940 AD 75). The standard cabinet colours were all in moulded brown or 'walnut' Bakelite and for around 10s.6d extra most were also available in black with chrome detailing. Various non-standard colours could be specially ordered with the AD 65 and the AD 36 models: Model A22 was shown in green Bakelite at the 1946 Britain Can Make It Exhibition but this 'one-off' exhibition model was the only A22 made in this colour. Today, round Ekco's in non-standard colours are extremely rare. Care should therefore be taken if offered one of these mouldings to ensure that the colour does not lie on the surface as a painted finish, for the colours were added to the Bakelite *before* moulding and as such go right through the cabinet.

1935 AD 76.

1934 AD 65.

1940 AD 75.

1935 AD 36.

1945 A22.

The B.B.C. Stamp & Post Office Registration Scheme

fig.907. (a). Left: BBC/PMG stamp, November 1st 1922 to September 1924. (b). Centre: BBC/EBM stamp, September 1924 to 1927. (c). Right: B.B.C. 'Trademark' stamp, September 1924 to 1927.

November 1st 1922.

The scheme was introduced whereby all commercially manufactured crystal sets, valve receivers and valve amplifiers bought for use under the Broadcast Licence (introduced on the same day) had to be of British manufacture, made by a member firm of the British Broadcasting Company and approved by the Post Master General. All such wireless equipment had to bear the BBC/PMG stamp (fig.907a) together with a G.P.O. registration number.

The letters 'BBC' signified that the equipment was made by a member firm of the British Broadcasting Company and was subject to a royalty payment, although the stamp was not a guarantee of the quality of workmanship.

Before going into production, a sample of each new model had to be sent to the Post Office and tested to see that it did not radiate electrical interference to a neighbouring aerial. In valve receivers, variable reaction was not allowed in the aerial circuit but fixed reaction was as long as it was incapable of causing oscillation. Variable reaction was permitted in subsequent stages if there was no specific coupling between these and the aerial circuit. Only non-radiating sets were approved and these were given their own G.P.O. registration number which had to be displayed on the set together with the embossed or transfer-printed BBC/PMG stamp which was circled with the words 'TYPE APPROVED BY POST MASTER GENERAL'. The approved model was secured with a seal and returned to the manufacturer. During the production run, it had to remain sealed and available for inspection by Post Office officials who had the power to select sets from the production line for comparison with the sealed approved model.

Accessories such as valves, headphones and loud-speakers also had to be of British manufacture and made by a member firm of the B.B.C., and while they were neither tested nor given G.P.O. registration numbers, they did have to bear the BBC/PMG stamp: in the case of valves, this was etched into the glass with hydrofluoric acid applied with a rubber stamp.

October 1st 1923.

Royalties on BBC/PMG-stamped equipment were reduced and were abolished altogether on valves, headphones and loud-speakers. Post Office requirements for broadcast receivers were drastically revised and the testing of sets with regard to reaction interference was abolished. Where any type of reaction was provided, manufacturers were now only responsible for advising the purchaser by label, leaflet or instruction booklet on how to use the set without causing it to oscillate and energise any neighbouring aerials.

Newly designed receivers still had to be submitted to the Post Office for testing and those approved were still given a G.P.O. registration number, but they were now merely given reception tests to see if they were capable of covering the Broadcast Band, now extended by the Sykes Comittee to cover 300 to 500 metres on both a short (30 ft.) and a long (100 ft.) aerial.

Any model which had been approved before October 1st

1923 could now have its seal broken and its circuit modified without the manufacturer having to re-submit it to the Post Office for testing. He simply sent a brief description of the proposed changes (these almost invariably involved the use of variable reaction in the aerial circuit) and when approved, the same G.P.O. registration number was assigned to the modified model.

July 1st 1924.

Royalties on BBC/PMG-stamped equipment were abolished together with the Post Office's testing and registration scheme. Under new regulations, receivers and valve amplifiers used with the Broadcast Licence could now be bought from *any* British manufacture and not solely from one who was a member of the B.B.C. - member firms, however, were still obliged to exhibit the BBC/PMG stamp on their wireless equipment, even though it was no longer submitted to, and had received no approval from, the Post Master General.

September 1924.

For receivers manufactured by member firms of the B.B.C., a second type of B.B.C. stamp appeared, replacing the original BBC/PMG stamp. This new type (known as the 'BBC/EBM' stamp, fig.907b) had the letters 'BBC' encircled with the phrase 'ENTIRELY BRITISH MANUFACTURE' which replaced the redundant phrase 'TYPE APPROVED BY POST MASTER GENERAL'. It was soon joined by a third, but little-used type of stamp without any peripheral wording, which was simply the B.B.C. trademark (fig.907c).

January 1st 1925.

The B.B.C. stamp regulations were abolished, and member firms were no longer obliged to exhibit any kind of B.B.C. stamp on their equipment. However, for prestige purposes and perhaps to show the patriotism of manufacturers, many receivers continued to be produced bearing the BBC/EBM stamp, or, to a lesser extent, the third type of stamp, until as late as 1927.

B.B.C. Royalties

During the first two years of its existence, the British Broadcasting Company's revenue depended quite heavily upon royalties levied on receivers and accessories made by its member manufacturing companies. The royalty was first introduced on November 1st 1922 and was levied on the wholesale price of all BBC/PMG-stamped wireless apparatus until its abolition on July 1st 1924. (Note the reduction in royalty charges from October 1st 1923).

	(1/11/22-30/9/23) Royalty	(1/10/23-1/7/24) Royalty
Crystal Set	7s.6d.	1s.0d.
Microphone Amplifier	7s.6d.	5s.0d.
1-Valve/Crystal Set	£1.7s.6d.	11s.0d.
2-Valve/Crystal Set	£2.2s.6d.	18s.6d.
1-Valve Set	£1.0s.0d.	10s.0d.
2-Valve Set	£1.15s.0d.	17s.6d.
Multi-Valve Set (extra valve)	10s.0d.	5s.0d.
Valve Amplifier (per valve)	10s.0d.	5s.0d.
Valve Itself	3d.	Charge Abolished
Headphones (per earpiece)	3d.	Charge Abolished
Loud-Speaker	3s.0d.	Charge Abolished

Price figures in the central column are from *The Wireless Trader*, page 280, November 1923.

The Wartime Civilian Receiver ("Utility Set")

Popularly known as the Utility Set, the 1944 Wartime Civilian Receiver was designed by Dr. G.D. Reynolds of Murphy Radio Ltd. It was an efficient but very basic, single waveband receiver covering the medium-waves only and its rather austere appearance echoed the fact that it had been designed to be produced with the minimum of raw materials and labour. The dial (fig.910) was calibrated in metres and, patriotically, also marked 'Home' and 'Forces' only (for the Home Service and General Forces Programme), although the single band circuit was quite capable of picking up foreign medium-wave stations including those in Germany.

The steel chassis, housed in a plain pinewood cabinet, appeared in both AC mains (fig.908) and battery (fig.909) versions of a standard Government specified design: a label on top of the cabinet announced that the set had been 'PRODUCED BY THE RADIO INDUSTRY UNDER GOVERNMENT DIRECTION'. It was made by over 40 British manufacturers with only very slight circuit divergencies and stamped on the back of the chassis was the manufacturer's identifying code number, (see list). This enabled retailers and service engineers to know where they should apply for any spare parts that were needed: purchasers received a three month's guarantee against faulty materials and workmanship. The valves supplied with the sets were also coded, with the third figure of the reference number printed on each valve denoting one of seven valve manufacturers to whom claims under the guarantee could be made.

During the twelve months from June 1944, over 175,000 AC mains and 75,000 battery Wartime Civilian Receivers were produced, which went a long way to eradicate the acute national shortage of wireless sets. So many of these receivers were in use throughout the country at the end of the war that there was a popular demand for them to be updated when long-wave broadcasting resumed with the opening on July 29th 1945 of the B.B.C.'s new Light Programme on 1,500 metres. While it is true that the Light Programme was also supplemented in certain areas on 261.1 metres on the medium waveband, reception outside these areas was commonly very poor and here, Wartime Civilian Receiver owners were generally deprived of the B.B.C.'s new programme. However, one solution to the problem was to connect an adaptor to extend the tuning range to cover the Light Programme on 1,500 metres, but commercially-made supplies of these did not become available until November, and meanwhile, service engineers were inundated by requests for made-up ones.

At last, the 'Longwave Adaptor' appeared on the market. It was brought out by Raleigh & Co. Ltd., of Kilburn, in a separate unit form priced at £2.2s.0d, but was made for the AC version only: it was planned to bring out an adaptor for the battery version, but it is not thought that one was ever commercially produced.

In effect, the unit duplicated (in two waveband form) the circuit of the AC Wartime Civilian Receiver up to the first valve. A valve adaptor on the end of a flexible cable was plugged into the first valve holder of the set, and the valve itself transferred to a holder provided in the unit. Tuning was then carried out on a variable condenser in the unit, with the other controls on the set itself being used in the normal manner. Aerial and earth leads were connected to suitable sockets provided on the unit which could be placed on top or alongside the receiver. The components were mounted on a metal chassis housed in a light metal cabinet finished in enamelled copper or gold. The tuning scale was calibrated for the medium and long wavebands which were selected by means of a two-position

fig.908. AC mains model 'Wartime Civilian Receiver'. June 1944. (des: Dr G.D. Reynolds of Murphy Radio Ltd.). A medium-wave only, 3-valve plus rectifier and Westector mains table model superhet housed in a plain pinewood cabinet. 13½ in. x 12 in. x 6½ in. Price £12.3s.4d inc PT.

fig.909. Battery model 'Wartime Civilian Receiver'. June 1944 (des: Dr G.D. Reynolds of Murphy Radio Ltd.). A medium-wave only, 4-valve battery table model receiver housed in a plain pinewood cabinet. 11½ in. x 17¾ in. x 8 in. Price £10.19s.0d inc PT.

wavechange switch mounted below a slow-motion tuning knob.

Closer examination of the chassis of Wartime Civilian Receivers will reveal that the same basic pressing was used for both the battery and the AC models, and this has provision for three spindles although only two of the three holes were used on the AC chassis (the centre hole on the battery version housed the spindle of a ON/OFF switch, but was left vacant on AC models). Soon after the war had ended, at least one manufacturer is known to have used the third unoccupied hole on the AC chassis to hold a wavechange switch when they produced a two waveband version of the AC Wartime Civilian Receiver (fig.912). These have dials printed with medium and long-wave settings in metre wavelengths only (fig.911), and despite being produced for post-war broadcasting conditions, it is believed that few people were tempted to buy them. Certainly, today, they are very rare.

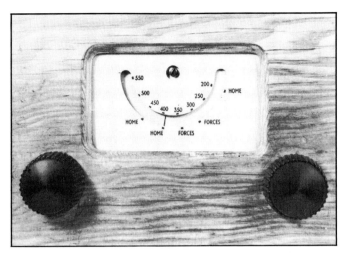

fig.910. Dial of 1944 medium-wave AC mains model 'Wartime Civilian Receiver', marked in metres and "Home" and "Forces". The same dial was used for the battery version.

fig.911. Dial of post-war two waveband version of the AC mains model 'Wartime Civilian Receiver' covering the medium and longwaves, marked in metres only.

fig.912. A post-war two waveband version of the AC mains model 'Wartime Civilian Receiver', released after July 1945. The back of the chassis has not been stamped with the manufacturer's identifying code number.

VALVE CODE NUMBERS

1	Cossor	5	Marconiphone
2	Ediswan	6	Mullard
3	Ferranti	7	S.T.C. (Brimar)
4	G.E.C. (Osram)		

RECEIVER MANUFACTURERS' CODE NUMBERS

U1	Bush Radio Ltd.	U21	Philco Radio & Tv. Corp. Ltd.
U2	E.K. Cole Ltd.	U22	Pilot Radio Ltd.
U3	A.C. Cossor Ltd.	U23	Plessey Co. Ltd.
U4	The Gramophone Co. Ltd.	U24	Regentone Products Ltd.
U4A	Marconiphone Co. Ltd.	U25	R.M. Electric Ltd.
U5	Ferguson Radio Corp. Ltd.	U26	Decca Record Co. Ltd.
U6	General Electric Co. Ltd.	U27	Dulci Co.
U7	Murphy Radio Ltd.	U28	R.N. Fitton Ltd.
U8	Philips Lamps Ltd.	U29	Portadyne Radio Ltd.
U9	Pye Ltd.	U30	Pamphonic Radio Ltd.
U10	Ultra Electric Ltd.	U31	Mains Radio Gramophones Ltd.
U11	A.J. Balcombe Ltd.	U32	Kolster-Brandes Ltd.
U12	Burndept Ltd.	U33	Roberts Radio Co. Ltd.
U12A	Vidor Ltd.	U34	Radio Gramophone Dev. Co. Ltd.
U13	Central Equipment Ltd.	U35	R.S.C. Radio Ltd.
U14	Ferranti Ltd.	U36	Beethoven Electric Equip. Co. Ltd.
U15	Felgate Radio Ltd.	U37	J.G. Graves Ltd.
U16	Hale Electrical Co. Ltd.	U38	Aren Radio & Television Ltd.
U17	Halcyon Radio Ltd.	U39	N.H. Radio Products Ltd.
U18	Invicta Radio Ltd.	U40	Ace Radio Ltd.
U19	Lissen Ltd. (Ever Ready).	U41	Solectric Ltd.
U20	McMichael Radio Ltd.	U42	Whiteley Electrical Co. Ltd.

Note: U41 & U42, battery model only.

Valves of The Broadcast Era, 1922 - 1950s (shown half actual size)

1922
'R' Valve

1923
Gettered DE3

1923
DEV

1923
Wecovalve and base

1923
DER

1923
LS5

1924
Thorpe K4

1925
Nelson Multi

1925
'Pipless' PM4

1926
Rectifier

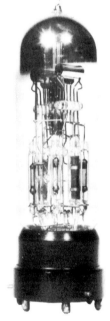

1926
Loewe 2NF

1927
Cosmos AC/G

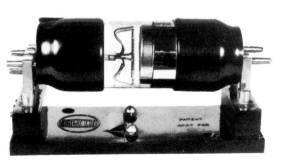

1927
S625 Screened-grid

1928
5-pin Mains Triode

1928
Pentode

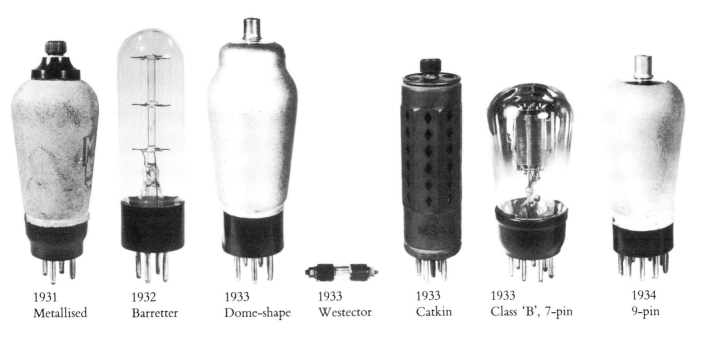

1931	1932	1933	1933	1933	1933	1934
Metallised	Barretter	Dome-shape	Westector	Catkin	Class 'B', 7-pin	9-pin

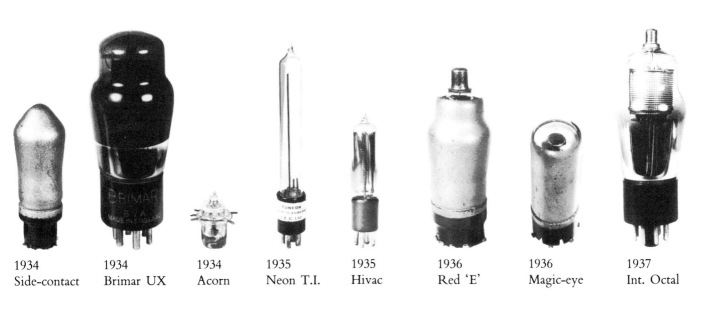

1934	1934	1934	1935	1935	1936	1936	1937
Side-contact	Brimar UX	Acorn	Neon T.I.	Hivac	Red 'E'	Magic-eye	Int. Octal

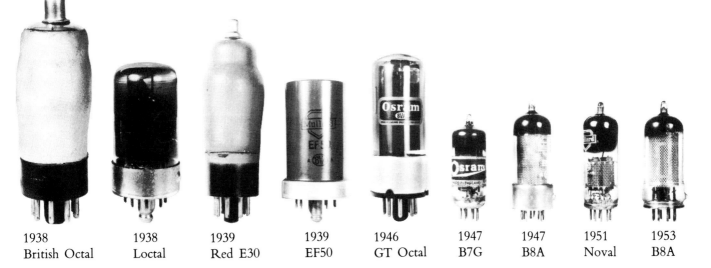

1938	1938	1939	1939	1946	1947	1947	1951	1953
British Octal	Loctal	Red E30	EF50	GT Octal	B7G	B8A	Noval	B8A

List of Important Wireless Exhibitions & Brief Summary of Exhibits (exhibition promoters in brackets)

October 28th 1919.
The first wireless exhibition to be held in Great Britain took place at the A.G.M. of the Wireless Society of London held at the Institution of Civil Engineers, Westminster, London SW1. 200 members and guests attended from many parts of the country. On display were a few amateur-built receivers and transmitters made by various members of the Society and several commercially-made receivers of the Military or other official type - no 'domestic' receivers were included.

January 29th 1920.
The Wireless Society of London's second exhibition. Far fewer pieces of apparatus of a Military or official nature were on show - the accent now was on 'domestic' wireless for amateur home use. (Note that the above two exhibitions were not open to the general public).

January 1922.
The *Model Engineer* Exhibition, Horticultural Hall, Vincent Square, London SW1. Seven wireless manufacturers showed various receiving apparatus and component parts designed solely for amateur use in the home. Leslie McMichael also had a stand at the exhibition but showed almost exclusively ex-Government wireless apparatus.

September 2nd - 8th 1922.
The International Radio Exhibition & Convention, Central Hall, Westminster, London SW1. The first public exhibition solely devoted to wireless - supported by over 40 British and Foreign manufacturers showing complete receivers, units and components.

September 30th - October 7th 1922.
The first All British Wireless Exhibition, Horticultural Hall, Vincent Square, London SW1. (Bertram Day & Co.). Featured 52 British wireless manufacturers - the most representative gathering ever held in this country. Aimed primarily at the requirements of the amateur experimenter and the general public. All the most up-to-date designs of complete valve receivers, crystal sets, amplifiers, headphones, horn loud-speakers, component parts and accessories were on show together with wireless magazines and books from the various publishers. Bright-emitters and sloping panels dominate. Waveband changing by 2-pin plug-in coils with dials calibrated in degrees. Unit-type receivers and home-construction very popular. Listening-in generally with headphones.

March 1st - 24th 1923.
The *Daily Mail* Ideal Home Exhibition, Olympia, London W14. There was a large wireless section (organised by the National Association of Radio Manufacturers - N.A.R.M.) of 42 manufacturers housed in the New Hall Gallery.

March 17th - 24th 1923.
The Manchester All British Wireless Exhibition, Burlington Hall, Burlington Street, Manchester. (Bertram Day & Co.) 30 principal exhibitors, mainly from the Manchester area.

November 8th - 21st 1923.
The second All British Wireless Exhibition, White City, London. (N.A.R.M.). Organised by Bertram Day & Co. with 56 principal exhibitors. Kit sets widely available for the first time, interest beginning in dull-emitters, cabinet design trend towards neatness beginning with valves and coils placed behind control panel on several sets - smoker's cabinet types of receiver popular, increasing use of horn loud-speakers. Slight decline in unit type of set.

September 27th - October 8th 1924.
The Wireless Exhibition, Royal Albert Hall, London.

(N.A.R.M.). 56 principal exhibitors. The first commercial appearance of battery supersonic heterodyne ('superhet') receivers, and hornless types of loud-speaker. Also, crystal sets with long-wave Chelmsford coils, square-law variable condensers, Marconiphone 'Ideal' LF transformer, 'Glazite' wiring, receivers with provision for using either bright or dull-emitters. Increasing use of dull-emitters. Unit type of set, and use of bright-emitters declining.

October 14th - 25th 1924.
The Manchester Wireless Exhibition, City Hall, Deansgate, Manchester. (*Evening Chronicle*). 121 principal exhibitors, mainly from the Manchester area.

September 12th - 23rd 1925.
The Wireless Exhibition, Royal Albert Hall, London. (National Association of Radio Manufacturers and Traders - N.A.R.M.A.T.). 109 principal exhibitors. Adoption of Neutrodyne circuits by several manufacturers. Increased interest in battery superhets. Introduction of the first commercial HT battery eliminator, the first 'pipless' valves and the first receivers calibrated in metres. Also introduction of the first 'mains' designated receivers, although all employed ordinary battery valve circuits supplied from a separate mains unit and some required also an LT battery. The use of crystal sets and the use of headphones begins to decline - many more valve receivers brought out for loud-speaker use, an increasing number of these are the cone type. Interest in outdoor battery portables begins.

October 10th - 16th 1925.
The Wireless Exhibition, Horticultural Hall, Vincent Square, London SW1, with 68 principal exhibitors.

September 4th - 18th 1926.
The first National Radio Exhibition, New Hall Gallery, Olympia, London W14. (N.A.R.M.A.T. and Society of Radio Manufacturers), with 182 principal exhibitors. This annual National Radio Exhibition at Olympia was known as 'Radiolympia' until the venue was changed in 1950. Simplicity of operation becoming important to manufacturers - four new types of tuning control introduced and a few more receivers appear calibrated in metres. Design neatness continues - valves (now dull-emitters) and coils etc. now generally placed behind the control panel. Further decline in crystal sets. Introduction of the first moving-coil cone loud-speaker, and the first AC 'mains' designated TRF receiver with a built-in mains unit supplying HT, LT and grid bias. Outdoor battery portables begin to rise in popularity.

September 24th - October 1st 1927.
The second National Radio Exhibition - Radiolympia. (Radio Manufacturers Association - R.M.A.). 184 principal exhibitors in the New Hall Gallery. Interest in outdoor battery portables rapidly increasing, but interest in battery superhets declines. Home-construction still very popular. Introduction of the first 'all-battery eliminators', the first screened-grid valve, and the first indirectly-heated AC mains valves (which led to the production of true AC mains receivers). Several short-wave only receivers appear on the market coinciding with the opening of the B.B.C.'s new experimental short-wave station (G5SW) at Marconi's Chelmsford Works. 2-pin plug-in coil waveband changing becoming obsolete, waveband-switching taking its place.

September 22nd - 29th 1928.
The third National Radio Exhibition - Radiolympia. (R.M.A.). 184 principal exhibitors in the New Hall Gallery.

Outdoor battery portables, especially the 'suitcase' type at height of popularity. Crystal sets practically disappeared, and interest in battery superhets dormant. Growing interest in AC and DC mains TRF receivers. Horn loud-speakers totally displaced by cone-types. Calibrations in metres feature in a growing number of sets. Baird 30-line Televisors exhibited for the first time.

September 23rd - October 3rd 1929.
The fourth National Radio Exhibition - Radiolympia. (R.M.A.). 185 principal exhibitors in the New Hall Gallery. Introduction of the first 'all-enclosed' AC mains table and transportable models - interest in mains TRF receivers grows, although DC receivers are outnumbered by AC by about 3:1. Bakelite begins to be used as a wireless cabinet material.

September 19th - 27th 1930.
The fifth National Radio Exhibition - Radiolympia. (R.M.A.). 186 principal exhibitors in the New Hall Gallery and the Empire Hall (added in 1929). Tremendous increase in mains TRF receivers and introduction of the first AC mains superhet - Radiolympia hailed as the "beginning of the All-Electric Season". Several manufacturers tending to bring out both AC and DC versions of particular models, although with the foreseeable phasing-out of DC supplies, DC-only sets remain in the minority. Growing use of Bakelite for cabinets. Most dials calibrated in metre wavelengths. First use of cord-driven cursor. Interest in outdoor battery portables drastically declines. Inductor-dynamic cone loud-speakers introduced and a gradual rise in the number of moving-coil types.

September 18th - 26th 1931.
The sixth National Radio Exhibition - Radiolympia. (R.M.A.). 210 principal exhibitors in the National and Empire Halls. Growing interest in AC mains superhets, although these are seen as an expensive luxury. In general, the all-enclosed class of TRF receiver with a moving-coil loud-speaker and a ganged tuning condenser dominates. DC mains valves introduced, leading to the first true DC mains receivers. Cone loud-speakers in decline. First 'midget' sets appear. First receiver with a dial printed with a full range of station names in addition to wavelengths appears. Design of cabinet begins to become very important to manufacturers, loud-speaker fret motifs now a feature of most cabinets.

August 19th - 27th 1932.
The seventh National Radio Exhibition - Radiolympia (R.M.A.). 241 principal exhibitors in the Grand and National Halls. First 'AC/DC' ('universal') receivers introduced. New receivers without an integral loud-speaker now rare. Interest in outdoor portables slight. Increase in dials printed with station names and wavelengths.

August 15th - 24th 1933.
The eighth National Radio Exhibition - Radiolympia. (R.M.A.). 210 principal exhibitors in the Grand and National Halls. Introduction of Class 'B' valves coupled with dramatic increase in battery receivers. Horizontal wooden cabinets popular with manufacturers. Mains superhets now take over from the larger class of mains TRF. Moving-coil loud-speaker now widespread.

August 16th - 25th 1934.
The ninth National Radio Exhibition - Radiolympia. (R.M.A.). 190 principal exhibitors in the Grand and National Halls. Several mains receivers with visual tuning indicators on the market and plain loud-speaker openings popular in receiver design. Notable decline in TRFs - 2-band AC superhets shown on practically every stand, AC/DC superhets becoming popular and displacing DC-only receivers. Most receivers generally with dials printed in station names and wavelengths. 'Clock-face' and 'aeroplane' dials first introduced.

August 14th - 24th 1935.
The tenth National Radio Exhibition - Radiolympia. (R.M.A.). 172 principal exhibitors in the Grand and National Halls. Having taken over completely from mains TRFs, AC superhets now dominate the market, and among these all-wave models increasingly popular. Crystal sets begin to make a small comeback as 'stand-by' receivers. Introduction of single-knob (or mono-knob) tuning by Decca.

August 26th - September 5th 1936.
The eleventh National Radio Exhibition - Radiolympia. (R.M.A.). 150 principal exhibitors in the Grand and National Halls. High-definition television demonstrated publicly for the first time anticipating the opening of the B.B.C.'s London area television service from Alexandra Palace on November 2nd - several wireless manufacturers begin to produce television sets. All-wave AC superhets become standard production of the Wireless Industry, very few DC-only receivers on show. Magic-eye tuning indicators introduced.

August 25th - September 4th 1937.
The twelfth National Radio Exhibition - Radiolympia. (R.M.A.). All-wave AC superhets continue to dominate. Tuning dials larger, clearer and easier to read than before. International ('American') octal valves introduced. Television attracting wide interest at the Exhibition.

August 24th - September 3rd 1938.
The thirteenth National Radio Exhibition - Radiolympia. (R.M.A.). British Octals introduced. Push-button and automatic-selective tuning devices exhibited on many receivers. Television continues to attract wide interest at the Exhibition.

August 23rd - September 1st 1939.
The fourteenth National Radio Exhibition - Radiolympia. (R.M.A.). Press-button receivers dominate the exhibition. New all-dry battery portables introduced. Television continues to hold the public's interest. Due to finish on September 2nd., Radiolympia closed a day early because of the worsening world political crisis - B.B.C.'s television service also closed down. With the outbreak of war, there is a great resurgence of interest in the crystal set as a stand-by receiver.

September 24th - October 31st 1946.
The Britain Can Make It Exhibition, Victoria & Albert Museum, South Kensington. (Council of Industrial Design). Twenty-five sets selected from the Radio and Television Industry were shown. Radios included Murphy's first baffle receiver, and the Romac midget portable using American 7-pin miniature all-glass valves. The Exhibition was described by Sir Stafford Cripps (President of the Board of Trade) as "British Industry's first great post-war gesture to the British people and the world". Receivers begin to be produced for the 'second-set' market.

October 1st - 11th 1947.
The fifteenth National Radio Exhibition - Radiolympia. (Radio Industry Council - R.I.C.). 170 principal exhibitors embracing radio and television receivers, communications and, for the first time, electronics (all other non-domestic radio equipment including industrial, scientific and medical radio apparatus). Fly-wheel tuning controls very popular. Experimental printed circuits shown at Radiolympia. In the following year, there was no 1948 Radiolympia, so that the industry could be allowed time and space to concentrate without distractions on achieving its export target.

September 28th - October 8th 1949.
The sixteenth National Radio Exhibition - Radiolympia. (R.I.C.). 218 principal exhibitors in the Grand Hall (domestic radio and television manufacturers), Grand Hall Annex (Wholesalers) and the National Hall (electronics). This was

the last Radiolympia to be held, and for the first time, television was the dominating feature.

September 6th -16th 1950.

The seventeenth National Radio Exhibition, B.I.F. Buildings, Castle Bromwich, Birmingham (R.I.C.). 108 principal exhibitors with electronics and television now taking on an even greater role. Germanium diodes introduced by G.E.C.

August 29th - September 8th 1951.

The eighteenth National Radio Exhibition, Earls Court, London SW5. (R.I.C.). 88 principal exhibitors with television the centre of attention. Among the radio exhibits, the 4-valve plus rectifier AC table model superhet in a polished wooden cabinet was the standard product of the Radio Industry.

August 27th - September 6th 1952.

The nineteenth National Radio Exhibition, Earls Court, London SW5. (R.I.C.). 108 principal exhibitors with radio receivers taking a lesser role behind television and electronics.

September 2nd - 12th 1953.

The twentieth National Radio Exhibition, Earls Court, London SW5. (R.I.C.). 112 principal exhibitors. Ferrite rod aerial introduced in receiver circuits. New 'female' market created in fancy portable receivers. Component transistors (low-power types) beginning to be used experimentally in hearing-aids and hi-fi amplifiers.

August 25th - September 4th 1954.

The twenty-first National Radio Exhibition, Earls Court, London SW5. (R.I.C.). 112 principal exhibitors. AM/FM receivers and FM tuner units introduced ready for the B.B.C.'s new VHF service planned for the following year. Printed circuits beginning to be used in receivers. Experimental transistor radio shown by G.E.C.

August 26th - September 3rd 1955.

The twenty-second National Radio Exhibition, Earls Court, London SW5. (R.I.C.). 121 principal exhibitors. (Opened two days late because of labour disputes). Great interest in new AM/FM receivers due to the B.B.C.'s new VHF servive. Continental influence in radio cabinet design: high-gloss finish, brass trim, piano-key tuning and multiple loud-speakers. Oversized circular dial controls in clear Perspex first introduced in a few receivers, and control knobs with gilded metal centres or outer rings generally become fashionable. I.T.A.'s new commercial television service creates massive television interest. Combined TV/FM sets introduced.

August 22nd - September 1st 1956.

The twenty-third National Radio Exhibition, Earls Court, London SW5. (R.I.C.). 117 principal exhibitors with the first British all-transistor radio on show: the Pam 710 portable. Several hybrid receivers with valves in the HF and IF stages and transistors in the LF stages appear around this time. Circuit miniaturisation techniques shown in many receivers. AM/FM receivers vastly outnumber AM-only types.

August 28th - September 7th 1957.

The twenty-fourth National Radio Exhibition, Earls Court, London SW5. (R.I.C.). AM/FM valve sets on show (mainly mains table models but a few battery portables) now generally as cheap as ordinary AM receivers. Pocket transistors first appeared - very expensive. Oversized circular dial controls in clear Perspex become popular for first time.

August 27th - September 6th 1958.

The twenty-fifth National Radio Exhibition, Earls Court, London SW5. (R.I.C.). With commencement of B.B.C.'s experimental stereo broadcasts and introduction of stereo records, pick-ups and record players, the Exhibition was heralded as the "start of the Stereo Season" - a separate Hall of Sound for the first time, comprising thirty-eight stands showing tape-recorders, hi-fi equipment, and loud-speakers. Combined TV/FM sets at height of popularity, and 'long, low look' introduced in table model cabinet design. Larger than ever selection of pocket transistor sets, but still regarded as an expensive novelty. No true transistorised battery table models shown.

August 26th - September 5th 1959.

The twenty-sixth National Radio Exhibition, Earls Court, London SW5. (Radio Industry Exhibitions Ltd.) Larger than ever Hall of Sound with stereo record players and tape-recorders the main attraction. Marked increase in the number of transistor sets, with a few transistorised battery table models being shown for the first time.

August 24th - September 3rd 1960.

The twenty-seventh National Radio Exhibition, Earls Court, London SW5. (R.I.E. Ltd.). First all-transistorised battery portable television set announced. Pocket and handbag-sized transistor portables making an impact, numbers of valve portables rapidly diminishing. Printed circuits now universal in all classes of receiver, and first transistorised AM/FM table models appear. First batch of cheap Japanese transistor sets arrive from the Far East. For the first time, Pye Ltd. have their own separate show at another venue.

August 23rd - September 2nd 1961.

The twenty-eighth National Radio Exhibition, Earls Court, London SW5. (R.I.E. Ltd.). New trade and technical section concerned with servicing requirements. Transistorised portables now widespread with very few valve portables being manufactured. VHF/FM band being used more in all classes of receiver including transistorised portables, and a few all-wave transistor sets introduced. Competition from Japanese imports begins to grow.

August 22nd - September 1st 1962.

The twenty-ninth National Radio Exhibition, Earls Court, London SW5. (R.I.E. Ltd.). Television emphasis on proposed introduction of B.B.C.'s 625-line service in 1964. Transistor radios growing rapidly, prices falling. Smallest transistor radio in the world: the Standard Micronic Ruby. A few mains valve stereo tuners, amplifiers and radios begin to appear.

1963

National Radio Exhibition cancelled. (R.I.E. Ltd.). Many firms hold their own 'Showtime Shows' around London instead. Drastic reduction in transistor radio prices.

August 26th - September 5th 1964.

The thirtieth (and last) National Radio Exhibition, Earls Court, London SW5. (R.I.E. Ltd.). Many more independant Showtime Shows at other venues around London and only the ground floor at Earls Court was occupied due to lack of industry support and large portions cordoned off for the trade-only.

Transistor portables and the new BBC-2 625-line television service dominated the show. All-wave and AM/FM transistor radios begin to increase - emphasis on being able to receive the Pop Pirates. British transistors suffering under Japanese competition - first Japanese Radio Exhibition held in London in June.

1965

International Radio & Television Show cancelled. (Industrial & Trade Fairs Ltd.) Due to be held at Earls Court from August 25th - September 4th. 50 international manufacturers agree to participate but lack of support from British companies, who simply carried on with their own independant shows around London. New cabinet design - portables housed in square-cut rectangular case with controls mounted on top on brushed-aluminium panel. Imports from Far East now account for 50 per cent of all transistor portables on sale in Britain.

August 22nd - 26th 1966.
Television & Radio Show '66, Earls Court, London SW5. (I. & T.F. Ltd.). An international, trade-only show. First integrated circuit miniature receiver introduced by Sony U.K. Sales Division (the ICR-100), and the world's smallest television (the pocket-sized Microvision) by Sinclair Radionics Ltd.

1967.
Television & Radio Show '67 cancelled. (I. & T.F. Ltd.). Cancellation caused by lack of support from the main television manufacturers in the year that the B.B.C.'s colour television service was introduced in the London area on BBC-2. I. & T.F.

Ltd. abandon any future hope of a National Television & Radio Show. Several trade-only exhibitions put on around London from August 20th - 25th. Among the exhibits, the first all-transistor colour television. A lot more emphasis on hi-fi with the display of radios thought of as disappointing. Still a few examples of valve circuits being used in mains table models.

August 25th - 29th 1968.
Manufacturers' trade-only exhibitions carried on at venues in and around London. Audio fairs now popular with public. Hybrid transistor/valve circuits commonplace in television circuits and most domestic radio/hi-fi equipment now transistorised.

The Wireless Licence, 1904 to 1971

From mid-Edwardian times until the early 1970s, the reception of transmitted wireless signals was subject to some form of licence limitation. Under the first *Wireless Telegraphy Act* of 1904, the Post Office had been given the authority to control both the transmission and the reception of wireless telegraphy, and this power was automatically extended to cover telephony as broadcasting developed after W.W.I.

Before the British Broadcasting Company was set up in November 1922, the Post Office had been the sole recipient of licence revenue, but a few weeks before the advent of official broadcasting, the new Broadcast Licence was introduced at 10s.0d. of which the B.B.C. took 50 per cent. This was needed to cover the cost of setting up transmitting stations and studios, making programmes and paying staff and artistes. At first the licence income was supplemented to a great extent by the sale of shares in the Company and by the levying of royalties on wireless equipment sold by its member firms (*see page 217*). But within a few years, with the royalty scheme abolished and the Company becoming a Corporation, the receiving licence became the major source of the B.B.C.'s revenue, just as the Television Licence is today.

1904. With the *Wireless Telegraphy Act* becoming law on August 15th, the operation of British wireless telegraphy stations on both land and sea was now subject to Post Office licence control. Whether the amateur enthusiast needed a licence to carry on with his private wireless experiments was at first uncertain. However, a letter from J.C. Lamb, Secretary of the G.P.O. in London to the editor of *The Model Engineer & Electrician*, and reprinted in their September 8th 1904 issue, made the position clear. *"SIR, — I am directed by the Post Master General to inform you that a licence will be required for the use of wireless apparatus for experimental purposes as well as for inter-communication on private premises and estates"*. Early in the following year, the first official printed licences for amateurs began to be issued by the Post Office.

1905. The first official printed licences for amateurs were issued by the Post Office. They were available free of charge to amateur enthusiasts wishing to conduct transmitting or receiving experiments in wireless telegraphy - it would be several more years before *telephony* developed. By June 13th 1906, 68 experimental licences had been granted by the Post Master General.

May 1913. The Post Office imposed a charge of £1.1s.0d. on all new experimental licences in an attempt to dissuade non bona-fide experimenters from applying and also to cover the cost of administering the licence documents and inspecting domestic wireless installations. By then, there were 405 amateurs licensed to transmit, and 360 licensed to receive.

August 1st 1914. With the imminent outbreak of World War One, the Post Master General ordered all experimental wireless apparatus to be dismantled and the aerial wires removed. No new wireless licences were issued until after the war, and in general, those then in current use (now deemed *"ineffective"*), were cancelled. Some amateur experimental licences though,

Broadcast Receiving Licence Figures 1922 to 1971

DATE SURVEY TAKEN	TOTAL RADIO LICENCES ISSUED	ISSUED FREE TO BLIND PERSONS	COMBINED RADIO & TV LICENCES	
			MONO	COLOUR
1922 (Oct. 31st)	18,061			
1922 (Dec. 31st)	35,774			
1923 (Mar. 31st)	122,155			
1924 (Mar. 31st)	721,002			
1925 (Mar. 31st)	1,349,294			
1926 (Jan. 31st)	1,840,268			
1927 (Mar. 31st)	2,269,644	(5,750)		
1928 (Mar. 31st)	2,482,873	(12,344)		
1929 (Mar. 31st)	2,731,872	(14,505)		
1930 (Mar. 31st)	3,092,324	(16,496)		
1931 (Mar. 31st)	3,647,722	(21,304)		
1932 (Mar. 31st)	4,621,805	(31,513)		
1933 (Mar. 31st)	5,497,217	(35,850)		
1934 (Mar. 31st)	6,259,653	(39,224)		
1935 (Mar. 31st)	7,011,753	(41,868)		
1936 (Mar. 31st)	7,616,822	(44,380)		
1937 (Mar. 31st)	8,127,636	(46,475)		
1938 (Mar. 31st)	8,588,676	(49,730)		
1939 (Mar. 31st)	8,968,338	(52,621)		
1940 (Mar. 31st)	8,951,045	(53,427)		
1941 (Mar. 31st)	8,752,454	(50,555)		
1942 (Mar. 31st)	8,683,098	(47,456)		
1943 (Mar. 31st)	9,242,040	(48,399)		
1944 (Mar. 31st)	9,554,838	(48,124)		
1945 (Mar. 31st)	9,710,230	(46,861)		
1946 (Mar. 31st)	10,395,551	(47,720)		
1947 (Mar. 31st)	10,763,144	(49,846)	14,560	
1948 (Mar. 31st)	11,134,112	(52,135)	45,564	
1949 (Mar. 31st)	11,620,881	(53,654)	126,567	
1950 (Mar. 31st)	11,875,566	(56,376)	343,882	
1951 (Mar. 31st)	11,605,086	(58,161)	763,941	
1952 (Mar. 31st)	11,304,246	(60,105)	1,449,260	
1953 (Mar. 31st)	10,749,779	(61,095)	2,142,452	
1954 (Mar. 31st)	10,187,901	(62,389)	3,248,892	
1955 (Mar. 31st)	9,476,730	(62,506)	4,503,766	
1956 (Mar. 31st)	8,521,958	(62,745)	5,739,593	
1957 (Mar. 31st)	7,558,843	(62,453)	6,966,256	
1958 (Mar. 31st)	6,556,347	(61,387)	8,090,003	
1959 (Mar. 31st)	5,480,991	(57,784)	9,255,422	
1960 (Mar. 31st)	4,535,258	(54,958)	10,469,753	
1961 (Mar. 31st)	3,908,984	(50,852)	11,267,741	
1962 (Mar. 31st)	3,538,507	(46,782)	11,833,712	
1963 (Mar. 31st)	3,256,185	(43,371)	12,442,806	
1964 (Mar. 31st)	2,999,348	(40,337)	12,885,331	
1965 (Mar. 31st)	2,793,558	(34,355)	13,253,045	
1966 (Mar. 31st)	2,611,066	(31,499)	13,567,090	
1967 (Mar. 31st)	2,505,934	(29,662)	14,267,271	
1968 (Mar. 31st)	2,557,314	(27,564)	15,068,079	20,428
1969 (Mar. 31st)	2,463,872	(24,966)	15,396,642	99,419
1970 (Mar. 31st)	2,301,191	(22,174)	15,609,131	273,397
1971 (Feb. 1st)	2,250,000	(19,500)	15,000,000	600,000

Notes:
1. Figure for October 31st 1922 is for Experimenter's Licence.
2. Figure for March 31st 1924 includes Constructor's Licence.
3. Figures before 1927 were published in *The Report of the Broadcasting Committee, 1925, Cmd 2599, 1926*. Other figures based on those published in *BBC Handbooks*.
4. Figures in second column include free licences issued to the blind.
5. Figures for Feb. 1st 1971 (the day the radio-only Broadcast Receiving Licence was abolished) are approximate. A true picture of the number of licences issued was not possible at the time due to industrial action within the P.O. between Jan. and Mar. 1971.

remained in force throughout the war in what appears to have been an oversight by the G.P.O., while a few others were issued with a special permit allowing them to operate under Government control for official purposes.

July 5th 1919. All amateur experimental licences issued before the war were cancelled and no new licences were issued until October.

October 21st 1919. The *'Experimenter's Licence'* was introduced at 10s.0d. a year for use with receiving apparatus only. Applicants had to be of British nationality (and be able to produce a birth certificate to that effect), were required to submit a description of the apparatus they proposed to install (plus a detailed circuit diagram if they wanted to use valves), and to give the name and address of the manufacturer if they intended to use a complete factory-built receiver. Receiving aerials were limited to 140 ft. for a single-stranded wire, and 100 ft. for a multi-stranded wire.

August 1st 1920. The *'Transmitting Licence'* was introduced for amateur experimenters.

November 1st 1922. The *'Broadcast Licence'* (*fig.913*), was introduced at 10s.0d. a year, some two weeks before official broadcasting commenced with the opening of the British Broadcasting Company's first station, 2LO London. While there were no restrictions as to the nationality, the qualifications or the experimental objectives of applicants, holders of the licence were legally bound to use it only in conjunction with British factory-built equipment which had been made by member firms of the British Broadcasting Company. Such equipment had to bear the BBC/PMG stamp together with a G.P.O. Registration Number (*see page 217*).

Since the B.B.C. received a percentage of the revenue from the Broadcast Licence together with royalties from the sale of BBC/PMG-stamped equipment, this measure ensured that financial support was received by them for the provision of a broadcasting service. Also, it gave protection against foreign import competition to the infant British Wireless Industry during the critical stages of its early development. The possession of a home-constructed receiver or one of commercial manufacture not bearing a BBC/PMG stamp was prohibited if it was used with the Broadcast Licence, although such receivers were able to be used legally with an Experimenter's Licence, and by November 1st 1922 over 18,000 of these had already been issued. The B.B.C. however, received no revenue from the Experimenter's Licence, nor royalties from the sets it covered.

October 4th 1923. The *'Constructor's Licence'* was introduced at 15s.0d. a year for amateurs wishing to construct their own receivers using British-made components only. (Under this licence the use of foreign-made components was prohibited). On the same day, the *'Interim Licence'* was introduced at 15s.0d. Lasting until the end of the month, this short-term licence was seen as an amnesty for all unlicensed equipment whether home-constructed or factory-built, or of British or foreign origin. By the time the amnesty had expired, about 200,000 Interim Licences had been applied for.

July 1st 1924. The Constructor's Licence was abolished.

January 1st 1925. The *'Receiving Licence'* was introduced at 10s.0d. a year. This was a single form of licence covering both experimental and broadcast reception and superseded all previous types of receiving licence. It was free from any restriction as to the origin or marking of apparatus, and with its introduction the embargo against foreign wireless equipment was lifted.

January 1st 1937. The stipulation that a separate Receiving Licence was needed for a wireless receiver fitted into a motor vehicle first appeared printed on the back of the licence.

June 1st 1946. For listeners who also owned a television set, a new combined radio and television licence (the *'Broadcast Receiving Licence [Including Television]'*), was introduced at £2 a year. On the same day, the radio-only Receiving Licence fee was doubled. Costing £1, it was now renamed the *'Broadcast Receiving Licence [Excluding Television]'*.

June 1st 1954. The combined radio and television licence fee was increased to £3.

August 1st 1957. Excise duty of £1 was imposed on the combined radio and television licence increasing the fee to £4.

October 1st 1963. Excise Duty abolished although the combined radio and television licence fee remained at £4.

August 1st 1965. The radio-only Broadcast Receiving Licence fee was increased to £1.5s.0d. and the combined radio and television licence fee was increased to £5.

January 1st 1968. A £5 Colour Television Supplement was introduced with the combined radio and television licence.

January 1st 1969. The combined radio and television licence fee was increased to £6.

February 1st 1971. The radio-only Broadcast Receiving Licence was abolished. At that time some 2,250,000 were in force and most people were surprised, and delighted, to find out that they no longer needed a licence to 'listen-in'.

fig.913.

How Old Is My Radio? — Dating a Receiver by its Tuning Dial

Many years ago, I had a protracted face-to-face discussion with a chap who had advertised a *"1936 Bush radio"* for sale in the *Exchange & Mart*. It had, he initially informed me over the telephone, been a wedding present to his parents when they had married that year. He even recalled, as a very small boy, listening-in to it during the war. He didn't know what model it was, but having journeyed across London and through a couple of Home Counties in order to buy it, I found the set to be a DAC 90A which I remembered from a *Trader* sheet to be 1950. No amount of gentle reasoning would convince him otherwise about its vintage and, as I wasn't interested then in anything but 1930s sets, it turned out to be a fruitless and wasted journey. Someone said later that I should have pointed out that the dial had the LIGHT and the THIRD PROGRAMME printed on it (both *post*-war stations) but this was very early on in my collecting career and I knew very little about such things. (I have also driven 175 miles to view a *"pre-war television set"* which turned out to be a radiogram . . . but that's another story!).

Following the DAC 90A episode, I resolved to do a bit of research which would help to pinpoint more accurately when a set was made by noting the stations and their wavelengths as they appeared on the tuning dial. Being very interested in the B.B.C.'s history, I also wanted to know exactly which of their stations would have been broadcasting in each particular year. I have had this information in scribbled note form for many years and compiling the third edition of this book has given me a welcome opportunity of laying it all out neatly to turn it into a useful reference section — an exercise which took some four weeks and prompted one of my daughters to tell me *"Dad, get a life!"*.

For a rough method of dating, see which B.B.C. stations appear on the dial and check them off against the QUICK DATING GUIDE list on the right; for more accuracy, see below.

QUICK DATING GUIDE
(examples of pre-1939 BBC AM stations)

DAVENTRY NATIONAL	*before* 1934
DROITWICH	*from* 1934
"NATIONALS"	*from* 1935
NORTH NATIONAL/REG.	*from* 1931
NORTHERN IRELAND	*from* 1935
SCOTTISH NATIONAL/REG.	*from* 1932
STAGSHAW	*from* 1937
WEST NATIONAL/REG.	*from* 1933
WELSH REGIONAL	*from* 1937

QUICK DATING GUIDE
(examples of post-1939 BBC AM stations)

A.E.F PROG.	*from* 1944
Clevedon	*from* 1939
FORCES	*from* 1940
GEN. FORCES PROG.	*from* 1944
HOME SERVICE	*from* 1939
LIGHT PROG.	*from* 1945
OVERSEAS	*from* 1940
RADIO 1, 2, 3, 4	*from* 1967
Start Point	*from* 1939
THIRD PROG. (203.5 metres)	*from* 1946
THIRD PROG. (194 metres)	*from* 1950

(VHF/FM Band	*from* 1955)

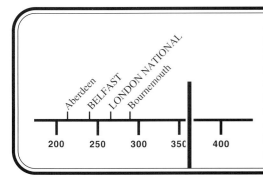

Although I have been able to put a date on around 4,000 different radios in this book, there must be thousands more in people's collections which I have been unable to include simply due to lack of space. In Britain, station names have appeared on tuning dials since 1931, and any radio which shows B.B.C. stations and wavelengths is easy to date by the following method. Write down the first three or four **B.B.C. medium-wave stations** and their **wavelengths** as they appear on the dial, starting with the one on the *lowest* wavelength (ie. Aberdeen, as left) and simply match these against the list below. NB: This method works for many radios, but not all, as some dials may not have had room to list *every* station (ie. the Philco 444 of 1936 left out Bournemouth and Plymouth at the top end of the scale). In this case, list all the radio's B.B.C. medium-wave stations on a piece of paper and check these against the in-depth analysis of stations and wavelengths that appears on pages 228 to 232.

ABERDEEN *(lowest wavelength on dial)*

Aberdeen	214.3	June 12th 1932
BELFAST	242.3	*to*
LONDON NATIONAL	261.3	July 23rd 1932
Bournemouth	288.5	

BELFAST *(lowest wavelength on dial)*

BELFAST	242.3	July 7th 1929
NEWCASTLE	261	*to*
Bournemouth	288.5	Nov. 2nd 1929
Bradford	288.5	
BELFAST	242.3	Nov. 3rd 1929
Bournemouth	288.5	*to*
Bradford	288.5	March 8th 1930
Dundee	288.5	
BELFAST	242.3	March 9th 1930
LONDON NATIONAL	261.3	*to*
Bournemouth	288.5	May 16th 1931
Bradford	288.5	
BELFAST	242.3	May 17th 1931
LONDON NATIONAL	261.3	*to*
Bournemouth	288.5	May 30th 1931
Dundee	288.5	
BELFAST	242.3	May 31st 1931
LONDON NATIONAL	261.3	*to*
Aberdeen	288.5	June 11th 1932
Bournemouth	288.5	

BOURNEMOUTH *(lowest wavelength on dial)*

Bournemouth	203.5	Jan. 15th 1934
Plymouth	203.5	*to*
Newcastle	209.9	Feb. 16th 1935
Aberdeen	233.5	
Bournemouth	203.5	Feb. 17th 1935
Plymouth	203.5	*to*
Aberdeen	233.5	June 13th 1939
NATIONALS	261.1	

Bournemouth	203.5	June 14th 1939
Clevedon	203.5	*to*
Plymouth	203.5	July 14th 1939
Aberdeen	233.5	

HOME SERVICE (WWII) *(lowest wavelength on dial)*

HOME SERVICE	391.1	Sept. 1st 1939
HOME SERVICE	449.1	*to*
		Dec. 18th 1939
HOME SERVICE	342.1	Dec. 19th 1939
HOME SERVICE	391.1	*to*
HOME SERVICE	449.1	Jan. 6th 1940
HOME SERVICE	203.5	Nov. 3rd 1940
OVERSEAS SERVICE	261.1	*to*
HOME SERVICE	296.2	March 1st 1941
FORCES	373.1	
HOME SERVICE	203.5	March 2nd 1941
OVERSEAS SERVICE	261.1	*to*
FORCES	342.1	March 5th 1942
OVERSEAS SERVICE	373.1	
HOME SERVICE	203.5	March 6th 1942
OVERSEAS SERVICE	261.1	*to*
FORCES	296.1	Feb. 26th 1944
FORCES	342.1	
HOME SERVICE	203.5	Feb. 27th 1944
OVERSEAS SERVICE	261.1	*to*
GEN. FORCES PROG.	296.1	June 6th 1944
GEN. FORCES PROG.	342.1	
HOME SERVICE	203.5	June 7th 1944
OVERSEAS SERVICE	261.1	*to*
ALLIED EX. F. PROG.	285.7	July 28th 1945
GEN. FORCES PROG.	296.1	

HOME SERVICE *(lowest wavelength on dial)*

HOME SERVICE (W.)	203.5	July 29th 1945
LIGHT PROG.	261.1	*to*
HOME SERVICE (N.)	285.7	June 1st 1946

HOME SERVICE (W.)	203.5	June 2nd 1946
LIGHT PROG.	261.1	*to*
HOME SERVICE (N.I)	285.7	Sept. 28th 1946
HOME SERVICE (Mid.)	296.2	

NEWCASTLE *(lowest wavelength on dial)*

Newcastle	211.3	July 24th 1932
Aberdeen	214.3	*to*
BELFAST	242.3	Nov. 12th 1932
LONDON NATIONAL	261.3	
Newcastle	211.3	Nov. 13th 1932
Aberdeen	214.3	*to*
BELFAST	242.3	Feb. 25th 1933
Swansea	245.9	
Newcastle	211.3	Feb. 26th 1933
Aberdeen	214.3	*to*
Plymouth	218.5	Jan. 14th 1934
BELFAST	242.3	

THIRD PROGRAMME *(lowest wavelength on dial)*

THIRD PROG.	203.5	Sept. 29th 1946
HOME SERVICE (W.)	216.8	*to*
LIGHT PROG.	261.1	Oct. 25th 1947
HOME SERVICE (N.I.)	285.7	
THIRD PROG.	203.5	Oct. 26th 1947
HOME SERVICE (W.)	216.8	*to*
LIGHT PROG.	261.1	March 14th 1950
HOME SERVICE (N.)	285.7	
THIRD PROG.	194	March 15th 1950
HOME SERVICE (W.)	206	*to*
LIGHT PROG.	247	Jan. 6th 1963
THIRD PROG.	194	Jan. 7th 1963
HOME SERVICE (W.)	206	*to*
HOME SERVICE (N.I)	224	Sept. 29th 1967

ANALYSIS OF STATIONS & WAVELENGTHS 1919 - 1978
(B.B.C. medium-wave and long-wave stations
unless otherwise stated).

1919 - 1922 (Pre-B.B.C., test transmissions)

1150	HAGUE (PCGG) *('Dutch Concerts')*	Nov. 6th 1919
2800	CHELMSFORD (MZX)* *(telephony)*	Jan. 15th 1920
1000	SLOUGH (2AA)** *(amateur telephony)*	Aug. 1st 1920
700	WRITTLE (2MT)*** *(telephony)*	Feb. 14th 1922
1000	WRITTLE (2MT)*** *(Morse)*	Feb. 14th 1922
360	LONDON (2LO) *(telephony)*	May 11th 1922
400	WRITTLE (2MT) *(telephony)*	May 30th 1922

*CHELMSFORD — 6 kW at first, increased to 15 kW on February 23rd 1920. (The station was closed down on Nov. 23rd 1920 by the P.M.G. due to interference with other stations).
**The 1000 metre wavelength was allotted to amateurs on August 1st 1920 for the transmission of wireless telephony with a maximum power of 10 Watts. SLOUGH (2AA) belonged to the Radio Communication Company.
***On May 30th 1922, these two wavelengths were replaced by telephony transmissions on 400 metres, and the Morse section was dropped. WRITTLE closed down on January 17th 1923.

1922 (B.B.C. Broadcasting Stations, November to December)

361	LONDON (2LO)	Nov. 14th
384	MANCHESTER (2ZY)	Nov. 15th
400	NEWCASTLE (5NO)	Dec. 23rd
420	BIRMINGHAM (5IT)	Nov. 15th

1923 (January 1st)

303	Sheffield (6FL)	Nov. 16th
353	CARDIFF (5WA)	Feb. 13th
361	LONDON	
370	MANCHESTER	
385	BOURNEMOUTH (6BM)	Oct. 17th
400	NEWCASTLE	
415	GLASGOW (5SC)	March 6th
420	BIRMINGHAM	
495	ABERDEEN (2BD)	Oct. 10th

BIRMINGHAM *changed to 475 metres on December 23rd.*

1924 (January 1st)

303	Sheffield	
306	Stoke (6ST)	Nov. 21st
310	Bradford (6BM)*	July 8th
318	Liverpool (6LV)	June 11th
318	Swansea (5SX)	Dec. 12th
320	Hull (6KH)	August 15th
325	Edinburgh (2EH)	May 1st
331	Dundee (2DE)	Nov. 9th
335	Plymouth (5PY)	March 28th
340	Nottingham (5NG)	Sept. 16th
346	Leeds (2LS)*	July 8th
353	CARDIFF	
365	LONDON	
375	MANCHESTER	
385	BOURNEMOUTH	
400	NEWCASTLE	
420	GLASGOW	
435	BELFAST (2BE)	Sept. 14th
475	BIRMINGHAM	
495	ABERDEEN	
1600	CHELMSFORD (5XX)	July 21st

Hull *changed to 335 metres on October 12th.*
Nottingham *changed to 322 metres on October 12th.*
* Bradford relayed the Leeds service from July 8th.

1925 (January 1st)

301	Sheffield	
306	Stoke	
310	Bradford	
315	Liverpool	
318	Swansea	
322	Nottingham	
328	Edinburgh	
331	Dundee	
335	Hull	
335	Plymouth	
346	Leeds	
353	CARDIFF	
365	LONDON	
375	MANCHESTER	
385	BOURNEMOUTH	
400	NEWCASTLE	
420	GLASGOW	
435	BELFAST	
475	BIRMINGHAM	
495	ABERDEEN	
1600	CHELMSFORD (5XX)*	
1600	DAVENTRY (5XX)	July 27th

Leeds *changed to 321 metres on December 27th.*
Swansea *changed to 485 metres on January 4th.*
*Chelmsford (5XX) closed down on July 27th— transferred to Daventry (5XX).

1926 (January 1st)

301	Sheffield
306	Stoke
310	Bradford
315	Liverpool
321	Leeds
326	Nottingham
328	Edinburgh
331	Dundee
335	Hull
338	Plymouth
353	CARDIFF
365	LONDON
378	MANCHESTER
385	BOURNEMOUTH
404	NEWCASTLE
422	GLASGOW
440	BELFAST
479	BIRMINGHAM
485	Swansea
495	ABERDEEN
1600	DAVENTRY (5XX)

Dundee *changed to 315 metres, Liverpool to 331 metres and Nottingham to 315 metres on March 14th. Sheffield changed to 306 metres and Stoke to 301 metres on June 13th.*

1926 (November 14th — GENEVA PLAN)

288.5	Dundee
288.5	Edinburgh
288.5	Hull
288.5	Liverpool
288.5	Nottingham
288.5	Plymouth
288.5	Sheffield
288.5	Stoke
288.5	Swansea
294.1	Bradford
297	Leeds
306.1	BOURNEMOUTH
312.5	NEWCASTLE
326.1	BELFAST
353	CARDIFF
361.4	LONDON
384.6	MANCHESTER
405.4	GLASGOW
491.8	ABERDEEN
491.8	BIRMINGHAM
1600	DAVENTRY (5XX)

ABERDEEN *changed to 500 metres on December 5th.*
BELFAST *changed to 306.1 metres on December 12th.*
BOURNEMOUTH *changed to 326.1 metres on December 12th.*
Bradford *changed to 254.2 metres on December 12th.*
Edinburgh *changed to 294.1 metres on December 12th.*
Leeds *changed to 277.8 metres on December 12th.*
Liverpool *changed to 297 metres on December 12th.*
Nottingham *changed to 275.2 metres on December 12th.*
Plymouth *changed to 400 metres on December 14th.*
Sheffield *changed to 272.7 metres on December 12th.*

1927 (January 1st)

254.2	Bradford	
272.7	Sheffield	
275.2	Nottingham	
277.8	Leeds	
288.5	Dundee	
288.5	Hull	
288.5	Stoke	
288.5	Swansea	
294.1	Edinburgh	
297	Liverpool	
306.1	BELFAST	
312.5	NEWCASTLE	
326.1	BOURNEMOUTH	
353	CARDIFF	
361.4	LONDON	
384.6	MANCHESTER	
400	Plymouth	
405.4	GLASGOW	
491.8	BIRMINGHAM*	
491.8	DAVENTRY EXP. (5GB)	Aug. 21st
500	ABERDEEN	
1600	DAVENTRY (5XX)	

Dundee *changed to 294.1 metres on January 30th.*
Edinburgh *changed to 288.5 metres on January 30th.*
Hull *changed to 294.1 metres January 30th.*
Stoke *changed to 294.1 metres on January 30th.*
Swansea *changed to 294.1 metres on January 30th.*
BOURNEMOUTH *changed to 491.8 metres on Jan. 30th, and 326.1 metres on August 21st).*
BIRMINGHAM *changed to 326.1metres on January 30th.*
DAVENTRY (5XX) *changed to 1604.8 metres on August 21st.*
*Birmingham closed down on August 21st. On the same day, DAVENTRY EXPERIMENTAL (5GB) was brought into service for experimental Regional Scheme broadcasts to the Midlands (see page 57).

1928 (January 1st)

252.1	Bradford
272.7	Sheffield
275.2	Nottingham (closed down on November 25th)
277.8	Leeds
288.5	Edinburgh
294.1	Dundee
294.1	Hull
294.1	Stoke
294.1	Swansea
297	Liverpool
306.1	BELFAST
312.5	NEWCASTLE
326.1	BOURNEMOUTH
353	CARDIFF
361.4	LONDON
384.6	MANCHESTER
400	Plymouth
405.4	GLASGOW
491.8	DAVENTRY EXPERIMENTAL (5GB)
500	ABERDEEN
1604.8	DAVENTRY (5XX)

Leeds *changed to 286 metres on November 4th*
DAVENTRY (5XX) *changed to 1562.5 metres November 11th*

1929 (January 1st)

252.1	Bradford
272.7	Sheffield
286	Leeds
288.5	Edinburgh
294.1	Dundee
294.1	Hull
294.1	Stoke
294.1	Swansea
297	Liverpool
306.1	BELFAST
312.5	NEWCASTLE
326.1	BOURNEMOUTH
353	CARDIFF
361.4	LONDON
384.6	MANCHESTER
400	Plymouth
405.4	GLASGOW
491.8	DAVENTRY EXPERIMENTAL (5GB)
500	ABERDEEN
1562.5	DAVENTRY (5XX)

1929 (January 13th — BRUSSELS PLAN)

243.9	NEWCASTLE (261 metres on June 30th)
261	Leeds (258 metres on February 10th)
272.7	Sheffield (288.5 metres on April 14th)
288.5	Bournemouth (relegated to a relay on January 13th)
288.5	Bradford (294 metres on April 14th)
288.5	Edinburgh
294.1	Dundee (288.5 metres on March 10th)
294.1	Hull (288.5 metres on February 10th)
294.1	Liverpool (288.5 metres on March 24th)
294.1	Stoke (288.5 metres on April 21st)
294.1	Swansea (288.5 metres on April 28th)
302.7	BELFAST
311.2	ABERDEEN
323.2	CARDIFF
358	LONDON
378.3	MANCHESTER
396.5	Plymouth (288.5 metres on May 12th)
401.1	GLASGOW
482.3	DAVENTRY EXPERIMENTAL (5GB)
1562.5	DAVENTRY (5XX)

1929 (July 7th — PRAGUE PLAN)

242.3	BELFAST
261	NEWCASTLE (288.5 metres/relegated to a relay on Nov. 3rd)
288.5	Bournemouth
288.5	Bradford (Bradford and Leeds merged on 288.5 metres on July 7th)
288.5	Dundee
288.5	Edinburgh
288.5	Hull
288.5	Liverpool
288.5	Plymouth
288.5	Sheffield
288.5	Stoke
288.5	Swansea
301.5	ABERDEEN
309.9	CARDIFF
356.3	LONDON (radiated by Brookmans Park X'ter from Oct. 21st)
376.4	MANCHESTER
398.9	GLASGOW
479.2	DAVENTRY EXPERIMENTAL (5GB)
1554.4	DAVENTRY (5XX)

1930 (January 1st)

242.3	BELFAST	
261.3	**LONDON NATIONAL**	**March 9th**
288.5	Bournemouth	
288.5	Bradford	
288.5	Dundee	
288.5	Edinburgh	
288.5	Hull	
288.5	Liverpool	
288.5	Newcastle	
288.5	Plymouth	
288.5	Sheffield	
288.5	Stoke	
288.5	Swansea	
301.5	ABERDEEN	
309.9	CARDIFF	
356.3	LONDON*	
356.3	**LONDON REGIONAL**	**March 9th**
376.4	MANCHESTER	
398.9	GLASGOW	
479.2	DAVENTRY EXP. (5GB)**	
479.2	**MIDLAND REGIONAL**	**March 9th**
1554.4	DAVENTRY (5XX)***	
1554.4	**DAVENTRY NATIONAL**	**March 9th**

*London (the B.B.C.'s original 2LO station) became London Regional on March 9th (*see page 96*).
**Daventry Experimental (5GB) became Midland Regional on March 9th (*see page 96*).
***Daventry (5XX) became Daventry National on March 9th (*see page 96*).

1931 (January 1st)

242.3	BELFAST	
261.3	LONDON NATIONAL	
288.5	Bournemouth	
288.5	Bradford*	
288.5	Dundee	
288.5	Edinburgh	
288.5	Hull*	
288.5	Liverpool*	
288.5	Newcastle	
288.5	Plymouth	
288.5	Sheffield*	
288.5	Stoke*	
288.5	Swansea	
301.5	ABERDEEN	
301.5	**NORTH NATIONAL**	**July 12th**
309.9	CARDIFF	
356.3	LONDON REGIONAL	
376.4	MANCHESTER*	
398.9	GLASGOW	
479.2	MIDLAND REGIONAL	
479.2	**NORTH REGIONAL**	**May 17th**
1554.4	DAVENTRY NATIONAL	

ABERDEEN *changed to 288.5 metres/became a relay on May 31st.*
GLASGOW *changed to 376.4 metres on April 12th.*
MANCHESTER *changed to 479.2 metres on April 12th.*
MIDLAND REGIONAL *changed to 398.9 metres on April 12th.*
1931 is marked as the year in which the first British receiver appeared which had a full range of station names printed on the dial, which of course made the process of tuning-in very much simpler (*see page 100, and fig.314 page 121*).
*Bradford, Hull, Liverpool, MANCHESTER (which was the last of the B.B.C.'s four original 1922 stations), Sheffield and Stoke stations all closed down on May 17th.

1932 (January 1st)

242.3	BELFAST	
261.3	LONDON NATIONAL	
288.5	Aberdeen	
288.5	Bournemouth	
288.5	Dundee*	
288.5	Edinburgh*	
288.5	Newcastle	
288.5	Plymouth	
288.5	**SCOTTISH NATIONAL** **	**Sept. 25th**
288.5	Swansea	
301.5	NORTH NATIONAL	
309.9	CARDIFF	
356.3	LONDON REGIONAL	
376.4	GLASGOW*	
376.4	**SCOTTISH REGIONAL**	**June 12th**
398.9	MIDLAND REGIONAL	
479.2	NORTH REGIONAL	
1554.4	DAVENTRY NATIONAL	

Aberdeen *changed to 214.3 metres on June 12th.*
Newcastle *changed to 211.3 metres on July 24th.*
Swansea *changed to 245.9 metres on November 13th.*
*Dundee, Edinburgh and GLASGOW stations all closed down on June 12th.
**On September 25th, the SCOTTISH NATIONAL and SCOTTISH REGIONAL full twin medium-wave service was inaugurated from a new transmitter built at Westerglen, near Falkirk, fed with programmes by landline live from the Edinburgh studios (SCOTTISH REGIONAL had already been on the air since June 12th).

1933 (January 1st)

211.3	Newcastle	
214.3	Aberdeen	
242.3	BELFAST	
245.9	Swansea*	
261.3	LONDON NATIONAL	
261.6	**WEST NATIONAL****	**Aug. 13th**
288.5	Bournemouth	
288.5	Plymouth	
288.5	SCOTTISH NATIONAL	
301.5	NORTH NATIONAL	
309.9	CARDIFF*	
309.9	**WEST REGIONAL****	**Aug. 13th**
356.3	LONDON REGIONAL	
376.4	SCOTTISH REGIONAL	
398.9	MIDLAND REGIONAL	
480	NORTH REGIONAL	
1554.4	DAVENTRY NATIONAL	

LONDON REGIONAL *changed to 356.3 metres on February 26th.*
Plymouth *changed to 218.5 metres on February 26th.*
*Cardiff and Swansea stations closed down on August 13th.
**The WEST NATIONAL and WEST REGIONAL programmes radiated from the new Washford Cross transmitter near Minehead.

1934 (January 1st)

211.3	Newcastle
214.3	Aberdeen
218.5	Plymouth
242.3	BELFAST
261.6	LONDON NATIONAL
261.6	WEST NATIONAL
288.5	Bournemouth
288.5	SCOTTISH NATIONAL
301.5	NORTH NATIONAL
309.9	WEST REGIONAL
356	LONDON REGIONAL
376.4	SCOTTISH REGIONAL
398.9	MIDLAND REGIONAL
480	NORTH REGIONAL
1554.4	DAVENTRY NATIONAL

1934 (January 15th — LUCERNE PLAN)

203.5	Bournemouth	
203.5	Plymouth	
209.9	Newcastle	
233.5	Aberdeen	
267.4	BELFAST	
261.1	LONDON NATIONAL	
261.1	WEST NATIONAL	
285.7	SCOTTISH NATIONAL	
296.2	NORTH NATIONAL	
307.1	WEST REGIONAL	
342.1	LONDON REGIONAL	
373.1	SCOTTISH REGIONAL	
391.1	MIDLAND REGIONAL	
449.1	NORTH REGIONAL	
1500	DAVENTRY NATIONAL*	
1500	**DROITWICH (NATIONAL)**	**Oct. 7th**

*DAVENTRY NATIONAL closed down on October 7th and was superceded by the B.B.C.'s new high-power longwave station at DROITWICH as the NATIONAL programme transmitter.

1935 (January 1st)

203.5	Bournemouth	
203.5	Plymouth	
209.9	Newcastle	
233.5	Aberdeen	
261.1	LONDON NATIONAL*	
261.1	WEST NATIONAL*	
267.4	BELFAST**	
267.4	**NORTHERN IRELAND**	**Jan. 6th**
285.7	SCOTTISH NATIONAL	
296.2	**MID. REG. (Droitwich X'ter)***	**February 17th**
296.2	NORTH NATIONAL*	
307.1	WEST REGIONAL	
342.1	LONDON REGIONAL	
373.1	SCOTTISH REGIONAL	
391.1	MID. REG. (Daventry X'ter)***	
449.1	NORTH REGIONAL	
1500	DROITWICH (NATIONAL)	

Newcastle *changed to 267.4 metres,* NORTHERN IRELAND *changed to 307.1 metres,* NORTH NATIONAL *changed to 261.1 metres,* WEST REGIONAL *changed to 373.1 metres, and* SCOTTISH REGIONAL *changed to 391.1 metres on February 17th.*
* After February 17th, the LONDON NATIONAL, NORTH NATIONAL and WEST NATIONAL stations on 261.1 metres appeared on tuning dials grouped together as "NATIONALS".
** BELFAST was renamed NORTHERN IRELAND on January 6th.
***The MIDLAND REGIONAL transmitter at Daventry closed down on February 17th and the programme was transferred to a new transmitter at Droitwich *(see page 110).*

1936 (January 1st)

203.5	Bournemouth
203.5	Plymouth
233.5	Aberdeen
261.1	NATIONALS*
267.4	Newcastle
285.7	SCOTTISH NATIONAL
296.2	MIDLAND REGIONAL
307.1	NORTHERN IRELAND
342.1	LONDON REGIONAL
373.1	WEST REGIONAL
391.1	SCOTTISH REGIONAL
449.1	NORTH REGIONAL
1500	DROITWICH (NATIONAL)

* The LONDON NATIONAL, NORTH NATIONAL and WEST NATIONAL stations on 261.1 metres appear on tuning dials grouped together as "NATIONALS".

1937 (January 1st)

203.5	Bournemouth	
203.5	Plymouth	
233.5	Aberdeen	
261.1	NATIONALS*	
267.4	Newcastle**	
267.4	**STAGSHAW****	**Oct. 19th**
285.7	SCOTTISH NATIONAL*	
296.2	MIDLAND REGIONAL	
307.1	NORTHERN IRELAND	
342.1	LONDON REGIONAL	
373.1	**WELSH REGIONAL**	**July 4th**
373.1	WEST REGIONAL****	
391.1	SCOTTISH REGIONAL	
449.1	NORTH REGIONAL	
1500	DROITWICH (NATIONAL)	

* The LONDON NATIONAL and NORTH NATIONAL stations on 261.1 metres (together, from July 4th, with SCOTTISH NATIONAL which changed on that date to 261.1 metres) appeared on tuning dials grouped together as "NATIONALS". Also on July 4th, the WEST NATIONAL transmitter at Washford Cross ceased putting out this service and instead broadcast the WEST REGIONAL service on 285.7 metres *(see also ****, below).*
** Newcastle (the sole survivor of the B.B.C.'s four original 1922 stations) closed on October 19th, its 267.4 metre wavelength taken over by STAGSHAW *(see ***, below).*
*** The new STAGSHAW (Northumberland) transmitter carried an improved NORTH REGIONAL service to listeners in Cumberland, Westmorland, Durham and Northumberland supplementing the existing NORTH REGIONAL transmitter at Moorside Edge.
**** In Wales, a new WEST REGIONAL transmitter opened at Penmon (Anglesey) on January 31st carrying an improved service to listeners in North Wales supplementing the existing WEST REGIONAL transmitter at Washford Cross. From July 4th, both these transmitters radiated the new WELSH REGIONAL service *(see also *, above, and page 113).*

1938 (January 1st)

203.5	Bournemouth
203.5	Plymouth
233.5	Aberdeen
261.1	NATIONALS*
267.4	STAGSHAW
285.7	WEST REGIONAL
296.2	MIDLAND REGIONAL
307.1	NORTHERN IRELAND
342.1	LONDON REGIONAL
373.1	WELSH REGIONAL
391.1	SCOTTISH REGIONAL
449.1	NORTH REGIONAL
1500	DROITWICH (NATIONAL)

*The LONDON NATIONAL, NORTH NATIONAL and SCOTTISH NATIONAL stations on 261.1 metres appeared on tuning dials grouped together as "NATIONALS".

1939 (January 1st)

203.5	Bournemouth *(closed down on July 14th)*	
203.5	**Clevedon*** *(WEST REGIONAL relay)*	**June 14th**
203.5	Plymouth *(closed down on July 14th)*	
233.5	Aberdeen*	
261.1	NATIONALS*/**	
267.4	STAGSHAW*	
285.7	**Start Point*** *(WEST REGIONAL relay)*	**June 14th**
285.7	WEST REGIONAL*	
296.2	MIDLAND REGIONAL*	
307.1	NORTHERN IRELAND*	
342.1	**HOME SERVICE****	**Dec. 19th**
342.1	LONDON REGIONAL*	
373.1	WELSH REGIONAL*	
391.1	**HOME SERVICE**	**Sept. 1st**
391.1	SCOTTISH REGIONAL*	
449.1	**HOME SERVICE**	**Sept. 1st**
449.1	NORTH REGIONAL*	
1500	DROITWICH (NATIONAL)*	

*All these stations were suspended on September 1st due to national emergency.
**The LONDON NATIONAL, NORTH NATIONAL and SCOTTISH NATIONAL stations.
***From December 19th, the HOME SERVICE was put out on 342.1 metres after 6pm as a means of testing reception for the proposed FORCES PROGRAMME *(see pages 116 and 158).*

<table>
<thead>
<tr><th colspan="3">1940 (January 7th)</th></tr>
</thead>
<tbody>
<tr><td>342.1</td><td>FORCES PROG. (EXP)* (after 6pm)</td><td rowspan="4">January 7th</td></tr>
<tr><td>342.1</td><td>HOME SERVICE (before 6pm)</td></tr>
<tr><td>391.1</td><td>HOME SERVICE</td></tr>
<tr><td>449.1</td><td>HOME SERVICE</td></tr>
</tbody>
</table>

*The experimental alternative FORCES PROGRAMME, aimed at the British Expeditionary Forces in France, went on the air after 6pm on 342.1 metres (during the day, this wavelength carried the HOME SERVICE, *see page 158*).

<table>
<thead>
<tr><th colspan="3">1940 (February 18th)</th></tr>
</thead>
<tbody>
<tr><td>342.1</td><td>FORCES PROGRAMME* (6-11pm)</td><td>February 18th</td></tr>
<tr><td>342.1</td><td>HOME SERVICE (before 6pm)</td><td></td></tr>
<tr><td>373.1</td><td>FORCES PROGRAMME* (11am-7pm)</td><td>February 18th</td></tr>
<tr><td>391.1</td><td>HOME SERVICE</td><td></td></tr>
<tr><td>449.1</td><td>HOME SERVICE</td><td></td></tr>
</tbody>
</table>

*12-hour FORCES PROGRAMME came on the air split between 342.1 metres and 373.1 metres (with a one-hour overlap between 6-7pm).

<table>
<thead>
<tr><th colspan="2">1940 (February 25th)</th></tr>
</thead>
<tbody>
<tr><td>342.1</td><td>FORCES PROGRAMME (8-11pm)</td></tr>
<tr><td>342.1</td><td>HOME SERVICE (before 8pm)</td></tr>
<tr><td>373.1</td><td>FORCES PROGRAMME (11am-8pm)</td></tr>
<tr><td>391.1</td><td>HOME SERVICE</td></tr>
<tr><td>449.1</td><td>HOME SERVICE</td></tr>
</tbody>
</table>

<table>
<thead>
<tr><th colspan="3">1940 (March 17th)</th></tr>
</thead>
<tbody>
<tr><td>261.1</td><td>OVERSEAS SERVICE*</td><td>March 17th</td></tr>
<tr><td>342.1</td><td>FORCES PROGRAMME (10-11pm)</td><td></td></tr>
<tr><td>342.1</td><td>HOME SERVICE (11pm-12.15am)</td><td></td></tr>
<tr><td>373.1</td><td>FORCES PROGRAMME (11am-10pm)</td><td></td></tr>
<tr><td>373.1</td><td>OVERSEAS SERVICE* (after 10pm)</td><td>March 17th</td></tr>
<tr><td>391.1</td><td>HOME SERVICE</td><td></td></tr>
<tr><td>449.1</td><td>HOME SERVICE</td><td></td></tr>
</tbody>
</table>

*On March 17th, the OVERSEAS SERVICE, which until then had been on shortwave only, was supplemented on the medium waveband on 261.1 and 373.1 metres *(see also pages 117 and 158)*.

<table>
<thead>
<tr><th colspan="3">1940 (June 9th)</th></tr>
</thead>
<tbody>
<tr><td>261.1</td><td>OVERSEAS SERVICE</td><td></td></tr>
<tr><td>296.2</td><td>HOME SERVICE</td><td>June 9th</td></tr>
<tr><td>342.1</td><td>FORCES PROGRAMME (10-11pm)</td><td></td></tr>
<tr><td>342.1</td><td>HOME SERVICE (11pm-12.15am)</td><td></td></tr>
<tr><td>373.1</td><td>FORCES PROGRAMME (6.15-8am, 10.30am-10pm)</td><td></td></tr>
<tr><td>373.1</td><td>OVERSEAS SERVICE (after 10pm)</td><td></td></tr>
<tr><td>391.1</td><td>HOME SERVICE</td><td></td></tr>
<tr><td>449.1</td><td>HOME SERVICE</td><td></td></tr>
</tbody>
</table>

<table>
<thead>
<tr><th colspan="2">1940 (September 15th)</th></tr>
</thead>
<tbody>
<tr><td>261.1</td><td>OVERSEAS SERVICE</td></tr>
<tr><td>296.2</td><td>HOME SERVICE</td></tr>
<tr><td>342.1</td><td>FORCES PROGRAMME (ceased on this wavelength)</td></tr>
<tr><td>342.1</td><td>HOME SERVICE (ceased on this wavelength)</td></tr>
<tr><td>373.1</td><td>FORCES PROGRAMME* (6.15am-11pm)</td></tr>
<tr><td>373.1</td><td>OVERSEAS SERVICE (after 11pm)</td></tr>
<tr><td>391.1</td><td>HOME SERVICE</td></tr>
<tr><td>449.1</td><td>HOME SERVICE</td></tr>
</tbody>
</table>

*Full daily FORCES PROGRAMME came on the air on September 15th, on 373.1 metres only.

<table>
<thead>
<tr><th colspan="3">1940 (October 11th)</th></tr>
</thead>
<tbody>
<tr><td>41.49</td><td>FORCES PROGRAMME*</td><td>October 11th</td></tr>
<tr><td>48.82</td><td>HOME SERVICE*</td><td>October 11th</td></tr>
<tr><td>261.1</td><td>OVERSEAS SERVICE</td><td></td></tr>
<tr><td>296.2</td><td>HOME SERVICE</td><td></td></tr>
<tr><td>373.1</td><td>FORCES PROG.* (6.15am-11pm)</td><td></td></tr>
<tr><td>373.1</td><td>OVERSEAS SERVICE (after 11pm)</td><td></td></tr>
<tr><td>391.1</td><td>HOME SERVICE</td><td></td></tr>
<tr><td>449.1</td><td>HOME SERVICE</td><td></td></tr>
</tbody>
</table>

*From October 11th, the HOME SERVICE was allocated a shortwave frequency (48.82 metres), as was the FORCES PROGRAMME, whose 41.49 metres wavelength was primarily intended for the Royal Navy.

<table>
<thead>
<tr><th colspan="3">1940 (November 3rd)</th></tr>
</thead>
<tbody>
<tr><td>41.49</td><td>FORCES PROGRAMME</td><td></td></tr>
<tr><td>48.82</td><td>HOME SERVICE</td><td></td></tr>
<tr><td>203.5</td><td>Home Service*</td><td>November 3rd</td></tr>
<tr><td>261.1</td><td>OVERSEAS SERVICE</td><td></td></tr>
<tr><td>296.2</td><td>HOME SERVICE</td><td></td></tr>
<tr><td>373.1</td><td>FORCES PROGRAMME</td><td></td></tr>
<tr><td>373.1</td><td>OVERSEAS SERVICE (after 11pm)</td><td></td></tr>
<tr><td>391.1</td><td>HOME SERVICE</td><td></td></tr>
<tr><td>449.1</td><td>HOME SERVICE</td><td></td></tr>
</tbody>
</table>

*A network of 60 low-powered Home Service relays (known collectively as the 'H-Group') came into service, synchronised on 203.5 metres *(see page 158)*. NOTE: Wartime station names and wavelengths did not generally appear on tuning dials until well into 1940, and even many new radios retained (optimistically) the old pre-war wavelengths in case the war ended *(see Ekco AD75, fig.635)*.

<table>
<thead>
<tr><th colspan="2">1941 (January 1st)</th></tr>
</thead>
<tbody>
<tr><td>41.49</td><td>FORCES PROGRAMME</td></tr>
<tr><td>48.82</td><td>HOME SERVICE</td></tr>
<tr><td>203.5</td><td>Home Service</td></tr>
<tr><td>261.1</td><td>OVERSEAS SERVICE</td></tr>
<tr><td>296.2</td><td>HOME SERVICE</td></tr>
<tr><td>373.1</td><td>FORCES PROGRAMME</td></tr>
<tr><td>373.1</td><td>OVERSEAS SERVICE (after 11pm)</td></tr>
<tr><td>391.1</td><td>HOME SERVICE</td></tr>
<tr><td>449.1</td><td>HOME SERVICE</td></tr>
</tbody>
</table>

<table>
<thead>
<tr><th colspan="3">1941 (March 2nd)</th></tr>
</thead>
<tbody>
<tr><td>41.49</td><td>FORCES PROGRAMME*</td><td></td></tr>
<tr><td>49.38</td><td>HOME SERVICE**</td><td></td></tr>
<tr><td>203.5</td><td>Home Service</td><td></td></tr>
<tr><td>261.1</td><td>OVERSEAS SERVICE</td><td></td></tr>
<tr><td>296.2</td><td>HOME SERVICE (ceased on this w/l)***</td><td></td></tr>
<tr><td>342.1</td><td>FORCES PROGRAMME***</td><td>March 2nd</td></tr>
<tr><td>373.1</td><td>FORCES PROG. (ceased on this w/l)***</td><td></td></tr>
<tr><td>373.1</td><td>OVERSEAS SERVICE****</td><td></td></tr>
<tr><td>391.1</td><td>HOME SERVICE</td><td></td></tr>
<tr><td>449.1</td><td>HOME SERVICE</td><td></td></tr>
</tbody>
</table>

*The shortwave FORCES PROGRAMME frequency changed to 48.86 metres on June 15th.
**The shortwave HOME SERVICE frequency changed to 49.38 metres on March 2nd.
***On March 2nd, the HOME SERVICE ceased broadcasting on 296.2 metres, and the FORCES PROGRAMME ceased broadcasting on 373.1 metres, but now went back on its old wavelength of 342.1 metres.
****The OVERSEAS SERVICE fully took over the 373.1 metres wavelength on March 2nd.

<table>
<thead>
<tr><th colspan="3">1942 (January 1st)</th></tr>
</thead>
<tbody>
<tr><td>48.86</td><td>FORCES PROGRAMME</td><td></td></tr>
<tr><td>49.38</td><td>HOME SERVICE</td><td></td></tr>
<tr><td>203.5</td><td>Home Service</td><td></td></tr>
<tr><td>261.1</td><td>OVERSEAS SERVICE</td><td></td></tr>
<tr><td>296.1</td><td>FORCES PROGRAMME</td><td>March 6th</td></tr>
<tr><td>342.1</td><td>FORCES PROGRAMME</td><td></td></tr>
<tr><td>373.1</td><td>OVERSEAS SERVICE</td><td></td></tr>
<tr><td>391.1</td><td>HOME SERVICE</td><td></td></tr>
<tr><td>449.1</td><td>HOME SERVICE</td><td></td></tr>
</tbody>
</table>

<table>
<thead>
<tr><th colspan="2">1943 (January 1st)</th></tr>
</thead>
<tbody>
<tr><td>48.86</td><td>FORCES PROGRAMME</td></tr>
<tr><td>49.38</td><td>HOME SERVICE</td></tr>
<tr><td>203.5</td><td>Home Service</td></tr>
<tr><td>261.1</td><td>OVERSEAS SERVICE</td></tr>
<tr><td>296.1</td><td>FORCES PROGRAMME</td></tr>
<tr><td>342.1</td><td>FORCES PROGRAMME</td></tr>
<tr><td>373.1</td><td>OVERSEAS SERVICE</td></tr>
<tr><td>391.1</td><td>HOME SERVICE</td></tr>
<tr><td>449.1</td><td>HOME SERVICE</td></tr>
</tbody>
</table>

<table>
<thead>
<tr><th colspan="3">1944 (January 1st)</th></tr>
</thead>
<tbody>
<tr><td>48.86</td><td>FORCES PROGRAMME*</td><td></td></tr>
<tr><td>48.86</td><td>GENERAL FORCES PROG.*</td><td>February 27th</td></tr>
<tr><td>49.38</td><td>HOME SERVICE</td><td></td></tr>
<tr><td>203.5</td><td>Home Service</td><td></td></tr>
<tr><td>261.1</td><td>OVERSEAS SERVICE</td><td></td></tr>
<tr><td>285.7</td><td>ALLIED EXPED. FORCES PROG.**</td><td>June 7th</td></tr>
<tr><td>296.1</td><td>FORCES PROGRAMME*</td><td></td></tr>
<tr><td>296.1</td><td>GENERAL FORCES PROG.*</td><td>February 27th</td></tr>
<tr><td>342.1</td><td>FORCES PROGRAMME*</td><td></td></tr>
<tr><td>342.1</td><td>GENERAL FORCES PROG.*</td><td>February 27th</td></tr>
<tr><td>373.1</td><td>OVERSEAS SERVICE</td><td></td></tr>
<tr><td>391.1</td><td>HOME SERVICE</td><td></td></tr>
<tr><td>449.1</td><td>HOME SERVICE</td><td></td></tr>
</tbody>
</table>

*The FORCES PROGRAMME ceased on February 27th, and a new GENERAL FORCES PROGRAMME took over using its three wavelengths *(see page 163)*.
**Following D-Day on June 6th, the new ALLIED EXPEDITIONARY FORCES PROGRAMME was inaugurated on June 7th for the benefit of British, American and Canadian forces in France.

<table>
<thead>
<tr><th colspan="2">1945 (January 1st)</th></tr>
</thead>
<tbody>
<tr><td>48.86</td><td>GENERAL FORCES PROG. (continued on this w/l only after July 29th)</td></tr>
<tr><td>49.38</td><td>HOME SERVICE (ceased on this wavelength on July 29th)</td></tr>
<tr><td>203.5</td><td>Home Service</td></tr>
<tr><td>261.1</td><td>OVERSEAS SERVICE (ceased on July 29th)</td></tr>
<tr><td>285.7</td><td>ALLIED EXPED. FORCES PROG. (ceased on July 29th)</td></tr>
<tr><td>296.1</td><td>GENERAL FORCES PROG. (ceased on July 29th)</td></tr>
<tr><td>342.1</td><td>GENERAL FORCES PROG. (ceased on July 29th)</td></tr>
<tr><td>373.1</td><td>OVERSEAS SERVICE (ceased on July 29th)</td></tr>
<tr><td>391.1</td><td>HOME SERVICE</td></tr>
<tr><td>449.1</td><td>HOME SERVICE</td></tr>
</tbody>
</table>

Following the unconditional surrender of Germany on May 8th, sweeping changes in the B.B.C.'s broadcasting service took place on July 25th when a regionally-based HOME SERVICE network was introduced on 9 medium wavelengths, with, for national coverage, the new LIGHT PROGRAMME on both the medium and the long waveband *(see next entry)*.

1945 (July 29th)

203.5	**HOME SERVICE (WEST REGION)** *(Clevedon X'ter)*
261.1	**LIGHT PROGRAMME***
285.7	**HOME SERVICE (NORTH REGION)**
285.7	**HOME SERVICE (NORTHERN IRELAND REGION)**
296.2	**HOME SERVICE (MIDLAND REGION)**
342.1	**HOME SERVICE (LONDON REGION)**
373.1	**HOME SERVICE (WELSH REGION)**
391.1	**HOME SERVICE (SCOTTISH REGION)**
449.1	**HOME SERVICE (NORTH REGION)**
514.6	**HOME SERVICE (WEST REGION)** *(Start Point X'ter)*
1500	**LIGHT PROGRAMME** *(Droitwich X'ter)*

The above listing shows the B.B.C.'s post-war peacetime broadcasting plan for the country which came into operation on July 29th. The HOME SERVICE was now divided up into seven regions (Scottish, North, Midland, London, West, Welsh and Northern Ireland), with each region having its own Programme Director and transmitting a certain amount of regional material.
*To improve reception of the B.B.C.'s new national LIGHT PROGRAMME in the London, Northern and Scottish areas, the 1500 metre longwave transmitter at Droitwich was supplemented by three medium-wave transmitters at Brookmans Park, Moorside Edge and Westerglen, synchronised on 261.1 metres.

1946 (September 29th)

203.5	**THIRD PROGRAMME***	September 29th
216.8	HOME SERVICE (WEST REGION)**	
261.1	LIGHT PROGRAMME	
285.7	HOME SERVICE (NORTHERN IRELAND REGION)	
296.2	HOME SERVICE (MIDLAND REGION)	
307.1	HOME SERVICE (WEST REGION)**	
342.1	HOME SERVICE (LONDON REGION)	
373.1	HOME SERVICE (WELSH REGION)	
391.1	HOME SERVICE (SCOTTISH REGION)	
449.1	HOME SERVICE (NORTH REGION)***	
514.6	**THIRD PROGRAMME***	September 29th
1500	LIGHT PROGRAMME	

*On September 29th, the B.B.C.'s new THIRD PROGRAMME was radiated on 203.5 metres by several low-power transmitters around the country *(see page 167)*, and for the benefit of listeners in the Midlands area, it was also put out on 514.6 metres by the Droitwich transmitter.
**The WEST REGIONAL HOME SERVICE transmitters at Clevedon and Start Point changed their wavelengths on September 29th to 216.8 metres and 307.1 metres respectively.
***The NORTH REGIONAL HOME SERVICE 285.7 metre wavelength had ceased on June 2nd.

1947 (January 1st)

203.5	THIRD PROGRAMME
216.8	HOME SERVICE (WEST REGION)
261.1	LIGHT PROGRAMME
285.7	HOME SERVICE (NORTHERN IRELAND REGION)
296.2	HOME SERVICE (MIDLAND REGION)
307.1	HOME SERVICE (WEST REGION)
342.1	HOME SERVICE (LONDON REGION)
373.1	HOME SERVICE (WELSH REGION)
391.1	HOME SERVICE (SCOTTISH REGION)
449.1	HOME SERVICE (NORTH REGION)*
514.6	THIRD PROGRAMME
1500	LIGHT PROGRAMME

*On October 26th, the B.B.C's NORTH REGIONAL HOME SERVICE on 449.1 metres was joined by its second wavelength of 285.7 metres.

1948 (January 1st)

203.5	THIRD PROGRAMME
216.8	HOME SERVICE (WEST REGION)
261.1	LIGHT PROGRAMME
285.7	HOME SERVICE (NORTH REGION)
285.7	HOME SERVICE (NORTHERN IRELAND REGION)
296.2	HOME SERVICE (MIDLAND REGION)
307.1	HOME SERVICE (WEST REGION)
342.1	HOME SERVICE (LONDON REGION)
373.1	HOME SERVICE (WELSH REGION)
391.1	HOME SERVICE (SCOTTISH REGION)
449.1	HOME SERVICE (NORTH REGION)
514.6	THIRD PROGRAMME
1500	LIGHT PROGRAMME

1949 (January 1st)

203.5	THIRD PROGRAMME
216.8	HOME SERVICE (WEST REGION)
261.1	LIGHT PROGRAMME
285.7	HOME SERVICE (NORTH REGION)
285.7	HOME SERVICE (NORTHERN IRELAND REGION)
296.2	HOME SERVICE (MIDLAND REGION)
307.1	HOME SERVICE (WEST REGION)
342.1	HOME SERVICE (LONDON REGION)
373.1	HOME SERVICE (WELSH REGION)
391.1	HOME SERVICE (SCOTTISH REGION)
449.1	HOME SERVICE (NORTH REGION)
514.6	THIRD PROGRAMME
1500	LIGHT PROGRAMME

1950 (March 15th — Copenhagen Plan)

194	THIRD PROGRAMME
206	HOME SERVICE (WEST REGION)
247	LIGHT PROGRAMME
261	HOME SERVICE (NORTH REGION)
261	HOME SERVICE (NORTHERN IRELAND REGION)
276	HOME SERVICE (MIDLAND REGION)
285	HOME SERVICE (WEST REGION)
330	HOME SERVICE (LONDON REGION)
341	HOME SERVICE (WELSH REGION)
371	HOME SERVICE (SCOTTISH REGION)
434	HOME SERVICE (NORTH REGION)
464	THIRD PROGRAMME
1500	LIGHT PROGRAMME

1955 (May 2nd — VHF/FM Broadcasting begins)

89.1Mc/s	**LIGHT PROGRAMME***	May 2nd
91.3Mc/s	**THIRD PROGRAMME***	May 2nd
93.5Mc/s	**HOME SERVICE***	May 2nd

194	THIRD PROGRAMME
206	HOME SERVICE (WEST REGION)
247	LIGHT PROGRAMME
261	HOME SERVICE (NORTH REGION)
261	HOME SERVICE (NORTHERN IRELAND REGION)
276	HOME SERVICE (MIDLAND REGION)
285	HOME SERVICE (WEST REGION)
330	HOME SERVICE (LONDON REGION)
341	HOME SERVICE (WELSH REGION)
371	HOME SERVICE (SCOTTISH REGION)
434	HOME SERVICE (NORTH REGION)
464	THIRD PROGRAMME
1500	LIGHT PROGRAMME

*On May 2nd, the first three of the B.B.C.'s high-power VHF/FM radio broadcasting stations were brought into regular service at Wrotham Hill in Kent, transmitting the LIGHT, THIRD and HOME SERVICE programmes to London and the Home Counties areas *(see page 184)*.

1963 (January 7th)

194	THIRD PROGRAMME
206	HOME SERVICE (WEST REGION)
224	**HOME SERVICE (NORTHERN IRELAND REGION)**
247	LIGHT PROGRAMME
261	HOME SERVICE (NORTH REGION)
276	HOME SERVICE (MIDLAND REGION)
285	HOME SERVICE (WEST REGION)
330	HOME SERVICE (LONDON REGION)
341	HOME SERVICE (WELSH REGION)
371	HOME SERVICE (SCOTTISH REGION)
434	HOME SERVICE (NORTH REGION)
464	THIRD PROGRAMME
1500	LIGHT PROGRAMME

1967 (January 1st)

194	THIRD PROGRAMME	
194	**RADIO 3***	September 30th
206	HOME SERVICE (WEST REGION)	
206	**RADIO 4***	September 30th
224	HOME SERVICE (NORTHERN IRELAND REG.)	
247	LIGHT PROGRAMME	
247	**RADIO 1***	September 30th
261	HOME SERVICE (NORTH REGION)	
276	HOME SERVICE (MIDLAND REGION)	
285	HOME SERVICE (WEST REGION)	
285	**RADIO 4***	September 30th
330	HOME SERVICE (LONDON REGION)	
341	HOME SERVICE (WELSH REGION)	
371	HOME SERVICE (SCOTTISH REGION)	
434	HOME SERVICE (NORTH REGION)	
464	THIRD PROGRAMME	
464	**RADIO 3***	September 30th
1500	LIGHT PROGRAMME	
1500	**RADIO 2***	September 30th

*On Sept. 30th, the B.B.C.'s *"swinging new radio service"* was inaugurated, led by a new all-pop music network, RADIO 1, with the other networks given a new image and being renamed RADIO 2 (old LIGHT PROGRAMME), RADIO 3 (old THIRD PROGRAMME) and RADIO 4 (old HOME SERVICE). On November 8th, the B.B.C's first local radio station, RADIO LEICESTER, went on the air on 95.05 Mc/s. Today (1996), the network has expanded to some forty stations.

1978 (November 23rd)

247	RADIO 3	Little red and blue diamond-shaped stickers *(right)* can often be seen stuck on the tuning dials of radios bought before 1978. They were provided by the B.B.C. so that listeners could use them to indicate the new November 23rd positions of the B.B.C.'s MW and LW stations.
275	RADIO 1	
285	RADIO 1	
330	RADIO 2	
433	RADIO 2	
1500	RADIO 4	

New wavelengths on the B.B.C.'s medium and longwave network (VHF frequencies were unchanged).

fig.914. Engineer Jack Cooper at the controls of the B.B.C.'s Birmingham (5IT) station in 1923 making sure everything is in order with its output on 420 metres. At this time, listeners-in had to make a separate note of where stations appeared in relation to the markings on their tuning dials (usually calibrated from 0 - 180 degrees, *see page 43*). This practice lasted beyond the end of the decade until, in 1931, station names began to appear printed on dials and the pointer was merely aimed at the name of the station required (*see page 100*).

An Edwardian Amateur Wireless Station (Call-Signal "S.I.X")

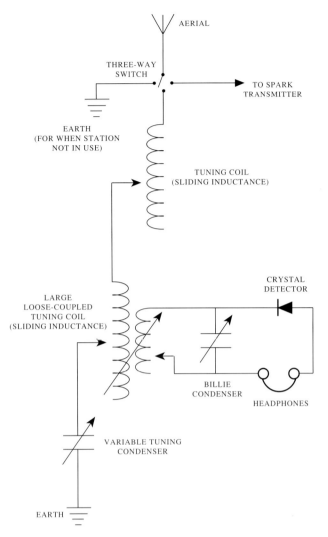

fig.915. Stapleton's crystal receiver circuit, 1911. Receiving range up to 600 miles, waverange between 250m and 4,000m.

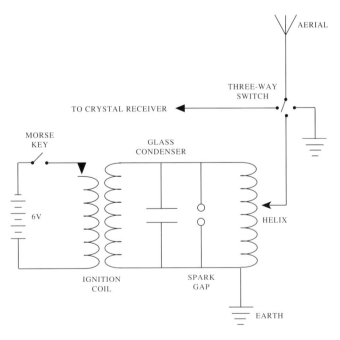

fig.916. Stapleton's spark transmitter circuit, 1913. Power 12 Watts, sending range 200 miles. *[Transmitter and receiver specifications from Gamage's Directory of Experimental Wireless Stations, published in March 1914].*

The transmitting and receiving station described here was put together between 1911 and 1913. It was assembled and operated under the call-signal S.I.X. by 'wireless amateur' Harold Stapleton who carried out experiments in Morse code with other enthusiasts in and around London until the outbreak of the First World War in August 1914 curtailed their activities. Within a short time, fearing a compromise to national security, Government officials began the process of confiscating all amateur wireless stations, including Stapleton's, which were then held in Post Office custody for the duration of the war.

There can be very few complete amateur wireless stations still surviving today that were operating in this country over 80 years ago. Technical progress in wireless communication during the First World War had been rapid. The world of spark transmitters and Morse code which Stapleton had shared with other wireless amateurs and which had been prevalent throughout the Edwardian era soon gave way in post-war years to valve circuits and broadcast telephony. It was towards this new area of wireless that Stapleton directed his interest when peace returned. However, his outdated spark equipment, instead of being dissected and utilised in a more modern set up (as was the fate of other amateur wireless stations) was simply kept in the boxes it was confiscated in and put away in an attic. It came to light again in the 1970s along with early correspondence conducted between Stapleton and the Post Office while he was establishing S.I.X. (summarised, right, *et seq.*) which provides a rare insight into a slower paced and more courteous age.

fig.917. Harold Stapleton operating his amateur wireless station in June 1913. The various bits and pieces which went to make up his spark transmitter and receiver are seen here set up on a desk in the front room of his home at 3 Prideaux Road, Clapham Rise, London.

fig.918. After a break during the WWI, Stapleton resumed his interest in experimental wireless, this time with 'modern' valve equipment for reception only (photograph, above, dated June 1920).

SUMMARY OF CORRESPONDENCE BETWEEN HAROLD STAPLETON AND THE POST OFFICE

1910 26th September: Stapleton first writes to the Postmaster General, General Post Office, London enquiring about obtaining a licence to conduct experiments in wireless telegraphy.

1910 30th September: G.P.O. sends Stapleton a wireless telegraphy licence application form inviting him *"to fill in the required particulars, and return the form to this office"* where his *"application shall be considered"*.

1910 1st October: Stapleton first applies to the Postmaster General, General Post Office, London for a licence to conduct experiments in wireless telegraphy.

1911 27th January: A Licence is issued to Stapleton, and his experimental station is given the call signal "S.I.X." (licences were issued free-of-charge until May 1913). He is advised in a letter from the G.P.O. accompanying his licence that *"with reference to Clause 5 (2) of the licence . . . the Postmaster General has found it desirable to lay down a general rule that stations should have a distinctive call-signal, and that each station, when signalling, should begin each transmission with the call signal of the station with which it desires to communicate and end with its own call signal"*. This ruling was first put into practice by the Postmaster General in May 1910.

1911 21st March: Licence cancelled. Stapleton is advised in the letter from the General Post Office that his existing licence is cancelled due to certain revisions of its provisions. He is asked to return his licence whereupon *"a fresh licence will be issued in due course if you still desire to continue your experiments"*.

1911 3rd April: Stapleton returns his licence to the General Post Office .

1911 13th September: A new licence is issued by the General Post Office. Stapleton is advised that he can continue using his original call signal - "S.I.X."

1911 27th November: Stapleton (now residing at 3 Prideaux Road, Clapham Rise, London SW) is informed that, in accordance with the terms of his licence, his wireless installation is to be inspected by an officer of the Post Office Telegraphs, Sectional Engineer's Office, Metropolitan (South) District, at 66 North Side, Wandsworth Common, London SW.

On the reverse of this letter in Stapleton's handwriting is a copy of the reply he gave, (on 29th November 1911), which clearly shows that up to this time, he only possessed a wireless receiver, viz:

Sir,

I am in receipt of letter dated 27th inst. re a visit to my wireless installation. I usually experiment on Tuesday and Friday evenings between 7.45 and 10.30, so I shall be pleased to see you or your representative any of the times mentioned above (excepting Tuesday 6th) but I will be in if you make an appointment for following Tuesday.

With regard to the installation, owing to my lack of spare time I have not made up any transmitting apparatus, only receiving, and that is not by any means as complete as I hope to have it. Will this Friday (the 1st) or next be the most convenient to the inspecting officer as I will be in on both dates,

I remain,
Your obedient servant,
H.S.

1911 8th December: Stapleton's wireless installation (comprising receiver only) is inspected by the Post Office at 8pm on Friday 8th December.

1912 22nd July: Mr. J.J.B. Grose of 388 Brixton Road, London applies to the General Post Office for permission to conduct wireless telegraphy experiments with Stapleton's station. He encloses with his application Stapleton's licence which will have to be amended to include details of this arrangement.

1912 25th July: The General Post Office informs Stapleton that Mr J.A. Fann of 36 Pine Road, Cricklewood, London NW has applied to them for permission to conduct wireless telegraphy experiments with Stapleton's station. He is asked to return his licence so that *"the necessary provision may be inserted therein"*. On the reverse of this letter in Stapleton's handwriting, is a copy of the reply he gave on 30th July thus:

Sir,

With reference to your letter of the 25th inst. I beg to inform you that Mr. J.J.B. Grose of 388 Brixton Road enclosed my licence with his application, No:97610/12 on 22nd inst., for experimenting with me also.
I am Sir,
Your obedient servant,
H.S.

1912 31st August: Stapleton's licence is returned having been amended with a permit to conduct wireless telegraphy experiments with Mr. J.J. Fann at 36 Pine Road, Cricklewood, London NW (call signal F.V.X.) and Mr J.J.B. Grose of 388 Brixton Road, London SW (call signal G.E.X.). Stapleton is advised that he can continue using his original call signal.

1913 June: By this date, Stapleton had assembled his spark transmitter — his wireless station was now complete. A month earlier the Post Office had for the first time imposed a charge (£1.1s.0d.) on all new experimental licences in an attempt to dissuade non bona-fide experimenters from applying, and also to cover the cost of administering licence documentation and inspecting amateur wireless installations. Stapleton was then one of only 405 amateurs licensed to transmit.

1913 20th August: The General Post Office informs Stapleton that Mr A. Vallins of 32 Edithna Street, London Road, Stockwell has applied to them for permission to conduct wireless telegraphy experiments with Stapleton's station. He is asked to return his licence so that *"the necessary provision may be inserted therein"*.

1913 14th October: Stapleton is issued with a fresh licence amended with a permit to conduct wireless telegraphy experiments with Mr A. Vallins of 32 Edithna Street, Stockwell. Stapleton is advised that he can continue using his original call signal.

1913 15th November: The General Post Office informs Stapleton that Mr H. Hildersley* *"with whom you are authorised to communicate, has changed his residence to 95 Minard Road, Catford"*. Stapleton is asked to return his licence so that it can be amended. It is not clear exactly when Stapleton was authorised to conduct experiments with Hildersley*, but it may have been when he first applied for a licence on 1st October 1910. *[This is more likely to be H. Hillesdey (call signal H.H.X. originally of Hither Green, London), who used to write articles on wireless telegraphy in The Model Engineer].

1914 14th February: Stapleton's licence is returned having been *"endorsed with particulars of Mr. H. Hildersley's new address"*. Stapleton is advised that he can continue using his original call signal.

1914 13th May*: Stapleton writes to the General Post Office asking them if he may transfer his wireless installation to his new address, Oakbank Grove, Herne Hill, London SE. *[Between this date and March 1920, he moves to 32 Grove Avenue, Twickenham].

1914 29th May: The G.P.O. informs Stapleton that they have no objection to him transferring his wireless installation to his new address, and ask him to return his licence so that it can be amended.

1914 1st August: A few days before Britain declared war on Germany, the Secretary of the G.P.O. sent the following telegram to Stapleton and all other amateur wireless licence holders which effectively put a stop to their experimental work for several years: *"TO STAPLETON CALL SIGNAL S I X • AUGUST 1 1914 • IN ACCORDANCE WITH YOUR WIRELESS LICENCE POSTMASTER GENERAL REQUIRES YOU TO REMOVE AT ONCE YOUR AERIAL WIRES AND DISMANTLE YOUR APPARATUS • ONE OF HIS OFFICERS WILL SHORTLY CALL UPON YOU • SIGNED KING SECRETARY GENERAL POST OFFICE"*

1914 28th November: Under the terms of Regulation 22 of the Defence of the Realm Consolidation Act, 1914 (dated 28/11/14), restrictions are introduced banning the manufacture, the purchase, the sale and the possession of all wireless apparatus intended for the transmission or reception of wireless telegraphy, even if the operator held an experimental licence. (A few amateur wireless stations were subsequently issued with a special permit allowing them to operate under Government control for official purposes, but the vast majority were eventually to be closed down for the duration of the war). An extract of the Regulation appears below:

"No person shall, without written permission of the Postmaster General, make, buy, sell or have in his possession, or under his control, any apparatus for the sending or receiving of messages by wireless telegraphy, or any apparatus intended to be used as a component part of such apparatus . . . and any person having in his possession or under his control any such apparatus, whether with or without the permission of the Postmaster General, shall on demand deliver the apparatus to the Postmaster General, or as he may direct . . . . For the purposes of this regulation any apparatus ordinarily used as a distinctive component part of apparatus for the sending or receiving of messages by wireless telegraphy shall be deemed to be intended to be so used unless the contrary is proved".

Over the next few months following the introduction of the above restrictions, the G.P.O. begins the process of confiscating the equipment of many wireless amateurs around the U.K. Their licences, now deemed *"ineffective"*, are cancelled — [letter from G.P.O. to wireless amateur R.J. Richardson dated 3rd March 1915]. Some amateur experimental licences, though, remain in force throughout the war in what appears to have been an oversight by the G.P.O. — all pre-war licences are finally cancelled on 5th July 1919.

1915 July: The Postmaster General acts more decisively and announces that <u>all</u> amateur wireless stations will be seized with immediate effect *"in order to simplify the control of wireless apparatus and to avoid the inspection to private premises . . . "* Stapleton's entire wireless station, by now dismantled, is packed up in cartons and confiscated by Post Office officials, and not released back to him until after April 1920.

1920 23rd March: Stapleton, whose stated occupation is a Wireless Instrument Maker at the War Department Wireless Factory, Soho (letter dated 23rd March 1920) writes to the Secretary of the General Post Office asking (a) to renew his experimental receiving and transmitting licence, first issued 27th January 1911, (b) to have all his wireless apparatus confiscated by the G.P.O. during the Great War returned to him, and (c) to have permission to resume experimental reception work. He encloses a 10/- (ten shilling) postal order as payment for the Experimenter's

Licence (first introduced on October 21st 1919 for reception only — transmitting licences were not issued again until August 1st 1920). Since having his pre-WWI equipment confiscated by the G.P.O., he has moved away from spark telegraphy and on to thermionic valves for use in both rectification and amplification, stating (in his letter of 23rd March 1920), that he wished *"to purchase valves (and other apparatus later) from Messrs. Mitchells; Messrs. Gamage, and the Radio Communication Co.".*

1920 13th April: Stapleton is notified in a letter/permit from the G.P.O. that he has been given permission by the Postmaster General to install and use apparatus for the reception of wireless signals at his Twickenham address (32 Grove Avenue), pending the issue of a formal receiving licence (the 10/- Experimenter's Licence), payment for which he sent with his letter of 23rd March 1920. One of the conditions was that the valves he intended to use in his receiver for rectification and amplification should *"be used in such a manner as to cause no interference with other stations"*. Enclosed with this letter was a separate permit authorising him to purchase valves and other apparatus from the various companies mentioned in his letter to the G.P.O. dated 23rd March 1920. Stapleton is informed that his old spark transmitting and receiving apparatus (held in Post Office custody since the war) is to be released back to him, but that he cannot use any *"apparatus for the transmission of wireless signals without the Postmaster General's specific authority"*. A summary of the conditions on which the P.M.G. was prepared to authorise the use of transmitters was also enclosed, together with a transmitting licence application form.

It appears that Stapleton did not subsequently apply for a transmitting licence, but settled instead for conducting experiments in wireless reception only, which by now included telephony. He never again went back to spark telegraphy and the complete wireless station he had assembled before the First World War remained packed up in the cartons it was confiscated in, and lay forgotten and gathering dust in the attic of his house in Grove Avenue for the next 50 years.

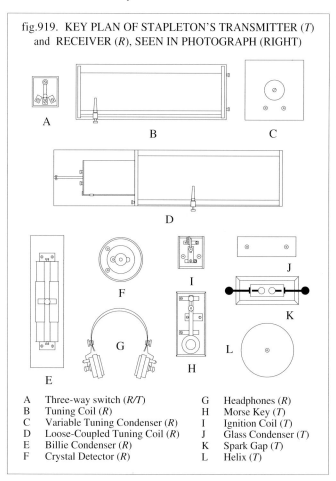

fig.919. KEY PLAN OF STAPLETON'S TRANSMITTER (*T*) and RECEIVER (*R*), SEEN IN PHOTOGRAPH (RIGHT)

A	Three-way switch (*R/T*)	G	Headphones (*R*)
B	Tuning Coil (*R*)	H	Morse Key (*T*)
C	Variable Tuning Condenser (*R*)	I	Ignition Coil (*T*)
D	Loose-Coupled Tuning Coil (*R*)	J	Glass Condenser (*T*)
E	Billie Condenser (*R*)	K	Spark Gap (*T*)
F	Crystal Detector (*R*)	L	Helix (*T*)

fig.920. The transmitting and receiving station operated before the First World War by wireless amateur, Harold Stapleton — one of only 405 such stations licensed at that time and perhaps the only complete and fully-documented example in existence today.

The Horophone - The 'Holy Grail' Of Early Wireless Receivers

The story surrounding the complete Edwardian amateur wireless station found in an attic and outlined on pages 234 to 237 of this book is at least matched (if not bettered) by the recent discovery of the unique wall-mounted Horophone crystal set of around the same period. Produced in 1913 by the Synchronome Company of London and designed by their founder and director Frank Hope-Jones, it was the first British 'domestic' wireless set designed specifically for receiving time-signals transmitted in Morse from various long-wave stations in Europe, most notably the Eiffel Tower Observatory in Paris (on 2,600 metres).

Although many people today are familiar with the basic appearance of the Horophone thanks to a single line-engraving of it that has appeared from time-to-time in various publications over the years (fig.23, p.24), it was until quite recently generally accepted that no actual 'living' specimen of this crystal set had managed to survive from before the First World War. Much research by dedicated collectors and historians in Britain and on the Continent had failed to uncover any trace of one. Because of this, and because of the Horophone's unique place as a landmark in both British wireless and horological history, many consider it to be the 'holy grail' of early British wireless receivers. In 1995, however, what may turn out to be the one and only surviving example was unearthed by a scientific instrument dealer in the North of England. Although now in a private collection, it has been possible to photograph and examine this wonderful instrument at close quarters. What is intriguing about this particular Horophone is that it has *provenance* (as Lovejoy would call it) for its history can be traced back over 80 years to when it hung on the wall of an address in Clerkenwell Road — an address which was at that time not only the London premises of the company that produced it, but also the business address of its designer. Dare we hope that this, the only Horophone known to exist, was the actual one owned and operated by Hope-Jones himself? We dare . . . so read on!

THE SYNCHRONOME COMPANY

By 1910, the world's first daily wireless time-signal service in Morse had begun from the Eiffel Tower Observatory in Paris (call-sign 'FL'). In Britain, the Paris time-signals were of great interest not only to the growing band of wireless amateurs thankful for something more to tune in to, but also to those to whom accurate time was of prime importance (*ie.* observatories, the Admiralty, shipping lines, railway companies and others running to precise timetables, and industrial firms including, of course, clock and watchmakers). Henceforth, wireless was to be used as an official and co-ordinated means of setting accurate time, and within a few years (mainly thanks to agreements following the International Radio-Telegraphic Convention held in London in 1912), wireless time-signals were being transmitted by stations around half the globe.

At this time, the Synchronome Company was well known for its involvement with electrically synchronised clock systems devised by Frank Hope-Jones in the 1890s for use in large factories *etc*. Here, a central master electric clock simultaneously drove a number of 'slave' clocks connected together by bell wire in various parts of the building. Each slave advanced one minute as it received an electric impulse from the master clock.

Hope-Jones was a respected figure in both horological and in wireless circles. A prominent member of the British Horological Society and (in 1913) the first chairman of the Wireless Society of London, he had first become interested in wireless as early as 1900, when he had begun to experiment with its use in time keeping, adapting his wired synchronised system to the wire-*less* broadcasting of electrical impulses. The introduction of the Paris time-signal service (not triggering slave clocks, but providing timed and measured signals — rather like

"the pips", *see p.47*) combined Hope-Jones' dual interests which eventually led him into designing the Horophone in 1913. Two versions were made — a Type 'A' (the one recently discovered and shown in the photograph opposite *et seq.*), and the similar Type 'B' (fig.921, this page — illustration courtesy Pat Leggatt) which, as well as a crystal detector, also had an electrolytic detector, a potentiometer and a changeover switch for selecting either detector (see also *The Wireless World*, Sept. 1913).

Examination of the Type 'A' Horophone allows some intriguing observations. Although bearing the Synchronome Company's name and London address, plus other labels engraved in English, its construction has a definite 'French feel' about it — the crystal detector is certainly French-made (*see fig.925*), and the patterning found on its turned ebonite control knobs is also echoed by the patterning found on other parts of the receiver, indicating the same hand. In all probability, therefore, the Horophone was made by a French manufacturer to Hope-Jones' own specification and to his own design.

This is not at all surprising, for he was already a frequent visitor to the Paris Observatory and would have built-up numerous wireless and horological contacts in France. Furthermore, by 1913, French-made time-signal wireless receivers had already gone on sale in France. One manufacturer, Louis Ancel, a scientific instrument maker based in Paris, was producing a range of such receivers which he had first demonstrated at the Paris Observatory in 1912 in conjunction with the International Radio-Telegraphic Convention. Ancel's receivers included two wall-mounted types not unlike the Horophone. It is inconceivable that Hope-Jones would not have known about them.

The Type 'A' Horophone came to light through the family of Edgar James Burroughs who has a direct connection with the Synchronome Company, for in 1910, at the age of 17, he began his working life as an apprentice watchmaker with them at Clerkenwell Road (Clerkenwell was then the centre of the Edwardian watch trade). According to family folklore, when Burroughs temporarily left in 1915 to join up following the outbreak of the war, the Type 'A' Horophone that had been used by Synchronome at their premises went with him. In the 1920s, by which time he had resumed his employment at Clerkenwell Road, Burroughs kept the Horophone at home and used it as a conventional crystal set to listen-in to the infant B.B.C. Over the years it was played with from time-to-time by family members until Burroughs' death in 1972. Since then it had been put away, finally leaving the Burroughs' family when sold in 1995.

CONCLUSION?

Future research may prove otherwise, but from the evidence I have so far been able to gather, it seems very likely that Hope-Jones had a single specimen of each type of Horophone made up in France in 1913. He then brought them back to Clerkenwell Road, where both he and his employees (including apprentice Edgar Burroughs) used them in connection with their work. In the months before the outbreak of W.W.I., Hope-Jones publicised the Horophone in one or two horological and wireless-related magazines including *The Wireless World*, with the intention of marketing it to the watch and clockmaking industry. Although a trade mark application (number 352,885 of 25/6/1913) was granted for the Horophone, no patent was ever taken out or even applied for. I therefore think it very unlikely that the Horophone ever got into quantity production, or that more than one of each type was made before W.W.I. intervened. Exactly how the Type 'A' Horophone shown here ended up in Burroughs' home is yet to be fully discovered. So too, is the whereabouts of the Type 'B' Horophone — but that, of course, may not have survived.

fig.922. The recently discovered Type 'A' Horophone crystal set of 1913 comprising a cat's whisker/crystal detector, buzzer, variable condenser, tuning coil, watch, headphones and aerial/earth shorting plug, all arranged on a wall-mounted mahogany board 18" high.

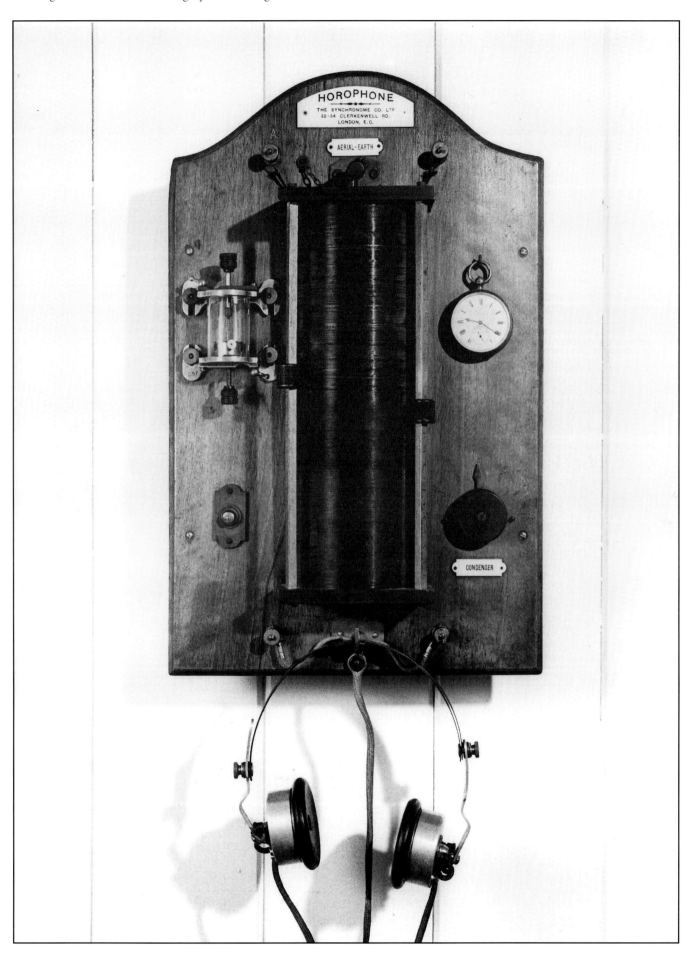

The following description of the operation of the Horophone was supplied by its designer Frank Hope-Jones for Caxton's 3-volume work *The Book Of Electrical Installations* prepared in 1914. (By the time it went to print in the following year, because of the war situation the possession of wireless equipment without special permission from the Postmaster General had been prohibited). Illustrating the article was the time signal chart shown below, right, and also the line-engraving shown in fig.23 on page 24, looking slightly different from the actual Horophone due to the artistic liberty taken by the engraver.

"*The instrument should be erected on a wall free from vibration, and preferably in a room where one is not disturbed by noise. Having joined up the aerial and earth wires to the terminals at the top of the board marked 'A' and 'E' respectively and withdrawn the plug in the centre, place the telephones over the ears and proceed to adjust the detector as follows: loosen the two clamps on the top and bottom of the crystal detector (on the left of the instrument) about half a turn, and manipulate the little vulcanite knobs until the pointed end of the spiral brass wire is resting on the crystal in the cup.*

"*Now press the button on the case underneath the detector and operate the buzzer which acts as a very weak transmitter of electrical waves, and if the detector is adjusted correctly a loud buzzing will be heard in the telephones. Some parts of the crystal are more sensitive than others and can only be found by trial. The transmitting station desired may now be tuned using the two sliders on the coil in conjunction with the condenser. The sliders and the condenser are calibrated to allow a note to be made of their particular settings for each transmitter. When the instrument is finished with, replace the plug at the top of the board. This connects the aerial direct to earth and protects the instrument from lightning.*

"*The detector is one of the class known as crystal detectors, and is fitted with two substantial aluminium castings mounted on the base by four screws. A cup with three screws is provided for holding the crystal and a brass point selector, perfect selection being obtained by means of the locked ball and socket adjustments. A glass cylinder encloses the crystal and point and the whole detector can be taken to pieces in a few seconds by simply loosening the fixing screws. The crystal supplied is prepared by special process, and will be found very sensitive and easy of adjustment. No local battery is required, in fact applied E.M.F. renders it less sensitive. Other crystals can of course be used if desired*".

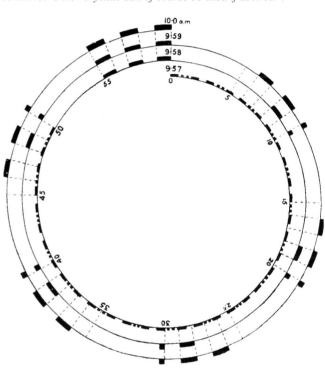

fig.924. The illustration above shows a diagrammatic representation of the 10am time-signals which were sent out between 9.57am and 10am from the Eiffel Tower Observatory in Paris. The pattern of these signals was devised by General Ferrié and they were also sent out between 10.44am and 10.48am, 11.44pm and 11.49pm and at midnight, together with regular weather forecasts and news reports in Morse.

The illustration might look more complicated than it is, but if you read the following description through a couple of times, the process should become clear!

Start from the inside of the spiral at figure '0', and follow the diagram in a clockwise direction. From 9.57, warning signals in the form of the Morse letter X (— . . —) were repeated for fifty seconds followed by silence for five seconds, after which the first time-signal was given, consisting of three dashes each lasting for one second, separated by intervals of one second - the end of the third dash coinciding precisely with the beginning of the 58th minute.

During this minute, the Morse letter N (— .) was sent out for every ten seconds followed by the second time-signal. For the 59th minute, the Morse letter G (— — .) was sent out for every ten seconds followed by the third time-signal of three dashes, the last dash ending precisely at the hour of 10 o'clock, enabling clocks and watches to be accurately set.

fig.923. The Type 'A' Horophone with its back off — a view that few people have seen! Note the buzzer mechanism (top right) and the rather primitive looking variable tuning condenser (centre left). This has two sets of rectangular sliding vanes made out of compressed cardboard which are covered on the back with silver foil (ten vanes per set). When the tuning knob is turned, an ingenious jointed mechanism slides the bottom set of vanes in and out of the top (fixed) set. The 4" x 11" tuning coil seen in the centre is wound on a cardboard former with exactly 440 turns of 24 swg black enamelled copper wire. The two sliders (*shown in fig.922*), which are used to tune the coil run along metal guide bars, calibrated from '0' to '27' (this measurement corresponded to 0-2700 metres, the actual waverange of the coil).

fig.925. A close-up of the Horophone's precision French-made "Omnium" crystal detector (galena crystal/cat's whisker contact), numbered 962, and marked in French *breveté* ('patented') and *S.G.D.G.* ('sans garantie du Gouvernement' — in other words, this meant that the French Government did not guarantee the quality of that particular product, even though they had granted it a patent!).

The end fittings are made of cast aluminium while the arms supporting the crystal and the cat's whisker are in brass, each with a turned* ebonite ('vulcanite') insulation cap. The arms are adjustable and can be held in position at any angle by means of a locking piece or clamp (top left and bottom right). The whole assembly is linked together by a glass tube which not only protects the crystal/cat's whisker contact from knocks, but also keeps out dust and dirt.

The pattern of the turning (cross-hatched to provide a grip) is echoed throughout the Horophone and appears also on the ebonite slider knobs, the variable condenser control knob, and the aerial/earth shorting plug. This attention to detail is one of the delights of the Horophone which is a most beautifully designed and well-made instrument.

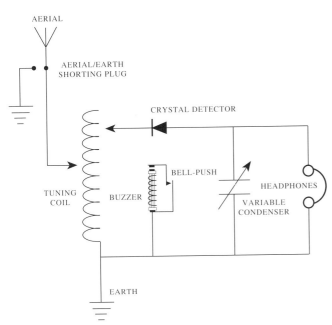

fig.926. The circuit diagram of the Type 'A' Horophone.

The Tempus Time-Signal Receiver

fig.927. The Horophone wasn't the only British wireless set designed to receive time-signals, as shown here by the Tempus crystal set made by W.J. Badman & Co. of Weston-Super-Mare in 1921 for use *"in Shop, Office or Work-room for the accurate regulation of Clocks or Watches"* (the illustration on the instruction booklet, above, shows a clockmaker setting his watch to the 10am time-signals). Original price £5.10s.0d. (Marconi's Wireless Telegraph Co. also brought out a time-signal wireless, the Crystal Receiver No:1, in c.1910/11, and their earlier Portable Magnetic Receiver of c.1906/7 [based on the 1902 Magnetic Detector] could also receive time-signals, although it wasn't specifically designed for this purpose. Both these sets were intended for official maritime use only, whereas the Horophone and the Tempus were 'domestic' sets, albeit with a commercial purpose).

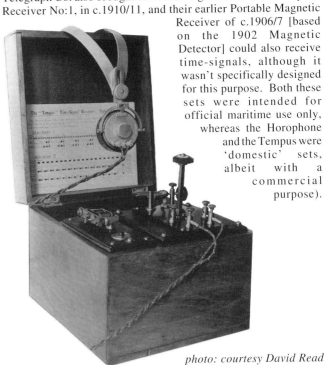

photo: courtesy David Read

241

A Directory of British Transistor Radios & Foreign Imports, 1956-1972

INTRODUCTION

This unique Directory briefly describes every popular model of British-made transistor radio (as well as many imported from abroad — from Europe, America and the Far East) available over the counter or by mail-order between 1956 and 1972.

During this period, the British transistor radio rapidly rose from very humble beginnings in 1956 with the introduction of just one set (the Pam 710), to a seemingly unassailable position by 1961, a year which witnessed British manufacturers completely abandoning the valve portable in favour of the transistor. Within a few years, though, unable to cope with competition from abroad (notably from Japan and the Far East), the British transistor went into rapid decline and all but disappeared along with our once proud radio industry. By the time the B.B.C. celebrated its 50th anniversary in 1972, many of our famous radio manufacturers whose names had been household words for decades, had fallen by the wayside and of those few that had managed to survive mainly by grouping together, Oriental chassis often lurked beneath the British brand name.

Transistor products issued by over 250 different manufacturers are featured in this Directory, and in addition to popular models (and by 'popular' I mean those which were well known at the time, and were good sellers), I have also included lesser known examples whose novelty, rarity or styling (bizarre in some cases) have demanded inclusion. If you are a transistor collector, then this Directory can be used as a comprehensive checklist or spotter's guide to transistors that you could have or should have in your collection (if you had every one listed then you would have getting on for 3,000!). Today, many radio collectors specialise in one particular manufacturer and with British firms in particular, whether large or small, I have tried to include every known model they produced within the period described, so you can at least see the ones you have missing.

Dates: The date accompanying each particular model shows the year in which it was first released onto the market in the U.K. — *ie.* when you would expect to see it on display if you wandered into a radio & electrical shop, or looked through a manufacturer's current product catalogue. If known, the month indicates its first mention in trade reviews or magazine advertisements.

At the end of each particular manufacturer's details appears a note on their transistor radio production run which shows the years during which they were active in producing or marketing transistor radios (*ie. "Transistor Production Run 1963-68"*). Where transistor production or sales continued outside the period covered by this Directory (*ie.* after 1972 and on into the 1970s), then this is indicated by a '+' sign (*ie.* 1968+).

Although some makes of transistor were only produced or distributed for one 12 month season, many models were current for several years. For example, one of the last Portadyne transistors to come off the production line, the International II of 1968, was still being shown as a current model in the 1974 edition of the *Electrical & Electronic Trader Yearbook*.

Prices: Prices shown refer to the advertised retail cost to the customer at the time of introduction, first trade review or advertisement. Changes may have occurred subsequently during a particular production run, due, for example, to fluctuations in the level of Purchase Tax or other market forces. For example, the Dynatron TP11 (Nomad) was priced at £19.9s.6d. plus £6.5s.0d. P.T. when introduced in 1959, but this had fallen to £17.3s.10d. plus £2.15s.2d. P.T. when it was withdrawn in 1963. More dramatically, Siemens model RT10

(an 8-transistor M/LW/FM portable) cost £30.9s.0d. including P.T. when introduced in 1959, but this price had more than halved, to just £15 including P.T. when withdrawn in 1964. For transistor radios introduced up to and including 1970, prices are shown in the old pounds, shillings and pence ('£.s.d.') monetary system. For those on the market from 1971 onwards, their prices are shown in the new decimal system — the changeover occurring on February 15th of that year.

Type of transistor radios: Almost all the transistor radios listed in this Directory are domestic types, intended either for the home or for outdoor use — in many cases, both. Several had a secondary, lesser function as car radios with car aerial sockets provided, and often a fixing bracket for in-car mounting. In this case they will be found described thus; 'portable/car radio'. With one exception (the Murphy Voxson), fully fledged transistorised car radios are not featured (that could be the subject of another book . . . . any takers?!).

Radios combined with clocks/watches are included, but those with cassette tape recorders/players are not. Unless stated otherwise, all the transistor radios listed are battery operated, mono receivers. The number of transistors employed in each circuit is indicated. (Diodes are not generally included, but some examples can be found listed under the section 'Typical Transistor Line-Ups' on page 283 *et seq.*).

Cabinet finishes and colour schemes: In the 1960s and 1970s, transistor radios were often produced in a choice of colour schemes. For example, with the Beolit 600 made by Bang & Olufsen (*see page 247*), customers could choose between a black, white, purple, mustard or coral coloured cabinet to match the decor of their sitting-rooms.

During these decades, saddle-stitched leather or leatherette cases (separate in the 1960s [*fig.814*]), and integral in the 1970s [*fig.959*]) were particularly popular — the latter a favourite with Binatone especially, and fashionable amongst Seventies teenagers. Padded leatherette coverings, often combined with teak, other matt-finished woods or moulded cabinets, also found favour from mid/late 1960s (*fig.815*). The minutiae of the various cabinet finishes found on the radios are outside the scope of this Directory, and are not generally referred to, except in a few cases where they are particularly alarming.

Different manufacturer/cabinet . . . but same chassis: Between 1957 and 1962, the structure of the British Radio Industry changed with many smaller firms like Cossor, McMichael, Pilot and Regentone being absorbed by large concerns like Philips, Radio & Allied Industries, Ultra and Kolster-Brandes *etc.*, so that groups of companies were formed. Usually the main company retained the use of the brand-name of the smaller company it had absorbed. The various radios that were put out by the group often shared the same basic chassis but had different model numbers and different brand-names. For example, within the Philips' group, the Cossor CR1310T and Stella ST415T share the same circuit and chassis of the Philips 241T, differing only in cabinet presentation.

As the 1960s wore on, chassis made in the Far East began to appear in radios carrying British brand names - a common enough sight today even with that bastion of British radio, Roberts Radio, whose more recent products have included radios bearing the legend "Made In China" (*eg.* the Roberts RP14, mains/battery portable of 1990. This set is further distinguished because it was the very first one to exhibit on its tuning dial the B.B.C.'s new Radio 5 station, which was inaugurated at 9am on Monday 21st August 1990 on 693kHz and 909kHz on the medium waveband).

fig.928. The K-B Sonata (Model SP31), a 6-transistor medium and longwave portable made by Kolster-Brandes Ltd. in 1961. Just the thing for a motoring trip in the country with a friend!

Ace (Ace Radio Ltd.), Tower Works, Tower Road, Pound Lane, Willesden, London NW10. From 1962, Cefndy Road, Rhyl, Wales. *Transistor Production Run 1957-1963.*

TR6-2. 6tr, M/LW portable. £13.17s.10d. plus £3.19s.2d. P.T. 1961.

TR257 (Courier). 7tr, M/LW portable. £22.16s.0d. plus £8.13s.0d P.T. December 1957.

Argosy Clubman. 6tr, M/LW portable. 1964.

Promenade. 6tr, M/LW portable. £9.19s.6d. including P.T. 1963.

Admiral (*dist.* **Denham & Morley Ltd.**), 173-175 Cleveland Street, London W1. *Transistor Production Run 1960.*

Admiral de Luxe. October 1960.

Aero [Japan] (*dist.* **Finex [Overseas] Ltd.**), 7 West End Lane, London NW6. Later, (from 1965) (*dist.* **Winter Trading Co. Ltd.**), 95-99 Ladbroke Grove, London W11. *Transistor Production Run 1961-65.*

ALM6. 7tr, M/LW pocket portable. 1965.

G-607. 6tr, MW Pocket portable. May 1961.

Aga (Aga Dictating Machine Co. Ltd.), 146 New Cavendish Street, London W1. *Transistor Production Run 1961.*

3140. 9tr, M/LW/FM portable. £28.13s.3d. plus £11.4s.9d. P.T. September 1961.

Aiwa [Japan] (*dist.* **B. Adler & Sons [Radio] Ltd.**), 32a Coptic Street, WC1. From 1968, (**Aiwa Co. Ltd.**), 31-36 Foley Street, London W1. *Transistor Production Run 1966-70+.*

AR122L. 12tr, M/LW/FM mains/battery portable. £20.9s.10d. plus £3.13s.2d. P.T. 1966. (Complete with built-in mains adaptor).

AR124. 10tr, S/M/LW/FM portable. £21.7s.3d. plus £3.16s.9d. P.T. 1966. (Mains adaptor, extra).

AR126L. 12tr, M/LW/FM mains/battery portable. £15.12s.2d. plus £2.15s.4d. P.T. 1966. (Complete with built-in mains adaptor).

AR132. 10tr, MW/FM pocket portable. £9.6s.0d. plus £1.13s.6d. P.T. 1966.

AR140. 10tr, S/M/LW/FM mains/battery portable. £25.7s.2d. plus £4.11s.4d. P.T. 1966. (Built-in mains adaptor, and tuning meter).

AR142. MW/FM mains/battery portable. £25.4s.0d. including P.T. 1970.

AR143H. 14tr, S/M/LW/FM mains/battery portable. £28.0s.9d. plus £5.18s.5d. P.T. 1968. (Built-in mains adaptor, tuning meter).

AR150. 15tr, 2S/M/LW/FM mains/battery portable/car radio. £49.12s.7d. plus £11.6s.5d. P.T. 1968. (For home, outdoor or in-car use).

AR150H. 15tr, 2S/M/LW mains/battery portable. £44.13s.4d. plus £9.8s.2d. P.T. 1968.

AR158H. 14tr, S/MW/FM/Aircraft Band/Marine Band mains/battery portable. £31.3s.7d. plus £6.12s.2d. P.T. 1968. (Built-in mains adaptor).

AR159H. 13tr, 2S/M/LW mains/battery portable. £31.3s.7d. plus £6.12s.5d. P.T. 1968.

AR160. 9tr, M/FM pocket portable. £8.14s.8d. plus £1.15s.4d. P.T. 1968.

AR614. 6tr, M/LW pocket portable. £4.0s.6d. plus 16s.10d. P.T. 1968.

AR734. 7tr, 2S/MW portable. 1969.

AR810L. 8tr, S/M/LW portable. £10.13s.5d. plus £1.18s.7d. P.T. 1966.

AR819. 2S/MW portable. £15.16s.3d. plus £3.12s.3d. P.T. 1968.

AR819L. 8tr, S/M/LW portable. £14.8s.8d. plus £3.0s.11d. P.T. 1968.

AR823. 8tr, MW portable. 1969.

AR865. 8tr, MW portable. 1969.

AR866. 8tr, MW portable. 1969.

Ajax [Hong Kong] (*dist.* **Acme Electric Co. [Finsbury] Ltd.**), 63 Gt. Eastern Street, London EC2. *Transistor Production Run 1961-72+.*

Ajax 6. 6tr, MW pocket portable. £2.15s.0d. including P.T. 1967.

Ajax 7. 7tr, MW pocket portable. 1967.

Ajax 8. 8tr, M/LW portable. £6.19s.6d. including P.T. 1965.

Ajax K600. 6tr, MW pocket portable. 1972.

Ajax TR190A. 6tr, MW pocket portable. £9 plus £2.18s.0d. P.T. May 1961.

Ajax TR220 de Luxe. 6tr, M/LW personal portable. £10.10s.0d. plus £3.7s.6d. P.T. July 1961.

Buccaneer. 7tr, M/LW portable. 1966.

Classic (770). M/LW/FM portable. 1972.

Commando. S/M/LW/FM/Aircraft Band mains/battery portable. 1972.

Continental. S/M/LW/FM/Aircraft Band/Marine Band mains/battery portable. 1972.

Coronet (P800). S/M/LW/FM mains/battery portable. 1972.

Craftsman. 2S/M/LW/FM/Aircraft Band/Marine Band/Public Service Band mains/battery portable. 1972.

Crestor Single Wave. 6tr, MW pocket portable. 1963.

Cromwell (1133). M/LW portable. 1972.

Dandy (641). MW pocket portable. 1972.

Diplomat (L1110LW). M/LW portable. 1971.

Flamingo. 8tr, M/LW portable. 1967.

Flamingo Mk.II. 8tr, M/LW portable. £5.9s.6d. including P.T. 1970.

Empress TR330. 10tr, S/M/LW portable. £14.14s.0d. including P.T. 1964.

Grosvenor. 12tr, M/LW mains/battery portable. 1967. (Complete with built-in mains adaptor).

International. MW/FM/Aircraft Band/Marine Band portable. 1971.

Londoner (876ML). 8tr, M/LW portable. £7.17s.6d. including P.T. 1967.

Mayfair (TM6A). M/LW/FM portable. 1970.

Minx. MW pocket portable. 1971.

Parisian. 14tr, MW/FM mains/battery portable. 1967. (Complete with built-in mains adaptor).

Passport (112). M/LW portable. 1972.

President. M/LW/FM portable. 1970.

Regal. 10tr, S/M/LW portable. 1967.

Regency. 10tr, M/LW/FM portable. 1967.

Royal TR220. 6tr, M/LW pocket portable. £5.5s.0d. including P.T. 1964.

Senator Mk.II. (TRL875). M/LW portable. 1970.

Serenade. 8tr, M/LW portable. £4.10s.0d. including P.T. 1970.

Serenade Mk.II (ST531). 8tr, M/LW portable. 1971.

Skymaster. M/LW/Aircraft Band portable. 1971.

Skymaster Mk.II. M/LW/Aircraft Band mains/battery portable. 1972.

Sovereign. M/LW/FM portable. 1971.

Stroller. M/LW pocket portable. 1971.

Super TR250. 6tr, M/LW pocket portable. £5.19s.6d. including P.T. 1964.

Symphonic (737). M/LW portable. 1972.

Two Wave. 6tr, M/LW pocket portable. 1963.

Ventura. M/LW portable. 1971.

Viscount. M/LW portable. 1971.

Akkord [West Germany] (*dist.* **A. Prince Industrial Products Ltd.**), 34 Marylebone High Street, London W1. From 1963, (*dist.* **Denham & Morley Ltd.**), 173-175 Cleveland Street, London W1. *Transistor Production Run 1957-1965.*

Akkord 770. 11tr, S/M/LW/FM portable. £51.9s.0d. including P.T. 1965.

Ambassador 605. 12tr, S/M/LW/FM portable. £30.9s.0d. including P.T. 1964.

Autotourist. 9tr, S/M/LW/FM portable/car radio. £40.19s.0d. including P.T. 1964. (Bracket available for in-car use, £3.13s.6d. extra).

Autotransistor 715. 11tr, M/LW/FM portable/car radio. £51.9s.0d. including P.T. 1963. (Complete with amplifier and bracket for in-car use).

Autotransistor Auto. 12tr, 3S/M/LW portable/car radio. £61.19s.0d. including P.T. 1963. (Complete with amplifier and bracket for in-car use).

Bluebell. 7tr, M/LW pocket portable. £11.0s.6d. including P.T. 1963.

Clipper 304/30C. 7tr, 3S/M/LW portable. £22.1s.0d. including P.T. 1964.

Clipper 304/65. 7tr, S/M/LW portable. £20.9s.6d. including P.T. 1964. (Complete with battery/tuning meter).

Club 105. 6tr, M/LW portable. £14.14s.0d. including P.T. 1964.

Filou 701. 9tr, M/LW/FM portable. £26.5s.0d. including P.T. 1963.

Flash 400. 7tr, S/M/LW portable. £23.12s.6d. including P.T. 1964.

Kessey 604. 9tr, M/LW/FM portable. £30.19s.0d. including P.T. 1963.

Kessy Lux. 9tr, S/M/LW/FM portable. £35.14s.0d. including P.T. 1963.

Motorette 690. 9tr, M/LW/FM portable. £30.9s.0d. including P.T. 1963.

Peggie. 5tr, MW personal portable. £20.17s.4d. plus £8.2s.8d. P.T. June 1957.

Pinguin 800. 11tr, S/M/LW/FM portable. £72.9s.0d. including P.T. 1965.

Pinguin de Luxe '63. 9tr, S/M/LW/FM portable. £40.19s.0d. including P.T. June 1963.

Pinguette 720. 9tr, S/M/LW/FM portable. £39.18s.0d. including P.T. 1964.

Rhythm 404. 9tr, M/LW/FM portable. £26.5s.0d. including P.T. 1964.

Selectar 505/65. 9tr, 2S/M/LW portable. £28.7s.0d. including P.T. 1964. (Complete with battery/tuning meter).

Trident 205/20C. 6tr, 2S/M/LW portable. £17.17s.0d. including P.T. 1964.

Aladdin (*dist.* **Winter Trading Co. Ltd.**), 95-99 Ladbroke Grove, London W11. *Transistor Production Run 1962.*

AL603. 6tr, MW pocket portable. £6.19s.6d. including P.T. August 1962.

Alba (Alba [Radio & Television] Ltd.), 52-70 Tabernacle Street, London EC2. *Transistor Production Run 1960-72+.*

22. 6tr, M/LW portable. £14.14s.3d. plus £4.14s.3d. P.T. March 1960.

33. Table model version of model 22 (above). £14.6s.3d. plus £4.11s.9d. P.T. August 1960.

44 (Swift). 6tr, M/LW portable/car radio. £15.15s.0d. including P.T. February 1961. (For home, outdoor or in-car use — fits into glove compartment with controls facing the driver).

55 (Sprite). 6tr, M/LW pocket portable (pre-set on LW for the Light Programme). £10.10s.0d. including P.T. February 1962.

55 (Sprite de Luxe). 6tr, M/LW pocket portable in presentation case (pre-set on LW for the Light Prog.). £12.1s.6d. including P.T. February 1962.

88 (Snipe). 6tr, M/LW portable. £12.12s.6d. including P.T. June 1962.

99 (Swallow). 6tr, M/LW portable. £18.7s.6d. including P.T. July 1962.

111 (Starling). 6tr, M/LW portable. £11.11s.0d. including P.T. August 1963.

131. 10tr, MW/FM portable. £14.18s.7d. plus £2.12s.8d. P.T. 1966.

131L. 10tr, M/LW/FM portable. £15.7s.8d. plus £2.14s.3d. P.T. 1967.

222 (Starlet). 6tr, M/LW pocket portable. £6.15s.6d. plus £1.9s.0d. P.T. 1968.

232. 10tr, M/LW/FM portable. £22.12s.5d. plus £3.19s.10d. P.T. 1966. (Bandspread tuning between 188-216 metres, for Radio Luxembourg).

243 (Starlight). 7tr, M/LW portable. £8.11s.10d. plus £1.10s.5d. P.T. 1966.

333. 8tr, S/M/LW portable. £12.14s.7d. plus £2.14s.5d. P.T. 1968.

444. 7tr, M/LW portable. £9.10s.2d. plus £2.4s.10d. P.T. 1969.

535. 7tr, M/LW portable. £12.14s.6d. plus £2.5s.0d. P.T. 1967.

555. 7tr, M/LW portable. £13.16.0d plus £2.19s.0d. P.T. 1968.

625. 7tr, M/LW portable. £10.18s.7d. plus £2.11s.5d. P.T. 1969.

636. 10tr, S/M/LW/FM portable. £24.8s.6d. plus £5.4s.6d. P.T. 1968.

636T. 10tr, M/LW/FM/Marine Band portable. £24.8s.6d. plus £5.4s.6d. P.T. 1968.

665. 8tr, MW/FM pocket portable. £7.19s.6d. plus £1.17s.6d. P.T. 1969.

666. 10tr, M/LW/FM portable. £14.8s.3d. plus £3.1s.9d. P.T. 1968.

675. 10tr, M/LW/FM portable. £16.0s.7d. plus £3.15s.5d. P.T. 1969.

676. 10tr, MW/FM portable. £13.05p. including P.T. 1971.

680. 7tr, M/LW portable/car radio. £19.07p. including P.T. 1971. (For home, outdoor and in-car use).

737 (Scout). 7tr, M/LW portable. £14.14s.0d. including P.T. 1965. (Bandspread tuning between 188-216 metres, for Radio Luxembourg).

775. 7tr, M/LW/FM portable. £20.77p. including P.T. 1971.

777 (Swan). 6tr, M/LW portable. £13.2s.6d. including P.T. May 1963.

780. 7tr, M/LW/FM portable. £23.85p. including P.T. 1972.

838 (Trans-Continental). 8tr, S/M/LW portable. £16.16s.0d. including P.T. 1965.

939 (Olympic). 7tr, S/M/LW portable. £18.18s.0d. including P.T. 1964.

Amcor (Tamaware). *Transistor Production Run 1962.*

8T11. Table model. August 1962.

8T21. Table model. August 1962.

Amplion (Amplion Ltd.), 175-179 Cricklewood Lane, London NW2. *Transistor Production Run 1959-62.*

A226 (Delegate). 6tr, M/LW portable. £13.1s.6d. plus £4.5s.0d. P.T. December 1959.

A230 (Skyport). 6tr, M/LW portable. £13.10s.3d. plus £4.6s.9d. P.T. July 1960.

A236. 6tr, M/LW pocket portable. £9.2s.10d. plus £2.18s.8d. P.T. June 1961.

A253. 6tr, M/LW portable. £9.15s.6d. plus £2.16s.6d. P.T. April 1962.

Arena (Trans-arena) (dist. B.C. Blazey & Clement Ltd.), Memfagimal House, 26 St. Cross Street, Hatton Garden, London EC1. From 1967, **(dist. Highgate Acoustics Ltd.)**, 184-188 Gt. Portland Street, London W1. *Transistor Production Run 1962-68.*

P319. 9tr, M/LW port. £30.9s.0d. inc. P.T. 1963.

PA9 Auto. 9tr, M/LW/FM portable. £33.12s.0d. including P.T. 1964.

PA9FM. 9tr, M/LW/FM portable. £13.19s.6d. including P.T. September 1962.

PA13. 13tr, 2S/M/LW/FM portable. £35.10s.0d. plus £5.19s.1d. P.T. 1966.

PA13FM. 13tr, 3S/M/LW/FM portable. £47.5s.0d. including P.T. September 1962.

PB7. 7tr, M/LW portable £15.4s.6d. including P.T. September 1962.

PB9FM. 9tr, M/LW portable. £24.3s.0d. including P.T. 1963.

PV7. 7tr, M/LW portable. £11.15s.3d. plus £2.6s.1d. P.T. 1966.

T1200 (Petite). 11tr, S/M/LW/FM mains table model. £41.0s.2d. plus £6.17s.4d. P.T. 1966.

T1500H. 28tr, S/M/LW/FM stereo mains table model. £60.4s.7d. plus £12.4s.5d. P.T. 1968. (Decoder for use in stereo mode, £7.7s.0d. extra).

T1900H (Stereo). 20tr, 2S/M/LW/FM stereo mains table model. £59.4s.9d. plus £9.18s.3d. P.T. (Tuning meter. Stereo decoder, extra). 1967.

T2500H. 34tr, S/M/LW/FM stereo mains table model. £84.13s.6d. plus £17.3s.6d. P.T. 1967. (Decoder for use in stereo mode, £6.6s.0d. extra).

TA10. 9tr, M/LW/FM portable. £31.7s.9d. plus £5.7s.3d. P.T. 1967.

TA12. 16tr, S/M/LW/FM portable. £42.15s.6d. plus £8.13s.6d. P.T. 1968.

Duo. 6tr, M/LW personal portable. £17.6s.6d. including P.T. September 1962.

Arnold (dist. S. Arnold Electronics Ltd.), 129 Whitechapel High Street, London E1. *Transistor Production Run 1965-66.*

Citadel. 6tr, MW pocket portable. £3.3s.0d. including P.T. 1966.

Globe. 8tr, S/MW spherical portable/novelty radio . £14.14s.0d. including P.T. 1965.

Raymor. 9tr, MW/FM portable. £12.12s.0d. including P.T. 1966.

Ringmaster (FM820). 16tr, 4S/M/LW/FM portable. £58.16s.0d. including P.T. 1965.

Swops. 6tr, MW pocket portable. £3.3s.0d. including P.T. 1966.

Wein. 7tr, MW/FM pocket portable. £9.19s.6d. including P.T. 1965.

Westminster. 10tr, M/LW/FM portable. £12.12s.0d. including P.T. 1965.

Antena (dist. Paschkes & Co. Ltd), 40 Craven Road, London W2. *Transistor Production Run 1963.*

Super 8-1. 8tr, S/M/LW portable. £23.12s.6d. including P.T. 1963.

Super 8-11. 8tr, 3S/MW portable. £25.4s.0d. including P.T. 1963.

Argosy (Argosy Radiovision Ltd.), Eastern Avenue West, Romford, Essex. *Transistor Production Run 1959-1963.*

Clubman. 7tr, M/LW portable. 1963.

TA1. 6tr, M/LW portable. £19.19s.0d. including P.T. August 1959.

Arim [West Germany] **(dist. Eric Wells [Merchants] Ltd.)**, 42 Botolph Lane, Eastcheap, London EC3. *Transistor Production Run 1963.*

Atlantic. 8tr, S/M/LW portable. February 1963.

Luxembourg. 7tr, M/LW portable. £11.11s.0d. including P.T. February 1963. (The Luxembourg radio was also available as part of the Arim-Travelgram, where it came clipped on to the side of a transistorised portable record player. Arim-Travelgram, price £21 complete including P.T.).

Trans-Europa. 7tr, M/LW portable. £16.5s.6d. including P.T. February 1963.

Trans-Europa de Luxe. 7tr, M/LW portable. £17.6s.6d. including P.T. February 1963.

Astrad [U.S.S.R.] **(dist. Technical & Optical Equipment [London] Ltd.)**, 15/17 Praed Street, London W2. *Transistor Production Run 1968-70.*

Altair. 8tr, 2S/M/LW portable. £9.17s.9d. plus £2.1s.9d. P.T. 1968.

Aquila. 7tr, M/LW pocket portable. £4.18s.8d. plus £1.0s.10d. P.T. 1968.

Auriga. 10tr, 6S/M/LW portable. £15.12s.2d. plus £3.5s.10d. P.T. 1968.

Corona. 6tr, M/LW pocket portable. £5.13s.6d. plus £1.4s.10d. P.T. 1968. (Includes rechargeable battery and charging unit).

Cygnus. 7tr, M/LW portable/watch radio. £9.6s.9d. plus £1.19s.3d. P.T. 1968.

Nova. 8tr, 2S/M/LW portable. £9.17s.9d. plus £2.1s.9d. P.T. 1968.

Orion Micro. 6tr, M/LW miniature portable (earpiece only). 1970. (This is a tiny, beautifully-made two-waveband set with circuit components, battery compartment and tuning coil, all crammed into a case measuring just 1 1/8" x 1 3/4" x 1/3". Something like a Russian version of a Sinclair product, only with the added ingredient of quality).

Riga 103. 18tr, 3S/M/LW/FM portable. £44.19s.6d. including P.T. 1968. (Includes tuning meter and two loudspeakers).

Solar. 17tr, 3S/M/LW/FM portable. £44.19s.6d. including P.T. 1969. (Includes tuning meter and two loudspeakers).

Aurora (dist. S. Arnold Electronics Ltd.), 129 Whitechapel High Street, London E1. *Transistor Production Run 1964.*

TMC86BS. 8tr, S/MW portable. £8.18s.6d. including P.T. 1964.

TMC86BL. 8tr, M/LW portable. £8.18s.6d. including P.T. 1964.

TMC106C. 10tr, MW portable. £8.8s.0d. including P.T. 1964.

Baird (Baird TV Distributors Ltd.), Empire House, High Road, London EC2. *Transistor Production Run 1962-65.*

103. 7tr, M/LW portable. £13.13s.0d. including P.T. 1965.

256. 6tr, M/LW portable. 1962.

262. 6tr, M/LW portable (pre-set on LW for the Light Programme). £13.2s.6d. including P.T. 1963.

264. 6tr, M/LW portable. £12.1s.6d. including P.T. 1963.

266. 6tr, M/LW portable. £12.1s.6d. including P.T. 1963. (Slightly modified version of 264).

268. 6tr, M/LW portable. £13.13s.0d. including P.T. 1963. (Slightly modified version of 264).

270. 6tr, M/LW table model. £16.5s.6d. including P.T. 1963. (Slightly modified version of 264).

276. 6tr, M/LW portable. £11.11s.0d. including P.T. 1963. (Slightly modified version of 264).

278. 6tr, M/LW portable. £16.16s.0d. including P.T. 1963. (Slightly modified version of 264).

290. 7tr, M/LW portable. £11.11s.0d. including P.T. 1963.

292. 7tr, M/LW portable. £11.0s.6d. including P.T. 1964.

294. 6tr, M/LW portable. £12.12s.0d. including P.T. 1963. (Slightly modified version of 264).

296. 10tr, M/LW portable/car radio. £17.17s.0d. including P.T. 1964. (For home, outdoor or in-car use).

298. 10tr, M/LW portable. £16.16s.0d. including P.T. 1964. (Basically as 296, but without provision for car aerial).

Baladin (*dist.* Denham & Morley Ltd.), 173-175 Cleveland Street, London W1. *Transistor Production Run 1961.*

Baladin 62. 6tr, M/LW portable. £13.10s.3d. plus £4.6s.9d. P.T. June 1961.

Bang & Olufsen [Denmark] (*dist.* **Aveley Electric Ltd.**), South Ockendon, Essex. From 1963, (*dist.* **St. Aldate Warehouse Ltd.**), Innsworth Lane, Gloucester. From 1965, (*dist.* **Debenhams Electrical & Radio Distribution Co. Ltd.**), Eastbrook Road, Gloucester. From 1969, (**Bang & Olufsen [U.K.] Ltd.**), of Easterbrook Road, Gloucester. *Transistor Production Run 1961-72+.*

Beolit 400. 9tr, FM portable. £27.77p. including P.T. 1971. (Available in black, white, red, violet or brown. Mains adaptor [Beopower 600], £6.90p. extra).

Beolit 500. 11tr, FM table model. £33.18s.3d. plus £5.19s.9d. P.T. 1966. Push-button selection of 5 stations.

Beolit 600. 9tr, S/M/LW/FM portable/car radio. £34.19s.9d. plus £4.8s.3d. P.T. 1966. (Bracket available for in-car use).

Beolit 600 (Colouradio). 9tr, M/LW/FM portable. £36.10s.0d. including P.T. 1970. (Interchangeable coloured panels were available in a variety of colours — white, black, purple, mustard or coral — a typically 'hippy' colour range. Mains adaptor [Beopower 600], £6.18s.0d. extra).

Beolit 609 AM/FM. 9tr, S/M/LW/FM portable. £28.2s.8d. plus £9.9s.11d. P.T. August 1961.

Beolit 609 AM Export II. 9tr, 3S/M/LW portable. £19.19s.0d. including P.T. 1964.

Beolit 609 FM Export II. 9tr, 2SW/MW/FM portable. £26.5s.0d. including P.T. 1963.

Beolit 611 de Luxe. 10tr, S/M/LW/FM portable. £40.19s.0d. including P.T. 1964.

Beolit 700. 10tr, S/M/LW/FM portable/car radio. £29.9s.0d. plus £5.4s.0d. P.T. 1967. (Bracket available for in-car use).

Beolit 800. 9tr, S/M/LW/FM portable/car radio. £34.16s.0d. plus 6.3s.0d. P.T. 1967. (Bracket available for in-car use).

Beolit 800T. 10tr, S/M/LW/FM portable. £40.19s.0d. including P.T. 1965.

Beolit 1000. 18tr, 2S/M/LW/FM portable/car radio. £62.5s.3d. plus £13.19s.9d. P.T. 1968. (Bracket available for in-car use. Model with Goatskin finish, £63.18s.0d. plus £14.7s.0d. P.T. Mains adaptor [Beopower 1000], £11.18s.0d. extra).

Beolit Teena FM. 11tr, M/LW/FM portable. £22.1s.0d. including P.T. 1964.

Beomaster 800. Integrated circuit TBA 460, M/LW/FM stereo mains table model. £99.50p. including P.T. 1972.

Beomaster 900K. 23tr, S/M/LW/FM stereo mains table model, with a pair of built-in loudspeakers. £58.16s.0d. plus P.T. 1964. (*"B & O's first all-transistor mains-operated stereo radio"* imported into Britain in preparation for the introduction of the B.B.C.'s stereo radio broadcasting service which was eventually inaugurated on Saturday July 30th 1966. Decoder for use in stereo mode, optional extra — otherwise it was used as a mono table model. One of the earliest mains-only transistorised table models to be introduced. *See fig.957, p.299*).

Beomaster 900M. £54.12s.0d. plus P.T. 1964. (As 900K, above, but without built-in loudspeakers — available as an optional extra).

Beomaster 900M Mk.II. 25tr, M/LW/FM stereo mains table model. £72.0s.0d. including P.T. 1969. (Decoder for use in stereo mode extra).

Beomaster 1000. 30tr, FM stereo mains table model. £95.0s.0d. including P.T. 1970. (Decoder for use in stereo mode, £9 extra).

Beomaster 1200. 45tr, M/LW/FM stereo mains table model. £105.6s.0d. including P.T. 1970. (Special wall-mounting bracket, optional extra).

Beomaster 1400K. 2S/M/LW/FM stereo mains table model. £101.5s.3d. plus £22.14s.9d. P.T. 1968. (Decoder for use in stereo mode, extra).

Beomaster 1600. 33tr, M/LW/FM stero mains table model. £121.6s.0d. including P.T. 1970.

Beomaster 3000. 63tr (+ 2 integrated circuits), FM stereo mains table model. £139.10s.0d. including P.T. 1970.

Beaumont (Beaumont [Television] Ltd.), 1 Wood Street, Brighouse, Yorkshire. *Transistor Production Run 1959-60.*

Arundel. 6tr, M/LW table model. £19.19s.0d. including P.T. December 1959.

Week-Enda. 7tr, M/LW portable radio/travelling case (pre-set on LW for the Light Programme). £17.9s.9d. plus £5.12s.3d. P.T. August 1960.

Belair [Hong Kong] (*dist.* **Harris & Russell Ltd.**), 51 Calthorpe Street, London WC1. *Transistor Production Run 1964-67.*

Belair 7TP. 7tr, S/M/LW portable. £12.1s.6d. including P.T. 1964.

Belair 8TP. 8tr, S/M/LW portable. £15.15s.0d. including P.T. 1964.

Belair FU19C. 15tr, 3S/MW/FM portable. £30.9s.0d. including P.T. 1964.

Belair FU101A. 9tr, MW/FM pocket portable. £8.2s.10d. plus £1.8s.10d. P.T. 1966.

Belair FU101EP. 11tr, MW/FM pocket portable. £6.0s.0d. plus £1.2s.0d. P.T. 1967.

Beltone [Hong Kong] (*dist.* **L.P.F. Photronic Ltd.**), Cricklewood Lane, London NW2. *Transistor Production Run 1964.*

Beltone. 6tr, MW pocket portable. £6.19s.6d. including P.T. 1964.

Benkson [Hong Kong/Japan] (*dist.* **Benkson Ltd.**), 351 Oxford Street, London W1. From 1970, (*dist.* **Benkert Ltd.**), of same address. *Transistor Production Run 1963-71.*

22. MW pocket port. £2.52p. inc. P.T. 1971.

33. M/LW pocket portable. £4.10p. including P.T. 1971.

44. M/LW portable. £8.65p. including P.T. 1971.

55. 7tr, M/LW pocket portable. £4.15s.0d. including P.T. 1970.

59. 7tr, S/M/LW portable. £8.11s.1d. plus £1.9s.4d. P.T. 1966.

66. 8tr, M/LW portable. £6.6s.0d. including P.T. 1970.

69. 7tr, S/M/LW portable. £12.19s.6d. including P.T. 1964.

75. 10tr, S/M/LW portable. £8.10s.2d. plus £1.10s.11d. P.T. 1966.

77. 8tr, M/LW portable. £7.7s.0d. including P.T. 1970.

83. 10tr, M/LW portable. £5.14s.6d. plus £1.5s.0d. P.T. 1968.

88. 6tr, M/LW pocket portable. £3.5s.3d. plus 14s.3d. P.T. 1968.

90. 12tr, MW/FM portable. £8.4s.8d. plus £1.15s.10d. P.T. 1968.

91. 6tr, MW portable radio/torch (white beam and red flashing light). £6.10s.11d. plus £1.8s.7d. P.T. 1968.

99. 10tr, M/LW/FM portable. £14.14s.0d. including P.T. 1970.

101. 8tr, M/LW pocket portable. £5.8s.3d. plus 18s.6d. P.T. 1966.

102. M/LW/FM portable. £16.40p. including P.T. 1971.

202. 8tr, M/LW portable. £4.6s.2d. plus 15s.5d. P.T. 1967.

250 (Telephone). 7tr, MW novelty radio in the shape of an old fashioned telephone. £8.12s.6d. plus £1.17s.9d. P.T. 1968.

303. 6tr, M/LW pocket portable. £6.19s.6d. including P.T. 1963.

323. 8tr, M/LW pocket portable. £4.1s.8d. plus 17s.10d. P.T. 1968.

333. 6tr, MW pocket portable. £2.11s.1d. plus 9s.3d. P.T. 1967.

444. 6tr, MW pocket portable. £2.0s.7d. plus 8s.11d. P.T. 1968.

450. 9tr, M/LW portable radio/clock. £7.0s.7d. plus 1.18s.11d. P.T. 1969.

458. 10tr, M/LW/FM portable. £10.3s.0d. plus £2.9s.0d. P.T. 1969.

459. M/LW/FM portable. £12.90p. including P.T. 1971.

460. 10tr, M/LW/FM portable. £9.19s.6d. including P.T. 1970.

555. 7tr, M/LW portable. £13.16s.0d. plus £2.19s.0d. P.T. 1968.

626. 10tr, M/LW/FM pocket portable. £7.7s.6d. plus £1.12s.0d. P.T. 1968.

666. 12tr, M/LW/FM portable. £13.19s.0d. including P.T. 1967.

707. 6tr, MW pocket portable. £5.5s.0d. including P.T. September 1963.

727. 10tr, MW/FM pocket portable. £6.10s.11d. plus £1.8s.7d. P.T. 1968.

808. 7tr, M/LW pocket portable. £7.19s.6d. including P.T. September 1963.

909. 7tr, M/LW personal portable. £8.8s.0d. including P.T. 1963.

929. 10tr, M/LW/FM portable. £9.9s.6d. plus £2.1s.6d. P.T. 1968.

999. 14tr, 2S/M/LW/FM portable. £22.14s.9d. plus £3.17s.4d. P.T. 1967.

CUP70. 6tr, MW novelty radio in the shape of a football. £3.7s.8d. plus 16s.4d. P.T. 1969.

Berec (Berec Radio Ltd.), Hercules Pl., Holloway, N7. *Transistor Production Run 1959-61.*

Bambino. 6tr, M/LW personal portable (pre-set on LW for the Light Programme). £15.18s.0d. plus £5.2s.0d P.T. August 1959. (Berec version of the Ever Ready Sky Personal).

Brigand. 6tr, M/LW table model. £18.10s.6d. including P.T. October 1961.

Demon. 6tr, M/LW portable. £15.8s.5d. plus £6.2s.7d. P.T. May 1958. (Berec version of the Ever Ready Sky Leader).

Musketeer. 6tr, M/LW table model (pre-set on LW for the Light Programme). £17.17s.9d. plus £5.14s.9d. P.T. March 1960. (Berec version of the Ever Ready Sky Baron).

Bestone [Hong Kong] (*dist. L.P.F. Photronic Ltd.*), Cricklewood Lane, London NW2. *Transistor Production Run 1963.*

Bestone S. 6tr, MW pocket portable. £4.19s.6d. including P.T. 1963.

Bestone 2B. 6tr, M/LW pocket portable. £6.19s.6d. including P.T. 1963.

Binatone [Japan] (*dist. J.Parkar & Co. [London] Ltd.*), 7 Broadwick Street, London W1. Later, from 1967, (**Binatone Electronics Ltd.**), 1 Paul Street, London EC2. *Transistor Production Run 1963-72+.*

008. 8tr, M/LW portable. £6.6s. inc. P.T. 1966.

606. 6tr, M/LW pocket port. £6.6s.0d. inc. P.T.

606 Mk.III. 6tr, M/LW pocket portable. £6.10s.0d. including P.T. 1964.

727. 7tr, M/LW port. £6.19s.0d. inc. P.T. 1964.

800. 8tr, M/LW portable. 1965.

990. 6tr, M/LW pocket portable. £6.6s.0d. including P.T. 1964.

V-8. 6tr, M/LW pocket portable. £5.15s.0d. including P.T. 1964.

VC-10. 6tr, M/LW pocket portable. £4.19s.6d. including P.T. 1964.

VC-10 (Mk.II). 8tr, M/LW pocket portable. £5.19s.6d. including P.T. 1969.

Admiral. 14tr, S/MW/FM portable. £14.20p. including P.T. 1972.

Airmarshal. 14tr, S/M/LW/FM portable. £28.50p. including P.T. 1972.

Apollo. 8tr, M/LW portable. £8.19s.6d. including P.T. 1970.

Atlantis. 10tr, M/LW/FM portable. £14.20p. including P.T. 1972.

Bandspread. 8tr, M/LW portable. £6.15s.0d. including P.T. 1966. (Bandspread tuning from 185-222 metres, for Radio Luxembourg).

Barracuda. 9tr, M/LW/FM portable. £16.10p. including P.T. 1972.

Barrel. 8tr, MW/LW portable radio/barrel. £10.0s.0d. including P.T. 1970.

Capri (01/243). 6tr, M/LW pocket portable. £3.90p. including P.T. 1971.

Challenger. 9tr, M/LW/FM portable. £16.10p. including P.T. 1972.

Champion. 12tr, M/LW/FM/Aircraft Band/Public Service Band portable. £16.10p. including P.T. 1972.

Chef Spice Rack Radio. 6tr, MW wall-mounted radio/spice rack. £3.99p. including P.T. 1972. (Complete with 12 glass jars for herbs and spices. Similar model sold by Shopertunities Ltd. of Holborn, *see fig.816, page 208*).

Classic. 9tr, MW/FM portable. £10.40p. including P.T. 1972.

Clipper. 7tr, M/LW portable. £5.95p. including P.T. 1972.

Commodore. 8tr, M/LW portable. £5.25p. including P.T. 1971.

Concord. 8tr, M/LW portable. £6.97p. including P.T. 1971.

Cosmos. M/LW table model. £10.0s.0d. including P.T. 1966.

Cougar. 7tr, M/LW portable. £5.95p. including P.T. 1972.

Crossworld. 9tr, M/LW pocket portable. £4.10s.0d. including P.T. 1967.

Desk Set. M/LW table model/writing pad, two pens in holders. £12.10s.0d. including P.T. 1969.

Desk Clock. M/LW clock radio complete with two pens in holders. £17.10s.0d. including P.T. 1969.

Diplomat. 10tr, M/LW/FM portable. £12.30p. including P.T. 1972.

Dunhill 8TR. MW pocket portable. £2.15s.0d. including P.T. 1969.

Dunhill Dual Speaker. S/M/LW table model. £12.5s.0d. including P.T. 1969. (Two loudspeakers "*for hi-fi effect*").

Dunhill Supersonic. 10tr, MW/FM mains/battery portable. £14.14s.0d. inc. P.T. 1970.

Euromatic. 10tr, M/LW portable. £10.10s.0d. including P.T. 1966.

Fleetwood (01/251). 8tr, M/LW pocket portable. £4.25p. including P.T. 1971.

Geranium. 14tr, M/LW/FM portable. £12.5s.0d. including P.T. 1969.

Globe M/L. 8tr, M/LW spherical portable/novelty radio. £11.11s.0d. including P.T. 1967.

Globe S/M. 8tr, S/MW spherical portable/novelty radio. £11.11s.0d. including P.T. 1967.

Globetrotter. 8tr, M/LW spherical portable/novelty radio. £14.14s.0d. including P.T. 1970.

Golf Club (01/258). 6tr, MW novelty radio. £6.95p. including P.T. 1971.

Grand Prix Car Radio. 8tr, M/LW/FM portable/car radio. £37.05p. including P.T. 1972. (For home, outdoor or in-car use).

Intercontinental. 8tr, M/LW portable. £7.17s.0d. including P.T. 1969.

International. 8tr, M/LW portable. £8.8s.0d. including P.T. 1970.

Jet. 6tr, M/LW pocket portable. £3.75p. including P.T. 1972.

Kissinger. 9tr, AM/FM mains/battery portable. £13.25p. inc. P.T. 1971. (Integral leatherette case. *See fig.959. p.299*).

Long Distance 10. 8tr, M/LW portable. £6.6s.0d. including P.T. 1966.

Magna. 9tr, M/LW/FM portable. £16.10p. including P.T. 1972.

Mambo. 8tr, MW pocket portable. £2.75p. including P.T. 1971.

Melody. 6tr, MW pocket portable. £3.3s.0d. including P.T. 1966.

Micro. 6tr, MW pocket portable. £2.80p. including P.T. 1972.

Music Master. 7tr, S/M/LW portable. £12.12s.0d. including P.T. 1964.

Mustang. 8tr, M/LW portable. £4.19s.6d. including P.T. 1970.

Navigator. 12tr, MW/FM/Aircraft Band. £19.50p. including P.T. 1971.

Play Boy. 6tr, MW pocket portable. £3.3s.0d. including P.T. 1966.

Play Boy Mk.II. 7tr, MW pocket portable. £2.19s.6d. including P.T. 1969.

Playmate (01/202). 6tr, MW pocket portable. £2.45p. including P.T. 1971.

Poodle Dog. 6tr, MW portable radio/toy poodle. £4.15s.0d. including P.T. 1967.

Puppy (01/076). 6tr portable radio/toy puppy. £4.95p. including P.T. 1971.

President. 8tr, M/LW pocket portable. £4.19s.6d. including P.T. 1967.

Riviera (01/276). 8tr, M/LW portable. £4.25p. inc. P.T. 1971. (Integral saddle-stitched case).

Silver Cloud (01/275). 8tr, M/LW portable. £5.25p. inc. P.T. 1971. (Integral saddle-stitched case).

Silver Shadow (01/248). 9tr, MW/FM portable. £12 including P.T. 1971.

Silver Star. 8tr, M/LW portable. £4.10s.0d. including P.T. 1969.

Stingray (01/272). 6tr, M/LW portable. £5.50p. including P.T. 1971.

Super 8. 8tr, MW pocket portable. £2.95p. including P.T. 1971.

Super de Luxe. 15tr, MW/FM portable. £12.12s.0d. including P.T. 1967.

Supersonic. 10tr, MW/FM portable. £15.15s.0d. including P.T. 1970.

Telephone. 6tr, M/LW novelty table model in the form of an early cradle-type telephone with lettered dial. £.9.0s.0d. including P.T. 1969.

Tokyo AM/FM AC/DC. 10tr, MW/FM portable. £11.5s.0d. including P.T. 1969.

Tokyo 7TR. 7tr, MW pocket portable. £2.12s.6d. including P.T. 1969. (Complete with wrist strap).

Tokyo Table. M/LW table model. £7.5s.0d. including P.T. 1969. (Designed for use in the kitchen).

Transworld. 10tr, M/LW/FM portable. £10.0s.0d. including P.T. 1966.

Travelmate (01/209). 6tr, M/LW portable/clock radio. £14.19s.6d. including P.T. 1969. (Folds into a wallet-sized case).

VHF Pocket Radio. 8tr, MW/FM pocket portable. £8.10p. including P.T. 1972.

Worldmaster. 14tr, 2S/M/LW/FM portable. £37.05p. including P.T. 1972.

Zodiac. 14tr, S/M/LW/FM portable. £20.0s.0d. including P.T. 1970.

Blaupunkt (*see Bluespot, next*).

Bluespot (Blaupunkt) [West Germany] (*dist. Bosch Ltd.*), 205 Gt. Portland Street, London W1. From 1968, at Rhodes Way, Radlett Road, Watford, Herts. *Transistor Production Run 1962-70+.*

L100L. 10tr, M/LW/FM portable. £35.0s.0d. including P.T. 1970. (Mains adaptor, £7.15s.0d. extra).

Derby de Luxe. 10tr, 2S/M/LW/FM portable/car radio. £48.9s.0d. plus £11.8s.0d. P.T. 1969. (For home, outdoor or in-car use. Car bracket and mains adaptor, extra).

Derby 651. 10tr, M/LW/FM portable. £39.19s.0d. plus £9.8s.0d. 1969. (Mains adaptor, extra).

Derby 691. 10tr, S/M/LW/FM portable/car radio. £45.6s.6d. plus £10.13s.4d. P.T. 1970. (For home, outdoor or in-car use. Car bracket and mains adaptor, extra).

Diva. 10tr, S/M/LW/FM portable. £32.6s.0d. plus £7.12s.0d. P.T. 1969. (Mains adaptor, extra).

Dixie. 9tr, MW/FM portable. £16.3s.0d. plus £3.16s.0d. P.T. 1969. (Mains adaptor, extra).

Lido. 9tr, M/LW/FM portable. £28.10s.4d. plus £8.4s.8d. P.T. May 1962.

Lido (Mk.II). 10tr, S/M/LW/FM portable. £33.12s.0d. 1966. (Mains adaptor, extra).

Flora. 7tr, 2S/MW portable. £29.8s.0d. including P.T. June 1963.

Genua. 11tr, M/LW/FM mains table model. £40.19s.0d. including P.T. 1967.

Nizza. S/M/LW/FM stereo mains table model. £84.3s.0d. plus £13.16s.0d. P.T. 1969. (Complete with two separate loudspeakers).

Ostia. 11tr, M/LW/FM mains table model. £47.5s.0d. including P.T. 1967.

Pisa. 11tr, M/LW/FM mains table model. £47.5s.0d. including P.T. 1967.

Supernova. 19tr, 7S/M/LW/FM mains/battery portable. £93.10s.0d. plus £3.16s.0d. P.T. 1969.

Swing. 9tr, MW/FM portable. £11.4s.11d. plus £2.8s.1d. P.T. 1968.

Bosch (*see Bluespot, above*).

Boy's Own (**Boy's Own Paper/Purnell & Sons Ltd.**). *Transistor Production Run 1963.*

B.O.P. Twin Transistor. 2tr, MW pocket portable (blueprint/instructions). £2.8s.0d. December 1963. (This was a schoolboy's radio designed by Gilbert Davey, the Radio Correspondent of the *Boy's Own Paper*, and was presented as an 8-page blueprint/instructions supplement in the Christmas issue of that paper. The transistors specified for the set were an OC44 and an OC71, with two OA81 germanium diodes).

Brandt [West Germany] (*dist.* **Layford [Electrical] Ltd.**), 7 Chesterfield Gardens, Curzon Street, London W1. *Transistor Production Run 1960.*

Brandt. 6tr, portable. March 1960.

Braun [West Germany] (*dist.* **Winter Trading Co. Ltd.**), 6 Harrow Road, London W2/95-99 Ladbroke Grove, London W11. From 1964, (*dist.* **Argelane Ltd.**), 251 Brompton Road, London SW3. From 1966, (*dist.* **Fi-Cord International**), Charlwoods Road, East Grinstead, Sussex. *Transistor Production Run 1958-68.*

KT2. 7tr, S/M/LW portable. £33.12s.0d. including P.T. 1958.

KT3. 6tr, M/LW personal portable. £14.15s.6d. plus £5.14s.0d. P.T. August 1958. *"Its French-grey plastic cabinet and simple tuning will immediately appeal to the feminine sex".*

T1. 4v + 3tr hybrid, S/M/LW personal portable/car radio. £31.9s.2d inc. P.T. July 1956.

T4. 7tr, S/M/LW personal portable. £17.9s.9d. plus £5.12s.3d. P.T. March 1960.

T22. 9tr, S/M/LW/FM portable. £35.15s.0d. plus £9.19s.0d. P.T. September 1960.

T23. 8tr, 4S/MW portable. £31 plus £9.19s.0d. P.T. September 1960.

T24. 7tr, S/M/LW portable. £25.8s.9d. plus £8.3s.3d. P.T. September 1960.

T31. 7tr, M/LW pocket portable. £14.14s.1d. plus £4.14.5d. P.T. March 1960.

T41. 7tr, S/M/LW pocket portable. £19.19s.0d. including P.T. 1963.

T52. 9tr, M/LW/FM portable/car radio. £40.19s.0d. including P.T. September 1961. (For home, outdoor and in-car use).

T510. 9tr, M/LW/FM portable. £30.9s.0d. including P.T. 1964.

T520. May 1962.

T540. 9tr, S/M/LW portable. £23.2s.0d. including P.T. 1963.

T580. 11tr, M/LW/FM portable. £44.2s.0d. including P.T. 1964.

T1000. 20tr, 8S/AM/FM portable. £195 including P.T. 1964. (Complete with tuning meter. Mains adaptor, extra).

T1000CD. 20tr, 2S/2M/2LW/FM portable. £185.17s.4d. (no Purchase Tax payable). 1968. (Came complete with tuning meter. Tuning on the medium waveband was divided into two sections with bandspread over both halves, giving MW1 (275-555 metres) and MW2 (185-280 metres).

TP1. 7tr, S/M/LW radiogram (the radio was detachable for use as pocket portable). £23.19s.1d. plus £7.10s.5d. P.T. September 1959.

Britram (*dist.* **Universal Distributing Co. Ltd.**), 66 Gt. Eastern Street, London EC2. *Transistor Production Run 1970-72+.*

34. 7tr, MW pocket portable. £2.16s.10d. including P.T. 1970.

39. 8tr, MW pocket portable. £4.16p. including P.T. 1972.

57. M/LW pocket portable. £4.5s.0d. including P.T. 1970.

77. 10tr, MW/FM pocket portable. £8.15s.0d. including P.T. 1970.

78. 10tr, MW/FM portable. £9.2s.6d. including P.T. 1970.

79. 10tr, M/LW/FM portable. £10.10s.0d. including P.T. 1970.

88. M/LW portable. £8.10s.0d. including P.T. 1970.

93. 13tr, MW/FM portable. £10.85p. including P.T. 1972.

98. 10tr, M/LW portable/car radio. £10.85p. including P.T. 1972. (For home, outdoor or in-car use).

99. 10tr, M/LW portable/car radio. £7.10s.0d. including P.T. 1970. (For home, outdoor or in-car use).

Brownie (*dist.* **Highgate Acoustics Ltd.**), 71-73 Gt. Portland Street, London W1. *Transistor Production Run 1964.*

777. 6tr, M/LW pocket portable. £10.10s.0d. including P.T. 1964.

Bruberry [Hong Kong] (*dist.* **Bruberry Supplies Ltd.**), 487 Otley Road, Adel, Leeds 16. *Transistor Production Run 1972+.*

K600. 7tr, MW pocket portable. £2.50p. including P.T. 1972.

Mk.II. 8tr, MW port. £3.45p. inc. P.T. 1972.

Brunswick (**Brunswick Radio & Television**), Ingate Place, Queenstown Road, London SW8. *Transistor Production Run 1963.*

BTP73. June 1963.

BTP74. June 1963.

Bush (**Bush Radio Ltd.**), Power Road, Chiswick, W4. From 1962, (**Rank-Bush Murphy Ltd. Bush Radio Division**) at same address. From 1972, (**Rank Radio International**) at same address. *Transistor Production Run 1959-72+.*

CR128 (Nightingale). 6tr, M/LW portable/clock radio. £13.19s.6d. including P.T. 1969.

TR82. 7tr, M/LW portable. £22.11s.6d. including P.T. May 1959. (The robust moulded cabinet of the TR82, shown in close-up on page 181 and in fig.800 page 197, was first used with the Bush MB60, [a mains/battery valve portable of 1957]. It also appeared on the Bush ETR82 [a 2S/MW valve/transistor hybrid export model of 1959], the Bush ETR92 [the all-transistor version of the ETR82, also of 1959], and with the Bush VTR103, *see below*. Further research may reveal a 'Luxembourg' bandspread model and a trawler band version to complete the set of variants! *Information from Bob Smallbone*).

TR90. 7tr, M/LW port. £14.5s.6d. plus £4.12s.6d. P.T. (Carrying case £1.10s.0d extra). May 1960.

TR91. 7tr, M/LW table model (long, low look). £15.17s.3d. plus £5.2s.10d. P.T. September 1960. (*See fig.804, p.199*).

TR102. 7tr, M/LW portable. £16.13s.3d. plus £4.17s.3d. P.T. January 1962.

TR104. 6tr, M/LW port. (pre-set on LW for the Light Prog.). £11.4s.6d. plus £4 P.T. July 1961.

TR106 (Slimline). 7tr, M/LW portable. £17.6s.6d. including P.T. August 1962.

TR112. 7tr, M/LW port. £17.19s.6d. + P.T. Feb. 1964.

TR114. 7tr, M/LW portable. £14.3s.6d. including P.T. August 1963.

TR116. 8tr, S/M/LW portable (plus pre-set on 208 metres for Radio Luxembourg). £17.17s.0d. including P.T. 1965.

TR116T. 1965. (As TR116, but with 'Trawler Band', 90-180 metres).

TR122. 7tr, M/LW portable. £11.19s.0d. including P.T. 1970.

TR124. 9tr, M/LW portable. £11.0s.6d. including P.T. 1968.

TR126. 7tr, M/LW pocket portable. £7.19s.6d. inc. P.T. 1969. (Complete with wrist strap).

TR129. 7tr, M/LW port. £8.93p. inc. P.T. 1971.

TR130. 7tr, M/LW port. (plus pre-set on 208 m. for Radio Lux.). £15.15s.0d. inc. P.T. 1965.

TR132. 7tr, M/LW portable. £17.17s.0d. including P.T. 1965.

TR146. 7tr, M/LW portable/car radio. £13.2s.6d. including P.T. 1967. (Complete with a logging-scale. For home, outdoor or in-car use. Bandspread tuning between 187-210 metres. Chassis identical to Murphy B822).

TR156. 7tr, M/LW port./car radio. £20.9s.6d. inc. P.T. 1968. (For home, outdoor or in-car use).

TR162. 7tr, M/LW port. £21.19s.0d. inc.P.T. 1968.

TR168. 8tr, M/LW port. £14.97p. inc. P.T. 1971.

TR230. 7tr, M/LW port. £18.29p. inc. P.T. 1971.

VHF101. 10tr, M/LW/FM mains table model. £30.19s.9d. including P.T. 1969.

VHF102. M/LW/FM mains table model. £39.18s.0d. inc. P.T. 1969. ("*Sealed Sound*" cabinet — entire cabinet acoustically sealed).

VTR103. 9tr, M/LW/FM portable. £22.9s.0d. plus £8 P.T. August 1961. (Same cabinet used on the Bush TR82, *etc*. See above).

VTR125. 10tr, MW/FM portable. £13.17s.10d. including P.T. 1969.

VTR127 (Sandpiper). M/LW/FM portable. £17.10s.0d. including P.T. 1970.

VTR131. 9tr, MW/FM portable. £9.19s.6d. including P.T. 1969.

VTR133. 9tr, M/LW/FM portable. £24.3s.0d. including P.T. 1965.

VTR143. 9tr, M/LW/FM portable. £19.19s.0d. including P.T. May 1967. (Bandspread tuning between 187-210 metres, for Radio Luxembourg. Came in three different cabinet versions, VTR143A, B and C — the VTR143C being made for the British Wireless For The Blind Fund with a non-tilting telescopic aerial).

VTR165. 11tr, M/LW/FM portable. £24.08p including P.T. 1971.

VTR 172 (Merlin). 9tr, M/LW/FM portable. £30.19s.9d. including P.T. 1969. (Pre-set push-button for B.B.C. Radio 1 on 247 metres).

VTR174. 9tr, M/LW/FM portable. £23.2s.0d. including P.T. 1968.

Candle (*dist.* **E.Joyce & Co. [Distributors] Ltd.**), 8 Queen's Gardens, London NW14. *Transistor Production Run 1961-62.*

OTR20. 2tr, MW radio/binoculars. £9.3s.0d. plus £2.13s.6d. P.T. September 1961.

OTR30. 3tr, MW radio/binoculars. £10.2s.9d. plus £2.19s.3d. P.T. 1962.

PTR21B. 2tr, MW pocket portable. £4.4s.3d. plus £1.4s.9d. P.T. 1962.

PTR22. 2tr, MW pocket portable. £4.2s.0d. plus £1.2s.0d. P.T. 1962.

PTR23. 2tr, MW pocket portable. £4 plus £1.3s.6d. P.T. September 1961.

PTR60S. 6tr, MW pocket portable. £8.1s.0d. plus £2.7s.0d. P.T. 1962.

PTR61. 6tr, MW pocket portable. £6.18s.6d. plus £2.0s.6d. P.T. 1962.

PTR62B. 6tr, MW pocket portable. £6.18s.6d. plus £2.0s.6d. P.T. 1962.

PTR63. 6tr, MW pocket portable. £8.1s.0d. plus £2.7s.0d. P.T. 1962.

PTR83. 8tr, MW personal portable. £9.3s.0d. plus £2.13s.6d. P.T. 1962.

Capri (*dist.* **Sloane Distributors Ltd.**), 4 Mossbury Road, London SW11. *Transistor Production Run 1964.*

Capri 64. 10tr, S/M/LW/FM portable. £38.6s.6d. including P.T. 1964. (Fixing kit for converting into car radio, price £5.11s.9d. extra).

Model 64. 9tr, M/LW/FM portable. £28.18s.6d. including P.T. 1964.

Caroline [Hong Kong] (*dist.* **Lee Products [Gt. Britain] Ltd.**), 10-18 Clifton Street, London EC2. *Transistor Production Run 1964-67.*

Caroline. 6tr, M/LW pocket portable. £6.6s.0d. including P.T. 1964.

Caroline 23. 8tr, M/LW portable. £4.9s.3d. plus 15s.9d. P.T. 1967.

Caroline 199. 6tr, MW pocket portable. £4.12s.3d. including P.T. 1964. Named after Radio Caroline 199 which was the first U.K. 'Pop Pirate' station to go the air. Inaugurated on Saturday 28th March 1964 on 199 metres, the station provided an all-day diet of pop music from 6am, and within just 3 weeks it had earned a staggering 7 million listeners (mostly teenagers). Its success quickly spawned many other Pop Pirates around the British Isles and marked the birth of off-shore radio. Accompanying this, was a corresponding massive increase in transistor radio sales, particular of cheap pocket portables imported from the Far East, eagerly bought by teenagers and young people for listening to pop music, day or night. (*See also Fidelity 199, page 255*).

Caroline 601. 6tr, MW pocket portable. £2.13s.6d. plus 9s.6d. P.T. 1967.

Channel (**Channel Electronic Industries Ltd.**), Dunstan Road, Burnham-on-Sea, Somerset. *Transistor Production Run 1958-61.*

Dixie. 6tr, M/LW portable. £12.12s.0d. plus £4.4s.0d. P.T. August 1960.

Escourt. 6tr, M/LW portable. January 1961.

Magpie. 6tr, M/LW portable. £15 plus £6 P.T. March 1958.

Transette 30. 6tr, M/LW (fixed tuned on LW). £12.15s.0d. plus £5.2s.0d. June 1958.

Clarville (*dist.* **Wholesale Supplies [Swinton] Ltd.**), 16 Worsley Road, Manchester. *Transistor Production Run 1962-63.*

PP8. 6tr, M/LW portable. £12.8s.4d. plus £3.11s.8d. P.T. March 1962.

PP10. 8tr, M/LW portable. £18.18s.0d. including P.T. 1963.

Clifton (*see Elpico, page 253*).

Concord (*dist.* **Concord Electronics**), 69 Preston Street, Brighton. By 1962, at 210 Church Road, Hove, Sussex. By 1965, at 9 Western Road, Hove, Sussex. By 1966, at 77 New Bond Street, London W1. Concord Electronics Ltd. (like Minisets Ltd., Henry's [Radio] Ltd. and Lasky's [Harrow Road] Ltd.) mainly specialised in the field of cheap (*"bargain"*) transistor kit sets specially for the home constructor (usually imported from abroad or the result of a *"frustrated export order"*). Often enticing would-be customers with slogans like *"Sensational liquidation sale . . . a 14 Guinea set for 4 Pounds! . . . . 500 only"*, their tempting advertisements were to be found gracing the pages of Practical Wireless from the late 1950s to the early 1970s. I have included Concord Electronics are a representative example of this genre, but studying this area alone would yield a fascinating book in itself. *Transistor Production Run 1958-72+.*

5 Star Volksradio. MW pocket portable (kit). 19s.0d. for complete set of parts and plans. 1962.

6 Star San Remo. MW pocket portable (kit). £1.12s.6d. for complete set of parts and plans. 1961. In simulated crocodile skin case.

Cigarette Packet Radio. MW pocket portable. 18s.6d. 1963. Built into a packet of Churchman's cigarettes (held ten cigarettes).

Concord Home Radio Course (construction kit for making 5 different transistor radios). £1.15s.0d. 1963.

Costa Brava. MW pocket portable (kit). 19s.0d. for complete set of parts and plans. 1962.

Lisbon. 2tr, MW pocket portable (kit). 19s.0d. for complete set of parts and plans. 1961.

Miami. MW miniature pocket portable (kit). 19s.0d. for complete set of parts and plans. 1962.

Minuette. 3tr, MW portable (kit). £1.17s.0d. 1961.

New Costa Brava. MW pocket portable (kit). £2.19s.0d. for complete set of parts and plans. 1963.

Satellite 8. 8tr, M/LW portable. £3.14s.6d. 1964.

Sky Pixie. 2tr, MW pocket portable (kit). £2.7s.6d. for complete set of parts and plans. 1958.

Sky Scout. 1tr, MW pocket portable (kit). £1.9s.6d. for complete set of parts and plans. 1958.

Skyscraper Communications Receiver. SW pocket portable (kit). £2.9s.6d. for complete set of parts and plans. 1963.

St. Tropez Mk.VI. MW pocket portable (kit). £1.5s.0d. for complete set of parts/plans. 1963.

Vantone. 8tr, M/LW pocket portable. £3.18s.0d. 1964. (*"Act now! . . . . 900 only!"*).

Worldwide. 7tr, MW pocket portable. £2.15s.0d. 1964.

Worldwide Mk. II. 7tr, MW pocket portable. £2.19s.6d. 1966.

Convair [U.S.S.R.] (*dist.* **Convair Time & Electronics Ltd.**), 51 Hatton Garden, London EC1. *Transistor Production Run 1966.*

Microsonic. 7tr, M/LW pocket portable. £3.4s.6d. plus 11s.6d. P.T. 1966. (Complete with mains charging unit).

Selga 600. 7tr, M/LW portable. £5.17s.6d. plus 18s.2d. P.T. 1966.

Sokol 800. 7tr, M/LW portable. £6.17s.6d. plus £1.0s.11d. P.T. 1966. (Complete with mains charging unit).

Co-op (*see Defiant, page 252*)

Cosmo (*dist.* **Denham & Morley Ltd.**), 173-175 Cleveland Street, London W1. *Transistor Production Run 1961.*

Cosmo 62. 7tr, S/M/LW portable. £20.13s.5d. plus £6.12s.7d. P.T. June 1961.

Cossor (**Cossor Radio & Television Ltd.**), Cossor House, Highbury Grove, London N5. From 1960, 71 Endell Street, London WC2. From 1961, 233 Tottenham Court Road, London W1. From 1965 (**Philips Electrical Ltd.**), Century House, Shaftesbury Avenue, London WC2. *Transistor Production Run 1957-66.*

546. 6tr, M/LW portable. £19.14s.3d. plus £7.11s.9d P.T. May 1957.

561 (Travellers Friend). 4tr, MW pocket portable. £14.18s.1d. plus £5.10d.11d. P.T. September 1957.

569 (Transistor Six). 6tr, M/LW portable/car radio. £16.13s.7d. plus £6.8s.6d. P.T. May 1958. (*"A new portable with a difference . . . in addition to normal operation out of doors or in the home, a simple socket for connection to a car aerial enables model 569 to be used inside a car or a caravan"*).

CR1300T. 6tr, M/LW portable. £19.8s.6d including P.T. 1959.

CR1301T. 6tr, M/LW portable. £14.6s.2d. plus £4.11s.10d. P.T. August 1960.

CR1302T. 6tr, M/LW portable. £13.11s.7d. plus £4.15s.11d. P.T. October 1961.

CR1304T. 6tr, M/LW portable. £14.3s.6d. including P.T. September 1962.

CR1305T (Melody Minor Seven). 7tr, M/LW portable. £12.12s.0d. including P.T. 1962.

CR1306T. 6tr, M/LW portable. £16.16s.0d. including P.T. 1963.

CR1310T. 6tr, M/LW portable. £13.13s.0d. including P.T. August 1963. (Identical chassis used in the Philips 241T and Stella ST415T).

CR1315T. 6tr, M/LW portable/car radio (bandspread section aligned on Radio Luxembourg's wavelength of 208 metres). £12.4s.4d. plus £2.3s.1d. P.T. 1966. (For home, outdoor or in-car use).

CR1341T. 9tr, M/LW/FM portable. £26.15s.6d. including P.T. 1964.

CR1350T. 8tr, M/LW/FM portable. £20.9s.6d. including P.T. 1963.

CR7225T. 9tr, M/LW/FM portable. £22.1s.0d. November 1963.

CR7243T. 10tr, S/M/LW/FM portable. £39.18s.0d. including P.T. 1964.

Cossor Transistor Kit. 4tr (Ediswan transistors), MW portable kit. £7.19s.6d. 1960. (Sold by Premier Radio Co., 23 Tottenham Court Road, London W1. Also available with Mullard transistors from Electronics [Fleet Street] Ltd.).

Crown [Asahi Radio Co., Japan] (*dist.* **Finex [Overseas] Ltd.**), 7 West End Lane, London NW6. From 1962, (*dist.* **Lee Products [Great Britain] Ltd.**), 10/18 Clifton Street, London EC2. From 1964, (*dist.* **Heddon Smith Group Ltd.**), 7 William Road, London W1. From 1966, (**Crown Radio Corporation**), Roman House, Wood Street, London EC2. From 1967, (**Crown Radio Co. Ltd.**), 137-149 Goswell Road, London EC1. From 1970, at128-129 Shoreditch High Street, London E1. *Transistor Production Run 1961-70.*

HT430S. 6tr, MW personal portable/money box. £8.2s.10d. plus 1.11s.4d. P.T. 1967.

HT460. 6tr, MW personal portable/jewel box. £9.1s.0d. plus £1.11s.11d. P.T. 1967.

TR124L. 12tr, 2S/M/LW portable. £24.3s.0d. including P.T. 1964.

TR145. 11tr, 2S/MW portable. £24.4s.6d. plus £5.14s.0d. P.T. 1969. (Sleep switch — when this is pressed, the set switches itself off after 30 minutes).

TR602L. 6tr, M/LW portable. £8.1s.6d. plus £1.18s.0d. P.T. 1969.

TR680. 6tr, MW pocket portable. £10.10s.0d. including P.T. November 1961.

TR690. 6tr, MW pocket portable. £5.15s.6d. including P.T. 1963.

TR702L. 7tr, M/LW portable. £18.18s.0d. including P.T. November 1961.

TR803L. 8tr, S/M/LW pocket portable. £17.0s.4d. including P.T. December 1962.

TR835L. 8tr, S/M/LW pocket portable. £13.13s.0d. including P.T. 1970. (Mains adaptor, optional extra).

TR905L. 9tr, S/M/LW personal portable. £20.16s.0d. including P.T. December 1962.

TR960L. 9tr, S/M/LW portable. £11.12s.0d. plus £2.9s.8d. P.T. 1968. (Mains adaptor, optional extra).

TR1200L. 12tr, M/LW/FM portable. £27.6s.0d. including P.T. 1964.

TR1600R. 9tr, MW/FM portable. £19.19s.0d. including P.T. 1964.

TR1800. 9tr, MW/FM pocket portable. £16.16s.0d. including P.T. 1964.

TR6026. 6tr, M/LW portable. £9.19s.6d. including P.T. 1970.

TRF16. 9tr, MW/FM pocket portable. £9.9s.2d. plus £1.13s.4d. P.T. 1967.

TRF145E. 11tr, S/M/LW/FM portable. £24.4s.6d. plus £5.14s.0d. P.T. 1969.

TRF800LW. 11tr, S/M/LW/FM mains/battery portable. £28.90p. including P.T. 1971.

TRF902L. 9tr, M/LW/FM portable. £17.25p. including P.T. 1971. (Mains adaptor, AD32E, £4.75p. extra).

TRF1300. 9tr, MW/LW pocket portable. £10.17s.2d. plus £1.18s.4d. P.T. 1967.

TRF1300L. 9tr, M/LW/FM portable. £11.3s.1d. plus £2.12s.6d. P.T. 1969.

TRF1400L. 14tr, S/M/LW/FM portable. £33.0s.5d. plus £5.16s.9d. P.T. 1967. (Mains adaptor, extra).

TRF1900L. 9tr, M/LW/FM pocket portable. £13.2s.5d. plus £2.6s.4d. P.T. 1967.

TRF2100L. 10tr, M/LW/FM portable. £17.17s.0d. plus £3.16s.0d. P.T. 1968.

TRF2200A. 18tr, M/LW/FM Broadcast Band/Aircraft Band mains/battery portable. £31.17s.3d. plus £5.18s.9d. P.T. 1967. (Built-in mains adaptor. Sleep switch — when this is pressed, the set switches itself off after 30 minutes).

TRF2200AL. 18tr, M/LW/FM/Aircraft Band mains/battery portable. £32.2s.7d. plus £7.11s.2d. P.T. 1969. (Built-in mains adaptor. Sleep switch — set switches off after 30 minutes).

TRF2200L. 16tr, S/M/LW/FM mains/battery portable. £28.19s.1d. plus £5.2s.3d. P.T. 1967. (Built-in mains adaptor. Sleep switch — set switches off after 30 minutes).

TRF2400L. 10tr, M/LW/FM portable. £13.7s.9d. plus £2.17s.4d. P.T. 1968.

TRF2610W. 4S/M/LW/FM mains/battery table model. £69.6s.0d. including P.T. 1970.

TRF2700L. 9tr, M/LW/FM portable. £15.15s.0d. including P.T. 1970. (Mains adaptor, extra).

TRF2800L. 10tr, M/LW/FM portable. £18.14s.0d. plus £4.0s.3d. P.T. 1968.

TRF2900L. 10tr, S/M/LW/FM portable. £45.15s.0d. including P.T. 1970. (Mains adaptor, extra).

Dansette (J. & A. Margolin Ltd.), Plus-a-Gram House, 112-116 Old Street, London EC1. From 1961, (**Dansette Products Ltd**), of same address. From 1963, Dansette House, Honeypot Lane, Stanmore, Middlesex. From 1972 (**Rank Radio Int.**), Power Road, Chiswick, London W4. *Transistor Production Run 1958-72+.*

RT60. 6tr, M/LW table model. £24.3s.0d. including P.T. 1958. (One of two pioneering British table model transistor radios to be released in 1958. *See also the Pam 365, page 265*).

RT66. 6tr, M/LW pocket portable. £8.10s.9d. plus £3.0s.3d. P.T. November 1961.

RT77. 6tr, M/LW personal portable. £9.6s.3d. plus £3.5s.9d. P.T. January 1962.

RT111. 6tr, M/LW portable. £19.19s.0d. including P.T. 1958.

RT111X. 6tr, M/LW portable. £10.10s.0d. including P.T. 1964.

RT222. 6tr, M/LW portable. £12.0s.7d. plus £4.4s.11d. P.T. March 1961. *"Housed in a plastics fabric covered glass-fibre case"*. . . (no further comment necessary).

TR1. 6tr, M/LW portable. £19.19s.0d. including P.T. 1959.

Cambridge (DTR45). 10tr, M/LW/FM portable. £19.0s.7d. plus £4.9s.7d. P.T. 1969.

Capri. 6tr, M/LW personal portable. £11.0s.6d. including P.T. January 1963.

Chorister. 7tr, M/LW portable. £12.1s.6d. including P.T. 1964.

Companion. 6tr, M/LW portable. 11.0s.6d. including P.T. 1964.

Diplomat. 8tr, M/LW portable. £12.13s.9d. plus £2.4s.9d. P.T. 1966.

Dorchester. 6tr, M/LW portable. £14.14s.0d. including P.T. June 1963.

Gem. 6tr, M/LW portable. £10.18s. plus £1.13s.5d. P.T. October 1962.

Hendon. 6tr, M/LW portable. £15.15s.0d. including P.T. 1964.

Herald. 6tr, M/LW portable. £15.15s.0d. including P.T. August 1963.

Hilton. 6tr, M/LW portable. 13.2s.6d. including P.T. 1964.

Imp. August 1963.

International. August 1963.

Medway. 10tr, MW/FM portable. £14.0s.6d. plus £2.9s.6d. P.T. 1966.

Richmond. 8tr, M/LW pocket portable. £6.9s.9d. plus £1.7s.9d. P.T. 1968.

Serenade. M/LW portable. £13.13s.0d. including P.T. 1964.

Stanmore. 10tr, M/FM pocket portable. £9.10s.0d. plus £2.0s.9d. P.T. August 1963.

Tempo (DTR35). M/LW portable. £14.97p. including P.T. 1972.

Windsor (DTR15). 7tr, M/LW portable. £13.8s.0d. plus £3.3s.1d. P.T. 1969.

Decca (Decca Radio & Television), Ingate Place, Queenstown Road, London SW8. From 1971, at Neachells Lane, Willenhall, Wolverhampton, Staffs. *Transistor Production Run 1959-72+.*

1125. 8tr, 3S/M/LW portable. £54.12s.0d. including P.T. 1964.

TP22. 6tr, M/LW portable. £15.2s.1d. plus P.T. September 1959.

TP33. (As TP22, but table model version). £15.18s.0d. plus P.T. September 1959.

TP44 (Debonaire). 7tr, M/LW portable. £13.10s.3d. plus £4.6s.9d. P.T. April 1960.

TP50 (Debonette). 6tr, M/LW portable. £12.8s.4d. plus £4.7s.8d. P.T. April 1961.

TP50A (Debonette). £12.8s.4d. plus P.T. January 1962. (Very similar to the earlier TP50, but in a larger cabinet and using larger capacity batteries).

TP60 (de Luxe Debonaire). 6tr, M/LW portable. £13.11s.7d. plus £4.15s.11d. P.T. August 1961.

TP74. 6tr, M/LW portable. £12.1s.6d. including P.T. 1964.

TP75 (Debutante). 6tr, M/LW portable. £13.2s.6d. including P.T. September 1962.

TP85. 9tr, M/LW/FM portable. £25.4s.0d. including P.T. July 1963.

TP86. 9tr, M/LW/FM portable. £26.5s.0d. including P.T. 1965.

TP89. 9tr, S/M/LW/FM portable. £31.10s.0d. including P.T. 1965.

TP90/A. 9tr, M/LW/FM portable/car radio. £21.0s.0d. including P.T. 1965. (For home, outdoor or in-car use).

TP99. 6tr, M/LW portable. £15.15s.0d. including P.T. May 1964.

TPW70. 6tr, M/LW circular wall-mounted receiver (for use in the kitchen or the bathroom). £13.11s.7d. plus £4.15s.11d. P.T. Nov. 1961. (*See fig.808, p.200*).

Cabaret (PR199). 9tr, MW/FM portable. £10.2s.4d. plus £2.7s.8d. P.T. 1969.

Carousel. 10tr, M/LW/FM portable. 1972.

Dauphine (PR200). S/M/LW/FM portable. £16.19s.6d. including P.T. 1970.

Diadem. M/LW/FM table model. £28.11s.2d. plus £5.0s.10d. P.T. 1966. (Unusual design with lift-up lid concealing tuning dial and controls).

Fantasia (PR204). Integrated circuit + 7tr, S/M/LW/FM portable. 1971.

Festival (PR201). 9tr, S/M/LW/FM portable. £15.15s.8d. plus £3.14s.4d. P.T. 1969.

Intercontinental 1125. 8tr, 3S/M/LW portable. £51.9s.0d. including P.T. 1963.

Mayfair (PR202). 10tr, M/LW/FM portable/car radio. £23.19s.0d. including P.T. 1970. (For home, outdoor or in-car use).

Defiant (Co-Operative Wholesale Society Ltd.), Alma Park, Warley Street, Upminster, Essex. *Transistor Production Run 1959-68.*

A4. 6tr, M/LW pocket portable (pre-set on LW for the Light Programme). £8.2s.6d. plus £2.7s.6d. P.T. 1961.

A5. 6tr, M/LW portable. £19.8s.6d. including P.T. June 1959.

A41. 6tr, M/LW portable (pre-set on LW for the Light Programme). £10.11s.3d. plus £3.1s.9d. P.T. 1961.

A42. 6tr, M/LW portable (pre-set on LW for the Light Programme). £10.11s.3d. plus £3.1s.9d. P.T. 1961.

A44. 7tr, M/LW portable (bandspread section aligned on Radio Luxembourg's wavelength of 208 metres). £12.12s.0d. including P.T. 1964.

A51. 6tr, M/LW portable. £17.17s.0d. including P.T. March 1960.

A52. £18.18s.0d. including P.T. 1960.

A53. £15.15s.0d. including P.T. 1960.

A55. 6tr, M/LW portable. £12.11s.11d. plus £3.13s.7d. P.T. June 1961.

A55 (de Luxe). 6tr, M/LW portable. £17.17s.0d. including P.T. 1963.

A55BS. 7tr, M/LW portable (bandspread section aligned on Radio Luxembourg's wavelength of 208 metres). 1965.

A56. 6tr, M/LW portable. £11.14s.10d. plus £1.18s.2d. P.T. 1961. (Identical chassis used in the A57).

A57. 6tr, M/LW portable. £10.16s.10d. plus £1.15s.2d. P.T. 1961. (Identical chassis used in the A56).

A58. 6tr, M/LW portable. £16.16s.0d. including P.T. 1964.

A59. 6tr, M/LW portable. £10.19s.5d. plus £3.4s.1d. P.T. 1961.

A501 (Mk.I). 6tr, M/LW portable. £12.12s.0d. including P.T. August 1959.

A501 (Mk.II). 7tr, M/LW portable. £13.2s.6d. including P.T. 1963.

A502. 7tr, M/LW portable. £11.15s.0d. plus £2.1s.10d. P.T. 1966.

A503. 7tr, M/LW portable. £11.5s.7d. plus £2.0s.5d. P.T. 1967. (Bandspread tuning between 187-21 metres, for Luxembourg).

AF504. 9tr, M/LW/FM portable. £18.15s.0d. plus £4.0s.0d. P.T. 1968.

Denco (Denco [Clacton] Ltd), Old Road, Clacton-on-Sea, Essex. *Transistor Production Run 1961.*

Maxi-Q Transistor Six. 6tr, MW portable. 1961. (Case in the form of a book. *See fig.809, p.201*).

Diamond (*dist.* **Denham & Morley Ltd.),** 173-175 Cleveland Street, London W1. *Transistor Production Run 1961.*

Diamond 91095. 9tr, M/LW/FM portable. £26.1s.5d. plus £7.10s.7d. P.T. 1961.

Diamond K9106. 9tr, M/LW/FM portable. £25.8s.9d. plus £8.3s.3d. P.T. May 1961.

Diamond de Luxe. 10tr, S/M/LW/FM portable. £30.2s.11d. plus £8.14s.1d. P.T. 1961.

Druker (*dist.* **D. & M. Druker Ltd.),** 6 Philpot Street, Stepney, London E1. *Transistor Production Run 1966.*

Spica. 6tr, MW pocket portable. £1.16s.0d. plus 12s.0d. P.T. 1966. .

Spiket. 6tr, M/LW pocket portable. £3.7s.0d. plus 18s.0d. P.T. 1966.

Dulci (*dist.* **Lee Products [Gt. Britain] Ltd.),** 10-18 Clifton Street, London EC2. *Transistor Production Run 1971-72+*

6Q15. 6tr, MW pocket portable. £3.86p. including P.T. 1971.

15F5. 15tr, MW/FM portable. £10.60p. including P.T. 1971.

16F5. 16tr, MW/FM/Aircraft Band/Police Band mains/battery portable. £18.34p. including P.T. 1971. (Came complete with built-in mains adaptor).

16F45. 16tr, M/LW/FM mains battery portable. £14.05p. including P.T. 1972. (Came complete with built-in mains adaptor).

642. 6tr, MW pocket portable. £2.44p. including P.T. 1972.

Dynaport (*see Portadyne, page 268*)

Dynatron (Dynatron Radio Ltd.), St.Peter's Road, Maidenhead, Berkshire. *Transistor Production Run 1958-69.*

TP10 (Nomad). 6tr, M/LW portable. £21.18s.2d. plus £8.10s.10d. P.T. August 1958.

TP11 (Nomad). 7tr, M/LW portable. £19.9s.6d. plus £6.5s.0d. P.T. August 1959. (Identical chassis used in the TP12 Linnet).

TP12 (Linnet). 7tr, M/LW table model. £19.9s.6d. plus £6.5s.0d. P.T. April 1960. (Identical chassis used in the TP11 Nomad).

TP14 (Tourist). 6tr, M/LW personal portable. £11.10s.6d. plus £3.14s.0d. P.T. August 1960.

TP14B (Tourist). 6tr, M/LW personal portable (pre-set on LW for the Light Programme). £12.1s.6d. including P.T. 1963.

TP15 (Commodore). 9tr, M/LW/FM portable. £25.8s.9d. plus £8.3s.3d. P.T. August 1961.

TP16 (Gypsy). 6tr, M/LW portable. £14.6s.2d. plus £4.11s.10d. P.T. August 1961.

TP21 (Nomad de Luxe). 7tr, M/LW portable. £26.5s.0d. including P.T. September 1962.

TP22 (Deputy). 6tr, M/LW portable. £18.7s.6d. including P.T. September 1962.

TP30 (Jewel). 7tr, M/LW portable. £16.16s.0d. including P.T. August 1963.

TP31 (Sapphire). 7tr, S/M/LW portable. £22.1s.0d. including P.T. 1964.

TP32 (Sapphire). 7tr, S/M/LW portable. £24.3s.0d. including P.T. 1964.

TP34 (Atlantis). 10tr, S/M/LW/FM portable/ car radio. £32.11s.6d. plus £5.14s.11d. P.T. 1966. (Came complete with a built-in tuning meter. Primarily for home, outdoor or in-car use).

TP35R. As model TP34, but housed in a rosewood cabinet. £36.9s.0d. plus £5.18s.2d. P.T. 1966.

TP35T. As model TP34, but in teak cabinet. £36.9s.0d. plus £5.18s.2d. P.T. 1966.

TP36 (Rally). 8tr, M/LW portable/car radio. £15.7s.8d. plus £2.14s.3d. P.T. 1966. (For home, outdoor or in-car use).

TP37T. As model TP36 (above), but in teak finish cabinet. £16.14s.0d. plus £2.19s.0d. P.T. 1966.

TP38T. 13tr, M/LW/FM portable/car radio. £27.4s.0d. plus £5.16s.4d. P.T. 1968. (For home, outdoor or in-car use).

TP39T. As TP38T (above), but housed in a teak finish cabinet. £29.15s.0d. plus £6.7s.4d. P.T. 1968.

TP40T. 8tr, M/LW portable/car radio. £18.14s.0d. plus £4.0s.0d. P.T. 1968. (For home, outdoor or in-car use).

TP41T. As TP40T (above), but housed in a teak finish cabinet. £20.8s.0d. plus £4.7s.3d. P.T. 1968.

TP42T. 8tr, M/LW portable/car radio. £5.14s.6d. plus £3.7s.3d. P.T. 1968. (For home, outdoor or in-car use).

TP43T. 9tr, M/LW/FM portable/car radio. £23.1s.5d. plus £5.8s.6d. P.T. 1969.

TRF2200L. 16tr, S/M/LW/FM mains/battery portable. £28.19s.1d. plus £5.2s.3d. P.T. 1967. (For home, outdoor or in-car use).

TRV15T. S/M/LW/FM mains table model. £38.0s.0d. plus £6.14s.2d. P.T. 1966. (Complete with tuning meter).

TRV16 (Ether Stereo). 30tr, M/LW/FM stereo mains table model. £78.15s.0d. including P.T. 1967. (Complete with tuning meter).

TRV17. 30tr, M/LW/FM stereo mains table model. £72.9s.0d. including P.T. 1967. (Complete with tuning meter).

E.A.R. (Electric Audio Reproducers Ltd.), The Square, Isleworth, Middlesex. *Transistor Production Run 1959-62.*

Astor. 6tr, M/LW portable. £10.3s.8d. plus £2.18s.10d. P.T. May 1961.

Goodwood. 6tr, M/LW portable. £18.18s.0d. including P.T. 1959.

Tourist. 7tr, M/LW portable. 1962.

Ekco (E.K. Cole Ltd.), Southend-on-Sea, Essex. From 1961, **(Ekco Radio & Television Ltd),** Southend-on-Sea, Essex. From 1969, **(Pye Group [Radio & Television] Ltd.),** PO Box 49, Cambridge. From 1972, **(Pye Ltd.),** at same address. *Transistor Production Run 1958-72+.*

A400. 21tr, M/LW/FM stereo mains table model. £49.15s.0d. including P.T. 1967.

A401. 10tr, M/LW/FM mains table model. £22.4s.10d. plus £4.15s.2d. P.T. 1968.

A402. 10tr, MW/FM mains table model/clock radio. £24.18s.0d. including P.T. 1970.

A410. 30tr, M/LW/FM stereo mains table model. £44.1s.6d. plus £9.8s.6d. P.T. 1968.

A449. S/M/LW/FM M/LW mains table model. £29.17s.2d. plus £5.5s.5d. P.T. 1966.

A455. 7tr, M/LW mains table model. £13.11s.5d. plus £2.7s.11d. P.T. 1966.

BPT333. 6tr, M/LW portable. £16.13s.6d. plus £6.8s.6d. P.T. April 1958. (Identical chassis used in the Ferranti PT1010).

BPT351. 6tr, M/LW portable. £15.10s.0d. plus £3.6s.4d. P.T. August 1959. (Identical chassis used in the Ferranti PT1030).

BT359. 8tr, M/LW table model. £21.9s.3d. plus £6.17s.9d. P.T. December 1960.

CP920 (Twin Set). 7tr, M/LW portable/car radio. £18.18s.0d. plus £3.9s.3d. P.T. 1962. (Complete with a "thief-proof" car bracket).

CP937. 6tr, M/LW portable/car radio. £21.6s.0d. plus P.T. 1967. (For home, outdoor or in-car use. Identical chassis used in the Pye 2009).

MBT414 (Transistor Twin). 8tr, M/LW mains/battery portable. £14.13s.3d. including P.T. July 1962. (Identical chassis used in the 1963 Ferranti MBT1089. The MBT414 was the first transistorised battery portable designed to operate also from the mains. It incorporated an AC mains unit, which could be bought separately from radio and electrical shops and used to provide auxilliary power for any other transistor portable. Transistorised mains-only table models were introduced in 1964 *[see the Bang & Olufsen Beomaster 900K, page 247]*).

MBT425 (Varsity). 8tr, M/LW mains/battery portable. £19.19s.0d. including P.T. June 1963.

P2010 (Two-in-One). 7tr, M/LW portable/car radio. £18.18s.0d. plus £3.9s.3d. P.T. 1966. (Complete with a "thief-proof" car bracket).

PT208. 7tr, M/LW portable (bandspread section aligned on Radio Luxembourg's wavelength of 208 metres). £14.3s.6d. including P.T. August 1964. (Identical chassis used in the Ferranti PT1127).

PT300. 9tr, S/M/LW/FM portable. £23.10s.6d. plus £4.3s.0d. P.T. 1966.

PT301 (Elf). 6tr, M/LW pocket portable. £4.10s.6d. plus £15s.11d. P.T. 1966.

PT302 (Stroller). 8tr, M/LW portable. £7.12s.7d. plus £1.6s.11d. P.T. April 1967. (Identical chassis used in the Pye P1369 and P1371).

PT304 (Wayfarer). 8tr, M/LW/FM portable. £17.7s.8d. plus £3.1s.4d. P.T. 1967. (Identical chassis used in the Ferranti 5501 and the Pye P1372).

PT305. 8tr, M/LW portable/car radio. £14.5s.7d. plus £2.10s.5d. P.T. 1967. (For home, outdoor or in-car use. Identical chassis used in the Ferranti 5503 and the Pye 1373).

PT306. 6tr, M/LW/FM portable. £12.12s.10d. plus £2.4s.8d. P.T. 1967. (Identical chassis used in the Pye 1374).

PT307 (Stroller). 8tr, M/LW portable. £8.3s.1d. plus £1.4s.4d. P.T. 1968.

PT308 (Elf). 6tr, M/LW portable. 4.17s.3d. plus £1.0s.9d. P.T. 1968.

PT310. 10tr, M/LW/FM/Marine Band mains/battery portable. £17.0s.0d. plus £4.0s.0d. P.T. 1969.

PT312. 9tr, M/LW/FM portable. £12.2s.2d. plus £2.11s.10d. P.T. 1968.

PT313. 8tr, M/LW/FM portable. £26.9s.2d. including P.T. 1970.

PT316 (Vanity). 6tr, M/LW portable. £6.16s.0d. including P.T. 1970.

PT318. 9tr, M/LW/FM portable. £10.2s.4d. plus £2.7s.8d. P.T. 1969.

PT320. 12tr, M/LW/FM portable/car radio. £18.10s.0d. including P.T. 1970. (For home, outdoor or in-car use).

PT321. 6tr, M/LW pocket portable. £5.99p. including P.T. 1971.

PT322. 11tr, M/LW/FM portable. £14.17p. including P.T. 1972.

PT352. 6tr, M/LW personal portable (pre-set on LW for the Light Programme). £10.6s.8d. plus £3.6s.4d. P.T. August 1960. Carrying case, 12s.6d. extra.

PT468. 7tr, M/LW portable. 1965.

PT378 (Vanity). 6tr, M/LW portable. £11.18s.5d. plus £3.16s.7d. P.T. April 1961.

PT378/1. 7tr, M/LW portable. £14.3s.0d. including P.T. September 1963. (Identical chassis used in the Ferranti PT1104).

PT379 (Verity). 9tr, M/LW/FM portable. £17.9s.9d. plus £5.12s.3d. P.T. August 1961.

PT399. 6tr, M/LW pocket portable (pre-set on LW for the Light Programme). £11.11s.0d. including P.T. August 1962. (Identical chassis used in the Ferranti PT1076. Circuit incorporates a complimentary symmetry transformerless output stage using matched n-p-n/p-n-p output transistors — NKT257/ NKT751).

PT399G. As PT399, but with jewelled loudspeaker grille.

PT424 (New Verity). 9tr, M/LW/FM portable. £23.2s.0d. including P.T. June 1963.

PT426/L (Valentine). 7tr, M/LW portable (bandspread section aligned on Radio Luxembourg's wavelength of 208 metres). £16.16s.0d. including P.T. 1963.

PT438. 7tr, M/LW portable. £11.0s.6d. including P.T. 1964.

PT447. 9tr, S/M/LW/FM portable. £26.5s.0d. including P.T. 1965.

PT454 (Vanity). 8tr, M/LW portable. £13.2s.6d. including P.T. 1965.

PTR313. 8tr, M/LW/FM portable. £21.8s.0d. plus £5.0s.10d. P.T. 1969.

Electrochord (G. Whitaker & Son Ltd.), 5-6 Lorimore Buildings, Olney Road, London SE17. *Transistor Production Run 1960.*

Transistor 6. 6tr, portable. March 1960.

Electronica (Europhon [Radio & Television] Ltd.), 70 Caledonian Road, London N1. *Transistor Production Run 1967.*

Mamaia 8651T. 10tr, S/M/LW/FM portable. £15.14s.8d. plus £3.13s.10d. P.T. 1967.

Elizabethan (Elizabethan Tape Recorders Ltd.), Bridge Close, Romford, Essex. From 1968, **(Elizabethan Products Ltd.)**, 10-18 Clifton Street, London EC2. From 1970, **(*dist.* Lee Products [Gt. Britain] Ltd.)**, at same address. *Transistor Production Run 1961-70.*

L216. 8tr, M/LW pocket portable. £4.9s.3d. plus 15s.9d. P.T. 1967.

L217. 10tr, M/LW/FM pocket portable. £8.0s.6d. plus £1.8s.4d. P.T. 1967.

L218. 14tr, M/LW/FM portable. £11.3s.3d. plus £1.19s.4d. P.T. 1967.

L299. 9tr, MW/FM portable. £7.16s.4d. plus £1.13s.4d. P.T. 1968.

LZ8. 8tr, S/M/LW portable. 1965.

LZ10. 10tr, S/M/LW portable. 1965.

LZ12. 10tr, MW/FM pocket portable. £8.18s.6d. plus £1.11s.6d. P.T. 1966.

LZ14. 12tr, M/LW/FM portable. £15.3s.5d. plus £2.13s.7d. P.T. 1967.

LZ16. 8tr, M/LW port. £5.5s.0d. inc. P.T. 1967.

LZ17. 10tr, S/M/LW portable. £9.9s.0d. plus P.T. 1967.

LZ18. 14tr, S/M/LW/FM mains/battery portable. £12.12s.6d. including P.T. 1967. (Built-in mains adaptor).

LZ800L. 8tr, M/LW portable. £14.5s.7d. plus £2.10s.5d. P.T. 1966. (Featured clockwork station hunting).

LZ837E. 8tr, S/M/LW portable. £13.7s.9d. plus £2.7s.3d. P.T. 1966.

LZTR2. 6tr, M/LW portable. 1961.

Apollo. 6tr, M/LW portable. £5.10s.0d. including P.T. 1970.

Corsair (PTR6). 6tr, M/LW portable. £12.8s.4d. plus £4.7s.8d. P.T. May 1961.

Roma. 6tr, M/LW portable. £12.1s.6d. including P.T. 1962.

Elpico (Clifton) (*dist.* Lee Products [Gt. Britain] Ltd.), 10-18 Clifton Street, London EC2. *Transistor Production Run 1962-70.*

8Q9 (Sandy). 8tr, MW/FM portable. £9.12s.3d. including P.T. 1970.

28. 7tr, M/LW pocket portable. £3.14s.5d. plus 13s.1d. P.T. 1967.

33. 10tr, M/LW portable. £4.15s.3d. plus £1.0s.3d. P.T. 1968.

92. 14tr, M/LW/FM mains/battery portable. £11.3s.2d. plus £1.19s.4d. P.T. 1967. (Built-in mains adaptor).

93. 10tr, M/LW/FM portable. £8.0s.8d. plus £1.8s.4d. P.T. 1967.

RV65. 6tr, MW pocket portable. £4.2s.9d. including P.T. 1964.

RV67. 6tr, MW pocket portable. 2.15s.3d. plus 9s.9d. P.T. 1966.

TP1. 6tr, M/LW portable. £10.9s.6d. plus £3.0s.6d. P.T. 1962.

Essex (TR862). 8tr, M/LW portable. £4.17s.2d. plus £1.2s.10d. P.T. 1969.

Emerson (Emerson Electronics Ltd.), Brent Crescent, N. Circular Road, London NW10. From 1962, **(Cockburn & Gunn Ltd.)**, Bridge Cl., Romford. *Transistor Production Run 1958-62.*

110. 9tr, M/LW/FM portable. £23.4s.0d. including P.T. September 1962.

505. 8tr, S/M/LW portable. £20.9s.6d. including P.T. September 1962.

555. 6tr, M/LW pocket portable. £19.19s.0d. including P.T. September 1959.

888. 6tr, M/LW portable. £19.19s.0d. including P.T. August 1958.

888 (Vanguard). 6tr, M/LW pocket portable. £18.18s.0d. including P.T. August 1959. (Similar to 888 but with different cabinet styling).

E666. 6tr, M/LW table model. £15.2s.1d. plus £4.16s.11d. P.T. November 1959.

911. 7tr, M/LW portable. £12.14s.5d. plus £4.1s.7d. P.T. August 1960.

988. 6tr, M/LW portable (pre-set on LW for the Light Programme). £10.11s.10d. plus £3.1s.2d. P.T. 1961.

Epic (*dist.* L.P.F. Photronics Ltd.), Cricklewood Lane, London NW2. *Transistor Production Run 1963.*

Epic Mk.I. 6tr, MW pocket portable. £3.19s.6d. including P.T. 1963.

Estyma (*dist.* Steven Strauss Ltd.), 69 Hatton Garden, London EC1. *Transistor Production Run 1966.*

Radiolarm. 6tr, M/LW portable radio/30-hour travel alarm clock. £12.12s.0d. plus £2.6s.2d. P.T. 1966. (8-day clock, £2.2s.0d. extra).

Radio Times. 6tr, M/LW portable radio/30-hour alarm clock in the form of a book. £13.1s.0d. plus £2.7s.10d. P.T. 1966. (8-day clock, £2.2s.0d. extra).

Ettinger (*dist.* G. Ettinger Ltd.), 11 Warwick Street, London W1. *Transistor Production Run 1966.*

Whisky Bottle (Ballantine Scotch Whisky label). 8tr, MW novelty radio. £10.19s.0d. plus £1.13s.0d. P.T. 1966.

Eumig [West Germany] **(*dist.* B.C. Blazey & Clement Ltd.)**, 137 Regent Street, London W1/ Memfagimal House, 26 St. Cross St., Hatton Garden, London EC1. *Transistor Production Run 1960-62.*

331 (de Luxe). 7tr, M/LW personal portable. £12.17s.11d. plus £3.11s.7d. P.T. 1961. (As Standard model, next, but with protective carrying case).

331 (Standard). 7tr, M/LW personal portable. £11.8s.1d. plus £3.5s.11d. P.T. 1961.

332. 9tr, S/M/LW/FM portable. £25.5s.1d. plus £7.5s.11d. P.T. 1961.

334. 7tr, M/LW personal portable. £11.16s.3d. plus £3.8s.3d. P.T. May 1962.

OKay. 7tr, M/LW personal portable. £13.18s.3d. plus £4.9s.3d. P.T. January 1960.

Country Club. MW pocket portable (converts into a table model by docking into a matching loudspeaker cabinet). May 1961.

Europhon (**Europhon [Radio & Television] Ltd.**), 174 Pentonville Road, London N1. From 1967, at 70 Caledonian Road, London N1. *Transistor Production Run 1961-72+.*

303. 7tr, M/LW portable. £18.18s.0d. including P.T. 1964.

523T. M/LW/FM mains/battery table model. £18.5s.9d. plus £3.15s.3d. P.T. 1968.

623T. M/LW/FM mains/battery table model. £20.17s.10d. £4.6s.2d. P.T. 1968.

723TA. 9tr, M/LW/FM mains/battery table model. £24.6s.2d. plus £5.1s.10d. P.T. 1968.

723ST. 15tr, M/LW/FM stereo mains table model. £30.1s.10d. plus £6.13s.2d. P.T. 1968.

800. 9tr, MW/FM mains/battery table model. £22.1s.0d. including P.T. 1970.

823T. S/M/LW/FM mains table model. £23.3s.5d. plus £5.5s.7d. P.T. 1968.

935. 9tr, M/LW/FM portable. £23 including P.T. 1971.

ES62. 7tr, MW portable. £9.19s.6d. including P.T. 1962.

FM1600. 11tr, S/M/LW/FM portable. £50.8s.0d. including P.T. 1964.

RC/A (Supreme). 7tr, M/LW portable. £15.4s.6d. including P.T. 1970.

RP440. 9tr, MW/FM portable. £14 including P.T. 1971.

SB60. 7tr, M/LW portable. £12.1sd.6d. including P.T. 1962.

SB64. 7tr, M/LW portable. £8.18s.6d. including P.T. 1963.

TR3 (Silver Star 22). 7tr, MW pocket portable. £14.14s.0d. including P.T. 1962.

TR3 (de Luxe). 7tr, 2S/M/LW portable. £14.14s.0d. including P.T. 1963.

TR4. 7tr, 2S/M/LW portable. £13.13s.0d. including P.T. 1964.

TR7. 7tr, MW pocket portable. £7.6s.8d. plus P.T. 1961.

TR67. 7tr, M/LW portable. £11 including P.T. 1971.

Eurostar Car. 8tr, S/M/LW portable. £16.16s.0d. including P.T. 1964. (For home, outdoor or in-car use. Mains adaptor, £2.2s.0d. extra).

Goldstar (S631T). 7tr, M/LW portable. £7 including P.T. 1971.

Eurostar Luxembourg. 8tr, S/M/LW portable (bandspread section aligned on Radio Luxembourg's wavelength of 208 metres). £15.15s.0d. including P.T. 1964. (Mains adaptor, £2.2s.0d. extra).

Lamp Radio. 7tr, M/LW mains table model/desk lamp. £11 including P.T. 1971. (Bright and dim lamp control).

Playboy. 9tr, S/M/LW/FM portable. £16.60p. including P.T. 1972.

Professional. 10tr, 2S/MW/FM/Marine Band mains/battery portable. £25.3s.5d. plus £5.5s.7d. P.T. 1968. (Built-in mains adaptor).

Professional Mk.II. 10tr, 3S/MW/FM/Marine Band mains/battery portable. £33.1s.6d. including P.T. 1970. (Built-in mains adaptor).

Radar. 9tr, MW/FM portable. £17.12s.11d. plus £3.2s.3d. P.T. 1966. (Mains adaptor, £2.2s.0d. extra).

Superla Silver Star. 7tr, MW pocket portable. 1961.

Three Stars. 6tr, M/LW portable. £8.8s.0d. including P.T. 1964.

Ever Ready (**Ever Ready Co. [Great Britain] Ltd.**), Hercules Place, Holloway, London N7. *Transistor Production Run 1958-65.*

Car Portable. 6tr, M/LW portable/car radio. £28.6s.0d. including P.T. May 1960. (Complete with shielded metal mounting box and auxilliary external loudspeaker for in-car use).

Sky Baby. 6tr, M/LW portable. £9.10s.0d. plus P.T. May 1965.

Sky Baron. 6tr, table model. M/LW table model (pre-set on LW for the Light Programme). £17.17s.9d. plus £5.14s.9d. P.T. March 1960. (Ever Ready version of the Berec Musketeer).

Sky Lark (Mk.I). 6tr, M/LW portable. £12.1s.6d. including P.T. March 1963.

Sky Lark (Mk.II). 6tr, M/LW portable. £12.1s.6d. including P.T. May 1963. (Circuit modified from Mk.I).

Sky Leader. 6tr, M/LW portable. £15.8s.5d. plus £6.2s.7d. P.T. May 1958. (Ever Ready version of the Berec Demon).

Sky Master. 6tr, M/LW portable. £13.17s.0d. plus £4 P.T. October 1962.

Sky Personal. 6tr, M/LW personal portable (pre-set on LW for the Light Programme). £15.18s.0d. plus £5.2s.0d P.T. August 1959. (Ever Ready version of the Berec Bambino).

Sky Prince. 6tr, M/LW table model. £18.10s.6d. including P.T. October 1961.

Sky Prince. 6tr, M/LW portable. £19.18s.6d. including P.T. November 1961.

Sky Queen Mk.III. 7tr, M/LW portable. £14.14s.0d. including P.T. July 1964.

Sky Tourer. 6tr, M/LW portable/car radio. £22.1s.0d. inc. P.T. 1964. (For home, outdoor or, with fixing kit provided, for in-car use).

Falcon (**John Street [Manufacturers] Ltd.**), Falcon Works, Barmeston Road, London SE6. *Transistor Production Run 1968.*

Escort 69. 7tr, M/LW portable. £12.12s.7d. plus £2.11s.11d. P.T. 1968.

Fantavox (*dist.* **E.R. [Factors] Ltd.**), 378 Harrow Road, London W9. *Transistor Production Run 1966.*

FAR102. 10tr, MW/FM portable. £12.0s.6d. plus £1.12s.6d. P.T. 1966.

TA8009. 8tr, MW pocket portable. £4.13s.9d. plus 11s.3d. P.T. 1966.

TM1015. 10tr, M/LW/FM portable. £13.18s.7d. plus £1.16s.5d. P.T. 1966.

TM1213. 12tr, S/M/LW/FM portable. £19.16s.6d. plus £2.15s.0d. P.T. 1966.

Ferguson (**Ferguson Radio Corporation Ltd.**), Thorn House, Upper St. Martins Lane, London WC2. From 1965, (**British Radio Corporation Ltd.**), 284 Southbury Road, Enfield, Middlesex. By 1968, some Ferguson models (*ie.* the 3158), were being made in Japan. *Transistor Production Run 1959-72+.*

348BT. 6tr, M/LW portable. £15.10s.0d. plus £4.9s.6d. P.T. August 1959. (Identical chassis used in the H.M.V. 1417 and Marconiphone T82B).

349BT. 6tr, M/LW portable. £13.18s.3d. plus £4.9s.3d. P.T. May 1960.

357BT. 6tr, M/LW personal portable (pre-set on LW for the Light Programme). £11.2s.7d. plus £3.11s.5d. P.T. May 1960.

358BT. 7tr, M/LW personal portable. £10.1s.9d. plus £3.4s.9d. P.T. June 1961.

433BT. 7tr, M/LW table model. £13.11s.8d. plus £4.7s.1d. P.T. August 1961.

453BT. 7tr, M/LW portable. £13.3s.11d. plus £4.4s.8d. P.T. June 1961.

626BT. 8tr, M/LW/FM table model. £22.5s.2d. plus £7.2s.10d. P.T. July 1960.

632BT. 9tr, M/LW/FM table model. £21.6s.10d. plus £6.17s.10d. P.T. August 1961.

3100 (Freeway). 7tr, M/LW portable. £13.2s.5d. plus P.T. 1962.

3102. 6tr, M/LW personal portable/alarm watch (pre-set on LW for the Light Programme). £12.12s.7d. plus P.T. May 1962.

3104 (Freelance). 6tr, M/LW portable. £11 plus £3.3s.6d. P.T. April 1962.

3108. 6tr, M/LW pocket portable. £9.15s.6d. plus £2.16s.6d. P.T. 1962.

3110. 6tr, M/LW portable. £6.6s.0d. inc. P.T. 1963.

3112 (Fairway). 9tr, M/LW/FM portable. £22.1s.0d. including P.T. September 1962.

3114 (Fieldfare). 7tr, M/LW portable. £15.15s.0d. including P.T. March 1963.

3120 (Wavecrest). 7tr, 2S/M/LW portable. £16.16s.0d. including P.T. August 1963.

3122 (Flight). 7tr, S/M/LW portable (bandspread section aligned on Radio Luxembourg's wavelength of 208 metres). £12.12s.0d. including P.T. 1964.

3124 (Autotwin). 9tr, M/LW portable/car radio. £17.17s.0d. including P.T. 1964. (For home, outdoor or in-car use).

3128 (Fieldsman). 9tr, M/LW/FM portable. £20.9s.6d. including P.T. July 1964.

3130 (Gemini-6). 6tr, M/LW pocket portable. £6.15s.9d. plus £1.3s.11d. P.T. 1966.

3132 (Flight). 7tr, S/M/LW portable (bandspread section aligned on Radio Luxembourg's wavelength of 208 metres). £12.12s.0d. including P.T. 1965.

3136 (Freelance). 8tr, M/LW portable. £15.15s.0d. including P.T. 1965.

3138 (Freshman). 10tr, M/LW/FM portable/car radio (bandspread section aligned on Radio Luxembourg's wavelength of 208 metres). £20.9s.6d. including P.T. 1965.

3140 (Autotwin Mk.II). 9tr, M/LW portable/car radio. 1965. (For home, outdoor or in-car use. *See fig.815, p.205*).

3144 (Rangefinder). 7tr, S/M/LW portable. £12.13s.4d. plus £2.4s.9d. P.T. 1966.

3146. 10tr, S/M/LW/FM portable. £22.12s.5d. plus £3.19s.8d. P.T. 1967.

3148 (President). 10tr, S/M/LW/FM portable/car radio. £15.16s.8d. plus 2.15s.10d. P.T. 1966. (For home, outdoor or in-car use).

3150 (Autotwin Mk.III). 9tr, M/LW portable/car radio. £15.16s.8d. plus P.T. 1966. (For home, outdoor or in-car use).

3152. 10tr, S/M/LW/FM portable/car radio. £29.17s.2d. plus £5.5s.4d. P.T. 1967. (For home, outdoor or in-car use).

3156 (Caravelle). 11tr, S/M/LW/FM portable/car radio. £23.10s.6d. plus £4.3s.0d. P.T. 1967. (An identical chassis was used in the Ultra 6158).

3158. 9tr, S/M/LW portable. £10.17s.2d. plus £1.18s.4d. P.T. 1967. (Complete with black leather case, shoulder strap and single earpiece. Made in Japan under the Ferguson trade-mark).

3160. 10tr, M/LW/FM portable. £13.2s.5d. plus £2.6s.4d. P.T. 1967.

3162 (Autotwin). 9tr, M/LW portable/car radio. £16.16s.2d. plus £3.11s.10d. P.T. 1968. (For home, outdoor or in-car use. Chassis identical to the Ultra 6150 Road Ranger).

3163. 7tr, M/LW table model/clock radio. £14.8s.4d. plus £3.1s.8d. P.T. 1968.

3164. 7tr, S/M/LW portable. £8.12s.2d. plus £1.16s.10d. P.T. 1968.

3165. 10tr, M/LW/FM portable. £12.15s.5d. plus £2.14s.7d. P.T. 1968.

3166 (Futura II). 10tr, S/M/LW/FM mains table model. £34.15s.1d. plus £7.10s.11d. P.T. 1968.

3167. 10tr, M/LW/FM portable. £14.0s.1d. plus £2.19s.11d. P.T. 1968.

3168. 10tr, S/M/LW/FM portable/car radio. £25.18s.1d. plus £5.10s.11d. P.T. 1968. (For home, outdoor or in-car use. Chassis identical to the H.M.V. 2156, H.M.V. 2158 and the Marconiphone 4156).

3169. 11tr, S/M/LW/FM portable/car radio. £28.15s.0d. including P.T. 1970. (For home, outdoor or in-car use).

3170. 7tr, M/LW portable/car radio. £17.4s.0d. including P.T. 1970. (For home, outdoor or in-car use).

3171. 11tr, M/LW/FM portable/car radio. £22.12s.0d. including P.T. 1970. (For home, outdoor or in-car use).

3173. 9tr, M/LW portable/car radio. £22.1s.0d. including P.T. 1970. (For home, outdoor or in-car use).

3176. 8tr, M/LW portable. £12.80p. including P.T. 1971.

3177. 8tr, M/LW portable. £15.95p. including P.T. 1971.

3179. M/LW/FM portable/car radio. £19.40p. including P.T. 1972. (For home, outdoor or in-car use).

3180. M/LW/FM portable/car radio. £19.75p. including P.T. 1972. (For home, outdoor or in-car use. Mains adaptor, extra).

3183. MW/FM portable. £10.50p. including P.T. 1972.

3184. M/LW/FM portable. £14.50p. including P.T. 1972.

Ferranti (Ferranti Radio & Television Ltd.), 41/47 Old Street, London EC1. *Transistor Production Run 1958-68.*

5501 (Greyhound). 8tr, M/LW/FM portable. £17.7s.8d. plus £3.1s.4d. P.T. 1967. (Identical chassis used in the Ekco PT304 and the Pye 1372).

5502. 8tr, M/LW portable. £11.9s.6d. plus £2.0s.6d. P.T. 1967.

5503. 8tr, M/LW portable/car radio. £14.5s.7d. plus £2.10s.5d. P.T. 1967. (For home, outdoor or in-car use. Identical chassis used in the Ekco PT305 and the Pye 1373).

5700. 7tr, M/LW mains table model. £17.5s.0d. including P.T. 1967.

5701. M/LW/FM mains table model. £23.1s.7d. plus £5.0s.5d. P.T. 1968.

A1143. 10tr, S/M/LW/FM mains table model. £29.17s.3d. plus £5.5s.4d. P.T. 1966.

A1149. M/LW mains table model. £13.11s.5d. plus 2.7s.11d. P.T. 1966.

BT1037. 8tr, MW/FM table model. £21.9s.3d. plus £6.17s.9d. P.T. August 1960.

MBT1089. 8tr, M/LW mains/battery portable. £18.18s.0d. including P.T. February 1963. (Identical chassis used in the 1962 Ekco MBT414 which was the first transistorised battery portable designed to operate also from the mains).

MBT1101. 7tr, M/LW mains/battery portable. £19.19s.0d. including P.T. 1964.

P1141. 9tr, S/M/LW/FM portable. £26.5s.0d. including P.T. 1965.

P1148. 7tr, M/LW portable. £13.2s.6d. including P.T. 1965.

PT1010. 6tr, M/LW portable. £16.13s.6d. plus £6.8s.6d. P.T. April 1958. (Identical chassis used in the Ekco BPT333).

PT1030. 6tr, M/LW portable. £15.10s.0d. plus £3.6s.4d. P.T. August 1959. (Identical chassis used in the Ekco BPT351).

PT1031. 6tr, M/LW pocket portable (pre-set on LW for the Light Programme). £10.6s.8d. plus £3.6s.4d. P.T. August 1960.

PT1056. 6tr, M/LW portable. £11.15s.6d. plus £3.16s.7d. P.T. April 1961.

PT1065. 9tr, M/LW/FM portable. £17.18s.5d. plus £5.3s.7d. P.T. 1961.

PT1076 (Pixie). 6tr, M/LW pocket portable (pre-set on LW for the Light Programme). £11.11s.0d. including P.T. August 1962. (Identical chassis used in the Ekco PT399. Circuit incorporates a complimentary symmetry transformerless output stage using matched n-p-n/p-n-p output transistors — NKT257/NKT751).

PT1079. 6tr, M/LW portable. £15.15s.0d. including P.T. 1962.

PT1100. 9tr, M/LW/FM portable. £23.2s.0d. including P.T. 1964.

PT1102. 7tr, M/LW portable. £16.16s.0d. including P.T. 1964.

PT1104. 7tr, M/LW portable. £14.3s.0d. including P.T. October 1963. (Identical chassis used in the Ekco PT378/1).

PT1127. 7tr, M/LW portable (bandspread section aligned on Luxembourg's wavelength of 208 metres). £14.3s.6d. inc. P.T. 1964. (Identical chassis used in the Ekco PT208).

Fida (*dist.* Kingsway Mill Co. [M/C] Ltd.), 1 Berry Street, London EC1. From 1966, (*dist.* Winter Trading Co. Ltd.), 95-99 Ladbroke Grove, London W11. *Transistor Production Run 1965.*

FR625P. 7tr, M/LW pocket portable. £4.19s.6d. including P.T. 1965.

Fidelity (Fidelity Radio Ltd.), 11-13 Blechynden Street, London W1. From 1964, at 6 Olaf Street, London W11. *Transistor Production Run 1960-72+.*

199 (Transistor Seven). 7tr, M/LW portable. 1965. Named after Radio Caroline 199 which, as the U.K.'s first 'Pop Pirate' station, first went on the air on Saturday 28th March 1964. (*See also under the brand-name Caroline, page 250*).

199A. As 199 (above), but in slightly different cabinet styling (metal grille instead of a plastics grille). £7.17s.6d. including P.T. 1966.

208. 7tr, M/LW portable. £13.13s.0d. including P.T. 1963. (Bandspread tuning between 185-211 metres, for Radio Luxembourg. One of a number of transistor radios brought out this time emphasising the pop station Radio Luxembourg and, like the 199 portable described above, aimed straight at the teenage market.

"*Standard sets three times the price can't get 208 the way Fidelity '208' can! For your radio-buying teens and twenties, it's the best thing that's happened to pop listening since Presley. This seven-transistor portable spreads Luxembourg's share of the tuning scale fifteen times wider than usual. Bandspread on Luxembourg means that the set has been manufactured with part of the medium wavelength around 208 metres expanded to give easy, spot-on tuning for Luxembourg fans. They get the stars, not the static, loud and clear the whole evening through. Fidelity '208' gives them volume for dancing, tone for listening. Fidelity '208' tunes straight in to today's rich young market! . . . ").*

Ayr. 6tr, M/LW portable. £13.2s.3d. plus £4.4s.3d. P.T. March 1960.

Comet. 7tr, M/LW portable. £9.19s.0d. plus £1.15s.3d. P.T. June 1966. (Bandspread tuning between 188-211 metres, for Radio Luxembourg).

Coronet Transistor Six. 6tr, M/LW pocket portable (pre-set on LW for the Light Programme). £9.19s.6d. including P.T. March 1961. (The first British-made transistor radio on sale for under £10 including P.T.).

Fairline. 12tr, S/M/LW portable. £16.14s.9d. plus P.T. May 1963. (Complete with tuning and battery meter).

Floret. 7tr, M/LW portable. £9.15s.6d. plus £2.16s.6d. P.T. May 1962. (The Floret was fitted with either Mullard or Texas Instruments transistors. Circuit incorporates a complimentary symmetry transformerless output stage using matched n-p-n/p-n-p output transistors — OC81M/AC127 [Mullard] or 2G381/2G339 [Texas Instruments]).

Florida. 6tr, M/LW portable. £10.17s.3d. plus £3.16s.9d. P.T. June 1961.

Fulmar. 7tr, M/LW portable. £9.9s.0d. including P.T. 1963.

Galaxy. 7tr, S/M/LW portable. £12.12s.0d. including P.T. 1963.

Kestrel. 9tr, M/LW/FM portable. £15.3s.6d. plus £2.13s.6d. P.T. 1967.

Rad 11. 7tr, M/LW portable. £10.5s.4d. plus £1.16s.2d. P.T. June 1967. (Bandspread tuning between 188-211 metres, for Radio Luxembourg).

Rad 11B. 7tr, M/LW portable. £10.7s.8d. plus £2.8s.10d. P.T. 1969.

Rad 12. 6tr, M/LW portable/car radio. £9.9s.0d. including P.T. May 1968. (For home, outdoor or in-car use).

Rad 14. 9tr, M/LW/FM portable. £14.14s.2d. plus £3.2s.10d. P.T. 1968.

Rad 15. 9tr, M/LW/FM portable/car radio. £17.17s.1d. plus £4.3s.11d. P.T. May 1969. (For home, outdoor or in-car use).

Rad 16. 7tr, S/M/LW/Marine Band (66.6-176 metres) portable/car radio. £14.9s.1d. plus £3.7s.11d. P.T. 1969. (For home, outdoor or in-car use).

Rad 18. 9tr, S/M/LW/Marine Band portable. £22.19s.2d. plus £5.7s.10d. P.T. 1969.

Rad 19. 8tr, M/LW/FM portable/car radio. £16.10s.0d. including P.T. 1970. (For home, outdoor or in-car use).

Rad 20. 6tr, M/LW port./car radio. £9.20p. inc. P.T. 1971. (For home, outdoor or in-car use).

Rad 21. 9tr, S/M/LW/FM/Marine Band portable. £33.50p. including P.T. 1972. (Mains adaptor, extra).

Rad 22. 7tr, M/LW portable £13.50p. including P.T. 1972.

Zodiac. 7tr, M/LW portable. £12.13s.4d. plus £2.4s.9d. P.T. 1966.

Fraikad (**Fraikad Ltd.**), 139-141 Farringdon Road, London EC1. *Transistor Production Run 1961.*

Princess 6. 6tr, MW pocket portable. March 1961.

G.B.C. (**G.B.C. Electronic Industries Ltd.**), 121-123 Edgware Road, Marble Arch, London W2. *Transistor Production Run 1961.*

Clarion Super-6. 6tr, MW pocket portable. June 1961.

Pizon. 6tr, MW pocket portable. Sept. 1961.

G.E.C. (**General Electric Co. Ltd.**), Magnet House, Kingsway, London WC2. From 1961, (**G.E.C. Radio & Television Ltd.**), Langley Park, Slough, Bucks. From 1966, (**G.E.C. Radio & Allied Holdings Ltd.**), Langley Park, Slough, Bucks. *Transistor Production Run 1957-70.*

BC501. 6tr, M/LW portable/car radio. £15.2s.1d. plus £4.16s.11d. P.T. June 1959. (For home, outdoor or in-car use).

BC502. 6tr, M/LW portable. £15.2s.1d. plus £4.16s.11d. P.T. September 1959. (Slightly modified version of BC501).

BC504. 6tr, M/LW pocket portable (pre-set on LW for the Light Programme). £11.18s.6d. plus £3.16s.6d. P.T. October 1961.

BC505. 7tr, M/LW portable. £18.18s.0d. plus P.T. October 1961.

BC506. 6tr, M/LW portable. £16.5s.6d. plus P.T. October 1961.

BC561. 6tr, M/LW portable. £17.9s.9d. plus £5.12s.3d. P.T. August 1960.

BC562. 9tr, FM portable. £19.1s.7d. plus £6.2s.5d. P.T. August 1960.

BC563. 9tr, M/LW/FM portable. £29.8s.0d. including Purchase Tax. October 1961. (Alternative transistor line-up provided — *see 'Typical Transistor Line-ups, 1961-1966', page 284*).

BC564. 7tr, M/LW portable. £23.12s.6d. including P.T. October 1961.

BC1650. 6tr, M/LW portable. £17.8s.9d. plus £6.14s.3d. P.T. August 1957.

G806 (Compact). 6tr, M/LW pocket portable (pre-set on LW for the Light Programme). £8.18s.6d. including P.T. November 1961. (An identical chassis was used in the Sobell S306).

G808 (Companion). 6tr, M/LW portable. £11.8s.1d. plus £3.5s.11d. P.T. January 1962.

G810. 6tr, M/LW portable. £12.4s.5d. plus £3.10s.7d. P.T. April 1962.

G812. 6tr, M/LW portable. £13.2s.6d. including P.T. 1962.

G814. 6tr, S/M/LW portable. £14.3s.6d. including P.T. April 1963.

G815. 6tr, S/M/LW portable. £14.3s.6d. including P.T. 1964.

G816. 9tr, M/LW/FM portable. £19.8s.6d. including P.T. March 1963.

G817. 10tr, M/LW/FM portable. £19.18s.2d. plus £3.10s.3d. P.T. 1966.

G818 (Luxembourg). 7tr, M/LW portable. £10.2s.1d. including P.T. 1963. (Bandspread tuning between 178-211 metres, for Radio Luxembourg).

G819. 9tr, S/M/LW portable. £17.6s.6d. including P.T. 1965.

G820 (Starfinder). 10tr, 2S/M/LW/FM portable. £31.13s.5d. plus £5.11s.9d. P.T. 1966. (With tuning/battery meter and world-time chart).

G822 (Transistomatic). 7tr, M/LW portable/camera. A transistor radio combined with a built-in Kodak Instamatic 100 camera, it came complete with a colour film, flash batteries, flash bulbs and a carrying strap. £19.19s.0d. including P.T. May 1964. (Bandspread tuning between 174-210 metres, for Radio Luxembourg).

G825. 8tr, S/M/LW portable. £14.3s.6d. including P.T. 1965. (Bandspread tuning between 183-211 metres for Luxembourg).

G826. 7tr, S/M/LW portable. £13.2s.5d. plus £2.6s.4d. P.T. 1966.

G827. 7tr, M/LW portable (pre-set station selection). £14.18s.7d. plus £2.12s.9d. P.T. 1966. (Bandspread tuning between 185-222 metres for Radio Luxembourg. Chassis identical to the Masteradio D527 and the Sobell S327).

G828. 7tr, S/M/LW portable. £13.2s.5d. plus £2.6s.4d. P.T. 1966.

G832. 8tr, M/LW mains/battery portable/car radio. £23.2s.0d. including P.T. 1967. (Complete with built-in mains adaptor. For home, outdoor or in-car use. Bandspread tuning between 185-220 metres for, Radio Luxembourg. Chassis identical to the Sobell S322).

G834. 10tr, M/LW/FM portable/car radio. £19.19s.0d. including P.T. 1967. (For home, outdoor or in-car use. Chassis identical to the Sobell S334).

G835 (Poppins). 7tr, M/LW portable. £7.17s.6d. including P.T. March 1967. (Recalling the 1964 film *Mary Poppins* perhaps? Complete with wrist strap).

G836. 10tr, 2S/M/LW/FM portable. £33.14s.8d. plus £7.4s.4d. P.T. 1968. (Complete with tuning/battery meter, and world-time chart).

G837. 10tr, M/LW/FM portable. £24.4s.5d. plus £5.3s.7d. P.T. 1968. (Complete with a built-in tuning/battery meter, and world-time chart).

G838. 9tr (5 transistors plus an encapsulated audio stage module containing 4 transistors and 1 diode), M/LW/FM portable/car radio. £15.15s.0d. including P.T. 1969. (For home, outdoor or in-car use. Chassis identical to the Sobell S338).

G989/1. 14tr, FM, stereo mains table model. £33.12s.0d. including P.T. 1970.

G2541. 11tr, 3S/M/LW/FM mains/battery portable. £48.10s.0d. including P.T. 1970.

General (*dist.* **Lee Products [Gt. Britain] Ltd.**), 10-18 Clifton Street, London EC2. *Transistor Production Run 1962-63.*

6GA-128L. 6tr, M/LW pocket portable. £12.15s.6d. plus £3.13s.10d. P.T. May 1962.

6GA-819. 6tr, MW pocket portable. £8.1s.6d. plus £2.9s.6d. P.T. May 1962.

8GA-701F. 10tr, MW/FM portable. £24.16s.9d. plus £7.3s.1d. P.T. May 1962.

9GA-131A. 9tr, 2S/MW portable. £22.5s.0d. including P.T. 1963.

C59. 8tr, S/MW pocket portable. £13.13s.0d. including P.T. 1963.

DC3350A. 8tr, S/MW portable. £17.17s.0d. including P.T. 1963.

Global (*dist.* **Watson Bros. [London] Ltd.**), 12 Kingly Street, London W1. *Transistor Production Run 1961.*

Global 6. 6tr, M/LW pocket portable. November 1961.

Gold Spot [Japan] (*dist.* **Cordes Marden & Co.Ltd.**), 18 Finsbury Circus, London EC2. *Transistor Production Run 1964.*

Gold Spot 6. 6tr, MW pocket portable. £4.16s.9d. including P.T. 1964.

Gold Spot 8. 8tr, M/LW portable. £9.0s.9d. including P.T. 1964.

Goldhorn (*dist.* **Denham & Morley Ltd.**), Denmore House, 175 Cleveland Street, London W1. *Transistor Production Run 1959-60.*

TK100. £17.6s.6d. including P.T. 1960.

TK102. £17.6s.6d. including P.T. 1960.

Amor. 6tr, M/LW portable. £15.10s.0d. plus P.T. October 1959. (In leather case).

Informant. (As Amor, above, but in plastic case). £14.9s.2d. plus P.T. October 1959.

Junior. 4tr, MW personal portable. £11.2s.6d. plus £3.11s.6d. P.T. October 1960.

Vogel. 7tr, M/LW portable. £17.9s.9d. plus £5.12s.3d. March 1960.

Grundig [West Germany] (**Grundig [Gt. Britain] Ltd.**), Newlands Park, Sydenham, London SE26. *Transistor Production Run 1957-72+.*

RF100A. 9tr, M/LW/FM mains table model. £23.16s.5d. plus £5.1s.1d. P.T. 1968.

RF110. M/LW/FM mains table model. £23.12s.7d. plus £5.11s.1d. P.T. 1969.

RF111. 9tr, M/LW/FM mains table model. £31.75p. including P.T. 1971.

RF430. M/LW/FM mains table model. £35.85p. including P.T. 1972.

TR600. 9tr, 4S/MW portable. £34.18s.0d. including P.T. 1970.

TR3005. 20tr, 4S/M/LW/FM portable. £78.25p. including P.T. 1972.

Automatic-Boy. 13tr, S/M/LW/FM portable. £63 including P.T. 1962.

City-Boy 204. 9tr, S/M/LW/FM portable. £35.14s.0d. including P.T. 1963.

Concert-Boy. 12tr, 2S/M/LW/FM portable. £50.13s.5d. plus £8.18s.10d. P.T. 1966. (Mains adaptor, £6.6s.0d. extra).

Elite-Boy 209. 10tr, S/M/LW/FM portable/car radio. £27.8s.8d. plus £6.8s.10d. P.T. 1969. (Mains adaptor extra).

Export-Boy 203. 8tr, 3S/MW portable. £38.17s.0d. including P.T. 1962.

Mariner TR860. 12tr, 2S/MW/FM portable. £33.17s.10d. plus £7.1s.2d. P.T. 1968. (Mains adaptor extra).

Mariner TR865. 12tr, 2S/MW/FM portable. £44.16s.9d. including P.T. 1970.

Melody-Boy (1000E). 13tr, 2S/M/LW/FM mains/battery portable. £53.10p. including P.T. 1972. (Built-in mains unit).

Micro-Boy. 6tr, MW pocket portable (converts into a table model by docking into a matching loudspeaker cabinet). £19.17s.6d. plus £6.7s.6d. P.T. July 1960. (*See fig.949, p.297*).

Mini-Boy. 6tr, MW pocket portable. (This ususual receiver converted into a table model by docking into a matching loudspeaker cabinet). £19.8s.1d. plus £6.4s.6d. P.T. October 1960.

Model 200. 4v + 2tr hybrid, S/M/LW portable. £31.10s.0d. including P.T. 1957. (Circuit line-up: DK96, DF96, DAF96 and DF97 valves, with a pair of Mullard OC72 transistors in push-pull output).

Music-Boy 204. 9tr, S/M/LW/FM portable. £40.19s.0d. including P.T. 1963.

Music-Boy 208A. 10tr, S/M/LW/FM portable. £24.5s.4d. plus £5.2s.8d. P.T. 1968. (Mains adaptor extra).

Music-Boy de Luxe. 11tr, S/M/LW/FM portable. £31.13s.5d. plus £5.11s.9d. P.T. 1966. (Mains adaptor, £6.6s.0d. extra).

Music-Boy Luxus 208A. 10tr, S/M/LW/FM portable. £24.4s.6d. plus £5.14s.0d. P.T. 1969. (Mains adaptor extra).

Music-Boy Universal. 9tr, M/LW/FM portable/car radio. £33.18s.8d. plus £5.19s.9d. P.T. 1966. (Bracket available for in-car use, £4.14s.6d. extra, mains adaptor, £6.6s.0d. extra).

Musicolor. 10tr, S/M/LW/FM portable. £25.10s.5d. plus £5.9s.1d. P.T. 1968. (Mains adaptor extra).

New Party-Boy. 9tr, S/M/LW/FM portable. £38.17s.0d. including P.T. 1963.

Ocean-Boy 205. 13tr, 4S/M/LW/FM portable. £91.7s.0d. including P.T. 1965. (Complete with tuning/battery meter, mains adaptor, £6.6s.0d. extra).

Party-Boy T203. 9tr, S/M/LW/FM portable. £37.16s.0d. including P.T. 1962.

Party-Boy 208. 9tr, M/LW/FM portable. £20.17s.5d. plus £4.18s.1d. P.T. 1969. (Mains adaptor extra).

Satellit. 17tr, 10S/M/LW/FM portable. £124.19s.0d. including P.T. 1965.

Satellit 6000. 19tr, 9S/M/LW/FM mains/battery portable. £123.12s.0d. plus £26.11s.0d. P.T. 1968. (Complete with tuning/battery meter, and built-in mains adaptor).

Satellit 6001/210. 23tr, 9S/M/LW/FM mains/battery portable. £179.14s.6d. including P.T. (Complete with tuning/battery meter, and built-in mains adaptor). 1969.

Solo-Boy 209. 9tr, M/LW/FM portable. £14.11s.0d. plus £3.8s.6d. P.T. 1969.

Trans-World TR16. 16tr, 3S/M/LW/FM portable. £75.12s.0d. including P.T. September 1962.

Transistor 17. 17tr, 3S/M/LW/FM portable. £90.17s.0d. including P.T. 1962.

Transistor 500. 9tr, M/LW/FM portable. £24.17s.8d. plus £4.8s.1d. P.T. 1966. (Mains adaptor, £6.6s.0d. extra).

Transit. 9tr, M/LW/FM portable. £14.14s.1d. plus £3.2s.1d. P.T. 1968.

Transonette 60. 7tr, MW/LW portable. £16.5s.6d. including P.T. 1965.

Transonette 70. 5tr, S/MW portable. £16.16s.0d. including P.T. 1965.

Transonette 99. S/M/LW portable. £47.5s.0d. including P.T. 1962.

Two-wave Micro-Boy. 6tr, M/LW pocket portable (converts into a table model by docking into a matching loudspeaker cabinet). £20.3s.7d. plus £6.9s.6d. P.T. August 1961.

Yacht-Boy. 11tr, M/LW/FM portable. £75.12s.0d. including P.T. September 1962.

Yacht-Boy 209. 10tr, S/M/LW/FM portable. £32.1s.7d. plus £7.10s.11d. P.T. 1969. (Includes battery meter. Mains adaptor extra).

H.M.V. (The Gramophone Company Ltd.),
Hayes, Middlesex. From 1960, **(British Radio Corporation Ltd.)**, 21 Cavendish Place, London W1. From 1965, at 284 Southbury Road, Enfield, Middlesex. *Transistor Production Run 1957-72+.*

1410. 3v + 2tr hybrid, M/LW portable. £9.16s.5d. plus P.T. Blue case (1410B), green case (1410G). June 1957. (Identical chassis

used in the Marconiphone P60B. Circuit line-up: DK96, DF96 and DAF96 valves, with a pair of Mullard OC72 transistors in push-pull output. *See fig.786, p.196, and fig. 943, p.294*).

1417. 6tr, M/LW portable. £15.10s.0d. plus £4.9s.6d. P.T. August 1959. (Identical chassis used in the Ferguson 348BT and Marconiphone T82B).

1420. 6tr, M/LW portable. £13.18s.3d. plus £4.9.3d. P.T. June 1960.

1421. 9tr, M/LW/FM table model. £22.5s.2d. plus £7.2s.10d. June 1960. (The first British transistorised table model to include FM tuning).

1424. 7tr, M/LW portable. £13.11s.8d. plus £4 15s.0d. P.T. May 1961.

1426. 6tr, M/LW table model. £12.16s.1d. plus £4.10s.5d. P.T. April 1961.

2104. 7tr, M/LW portable/car radio. £16.5s.11d. plus £4.14s.1d. P.T. 1961. (For home, outdoor or in-car use).

2108. 6tr, M/LW portable. £11.16s.3d. plus £3.8s.3d. P.T. 1961.

2112. 7tr, M/LW portable. £13.2s.6d. including P.T. October 1963.

2114. 7tr, M/LW portable. £13.11s.5d. plus £2.3s.7d. P.T. February 1963.

2116. 9tr, M/LW portable. £20.9s.6d. including P.T. April 1963.

2120. 7tr, S/M/LW portable/car radio. £12.4s.4d. plus P.T. March 1964. (For home, outdoor or in-car use).

2122. 7tr, S/M/LW portable/car radio. £17.17s.0d. including P.T. 1964. (For home, outdoor or in-car use).

2124. 9tr, M/LW portable/car radio. £19.8s.6d. including P.T. 1964. (For home, outdoor or in-car use. Bandspread tuning between 187.5-214 metres, for Radio Luxembourg).

2126. 10tr, S/M/LW portable. £25.4s.0d. including P.T. 1964.

2128. 7tr, S/M/LW portable/car radio. £14.14s.0d. including P.T. 1964. (For home, outdoor or in-car use. Bandspread tuning between 176-214 metres, for Luxembourg).

2130. 11tr, M/LW/FM portable/car radio. £27.6s.0d. including P.T. 1965. (For home, outdoor or in-car use. Bandspread tuning between 185-216 metres, for Luxembourg).

2134. 7tr, S/M/LW portable. £14.0s.6d. plus P.T. 1966.

2138. 8tr, S/M/LW portable/car radio. £19.0s.0d. plus £3.7s.1d. P.T. 1966. (For home, outdoor or in-car use).

2140. 10tr, S/M/LW/FM portable/car radio. £24.8s.7d. plus £4.6s.3d. P.T. 1966. (For home, outdoor or in-car use).

2148. 10tr, S/M/LW/FM portable/car radio. £25.6s.9d. plus £4.9s.5d. P.T. 1967. (For home, outdoor or in-car use).

2150. 9tr, M/LW/FM portable. £15.16s.8d. plus £2.15s.10d. P.T. 1967.

2152. 26tr, S/M/LW/FM stereo mains table model. £62.16s.2d. including P.T. 1967. (With separate loudspeaker).

2154. 7tr, S/M/LW portable. £12.13s.4d. plus £2.4s.9d. P.T. 1967.

2156. 10tr, S/M/LW/FM portable/car radio. £25.18s.1d. plus £5.10s.11d. P.T. 1968. (For home, outdoor or in-car use. Chassis identical to the Ferguson 3168, H.M.V. 2158 and the Marconiphone 4156).

2158. 10tr, S/M/LW/FM portable/car radio. £25.18s.1d. plus £5.10s.11d. P.T. 1968. (For home, outdoor or in-car use. Chassis identical to the Ferguson 3168, H.M.V. 2156 and the Marconiphone 4156).

2161. 10tr, M/LW/FM portable. £12.6s.3d. plus £2.12s.9d. P.T. 1968. (Identical chassis used in the Marconiphone 4161).

2163. 11tr, M/LW/FM portable. £21.19s.2d. plus £4.11s.10d. P.T. 1968.

2164. 10tr, M/LW/FM portable/car radio. £20.17s.0d. including P.T. 1970. (For home, outdoor or in-car use).

2165. 7tr, M/LW portable/car radio. £11.14s.9d. plus £2.15s.3d. P.T. 1969. (For home, outdoor or in-car use).

2166. 10tr, M/LW/FM portable/car radio. £11.18s.10d. plus £2.16s.2d. P.T. 1969. (For home, outdoor or in-car use).

2167. 7tr, M/LW/FM portable/car radio. £15.20p. including P.T. 1971. (For home, outdoor or in-car use).

2169. 7tr, S/M/LW portable. £9.6s.2d. plus £2.3s.10d. P.T. 1969.

2170. 13tr S/M/LW/FM portable/car radio. £32.10s.0d. including P.T. 1970. (Mains adaptor, £5.0s.0d. extra. For home, outdoor or in-car use).

2171. 13tr, M/LW/FM portable/car radio. £32.10s.0d. including P.T. 1970. (Mains adaptor, £5.0s.0d. extra. For home, outdoor or in-car use).

2174. 11tr, M/LW/FM portable/car radio. £22.85p. including P.T. 1971. (For home, outdoor or in-car use).

2175. 8tr, M/LW portable/car radio. £18.05p. including P.T. 1971. (For home, outdoor or in-car use).

2176. FM table model. £25.30p. including P.T. 1972.

2181. M/LW/FM portable/car radio. 1972. (For home, outdoor or in-car use).

Hacker (Hacker Radio Ltd.), Norreys Drive, Cox Green, Maidenhead, Royal Berkshire. *Transistor Production Run 1960-72+*

RP10 (Herald). 7tr, M/LW portable. £20.13s.4d. plus £6.12s.8d. P.T. April 1960. (Also available, a tan coloured zip carrying bag, price £2.2s.0d. optional extra, and a tartan zip carrying bag, price £1.5s.0d. optional extra. *See fig.947, p.296*).

RP17 (Mini-Herald). 7tr, M/LW portable. £18.7s.6d. including P.T. August 1962.

Talisman. 8tr, M/LW portable. £20.13s.4d. plus £6.12s.8d. P.T. August 1960.

RP18 (Sovereign). 15tr, M/LW/FM portable. £40.19s.0d. including P.T. 1964. (Zip carrying bag £2.2s.7d. optional extra).

RP25 (Sovereign II). 16tr, M/LW/FM portable. £35.5s.6d. plus £6.4s.6d. P.T. 1967. (Carrying case, £2.8s.10d. optional extra).

RP30 (Herald). 9tr, M/LW portable. £23.2s.0d. including P.T. 1964. (Zip carrying bag £2.2s.7d. optional extra).

RP31SW (Herald). 11tr, S/M/LW portable. £27.6s.0d. including P.T. 1964. (Zip carrying bag £2.2s.7d. optional extra).

RP33 (Autocrat). 9tr, M/LW portable/car radio. £16.14s.10d. plus £2.19s.0d. P.T. 1966. (For home, outdoor or in-car use. Car bracket, £2.16s.0d. extra, case, £2.2s.0d. optional extra).

RP34 (Democrat). 9tr, M/LW portable. £15.4s.4d. plus £2.3s.8d. P.T. 1967. (Case, £1.10s.0d. optional extra).

RP35 (Herald). 10tr, M/LW portable. £20.1s.1d. plus £3.10s.11d. P.T. 1967. (Case, £2.2s.0d. optional extra).

RP36 (Helmsman). 11tr, 3S/M/LW portable. £28.1s.0d. plus £4.19s.0d. P.T. 1967. (A carrying case, £2.2s.0d., was available as an optional extra).

RP37 (VHF Herald). 13tr, FM portable. £24.4s.1d. plus £5.13s.11d. Purchase Tax 1969. (A carrying case, £2.8s.10d., was available as an optional extra).

RP38 (Hunter). 9tr, M/LW/FM portable. £27.18s.0d. plus £6.11s.5d. P.T. 1969. (A carrying case, price £2.8s.10d., was available as an optional extra).

RP38T (Hunter). 9tr, M/LW/FM portable. £28.14s.9d. plus £6.15s.3d. P.T. 1969. (The Hunter was supplied in a cabinet with Afrormosia hardwood sides. Also available, was a carrying case, price £2.8s.10d. as an optional extra).

RP71 (Harrier). 7tr, FM portable. £28.50p. including P.T. 1972.

RP73 (Autocrat 2). Integrated circuit + 5tr, M/LW portable/car radio. £25.25p. including Purchase Tax. 1971. (For home, outdoor or in-car use).

Halcyon (Halroy Products Ltd.), The Power House, Headstone Lane, North Harrow, Middlesex. *Transistor Production Run 1967-69.*

226. 8tr, M/LW portable. £9.1s.0d. plus £1.18s.6d. P.T. 1968.

Coronado. 8tr, M/LW pocket portable. £5.17s.3d. plus 19s.3d. P.T. 1967.

Corvette. 8tr, M/LW portable. £12.3s.9d. plus £1.19s.9d. P.T. 1967.

Corvette Mk.II. 8tr, M/LW portable. £12.2s.9d. plus £3.0s.5d. P.T. 1969.

County Ten. 8tr, M/LW pocket portable. £4.12s.8d. plus 16s.2d. P.T. 1967.

Hammond (C.E. Hammond & Co.), 90 High Street, Eton. *Transistor Production Run 1964.*

Piccolone Mobil 643. 10tr, S/M/LW/FM portable. £28.7s.0d. including P.T. August 1964.

Heathkit (Daystrom Ltd.), 900 Southgate Street, Gloucester. From 1970, **(Heath [Gloucester] Ltd.)** at same address. *Transistor Production Run 1960-69+.*

EW-1. Junior Experimental Workshop (kit). £7.13s.6d. including P.T. (*"More than a toy! Will make over 20 exciting electronic devices, incl: Radios, Burglar Alarms, etc. 72 page Manual. The ideal present!"*). 1964.

GC-1U (Mohican). 10tr, S/MW portable (kit). £39.16s.0d. including P.T. 1969.

UJR-1. 1tr, MW portable (kit). £2.7s.6d. including P.T. 1963.

UXR-1. 6tr, M/LW portable (kit). £15.18s.6d. including P.T. 1960.

UXR-2 (Oxford). 7tr, M/LW portable (kit). £14.18s.0d. including P.T. 1961.

Severn. 12tr, M/LW/FM portable (kit). £19.15s.0d. (kit) including P.T., £26.18s.0d. (assembled) including P.T. 1969.

Hi-Sonic [Japan] (*dist.* **Holiday Brothers [Electrical Wholesalers] Ltd.**), 61b Shawheath, Stockport, Cheshire. *Transistor Production Run 1964.*

6033. 6tr, MW pocket portable. £3.1s.3d. (wholesale trade price). 1964.

8322. 6tr, M/LW pocket portable. £5.2s.11d. (wholesale trade price). 1964.

Hitachi [Japan] (*dist.* **Lee Products [Gt. Britain] Ltd.**), 10-18 Clifton Street, London EC2. From 1971, **(Hitachi Sales [U.K.] Ltd.)**, Park House, Coronation Road, Park Royal, London NW10. *Transistor Production Run 1961-72+.*

K-700H. MW/FM mains table model. £19.8s.7d. plus £4.11s.5d. P.T. 1969.

KC-770. 7tr, MW/FM table model/digital clock radio. £28 including P.T. 1971.

KC-783. MW/FM mains table model/clock radio. £29.90p. including P.T. 1972.

KH-907H. 9tr, S/M/LW/FM stereo portable. £28.7s.0d. including P.T. 1963. (Decoder for use in stereo mode, optional extra).

KH-910. 9tr, M/LW/FM portable. £25.4s.0d. including P.T. 1964.

KH-920L. 9tr, S/M/LW/FM portable. £31.10s.0d. including P.T. 1965.

KH-930. 9tr, M/LW portable. £11.6s.8d. plus £2.13s.4d. P.T. 1969.

KH-931E. MW/FM portable. £12.15s.0d. including P.T. 1970. (Mains adaptor, extra).

KH-970H. 9tr, MW/FM portable. £19.3s.3d. including P.T. 1966.

KH-980L. 9tr, M/LW/FM portable. £14.14s.6d. plus £2.12s.0d. P.T. 1967.

KH-985. 9tr, S/M/LW/FM portable. £23.10s.0d. including P.T. 1970.

KH-1002R. 10tr, M/LW/FM portable. £26.5s.0d. including P.T. 1963.

KH-1006L. 10tr, M/LW/FM portable. £20.15s.2d. plus £4.8s.10d. P.T. 1968.

KH-1013E. 10tr, M/LW/FM portable. £19.19s.0d. including P.T. 1970.

KH-1014L. 10tr, M/LW/FM portable. £17.19s.0d. including P.T. 1970. (Mains adaptor, extra).

KH-1026H. 10tr, S/M/LW/FM portable. £21.10s.0d. including P.T. 1970. (Mains adaptor, extra).

KH-1108H. 11tr, S/M/LW/FM portable. £23.7s.1d. plus £4.19s.11d. P.T. 1968.

KH-1230H. 12tr, MW/FM portable. £23.7s.1d. plus £4.19s.11d. P.T. 1968.

KH-1290H. 12tr, 2S/M/LW/FM portable. £34.12s.0d. plus £7.8s.0d. P.T. 1968.

KH-1325. 13tr, 2S/M/LW/FM portable/car radio. £31.2s.6d. plus £5.13s.6d. P.T. 1967. (For home, outdoor or in-car use).

KM-900L. 9tr, M/LW/FM portable/car radio. £30.9s.0d. including P.T. 1966. (Complete with car bracket. For home, outdoor or in-car use).

KS1700H. 17tr, MW/FM stereo portable. £38.18s.6d. plus £8.6s.6d. P.T. 1968. (Detachable loudspeakers).

LH-980L. 9tr, M/LW/FM portable. £19.4s.8d. including P.T. 1970.

TH-600. 6tr, MW pocket portable. £10.10s.0d. including P.T. 1964.

TH-610. 6tr, MW pocket portable. £6.10s.0d. including P.T. 1964.

TH-622. 6tr, MW pocket portable. £5.10s.0d. including P.T. 1970.

TH-650. 6tr, MW pocket portable. £6.6s.0d. including P.T. 1963.

TH-660. 6tr, MW pocket portable. £9.11s.4d. plus £2.15s.3d. P.T. 1961. This was Hitachi's first transistor radio exported to Britain.

TH-662. 6tr, MW pocket portable. £5.50p. including P.T. 1971.

TH-666F. 6tr, MW pocket portable. £8.8s.0d. including P.T. 1965.

W-734. 7tr, S/MW table model/clock radio. £27.6s.0d. including P.T. 1963.

W-752. 7tr, S/MW portable. £16.16s.0d. including P.T. 1963.

WH-628R. 6tr, M/LW personal portable. £12.3s.11d. plus £3.10s.6d. P.T. January 1962.

WH-638. 6tr, M/LW pocket portable. £7.2s.8d. plus £1.5s.4d. P.T. 1967.

WH-800L. 8tr, M/LW portable. £16.16s.0d. including P.T. 1966.

WH-829H. 8tr, S/MW personal portable. £15.12s.3d. plus £4.10s.2d. P.T. January 1962.

WH-837. 8tr, S/M/LW portable. £19.19s.0d. including P.T. February 1963.

WH-837E. 8tr, S/M/LW portable. £16.11s.3d. including P.T. 1970.

WH-838. 8tr, M/LW pocket portable. £14.5s.0d. including P.T. 1964.

WH-844H. 8tr, S/MW portable. £15.4s.6d. including P.T. 1963.

WH-855. 8tr, S/MW port. £21 inc. P.T. 1962.

WH-888L. 8tr, M/LW portable. £15.15s.0d. including P.T. 1964.

WH-900. 9tr, 3S/MW portable. £26.5s.0d. including P.T. 1963.

WH-1160. 11tr, S/M/LW/Marine Band. £24.2s.0d. plus £4.5s.0d. P.T. 1967.

WM-800L. 8tr, M/LW portable. £26.5s.0d. including P.T. 1963.

XH-1002. 10tr, M/LW/FM portable. £27.18s.9d. plus £8.1s.4d. P.T. 1962.

Auto 9. 8tr, MW portable. £18.18s.0d. including P.T. 1965.

Hobday (Hobday Bros. Ltd.), 21-27 Great Eastern Street, London EC2. *Transistor Production Run 1958.*

Hobday 1. 6tr, M/LW portable. Sept. 1958.

Holiday [Hong Kong] (*dist.* **Holiday Brothers [Electrical Wholesalers] Ltd.**), 61b Shawheath, Stockport, Cheshire. *Transistor Production Run 1964.*

AT-65 (Holiday). 6tr, MW pocket portable. £6.6s.0d. including P.T. 1964. (*See fig.814, page 204*). This set, protected by a saddle-stitched case (a style, in integral form, destined to be popular in the 1970s, *see fig.959, p.299*), was distributed by several companies in the U.K. who, like Holiday Brothers, had it customised with their own particular trade name.

I.T.C. [Hong Kong] (*dist.* **ITC [Bradford] Ltd.**), Bradford. *Transistor Production Run 1968.*

F2212. 12tr, MW/FM port. £8.8s.6d. inc. P.T. 1968.

I.T.T. (*see K-B, page 260, and R.G.D., page 269*).

Ingelen (*dist.* **Highgate Acoustics Ltd.**), 71-73 Gt. Portland Street, London W1. *Transistor Production Run 1961-65.*

TR113. 8tr, 2S/MW portable. £22.15s.0d. plus £6.13s.0d. P.T. October 1961.

TR114. 8tr, S/M/LW portable. £22.15s.0d. plus £6.13s.0d. P.T. October 1961.

TR414. 9tr, M/LW/FM portable. £25.4s.0d. including P.T. June 1963.

TR415 (Golf). 9tr, M/LW/FM portable/car radio. £22.11s.6d. including P.T. 1964. (Bracket available for in-car use).

TR500. 10tr, S/M/LW/FM portable. £29.5s.0d. plus £8.11s.0d. P.T. 1961.

TR800. 10tr, S/M/LW/FM portable. £30.9s.0d. including P.T. August 1963.

TR808 (Marquis). 10tr, S/M/LW/FM portable. £25.4s.0d. including P.T. 1965.

TR900. 9tr, M/LW/FM portable. £30.9s.0d. including P.T. 1965.

TR1003. 12tr, 2S/M/LW/FM portable. £39.16s.0d. plus £11.13s.0d. P.T. August 1962.

TR1005. 8tr, 3S/M/LW portable. £42. including P.T. May 1962.

TR2000. 10tr, S/M/LW/FM portable. £37.16s.0d. including P.T. August 1963.

TR3000. 10tr, S/M/LW/FM portable/car radio. £51.9s.0d. including P.T. 1965. (Bracket available for in-car use).

Intel (*dist.* **Interelectronic Transistor Service Ltd.**), 3 The Pantiles, Elmers End Road, Beckenham, Kent. *Transistor Production Run 1967.*

Skandia. 9tr, mains/battery table model. £28.17s.0d. including P.T. 1967.

Internet (*dist.* **Internet Radio [Products] Ltd.**), Oakfield House, 56-60 Oakfield Road, London SE20. *Transistor Production Run 1968-71+.*

Internet 14. 14tr, M/LW/FM portable. £12.12s.0d. including P.T. 1970.

Internet 3001. 12tr, 6S/M/LW/FM mains/battery portable. £157.10s.0d. including P.T. 1970. (Built-in mains adaptor. Complete with world-time chart).

Internet 7000. 17tr, 7S/M/LW/FM mains/battery portable. £180.0s.0d. (no Purchase Tax). 1970. (Built-in mains adaptor).

Internet A1000. MW/LW/FM mains/battery portable. £14.14s.0d. including P.T. 1969. (Built-in mains adaptor).

Internet J67A. 10tr, M/LW portable. £5.5s.0d. including P.T. 1968.

Internet J80. 14tr, MW/FM/Aircraft Weather Band portable. £10.10s.0d. including P.T. 1968.

Internet J82A. 10tr, M/LW portable. £7.7s.0d. including P.T. 1968.

Internet J95. MW/FM mains/battery portable. £14.14s.0d. including P.T. 1970. (Built-in mains adaptor).

Internet S1000. 6tr, MW pocket portable. £2.97p. including P.T. 1971.

Internet S4000J. 8tr, MW pocket portable. £2.19s.6d. including P.T. 1969.

Internet Mark Ten. M/LW portable. £7.7s.0d. including P.T. 1970.

Invicta (**Invicta Radio Ltd.**), 100 Great Portland Street, London W1. From 1970, (**Pye Group [Radio & Television] Ltd.**), P.O. Box 49, Cambridge. *Transistor Production Run 1958-72+.*

30. 6tr, M/LW portable. £17.16s.4d. plus £6.17s.2d. P.T. May 1958.

31. 6tr, M/LW portable. £13.18s.3d. plus £4.9s.3d. P.T. August 1959.

320. 6tr, M/LW table model. £13.2s.4d. plus £4.4s.2d. P.T. August 1959.

321. 6tr, M/LW personal portable. £10.6s.8d. plus £3.6s.4d. P.T. November 1960.

322. 6tr, M/LW portable. £12.4s.5d. plus £4.1s.7d. P.T. September 1961.

331. 9tr, M/LW/FM portable. £19.1s.7d. plus £6.2s.5d. P.T. September 1961.

332 (Vest-Pocket Vicki). 6tr, M/LW pocket portable (pre-set on LW for the Light Programme). £8.6s.11d. plus £2.13s.7d. P.T. September 1961.

332/L. 6tr, M/LW personal portable (pre-set on LW for the B.B.C.'s Light Programme). £9.10s.10d. plus £3.1s.2d. P.T. December 1961.

8004. 7tr, M/LW portable. £13.2s.6d. including P.T. March 1963.

8005. 7tr, 2S/MW portable. £13.2s.6d. including P.T. 1963.

8007. 6tr, M/LW portable (bandspread section aligned on Radio Luxembourg's wavelength of 208 metres). £14.14s.0d. including P.T. 1964.

8010. 7tr, M/LW portable. £12.12s.0d. including P.T. 1965.

8015. 6tr, M/LW pocket portable. £5.5s.0d. including P.T. 1967.

8017. 8tr, M/LW/FM portable. £26.0s.0d. including P.T. 1968.

8020. 10tr, M/LW/FM portable. £16.10s.0d. including P.T. 1969.

8021. 11tr, M/LW/FM portable. £12.15s.0d. including P.T. 1970.

8022. 11tr, M/LW/FM portable. 1970.

8023. 6tr, MW pocket portable. £7.0s.0d. including P.T. 1970.

8025. 14tr, S/M/LW/FM/Marine Band mains/battery portable/car radio. 1972. (For home, outdoor, or in-car use).

Vicki 8. 8tr, M/LW portable. £8.8s.0d. including P.T. 1967.

Vicki 611. 6tr, M/LW portable. £6.16s.6d. including P.T. 1967.

Vicki 633. 6tr, M/LW portable. 1968.

Vicki FM68. 9tr, M/FM portable. 1968.

Vicki K. 6tr, M/LW pocket portable. £4.14s.6d. including P.T. 1967.

Ishikawa [Japan — specialised in novelty transistor radios] (*dist.* **Denham & Morley Ltd.**), Denmore House, 175 Cleveland Street, London W1. *Transistor Production Run 1966-67.*

Barrel. 6tr, MW novelty radio. £6.10s.0d. plus £1.13s.6d. P.T. August 1966.

Barrel. 10tr, MW/FM novelty radio. £13.11s.6d. plus £2.8s.0d. P.T. August 1966.

Bowling Ball. 6tr, MW novelty radio. £9.10s.0d. plus £1.13s.6d. P.T. August 1966.

Bowling Pin. 8tr, MW novelty radio. £11.15s.0d. plus £2.1s.6d. P.T. August 1966.

Car Wheel & Tyre. 6tr, MW novelty radio. £9.10s.0d. plus £1.13s.6d. P.T. August 1966.

Gin Bottle (White Satin Gin label). 8tr, MW novelty radio. £10.8s.0d. plus £1.16s.9d. P.T. August 1966.

Hip Flask. 7tr, MW novelty radio. £8.10s.0d. plus £1.10s.4d. P.T. August 1966.

Miniature Bottle. 8tr, MW novelty radio. £6.17s.0d. plus £1.4s.9d. P.T. 1967.

Pepsi Cola Dispenser. 9tr, MW novelty radio. £11.15s.0d. plus £2.1s.6d. P.T. August 1966.

Sphere. 8tr, MW novelty radio. £11.15s.0d. plus £2.1s.6d. P.T. August 1966.

Whisky Bottle (Grand Old Parr Scotch Whisky label). 6tr, MW novelty radio. £6.17s.0d. plus £1.4s.9d. P.T. August 1966.

J.V.C. (*see Nivico, page 264*).

Jackson (*dist.* **Winter Trading Co. Ltd.**), 95-99 Ladbroke Grove, London W11. *Transistor Production Run 1965-72+.*

706L. 7tr, S/M/LW portable. £11.11s.0d. including P.T. 1965.

803L (8TP). 8tr, S/M/LW portable. £17.6s.6d. including P.T. 1965.

FU81A. 9tr, M/LW pocket portable. £13.2s.6d. including P.T. 1965.

M32A. 11tr, 2S/M/LW portable. £26.5s.0d. including P.T. 1965.

T15A. 9tr, 2S/MW portable. £20.9s.6d. including P.T. 1965.

TR62. 10tr, 3S/M/LW portable. £30.19s.6d. including P.T. 1965.

Jackson. 6tr, M/LW portable. £3.40p. including P.T. 1972.

Jason (**Jason Motor & Electronic Co.**), 3-4 Great Chapel Street, Oxford Street, London W1. *Transistor Production Run 1959.*

Everest 6. 6tr, MW portable (kit). £13.9s.9d. including P.T. November 1959.

Everest 7. 7tr, MW portable (kit). £15.18s.9d. including P.T. November 1959. (The Everest 7 was the same as Everest 6, but incorporated an extra RF stage for more power and selectivity).

Jenkins (**M. Jenkins**), 24 Victoria St., Altrincham. *Transistor Production Run 1958.*

Jenkins 1. 1tr, MW pocket portable. June 1958.

Juliette [Japan] (*dist.* **Winter Trading Co. Ltd.**), 95-99 Ladbroke Grove, London W11. From 1966, (*dist.* **Veritone Ltd.**), Eden Grove, London N7. From 1967, (*dist.* **Goodman [Radio 1950]**). From 1969, (*dist.* **Elsworthy Electronics Ltd.**), 27/31 Broadley Terrace, London NW1. *Transistor Production Run 1965-69.*

1880 (Interceptor). 17tr, S/M/LW/FM/Aircraft Band/Marine Band mains/battery portable. £48.0s.0d. (no Purchase Tax). 1969.

AT65. 6tr, MW pocket portable. £3.19s.6d. including P.T. 1967.

DTF180. 18tr, MW/FM portable. £20.3s.8d. plus £2.18s.4d. P.T. 1966. (Complete with mains adaptor).

NA5018. 15tr, 3S/MW/FM Broadcast Band/Aircraft Band/Marine Band mains/battery portable. £30.6s.10d. plus £4.6s.2d. P.T. 1966.

NA7021. 21tr, 3S/MW/FM Broadcast Band/Aircraft Band /Marine Band mains/battery portable. £65.2s.0d. (no Purchase Tax). 1969.

Re 1018. 14tr (silicon transistors), S/M/LW/FM/Aircraft Band. £16.10s.8d. plus £3.18s.10d. P.T. 1969.

TR10M. 10tr, MW portable. £11.1s.1d. plus £1.10s.11d. P.T. 1966.

TR73. 7tr, MW pocket portable. £3.19s.6d. including P.T. 1967.

TR91M. 9tr, MW portable. £9.12s.9d. plus £1.7s.3d. P.T. 1966.

TR777. 7tr, MW pocket portable. £4.3s.6d. plus £11s.0d. P.T. 1965.

TR3012M. 12tr, MW/FM/Marine Band. £22.1s.0d. including P.T. 1967. (Mains adaptor, extra).

K-B (**Kolster-Brandes Ltd.**), Footscray, Sidcup, Kent. From 1966, (**Standard Telephones & Cables Ltd.**), 190 Strand, London WC2. From 1970, products appear under the **I.T.T.-KB** trade name, (**I.T.T. Consumer Products [U.K.] Ltd.**), Footscray, Sidcup, Kent. *Transistor Production Run 1957-72+.*

KR010. 8tr, S/M/LW portable. £13.13s.0d. including P.T. 1964. (Bandspread tuning between 195-215 metres, for Radio Luxembourg).

KR012. 8tr, S/M/LW portable. £16.16s.0d. including P.T. 1964. (Bandspread tuning between 195-215 metres, for Luxembourg).

KR016. 9tr, 2S/MW/FM portable. £26.5s.0d. including P.T. 1964.

KR017. 9tr, MW/FM portable. £14.14s.0d. including P.T. 1965.

KR019. 12tr, M/LW/FM portable. £20.9s.6d. including P.T. 1965.

KR021 (Cobra). 7tr, 2M/LW portable/car radio. £11.6s.2d. plus £2.0s.0d. P.T. 1966. (Identical chassis used in the R.G.D. RR211 Rover. Medium waveband tuning is divided into two with bandspread over both halves, giving MW1 [275-555 metres] and MW2 [185-280 metres]. For home, outdoor or in-car use).

KR022 (Commodore). 6tr, 2M/LW portable. £16.5s.8d. plus £2.17s.7d. P.T. 1966. (Identical chassis used in the R.G.D. RR222 Rambler. Medium waveband tuning is divided into two with bandspread over both halves, giving MW1 [275-555 metres] and MW2 [185-280 metres]. For home, outdoor or in-car use).

KR023. 7tr, 2M/LW portable. £14.15s.4d. plus £2.11s.2d. P.T. 1967. (Medium waveband tuning is divided into two with bandspread over both halves, giving MW1 [275-555 metres] and MW2 (185-280 metres).

KR026. 9tr, S/M/LW/FM portable. £24.3s.0d. including P.T. 1964.

KR028. 7tr, M/LW portable/car radio. £16.10s.11d. plus £3.12s.2d. P.T. 1968. (For home, outdoor or in-car use).

KR029 (Chieftain). 7tr, M/LW portable. £14.15s.4d. plus £3.2s.0d. P.T. 1968.

KR600. 8tr, 2M/LW portable. £20.19s.5d. plus £3.14s.1d. P.T. 1967. (Medium waveband tuning is divided into two with bandspread over both halves, giving MW1 [275-555 metres] and MW2 [185-280 metres]. For home, outdoor or in-car use).

KR601. 10tr, M/LW/FM portable. £26.18s.10d. plus £5.12s.8d. P.T. 1968.

KR606 (Rhapsody 2000FM). 10tr, M/LW/FM portable. £21.0s.1d. plus £4.18s.6d. P.T. 1969.

KR607. 9tr, M/LW/FM portable. £12.10s.10d. plus £2.13s.8d. P.T. 1968.

KR608. 10tr, M/LW/FM mains table model. £26.10s.2d. plus £6.4s.10d. P.T. 1969.

KR609 (Rhapsody). 10tr, M/LW/FM portable. £24.12s.0d. including P.T. 1970.

KR610. 10tr, S/M/LW/FM portable. £14.9s.0d. plus £3.8s.0d. P.T. 1969.

KR611. 7tr, M/LW portable. £8.17s.3d. plus £2.1s.9d. P.T. 1969.

KR612. 9tr, S/M/LW/FM portable. £21.16s.4d. plus £5.2s.8d. P.T. 1969.

KR614 (Super 4). 10tr, S/M/LW/FM portable. £16.90p. including P.T. 1971.

ML2 (Junior). 8tr, M/LW portable. £6.9s.4d. plus £1.10s.8d. P.T. 1969.

OP21 (Rhapsody). 6tr, M/LW portable. £17.8s.8d. plus £6.14s.4d. P.T. November 1957. (Housed in a midnight blue plastics cabinet with chrome stars and trim).

PP31 (Rhapsody de Luxe). 6tr, M/LW portable. £22.11s.6d. including P.T. May 1958. (As OP21 but housed in a fabric-covered wooden case instead of a plastics cabinet).

QP21 (Gaiety). 6tr, M/LW portable. £14.6s.2d. plus £4.11s.10d. P.T. September 1959. *"For the car, outdoors and any room in the house . . . . the miniature suitcase cabinet has a detachable lid enabling it to be used as a conventional bedside or kitchen set"*.

RP21 (Romance). 6tr, M/LW portable. £12.14s.4d. plus £4.1s.8d. P.T. August 1960.

SP31 (Sonata). 6tr, M/LW portable. £12.16s.1d. plus £4.10s.5d. P.T. September 1961. (de Luxe version of RP21).

TP11 (Bikini). 6tr, M/LW personal portable. £10.9s.6d. plus £3.14s.0d. P.T. Leather carrying case with shoulder strap and earpiece pouch, £1.12s.6d. extra, ear-piece, 17s.6d. extra. August 1961. (Circuit fitted with either G.E.C. or Texas Instruments transistors).

TP41 (Cavalier). 7tr, M/LW portable. £15.18s.2d. plus £5.12s.4d. P.T. Microphone and 50' of cable, £1.10s.0d. extra. August 1961. *"Used with microphone, this unique set can be a baby alarm or a calling system between garage, tool shed or any part of the house"*. (Circuit fitted with S.T.C., G.E.C. or Texas Instruments transistors).

TR11 (Tango). 6tr, M/LW table model. £11.5s.1d. plus £3.19s.5d. P.T. August 1961. (Circuit fitted with S.T.C., G.E.C. or Texas Instruments transistors).

UP11 (Cadet). 8tr, M/LW portable. £14.14s.0d. including P.T. August 1962. (Circuit fitted with S.T.C., G.E.C., Texas Instruments or Mullard transistors).

UP21 (Rhapsody). 6tr, M/LW portable. £12.12s.7d. plus £3.12s.11d. P.T. April 1962. (Available in a midnight blue plastics cabinet with chrome stars and trim [Starlight Rhapsody], or in an opal white plastics cabinet with gold stars and trim [Golden Rhapsody]).

UP31 (Rhapsody de Luxe). 6tr, M/LW portable. £14.13s.4d. plus £4.4s.8d. P.T. 1962. (As UP21 but housed in a fabric-covered wooden case instead of a plastics cabinet).

VP21 (Rhapsody Super 8). 8tr, M/LW portable. £13.13s.0d. including P.T. 1963. *"The Rhapsody, Britain's most popular portable, now has 8 transistors for high quality listening"*. (Plastics cabinet available in Venetian red with chrome trim [Carmina], midnight blue with chrome trim [Starlight], clear red and white [Scarlet], and pearl white and gilt trim [Golden]).

VP31 (Rhapsody Super 8 de Luxe). 8tr, M/LW portable. £15.15s.0d. including P.T. 1963. (As the Super 8, above, but with an extra sensitive internal aerial and housed in a special fabric-covered wooden cabinet to enhance sound reproduction).

WP11 (Carioca). 6tr, M/LW portable (bandspread section aligned on Radio Luxembourg's wavelength of 208 metres). £11.0s.6d. including P.T. 1963.

WP21 (Lyric). 9tr, M/LW portable. £13.13s.0d. including P.T. Microphone and 50' of cable, £1.10s.0d. extra, telephone adaptor, £1.1s.0d. extra. August 1963. (Bandspread tuning between 195-215 metres, for Radio Luxembourg. Fitted with baby alarm socket and telephone socket).

WP31 (Calypso). 9tr, M/LW. £5.15s.0d. including P.T. Microphone and 50' of cable, £1.10s.0d. extra, telephone adaptor, £1.1s.0d. extra. July 1963. (Fitted with baby alarm socket and telephone socket).

XR51. 11tr, M/LW/VHF table model. £26.5s.0d. including P.T. Mains adaptor, £4.4s.0d. extra. 1964.

Golf. 10tr, S/M/LW/FM portable/car radio. £31.19s.0d. including P.T. 1970. (For home, outdoor or in-car use).

Junior de Luxe. 10tr, MW/FM portable. £10.65p. including P.T. 1972.

Junior Super. 10tr, MW/FM portable. £10.15s.0d. including P.T. 1970. *(For Junior, see ML2, bottom left).*

Junior Two. 8tr, M/LW portable. £6.95p. including P.T. 1972.

Tiny 33. 9tr, M/LW/FM portable. £13.10s.0d. including P.T. 1970.

Tiny Super. 10tr, M/LW/FM portable. £13.95p. including P.T. 1972.

Touring International. 4S/2M/LW/FM mains/battery portable/car radio. £56.0s.0d. including P.T. 1970. (Medium waveband tuning is divided into two with bandspread over both halves, giving MW1 [275-555 metres] and MW2 [185-280 metres]. For home, outdoor or in-car use).

Touring International Marine. LW/FM/2 x Marine Bands portable/car radio. £55 including P.T. 1972. (For home, outdoor or in-car use).

Weekend. 10tr, S/M/LW/FM portable. £20.50p. including P.T. 1971.

(NB: Some K-B <u>valve</u> portables were also called Rhapsody, *eg.* PP11, March 1958, PP21 and PP251, both May 1958).

Kaydon (*dist. L.P.F. Photronic Ltd.*), Cricklewood Lane, London NW2. *Transistor Production Run 1964.*

Caravelle. 8tr, M/LW portable. £6.19s.6d. including P.T. 1964

Clipper. 6tr, MW pocket portable. £3.19s.6d. including P.T. 1964.

Rambler. 6tr, M/LW portable. £5.19s.6d. including P.T. 1964.

Kendy [Hong Kong] (*dist. Bruce Brent Ltd.*), 26-34 Emerald Street, Theobald's Road, London WC1. *Transistor Production Run 1961-62.*

TR-D (Universal-6). 6tr, pocket portable. September 1961.

TR-610. 6tr, MW pocket portable. July 1962.

TR-612. 6tr, MW pocket portable. £8.18s.6d. including P.T. April 1962.

TR-712 (Enterprize). 7tr, pocket portable. September 1961.

TR-720 (Global). 7tr portable. July 1962.

Klarad (*dist. Highgate Acoustics Ltd.*), 71-73 Gt. Portland Street, London W1. *Transistor Production Run 1964-65.*

720-C4. 2S/M/LW portable. £24.3s.0d. including P.T. 1964.

720-C5AM. 8tr, 3S/M/LW portable. £27.6s.0d. including P.T. 1965.

720-FM. S/M/LW/FM portable. £30.9s.0d. including P.T. 1964.

720-FMAS. 10tr, S/M/LW/FM portable. £30.9s.0d. including P.T. 1965.

730-C5. 3S/M/LW portable. £28.17s.0d. including P.T. 1964.

760-OS4. 8tr, 2S/M/LW portable. £22.1s.0d. including P.T. 1965.

760-OS4FM. 10tr, 2S/M/LW/FM portable. £30.9s.0d. including P.T. 1965.

Koden (*dist.* **Videorama Ltd.**), International House, 56 Garden Street, Stafford, Staffs. *Transistor Production Run 1970.*

Koden 72. 8tr, M/LW pocket portable. £5.12s.11d. including P.T. 1970.

Korting [West Germany] (*dist.* **Europa Electronics Ltd.**), Howard Place, Shelton, Stoke-on-Trent. From 1971, products appear under the **Korting-Transmare** trade name. *Transistor Production Run 1963-72+.*

24021. 7tr, M/LW portable. £18.7s.6d. including P.T. July 1963.

24041. 9tr, M/LW portable. £27.16s.0d. including P.T. July 1963.

25021. 7tr, M/LW portable. £18.7s.6d. including P.T. 1964.

25031. 9tr, M/LW/FM portable. £25.14s.6d. including P.T. 1963.

25041. 9tr, M/LW/FM portable. £28.17s.6d. including P.T. 1964.

25064. 9tr, S/M/LW/FM portable. £39.7s.6d. including P.T. 1964.

TR621. 7tr, M/LW portable. £19.8s.6d. including P.T. 1964.

TR641. 10tr, M/LW/FM portable. £28.17s.6d. including P.T. 1964.

TR642. 10tr, M/LW/FM portable. £30.19s.6d. including P.T. 1964.

TR643. 10tr, M/LW/FM portable. £30.19s.6d. including P.T. 1965.

TR680. 10tr, S/M/LW/FM portable. £39.7s.6d. including P.T. 1964.

TR684. 10tr, S/M/LW/FM portable. £41.9s.6d. including P.T. 1964.

TR721. 7tr, M/LW portable. £16.14s.10d. plus £2.19s.0d. P.T. 1966. (Mains adaptor, £4.4s.0d. extra).

TR741. 11tr, M/LW/FM portable. £25.15s.9d. plus £4.11s.0d. P.T. 1966. (Mains adaptor, £4.4s.0d. extra).

TR742. As TR741. 1966.

TR743. 10tr, M/LW/FM portable. £26.14s.0d. plus £4.14s.1d. P.T. 1966. (Mains adaptor, £4.4s.0d. extra).

TR782. 10tr, S/M/LW/FM portable/car radio. £35.14s.10d. plus £6.6s.2d. P.T. 1966. (Mains adaptor, £4.4s.0d. extra, bracket for in-car use, £5.5s.0d. extra).

TR784. 10tr, S/M/LW/FM portable. £35.14s.10d. plus £6.6s.2d. P.T. 1966. (Mains adaptor, £4.4s.0d. extra).

TR810. 7tr, M/LW portable/car radio. £11.6s.2d. plus £2.0s.0d. P.T. 1967.

TR832. 9tr, S/MW/FM portable. 1969. (Mains adaptor, £5.5s.0d. extra).

TR884. 10tr, S/M/LW/FM portable. £40.13s.1d. plus £8.13s.11d. P.T. 1968.

TR928. 7tr, M/LW portable/car radio. £16.17s.4d. plus £3.12s.2d. P.T. 1968.

TR963. 11tr, S/M/LW/FM portable. £25.10s.4d. plus £5.9s.2d. P.T. 1968. (Mains adaptor, £5.5s.0d. extra).

TR968. 10tr, S/M/LW/FM portable. 1969.

TR983. 11TR, S/M/LW/FM portable/car radio. £35.8s.6d. plus £8.6s.0d. Purchase Tax. 1969. (For home, outdoor or in-car use. Mains adaptor, £5.5s.0d. optional extra; car bracket, optional extra).

TR988. As TR983 (above), but with additional diode for electronic tuning.

TR1075. 13tr, S/M/LW/FM portable/car radio. £67.50p. including P.T. 1971. (For home, outdoor or in-car use).

TR1263. S/M/LW/FM portable. £33.50p. including P.T. (Mains adaptor, £5.25p. extra).

Novan. S/M/LW/FM mains/battery table model/portable. £42.50p. including P.T. 1972.

Novita. S/M/LW/FM mains table model. £39.75p. including P.T. 1972.

Novum 70. 11tr, S/M/LW/FM mains/battery table model. £35.1s.9d. plus £8.13s.3d. P.T. 1969. (Complete with tuning meter).

Kowa [Hong Kong] (*dist.* **L.P.F. Photronic Ltd.**), Cricklewood Lane, London NW2. *Transistor Production Run 1963-64.*

Kowa 71F. 7tr, MW pocket portable. £11.11s.0d. including P.T. 1964.

Kowa 91L. 9tr, MW/FM pocket portable. £13.13s.0d. including P.T. 1964.

Kowa 102L. 11tr, M/LW/FM portable. £21.10s.0d. including P.T. 1964.

Kowa HF KTF-115. 11tr, MW/FM portable. £18.18s.0d. including P.T. 1963.

Kowa KTF-1021. 11tr, M/LW/FM portable. £20.9s.6d. including P.T. 1963.

Koyo [Hong Kong] (*dist.* **Light & Sound Ltd.**), 125 Gunnersbury Lane, Acton, London W3. From 1967, (*dist.* **Kingsway Mill Co. [M/C] Ltd.**), 1 Berry Street, London EC1. From 1968, at 5 Worship Street, London EC2. *Transistor Production Run 1966-68.*

KTR831. 8tr, MW/LW pocket portable. £10.9s.9d. plus £1.13s.0d. P.T. 1966.

KTR837. 8tr, S/MW portable. £8.12s.7d. plus £1.17s.5d. P.T. 1968.

KTR879L. 8tr, S/M/LW portable. £13.17s.5d. plus £2.18s.7d. P.T. 1968.

KTR881L. 9tr, M/LW portable. £8.12s.7d. plus £1.17s.5d. P.T. 1968.

KTR964. 9tr, MW/FM portable. £8.12s.7d. plus £1.17s.5d. P.T. 1968.

KTR1036. 10tr, MW/FM portable. £13.19s.6d. plus £2.3s.11d. P.T. 1966.

KTR1041. 10tr, MW/FM portable. £10.19s.9d. plus £1.12s.3d. P.T. 1967.

KTR1058. 10tr, MW/FM portable. £11.18s.1d. plus £1.14s.11d. P.T. 1967.

KTR1251. 12tr, MW/FM portable. £16.18s.9d. plus £2.9s.9d. P.T. 1967. (Mains adaptor, extra).

KTR1252L. 12tr, M/LW/FM portable. £18.6s.3d. plus £2.13s.9d. P.T. 1967.

KTR1361L. 13tr, M/LW/FM portable. £18.6s.9d. plus £3.7s.3d. P.T. 1966.

KTR1365L. 13tr, M/LW/FM portable. £20.19s.5d. plus £3.5s.11d. P.T. 1966. (Employs two loudspeakers).

KTR1377L. 13tr, M/LW/FM portable. £15.12s.2d. plus £2.4s.4d. P.T. (Twin loudspeakers).

KTR1381. 12tr, S/M/LW/FM portable. £21.11s.6d. plus £4.13s.6d. P.T. 1968.

KTR1451L. 14tr, S/M/LW/FM portable. £37.17s.6d. plus £5.19s.1d. P.T. (Complete with world-time chart).

KTR1571L. 15tr, 3S/M/LW/FM portable. £33.0s.0d. plus £4.16s.9d. P.T. 1967. (World-time chart. Mains adaptor, extra).

KTR1651L. 16tr, 2S/M/LW/FM portable. £32.7s.3d. plus £7.0s.3d. P.T. 1968.

KTR1883. 18tr, S/MW/FM/Aircraft Band mains/battery portable. £32.7s.3d. plus £7.0s.3d. P.T. 1968.

RE1910. 10tr, M/FM portable. £15.7s.6d. plus £2.8s.4d. P.T. 1966.

Loewe Opta [West Germany] (*dist.* **Highgate Acoustics Ltd.**), 71-73 Gt. Portland Street, London W1. The names chosen by Loewe Opta for some of their transistor radios must rank among the most ludicrous in the entire history of radio manufacture; *ie.* Dolly, Ronny, Freddy and Percy . . . . . . CALL THE POLICE! *Transistor Production Run 1961-66.*

Lissy. 9tr, M/LW/FM portable/car radio. £35.4s.0d. including P.T. 1963.

5910 (Luxy). 6tr, M/LW pocket portable. £15.4s.6d. including P.T. June 1961.

6945 (Ronny). 9tr, M/LW/FM portable. £22.8s.8d. plus £9.0.4d. P.T. November 1961.

6950 (Percy). 9tr, M/LW/FM portable. £23.11s.2d. plus £6.17s.10d. P.T. March 1962.

6955. 9tr, S/MW/FM portable. £27.6s.0d. including P.T. 1963.

52330 (Auto Lord). 10tr, S/M/LW/FM portable/car radio. £42. including P.T. 1963. (Bracket available for in-car use).

52350 (Freddy). 9tr, S/M/LW/FM portable/car radio. £35.14s.0d. including P.T. 1964. (Bracket available for in-car use).

52355 (Auto-Toxy). 9tr, M/LW/FM portable/car radio. £42.2s.0d. including P.T. 1964. (Bracket available for in-car use).

52385 (Autoport). 10tr, S/M/LW/FM portable/car radio. £46.4s.0d. including P.T. 1963. (Bracket available for in-car use).

T37K (Dolly). 9tr, M/LW/FM portable. £30.9s.0d. including P.T. 1965. (Mains adaptor extra).

T47 (Autoport). 9tr, S/M/LW/FM portable/car radio. £35.5s.6d. plus £6.4s.10d. P.T. 1966. (Bracket available for in-car use. Mains adaptor extra).

TS40 (Autoport). 10tr, M/LW/FM portable/car radio. £37.16s.0d. including P.T. 1965. (Bracket available for in-car use).

TS50 (Autoport). 10tr, 2S/M/LW/FM portable/car radio. £51.9s.0d. including P.T. 1965. (Bracket available for in-car use).

TS52 (Autoport). 10tr, 2S/M/LW/FM portable/car radio. £49.15s.3d. plus £8.15s.9d. P.T. 1966. (Bracket available for in-car use).

TS57 (Autoport). 10tr, 2S/M/LW/FM portable/car radio. £53.11s.6d. plus £9.8s.8d. P.T. 1966. (Bracket available for in-car use).

Luxor [Sweden] (*dist.* **Scandinavian Sound Corporation Ltd.**), 50 Todd Lane, Preston, Lancashire. From 1968, (*dist.* **Luxitone**), 84 Bolsover Street, London W1. *Transistor Production Run 1967-68.*

B4673. 9tr, M/LW/FM portable. £34.0s.11d. plus £6.18s.1d. P.T. 1968.

B4773. 9tr, M/LW/FM portable. £35.15s.10d. plus £7.5s.2d. P.T. 1968.

Malmo. 28tr, FM stereo mains table model. £82.19s.0d. including P.T. 1967. (Decoder for use in stereo mode, optional extra).

Motala. 28tr, M/LW/FM stereo mains table model. £90.6s.0d. including P.T. 1967. (Decoder for use in stereo mode, optional extra).

Magnavox [Japan] (*dist.* **Magnavox Electronics Ltd.**), Ripple Works, By-Pass Road, Barking, Essex. Later, Alfred's Way, Barking, Essex. *Transistor Production Run 1960-64.*

7P22L. 7tr, M/LW portable. £12.12s.0d. including P.T. 1964.

7P226. 7tr, M/LW portable. £12.12s.0d. including P.T. 1963.

300TR (Mercury). 6tr, M/LW table model. £14.6s.2d. plus £4.11s.10d. P.T. October 1960.

AM60 (Pocketmate). 6tr, MW pocket portable. £9.6s.3d. plus £2.13s.9d. P.T. December 1960.

AM80 (Companion). 8tr, MW pocket portable. £10.17s.3d. plus £3.2s.9d. P.T. December 1960.

TP320 (Voyager). 6tr, M/LW portable/car radio. £13.10s.3d. plus £4.6s.9d. P.T. February 1961. (For home, outdoor or in-car use).

Magneta (B.V.C. Electronic Developments Ltd.), Goblin Works, Ermyn Way, Leatherhead, Surrey. *Transistor Production Run 1966-70.*

PTR. 8tr, M/LW/FM portable. £30.0s.0d. plus £5.12s.0d. P.T. 1966. (The PTR transistor was from the same stable that gave us the famous Goblin 'Time-Spot' receiver in 1947. *See fig.682, p.175*).

PTR/2. 8tr M/LW portable. £30.0s.0d. including P.T. 1968.

Marconiphone (Marconiphone Radio & Television Sales Ltd.), 21 Cavendish Place, London W1. From 1960, **(British Radio Corporation Ltd.)**, at the same address. From 1965, at 284 Southbury Road, Enfield, Middlesex. *Transistor Production Run 1957-72 ¹.*

4102 (Troubadour). 6tr, M/LW portable. £10.19s.4d. plus £3.4s.2d. P.T. April 1962.

4104 (Minstrel). 6tr, M/LW pocket portable (pre-set on LW for the Light Programme). £8.10s.7d. plus £2.9s.11d. P.T. 1961.

4106. 6tr, M/LW portable. £9.18s.9d. plus £1.12s.3d. P.T. January 1963.

4110 (de Luxe). 7tr, M/LW portable. £12.3s.10d. plus £1.19s.8d. P.T. January 1963.

4112. 7tr, M/LW portable. £12.12s.0d. including P.T. 1964.

4114. 9tr, M/LW portable. £15.4s.6d. including P.T. 1964.

4116. 7tr, S/M/LW portable. £12.3s.10d. plus P.T. March 1964.

4120. 7tr, S/M/LW portable. £14.14s.0d. including P.T. 1964.

4122. 9tr, M/LW portable/car radio. £19.8s.6d. including P.T. 1965. (For home, outdoor or in-car use. Bandspread tuning between 187.5-214 metres, for Radio Luxembourg).

4126. 11tr, M/LW/FM portable. £25.4s.0d. including P.T. 1965.

4128. 7tr, S/M/LW portable/car radio. £14.0s.0d. plus £2.10s.1d. P.T. 1966. (For home, outdoor or in-car use).

4130 (Travelmate). 8tr, S/M/LW portable/car radio. £18.19s.4d. plus £3.7s.10d. P.T. 1966. (For home, outdoor or in-car use).

4132 (Grand Prix). 10tr, S/M/LW/FM portable/car radio. £24.7s.9d. plus £4.7s.2d. P.T. 1966. (For home, outdoor or in-car use).

4138. 9tr, M/LW/FM portable. £16.0s.6d. plus £2.17s.6d. P.T. 1967. (Bandspread tuning between 188-216 metres, for Radio Luxembourg. Identical chassis used in the Ultra 6142).

4140. 7tr, S/M/LW portable. £13.7s.1d. plus £2.7s.11d. P.T. 1967.

4142 (Merrymaker). 7tr, S/M/LW portable. £8.11s.0d. plus £1.10s.4d. P.T. 1966. (Identical chassis used in the Ultra 6146).

4156. 10tr, S/M/LW/FM portable/car radio. £25.18s.1d. plus £5.10s.11d. P.T. 1968. (For home, outdoor or in-car use. Chassis identical to the Ferguson 3168, H.M.V. 2156 and H.M.V. 2158).

4159. 7tr, S/M/LW portable. £14.17s.6d. plus £3.3s.8d. P.T. 1968. (Bandspread tuning between 185-216 metres, for Radio Luxembourg. Identical chassis used in the Ultra 6159).

4160. 9tr, M/LW/FM portable. £17.12s.9d. plus £3.15s.5d. P.T. 1968. (Bandspread tuning between 185-216 metres, for Radio Luxembourg. Identical chassis used in the Ultra 6160).

4161. 10tr, M/LW/FM portable. £12.6s.6d. plus £2.12s.9d. P.T. 1968. (Identical chassis used in the H.M.V. 2161).

4163. 11tr, M/LW/FM portable. £21.9s.3d. plus £4.11s.10d. P.T. 1968.

4166. 10tr, M/LW/FM portable. £11.18s.10d. plus £2.16s.2d. P.T. 1969.

4167. 8tr, S/M/LW portable/car radio. £14.3s.4d. plus £3.6s.8d. P.T. 1969. (For home, outdoor or in-car use).

4168. 11tr, M/LW/FM portable. £16.15s.11d. plus £3.19s.1d. P.T. 1969.

4169. 7tr, S/M/LW portable. £9.6s.2d. plus £2.3s.10d. P.T. 1969.

4170. 13tr, S/M/LW/FM portable/car radio. £32.10s.0d. including P.T. 1970. (For home, outdoor or in-car use. Mains adaptor, £5.0s.0d. extra).

4173. 8tr, M/LW portable/car radio. £21.30p. including P.T. 1971. (For home, outdoor or in-car use).

4174. 8tr, M/LW portable/car radio. £16.90p. including P.T. 1971. (For home, outdoor or in-car use).

4175. 11tr, M/LW/FM portable/car radio. £21.30p. including P.T. 1971. (For home, outdoor or in-car use).

4177. 7tr, M/LW portable/car radio. £15.95p. including P.T. 1971. (For home, outdoor or in-car use).

4178. 10tr, MW/FM portable. £15.45p. including P.T. 1971.

4179. M/LW/FM portable/car radio. £19.40p. including P.T. 1972. (For home, outdoor or in-car use).

4180. M/LW/FM portable/car radio. £19.75p. including P.T. 1972. (Mains adaptor, extra. For home, outdoor or in-car use).

4181. M/LW/FM portable/car radio. 1972. (Mains adaptor, extra. For home, outdoor or in-car use).

P60B. 3v + 2tr hybrid, M/LW portable. £9.16s.5d. plus P.T. June 1957. (Identical chassis used in the H.M.V. 1410. Circuit line-up: DK96, DF96 and DAF96 valves, with a pair of Mullard OC72 transistors in push-pull output).

T82B. 6tr, M/LW portable. £15.10s.0d. plus £4.9s.6d. P.T. August 1959. (Identical chassis used in the H.M.V. 1417 and Ferguson 348BT).

T84B. 9tr, M/LW/FM table model. £19.16s.3d. plus £6.8s.9d. P.T. July 1960.

T85B. 6tr, M/LW portable. £13.1s.6d. plus £4.5s.0d. P.T. July 1960.

T96B. 6tr, M/LW portable. £13.3s.0d. plus £4.14s.0d. P.T. March 1961.

T98B. 6tr, M/LW table model. £12.15s.3d. plus £4.11s.3d. P.T. March 1961.

Masteradio (Masteradio Ltd.), Langley Park, Slough, Bucks. *Transistor Production Run 1963-68.*

D514. 6tr, S/M/LW portable. £14.3s.6d. including P.T. May 1963.

D516. 9tr, M/LW/FM portable. £19.8s.6d. including P.T. May 1963.

D517. 10tr, M/LW/FM portable. £19.18s.2d. plus £3.10s.3d. P.T. 1966.

D518. 7tr, M/LW (bandspread section aligned on Radio Luxembourg's wavelength of 208 metres). £14.3s.6d. including P.T. 1963.

D519. 9tr, S/M/LW portable. £17.6s.6d. including P.T. 1965.

D525. 8tr, S/M/LW portable. £14.3s.6d. including P.T. 1965.

D527. 7tr, M/LW portable (pre-set station selection). £14.18s.7d. plus £2.12s.9d. P.T. 1966. (Bandspread tuning between 185-222 metres, for Radio Luxembourg. Chassis identical to the G.E.C. G827 and the Sobell S327).

D532. 8tr, M/LW mains/battery portable/car radio. £19.17s.11d. plus £4.5s.1d. P.T. 1968. (For home, outdoor or in-car use. Built-in mains adaptor).

D534. 10tr, M/LW/FM portable/car radio. £17.6s.0d. plus £3.14s.0d. P.T. 1968. (For home, outdoor or in-car use).

Matsushita (*see National, page 263*).

McMichael (McMichael Radio & Electronics Ltd.), Langley Park, Slough, Bucks. From 1966, **(Radio & Allied Industries Ltd.)**, Langley Park, Slough, Bucks. *Transistor Production Run 1960-66.*

M103BT. 7tr, M/LW personal portable. £10.6s.8d. plus £3.6s.4d. P.T. November 1960.

M104BT (Gadabout). 6tr, M/LW portable. £12.0s.7d. plus £4.4s.11d. P.T. April 1961. (Identical chassis used in the Sobell S304BT).

M105BT. 6tr, M/LW portable. £13.11s.8d. plus £4.15s.10d. P.T. April 1961.

M107. 6tr, M/LW portable (pre-set on LW for the Light Prog.). £13.2s.6d. inc. P.T. 1962.

M108. 6tr, M/LW portable. £11.8s.1d. plus £3.5s.11d. P.T. April 1962.

M110. 6tr, M/LW portable. £15.15s.0d. including P.T. May 1962.

M112. 6tr, M/LW portable. £13.2s.6d. including P.T. May 1962.

M113. 6tr, M/LW pocket portable. £12.1s.6d. including P.T. May 1962.

M114. 6tr, S/M/LW portable. £14.3s.6d. including P.T. 1963.

M126. 7tr, S/M/LW portable. £13.2s.5d. plus £2.6s.4d. P.T. 1966.

M150BT (Luxury Consort). April 1961.

MT102. 6tr, M/LW portable. £13.2s.4d. plus £4.4s.2d. P.T. August 1960. (Identical chassis used in the Sobell ST301).

Meeta (*dist.* **J.T. Chanrai & Co. [U.K.] Ltd.**), 1-2 Finsbury Square, London EC2. *Transistor Production Run 1967.*

Meeta TR-804. 7tr, M/LW portable. £4.19s.6d. including P.T. 1967.

Mercury (*dist.* **Wye Electronics Ltd.**), Queen Street North, Whittington Moor, Chesterfield. *Transistor Production Run 1967-70.*

247. 6tr, M/LW portable. £15.2s.9d. plus £3.4s.9d. P.T. 1967. (The '247' was aimed at the teenage market, and brought out in celebration of the B.B.C.'s new "*swinging*" radio station, Radio 1, which was launched on 247 metres on Saturday 30th September 1967).

500. 9tr, M/LW/FM portable. £20.15s.2d. plus £4.8s.10d. P.T. 1968.

747. 9tr, M/LW/FM portable. £27.8s.6d. including P.T. 1970.

AM/FM Mercury. M/LW/FM portable. £24.7s.6d. plus £3.19s.6d. P.T. 1967.

Mercury One. 6tr, M/LW portable. £14.0s.6d. plus £2.9s.6d. P.T. 1967.

Mikado [Japan] (*dist.* **D.Tandon [London] Ltd.**), 244 Edgware Road, London W2. *Transistor Production Run 1966.*

1 Band. 6tr, MW pocket portable. £2.17s.6d. including P.T. 1966.

2 Band. 7tr, M/LW portable. £5.10s.0d. including P.T. 1966.

Minivox [Switzerland] (**Minivox S.A., Nepro Watch Division**), Avenue Leopold Robert 88, La Chaux-de-Fonds, Switzerland. *Transistor Production Run 1963.*

RR-34 (Minivox Clock Radio). 6tr, MW pocket portable/alarm watch movement. 1963. (This beautiful little radio came complete with an earphone, set of batteries and instructions, and was presented in a red and gold case lined with ivory coloured silk. It was assembled in Switzerland using Toshiba components in the radio circuit. *See fig.950, p.297*).

Monogram (**Monogram Electric Ltd.**), Gatwick Road, Crawley, Sussex. From 1967, new address at Lincoln House, 296 High Holborn, London WC1. *Transistor Production Run 1966-67.*

C1425. MW mains table model/clock radio. £11.2s.6d. plus £2.0s.0d. P.T. 1966.

C1570. MW/FM mains table model/clock radio. £20.0s.7d. plus £3.11s.11d. P.T. 1966.

C1590. MW/FM mains table model/clock radio. £32.1s.0d. plus £5.15s.0d. P.T. 1966.

P975. 15tr, MW/FM portable. £12.16s.8d. plus P.T. 1966.

P976. 15tr, M/LW/FM portable. 16.0s.8d. plus £2.17s.4d. P.T. 1967. (Mains adaptor, optional extra).

P990. 17tr, 2S/M/LW/FM portable. £39.3s.4d. plus £7.0s.8d. P.T. 1966. (Complete with logging scale, and battery check).

P1720. 10tr, M/FM pocket portable. £9.6s.11d. plus £1.13s.7d. P.T. 1966.

P1735. 6tr, MW pocket port. £2.18s.11d. +P.T. 1966.

P1736. 8tr, M/LW pocket portable. £4.0s.2d. plus £14s.4d. P.T. 1966.

P1800. 6tr, MW pocket portable. £6.4s.6d. plus £1.2s.6d. P.T. 1966.

P1820. 11tr, MW/FM pocket portable. £12.16s.8d. plus £2.7s.10d. P.T. 1966.

P1831. 8tr, M/LW portable. £8.11s.10d. plus £1.11s.10d. P.T. 1967.

P1911. 16tr, M/LW/FM portable. £24.18s.0d. plus 4.9s.2d. P.T. 1967.

P1980. 11tr, MW/FM portable. £15.12s.7d. plus £2.15s.11d. P.T. 1966.

P1986. 8tr, M/LW/FM portable. £12.9s.5d. plus £2.4s.7d. P.T. 1967.

T143. MW mains table model. £8.9s.3d. plus £1.10s.3d. P.T. 1966.

T1270. MW/FM mains table model. £16.9s.4d. plus £2.19s.2d. P.T. 1966.

UKC1436. M/LW mains table model/clock radio. £13.12s.6d. including P.T. 1967. (With "Snooz" alarm).

UKC1570. 9tr, MW/FM mains table model/clock radio. £23.12s.0d. including P.T. 1967. (With "Snooz" alarm).

UKC1576. 9tr, M/LW/FM mains table model/clock radio. £26.5s.0d. including P.T. 1967. (With "Snooz" alarm).

UKC1590. 10tr MW/FM mains table model/clock radio. £37.16s.0d. including P.T. 1967. (With "Snooz" alarm).

UKT1270. 9tr, MW/FM mains table model. £19.8s.6d. including P.T. 1967.

Motorola [U.S.A.] (*dist.* **World Radio Ltd.**), Edgware Road, London NW2. *Transistor Production Run 1963.*

X21. 6tr, MW pocket portable. 1963. (Gold-plated fascia, inset with paste diamonds. Came complete with batteries, earphone and silk-lined presentation case. This set was actually made in Japan for the American company Motorola - it merely bore their brand-name. *See fig.951, p.297*).

Playmate. 7tr, M/LW portable. £17.5s.8d. including P.T. 1963.

Murphy (**Murphy Radio Ltd.**), Welwyn Garden City, Herts. From 1962, (**Rank-Bush Murphy Ltd., Murphy Radio Division**) at same address. From 1972 (**Rank Radio International**) at same address. *Transistor Production Run 1959-72+.*

A857. 9tr, M/LW/FM mains table model. £31.10s.5d. including P.T. 1969.

A858. 13tr, S/M/LW/FM mains table model. £52.7s.2d. including P.T. 1969.

A859. 24tr, S/M/LW/FM stereo mains table model. £73.14s.7d. including P.T. 1969.

A860. 24tr, S/M/LW/FM stereo mains table model. £80.2s.9d. including P.T. 1969. (Similar specification to A859 but with separate loudspeakers).

B385. 8tr, M/LW portable. £22.1s.0d. including P.T. September 1959. (Optional wooden loudspeaker cabinet [model B1] used to convert B385 into a table model, price £3.19s.3d. plus £1.5s.9d. P.T. extra. Still being sold as a current model in 1961. *See fig.807, p.200*).

B483. 6tr, M/LW portable. £11.17s.9d. plus £3.17s.3d. P.T. July 1960.

B485. 7tr, M/LW portable. £15.5s.4d. plus £4.8s.2d. P.T. February 1961. (Later, slightly modified version of B385).

B493. 6tr, M/LW table model. £12.14s.1d. plus P.T. January 1962.

B495. 6tr, M/LW portable. £11.6s.10d. plus P.T. May 1962.

B581. 6tr, M/LW pocket portable (pre-set on LW for the Light Programme) personal portable. £8.16s.8d. plus £3.2s.4d. P.T. (Earpiece and leather carrying case £2.2s.0d. — these were available as optional extras). October 1961.

B583. 7tr, M/LW portable. £13.2s.0d. plus P.T. March 1962.

B585. 9tr, MW/FM portable. £16.4s.6d. plus £5.14s.6d. P.T. June 1961. (Leather carrying case and earpiece included).

B605. 7tr, M/LW table model. £13.10s.3d. plus P.T. April 1961.

B801. 7tr, M/LW portable. £14.3s.6d. including P.T. June 1963.

B812. 7tr, M/LW portable. £16.16s.0d. including P.T. August 1963.

B813. 7tr, M/LW portable. £15.15s.0d. including P.T. August 1963.

B815. 8tr, M/LW portable/car radio. £14.9s.7d. plus P.T. 1966. (For home, outdoor or in-car use. Bandspread tuning between 187-210 metres, for Radio Luxembourg).

B818. 7tr, M/LW portable (pre-set on 208 metres for the Radio Luxembourg). £15.15s.0d. including P.T. 1965.

B822. 7tr, M/LW portable/car radio. £13.2s.6d. including P.T. 1967. (Complete with a logging-scale. For home, outdoor or in-car use. Bandspread tuning between 187-210 metres, for Radio Luxembourg. Chassis identical to the Bush TR146).

B831. 9tr, M/LW/FM portable. £21.0s.0d. including P.T. 1965.

B837. 9tr, M/LW/FM portable. £24.3s.0d. including P.T. 1965. (Bandspread tuning between 187-210 metres, for Radio Luxembourg).

B840. 8tr, M/LW portable. £18.7s.6d. including P.T. 1967.

B841. 10tr, M/LW/FM portable. £23.2s.0d. including P.T. 1967.

B842. 9tr, S/M/LW/FM portable/car radio. £20.9s.6d. including P.T. 1967. (For home, outdoor or in-car use).

B844. M/LW/FM portable. £28.18p. including P.T. 1972.

B845. 10tr, 2S/M/LW/FM portable. £32.17s.0d. plus £7.0s.0d. P.T. 1968.

B846. 7tr, M/LW portable. £18.3s.4d. including P.T. 1969.

B848. 10tr, M/LW/FM portable. £12.19s.6d. plus £2.15s.6d. P.T. 1968.

B861. 7tr, M/LW portable. £8.8s.0d. including P.T. 1969. (Complete with wrist strap).

B865. 10tr, M/LW/FM portable. £16.10s.0d. including P.T. 1970.

B866. 6tr, M/LW portable. £11.10s.0d. including P.T. 1970.

B868. 11tr, MW/FM portable. £14 including P.T. 1971.

B870. M/LW, integrated circuit portable/car radio with pre-set push-button for the pop station B.B.C. Radio 1 on 247 metres. £17.85p. including P.T. 1971. (For home, outdoor or in-car use).

Voxson MR750. 5tr, M/LW car radio/rear view mirror. In two separate units — a receiver tuning head (complete with rear view mirror) and a loudspeaker unit. £16.6s.0d. plus P.T. September 1960. (Although not a domestic radio, the Voxson has been included because it is so unusual. I am afraid I couldn't resist it!).

Nanaola (*dist.* **Dallas Electrical Ltd.**), 10 Clifton Street, London EC2. *Transistor Production Run 1964.*

8TP-803L. 8tr, S/M/LW portable. £18.7s.6d. including P.T. 1964.

10NT-504. 10tr, 3S/M/LW portable. £27.6s.0d. including P.T. 1964.

National [Matsushita Electric Industrial Co. Ltd., Osaka, Japan] (*dist.* **Winter Trading Co. Ltd.**), 95-99 Ladbroke Grove, London W11. From 1964, (*dist.* **United Africa Mechanical & Electrical Ltd. [UNAMEC]**), United Africa House, Blackfriars Road, London SE1. Later became **National Panasonic**. *Transistor Production Run 1960-72+.*

AB210T. 9tr, S/MW portable. 1963. (Similar to AB210U, but with 7-18mHz SW coverage)

AB210U. 9tr, S/MW portable. 1963. (Similar to AB210T, but with 3.9-11mHz SW coverage).

R70. 6tr, MW pocket portable (spherical radio, c.5" diameter). £7.15s.0d. including P.T. 1970. (Available in red, blue or white. Can be suspended from the metal chain provided).

R100. 9tr, 3S/MW portable. £35.5s.8d. plus £7.10s.11d. P.T. 1968. (Complete with tuning meter).

R108 (Panasonic). 6tr, MW pocket portable. 1964.

R203L. 7tr, M/LW portable. £13.13s.0d. including P.T. 1964. (Complete with tuning meter).

R211L. 6tr, M/LW portable. 1965.

R289L. 6tr, M/LW portable. £13.10s.0d. including P.T. 1970.

R411B. 8tr, 3S/MW mains/battery portable. £23.7s.1d. plus £4.19s.11d. P.T. 1968.

R411L/B. 8tr, 2S/M/LW mains/battery portable. £23.7s.1d. plus £4.19s.11d. P.T. 1969.

R470. 10tr, 3S/MW portable. £25.19s.0d. plus £4.10s.0d. P.T. 1967. (Complete with battery/ tuning meter).

R807L. 6tr, M/LW pocket portable. £9.1s.0d. plus £1.11s.11d. P.T. 1965.

R1000. 10tr, MW portable. £17.3s.10d. plus £3.0s.6d. P.T. 1965. (Featuring 'RadarMatic' auto station hunting).

R2079L. 6tr, M/LW portable. £9.13s.11d. plus £2.5s.7d. P.T. 1969.

RC702. 8tr, MW/FM mains table model/digital clock radio. £27 including P.T. 1972.

RC703. 9tr, M/LW/FM mains table model/ digital clock radio. £33.79p. including P.T. 1971.

RC705B. 9tr, MW/FM mains/battery portable/ clock radio. £40.0s.0d. including P.T. 1970. (Synchronous clock with time-setting of radio. Built-in mains adaptor).

RE7670. 25tr, MW/FM stereo mains table model. £77.23p. including P.T. 1971. (Separate loudspeakers).

RF60. 3tr, FM stereo portable. £50.0s.0d. including P.T. 1970. (Stereo headset receiver).

RF531. 8tr, 4S/MW portable. 31.59p. including P.T. 1972.

RF602. 9tr, MW/FM portable. £13.7s.10d. plus £3.2s.11d. P.T. 1969.

RF603. 9tr, MW/FM portable. £16.10s.11d. including P.T. 1970.

RF610. 9tr, M/FM portable. £14.9s.7d. plus £2.11s.1d. P.T. 1966.

RF621. 9tr, M/LW/FM portable. £14.14s.6d. plus £2.12s.0d. P.T. 1967.

RF680L. 8tr, M/LW/FM portable. £15.16s.8d. plus £2.15s.11d. P.T. 1967.

RF670. 9tr, M/LW/FM portable. £14.14s.6d. plus £3.9s.4d. P.T. 1969.

RF811. 8tr, MW/FM pocket portable. £14.9s.7d. plus £2.11s.1d. P.T. 1965.

RF820L. 8tr, M/LW/FM portable. £18.7s.6d. including P.T. 1964. (Mains adaptor, optional extra).

RF823. 9tr, M/LW/FM portable. £21.0s.0d. including P.T. 1970.

RF829L. 8tr, M/LW/FM portable. £19.95p. including P.T. 1972.

RF843L. 9tr, M/LW/FM portable. £28.90p. including P.T. 1971.

RF849. 9tr, M/LW/FM portable. £22.19s.2d. plus £5.7s.10d. P.T. 1969.

RF894L. S/M/LW/FM portable. £43.16s.2d. including P.T. 1970.

RF902L. 9tr, S/M/LW/FM portable. £29.15s.2d. plus £6.19s.10d. P.T. 1969.

RF939. S/M/LW/FM portable. £35.48p. including P.T. 1971.

RF959. S/M/LW/FM portable. £40.04p. including P.T. 1971.

RF1006L. 10tr, M/LW/FM portable. £26.5s.0d. including P.T. 1964.

RF2079L. 6tr, M/LW portable. £11.19s.7d. including P.T. 1970.

RF3000. 19tr, 2S/M/LW/FM/Marine Band. £78.14s.3d. plus £16.16s.9d. P.T. 1968. (Inc. tuning meter. Mains adaptor, extra).

RF5000. 19tr, 8S/M/LW/FM portable. £169.0s.0d. (no Purchase Tax). 1969.

SPT501. Extension loudspeaker in the form of a flying saucer on tripod legs (body 8 1/2" diameter, loudspeaker 4 3/4" diameter). This transistor radio accessory was designed to plug into the earphone socket of any pocket transistor, thus considerably improving the sound quality. 1961. (Two-tone grey and burnt sienna plastics body resting on a gilded metal tripod).

T10. 6tr, MW pocket portable. £9.11s.9d. plus £2.9s.9d. P.T. December 1960.

T15L. 6tr, M/LW personal portable. £13.0s.6d. plus £3.5s.0d. P.T. 1961.

T46. 8tr, S/MW pocket portable. £15.15s.0d. including P.T. 1963.

T81. 8tr, M/LW/FM portable. £22.1s.0d. including P.T. April 1963.

T82L. 8tr, M/L/FM portable. £24.0s.10d. plus £6.8s.2d. P.T 1961.

T94. 7tr, S/MW portable/alarm watch. £20.7s.4d. plus £5.17s.8d. P.T. 1961.

T100. 9tr, 3S/MW portable. £47.5s.0d. including P.T. April 1963.

T100D. 9tr, 3S/MW portable. £35.5s.8d. plus £6.4s.8d. P.T. 1965. (Complete with battery/ tuning meter).

T100F. 12tr, S/M/LW/FM portable. £44.2s.0d. including P.T. 1964. (Complete with battery/ tuning meter).

T211L. 6tr, M/LW pocket portable. £11.0s.6d. including P.T. April 1963.

T370. 8tr, S/MW portable. £30.19s.6d. including P.T. April 1963.

National Panasonic (*see National, page 263*).

Newmatic (Newmatic Electrical Ltd.), Manor Trading Estate, Thundersley. *Transistor Production Run 1964.*

Dualmaster. 6tr, M/LW portable/car radio. £19.8s.6d. including P.T. 1964. (For home, outdoor or in-car use).

Niccol (*dist.* Lee Products [Gt. Britain] Ltd.), 10-18 Clifton Street, London EC2. *Transistor Production Run 1963.*

1807L. 7tr, M/LW pocket portable. £11.11s.0d. including P.T. 1963.

Nishinan [Japan] (*dist.* Lee Products [Gt. Britain] Ltd.), 10-18 Clifton Street, London EC2. *Transistor Production Run 1962.*

TRN-66. 6tr, MW pocket portable. £7.15s.3d. plus £2.4s.10d. P.T. 1962.

Nivico (J.V.C.) [Japan] (*dist.* Winter Trading Co. Ltd.), 95-99 Ladbroke Grove, London W11. From 1967, (*dist.* Denham & Morley Ltd.), Denmore House, 175 Cleveland Street, London W1. *Transistor Production Run 1965-72+.*

6TA. 6tr, M/LW pocket portable. £6.6s.0d. including P.T. 1965.

8A-260E. 8tr, S/MW pocket portable. £10.37p. including P.T. 1972.

8A-260L. 8tr, M/LW pocket portable. £9.19s.0d. including P.T. 1970.

8A-353ALR. S/M/LW portable. £18.18s.0d. including P.T. 1968.

8TA. 8tr, M/LW portable. £13.2s.6d. including P.T. 1965.

10F-353LS. 10tr, M/LW/FM portable. £18.7s.6d. 1970.

10F-407. 10tr, S/M/LW/FM portable. £29.8s.0d. including P.T. 1968. (Mains adaptor, extra).

12F-343L. 12tr, M/LW/FM portable. £28.7s.0d. including P.T. 1968.

10F-353LS. 10tr, M/LW/FM portable. £18.7s.6d. including P.T. 1970.

10TA-1. 10tr, 2S/MW portable. 1965.

FA-40L. 10tr, S/M/LW/FM mains/battery portable/car radio. £40.19s.0d. including P.T. 1970. (Complete with tuning meter. For home, outdoor or in-car use).

FA-900N. 12tr, 6S/M/LW/FM portable. £68.5s.0d. including P.T. 1968. (Complete with tuning meter. Mains adaptor, optional extra).

FA-6000T. 11tr, 3S/M/LW/FM portable. £82.19s.0d. including P.T. 1968. (Complete with tuning meter, and world-time chart. Mains adaptor, extra).

FA-8500L. 6S/M/LW/FM mains/battery portable. £55.0s.0d. including P.T. 1970. (Complete with tuning meter).

Normende [West Germany] (*dist.* T.A.K. Continental Importers), 16a High Street, Stone, Staffordshire. *Transistor Production Run 1958-72+.*

Ascot. 10tr, M/LW portable. £14.14s.0d. including P.T. 1970. (Mains adaptor, optional extra).

Ascot 6. MW/FM portable. £11.50p. including P.T. 1971. (Mains adaptor available, optional extra).

Bornholm. S/M/LW/FM mains table model. £38.18s.6d. plus £8.6s.6d. P.T. 1968.

Carrera. 9tr, M/LW/FM portable. £17.17s.6d. plus £4.3s.6d. P.T. 1969. (Mains adaptor, optional extra).

Charleston. 10tr, S/M/LW/FM portable. £28.10s.0d. including P.T. 1970. (Mains adaptor, optional extra).

Clipper K. 7tr, S/MW portable. £28.7s.0d. including P.T. 1958.

Clou. 9tr, S/MW/FM portable/car radio. £40.95p. including P.T. 1971. (Mains adaptor, £6 extra, bracket for in-car use, £7 extra).

Club Flamingo. 9tr, S/2M/LW/FM portable. £33.7s.3d. plus £7.11s.9d. P.T. 1968. (Mains adaptor, extra. Medium waveband tuning is divided into two with bandspread over both halves, giving MW1 (275-555 metres) and MW2 (185-280 metres).

Corvette. 10tr, M/LW/FM portable. £21.50p. including P.T. 1971. (Mains adaptor, optional extra).

Dixieland. 9tr, 2S/M/LW/FM portable. £41.9s.0d. including P.T. 1970. (Mains adaptor, extra).

Electra. S/M/LW/FM mains table model. £39.50p. including P.T. 1972.

Euro. 9tr, S/2M/LW/FM portable. £33.7s.3d. plus £7.11s.10d. P.T. 1968. (Mains adaptor, extra. Medium waveband tuning is divided into two with bandspread over both halves, giving MW1 (275-555 metres) and MW2 (185-280 metres).

Euro Perfect. 9tr, S/2M/LW/FM portable. £37.7s.0d. including P.T. 1970. (Mains adaptor, extra. Medium waveband tuning is divided into two with bandspread over both halves, giving MW1 (275-555 metres) and MW2 (185-280 metres).

Exclusive. S/M/LW/FM mains table model. £38.2s.6d. plus £9.2s.6d. P.T. 1969.

Dingy. 10tr, S/M/LW/FM portable. £21.10s.0d. including P.T. 1970. (Mains adaptor, extra).

Galaxy Mesa 2000. 10tr, S/MW/FM mains/battery portable. £44 including P.T. 1971. (Complete with built-in mains adaptor).

Galaxy Mesa 4000. 10tr, 3S/M/LW/FM mains/battery portable. £55 including P.T. 1971. (Complete with built-in mains adaptor).

Galaxy Mesa 6000. 13tr, 6S/M/LW/FM mains/battery portable. £69 including P.T. 1971. (Complete with built-in mains adaptor).

Globemanager. 21tr, 11S/M/LW/FM mains/battery portable. £115.50p. including P.T. 1971. (Complete with built-in mains adaptor, and twin loudspeakers).

Globetraveller IV. 18tr, 11S/M/LW/FM/Public Service Bands mains/battery portable. £96.10s.0d. including P.T. 1970. (Complete with built-in mains adaptor).

Globetrotter Amateur. 17tr, 11S/M/LW/FM mains/battery portable. £84.10s.3d. plus £19.8s.9d. P.T. 1968. (Built-in mains adaptor).

Globetrotter TN600. 14tr, 11S/M/LW/FM mains/battery portable. £76.4s.4d. plus £17.4s.8d. P.T. 1968. (Built-in mains adaptor).

Golden Dixieland. 9tr, S/M/LW/FM portable. £24.17s.0d. plus £3.18s.6d. P.T. 1967.

Hit. M/LW/FM portable. £17.17s.0d. including P.T. 1970. (Mains adaptor, extra).

Kadett. 9tr, MW/FM portable. £9.18s.2d. lus £2.3s.4d. P.T. 1968. (Mains adaptor, optional extra).

Mambino. 5tr, M/LW portable. £15.9s.6d. plus £4.9s.6d. P.T. 1961.

Mambo. 7tr, M/LW portable. £26.5s.0d. including P.T. 1958.

Mambo (Mk.II). 10tr, M/LW/FM portable. £14.5s.6d. plus £3.1s.0d. P.T. 1968. (Mains adaptor, extra).

Mikrobox. 6tr, M/LW personal portable. £13.1s.0d. plus £3.15s.0d. 1961.

Minibox. 6tr portable. £21. including P.T. 1958.

Othello. S/M/LW/FM mains table model. £39.50p. including P.T. 1972.

Oxford L. 11tr, M/LW/FM portable. £18.10s.0d. including P.T. 1970. (Mains adaptor, extra).

Regina. S/M/LW/FM stereo mains table model. £75.0s.4d. plus £18.18s.8d. P.T. 1969. (Separate loudspeakers).

Rumba. 8tr, 3S/MW portable. £27.6s.0d. including P.T. 1964.

Skandia. S/M/LW/FM mains table model. £38.2s.6d. plus £9.2s.6d. P.T. 1969.

Spectra 4002. S/M/LW/FM mains table model. £39.85p. plus £7.85p. P.T. 1971.

Spectra-Futura M. S/M/LW/FM mains table model. £41.19s.9d. plus £9.9s.3d. Purchase Tax. 1968.

Spectra-Futura S. S/M/LW/FM stereo mains table model. £59.2s.3d. plus £13.6s.9d. P.T. 1968.

Spectra-Futura ST. S/M/LW/FM stereo mains table model. £76.4s.4d. plus £17.4s.8d. P.T. 1968.

Spectra-Phonic. 10tr, MW/FM mains table model. £29.8s.0d. including P.T. 1967.

Spectra-Phonic 4004. S/M/LW/FM mains table model. £49.50p. including P.T. 1972.

Starlet. 9tr, MW/FM pocket portable. £12.2s.3d. plus £2.11s.9d. P.T. 1968. (Mains adaptor, extra).

Stradella. 9tr, MW/FM portable. £22 plus £6.7s.0d. P.T. September 1962.

Tasti. 10tr, FM portable. £16.2s.9d. plus £2.15s.3d. P.T. 1967. (Push-button selection of three FM stations — three huge buttons! Mains adaptor, extra).

Windsor. 9tr, M/FM portable. £12.1s.4d. plus £2.2s.2d. P.T. 1967. (Mains adaptor, extra).

Transista E. 9tr, M/LW/FM portable. £23.14s.0d. plus £6.15s.0d. P.T. 1961.

Transista GC. 9tr, M/FM/Marine band portable. £23.14s.0d. plus £6.15s.0d. P.T. 1961.

Transista K. 9tr, S/MW/FM portable. £23.14s.0d. plus £6.15s.0d. P.T. 1961.

Transista Automatic. 11tr, S/M/LW/FM portable/car radio. £40.19s.0d. including P.T. 1964. (Bracket for in-car use, £7.10s.0d. optional extra).

Transista Comfort. 8tr, S/M/LW/FM portable. £40.19s.0d. including P.T. 1970. (Mains adaptor, extra).

Transista Exact. 13tr, S/2M/LW/FM mains/battery portable. £50.10s.7d. plus £11.8s.5d. P.T. 1968. (Built-in mains adaptor. Medium waveband tuning is divided into two with bandspread over both halves, giving MW1 (275-555 metres) and MW2 (185-280 metres).

Transista Export. 9tr, S/M/LW/FM portable. £28.10s.0d. plus £8.5s.0d. P.T. September 1962. (Mains adaptor, £6 extra).

Transista GT. 11tr, 2S/M/LW/FM portable. £41.19s.0d. plus £9.9s.3d. P.T. 1968. (Mains adaptor, extra).

Transista Globetrotter. 14tr, 11S/M/LW portable. £72.12s.0d. including Purchase Tax. 1964. (Complete with tuning meter and mains adaptor connector; mains adaptor, £6 extra. Bracket for in-car use available, price £8.12s.6d. extra).

Transista Globetrotter TN6001. 15tr, 11S/M/LW/FM mains/battery portable. £96.10s.0d. including P.T. 1970. (Built-in mains adaptor).

Transista Luxus. 9tr, M/LW/FM portable. £26.1s.3d. plus £7.10s.9d. P.T. September 1962.

Transista Recorder. 12tr, S/MW/FM portable. £47.10s.0d. including P.T. 1970. (Mains adaptor, extra).

Transista Royal. 9tr, M/LW/FM portable. £34.14s.0d. including P.T. 1964.

Transista Royal Mk.II. S/M/LW/FM portable. £34.13s.0d. including P.T. 1970.

Transista Special. 9tr, S/M/LW/FM portable. £30.19s.6d. including P.T. 1964. (Mains adaptor, £6 extra).

Transista Stereo de Luxe. 24tr, S/M/LW/FM stereo mains/battery portable. £72.9s.0d. including Purchase Tax. 1970. (Built-in mains adaptor).

Transista Super. 14tr, 2S/M/LW portable. £70.7s.0d. including P.T. 1964.

Transista T.S. Special. 11tr, 2S, M/LW/FM portable. £51.9s.0d. including P.T. 1964. (Mains adaptor, £6 extra. Bracket for in-car use, £8.5s.0d. extra).

Transista Universal. 9tr, M/LW/FM portable. £30.19s.6d. including P.T. 1963.

Oceanic (*dist. Sound Song Ltd.*), 1-3 Jacob's Well Mews, George Street, London W1. From 1963, *(dist. H.K. Harrisson & Co. Ltd.)* of same address. *Transistor Production Run 1962-63.*

Monaco. 9tr, M/LW/FM portable. £30.9s.0d. including P.T. March 1963.

Tonic. 6tr, M/LW portable. £16.16s.0d. including P.T. March 1963.

Traffic. 6tr, 3S/MW portable. £21.5s.6d. plus £6.4s.6d. P.T. April 1962.

Triton. 6tr, M/LW portable. £15.8s.8d. plus £4.10s.4d. P.T. April 1962.

Tropic. 6tr, S/M/LW portable. £18.11s.4d. plus £5.8s.8d. P.T. April 1962.

Optalix (*dist. Paschkes & Co. Ltd*), 40 Craven Road, W2. *Transistor Production Run 1963.*

Turny. 7tr, M/LW portable. £21.1s.0d. including P.T. 1963.

Pam (Pam [Radio & Television] Ltd.), 295 Regent Street, London W1. *Transistor Production Run 1956-66.*

222. 6tr, M/LW pocket portable. £10.6s.8d. plus £3.6s.4d. P.T. August 1960.

333. 6tr, M/LW pocket portable. £11.0s.6d. plus P.T. 1962.

365. 6tr, M/LW table model. £21 including P.T. November 1958. (One of two pioneering British table model transistor radios to be released in 1958. *See also the Dansette RT60, page 251*).

710. 8tr, M/LW portable (pre-set on LW for the Light Programme). £31.10s.0d. including P.T. March 1956. (This was the first British transistor radio to be released onto the U.K. market. Very few Pam 710's seem to have been sold, and certainly, few have survived over the years with little more than half a dozen examples known today. *See pages 288-291*).

720. 6tr, M/LW portable (pre-set on LW for the Light Programme). £17.8s.9d. plus £6.14s.3d. P.T. April 1957.

5215. 7tr, M/LW portable. £13.2s.6d. including P.T. June 1963.

5217. 7tr, M/LW portable. £17.17s.0d. including P.T. June 1963.

5219. 8tr, M/LW portable. £19.19s.0d. including P.T. June 1963.

5220. 8tr, M/LW portable. £13.2s.6d. including P.T. 1964.

5222. 9tr, S/M/LW/FM portable. £25.4s.0d. including P.T. 1964.

5224. 9tr, S/M/LW/FM portable. £22.12s.5d. plus £3.19s.10d. P.T. 1966.

5225. 7tr, M/LW portable (bandspread section aligned on Radio Luxembourg's wavelength of 208 metres). £12.1s.6d. including P.T. 1965.

5230. 10tr, S/M/LW/FM mains table model. 1966.

5430. 7tr, S/MW portable. 1964.

5446. 7tr, 3S/MW portable. 1966.

TB20. 6tr, M/LW portable. £17.8s.9d. plus £6.14s.3d. P.T. May 1958.

TB59. 6tr, M/LW portable. £18.18s.0d. including P.T. May 1959.

TB60. 6tr, M/LW portable. £13.10s.3d. plus £4.6s.9d. P.T. May 1960.

TB61. 6tr, M/LW portable. £12.4s.5d. plus £3.10s.7d. P.T. 1961.

TB71. 9tr, M/LW/FM table model. £23.12s.6d. plus P.T. April 1962.

TB77. 7tr, M/LW table model. £22.5s.2d. plus £7.2s.10d. P.T. August 1960.

TB81T (Courier). 8tr, 2S/M/LW portable. £19.19s.2d. plus £5.15s.4d. P.T. July 1961.

TB90. 7tr, M/LW table model. £14.3s.6d. plus P.T. November 1961.

TXP185. 8tr, 2S/M/LW portable. £23.2s.0d. including P.T. 1963.

Gayplay III. 5tr, M/LW pocket portable. £13.12s.11d. plus £5.5s.1d. P.T. May 1958.

Miniset 333. 6tr, M/LW personal portable. £8.6s.11d. plus £2.18s.11d. P.T. September 1961.

Park Air (Park Air Electronics Ltd.), 22a High Street, Stamford, Lincs. *Transistor Production Run 1966-69.*

Air Buddy. 10tr, MW/Aircraft Band portable. £28.0s.0d. plus £5.13s.9d. P.T. 1966.

Concorde. 10tr, MW/Aircraft Band portable. £15.0s.0d. plus £3.11s.6d. P.T. 1969.

Jet Set. 10tr, MW/Aircraft Band portable. £10.2s.4d. plus £1.17s.8d. P.T. 1967.

Jet Stream. 9tr, M/LW/Aircraft Band. £15.0s.0d. plus £3.11s.6d. P.T. 1969.

Monitor 10SS (series). 10tr, Aircraft Band only, mains/battery portable. £52.16s.0d. to £96.16s.0d. (no Purchase Tax). 1969. Six different models were available in the SS series.

Sky Bandit. 9tr, M/LW/Aircraft Band. £19.8s.6d. plus £3.11s.6d. P.T. 1967.

Sky Monitor. 12tr, S/M/LW/Aircraft Band portable. 1966.

Sky King. 9tr, M/LW/Aircraft Band portable. £17.13s.0d. plus £3.12s.0d. P.T. 1966.

Perdio (Perdio Ltd.), Dunstan House, St. Cross Street, London EC1. From 1963, **(Perdio Electronics Ltd.),** Perdio House, Bonhill Street, London EC2. From 1965, **(Perdio Products Ltd.),** Lowther Road, Stanmore, Middlesex. Perdio went into liquidation in October 1965, and soon after, Perdio products began to be made in Hong Kong and started to appear bearing the legend *"Empire Made"*. Later, from 1971, **(dist. Brown Bros. Ltd.),** Gt. Eastern Street, London EC2. *Transistor Production Run 1957-72+.*

AM/FM 10. 10tr, MW/FM pocket portable. £9.1s.0d. plus £1.11s.11d. P.T. 1965.

AM/FM 95. 9tr, M/LW/FM portable. £22.5s.3d. plus £7.2s.9d. P.T. August 1960.

AM/FM 100. 9tr, M/LW/FM portable. £22.10s.1d. plus P.T. September 1961.

PR1. 5tr, MW pocket portable. £16.13s.7d. plus £6.8s.5d. P.T. June 1957.

PR2. 5tr, M/LW pocket portable. £18.3s.10d. plus £7.0s.2d. P.T. February 1958.

PR3. Unknown. Was a PR3 ever produced? — we would all like to know.

PR4. 4tr, M/LW portable. £9.17s.10d. plus £3.15s.2d. P.T. February 1958. (A modification kit was available from the manufacturers for installing an external aerial socket or an earphone socket).

PR5 (de Luxe). 6tr, M/LW portable. £16.14s.10d. plus £6.7s.2d. P.T. May 1958. (With external aerial, earphone and tape recorder sockets).

PR5 (Standard). 6tr, M/LW portable. £14.9s.2d. plus £5.9s.10d. P.T. May 1958. (As PR5 de Luxe but without external aerial, earphone and tape recorder sockets).

PR7 (Super-7 de Luxe). 7tr, M/LW pocket portable/car radio. £17.17s.7d. plus £6.15s.11d. P.T. August 1958. (In Morocco leather case). *"The Super-7 sets have an added selling point . . . they will fit a special bracket available as an extra for your customers' cars".* (For home, outdoor or in-car use).

PR7 (Super-7 Standard). 7tr, M/LW pocket portable/car radio. £16.7s.3d. plus £6.4s.4d. P.T. August 1958. (As Super-7 de Luxe, but in rexine case. For home, outdoor or in-car use).

PR12. 7tr, M/LW portable. £7.17s.6d. including P.T. 1965. (One of the first Perdio products to appear bearing the logo *"Empire Made"*).

PR22. 7tr, M/LW table model. £15.10s.1d. plus £4.19s.5d. P.T. March 1960. (M/LW table model version of PR73 Continental).

PR23 (Park Lane). 7tr, M/LW personal portable. £12.16s.1d. plus £4.10s.5d. P.T. January 1961.

PR24 (Mini-6). 6tr, M/LW pocket portable. £12.12s.0d. including P.T. August 1960. (See also PR33, below).

PR25. 7tr, M/LW portable. £13.19s.6d. including P.T. March 1961. (Identical chassis used in the PR36 Fanfare). Housed in possibly the world's worst radio cabinet (*see comment under fig.811, page 201*).

PR29. 6tr, M/LW portable. £9.6s.2d. plus £2.13s.9d. P.T. January 1962.

PR30 (Londoner). 7tr, M/LW portable. £11.2s.1d. plus £3.1s.5d. P.T. March 1962.

PR32 (Town & Country). 7tr, M/LW/Marine Band portable. £19.19s.0d. including P.T. September 1962.

PR33 (Mini-66). 6tr, M/LW pocket portable (pre-set on LW for the Light Programme). £13.2s.6d. including P.T. January 1962. (Re-styled version of the PR24, above. Circuit fitted with either Mullard or Impex transistors).

PR36 (Fanfare). 7tr, M/LW portable. £16.16s.0d. including P.T. January 1962. (Identical chassis used in the PR25).

PR37 (Carnival). 5tr, M/LW portable. £11.11s.0d. including P.T. July 1962.

PR40 (Knightsbridge). 7tr, M/LW/FM portable. £29.8s.0d. including P.T. 1963.

PR41 (Town & Country). 7tr, S/M/LW portable. £19.19s.0d. including P.T. August 1962.

PR-43 (Mini-77). 7tr, M/LW pocket portable. £9.19s.6d. including P.T. May 1963. (De Luxe version, price £10.10s.0d. including P.T. May 1963).

PR44 (Strand). 7tr, M/LW portable. £11.11s.0d. including P.T. 1963.

PR51 (Pall Mall). 7tr, M/LW portable. £11.11s.0d. including P.T. August 1962. (In a padded leathercloth case).

PR73 (Continental). 7tr, M/LW/Trawler Band (87-197 metres) portable. £14.15s.1d. plus P.T. June 1959. (One of the first transistor receivers to include the Trawler Band. *See fig.802, p.197*).

PR74 (Town & Country). 7tr, 2S/MW portable. £19.19s.0d. including P.T. January 1963.

PR76 (Berkeley). 7tr, M/LW portable. £14.14s.0d. including P.T. May 1963.

PR99 (Curzon). 7tr, M/LW port. £10.8s.1d. +P.T. May 1964.

PR95. 9tr, M/LW/FM portable. 1961.

PR100. 9tr, M/LW/FM portable. £22.10s.0d. plus P.T. September 1961.

PR110 (Grosvenor). 7tr, S/M/LW portable. £15.16s.8d. plus P.T. May 1964.

PR120 (Marco Polo). 17tr, 6S/M/LW/FM portable. £99.15s.0d. including P.T. 1964. (Continuous coverage from 1.6 to 30 Mc/s. World-time chart inside front cover).

PR159 (Parade). 7tr, M/LW portable. £11.0s.6d. including P.T. 1964.

PR167 (Caralux). 7tr, M/LW portable (bandspread section aligned on Radio Luxembourg's wavelength of 208 metres). £16.5s.6d. including P.T. 1964.

PR 189 (Polka). 7tr, M/LW portable. £8.18s.6d. including P.T. 1964.

PR190 (Popsy). 6tr, M/LW pocket portable. £5.17s.0d. including P.T. 1964.

PR191 (Radio Alarm). M/LW table model/clock radio. £10.17s.2d. plus £1.18s.4d. P.T. 1966.

PR608. 6tr, M/LW pocket portable. £6.19s.6d. including P.T. 1964.

PR712. 7tr, M/LW pocket portable. £8.18s.6d. including P.T. 1964.

PR713 (Pennant). 7tr, M/LW portable. £12.1s.6d. including P.T. 1964.

PR721 (Piccadilly). 7tr, M/LW pocket portable. £11.10s.6d. plus £3.14s.0d. P.T. August 1959. (This model also came in a gift set comprising the PR721, a leather case, a bracket for converting into a car radio, an earphone and a battery, price £14.11s.6d. plus £4.6s.0d. P.T. April 1961).

Berkeley (see PR76).

Burford. 6tr, S/M/LW portable. £7.15p. including P.T. 1971.

Caralux (see PR167). 7tr, M/LW portable. £16.5s.6d. including P.T. 1964.

Carnival (see PR37).

Continental (see PR73).

Curzon (see PR99).

Devon. 7tr, M/LW portable. £11.13s.6d. plus £2.10s.0d. P.T. 1968.

Fanfare (see PR36).

Grosvenor (see PR110).

Kenilworth. 11tr, MW/FM portable/car radio. £9.15p. including P.T. 1972. (For home, outdoor or in-car use).

Knightsbridge (see PR40).

Londoner (see PR30).

Marcolo (see PR120).

Mayfair. 6tr, M/LW portable. £9.6s.2d. plus £2.13s.9d. P.T. 1961.

Mini-6 (see PR24).

Mini-66 (see PR33).

Mini-77 (see PR43).

Multi-Band 91. 9tr, 3S/M/L portable. £19.17s.6d. plus £6.7s.6d. Purchase Tax. August 1960.

Multi-Band 102. 10tr, 3S/M/LW portable. £22.10s.2d. plus £7.18s.11d. Purchase Tax. October 1961.

New Continental. 7tr, S/M/LW portable. £25.4s.0d. including P.T. 1963.

Norfolk. 8tr, M/LW/Marine Band. £19.17s.11d. plus £4.13s.7d. P.T. 1969.

Pall Mall (see PR51).

Parade (see PR159).

Park Lane (see PR23).

Pennant (see PR713).

Piccadilly (see PR721).

Polka (see PR189).

Popsy (see PR190).

Popsy II. 6tr, M/LW pocket portable. £5.3s.9d. plus £1.2s.3d. P.T. 1968.

Radio Alarm (see PR191).

Somerset. 10tr, M/LW/Marine Band. £25.19s.0d. plus £6.2s.1d. Purchase Tax. 1969.

Strand (*see PR44*).

Strand de Luxe. 7tr, M/LW portable. £12.12s.0d. including P.T. 1963.

Super-7 de Luxe (*see PR7*).

Super-7 Standard (*see PR7*).

Town & Country (*see PR32, PR41 and PR74*).

Perth (Perth Radios Ltd.), Marten House, 39/47 East Road, London N1. *Transistor Production Run 1959-60.*

Mercury K766. 7tr, S/M/LW portable. £24.13s.0d. plus £7.18s.0d. P.T. June 1959.

Mercury Mk.II. 6tr, M/LW portable. £17.2s.0d. plus £5.9s.6d. P.T. August 1960.

Peto Scott (Peto Scott Electrical Instruments Ltd.), Addlestone Road, Weybridge, Surrey. *Transistor Production Run 1961.*

RA73. 6tr, M/LW portable. £8.11s.4d. plus £4.9s.6d. P.T. June 1961.

Philco (Philco [Gt. Britain] Ltd.), 30-32 Grays Inn Road, London WC1. From 1960, **(British Radio Corporation Ltd.)**, 21 Cavendish Place, London W1. From 1963, **(P.G.B. Electronics Ltd)**, of same address. From 1966, **(Philco International Ltd.)**, 42 Leicester Square, London WC2. Products appeared under the **Philco-Ford** trade name from 1968. *Transistor Production Run 1959-71.*

8J21. 8tr, MW pocket portable. £5.7s.1d. plus £18.11d. P.T. 1966.

9J43TL. 9tr, S/M/LW table model. £16.19s.2d. plus £2.19s.10d. P.T. 1966. (Mains adaptor extra).

11J44TL. 11tr, S/M/LW/FM table model. £27.4s.5d. plus £4.16s.1d. P.T. 1966. (Mains adaptor, £3.13s.6d. extra).

13J63PL. 13tr, M/LW/FM portable. £15.7s.8d. plus £2.14s.3d. P.T. 1967. (Two loudspeakers).

14J65PL. 14tr, 2S/M/LW/FM portable. £28.1s.0d. plus £4.19s.0d. P.T. 1967.

124. 6tr, M/LW table model. £13.3s.11d. plus £4.13s.1d. P.T. June 1961.

200 (Transitone). 6tr, M/LW pocket portable. £18.18s.0d. including P.T. 1959. (A special carrying handle supplied with the set enabled it to hang from the back of a car seat or a deckchair [I wonder if that annoyed anyone on the beach?]. Inverted, it acted as a support).

202 (Courier). 6tr, M/LW personal portable (pre-set on LW for the Light Programme). £11.2s.7d. plus £3.11s.5d. P.T. July 1960.

204. 7tr, M/LW personal portable. £10.1s.9d. plus £3.4s.9d. P.T. June 1961.

300 (Transporta). 6tr, M/LW portable. £14.6s.2d. plus £4.11s.10d. March 1960.

302. 7tr, M/LW portable. £13.11s.8d. plus £4.15s.10d. P.T. June 1961.

304. 9tr, M/LW/FM portable. £23.5s.8d. plus £7.9s.5d. P.T. August 1961.

425. 8tr, MW/FM mains table model. £19.26p. including P.T. 1971.

5100 (Sprite). 6tr, M/LW pocket portable. £8.11s.1d. plus £2.9s.5d. P.T. February 1962.

B470 (Transglobe). 10tr, 7S/MW portable. £55.6s.9d. plus £9.15s.5d. P.T. 1966. (Mains adaptor extra. Complete with world-time chart).

R425WA. 9tr, MW/FM mains table model. £17.17s.0d. including P.T. 1970. (Uses two loudspeakers).

T12. 9tr, M/LW portable. £10.7s.6d. plus £2.9s.0d. P.T. 1969.

T85. 8tr, MW pocket portable. £5.16s.0d. plus £1.0s.6d. P.T. 1966.

T91. 9tr, MW/FM pocket portable. £9.0s.11d. plus £1.12s.1d. P.T. 1967.

T92. 9tr, MW/FM portable. £8.9s.7d. plus £1.9s.11d. P.T. 1966.

T93. 10tr, MW/FM portable. £9.7s.5d. plus £1.13s.1d. P.T. 1966.

T96. 12tr, M/FM portable. £12.9s.11d. plus £2.4s.1d. P.T. 1966.

T97. 12tr, MW/FM portable. £15.12s.4d. plus £2.15s.2d. P.T. 1966.

T150. 9tr, MW/FM portable. £7.12s.4d. plus £1.12s.8d. P.T. 1968.

T160. 6tr, MW/LW portable. £6.15s.0d. including P.T. 1970.

T162. 7tr, M/LW portable. £8.4s.3d. plus £1.15s.3d. P.T. 1968.

T164. 7tr, M/LW portable. £10.15s.0d. including P.T. 1970.

T170. 10tr, M/LW/FM portable. £15.19s.0d. including P.T. 1970. (Mains adaptor extra).

T180. 10tr, M/LW/FM portable. £16.8s.11d. plus £3.10s.7d. P.T. 1968.

T182. 10tr, M/LW/FM portable. £18.19s.0d. including P.T. 1970.

T202. 10tr, M/LW/FM portable. £17.10s.0d. plus £3.15s.0d. P.T. 1968.

T204. 10tr, M/LW/FM portable/car radio. £25.19s.0d. including P.T. 1970. (For home, outdoor or in-car use. Mains adaptor extra).

T226. 11tr, S/M/LW/FM portable/car radio. £33.19s.0d. including P.T. 1970. (For home, outdoor or in-car use. Mains adaptor extra).

T240. 13tr, 2S/M/LW/FM portable/car radio. £43.19s.0d. including P.T. 1970. (For home, outdoor or in-car use. Provision for housing a mains adaptor within the cabinet).

T611. 6tr, MW pocket portable. £3.12s.4d. plus 12s.10d. P.T. 1967.

T914. 13tr, 3S/M/LW/FM portable. £35.5s.1d. plus £6.4s.3d. P.T. 1966. (Mains adaptor extra).

T980. 10tr, M/LW/FM portable. £13.19s.6d. plus £3.6s.0d. P.T. 1969.

T993. 10tr, MW/FM portable. £12.2s.1d. plus £2.11s.11d. P.T. 1968.

T995. 10tr, MW/FM portable. £13.19s.6d. plus £3.0s.0d. P.T. 1968.

Philips (Philips Electrical Ltd.), Century House, Shaftesbury Avenue, London WC2. Philips' model numbers often appear in an alternative version prefixed by or intersperced with letters — *eg.* models 390 and 395 were also known as P3G90T and L3G95T respectively *etc.* ('T' at the end meaning Transistor). For simplification, I have gone for the numerical version, although care might be needed in some cases in order to work out exactly which model is being referred to. *Transistor Production Run 1959-72+.*

011. 6tr, M/LW portable. £9.47p. including P.T. 1972.

56. S/M/LW/FM stereo mains table model. £77.2s.6d. including P.T. 1969. (Complete with tuning meter).

75 (Personic). 7tr, MW personal portable. £18.7s.6d. including P.T. May 1959.

90 (Personic). 7tr, M/LW personal portable. £12.0s.7d. plus P.T. June 1960.

91 (Philette). 6tr, M/LW portable. £20.9s.6d. including P.T. May 1959.

091 (Personic). 7tr, M/LW pocket portable. £9.15s.6d. plus £2.16s.6d. P.T. April 1962.

110. 8tr, M/LW portable. £7.30p. including P.T. 1972.

114. 11tr, MW/FM portable. £12.25p. including P.T. 1972.

130. 6tr, M/LW pocket portable. £11.11s.0d. including P.T. 1963.

141. 6tr, M/LW portable. £7.19s.6d. including P.T. 1965.

151 (Popmaster). Pocket portable. £7.19s.6d. including P.T. 1965. (Designed to combat the increasing sales of small low-priced transistor radios imported from the Far East. During 1965, the low-priced end of the market began to be dominated for the first time by sets assembled in Japan and Hong Kong, and even some British firms were beginning to have their own chassis made there).

152. 6tr, M/LW pocket portable. £6.16s.6d. plus 1.5s.3d. P.T. 1966. (Case, 15s.0d. extra).

161 (Popmaster Prince). 6tr, M/LW portable. £8.10s.5d. including P.T. 1967.

180 (Musicman). 7tr, M/LW portable. £6.15s.6d. plus £1.4s.0d. P.T. 1967.

192. 8tr, MW/FM mains table model. £25.10p. including P.T. 1971.

194. 11tr, MW/FM portable. £10.19s.7d. including P.T. 1970.

200. 7tr, S/M/LW personal portable. £14.13s.3d. plus £4.4.9d. P.T. May 1962.

210. 7tr, S/M/LW portable. £17.17s.0d. including P.T. December 1962.

210 (RL). 8tr, M/LW portable. £12.15p. including P.T. 1972.

221. 6tr, M/LW portable. £14.3s.6d. plus P.T. September 1962.

232. 6tr, M/LW portable. £13.13s.0d. including P.T. 1965.

237. 6tr, M/LW portable. £11.11s.0d. including P.T. August 1964.

241. 6tr, M/LW portable. £13.13s.0d. including P.T. August 1963. (Identical chassis used in the Cossor CR1310T and Stella ST415T).

242. 9tr, S/M/LW/FM portable. £23.2s.0d. including P.T. 1965.

243 (Trieste). 6tr, M/LW portable/car radio. £12.4s.4d. plus £2.3s.1d. P.T. 1966. (For home, outdoor or in-car use).

247. 6tr, M/LW portable. £9.19s.0d. plus £1.15s.3d. P.T. 1966.

248 (New Yorker). 7tr, S/M/LW portable. £13.2s.5d. plus £2.6s.4d. P.T. 1966.

250. 6tr, M/LW portable. £9.19s.6d. plus £1.11s.8d. P.T. 1966.

261. 6tr, M/LW mains table model/clock radio. £16.5s.6d. including P.T. 1967.

262. 6tr, M/LW mains table model. £13.13s.0d. including P.T. August 1967. (Identical chassis used in the Stella 4500).

265 (Popmaster Sovereign). 6tr, M/LW portable. £8.10s.9d. plus £1.18s.5d. P.T. September 1967.

269. 7tr, M/LW portable. £11.13s.6d. plus £2.10s.0d. P.T. 1968.

272. 6tr, M/LW mains table model. £14.14s.0d. including P.T. 1969.

273. 6tr, M/LW mains table model/clock radio. £18.18s.0d. including P.T. 1969.

274 (Executive). 9tr, M/LW/FM mains table model/clock radio. £30.6s.11d. plus £6.9s.10d. P.T. 1968. (Bizarre design — long, thin cabinet with a long, thin dial and the clock perched on top seemingly as an after-thought. The 274 would certainly look at home on the set of the "Thunderbirds" tv series).

280. 7tr, M/LW portable. 1966. (With twin loudspeakers).

282. 9tr, M/LW/FM portable. £13.19s.8d. plus £2.19s.10d. P.T. 1968.

284. 9tr, MW/FM portable. £11.10s.3d. plus £2.9s.3d. P.T. 1968. (Identical chassis used in the Stella 6003).

290. 11tr, M/LW/FM portable. £11.10p. including P.T. 1971. (Mains adaptor, extra).

291. Integrated circuit, M/LW mains table model/clock radio. £20.30p. inc. P.T. 1971.

292. 10tr, S/2M/LW/FM mains table model. £36.20p. including P.T. 1971. (Medium waveband tuning is divided into two with bandspread over both halves, giving MW1 (275-555 metres) and MW2 (185-280 metres).

294. MW/FM mains table model/clock radio. £26.42p. plus £5.08p. P.T. 1971.

301. 6tr, M/LW portable. £14.6s.2d. plus £4.11s.10d. P.T. June 1960. (Identical chassis used in the 395).

303. 6tr, M/LW portable. £13.3s.10d. plus £4.13s.2d. P.T. June 1961.

304. 6tr, M/LW portable. £14.7s.1d. plus £5.1s.11d. P.T. August 1961.

312. 8tr, M/LW/FM portable. £21.3s.8d. plus £6.2s.4d. P.T. 1961.

313. 6tr, M/LW portable. £12.12s.6d. plus £3.13s.0d. P.T. May 1962.

322. 9tr, M/LW/FM portable. £23.2s.0d. including P.T. August 1962.

323. 7tr, M/LW portable. £15.15s.0d. including P.T. 1962.

323/01. 7tr, M/LW portable. £16.5s.6d. including P.T. 1963.

336. 6tr, M/LW portable. £17.6s.6d. including P.T. 1964.

338. 6tr, M/LW portable/car radio. £18.1s.3d. plus £3.4s.8d. P.T. 1966. (Bracket for converting into car radio included).

345. 6tr, M/LW portable/car radio. £14.0s.6d. plus £2.9s.6d. P.T. 1966. (For home, outdoor or in-car use. A "power boost" switch enables a choice of high or low output from the receiver, with increased battery life in the "Min" position).

360. 6tr, M/LW portable. £18.2s.0d. including P.T. 1967.

370. 9tr, M/LW/FM portable. £15.12s.0d. plus £3.6s.9d. P.T. 1968.

372. 10tr, M/LW/FM portable. £17.8s.1d. plus £3.1s.5d. P.T. 1967.

382. 12tr, M/LW/FM portable. £29.6s.9d. including P.T. 1969.

386. 9tr, M/LW/FM portable. £26.4s.0d. including P.T. 1969. (Mains adaptor, extra).

390. 6tr, M/LW portable/car radio. £21.14s.6d. including P.T. May 1962. (Bracket and mounting kit for converting into car radio extra).

391. 6tr, M/LW portable. £18.18s.0d. including P.T. May 1959.

392. 9tr, M/LW/FM portable. £20.0s.0d. including P.T. 1970.

393. 9tr, M/LW/FM portable. £25.15s.0d. including P.T. 1970. (Mains adaptor, extra).

395. 6tr, M/LW portable. £13.2s.4d. plus £4.4s.2d. P.T. August 1960. (Identical chassis used in the 301).

402. 6tr, M/LW table model. £15.2s.1d. plus £4.16s.11d. P.T. August 1960.

410. 7tr, 3S/MW portable. £28.7s.0d. including P.T. 1970.

425. 6tr, M/LW pocket portable. 1964.

430. 9tr, M/LW/FM portable. 1964.

439. 7tr, S/M/LW portable. £25.4s.0d. including P.T. 1964.

442. 10tr, M/LW/FM portable. £28.17s.0d. including P.T. 1964.

486. 15tr, M/LW/FM portable. £30.9s.0d. including P.T. 1969.

500. 9tr, M/LW/FM portable. £20.0s.0d. including P.T. 1970. (Mains adaptor, extra).

534. 9tr, S/M/LW/FM portable. £39.18s.0d. including P.T. 1964.

544. 9tr, S/M/LW portable. £38.0s.0d. plus £6.14s.1d. P.T. 1966.

560. S/M/LW/FM stereo mains table model. £57.0s.1d. plus £10.1s.3d. P.T. 1966. (Decoder for use in stereo mode, available as an optional extra).

561. 23tr, S/M/LW/FM stereo mains table model. £73.9s.1d. including P.T. 1967.

570. 9tr, S/M/LW/FM portable. £40.3s.3d. plus £7.1s.9d. P.T. 1967.

583. 10tr, S/M/LW/FM portable. £32.0s.1d. plus £6.16s.11d. P.T. 1968.

586. 9tr, M/LW/FM portable. £19.17s.10d. plus £4.5s.2d. P.T. 1968. (Mains adaptor, extra).

638. 11tr, 4S/M/LW/FM portable. £90.9s.8d. plus £15.19s.3d. P.T. 1966. (Complete with radio compass).

693. 11tr, S/2M/LW/FM mains/battery portable. £78.16s.0d. including Purchase Tax. 1969. (The model 693 employed two loudspeakers and was housed in an unusual cabinet which slid apart to reveal the controls and vertical scales for the various wavebands. Medium waveband tuning is divided into two with bandspread over both halves, giving MW1 (275-555 metres) and MW2 (185-280 metres).

798. 11tr, 4S/M/LW/FM portable. £105.0s.0d. including P.T. 1969.

IC-103. Integrated circuit, M/LW portable. £13.10s.0d. including P.T. 1970.

IC-105. Integrated circuit, M/LW portable. £14.5s.0d. including P.T. 1970.

IC-321. Integrated circuit, M/LW/FM portable. £26.75p. including P.T. 1972.

IC-322. Integrated circuit, S/M/LW/FM portable. £31.65p. including P.T. 1971. (Complete with tuning meter).

IC-323. Integrated circuit, S/M/LW/FM mains/battery portable. £35.75p. including P.T. 1972. (Built-in mains adaptor).

IC-326. Integrated circuit, S/M/LW/FM mains/battery portable. £30.90p. including P.T. 1972. (Built-in mains adaptor).

IC-361. Integrated circuit, 3S/M/LW/FM mains/battery portable. £79.95p. inc. Purchase Tax. 1972.

Pilot (Pilot Radio & Television Ltd.), Television House, Eastcote, Ruislip, Middlesex. *Transistor Production Run 1960-63.*

7100. 7tr, M/LW portable. £11.19s.6d. including P.T. 1963.

7102. 6tr, M/LW portable. £13.2s.6d. including P.T. 1963.

PR251. 6tr, M/LW portable. £14.14s.2d. plus £4.14s.4d. P.T. March 1960. (Identical chassis used in the Ultra 101).

PR260. 6tr, M/LW pocket portable. £12.6s.5d. plus £3.19s.1d. Purchase Tax. August 1960.

PR270. 7tr, M/LW portable. £13.18s.2d. plus £4.9s.4d. P.T. August 1960.

PR280. 6tr, M/LW portable. £17.17s.0d. plus £5.14s.6d. P.T. April 1961.

PR281. 9tr, M/LW/FM portable. £23.5s.8d. plus £6.14s.6d. P.T. April 1961.

PR288. 6tr, M/LW personal portable. £9.6s.3d. plus £2.19s.9d. P.T. April 1961.

Playcraft (Playcraft Toys Ltd.), Sutherland House, 5-6 Argyll Street, London W1. *Transistor Production Run 1963.*

Y4500. 4tr, M/LW portable. £6.6s.0d. including P.T. 1963. (Adaptable as a baby alarm).

Y4502. 6tr, M/LW portable. £8.19s.0d. including P.T. 1963. (Adaptable as a baby alarm).

Poodle (*dist.* **Winter Trading Co. Ltd.**), 95-99 Ladbroke Grove, London W11. *Transistor Production Run 1966.*

TR6 (Poodle Dog). 6tr, MW portable radio/toy poodle. £6.15s.0d. plus £1.4s.9d. P.T. 1966.

Portadyne (Dynaport Radio & Television Ltd.), 30/34 Gorst Road, North Acton, London NW10. *Transistor Production Run 1959-69+.*

3B2. 6tr, S/M/LW portable. £13.16s.6d. plus £2.9s.0d. P.T. 1967.

S3B (*see Super Three Band, below*).

TP1. 6tr, M/LW portable. £12.6s.1d. plus £3.19s.5d. P.T. September 1959.

TP6. 6tr, M/LW portable. £11.16s.0d. plus £3.8s.6d. P.T. 1961. (Similar to Minx, but in cream leathercloth cabinet and with push-button wavechange).

TP484. 6tr, M/LW portable. £11.4s.9d. plus £3.19s.9d. P.T. June 1961.

TP500. 6tr, M/LW portable. £9.13s.9d. plus £3.8s.9d. P.T. 1961.

TP700. 6tr, M/LW personal portable (pre-set on LW for the Light Programme). £7.9s.6d. including P.T. 1963.

Escort. 8tr, S/M/LW portable. £13.3s.6d. plus £3.2s.0d. P.T. 1969.

International. 7tr, M/LW portable. £9.19s.6d. including P.T. 1964.

International II. 7tr, M/LW portable. £9.1s.8d. plus £1.18s.10d. P.T. 1968.

Minx. 6tr, M/LW portable. £11.0s.6d. including P.T. June 1962. (Similar to TP6, but in two-tone leathercloth cabinet and with wavechange switch).

Super Three Band (S3B). 6tr, S/M/LW portable. £14.3s.6d. including P.T. 1963.

Viscount. 6tr, M/LW portable (pre-set on LW for the Light Programme). £7.7s.3d. plus £2.12s.3d. 1961.

Portogram (Portogram Radio Electrical Industries Ltd.), Paxton Road, Tottenham, London N17. *Transistor Production Run 1959.*

Prefect. 7tr, M/LW portable. £17.9s.9d. plus £5.12s.3d. P.T. August 1959.

President (*dist.* **Kingsway Mill Co. [M/C] Ltd.**), 1 Berry Street, London EC1. Later, from 1966 (*dist.* **Winter Trading Co. Ltd.**), 95-99 Ladbroke Grove, London W11. *Transistor Production Run 1965-72.*

TR602. 6tr, M/LW pocket portable. £4.9s.6d. including P.T. 1965.

TR1030. S/M/LW portable. £9.95p. including P.T. 1972.

Pye (Pye Ltd.), Cambridge. From 1969, **(Pye Group [Radio & Television] Ltd.),** P.O. Box 49, Cambridge. *Transistor Production Run 1957-72+*

P123BQ. 6tr, M/LW portable (pre-set on LW for the Light Programme). £17.6s.4d. plus £6.17s.2d. P.T. January 1957. (*See fig.940, p.293.* With many parts borrowed from the Pam 710, the P123BQ has always been thought of as Pye's first transistor radio made under its own label, but now this may not turn out to be the case —*see under fig.940, p.293*).

P128B (Slim Six). 6tr, M/LW 'mantel' radio (pre-set on LW for the Light Programme). 1958. (Designed, not for outdoor use as a portable, but rather for indoor use on a mantelpiece . . . well, it did look like a mantel clock, so why not? *See fig.789, p.196*).

P150BQ. 5tr, M/LW personal portable. £13.12s.11d. plus £5.5s.1d. P.T. June 1958.

P152BQ. 6tr, M/LW portable. £14.14s.0d. including P.T. 1959.

P160PQ. 6tr, M/LW pocket portable (pre-set on LW for the Light Programme). £15.15s.0d. including P.T. March 1959.

P170BQ. 6tr, M/LW portable. £9.18s.9d. plus £3.3s.9d. P.T. May 1960.

P180BQ. 6tr, M/LW portable. £11.10s.6d. plus £3.14s.0d. P.T. August 1960.

P190BQ. 6tr, M/LW pocket portable. £9.18s.9d. plus £3.3s.9d. P.T. February 1961.

P191BQ. 6tr, M/LW pocket portable. (Leather cased version of P190BQ). £11.10s.6d. plus £3.14s.0d. P.T. February 1961.

P200BQ. 6tr, M/LW port. (pre-set on LW for the Light Prog.). £11.0s.6d. +P.T. August 1962.

P201BQ. 6tr, M/LW pocket portable (pre-set on LW for the Light Programme). £9.2s.10d. plus £2.18s.8d. P.T. September 1961.

P202BQ. 6tr, M/LW pocket portable (pre-set on LW for the Light Programme). £8.6s.11d. plus £2.13s.7d. P.T. September 1961. (Employed the same basic chassis as the P201BQ but with different case styling).

P444 (Cruiser). 6tr, M/LW/Trawler Band (90-180 metres) portable. £18.5s.8d. plus £5.17s.4d. P.T. August 1959. (One of the first receivers to include the Trawler Band).

P1108. 9tr, S/M/LW/FM mains table model. £32.11s.6d. plus £5.14s.11d. P.T. 1966. (As P1110, but with different cabinet styling).

P1110. 9tr, S/M/LW/FM mains table model. £28.19s.1d. plus £5.2s.2d. P.T. 1966. (As P1108, but with different cabinet styling).

P1111. S/M/LW/FM stereo mains table model. £44.15s.10d. plus £7.18s.0d. P.T. 1966. (Complete with stereo decoder and extension loudspeaker).

P1113. 7tr, M/LW mains table model. £16.16s.0d. including P.T. 1967.

P1351. 7tr, M/LW table model. £16.16s.0d. plus P.T. 1961.

P1352. 7tr, M/LW portable/car radio. £13.2s.6d. including P.T. August 1964. (For home, ourdoor or in-car use).

P1353. 9tr, M/LW/FM portable. £23.2s.0d. including P.T. March 1963.

P1354. 9tr, M/LW mains/battery portable. £17.17s.0d. including P.T. December 1962.

P1355. 7tr, M/LW portable. £16.16s.0d. including P.T. 1963.

P1356. 9tr, S/M/LW/FM portable. £25.4s.0d. including P.T. 1964.

P1357. 7tr, M/LW portable. £13.13s.0d. including P.T. 1964.

P1359. 6tr, M/LW pocket portable. £5.5s.0d. including P.T. 1964.

P1362 (Astronaut). 9tr, S/M/LW/FM portable. £25.4s.0d. including P.T. 1964.

P1363 (Popliner). 7tr, M/LW portable. £10.8s.1d. plus £1.16s.9d. P.T. 1965. (Bandspread tuning between 182-215 metres, for Radio Luxembourg).

P1366 (Poppet). 6tr, M/LW pocket portable. £4.10s.6d. plus 15s.11d. P.T. 1966.

P1367 (Playalong). 8tr, M/LW portable. £6.6s.8d. plus P.T. November 1965.

P1369 (Playboy). 8tr, M/LW portable. £8.2s.10d. plus £1.8s.9d. P.T. March 1967. (Identical chassis used in the Pye P1371 and the Ekco PT302).

P1370 (Finlandia). 9tr, S/M/LW/FM portable. £24.8s.7d. plus £4.6s.3d. P.T. 1966.

P1371 (Playalong). 8tr, M/LW portable. £6.6s.8d. plus £1.2s.4d. P.T. November 1966. (Identical chassis used in the Pye P1369 and the Ekco PT302).

P1372 (Venturer). 8tr, M/LW/FM portable. £17.16s.7d. plus £3.2s.11d. P.T. 1967. (Identical chassis used in the Ekco PT304 and the Ferranti 5501).

P1373. 8tr, M/LW portable/car radio. £14.5s.7d. plus £2.10s.5d. P.T. 1967. (For home, outdoor or in-car use. Identical chassis used in the Ekco PT305 and the Ferranti 5503).

P1374. 6tr, M/LW/FM portable. £12.5s.2d. plus £2.3s.4d. P.T. 1967. (Identical chassis used in the Ekco PT306).

P1375 (Popalong). 9tr, M/LW/FM portable. £7.13s.3d. plus £1.12s.9d. P.T. February 1968.

P1376 (Playalong). 8tr, M/LW portable. £7.3s.4d. plus £1.10s.8d. P.T. 1968.

P1377 (Playboy). 8tr, M/LW portable. £8.13s.0d. plus £1.17s.0d. P.T. 1968.

P1380 (Poppet). 6tr, M/LW pocket portable. £5.0s.6d. plus £1.1s.6d. P.T. 1968.

P1382. 9tr, M/LW/FM portable. £12.2s.2d. pus £2.11s.10d. P.T. 1968.

P1383. 9tr, M/LW/FM portable. £28.0s.2d. plus £5.19s.10d. P.T. 1968. (Mains adaptor, extra).

P1385. 9tr, M/LW/FM portable. £14.3s.4d. plus £3.6s.8d. P.T. 1969.

P1388. 11tr, M/LW/FM portable. £10.2s.4d. plus £2.7s.8d. P.T. 1969.

P1392. 6tr, M/LW portable. £5.16s.0d. including P.T. 1970.

P1393. 9tr, M/LW/FM portable. £28.8s.0d. including P.T. 1970. (Mains adaptor, extra).

P1394. 10tr, M/LW/FM mains/battery portable. £35.04p. including P.T. 1971. (Built-in mains adaptor).

P1395. 9tr, M/LW/FM portable/car radio. £20.52p. including P.T. 1972. (For home, outdoor and in-car use).

P1400. 6tr, M/LW pocket portable. £6.18s.0d. including Purchase Tax. 1970. (Housed in a *"camera-style"* cabinet complete with wrist strap).

P1403 (The Mistral). 10tr, M/LW/FM portable. £13.18s.0d. including Purchase Tax. 1970.

P1404 (Tempest). 10tr, S/M/LW/FM portable. £22.18s.0d. including P.T. 1970. (Mains adaptor, extra).

P2009. 6tr, M/LW portable/car radio. £21.6s.0d. plus P.T. 1967. (For home, outdoor or in-car use. Identical chassis used in the Ekco CP937).

P2010 (Two-In-One). 7tr, M/LW portable/car radio. 1963.

P6000 (Piccadilly). 22tr, 4S/M/LW/FM portable. £82.7s.7d. plus £17.12s.5d. P.T. 1968. (Complete with tuning/battery meter. Mains adaptor, extra).

Q1 (President). 6tr, M/LW cigarette box/receiver. £13.18s.3d. plus £4.9s.3d. P.T. August 1959.

Q3 (Jewel Case). 6tr, M/LW portable. £15.10s.0d. plus £4.19s.6d. P.T. August 1959.

Q4 (Jewel Case). 6tr (Pye Yellow Circle Transistors), or 7tr (Pye Green Circle Transistors), M/LW portable. £14.14s.2d. plus £4.14s.4d. P.T. August 1960.

Q5. 6tr, M/LW portable. £17.17s.0d. including P.T. 1959.

Q6. 6tr, M/LW portable. £12.14s.5d. plus £4.1s.7d. P.T. May 1960.

Q7. (7tr version of Q6). £13.2s.4d. plus £4.4s.2d. P.T. September 1961.

Q8. 6tr, M/LW portable. £12.4s.5d. plus £3.10s.7d. P.T. September 1961.

Q9. 8tr, S/M/LW portable. £24.13s.6d. including P.T. May 1962.

R32. 7tr, M/LW table model. £14.16s.9d. plus £7.2s.10d. P.T. March 1960.

R38. 9tr, M/LW/FM table model. £22.5s.2d. plus £7.2s.10d. P.T. August 1960.

Pygmy [France] (*dist.* **Wholesale Supplies [Swinton] Ltd.),** 16 Worsley Road, Manchester. From 1963, **(dist. Europa Electronics Ltd.),** Howard Place, Shelton, Stoke-on-Trent. From 1968, **(dist. Perry & Pharo Ltd.),** 56 Garden Street, Stafford. *Transistor Production Run 1961-68.*

501. 7tr, M/LW portable. £16.5s.6d. including P.T. 1963.

601. 7tr, M/LW portable. £15.4s.6d. including P.T. August 1963.

701. 7tr, M/LW portable. £17.17s.0d. including P.T. August 1963.

850. 7tr, 3S/M/LW portable. £22.1s.2d. plus £4.14s.4d. P.T. 1968.

1650. 9tr, 2S/M/LW/FM portable/car radio. £34.3s.4d. plus £7.6s.2d. P.T. 1968. (For home, outdoor or in-car use).

1901. 10tr, 3S/M/LW/FM portable. £42.7s.8d. plus £9.1s.4d. P.T. 1968. (For home, outdoor or in-car use).

2001 (Super). 15tr, S/M/LW/FM portable/car radio. £72.9s.0d. including P.T. 1965. (For home, outdoor or in-car use).

Lystron. 7tr, M/LW portable. £15.17s.9d. plus £4.11s.9d. P.T. September 1961.

Isotron. 7tr, 2S/M/LW portable. £22.8s.0d. plus £6.9s.6d. P.T. September 1961.

Varitron. 8tr, 3S/M/LW portable. £30.3s.0d. plus £8.14s.0d. P.T. September 1961.

Waltron. 10tr, M/LW/FM portable. £30.19s.6d. including P.T. 1963.

R.G.D. **(Radio Gramophone Development Co.Ltd.),** Eastern Avenue West, Romford, Essex. From 1961, Foots Cray, Sidcup, Kent. From 1966, **(dist. Standard Telephones & Cables Ltd.),** 190 Strand, London WC2. From 1971, **(ITT Consumer Products [U.K.] Ltd.),** Footscray, Sidcup, Kent. *Transistor Production Run 1958-72+.*

B56. 6tr, M/LW portable. £14.15s.8d. plus £5.13s.10d. P.T. July 1958.

B57. 6tr, M/LW portable. £12.14s.5d. plus £4.1s.7d. P.T. May 1960.

B58. 6tr, M/LW portable. £10.1s.9d. plus £3.11s.3d. P.T. April 1961.

B59. 6tr, M/LW portable. £14.14s.0d. including P.T. April 1962.

B60. 6tr, M/LW personal portable. £12.1s.6d. plus P.T. June 1962.

B61. 7tr, M/LW portable. £12.1s.6d. including P.T. August 1963.

B62. 8tr, M/LW portable. £15.15s.0d. including P.T. August 1963.

B64 (Toledo). 6tr, M/LW portable. £10.10s.0d. including P.T. 1964.

BT14. Portable. April 1960.

R75. 6tr, M/LW (adjustable pre-set on the long waveband). £5.95p. including Purchase Tax. 1972.

R100. 8tr, M/LW portable. £7.25p. including P.T. 1971.

R125. 7tr, M/LW portable. £10.60p. including P.T. 1971.

R130. 10tr, MW/FM portable. £10.90p. including P.T. 1972.

R155. 9tr, M/LW/FM portable. £15.95p. including P.T. 1972.

R200. 11tr, S/M/LW/FM portable. £27.75p. including P.T. 1972.

RR210. 8tr, S/M/LW portable (bandspread section aligned on Radio Luxembourg's wavelength of 208 metres). £13.13s.0d. including Purchase Tax. 1964.

RR214 (International). 9tr, 2S/MW/FM portable. £30.9s.0d. including P.T. 1964.

RR219. 10tr, M/LW/FM portable. £36.4s.0d. including P.T. 1966.

RR221 (Rover). 7tr, 2M/LW portable/car radio. £11.6s.2d. plus £2.0s.0d. P.T. 1966. (Identical chassis used in the K-B KR021 Cobra. Medium waveband tuning is divided into two with bandspread over both halves, giving MW1 (275-555 metres) and MW2 (185-280 metres). For home, outdoor or in-car use).

RR222 (Rambler). 6tr, 2M/LW portable. £16.5s.8d. plus £2.17s.7d. Purchase Tax. 1966. (Identical chassis used in the KR022 Commodore. Medium waveband tuning is divided into two with bandspread over both halves, giving MW1 (275-555 metres) and MW2 (185-280 metres). For home, outdoor or in-car use).

RR223. 7tr, 2M/LW portable. £14.15s.4d. plus £2.11s.2d. P.T. 1967. Medium waveband tuning is divided into two with bandspread over both halves, giving MW1 (275-555 metres) and MW2 (185-280 metres).

RR700. 8tr, 2M/LW portable. £20.19s.5d. plus £3.14s.1d. P.T. 1967. Medium waveband tuning is divided into two with bandspread over both halves, giving MW1 (275-555 metres) and MW2 (185-280 metres).

RR701. 10tr, M/LW/FM portable. £26.18s.4d. plus £5.12s.8d. P.T. 1968.

Radialva (*dist.* **Sound Song Ltd.**), 1-3 Jacob's Well Mews, Gearge Street, London W1. *Transistor Production Run 1962.*

Prestige. 9tr, 3S/M/LW portable. £42.11s.0d. plus £12.9s.0d. P.T. June 1962.

Radiomatic (*dist.* **Highgate Acoustics Ltd.**), 71-73 Gt. Portland Street, London W1. *Transistor Production Run 1965.*

Mexico. 8tr, M/LW portable. £16.16s.0d. including P.T. 1965.

Radionette (*dist.* **Denham & Morley Ltd.**), Denmore House, 175 Cleveland Street, London W1. *Transistor Production Run 1966-72+.*

Explorer. 7tr, 2S/M/LW/Marine Band portable. £30.16s.0d. plus £5.8s.6d. P.T. 1967.

Explorer FM. 12tr, S/M/LW/FM/Marine Band portable. £50.17s.4d. plus £8.19s.8d. P.T. 1967.

Explorer FM Mk.II. 12tr, 2S/M/LW/FM portable/car radio. £64.0s.0d. including P.T. 1967. (Mains adaptor, extra. For home, outdoor or in-car use).

Kurer Aircraft. 9tr, S/M/LW/Aircraft Band portable. £42.10s.6d. including P.T. 1968. (Mains adaptor, extra).

Kurer Automatic. 12t, S/M/LW/FM portable. £51.9s.0d. including P.T. 1968. (Mains adaptor, extra).

Kurer FM. 9tr, S/M/LW/FM portable. £30.16s.0d. plus £5.8s.6d. P.T. 1966. (Mains adaptor, extra).

Kurer Marine. 9tr, M/LW/FM/Marine Band. £30.16s.0d. plus £5.8s.6d. P.T. 1967. (Mains adaptor, extra).

Kurer 501. 10tr, FM portable. 1972.

Kurer 1001. 12tr, M/LW/FM portable. £47.17s.6d. including Purchase Tax. 1970. (Optional mains adaptor available, £6.6s.0d. extra).

Realtone (*dist.* **L.P.F. Photronics Ltd.**), Cricklewood Lane, London NW2. Later, from 1966, (*dist.* **Winter Trading Co. Ltd.**), 95-99 Ladbroke Grove, London W11. *Transistor Production Run 1963-66.*

TR1628 (Rambler). 6tr, MW pocket portable. £4.19s.6d. including Purchase Tax. June 1963.

TR1660 (Duke). 6tr, MW pocket portable. 1963.

TR1820 (Lancer 8). 8tr, MW pocket portable. 1963.

TR2011. 10tr, MW/FM portable. £8.11s.9d. plus £1.10s.6d. P.T. 1966.

TR2051 (Melody). 10tr, AM/FM portable. £16.5s.6d. including P.T. 1963.

TR2663. 16tr, 5S/M/LW/FM portable. £61.19s.0d. including P.T. 1965.

TR2868. 8tr, M/LW pocket portable. £7.19s.6d. including P.T. 1963.

TR2884. 8tr, AM/FM pocket portable. £13.2s.6d. including Purchase Tax. 1965.

TR3002. 10tr, MW/FM/Marine Band portable. £14.18s.7d. plus £2.12s.9d. P.T. 1966. (Mains adaptor extra).

TR3047 (Commander). 10tr, S/M/LW portable. £14.3s.6d. including P.T. 1963.

TR3283. 12tr, M/LW/FM portable. £17.6s.6d. including P.T. 1965.

TR3414. 14tr, S/MW/FM portable. 1966.

TR3449 (International). 14tr, S/M/LW/FM portable. £35.15s.0d. including Purchase Tax. 1963.

TR4250 (Navigator). 12tr, 2S/M/LW portable. £30.9s.0d. including P.T. 1963.

TR4525. 14tr, 3S/MW portable. £22.12s.4d. plus £4.0s.0d. P.T. 1966.

TR4597. 15tr, S/MW/FM/Marine Band portable. £22.12s.4d. plus £4.0s.0d. P.T. 1966. (Mains adaptor extra).

Voyager. 9tr, 2S/M/LW portable. £13.13s.0d. including P.T. 1963.

Recording Devices (**Recording Devices Ltd.**), 44 Southern Row, London W10. *Transistor Production Run 1960-62.*

Aurora. 6tr, MW pocket portable. £5.0s.10d. plus £1.9s.0d. P.T. 1962.

Minerva. 8tr, M/LW/FM portable. £27.11s.3d. plus £9.3s.9d. P.T. August 1960.

Riviera. 6tr, M/LW personal portable. £11.5s.0d. plus £3.19s.6d. P.T. August 1961.

Reela (*dist.* **Paschkes & Co. Ltd**), 40 Craven Road, London W2. *Transistor Production Run 1963.*

Lucky. 6tr, S/M/LW portable. £14.14s.0d. including P.T. 1963.

Punch. 6tr, M/LW portable. £13.2s.6d. including P.T. 1963.

Regentone (**Regentone Radio & Television Ltd.**), Eastern Avenue West, Romford, Essex. From 1961, Foots Cray, Sidcup, Kent. *Transistor Production Run 1959-65.*

BT11. 6tr, M/LW (pre-set on LW for the Light Programme). £18.18s.0d. including P.T. 1959.

BT12. 6tr, M/LW portable (in plastics case). £16.5s.6d. including P.T. November 1959.

BT14. 6tr, M/LW portable (as BT12 but in wooden case). £17.17s.0d. inc. P.T. April 1960.

BT16. 6tr, M/LW portable. £10.17s.3d. plus P.T. August 1961.

BT17. 6tr, M/LW portable. £9.14s.0d. plus P.T. June 1961.

BT18 (Minim). 6tr, M/LW pocket portable. £8.19s.3d. plus £2.11s.9d. P.T. September 1961.

BT20 (Adelphi). 7tr, M/LW portable. £12.1s.6d. including P.T. 1963.

BT21 (Tivoli). 7tr, M/LW portable. £13.2s.6d. including P.T. 1963.

BT22 (Savoy). 8tr, M/LW portable. £15.15s.0d. including P.T. 1963.

BT23 (Regenteener). 6tr, M/LW portable. £9.19s.6d. including P.T. 1963. (Priced so as to appeal to the teenage market).

TR410. 8tr, S/M/LW portable (bandspread section aligned on Radio Luxembourg's wavelength of 208 metres). £13.13s.0d. including P.T. 1964.

TR415. 10tr, MW/FM pocket portable. £17.17s.0d. including P.T. 1964.

TR419. 12tr, M/LW/FM portable. £20.9s.6d. including P.T. 1965.

Retra (*dist.* **Heddon Smith Group Ltd.**), 7 William Road, London W1. *Transistor Production Run 1964-65.*

Ministar II. 7tr, M/LW pocket portable. £7.19s.6d. including P.T. 1964.

Nightstar. 8tr, S/M/LW portable. £14.14s.0d. including P.T. 1965.

Songstar II. 6tr, MW pocket portable. £4.19s.6d. including P.T. 1964.

Riviera (*dist.* **Denham & Morley Ltd.**), 173-175 Cleveland Street, London W1. From 1963, (*dist.* **Highgate Acoustics Ltd.**), 71-73 Gt. Portland Street, London W1. *Transistor Production Run 1961-63.*

Riviera. 6tr, MW pocket portable. £8.18s.6d. plus £3.3s.0d. P.T. September 1961.

Riviera ML610. 6tr, M/LW pocket portable. £11.0s.6d. including P.T. 1963.

Roberts (Roberts Radio Co.Ltd.), Creek Road, East Molesey, Surrey. *Transistor Production Run 1958-72+.*

R200 (1st circuit version, serial numbers up to 36,546). 6tr, M/LW portable. £14.6s.0d. plus £4.12s.0d. Purchase Tax. January 1960. (This model was also made as a one-off set in a solid gold case [present-day value c. £35,000] priced then at £2,100, plus 3s.6d. for the battery! It was subsequently stolen from Harrods while on display, and presumably melted down . . . unless you know otherwise?!).

R200 (2nd circuit version, serial numbers 36,547 to 70,000). February 1961.

R200 (3rd circuit version, serial numbers 70,001 onwards). January 1962. The R200 serves to illustrate how some manufacturers continually sought to improve the performance of their sets while they were in production. While the outward appearance of this popular transistor radio remained unaltered during its lifetime, its circuit went through three distinct changes and over half a dozen modifications.

For those who will find life completely unbearable without knowing, "Trader" Service Sheet 1602 (published 25th May 1963) lists all the minutiae of the R200's modifications.

R300. 6tr, M/LW portable. £15.15s.0d. including P.T. May 1964. (Carrying case £1.10s.0d. extra).

R303. 8tr, M/LW portable. £15.15s.0d. including P.T. 1967. (Carrying case £1.12s.6d. extra).

R404. 7tr, M/LW portable. £15.7s.7d. plus P.T. March 1965. (Carrying case £1.15s.0d. extra).

R500. 7tr, S/M/LW portable. £18.10s.6d. including P.T. September 1963. (Carrying case £1.15s.0d. extra).

R600. 11tr, M/LW/FM portable. £24.3s.0d. including P.T. 1968. (Carrying case £2.0s.0d. extra).

R700. 14tr, M/LW/FM portable. £30.19s.6d. including P.T. 1966. (Carrying case £1.18s.6d. extra).

R707. 12tr, S/M/LW/FM portable. £27.18s.6d. plus £6.11s.6d. P.T. 1969. (Carrying case £2.10s.0d. extra).

RIC-1. 3tr, plus a TAD 100 integrated circuit, M/LW portable. £15.15s.0d. including Purchase Tax. August 1968. This was the first British-made transistor radio incorporating an integrated circuit (microchip) to be placed on the market. The IC used was a TAD100, manufactured by Mullard and primarily intended for use in AM radio receivers.

The TAD100 housed 11 transistors and 11 resistors in an area occupying just less than 1/500th part of a square inch, incorporating mixer, oscillator, IF amplifier, ACG and audio pre-amplifier stages - audio output transistors were not included so that different output power stages might be added to suit individual receiver requirements. In the RIC-1's case, an OC44/5 was used as the audio driver, with an AC187 and an AC188 as the complementary output pair — a BA114 was employed as the oscillator diode.

The RIC-1's wooden cabinet was embellished with either red, Oxford blue, conifer green or black Rexine leathercloth as standard, but it was also available exclusively from Harrods in Knightsbridge, London in a yellow/orange/green Paisley cloth covering. . . . . *very* Sixties!

RIC-2. 3tr (OC71/T7, AC187, AC188), plus a TAD 100 integrated circuit, M/LW portable. £16.80p. including P.T. 1971. (Carrying case £1.70p. extra).

RM40. 18tr, M/LW/FM mains table model. 1972.

RT1. 6tr, M/LW portable. £17.8s.9d. plus £6.14s.3d. P.T. Waterproof cover £1.11s.6d. extra. April 1958. (Roberts' first commercially produced transistor radio, *see fig.948, p.296*. At the time of their release, and by special order, RT1's were also available in mink, pony skin, leopard skin and jewel-encrusted suede coverings. This idea has been repeated in the last few years by wireless collector John Fenwick who has clothed Roberts' radios in, among other things, mock mink and tartan cloth. These appear for sale from time to time).

RT7. 7tr, M/LW portable. £18.5s.8d. plus £5.17s.4d. P.T. August 1960.

RT8. 7tr, M/LW portable. £23.2s.0d. plus P.T. August 1962.

Personal Portable. M/LW. March 1958. Strictly speaking, this was Roberts' first transistor radio, although it was a "one-off" produced privately and presented to H.M. The Queen as a gift from the Radio Industry Council.

Ross [Hong Kong] (*dist.* **Benross Trading Co.Ltd.**), 29-33 Everton Brow, Liverpool 3. *Transistor Production Run 1964.*

2-Band. 6tr, M/LW pocket portable. £3.11s.1d. including P.T. (nett trade price per item. Carton of 24, less 2s.0d. plus P.T. each). 1964.

International 3-Band. 7tr, S/M/LW port. 1964.

Jubilee RE777. 7tr, MW portable. 1964.

Orion. 6tr, M/LW pocket portable. £4.12s.9d. including P.T. (nett trade price per item. Carton of 24, less 2s.0d. plus P.T. each). 1964.

Supreme. 6tr, MW pocket portable. £2.11s.6d. including P.T. (nett trade price per item. Carton of 24, less 2s.0d. plus P.T. each). 1964.

Royal (*see Zenith, page 281*).

Saba (Saba Electronics Ltd.), 3 Eden Grove, London N7. *Transistor Production Run 1964-66.*

Transatlantic. 10tr, S/MW/FM portable/car radio. £45.3s.0d. including P.T. 1964. (Bracket available for in-car use, £7.7s.0d. optional extra, mains adaptor, £7.0s.0d. optional extra).

Transeuropa I. 12tr, S/M/LW/FM portable/car radio. £51.9s.0d. including P.T. 1964. (Bracket available for in-car use, £8.8s.0d. extra, mains adaptor, £7.0s.0d. extra).

Transeuropa II. 10tr, M/LW/FM portable/car radio. £42 including P.T. 1964. (Bracket available for in-car use, £7.7s.0d. extra, mains adaptor, £7.0s.0d. extra).

Transeuropa III. 10tr, M/LW/FM portable/car radio. £42.11s.6d. including P.T. 1966. (Bracket available for in-car use, £7.7s.0d. extra, mains adaptor, £7.0s.0d. extra).

Sagaya [Japan] (*dist.* **Cromptons [Manchester] Ltd.**), 29 Minshull Street, Manchester 1. *Transistor Production Run 1960-61.*

STR66 (Mascot). 6tr, MW pocket portable. £8.4s.0d. including P.T. November 1960. (Uses 3 x U12 batteries).

STR67 (Mascot). 6tr, MW pocket portable. £8.4s.0d. including P.T. November 1960. (As STR66, but using PP3 battery).

Winston. 6tr, MW pocket portable. £8 including P.T. 1961.

Sakura [Japan] (*dist.* **Marubeni-Iida Co. Ltd.**), Moor House, London Wall, London EC2. *Transistor Production Run 1963.*

TR614. 6tr, MW pocket portable. £4.9s.6d. including P.T. 1963.

Sankoh (*dist.* **D.Tandon [London] Ltd.**), 244 Edgware Road, London W2. *Transistor Production Run 1966.*

SP8A. 8tr, MW portable/car radio. £18.15s.0d. including P.T. 1966. (Bracket for in-car use).

Sanyo [Japan] (*dist.* **Marubeni-Iida Co. Ltd.**), Moor House, London Wall, London EC2. From 1965, (**Sanyo Service & Sales**), 23 Savage Gardens, London EC3. From 1966, at 164 Clapham Park Road, London SW4. From 1971, (**Sanyo Marubeni [U.K.] Ltd.**), Bushey Mill Lane, Watford, Hertfordshire. (The numerical prefix [usually] refers to the number of transistors used). *Transistor Production Run 1962-72+.*

104850 (Cantabile). 10tr, S/M/LW/FM portable. £23.2s.0d. including P.T. 1967.

6C11. 6tr, MW personal portable. £8.9s.3d. plus £2.15s.9d. P.T. May 1962.

6C18. 6tr, MW personal portable. £8.9s.3d. plus £2.15s.9d. P.T. April 1963.

6C64D. 6tr, MW pocket portable. £5.19s.6d. including P.T. 1965.

6C302. 6tr (integrated circuit), MW pocket portable. £6.15s.0d. including P.T. 1970. (Complete with snap-on carrying strap).

6C318. 6tr, MW pocket portable. £8.8s.0d. including P.T. 1964.

6C640 (Solo). 6tr, MW pocket portable. £6.1s.2d. including P.T. 1967.

6L610 (Mirabelle). 6tr, M/LW portable. £7.1s.5d. including P.T. 1967.

6L714 (Sandown). 6tr, M/LW portable. £6.17s.6d. plus £1.4s.2d. P.T. 1967.

6LO8. 6tr, M/LW portable. £14.14s.0d. including P.T. April 1963.

6LP4. 6tr, M/LW personal portable. £13.1s.8d. plus £3.18s.4d. P.T. May 1962.

6LP11. 6tr, M/LW pocket portable. £12.12s.0d. including P.T. 1963.

6LP19. 6tr, M/LW portable. £12.12s.0d. including P.T. August 1963.

6LP25. 6tr, M/LW portable. £19.19s.0d. including P.T. 1964. (Rechargeable battery also available).

7C305. 7tr, MW pocket portable. £6.0s.3d. plus £1.1s.2d. P.T. 1966.

7L706 (Society). 7tr, M/LW portable. £10.19s.6d. including P.T. 1965.

7L706 (Mk.II). 7tr, M/LW portable. £9.10s.5d. plus £2.0s.7d. Purchase Tax. 1968.

7L718E. 7tr, M/LW pocket portable. £7.17s.6d. including P.T. 1965.

8F801. 8tr, M/FM portable. £9.9s.2d. plus £1.13s.4d. P.T. 1966.

8L742E. 8tr, M/LW portable. £10.13s.8d. plus £1.18s.4d. P.T. 1967.

8LP24. 9tr, 2S/M/LW portable. £26.5s.0d. including P.T. 1963.

8LP39. 8tr, S/M/LW portable. £18.18s.0d. including P.T. (Rechargeable battery also available). 1964.

8MP20. 8tr, S/MW personal portable. £15.15s.0d. including P.T. August 1963.

8SP2. 8tr, S/MW personal portable. £14.14s.0d. including P.T. April 1963.

8SP22. 9tr, S/MW portable. £18.18s.0d. including P.T. August 1963.

8SP25. 8tr, S/MW portable. £18.18s.0d. including P.T. 1964. (Rechargeable battery also available).

8U604E. 8tr, S/M/LW portable. £18.18s.0d. including P.T. 1965.

8U605E. 8tr, S/M/LW portable. £15.7s.8d. plus £2.14s.3d. P.T. 1966.

8U743. 8tr, S/M/LW portable. £12.18s.2d. plus £2.6s.4d. P.T. 1967.

8XP24. 9tr, 3S/MW portable. £26.5s.0d. including P.T. 1963.

9F820. 9tr, MW portable. £9.17s.8d. plus £2.2s.4d. P.T. 1968. (Mains adaptor, £15.95p. extra).

10F803. 7tr, MW/FM pocket portable. £13.15s.0d. including P.T. 1970.

10F806. 7tr, MW/FM portable. £15.95p. including P.T. 1971. (Mains adaptor, £15.95p. extra).

10F811. 7tr, MW/FM pocket portable. £14.95p. including P.T. 1971.

10F892. 7tr, MW/FM portable. £10.5s.0d. including P.T. 1970.

10F893. 7tr, MW/FM mains/battery portable. £14.15s 0d. including P.T. 1970.

10FA406. 7tr, MW/FM mains table model/clock radio. £36.15s.0d. including P.T. 1970.

10FAT40. 7tr, MW/FM mains table model/digital clock radio. £33.15s.0d. including P.T. 1970.

10G831 (Colorano). 10tr, M/LW/FM portable. 12.4s.3d. plus £2.3s.2d. P.T. 1967.

10G850. 10tr, S/M/LW/FM portable. £19.11s.8d. plus £3.10s.4d. P.T. 1967.

10G888L. 10tr, S/M/LW/FM portable. £17.12s.2d. plus £3.2s.3d. P.T. 1966.

10G895LE. 7tr, M/LW/FM portable. £19.95p. including P.T. 1971. (Mains adaptor, extra).

10HA670L. M/LW/FM stereo mains/battery portable. 1972. ('Stereocast' headphone adaptor, extra).

10HA896. 7tr, S/M/LW/FM £26.15s.0d. including P.T. 1970. (Mains adaptor, extra).

10H850. 10tr, S/M/LW/FM portable. £21.0s.1d. plus £4.9s.11d. Purchase Tax. 1968.

10LP10. 10tr, S/M/LW portable. £22.14s.0d. plus £6.16s.0d. P.T. May 1962.

10S81. 10tr, M/LW/FM mains table model. 1972.

10SP10N (Transcontinental). 10tr, 2S/MW portable. £22.6s.4d. plus £6.13s.8d. P.T. May 1962. (Came complete with tuning meter).

10UP10. 10tr, 2S/MW portable. £19.15s.0d. including P.T. 1970.

12H864. 12tr, S/M/LW/FM portable/car radio. £32.19s.9d. plus £7.15s.3d. Purchase Tax. 1969. (For home, outdoor or in-car use).

13GAB77 (Transworld). 13tr, S/M/FM mains/battery portable. £38.15s.0d. including P.T. 1970.

14H636 (Sharon). 14tr, S/M/LW/FM portable. £26.5s.4d. plus £4.14s.2d. P.T. 1967.

15H860. 15tr, 4S/M/LW/FM portable. £50.13s.0d. plus £11.5s.3d. P.T. 1968. (Complete with tuning meter. Mains adaptor, extra).

17H815 (Transworld). 17tr, 3S/M/LW/FM portable/car radio. £53.7s.7d. plus £9.8s.7d. P.T. 1967. (Complete with tuning meter. Mains adaptor, £6.6s.0d. extra. For home, outdoor or in-car use).

18H815. 18tr, 3S/M/LW/FM mains/battery portable/car radio. £56.5s.3d. plus £13.4s.9d. P.T. 1969. (For home, outdoor or in-car use. Complete with tuning meter and built-in mains adaptor).

21FA454. 18tr, MW/FM stereo mains table model. £79.15s.0d. including P.T. 1970. (Separate matching loudspeakers).

38U743E (Stratford). 8tr, S/M/LW portable. £15.4s.6d. including P.T. 1967.

106A896. 7tr, S/M/LW/FM portable. £19.15s.0d. including P.T. 1970. (Mains adaptor, extra).

AFT1. 14tr, MW/FM portable. £26.18s.8d. plus £8.1s.4d. P.T. May 1962.

AFT2. 12tr, S/M/LW portable. £37.17s.9d. plus £11.7s.3d. P.T. May 1962.

AFT6. 9tr, M/LW/FM portable. £21.10s.6d. including P.T. 1963.

AFT8. 9tr, M/LW/FM portable. £27.6s.0d. including P.T. 1963.

AFT9L. 9tr, M/LW/FM portable. £25.4s.0d. including P.T. 1963.

AFT9S. 9tr, S/MW/FM portable. 1963.

RM5340. M/LW/FM stereo mains/battery table model/clock radio. 1972. ('Stereocast' headphone adaptor, extra).

RP1711. 6tr, MW portable/cube radio in the form of a die. £7.95p. including P.T. 1972. (Available in red, blue or green).

RP5210. MW/FM stereo portable. £11.75p. including P.T. 1972. ('Stereocast' headphone adaptor, extra).

RP5310. M/LW/FM stereo portable. £16.50p. including P.T. 1972. ('Stereocast' headphone adaptor, extra).

RP7412. M/LW/FM stereo mains/battery portable. £23.95p. including P.T. 1972. ('Stereocast' headphone adaptor, extra).

RP8110. M/LW/FM stereo mains/battery portable. £29.75p. including P.T. 1972. ('Stereocast' headphone adaptor, extra).

VH26 (Jet Set). 9tr, MW/Aircraft Band portable. £14.9s.6d. plus £2.11s.2d. P.T. 1967.

Satellite [Japan] (dist. Satellite Electronics Ltd.), 70/72 Old Street, London EC1. *Transistor Production Run 1968-72+*.

010. 6tr, MW pocket portable. £2.2s.2d. plus 10s.4d. P.T. 1969.

014. 6tr, MW pocket portable. £2.17s.6d. including P.T. 1970.

7. 7tr, MW pocket portable. £2.9s.11d. including P.T. 1968.

10. 10tr, MW/FM portable. £8.19s.6d. including P.T. 1968.

15F7. 10tr, M/LW/FM mains/battery portable. £12.90p. including P.T. 1971.

101. 6tr, MW pocket portable. £2.90p. including P.T. 1971.

134L. 13tr, M/LW/FM portable. £11.17s.0d. including P.T. 1968.

153L. 12tr, 2S/M/FM mains/battery portable. £24.9s.0d. including P.T. 1968. (Built-in mains adaptor).

605. 6tr, MW pocket portable. £2.80p. including P.T. 1971.

700. 8tr, M/LW portable. £5.80p. including P.T. 1971.

747. 8tr, M/LW portable. £8.19s.6d. including P.T. 1970.

888. 8tr, M/LW portable. £8.90p. including P.T. 1971.

1000. 6tr, MW pocket portable. £2.0s.3d. plus 9s.8d. P.T. 1969.

5000. 8tr, M/LW mains/battery portable. £8.90p. including P.T. 1971.

AFM/2. 10tr, MW/FM portable. £7.40p. including P.T. 1971.

AM/FM. 10tr, MW/FM portable. £6.16s.8d. plus £1.13s.4d. P.T. 1969.

AS117. 10tr, MW/FM mains/battery portable. £11.50p. including P.T. 1971.

F210. 10tr, MW/FM portable. £7.1s.5d. plus £1.14s.7d. P.T. 1969.

P300 (Twin Speaker). 10tr, S/M/LW portable. £11.17s.0d. including P.T. 1968.

SE500. 8tr, M/LW portable. 1972.

Apollo. 6tr, MW pocket portable. £2.6s.4d. plus 11s.2d. P.T. 1969.

Avenger. 8tr, M/LW portable. £5.90p. including P.T. 1971.

Concord. 8tr, M/LW portable. £4.13s.6d. including P.T. 1968.

Silver Star. 8tr, M/LW portable. £5.5s.0d. including P.T. 1968.

Magnasonic. 9tr, M/LW portable. £4.19s.6d. including P.T. 1968.

Melody Master. 8tr, M/LW portable. £5.5s.0d. including P.T. 1968.

Rhythm Master. 10tr, S/M/LW portable. £9.19s.6d. including P.T. 1968.

Stingray. 10tr, S/M/LW portable. £15.60p. including P.T. 1971.

Supersonic. 8tr, M/LW portable. £5.15s.6d. including P.T. 1968.

Schaub Lorenz [West Germany] (dist. Winter Trading Co. Ltd.), 95-99 Ladbroke Grove, London W11. *Transistor Production Run 1962-63*.

T20A (Amigo). 9tr, M/LW/FM portable. £30.19s.6d. including P.T. 1962.

T30K (Kolibri). 9tr, M/LW/FM portable. £26.5s.0d. including P.T. 1962.

T30T (Touring). 9tr, S/M/LW/FM portable. £47.5s.0d. including P.T. 1962.

T30W (Weekend). 9tr, M/LW/FM portable. £40.19s.0d. including P.T. 1962.

T40 (Polo). 9tr, M/LW/FM portable. £30.9s.0d. including P.T. 1963.

T40 (Touring). 9tr, S/M/LW/FM portable/car radio. £47.5s.0d. including P.T. 1963. (Bracket available for in-car use).

T40 (Weekend). 9tr, M/LW/FM portable. £36.15s.0d. including P.T. 1963.

T101 (Camping). 8tr, 2S/M/LW portable. £28.7s.0d. including P.T. 1963.

T103 (Camping). 8tr, 3S/MW portable. £28.7s.0d. including P.T. 1963.

T203C (Camping). 8tr, 3S/MW portable. £30.19s.6d. including P.T. 1962.

Schneider [West Germany] (dist. Light & Sound Ltd.), 414 High Road, Chiswick, W4. From 1963, 125 Gunnersbury Lane, Acton, W3. *Transistor Production Run 1961-64*.

Bip. 6tr, M/LW personal portable. £12.4s.6d. plus £3.10s.6d. P.T. December 1961.

Caprice. 6tr, M/LW personal port. £12.4s.6d. plus £3.10s.6d. P.T. December 1961.

Cithare. 7tr, S/M/LW portable. £22.11s.6d. including P.T. 1963.

Cithare FM. 9tr, M/LW/FM portable. £30.19s.6d. including P.T. 1964.

Fifre C84 (FM). M/LW/FM portable/car radio. £24.3s.0d. including P.T. 1963. (For home, outdoor or in-car use).

Fifre C85. 8tr, M/LW/FM portable. £24.3s.0d. including P.T. 1963.

Fifre D84. 6tr, M/LW portable. £13.2s.6d. including P.T. August 1963.

Fifre E84 (LUX). 6tr, M/LW portable/car radio. £15.4s.6d. including P.T. 1963. (Marketed with special reference to Radio Luxembourg on 208 metres. For home, outdoor or in-car use).

Lutin. 6tr, M/LW portable. £17.18s.6d. plus £5.3.s.6d. P.T. December 1961.

Puck. 6tr, M/LW portable. £14.5s.3d. plus £4.2s.3d, P.T. December 1961.

Surf. 6tr, M/LW/FM portable. £18.7s.6d. including P.T. 1964.

Tabourin FM. 10tr, S/M/LW/FM portable. £41.9s.6d. including P.T. 1964.

Troubadour. 7tr, S/M/LW portable. £24.9s.0d. plus £7.1s.0d. P.T. Dec. 1961.

Troubadour FM. 7tr, M/LW/FM portable. £37.5s.6d. including P.T. 1964.

Sharp [Japan] (*dist.* **Wholesale Supplies [Swinton] Ltd.**), 16 Worsley Road, Manchester. From 1967, (**Sharp Sales & Service**) of same address. From 1971, (**Sharp Electronics [U.K.] Ltd.**), 48 Derby Street, Manchester 8. *Transistor Production Run 1961-72+.*

1CX20B. 5tr, MW/FM portable. £14 including P.T. 1971.

AXL329. 7tr, M/LW pocket portable. £10.10s.0d. including P.T. 1963.

BHL354. 7tr, M/LW portable. £18.18s.0d. including P.T. April 1963. (Mains adaptor extra).

BP100. 6tr, MW pocket portable. £7.17s.6d. including P.T. 1964.

BP101. 6tr, MW pocket portable. £4.1s.6d. plus 14s.3d. P.T. 1967.

BP102A. 6tr, MW pocket portable. £5.5s.0d. including P.T. 1970.

BP110. 6tr, MW pocket portable. £5.5s.0d. including P.T. 1970.

BP200. 6tr, MW pocket portable. £10.10s.0d. including P.T. 1970.

BP322. 7tr, MW pocket portable (powder compact/radio, 3 1/2" diameter with circular mirror). £9.10s.0d. including P.T. April 1963.

BP460. 6tr, MW pocket portable. £8.18s.6d. including P.T. April 1963.

BPC12. 7tr, MW portable/clock radio. £13.10s.0d. including P.T. 1970.

BX326. 10tr, S/MW portable. 1962.

BX327. 8tr, S/MW personal portable. £15.2s.0d. plus £4.7s.6d. P.T. October 1961. (Mains adaptor extra).

BX371. October 1961.

BX381. 8tr, M/LW personal portable. £18.5s.8d. plus £5.5s.7d. Purchase Tax. October 1961.

BX489. 8tr, S/MW portable. £15.15s.0d. including P.T. 1964. (Mains adaptor optional extra).

BX6403. October 1961.

BXC12L. 6tr, M/LW portable. £18.0s.0d. including P.T. 1970.

BXL184. 6tr, M/LW pocket portable. £8.0s.0d. including P.T. 1970.

BXL372. 6tr, M/LW pocket portable. £11.11s.0d. including P.T. 1963.

BXL377. 7tr, M/LW personal portable. £11.0s.6d. including P.T. 1964.

BXL403. 8tr, S/M/LW portable. £22.5s.3d. plus £6.8s.6d. P.T. 1961.

BXL468. 6tr, M/LW portable. £13.13s.0d. including P.T. 1964. (Mains adaptor extra).

BYL14. 8tr, S/M/LW portable. £20.9s.6d. including P.T. 1965. (Mains adaptor extra).

BYL488. 8tr, S/M/LW portable. £24.3s.0d. including P.T. 1964. (Complete with battery/tuning meter. Mains adaptor available).

BZ23. 13tr, 3S/MW portable. £26.4s.9d. plus £4.12s.8d. P.T. 1966. (Complete with battery/tuning meter).

BZ480. 8tr, 3S/MW portable. 1963.

BZ490. 9tr, 3S/MW portable. £23.19s.6d. plus £3.17s.6d. P.T. 1963.

BZL606. 10tr, 3S/MW portable. £29.8s.0d. including P.T. 1965. (Complete with battery/tuning meter. Mains adaptor extra).

BZL480. 8tr, 2S/M/LW portable. £32.11s.0d. including P.T. 1963.

BZL490. 9tr, 2S/M/LW portable. £23.17s.0d. plus £6.17s.6d. P.T. 1961.

BZL580. 8tr, 2S/M/LW portable. £30.19s.0d. including P.T. 1964.

BZL606. 10tr, 2S/M/LW portable. £26.15s.6d. including P.T. 1964.

FMA22. 10tr, MW/FM mains/battery table model. £22.7s.1d. including P.T. 1967.

FMA31. 10tr, MW/FM mains/battery table model. £29.16s.2d. including P.T. 1967.

FV16. 13tr, S/M/LW/FM mains/battery portable. £48.75p. including P.T. 1972.

FV507. 12tr, S/M/LW/FM mains/battery portable. £33.0s.0d. including P.T. 1970.

FV1700 (Intercontinental). 17tr, 3S/M/LW/FM portable/car radio. £72.9s.0d. including P.T. 1965. (Complete with world-time chart and beat frequency oscillator. Bracket available for in-car use).

FV1710. 18tr, 3S/M/LW/FM mains/battery portable/car radio. £59.13s.9d. plus £12.15s.3d. P.T. 1968. (Complete with built-in mains adaptor. For home, outdoor or in-car use).

FV1800. 17tr, 3S/M/LW/FM mains/battery portable. £65.0s.0d. including Purchase Tax. 1970.

FW26L. 10tr, S/M/LW/FM portable/car radio. £32.11s.6d. plus £5.14s.11d. P.T. 1966. (Bracket available for in-car use. Mains adaptor extra).

FW401. 8tr, S/M/LW/FM mains/battery portable. £30 including P.T. 1972.

FW503. 12tr, S/M/LW/FM portable. £34.13s.0d. including P.T. 1964.

FW509. 10tr, S/M/LW/FM portable. £23.12p. including P.T. 1971.

FX28D. 11tr, M/FM portable/car radio. £25.0s.0d. including P.T. 1970. (Bracket available for in-car use).

FX109. 10tr, MW/FM pocket portable. £17.17s.0d. including P.T. 1964.

FX113. 9tr, M/FM portable. £14.9s.6d. plus £2.11s.2d. P.T. 1966.

FX180. 9tr, MW/FM portable. £14.10s.0d. including P.T. 1970.

FX183. 9tr, MW/FM portable. £14.10s.0d. including P.T. 1970.

FX184. 9tr, MW/FM portable. £11.0s.0d. including P.T. 1970.

FX184AU. 8tr, MW/Aircraft Band portable. £10.95p. including P.T. 1972.

FX404. October 1961.

FX502. 10tr, MW/FM portable. £24.3s.0d. including P.T. 1963.

FXC12. 9tr, MW/FM portable/mechanical clock radio. £19.19s.0d. including P.T. 1970.

FY25. 10tr, M/LW/FM portable/car radio. £29.8s.0d. including P.T. 1965. (Bracket available for in-car use. Mains adaptor, optional extra).

FY27L. 10tr, M/LW/FM portable/car radio. £21.10s.0d. including P.T. 1970. (Bracket for in-car mounting, extra).

FY178L. 10tr, M/LW/FM portable. £17.0s.0d. including P.T. 1970.

FY301L. 7tr, M/LW/FM portable. £18.60p. including P.T. 1972.

FYL30D. 11tr, M/LW/FM portable/car radio. £26.0s.0d. including Purchase Tax. 1970. (Bracket for in-car mounting, £6.17s.6d., optional extra).

FYL119. 10tr, M/LW/FM portable. £27.6s.0d. including P.T. 1965.

FYL151. 10tr, M/LW/FM portable. £29.8s.0d. including P.T. 1965. (Mains adaptor extra).

FYL414. 10tr, M/LW/FM portable. £29.8s.0d. including P.T. 1963.

FYL512. 10tr, M/LW/FM portable. £28.7s.0d. including P.T. 1964.

ICX20B. 5tr, MW/FM portable. £15.55p. including P.T. 1972.

LY412. 10tr, S/M/LW portable. £30.9s.0d. including P.T. 1963.

TRL237. 6tr, M/LW personal portable. £13.10s.3d. plus £3.18s.0d. P.T. 1961.

UW121. October 1961.

Shira [Hong Kong] (*dist.* **Winter Trading Co. Ltd.**), 95-99 Ladbroke Grove, London W11. *Transistor Production Run 1964-72+.*

1. 6tr, MW pocket portable. £3.9s.9d. including P.T. 1964.

2. 6tr, M/LW pocket portable. £5.4s.8d. including P.T. 1964.

3. 9tr, S/M/LW portable. £13.0s.3d. plus £2.6s.6d. P.T. 1966.

650. MW/FM pocket portable. £6.30p. including Purchase Tax. 1972. (Wrist strap radio).

670. MW/FM portable. £6.50p. including P.T. 1972.

707. 7tr, S/M/LW portable. £8.11s.0d. plus £1.11s.4d. P.T. 1966.

ST531. 8tr, M/LW pocket portable. £4.8s.7d. including P.T. 1970.

County. MW/FM table model. £9.95p. including P.T. 1971.

Euston. 7tr, M/LW portable. £6.19s.6d. including P.T. 1964.

Go Go. 6tr, M/LW portable. £4.95p. including P.T. 1972.

Imperial. 6tr, MW pocket portable. £3.3s.6d. including P.T. 1964.

Jumbo. 16tr, MW/FM/Aircraft Band mains/battery portable. 1970.

Micro. MW miniature portable. £4.25p. including P.T. 1972.

Nobility. 8tr, MW pocket portable. £10.11s.10d. including P.T. 1970.

Poodle. MW portable (*"fluffy dog shape radio"*). £4.55p. inc. P.T. 1972.

Shira-8 (P4108). 8tr, MW pocket portable. £3.3s.0d. including P.T. 1970.

Shira-FM. 10tr, MW/FM pocket portable. £6.2s.4d. including P.T. 1970.

Shira de Luxe. 10tr, M/LW portable. £5.12s.1d. including P.T. 1970.

Shirabell. 14tr, MW/FM mains/battery portable. £11.9s.6d. including P.T. 1970.

Shiralarm (CTR620). 6tr, M/LW table model/clock radio. £11.4s.3d. including P.T. 1970.

Shirateen (PP63). 6tr, MW pocket portable. £3.3s.0d. including P.T. 1970.

Shirawake. 6tr, MW port. £8.1s.2d. inc.P.T. 1970.

Worldmaster. 2S/M/LW/FM/Aircraft Band/Marine Band mains/battery port. £29.50p. inc. P.T. 1972. (Includes time zone chart).

Shopertunities (Shopertunities Ltd.), Holborn, London WC1.

De-luxe Transistor Radio/Spice Rack. 6tr, MW. £3.99p. inc. P.T. 1972. (Wall-mounted. Complete with 12 glass jars for herbs & spices. *See fig.816, p.208.* A similar model was also sold by Binatone).

Shorrock (Shorrock Developments Ltd.), 51 Preston New Road, Blackburn, Lancashire. *Transistor Production Run 1964-66.*

Clubman. 10tr, M/LW/Aircraft Band portable. £28 including P.T. 1964.

Mark V. 10tr, M/LW/Aircraft Band portable. £36 including P.T. 1964.

Mark VI. 10tr, M/LW/Aircraft Band portable. £31.2s.3d. plus £5.12s.9d. P.T. 1966.

Monitor. 11tr, M/LW/Aircraft Band port. £42 inc. P.T. 1964. (External speaker, extra).

Siemens [West Germany] **(dist. Lonor Ltd.),** 1 Maddox Street, London W1. *Transistor Production Run 1959.*

RT10. 8tr, M/LW/FM port. £30.9s.0d. inc.P.T. 1959.

T2. £19.19s.0d. including P.T. 1959.

Silver (J.J. Silber Ltd.), 11 Northburgh St., EC1. *Transistor Production Run 1970-71.*

9F-155. 9tr, M/LW/FM portable. £12.97p. including P.T. 1971.

10F-255. 10tr, S/MW/FM portable. £15.19s.6d. including P.T. 1970.

10F-255L. 10tr, M/LW/FM port. £15.19s.6d. inc. P.T. 1970.

10F-455. 10tr, S/M/LW port. £24.94p. inc.P.T. 1971.

14F-911L. 14tr, 2S/M/LW/FM portable. £37.12s.6d. including P.T. 1970.

15AF-29B. 15tr, 3S/M/LW/FM portable. £52.10s.0d. including P.T. 1970.

Silvertone [Hong Kong] **(dist. W.Wood & Son Ltd.),** Kelvin Works, Power Road, London W4. *Transistor Production Run 1964.*

T18. 6tr, M/LW port. £17.17s.0d. inc.P.T. 1964.

Sinclair (Sinclair Radionics Ltd.), 69 Histon Road, Cambs. From 1967, 22 Newmarket Road, Cambs. *Transistor Production Run 1958-69+.*

Micro-6. 3tr, MW miniature portable (kit). £2.19s.6d inc. earpiece and full set of parts. 1964. ('Transrista' nylon strap to convert the Micro-6 into a wrist-radio, price 7s.6d. Amplifier kit, model TR.750, for use with Micro-6, price £1.19s.6d. *See also p.298*).

Micro FM. 7tr, FM miniature portable (kit). £5.19s.6d. complete with earpiece and full set of parts. 1965. (*See also p.298*).

Micro-Midget. 3tr, MW miniature portable (circuit design/article). November 1958. (This simple receiver, less than half the size of a matchbox, was designed by Clive Sinclair for readers of *Practical Wireless* magazine, featuring on pages 712-715 of the November 1958 issue, and also on the colourful cover. It could be built for less than £4 using components bought from surplus stores such as G.W. Smiths Ltd. of Lisle Street in London. *See fig.952, p.298*).

Micromatic Mk.I. 3tr, MW miniature portable (kit). £2.19s.6d. inc. earpiece and full set of parts. 1967. (Ready-built and tested £3.19s.6d. *See fig.955, p.298*).

Micromatic Mk.II. 2tr, MW miniature portable (kit). £2.9s.6d. complete with earpiece and full set of parts. 1969. (Ready-built and tested £2.19s.6d. Outwardly identical to the 3tr version of 1967, but with a modified 2-transistor circuit, and the earpiece socket on the right hand side instead of the left. *See fig.956, p.298*).

Slimline. 2tr, MW miniature portable (kit). £2.9s.6d. complete with earpiece and full set of parts. Feb. 1963. (*See figs.953 and 954, p.298*).

Sobell (Radio & Allied Industries Ltd.), Langley Park, Slough, Bucks. *Transistor Production Run 1961-70.*

S303BT. 7tr, M/LW personal portable. £10.9s.7d. plus £3.13s.11d. P.T. April 1961.

S304BT (Playmate). 6tr, M/LW portable. £11.5s.1d. plus £3.19s.5d. P.T. April 1961. (Chassis identical to McMichael M104BT).

S305BT (Traveller). 6tr, M/LW portable. £13.11s.8d. plus £4.15s.10d. Purchase Tax. April 1961.

S306BT (Baby Grand). 6tr, M/LW pocket portable (pre-set on LW for the B.B.C.'s popular Light Programme). £11.0s.6d. including Purchase Tax. November 1961. (The S306BT's chassis was identical to the G.E.C. G806).

S308BT. 6tr, M/LW portable. £11.8s.1d. plus £3.5s.11d. P.T. April 1962.

S310. 6tr, M/LW portable. £12.4s.5d. plus £3.10s.7d. P.T. April 1962.

S312. 6tr, M/LW portable. £13.2s.6d. plus P.T. September 1962.

S314. 6tr, S/M/LW portable/car radio. £13.13s.0d. including P.T. January 1963. (For home, outdoor or in-car use).

S316. 9tr, M/LW/FM portable. £19.8s.6d. including P.T. 1964.

S319. 7tr, S/M/LW portable. £17.6s.6d. including P.T. 1964.

S322. 8tr, M/LW mains/battery portable/car radio. £23.2s.0d. including P.T. 1967. (Complete with built-in mains adaptor. For home, outdoor or in-car use. Bandspread tuning between 185-220 metres, for Radio Luxembourg. Chassis identical to the G.E.C. G832).

S324 (Fidelio). 7tr, S/M/LW portable. £15.16s.10d. plus £2.19s.0d. P.T. 1965. (Bandspread tuning between 176-211 metres, for Radio Luxembourg).

S325. 7tr, S/M/LW portable. £13.13s.0d. including P.T. 1964. (Bandspread tuning between 183-211 metres, for Radio Luxembourg).

S327 (Duplex Autotune). 7tr, M/LW portable (pre-set station selection). £14.18s.7d. plus £2.12s.9d. P.T. 1966. (Bandspread tuning between 185-222 metres, for Radio Luxembourg. Chassis identical to the G.E.C. G827 and the Masteradio D527).

S332. 8tr, M/LW mains/battery portable/car radio. £23.2s.0d. incwith earpiece and full set of partsluding P.T. 1967. (Built-in mains adaptor. For home, outdoor or in-car use).

S334. 10tr, M/LW/FM portable/car radio. £19.19s.0d. including P.T. 1967. (For home, outdoor or in-car use. Chassis identical to the G.E.C. G834).

S336. 10tr, 2S/M/LW/FM portable/car radio. £42.13s.0d. including P.T. 1970. (For home, outdoor or in-car use).

S337. 10tr, M/LW/FM portable/car radio. £30.18s.0d. including P.T. 1970. (For home, outdoor or in-car use).

S338. 9tr (5 transistors plus an encapsulated audio stage module containing 4 transistors and 1 diode), M/LW/FM portable/car radio. £15.15s.0d. including P.T. 1969. (For home, outdoor or in-car use. Chassis identical to the G.E.C. G838).

S1541. 11tr, 3S/M/LW/FM portable. £48.10s.0d. including P.T. 1970.

ST301. 6tr, M/LW battery portable. £11.18s.6d. plus £3.16s.6d. P.T. August 1960. (Chassis identical to the McMichael MT102).

Socradel (dist. Paschkes & Co. Ltd), 40 Craven Road, London W2. *Transistor Production Run 1963.*

Major Metropolitan. 7tr, S/M/LW portable. £34.2s.6d. including P.T. 1963.

Major Overseas. 7tr, 3S/MW portable. £36.4s.6d. including P.T. 1963.

Meteor. 7tr, S/M/LW portable. £30.19s.6d. including P.T. 1963.

Minor Overseas. 7tr, 2S/MW portable. £19.19s.0d. including P.T. 1963.

Senior Export. 7tr, S/M/LW portable. £25.4s.0d. including P.T. 1963.

Senior Metropolitan. 7tr, M/LW portable. £23.2s.0d. including P.T. 1963.

Senior Overseas. 7tr, 3S/MW portable. £26.15s.6d. including P.T. 1963.

Sonolor [France] **(dist. Denham & Morley Ltd.),** 173-175 Cleveland Street, London W1. *Transistor Production Run 1961-71.*

62. 6tr, S/M/LW portable. £17.17s.9d. plus £5.14s.9d. P.T. May 1961.

62/30C. 7tr, 3S/M/LW portable. £18.5s.6d. plus £5.17s.6d. P.T. June 1961.

62/35. 6tr, 3S/M/LW portable. £18.5s.6d. plus £5.17s.6d. P.T. June 1961.

Clipper 304. 7tr, S/M/LW portable. £20.9s.6d. including P.T. 1963.

Clipper Continental 304/30C. 7tr, 3S/M/LW portable. £22.1s.0d. including P.T. 1965.

Club 104. 6tr, M/LW portable. £14.14s.0d. including P.T. 1965.

Continent. 9tr, 4S/M/LW mains/battery portable. £35.02p. including P.T. 1971.

Croisiere 504. 7tr, 2S/M/LW portable. £28.7s.0d. including P.T. 1965.

Derby. 6tr, M/LW portable. £11.9s.0d. plus £2.0s.5d. P.T. 1967.

Electra 7. 7tr, S/M/LW portable. £20.7s.3d. plus £5.17s.9d. P.T. 1961.

Electra (Continental). 7tr, 3S/M/LW portable. £20.15s.6d. plus £6 P.T. 1961.

Flash 64. 7tr, S/M/LW portable. £23.12s.6d. including P.T. 1963.

Gouverneur. 10tr, 2S/M/LW/FM portable/car radio. £29.0s.0d. plus £5.1s.3d. P.T. 1966. (For home, portable or in-car use).

Jet 64. 6tr, M/LW portable. £14.3s.6d. including P.T. July 1963.

Plein Air 7. 7tr, S/M/LW portable. £17.18s.6d. plus £5.3s.6d. P.T. 1961.

Plein Air 63. 7tr, S/M/LW portable. £22.1s.0d. including P.T. 1962.

Plein Air 64. 7tr, S/M/LW portable. £22.1s.0d. including P.T. 1963.

Plein Air (Continental). 8tr, 3S/M/LW port. £18.14s.9d. plus £5.8s.3d. P.T. 1961.

Plein Feu. 7tr, 4S/M/LW portable/car radio. £20.7s.2d. plus £3.11s.11d. P.T. 1966. (For home, portable or in-car use).

Racing. 6tr, M/LW portable. £15.15s.0d. including P.T. September 1962.

Racing 64. 6tr, M/LW portable. £15.15s.0d. including P.T. 1963.

Racing Continental. 7tr, S/M/LW portable. £26.15s.0d. including P.T. February 1963.

Rhythm 64. 9tr, M/LW/FM portable. £25.4s.0d. including P.T. 1963.

Selection 63. 9tr, S/M/LW portable. £27.6s.0d. including P.T. 1962.

Selection 64. 7tr, S/M/LW portable. £26.5s.0d. including P.T. July 1963.

Selection Ambassador. 12tr, S/M/LW/FM portable. £30.9s.0d. including P.T. July 1963.

Selection Continental. 9tr, 3S/M/LW portable. £28.7s.0d. inc. P.T. July 1963.

Solo. 6tr, 2S/M/LW table model. £14.0s.6d. plus £2.9s.6d. P.T. 1967.

Touring 604. 10tr, S/M/LW/FM portable. £30.9s.0d. including P.T. 1965.

Trident 204/20C. 6tr, 2S/M/LW portable. £17.17s.0d. including P.T. 1965.

Univers. 9tr, 2S/M/LW/FM mains/battery portable. £45.21p. including P.T. 1971.

Sony [Japan] (*dist.* **Tellux Ltd.**), Brunel Road, London W3. From 1962, at Avenue Works, Chelmsford Road, Romford, Essex. From 1964, (*dist.* **St. Aldate Warehouse Ltd.**), Innsworth Lane, Gloucester. From 1965, (*dist.* **Debenhams Electrical & Radio Distribution Co. Ltd.**), Eastbrook Road, Gloucester. From 1966, (*dist.* **Sony U.K. Sales Division**), Debenhams Electrical & Radio Distribution, Eastbrook Road, Gloucester**.** From 1968, (**Sony U.K. Ltd.**), Ascot Road, Bedfont, Middlesex. From 1971, at Pyrene House, Sunbury Cross, Sunbury-on-Thames, Middlesex. *Transistor Production Run 1960*-72+.* **(Although Sony-brand transistor radios were first made in 1955, exports to the U.K. did not begin until 1960 [see Model 620, page 276]. Sony-brand radios were first made by Tokyo Tsushin Kogyo Ltd. who wisely changed their name in January 1958 to the Sony Corporation).*

3F66W. 9tr, MW/FM pocket portable. £9.0s.0d. plus £2.0s.0d. P.T. 1968.

3F70W. 8tr, MW/FM pocket portable. £12.40p. including P.T. 1972.

4F53L. 8tr, M/LW/FM pocket portable. £16.10s.3d. plus £2.18s.3d. P.T. 1966. (Employs two loudspeakers).

5F94L. 10tr, S/M/LW/FM portable (convertable into stereo). £24.3s.0d. including P.T. 1967. (Socket provided for connecting 9tr FM stereo adaptor model STA-110, price £16.16s.0d. extra). Mains adaptor, extra).

6F21L. 10tr, M/LW/FM portable (convertable into stereo). £17.3s.7d. plus £3.16s.5d. P.T. 1968. (Socket provided for connecting 9tr FM stereo adaptor model STA-110, price £16.16s.0d. extra).

6R24. 8tr, S/MW portable. £12.17s.6d. including P.T. 1970. (Mains adaptor, £4.0s.0d. extra).

6R24L. 8tr, M/LW portable. £12.15s.0d. including P.T. 1970. (Mains adaptor, £4.0s.0d. extra).

6RC15. 6tr, MW mains table model/digital clock radio. £18.83p. including Purchase Tax. 1971.

7F74L. 11tr, S/M/LW/FM portable/car radio (convertable into stereo). £25.17s.9d. plus £4.11s.3d. P.T. 1966. (A separate car bracket accessory was available for in-car use. Socket provided for connecting a 9tr FM stereo adaptor, model STA-110, price £16.16s.0d. extra).

7F83L. 10tr, M/LW/FM portable. £15.19s.9d. plus £3.15s.3d. P.T. 1969. (Mains adaptor, extra).

7R33. 8tr, 3S/MW mains/battery portable. £27.15s.0d. including P.T. 1970. (Built-in mains adaptor).

7R33L. 8tr, 2S/M/LW mains/battery portable. £27.15s.0d. including P.T. 1970. (Built-in mains adaptor).

7R76L. 8tr, S/M/LW portable. £11.17s.3d. plus £2.12s.9d. P.T. 1968.

7R77. 8tr, 3S/MW mains/battery portable. £32.15s.0d. including P.T. 1970. (Built-in mains adaptor).

8FC59W. MW/FM mains table model/digital clock radio (numbers flip over). £24.4s.5d. plus £5.10s.7d. P.T. 1968. (Pillow loudspeaker, £2.2s.6d. optional extra).

8FC69W. 8tr, MW/FM mains table model/digital clock radio. £32.5s.0d. including P.T. 1970. (Pillow loudspeaker, £2.2s.6d. optional extra).

8FC79. MW/FM mains table model/digital clock radio. £38.70p. including Purchase Tax. 1972.

8RC25. MW mains table model/digital clock radio. £18.12s.6d. plus £4.7s.6d. P.T. 1969.

CRF-150. 21tr, 10S/M/LW/FM mains/battery portable/car radio. £125.0s.0d. including Purchase Tax. 1970. (Built-in mains adaptor. For home, outdoor, in-car or in-boat use).

CRF-160. 10S/M/LW/FM mains/battery portable/car radio. £124.75p. including P.T. 1972. (Built-in mains adaptor. For home, outdoor, in-car or in-boat use).

CRF-230. 48tr, 19S/M/LW/FM mains/battery portable/car radio. £361.15s.0d. including Purchase Tax. 1970. (Built-in mains adaptor. For home, outdoor, in-car or in-boat use).

ICF-110W. 10tr, MW/FM portable. £33.85p. including P.T. 1972. (Complete with tuning meter).

ICF-111L. 10tr, M/LW/FM portable. £41.40p. including P.T. 1972.

ICF-8500. 18tr (2 integrated circuits), MW/FM/Aircraft Band/Marine Band portable. £40.0s.0d. (no Purchase Tax). 1969. (Mains adaptor, extra).

ICR-100. 3tr (integrated circuit), MW miniature portable. 1966. (The ICR-100 was the first integrated circuit transistor radio to be placed on the market in Britain and it used a tiny single silicon chip incorporating 9 transistors, 4 diodes and 14 resistors. See also the Roberts RIC-1 of 1968).

ICR-120. 3tr (integrated circuit), MW miniature portable. £24.15s.0d. including P.T. 1970. (Built-in rechargeable battery. Supplied with battery charger/mains unit).

ICR-200. 3tr (integrated circuit), MW miniature portable. £14.11s.6d. plus £3.8s.3d. P.T. 1969. (Built-in rechargeable battery. Supplied with battery charger/mains unit).

ST70. MW/FM stereo mains table model. £39.75p. including P.T. 1972.

ST80F. MW/FM stereo mains table model. £48.35p. including P.T. 1972. (Field Effect Transistors front end).

ST5055L. M/LW/FM stereo mains table model. £79.75p. including P.T. 1972. (Field Effect Transistors RF amplifier and mixer stage).

ST5100. MW/FM stereo mains table model. £97 including P.T. 1972. (Field Effect Transistors front end).

ST5600. MW/FM stereo mains table model. 60 including P.T. 1972. (Field Effect Transistors front end).

TFM95L. 9tr, M/LW/FM portable/car radio. £27.13s.8d. plus £8.0s.4d. P.T. 1961. (Bracket available for in-car use).

TFM96. 9tr, MW/FM portable. £18.18s.0d. including P.T. October 1963.

TFM116A. 11tr, MW/FM/Marine Band). £35.14s.0d. including P.T. October 1963.

TFM116L. 11tr, M/LW/FM portable. £33.12s.0d. including P.T. October 1963.

TFM117L. 11tr, S/M/LW/FM portable. £32.11s.0d. including P.T. 1964.

TFM122. 9tr, FM table model. £55.13s.0d. including P.T. June 1962.

TFM825L. 8tr, M/LW/FM pocket portable. £20.10s.6d. including P.T. 1964.

TFM834L. 8tr, M/LW/FM pocket portable. £18.7s.6d. including P.T. 1965.

TFM951B. 9tr, S/M/LW portable. £27.16s.0d. including P.T. 1964.

TFM951L. 9tr, M/LW/FM portable. £27.16s.0d. including P.T. 1964.

TFM1000L. 14tr, S/M/LW/FM portable. £31.18s.2d. plus £7.1s.10d. P.T. 1968. (Mains adaptor, extra).

TFM1500L. 14tr, S/M/LW/FM portable. £31.18s.2d. plus £7.10s.4d. P.T. 1969. (Mains adaptor, extra).

TFM1600W. 17tr, 4S/MW/FM mains/battery portable. £59.15s.0d. including P.T. 1970. (Built-in mains adaptor).

TFM6600L. 9tr, M/LW/FM portable. £17.12s.3d. plus £4.2s.9d. P.T. 1969. (Mains adaptor, extra).

TMF8030L. 11tr, M/LW/FM portable. £24.1s.9d. plus £5.13s.3d. P.T. 1969. (Mains adaptor, extra).

TMF8251. 8tr, MW/FM pocket portable. £15.35p. including P.T. 1972.

TFM8601L. 12tr, S/M/LW/FM portable. £48.40p. including P.T. 1972.

TFM8800L. M/LW/FM portable/car radio. £27.15s.0d. including P.T. 1970. (Bracket available for in-car use, £5.5s.0d. extra).

TFMC590UK. MW/FM mains table model/digital clock radio. £28.95p. 1972.

TFMC690UK. MW/FM mains table model/digital clock radio. £29.75p. 1972.

TR55. (*See the TR620, below*).

TR63. (*See the TR620, below*).

TR72. (*See fig.944, p.295. See also the TR620, below*).

TR84. 8tr, MW portable. £22.1s.0d. including P.T. June 1962.

TR608. 6tr, MW portable. 1963.

TR609. 6tr, MW pocket pocket portable. £14.3s.6d. including P.T. June 1962.

TR610. (See the TR620, below).

TR614L. 6tr, M/LW personal portable. £13.8s.8d. plus £3.17s.10d. P.T. 1961.

TR615. 6tr, M/LW pocket portable. £12.1s.6d. including P.T. 1964.

TR620. 6tr, MW pocket portable. £18.18s.0d. including P.T. November 1960. (Complete with carrying case, battery and earpiece all housed in an attractive presentation box. Although the TR620 was the first Sony-brand transistor radio to be officially placed onto the market in the U.K., a handful of Sony's earlier models [originally exported from Japan to the United States] seem to have already found their way into this country via, for example, American airmen stationed at American air bases in East Anglia, or businessmen bringing back souvenirs. Look out for the TR55 [1955], TR63 [1957], TR72 [1957] — all by Tokyo Tsushin Kogyo Ltd. — and the TR610 [1958]. Discovering these models today is a rare and unexpected treat!).

TR623. 6tr, MW personal portable. £11.5s.1d. plus £3.19s.5d. P.T. (including carrying case, battery and earpiece all housed in presentation box). July 1961.

TR624. 6tr, MW desk radio. £14.14s.11d. plus £5.4s.1d. P.T. May 1961.

TR630. 6tr, MW pocket portable. £12.1s.6d. including P.T. June 1962.

TR650. 6tr, MW pocket portable. £8.18s.6d. including P.T. 1964.

TR710B. 7tr, S/MW personal portable. 1962. (SW covering 3.9-12mHz).

TR710L. 7tr, M/LW personal portable. £15.9s.4d. plus £4.9s.8d. P.T. March 1962.

TR710Y. 7tr, S/MW personal portable. 1962. (SW covering 6-18mHz).

TR711. 7tr, S/MW table model. 1963.

TR712. 7tr, MW table model. 1963.

TR716B. 7tr, S/MW personal portable. £20.9s.6d. including P.T. June 1962. (SW covering 3.9-12mHz).

TR716Y. 7tr, S/MW personal portable. £20.9s.6d. including P.T. June 1962. (SW covering 6-18mHz).

TR717Y. 7tr, S/MW portable. £23.2s.6d. including P.T. July 1962.

TR719. 3S/MW table model. £30.19s.6d. June 1962.

TR720. 7tr, M/LW portable. £12.1s.6d. including P.T. September 1963.

TR725. 7tr, S/MW personal portable. £13.16s.10d. plus £4.0s.2d. P.T. June 1962.

TR729. 7tr, S/MW pocket portable. £14.3s.6d. inc. Purchase Tax. April 1963.

TR730. 7tr, MW pocket portable. £13.8s.11d. plus £3.17s.7d. P.T. June 1962. (Complete with carrying case, battery and earpiece).

TR810. 8tr, MW portable. 1963.

TR812. 8tr, 2S/MW portable. £37.16s.0d. including P.T. June 1962.

TR814. 8tr, 2S/MW portable. £27.6s.0d. including P.T. 1963.

TR815Y. 8tr, S/MW portable. £28.7s.0d. including P.T. June 1962.

TR816Y. 8tr, S/MW portable. £24.13s.6d. including P.T. March 1963.

TR818. 8tr, MW portable. £19.8s.0d. including P.T. 1963.

TR819. 8tr, S/MW portable. £17.17s.0d. including P.T. 1963.

TR820. 8tr, S/MW portable. £18.18s.0d. including P.T. December 1963.

TR826. 8tr, MW pocket portable. £17.17s.0d. including P.T. 1964.

TR911. 9tr, 2S/MW portable. £30.19s.6d. including P.T. March 1963.

TR1000. 10tr, 3S/MW portable. £29.9s.0d. plus £5.4s.0d. P.T. 1966. (Complete with tuning meter).

TR1300. 12tr, 4S/MW mains/battery portable. £45.0s.0d. including P.T. 1970. (Built-in mains adaptor).

TR1819. 6tr, MW table model/portable (cube shape case, finished in simulated walnut). £5.3s.11d. plus £1.3s.1d. P.T. 1968.

TR1823. 6tr, MW table model/portable (cube shape case, finished in red, white or green). £5.68p. plus £1.12p. P.T. 1971.

TR1825. 6tr, MW pocket portable. £8.21p. including P.T. 1971.

TR1829. 6tr, MW table model/portable (cylinder shape case, finished in simulated walnut). £6.15s.0d. plus £1.10s.0d. P.T. 1968.

TR1829C. 6tr, MW table model/portable (cylinder shape case, finished in red, yellow or white). £6.80p. plus £1.30p. P.T. 1971.

TR1839. 6tr, MW portable (cigarette box shape case). £7.13s.10d. plus £1.14s.2d. P.T. 1968.

TR6080. 6tr, MW portable. £16.16s.0d. including P.T. June 1962.

TR7120L. 7tr, M/LW portable. £16.6s.0d. plus £5.15s.0d. P.T. November 1961.

TR8460. 10tr, Aircraft Band portable. £24.10p. including P.T. 1972.

TRW621. 6tr, MW personal portable/alarm watch. £15.17s.6d. plus £4.12s.0d. P.T. May 1961.

Standard [Japan] (*dist.* **Denham & Morley Ltd.**), 173-175 Cleveland Street, London W1. From 1970, (*dist.* **Telerenters [London & Provincial] Ltd.**), Standard House, 1-2 Church Way, Edgware, Middlesex. *Transistor Production Run 1961-72+*.

F-205L. 6tr, M/LW pocket portable. £12.1s.6d. including P.T. 1963.

F-408L. 6tr, M/LW pocket portable. £6.7s.0d. including P.T. 1970.

F-416L. 6tr, M/LW pocket portable. £7.19s.6d. including P.T. 1965.

F-426. 8tr, M/LW pocket portable. £8.12s.6d. including P.T. 1965.

F-4000 (Alarm). 6tr, MW pocket portable/alarm watch. £11.0s.6d. including Purchase Tax. 1963.

G-700. 7tr, S/MW pocket portable. £13.13s.0d. including P.T. 1963.

G-700L. 7tr, M/LW pocket portable. £13.13s.0d. including P.T. 1963.

GL-500. Portable. September 1961.

H-115. 10tr, 2S/MW portable. £17.17s.0d. including P.T. 1963.

H-115L. 8tr, S/M/LW portable. £17.17s.0d. including P.T. 1963.

H-426L. 8tr, M/LW pocket portable. £7.9s.0d. plus £1.5s.10d. P.T. 1966.

H-504L. 8tr, S/M/LW portable. £14.14s.0d. including P.T. 1965.

H-741L. 8tr, S/M/LW portable. £8.8s.0d. including P.T. 1965.

J-672FL. 10tr, M/LW/FM mains table model. £20.67p. including P.T. 1971.

J-802FL. 10tr, S/M/LW/FM portable. £33.12s.0d. including P.T. May 1963.

J-862FL. 10tr, S/M/LW/FM portable. £22.18s.0d. plus £4.0s.10d. Purchase Tax. 1967.

J-920F. 10tr, M/LW portable. 1966.

K-17X. 11tr, portable receiver/transmitter. 1965. (This compact, 27mHz "Citizen's Band" transceiver was capable of two-way communication over short distances. It is included as an example of a type of equipment widely marketed in the U.K. in the mid-1960s despite the fact that, at the time, no official "Citizen's Band" permits existed or were being issued).

L-555F. 12tr, 3S/M/LW/FM portable. £40.19s.0d. including P.T. 1964.

M-809FLR. 11tr, S/M/LW/FM mains/battery portable. £27.0s.0d. including Purchase Tax. 1970.

N-512FL. 14tr, S/M/LW/FM portable. £40.19s.0d. including P.T. 1964.

N-515FL. 14tr, 2S/M/LW/FM portable. £35.14s.10d. plus £6.6s.2d. P.T. 1965.

Q-110. Portable. September 1961.

Q-771FL. 9tr, M/LW/FM portable. £13.2s.0d. plus £2.5s.9d. P.T. 1966.

Q-822FL. 9tr, M/LW/FM portable. £14.0s.6d. plus £2.9s.6d. Purchase Tax. 1966.

Q-832FL. 9tr, M/LW/FM portable. £19.19s.0d. including P.T. 1963.

Q-918FL. 9tr AM/FM pocket portable. £17.6s.6d. including P.T. 1964.

RF-300. 9tr, M/LW/FM mains/battery portable. £13.36p. including P.T. 1972.

RF-950E. 15tr, M/LW/FM/Aircraft Band mains/battery portable. £30.60p. including P.T. 1972.

RL-815. 12tr, MW/FM mains table model/digital clock radio. £32.48p. including P.T. 1971. (Pillow loudspeaker available as an optional extra).

RK-552FL. 9tr, M/LW/FM mains/battery portable. £18.49p. including Purchase Tax. 1972.

RQ-520FL. 11tr, S/M/LW/FM portable. £19.9s.9d. including P.T. 1970.

RQ-522FL. 9tr, M/LW/FM mains/battery portable. £17.95p. including Purchase Tax. 1971.

RV-600FL. 16tr, 2S/M/LW/FM/Marine Band mains/battery portable. £78.13s.0d. including P.T. 1970.

RV-4000FL. 17tr, 3S/M/LW/FM portable. £73.13s.6d. including P.T. 1970.

SR-107. 8tr, M/LW portable. £14.9s.6d. plus £2.6s.6d. Purchase Tax. September 1961.

SR-115. 8tr, S/M/LW portable. £22.1s.0d. including P.T. 1962.

SR-205. 6tr, M/LW pocket portable. £15.4s.6d. including P.T. 1963.

SR-400. Pocket portable/alarm watch. September 1961.

SR-505. S/M/LW portable. £28.7s.0d. including P.T. 1962.

SR-900. 7tr, M/LW port. September 1961.

SR-G430 (Micronic Ruby). 7tr, MW miniature pocket portable with gold-plated loudspeaker grille. £13.13s.0d. including P.T. July 1962. (Also came complete with a silk-lined presentation case, leather carrying pouch, earpiece, carrying strap and mercury-type batteries, price £24.3s.0d. including P.T. — a transistor collector's dream! *Figs.812, 813, p.202*).

SR-G433 (Micronic Ruby). 7tr, MW miniature pocket portable. £9.19s.6d. including P.T. 1964.

SR-G437 (Micronic Ruby). 8tr, MW miniature pocket portable. £15.15s.0d. including P.T. 1963.

SR-H35 (Micronic Ruby). 9tr, MW miniature pocket portable. £17.17s.0d. inc. P.T. 1965.

SR-H436 (Micronic Ruby). 8tr, MW miniature pocket portable. £17.17s.0d. including P.T. 1964.

SR-H438 (Micronic Ruby). 8tr, MW miniature pocket portable. £17.17s.0d. including P.T. 1965.

SR-Q460F (Micronic Ruby). 9tr, MW/FM miniature pocket portable. £20.9s.6d. including P.T. 1965.

SR-Q466 (Micronic Ruby). 11tr, MW/FM miniature portable. £24.3s.0d. including P.T. 1968. (Although these and other models of Micronic Ruby were sold in the United States in the 1960s, the eight different models listed above were the only ones imported into Britain from Japan during this time).

TK-1848L. 18tr, S/M/LW/FM/Aircraft Band mains/battery portable. £36.17s.0d. including P.T. 1970.

Sky Bandit. 9tr, M/LW/Aircraft Band. £19.10s.0d. plus £3.11s.6d. P.T. 1967.

Steepletone (Steepletone Products Ltd.), 2 Station Approach, Bicester, Oxon. Works at Croughton, Northants. *"Steepletone Products Ltd. are in their 25th year - a quarter of a century specialising in manufacturing and distributing competitive consumer electronic products. Until the early 1990's products were manufactured 'in-house' at the Croughton base. Then, as other top brands in the industry, Steepletone had to move their manufacturing facility to the Far East to remain competitive"* (from a 1996 Steepletone brochure, which heavily featured their 'Nostalgic Radio' collection of contemporary table model radios housed in 1930s-style wireless cabinets. They have also very recently brought out a 1920s style set with sloping panel and imitation bright-emitter valves, the 'Valve 1', *see fig.960, p.299*). *Transistor Production Run 1972+.*

SR300. M/LW/FM mains/battery portable. £16.63p. including P.T. 1972.

SR700. 6tr + integrated circuit S/M/LW/FM portable/car radio. £23.96p. including P.T. 1972. (For home, outdoor or in-car use).

SRLM2. M/LW port. £5.54p. inc. P.T. 1972.

SRLM3. M/LW port. £6.27p. inc. P.T. 1972.

SRLM4. M/LW port. £7.34p. inc. P.T. 1972.

STR40. M/LW/FM port.£10.33p.inc.P.T. 1972.

STR50. M/LW/FM mains/battery portable. £14.33p. including P.T. 1972.

STR60. 10tr, M/LW/FM mains/battery portable. £16.95p. including Purchase Tax. 1972.

STR70. 9tr + integrated circuit, M/LW/FM mains/battery portable. £19.20p. including P.T. 1972.

STR1010. M/LW/FM portable. £8.27p. including P.T. 1972.

STR1212. MW/FM portable. £11.23p. including P.T. 1972.

Stella (Stella Radio & Television Ltd.), 121-123 Shaftesbury Avenue, London WC2. All model numbers prefixed by 'ST'. *Transistor Production Run 1959-68.*

402. 6tr, M/LW portable. £18.18s.0d. including P.T. 1959.

403. 6tr, M/LW portable. £13.18s.3d. plus £4.9s.3d. P.T. August 1960.

404. 7tr, M/LW personal portable. £12.6s.5d. plus £3.19s.1d. P.T. August 1960.

405. 6tr, M/LW portable. £13.3s.10d. plus £4.13s.2d. P.T. July 1961.

414. 7tr, M/LW personal portable. £9.7s.4d. plus £2.14s.2d. P.T. 1961.

415. 6tr, M/LW portable. £14.3s.6d. including Purchase Tax. August 1962. (Identical chassis used in the Cossor CR1310T).

416. 7tr, S/M/LW portable. £19.19s.0d. including P.T. August 1962. (On the front of this radio there a small clear Perspex window designed to accept a favourite photograph *etc.*).

419. 6tr, M/LW portable. £15.15s.0d. including P.T. March 1963.

420. 9tr, M/LW/FM portable. £25.4s.0d. including P.T. August 1962.

425. 6tr, M/LW pocket portable. £11.11s.0d. including P.T. 1964.

426. 6tr, M/LW pocket portable. £8.11s.11d. plus £1.10s.5d. P.T. 1966.

427. 6tr, M/LW portable. £13.13s.0d. including P.T. 1964.

428. 6tr, M/LW portable. £17.6s.6d. including P.T. 1964.

429. 6tr, M/LW portable. £14.0s.6d. plus £2.9s.6d. P.T. 1966.

430. 9tr, M/LW/FM portable. £24.3s.0d. including P.T. August 1963.

431. 6tr, M/LW portable. £11.11s.0d. including P.T. 1964.

438. 7tr, M/LW portable. £12.18s.10d. plus 2.15s.5d. P.T. 1967.

4500. 6tr, M/LW mains table model. £13.13s.0d. including Purchase Tax. August 1967. (Identical chassis used in the Philips 262).

6003. 9tr, MW/FM portable. £11.10s.3d. plus £2.9s.3d. P.T. 1968. (Identical chassis used in the Philips 284).

6143. 9tr, M/LW/FM portable. £17.19s.6d. including P.T. 1967.

6239. 7tr, M/LW portable. 1967.

7005. 6tr, M/LW portable. £15.12s.0d. plus £3.6s.9d. P.T. 1968.

7008. 9tr, M/LW/FM portable. £21.3s.10d. plus £4.10s.8d. P.T. 1968. (Mains adaptor, extra).

7204. 9tr, M/LW/FM portable. £16.0s.0d. plus £3.8s.6d. P.T. 1967.

7219. 10tr, S/M/LW/FM portable. £32.0s.1d. plus £6.16s.11d. P.T. 1968.

7226. 10tr, M/LW/FM portable. £25.14s.6d. including P.T. 1967.

7228. 9tr, M/LW/FM portable. £23.1s.6d. plus £4.1s.5d. P.T. 1966.

7230. 10tr, M/LW/FM portable. £29.8s.0d. including P.T. 1964.

7288. 7tr, 3S/MW portable. £38.0s.0d. plus £6.14s.3d. P.T. 1966.

7570. 9tr, S/M/LW/FM portable. £38.7s.6d. plus £6.15s.6d. P.T. 1967.

7581. 9tr, S/M/LW/FM portable/car radio. £49.7s.0d. including P.T. 1968. (For home, outdoor or in-car use).

Stereosound (Stereosound Production Limited), 12-14 Wakefield Road, Brighouse, Yorkshire. *Transistor Production Run 1959.*

T6 (Carousel). 6tr, M/LW portable. £15.10s.0d. plus £4.19s.6d. P.T. November 1959.

Stokvis (R.S. Stokvis & Sons Ltd.), 12 High Street, Walton-on-Thames. *Transistor Production Run 1962.*

620P. 7tr, M/LW portable. £15.1s.0d. plus £4.7s.0d. P.T. March 1962.

621P. 7tr, S/M/LW portable. £19.17s.11d. plus £5.16s.7d. P.T. March 1962.

Sudfunk [West Germany] **(dist. Denham & Morley)**, 173-175 Cleveland Street, London W1. *Transistor Production Run 1960.*

Sudfunk 766. £27.16s.6d. including P.T. October 1960.

Sudfunk K9106. October 1960.

Suma (dist. Kingsway Mill Company [M/C] Limited), 1 Berry Street, London EC1. *Transistor Production Run 1965.*

Suma. 8tr, M/LW pocket portable. £6.6s.0d. including P.T. 1965.

Summitone (dist. Kingsway Mill Company [M/C] Limited), 1 Berry Street, London EC1. *Transistor Production Run 1965.*

Summitone. 6tr, MW pocket portable. £3.9s.6d. including P.T. 1965.

T.A.K. Continental (*see Normende, page 264*).

T.E.D. (dist. Paschkes & Company Limited), 40 Craven Road, London W2. *Transistor Production Run 1963.*

St. Germain. 6tr, M/LW personal portable. Gold-plated fittings, with the case covered in box calf or pig skin, £21 including Purchase Tax. 1963. (Also available in lizard-covered case, price £24.3s.0d. including Purchase Tax).

Tandberg (Farnell-Tandberg Ltd.), 81 Kirkstall Road, Leeds. *Transistor Production Run 1970+.*

TP-3S. M/LW/FM portable/car radio. £54.5s.0d. including P.T. 1970. (Bracket for in-car use, £3.0s.0d. extra; mains adaptor, £6.10s.0d. extra).

TP-41W. 13tr, S/M/LW/FM portable/car radio. £59.0s.0d. including P.T. 1970. (Bracket for in-car use, £3.0s.0d. extra; mains adaptor, £6.10s.0d. extra).

Telefunken [West Germany] (*dist.* **Tellux Ltd.**), 146 New Cavendish Street, London W1. From 1960, (*dist.* **Welmec Corporation Ltd.**), 147-148 Strand, London WC2. From 1965, (**A.E.G. [Gt. Britain] Ltd.**), 27 Chancery Lane, London WC2. *Transistor Production Run 1957-72+.*

Andante (101). S/M/LW/FM stereo mains table model. £87.13s.6d. inc. P.T. 1968.

Atlanta (101). 12tr, 2S/2M/LW/FM mains/battery portable. £59.13s.0d. plus £14.0s.10d. P.T. 1969. (Built-in mains unit. Medium waveband tuning is divided into two with bandspread over both halves, giving MW1 (275-555 metres) and MW2 (185-280 metres).

Atlanta de Luxe (101). 17tr, 3S/2M/LW/FM stereo mains/battery portable. £63.15s.0d. plus £15.0s.0d. P.T. 1969. (Built-in mains unit. Decoder for use in stereo mode, optional extra. Medium waveband tuning is divided into two with bandspread over both halves, giving MW1 (275-555 metres) and MW2 (185-280 metres).

Bajazzo. 9tr, S/M/LW/FM portable. £35.15s.6d. plus £11.9s.6d. P.T. 1960.

Bajazzo (TS101). 11tr, S/M/LW/FM portable/car radio. £49.15s.4d. plus £8.15s.8d. P.T. 1966. (Bracket available for in-car use, £7.7s.0d. extra).

Bajazzo (TS101 de Luxe). 11tr, S/M/LW/FM portable/car radio. £66.1s.0d. plus £11.13s.1d. P.T. 1966. (Bracket available for in-car use, £7.7s.0d. extra).

Bajazzo (TS201). 11tr, S/M/LW/FM portable/car radio. £61.19s.0d. including P.T. 1970. (Bracket available for in-car use, extra; mains adaptor, extra).

Bajazzo (TS201 de Luxe). 11tr, S/M/LW/FM portable/car radio. £77.13s.6d. including P.T. 1970. (Bracket available for in-car use, extra; mains adaptor, extra).

Bajazzo (TS 3511). 11tr, S/M/LW/FM portable/car radio. £57.15s.0d. including P.T. 1964. (Bracket available for in-car use, £7.7s.0d. extra).

Bajazzo (TS 3511M). 11tr, M/LW/FM/Marine Band portable/car radio. £57.15s.0d. including P.T. 1964. (Bracket available for in-car use, £7.7s.0d. extra).

Bajazzo (TS 3611 de Luxe). 11tr, S/M/LW/FM portable. £76.13s.0d. including P.T. 1965.

Bajazzo (TS 5511M). 11tr, 2S/M/LW portable/car radio. £57.15s.0d. including P.T. 1964. (Bracket available for in-car use, £7.7s.0d. extra).

Bajazzo (Junior 201). 9tr, M/LW/FM portable/car radio. £36.3s.10d. plus £6.7s.10d. P.T. 1967. (Mains adaptor, extra).

Bajazzo (Sport 101E). 9tr, M/LW/FM portable/car radio. £43.8s.8d. plus £7.13s.3d. P.T. 1966. (Bracket available for in-car use, £7.7s.0d. extra).

Bajazzo (Sport 201). 10tr, S/2M/LW/FM portable/car radio. £47.15s.6d. including P.T. 1970. (Bracket available for in-car use, £8.12s.0d. extra. Mains adaptor, £6.11s.6d. available as an optional extra. Medium waveband tuning is divided into two with bandspread over both halves, giving MW1 [275-555 metres] and MW2 [185-280 metres]).

Bajazzo (Sport 3591L). 9tr, M/LW/FM portable/car radio. £58.8s.0d. including P.T. 1964. (Bracket available for in-car use, £7.7s.0d. extra.

Bajazzo (Sport 3591S). 9tr, S/MW/FM portable/car radio. £58.8s.0d. inc. P.T. 1964. (Bracket for in-car use, £7.7s.0d. extra).

Bandola 201. 9tr, S/M/LW/FM portable. £26.15s.0d. plus £6.6s.0d. P.T. 1969. (Mains adaptor, extra).

Banjo Automatic. 9tr, M/LW/FM portable. £22.19s.0d. plus £5.8s.0d. P.T. 1969. (Mains adaptor, extra).

Caprice (TL3291). 9tr, MW/L/FM table model. £37.16s.0d. including P.T. 1961.

Digitale (101). 9tr, MW/FM mains table model/digital clock radio. £34.67p. inc. P.T. 1971.

Famulus (101). 10tr, M/LW/FM portable. £20.8s.0d. plus £4.16s.0d. P.T. 1969. (Mains adaptor, extra).

Famulus (3371). 7tr, S/M/LW portable. £25.10s.0d. including P.T. 1963.

Filius (101). 7tr, M/LW portable/car radio. £21.15s.0d. plus £3.16s.9d. P.T. 1967. (Mains adaptor, extra).

Gavotte (1691). 9tr, S/M/LW/FM mains table model. £69.3s.11d. including P.T. 1967.

Jubilate (301). 9tr, M/LW/FM mains table model. £40.9s.0d. including P.T. 1967.

Kavalier (3291L). 9tr, MW/L/FM portable. £40.19s.0d. including P.T. 1961.

Mini-Partner (101). 10tr, MW/FM portable. £14.14s.1d. including P.T. 1970. (Mains adaptor, extra).

Partner. 5tr, MW personal port. £13.15s.0d. plus £8.5s.0d. P.T. October 1957.

Partner (III). 7tr, M/LW portable. £16.13s.11d. plus £5.7s.1d. P.T. 1960.

Partner (IV). 7tr, S/M/LW portable. £25.4s.0d. including P.T. 1961.

Partner (201). 9tr, M/LW/FM portable. £14.0s.6d. plus £3.6s.0d. P.T. 1969. (Mains adaptor, extra).

Partner (UKW). 8tr, MW/FM portable. £31.10s.0d. including P.T. 1961.

Partner Exclusive (201). 9tr, S/M/LW/FM mains/battery portable. £19.95p. 1971. (Built-in mains adaptor).

Partner Universal (201). 9tr, S/M/LW/FM mains/battery portable. £28 including P.T. 1972. (Push-button for Radio Luxembourg. Built-in mains adaptor).

Rytmo 201. 9tr, S/M/LW/FM portable. £26.15s.0d. plus £6.6s.0d. P.T. 1969. (Mains adaptor, extra).

Telestar II (7501). 10tr, 4S/MW portable. £57.0s.0d. plus £10.1s.4d. P.T. 1966.

Ticcolo (101). 10tr, MW/FM portable/clock radio. £19.80p. including P.T. 1971.

Ticcolo (3361). 6tr, M/LW pocket portable/clock radio. £18.8s.9d. including P.T. 1963.

Tramp (101). 11tr, MW/FM portable. £17.17s.1d. including P.T. 1970.

Telec (Telec Tronic Ltd.), 12 Whitehall, London SW1. *Transistor Production Run 1961.*

Par Kanal. Pocket portable. January 1961.

Teleton [Japan] (*dist.* **Teleton Electro [U.K.] Ltd.**), 24/32 Kilburn High Road, London NW6. *Transistor Production Run 1968-71+.*

6X615. 6tr, MW pocket portable. £3.12s.0d. plus 13s.5d. P.T. 1968.

6X705. 6tr, MW pocket portable. £2.5s.0d. plus 10s.0d. P.T. 1969.

15FI. 11tr, MW/FM mains/battery portable. £9.3s.0d. plus £2.2s.0d. P.T. 1969.

46F10. 9tr, MW/FM portable. £7.6s.4d. plus £1.13s.8d. P.T. 1969.

770. M/LW/FM mains/battery portable. £14.0s.0d. including P.T. 1970.

850. 6tr, MW pocket portable. £2.15s.0d. including P.T. 1970.

855. 6tr, MW pocket portable. £2.15s.0d. including P.T. 1970.

8001. M/LW pocket portable. £6.5s.0d. including P.T. 1970.

8002. 10tr, MW/FW portable. £9.15s.0d. including P.T. 1970.

8003. 12tr, M/LW/FM portable. £10.15s.0d. including P.T. 1970.

AB21. 17tr, S/MW/FM/Aircraft Band mains/battery portable. £30.9s.5d. plus £5.10s.1d. P.T. 1968. (Complete with tuning meter, and built-in mains adaptor).

F5124. 12tr, MW/FM portable. £6.18s.1d. plus £1.11s.11d. P.T. 1969.

GE702. S/M/LW/FM portable. £24.09p. including P.T. 1971.

N1000. 10tr, MW pocket portable. £3.38p. including P.T. 1971.

STG50. 12tr, MW/FM portable. £8.5s.0d. including P.T. 1970.

TF161 (General). 18tr, 2S/M/LW/FM/Marine Band mains/battery portable. £34.9s.3d. plus £6.5s.2d. P.T. 1968. (Complete with world-time chart, tuning meter, two loudspeakers and built-in mains adaptor).

TF163. 12tr, 3S/M/LW/FM portable. £38.0s.0d. including P.T. 1970.

TF181. 28tr, 2S/M/LW/FM/2xPublic Service Bands mains/battery portable. £55.15s.0d. (no Purchase Tax). 1969.

TF182. 28tr, 3S/M/LW/FM/Marine Band mains/battery portable. £55.15s.0d. (no Purchase Tax). 1969.

TF911(Hit Parade). 9tr, M/FM pocket portable. £7.17s.1d. plus £1.9s.1d. P.T. 1968.

Goal 1. 6tr, MW novelty radio in the shape of a football. £2.16s.5d. plus 13s.1d. P.T. 1969.

Teletron (The Teletron Co.Ltd.), 112b Station Road, Chingford, London E4. *Transistor Production Run 1960-64.*

AW6. 6tr, S/M/LW portable. £13.10s.4d. plus £4.6s.8d. P.T. December 1960.

DW6. 6tr, M/LW personal portable. £7.19s.0d. plus £2.11s.0d. P.T. April 1961.

T6. 6tr, M/LW portable. £9.9s.0d. including P.T. 1964.

T66. 6tr, S/MW portable. £9.15s.0d. including P.T. 1964.

T300. 6tr, M/LW portable. £11.0s.6d. including P.T. 1964.

Tesla [Japan] (*dist.* **Hall Electric Limited**), Haltron House, Anglers Lane, Kentish Town, London NW5. *Transistor Production Run 1963.*

2805B. 7tr, S/M/LW portable. £13.2s.6d. including P.T. 1963.

Tobisonic (*dist.* **D.Tandon [London] Ltd.**), 244 Edgware Road, London W2. *Transistor Production Run 1966.*

TR211. 11tr, MW/FM portable. £12.0s.0d. including P.T. 1966. (Complete with local/distant switch).

TR293. 6tr, M/LW portable. £7.7s.0d. including P.T. 1966.

Tokai [Japan] (*dist.* **Holiday Bros. [Electrical Wholesalers] Ltd.**), 61b Shawheath, Stockport, Cheshire. From 1966, (*dist.* **D.Tandon [London] Ltd.**), 244 Edgware Road, W2. *Transistor Production Run 1964-66.*

CR-105. 9tr, MW/FM portable/car radio. £26.0s.0d. including P.T. 1966. (Complete with bracket for in-car use).

LA-611. 6tr, M/LW pocket portable. £4.19s.11d. (wholesale trade price). 1964.

Toshiba [Tokyo Shibaura Electric Co. Ltd., Japan] (*dist.* **Hall Electric Limited**), Haltron House, Anglers Lane, Kentish Town, London NW5. From 1970 (*dist.* **Hanimex U.K. Ltd.**), 15 Gt. Dover Street, London SW1. *Transistor Production Run 1960-72+.*

6C-600. 6tr, MW pocket portable. £15.2s.6d. including P.T. 1963.

6P-15. 6tr, MW pocket portable. £7.7s.0d. including P.T. 1963.

6TP-354. 6tr, MW pocket portable. £12.12s.0d. including P.T. December 1960. (This was Toshiba's first transistor radio exported to Britain).

7P-120L. 7tr, M/LW portable. £11.19s.6d. including P.T. 1963.

7P-130L. 7tr, M/LW portable. £12.12s.0d. including P.T. 1964.

7TP-440L. 7tr, portable. July 1961.

7TH-486S. 7tr, portable. September 1962.

8M-210R. 8tr, S/MW portable. £15.10s.0d. including P.T. 1963.

8M-340R. 8tr, S/MW portable. £19.8s.6d. including P.T. 1963.

8L-450L. 8tr, M/LW portable. £14.3s.6d. including P.T. 1964.

8L-450R. 8tr, S/MW portable. £15.4s.6d. including P.T. 1964.

8L-688L. 8tr, 2S/M/LW portable. £17.17s.0d. including P.T. 1964.

8TL-463R. 8tr, S/MW portable. £15.9s.6d. plus £4.9s.6d. P.T. March 1962.

8TM-373S. 8tr, S/MW port. September 1962.

9TL-641R. 9tr, 2S/MW portable. £26.5s.0d. including P.T. 1964.

10TL-429F. 10tr, MW/FM portable. £26.10s.0d. including P.T. September 1962.

16TL-625FB. 16tr, 3S/M/LW/FM portable. £52.10s.0d. including P.T. 1964.

IC70. MW/FM mains table model/clock radio. £22.98p. including P.T. 1972.

IC'70. Integrated circuit, MW/FM portable. £19.19s.0d. including P.T. 1970. (Field Effect Transistors. Mains adaptor available, extra).

IC700. S/MW/FM mains/battery portable. £33.35p. including P.T. 1971. (Built-in mains adaptor).

RM-341F. MW/FM mains/battery portable. £28.10s.0d. including P.T. 1970.

RR-34 (Minivox Watch Radio) — *see under Minivox, page 263.*

Tourist (*dist.* **Highgate Acoustics Ltd.**), 71-73 Gt. Portland Street, London W1. *Transistor Production Run 1964.*

720/C4. 7tr, 2S/M/LW portable. £22.1s.0d. including P.T. 1964.

720FMAS. 10tr, S/M/LW/FM portable. £28.7s.0d. including P.T. 1964.

730/C5. 8tr, 3S/M/LW portable. £26.5s.0d. including P.T. 1964.

Toyo [Japan] (**Toyo Trading Co. Ltd.**), No.2, 1-Chome, Hongoku-Cho, Nihonbashi, Chuo-Ku, Toyko. *Transistor Production Run 1960.*

6G-397. 6tr, MW pocket portable. 1960.

6GA-441. 6tr, SW/MW personal portable. 1960. (These two models were advertised and illustrated in the April issue of *Wireless World* and were among the first Japanese transistor radios that the British listening public had been given sight of).

Trans-arena (*see Arena, page 246*).

Transmobile (*dist.* **Lee Products [Gt. Britain] Ltd.**), 10-18 Clifton Street, London EC2. *Transistor Production Run 1963.*

Transmobile. 8tr, M/LW portable. £18.16s.3d. including P.T. 1963.

Transwave (*dist.* **Euramasia Ltd.**), 3 Poplar Court Parade, East Twickenham. From 1964, (*dist.* **Green Arrow Intercontinental Ltd.**), 702 Tudor Estate, Abbey Road, Park Royal, London NW10. *Transistor Production Run 1963-64.*

HTR.600L. 6tr, M/LW portable. £5 including P.T. (wholesale price). 1963.

HTR.605S. 6tr, MW portable. £3 including P.T. (wholesale price). 1964.

HTR.700L. 7tr, M/LW portable. £5 including P.T. (wholesale price). 1964.

HTR.720SL. 7tr, M/LW pocket portable. £3.17s.4d. including P.T. (wholesale price). 1964.

HTR.808S. 8tr, MW pocket portable. £3.5s.0d. including P.T. (wholesale price). 1964.

HTR.825SL. 8tr, M/LW portable. £5 including P.T. (wholesale price). 1964.

HTR.1010S. 10tr, MW pocket portable. £3.11s.0d. including P.T. (wholesale price). 1964.

HTR.1026. 10tr, M/LW portable. £5 including P.T. (wholesale price). 1964.

Tri-ang (**Minimodels Ltd.**). *Transistor Production Run 1961-62.*

Tri-onic Kit 'A'. 1961. (An electronic construction set aimed at children and young people. It included components for making six different crystal and transistor radios for headphone use. *See fig.806, p.200*).

Tri-onic Kit 'A/B'. 1962. (An add-on kit for use with the above, upgrading the transistor radios for loudspeaker use).

Tricity (**Tricity Cookers Ltd.**), Thorn House, Upper St. Martins Lane, London WC2. *Transistor Production Run 1965.*

Melodie. 6tr, M/LW mains operated transistor radio built into the Tricity electric cooker Model 620. 1965. Yes, a combined electric cooker and transistor radio — try finding one of these today at a boot fair! Does anyone collect these strange hybrids? (The Melodie was made by Ferguson, who were registered at the same address as Tricity Cookers).

Trixie (*dist.* **Highgate Acoustics Limited**), 71-73 Gt. Portland Street, London W1. *Transistor Production Run 1963.*

Trixie II. 7tr, M/LW portable. £13.13s.0d. including P.T. 1963.

Ultra (**Ultra ElectricLimited**), Stonefield Way, South Ruislip, Middlesex. From 1960 (**Ultra Radio & Television Limited**), Television House, Eastcote, Ruislip, Middlesex. From 1967, (**British Radio Corporation Limited**), 284 Southbury Road, Enfield, Middlesex. *Transistor Production Run 1958-71.*

6100. 6tr, M/LW portable (pre-set on LW for the Light Programme). £11.10s.6d. including P.T. June 1962.

6102. 6tr, M/LW portable. £13.13s.0d. including P.T. June 1962.

6104. 7tr, M/LW portable. £19.8s.6d. including P.T. June 1962.

6110. 7tr, M/LW portable. £13.13s.0d. including P.T. March 1963.

6112. 7tr, M/LW portable/car radio. £11.10s.6d. including P.T. March 1963. (For home, outdoor or in-car use).

6114. 9tr, M/LW/FM portable. £18.10s.6d. August 1963.

6116 (Road Ranger I). 9tr, M/LW portable/car radio. £20.6s.4d. including P.T. April 1964. (For home, outdoor or, as its name implies, for in-car use).

6118 (Globetrotter). 7tr, S/M/LW portable. £14.18s.9d. including P.T. November 1963.

6120. 7tr, S/M/LW portable/car radio. £14.3s.6d. including P.T. 1964. (For home, outdoor or in-car use. Bandspread tuning between 185-216 metres, for Radio Luxembourg).

6122. 9tr, M/LW/FM portable. £17.17s.0d. including P.T. April 1965.

6126 (Road Ranger II). 9tr, M/LW portable/car radio. £15.7s.8d. plus £2.14s.3d. P.T. 1966. (For home, outdoor or, as its name implies, for in-car use).

6128. 10tr, M/LW/FM portable/car radio. £20.16s.3d. plus £3.13s.5d. P.T. 1966. (For home, outdoor or in-car use. Bandspread tuning between 185-216 metres, for Radio Luxembourg).

6130. 7tr, M/LW portable. £12.13s.4d. plus £2.4s.9d. P.T. 1966. (Bandspread tuning between 176-214 metres, for Radio Luxembourg).

6132. 11tr, S/M/LW/FM portable/car radio. £23.10s.6d. plus £4.3s.0d. P.T. 1966. (For home, outdoor or in-car use).

6142. 9tr, M/LW/FM portable. £16.5s.9d. plus £2.17s.6d. P.T. 1967. (Bandspread tuning between 188-216 metres, for Radio Luxembourg. Identical chassis used in the Marconiphone 4138).

6144. 7tr, S/M/LW portable. £13.11s.5d. plus £2.7s.11d. P.T. 1967.

6146. 7tr, S/M/LW portable. £8.11s.11d. plus £1.10s.4d. P.T. 1966. (Identical chassis used in the Marconiphone 4142).

6148. 6tr, M/LW pocket portable. £5.17s.8d. plus £1.0s.9d. P.T. 1967.

6150 (Road Ranger III). 9tr, M/LW portable/car radio. £16.16s.2d. plus £3.11s.10d. P.T. 1968. (For home, outdoor or, as its name implies, for in-car use. Chassis identical to the Ferguson 3162 Autotwin).

6151. 10tr, M/LW/FM portable. £12.11s.3d. plus £2.13s.9d. P.T. 1968.

6158. 11tr, S/M/LW/FM portable/car radio. £23.10s.6d. plus £4.3s.0d. P.T. 1967. (For home, outdoor or in-car use. Identical chassis used in the Ferguson 3156).

6159. 7tr, S/M/LW portable. £14.17s.4d. plus £3.3s.8d. P.T. 1968. (Bandspread tuning between 185-216 metres, for Radio Luxembourg. Identical chassis used in the Marconiphone 4159).

6160. 9tr, M/LW/FM portable. £17.12s.7d. plus £3.15s.5d. P.T. 1968. (Bandspread tuning between 185-216 metres, for Radio Luxembourg. Identical chassis used in the Marconiphone 4160).

6167. 8tr, S/M/LW portable/car radio. £14.3s.4d. plus £3.6s.8d. P.T. 1969. (For home, outdoor or in-car use).

6168. 11tr, M/LW/FM portable/car radio. £16.15s.11d. plus £3.19s.1d. P.T. 1969. (For home, outdoor or in-car use).

6169. 11tr, S/M/LW/FM portable/car radio. £28.15s.0d. including P.T. 1970. (For home, outdoor or in-car use).

6170. 8tr, M/LW portable/car radio. £21.30p. including P.T. 1971. (For home, outdoor or in-car use).

6174. 8tr, M/LW portable. £16.90p. including P.T. 1971.

6175. 11tr, M/LW/FM table model. £17.86p. plus £3.44p. P.T. 1971.

TR60. 6tr, M/LW pocket portable. £12.6s.5d. plus £4.9s.4d. P.T. August 1960.

TR70. 7tr, M/LW portable. £12.6s.5d. plus £3.19s.1d. P.T. August 1960.

TR80. 6tr, M/LW table model. £15.18s.0d. plus £5.2s.0d. P.T. 1961. (See fig.810, p.201).

TR81 (Rio). 9tr, M/LW/FM table model. £21.9s.4d. plus £6.17s.8d. P.T. August 1960.

TR81A. 9tr, M/LW/FM table/portable. £17.12s.10d. plus £2.16s.8d. P.T. June 1962.

TR88. 6tr, M/LW personal portable (pre-set on LW for the Light Programme). £8.3s.0d. plus £2.12s.3d. P.T. 1960.

TR100 (Transistor Six). 6tr, M/LW portable/car radio. £15.3s.3d. plus £5.16.9d. P.T. August 1958. (See fig.790, p.196. Despite having a car radio socket plus all the characteristics, including a carrying handle, of a typical outdoor portable, the TR100 was thought of by Ultra as *"the first completely self-contained home radio"*. True transistorised 'home radios', if that's what we have to call them, [ie. table models for indoor use only], were by now only just starting to appear, the first ones being the Dansette RT60 and Pam 365. Because they were battery-powered and therefore had no trailing mains cable, they were soon being referred to in the trade as 'cordless sets'. Mains-only transistorised table models appeared in 1964 *[see the Bang & Olufsen Beomaster 900K, page 247]*, two years after the first mains/battery portables).

TR101. 6tr, M/LW portable. £14.14s.2d. plus £4.14s.4d. P.T. March 1960. (Identical chassis used in the Pilot PR251).

Universal [Champagne Engineering Corporation Limited, Hong Kong] (*dist.* **Winter Trading Co. Limited**), 95-99 Ladbroke Grove, London W11. *Transistor Production Run 1963.*

6TR-D. 6tr, MW pocket portable. £4.4s.0d. including P.T. 1963.

Vantone (*dist.* **Vantone Electronics Ltd.**), 186-188 George Lane, London E18. From 1965, (*dist.* **Kingsway Mill Co. [M/C] Ltd.**), 1 Berry Street, London EC1. (*See also Concord Electronics, page 250*). *Transistor Production Run 1962-68.*

803. 8tr, M/LW pocket portable. 1967.

900. 9tr, M/LW pocket portable. 1967.

1030. 10tr, S/M/LW portable. 1967.

K17. 7tr, MW pocket portable. 1968.

KM28. 8tr, M/LW portable. 1968.

TR6. 6tr, MW pocket portable. £3.9s.6d. including P.T. 1965.

TR661. 6tr, M/LW portable. January 1962.

TR800. 8tr, M/LW pocket portable. 1967.

V600. 6tr, MW pocket portable. 1967.

Velvetone (*dist.* **Philimpex Ltd.**), 59 Hatton Garden, London EC1. *Transistor Production Run 1964.*

Velvetone 1. 6tr, MW pocket portable. 1964.

Velvetone 2. 6tr, M/LW pocket port. 1964.

Velvetone II. 11tr, M/LW portable. 1964.

Velvetone Super. 6tr, M/LW pocket port. 1964.

Vicki (*see Invicta, page 259*).

Victor (*dist.* **Winter Trading Co. Ltd.**), 95-99 Ladbroke Grove, London W11. *Transistor Production Run 1961.*

7TA4. 7tr, S/MW personal portable. £18.4s.7d. plus £4.17s.1d. P.T. 1961.

10TA1. 10tr, S/M/LW portable. £24.0s.10d. plus £6.8s.2d. P.T. 1961.

Vidor (**Vidor Ltd.**), West Street, Erith, Kent. *Transistor Production Run 1957.*

CN440 (Gem). 6tr, M/LW portable (pre-set on LW for the Light Programme). £15.8s.5d. plus £6.2.7d. P.T. 1957.

Viscount (*dist.* **Acme Electric Co. [Finsbury] Ltd.**), 63 Gt. Eastern Street, London EC2. *Transistor Production Run 1963-68.*

Viscount 8. 8tr, MW pocket portable. 1967.

Viscount G613. 6tr, MW pocket portable. £3.19s.6d. 1964.

Viscount Serenade. 8tr, M/LW portable. 1968.

Viscount Single Wave. 6tr, MW pocket portable. 1963.

Viscount Two Wave. 6tr, M/LW pocket portable. 1963.

Webster (**Webster's Electronic Devices Ltd.**), 77 James' Street, Burnley, Lancs. *Transistor Production Run 1958-60.*

PPL. 6tr, M/LW pocket portable (pre-set on LW for the Light Programme). £17.1s.0d. plus £6.11s.6d. P.T. (2-band version of the Pocket Princess). August 1958.

Pocket Princess. (As PPL but for the medium waveband only). £16.14s.6d. plus £6.7s.6d. P.T. August 1958.

Pocket Princess. (Later 2-band version). 6tr, M/LW pocket portable (pre-set on LW for the Light Programme). £11.17s.9d. plus £3.17s.3d. P.T. August 1960.

Welco (*dist.* **Eric Wells [Merchants] Ltd.**), 42 Botolph Lane, Eastcheap, London EC3. From 1964, (*dist.* **Wells Electronics Ltd.**), 338 St. John Street, London EC1. *Transistor Production Run 1963-64.*

Corona. 7tr, MW pocket portable. £4.4s.0d. including P.T. 1963.

Bermuda. 6tr, M/LW portable. £11.11s.0d. including P.T. 1964.

Pacific. 6tr, M/LW portable. £6.6s.0d. including P.T. 1964.

Wien [West Germany] (*dist.* **H.O.Thomas Electronics Ltd.**), 67 Avenue Chambers, Vernon Place, London WC1. *Transistor Production Run 1966-71+.*

Wien 2. M/LW pocket portable. £4.17s.0d. including P.T. 1970.

Wien 3. 10tr, MW/FM pocket portable. £8.17s.0d. including P.T. 1970.

Wien 4. MW/FM portable. £8.50p. including P.T. 1971.

Wien 5. MW/FM portable. £9.85p. including P.T. 1971.

Wien 6. 10tr, M/LW mains/battery portable. £7.19s.0d. including P.T. 1970.

Wien 7. MW/FM portable. £12.19s.0d. including P.T. 1970.

Wien 9. 10tr, MW/FM mains/battery portable. £15.9s.10d. including P.T. 1970.

Wien 9L. As 9, but with addition of LW band. £17.1s.11d. including P.T. 1970.

Wien 10. M/LW portable. £9.25p. including P.T. 1971.

Wien 22. M/LW portable. £4.20p. including P.T. 1971.

Wien 23. M/LW/FM portable. £11.85p. including P.T. 1971.

Wien 24/25. M/LW/FM portable. £13.50p. including P.T. 1971. (Two loudspeakers).

Wien 666. 6tr, M/LW pocket portable. £4.19s.6d. plus £17s.7d. P.T. 1966.

Wien 900. 9tr, MW/FM mains/battery portable. £10.14s.0d. plus £1.18s.0d. P.T. 1967. (Built-in mains adaptor).

Wien 909. 9tr, MW/FM pocket portable. £7.13s.10d. plus £1.7s.1d. P.T. 1966.

Wien 1010. 10tr, M/LW/FM portable. £12.13s.5d. plus £2.4s.7d. P.T. 1966.

Wien C1. M/LW mains table model/clock radio. £10.19s.0d. including P.T. 1970.

Wien C2FM. MW/FM mains table model/ clock radio. £15.19s.0d. including Purchase Tax. 1970.

Wien C3D. MW/FM mains table model. £24.0s.0d. including P.T. 1970.

Wien H. 8tr, MW/FM mains table model. £17.6s.6d. including P.T. 1967.

Wien T83. 8tr, MW/FM mains table model. £22.8s.9d. including P.T. 1970. (Two loudspeakers).

Wien T85. 8tr, MW/FM mains table model. £16.0s.6d. including P.T. 1970.

Wien TFM10. 10tr, MW/FM mains/battery portable. £14.14s.3d. plus £2.12s.3d. P.T. 1967. (Built-in mains adaptor).

Wien Flight 4. MW/Aircraft Band/Public Service Band portable. £16.19s.0d. including P.T. 1970.

Wien Freddy. 6tr, MW pocket portable. £2.14s.4d. plus £9s.6d. P.T. 1966.

Wien Mainz 1. 8tr, MW/FM mains table model. £17.6s.6d. including P.T. 1967.

Wien Multi 66. 20tr, S/M/LW/FM/Aircraft Band/Marine Band/Public Service Band mains/battery portable. £33.10s.0d. including P.T. 1970.

Wien Pilot 2. 9tr, MW/Aircraft Band pocket portable. £8.18s.4d. plus £1.11s.8d. P.T. 1967.

Wien Pilot 3. 9tr, MW/FM/Aircraft Band pocket portable. £10.5s.1d. plus £1.16s.5d. P.T. 1967.

Wien Sport. 6tr, M/FM pocket portable. £7.2s.8d. plus £1.5s.4d. P.T. 1967.

Wilco (*dist.* **S. Arnold Electronics Limited**), Arnold House, 129 Whitechapel High Street, London E1. *Transistor Production Run 1965.*

FA103. 10tr, MW/FM portable. £18.18s.0d. including P.T. 1965.

FT129. 12tr, M/LW/FM portable. £23.12s.0d. including P.T. 1965.

YS83. 8tr, S/MW portable. £16.16s.0d. including P.T. 1965.

YS83L. 8tr, S/M/LW portable. £17.17s.0d. including P.T. 1965.

Zephyr [Hong Kong] (*dist.* **B.Adler & Sons [Radio] Limited**), 32a Coptic Street, London WC1. From 1966, (*dist.* **Light & Sound Limited**), 125 Gunnersbury Lane, Acton, London W3. *Transistor Production Run 1964-66.*

600. 6tr, MW pocket portable. £2.19s.6d. including P.T. 1966.

712. 7tr, M/LW pocket portable. £6.6s.0d. including P.T. 1964.

722. 6tr, M/LW pocket portable. £6.17s.6d. including P.T. 1964.

730. 7tr, MW pocket portable. £4.9s.6d. including P.T. 1964. Employed transistors made by Texas Instruments in the U.S.

830. 7tr, M/LW pocket portable. £4.4s.0d. including P.T. 1966.

930. 9tr, MW pocket portable. £5.11s.0d. including P.T. 1964.

1011. 10tr, MW pocket portable. £6.1s.0d. including P.T. 1964.

Zenith (U.S.A.) (*dist.* **United Mercantile Co. Limited**), 13-14 Queen Street, Mayfair, London W1. *Transistor Production Run 1959-72+.*

A279. MW table model/clock radio. £24.0s.0d. plus £5.12s.11d. Purchase Tax. 1969.

A289. MW table model/clock radio/desk stand. A novel and useful radio for the office, complete with two pens and pen holders. £33.15s.0d. plus £7.19s.1d. P.T. 1969.

A424. MW/FM mains table model. £37.2s.6d. plus £8.14s.8d. Purchase Tax. 1969.

B47. 9tr, MW/FM portable. £22.35p. including P.T. 1971.

B77. 9tr, MW/FM portable. 1971.

B416. MW/FM portable. £28.13p. plus £5.41p. P.T. 1971.

Y280. MW table model/clock radio. £27.0s.0d. plus £5.15s.6d. P.T. 1968.

Y290. MW table model/clock radio/desk stand. A novel and useful radio for the office, complete with two pens and pen holders. £37.10s.0d. plus £8.0s.5d. P.T. 1968.

Z434. MW/FM mains table model. £60.0s.0d. plus £12.16s.8d. P.T. 1968.

Z448. MW/FM stereo mains table model. £126.0s.0d. plus £29.12s.11d. P.T. 1969.

Royal 20. 8tr, MW pocket portable. £13.10s.0d. plus £2.7s.8d. P.T. 1966.

Royal 25. 8tr, MW/FM pocket portable. £15.0s.0d. plus £3.4s.2d. P.T. 1968.

Royal 28. 9tr, MW/FM pocket portable. £15.0s.0d. plus £3.10s.7d. P.T. 1969.

Royal 40. 6tr, MW pocket portable. £13.1s.1d. including P.T. 1963.

Royal 41. 8tr, MW portable. £21.0s.0d. plus £3.14s.1d. P.T. 1967.

Royal 45. 9tr, MW/FM portable. £18.15s.0d. plus £4.8s.6d. P.T. 1969.

Royal 46. 9tr, MW/FM portable. £25.18s.10d. including P.T. 1970.

Royal 50. 6tr, MW personal portable. £15.10s.0d. plus £5.9s.6d. P.T. November 1960.

Royal 51. 9tr, MW/FM portable. £30.0s.0d. plus £5.5s.11d. P.T. 1967.

Royal 55. 6tr, MW personal portable. £21.9s.4d. plus £7.11s.5d. P.T. May 1961.

Royal 56. 8tr, MW portable. £36.0s.0d. plus £5.7s.0d. P.T. 1967. (The set of batteries stored in the carrying handle may be re-charged directly from sunlight [asuming there is some], or if not, from the separate mains charging unit provided).

Royal 64. 6tr, M/LW (pre-set on LW for the Light Programme). £19.10s.0d. plus £3.8s.10d. P.T. 1967.

Royal 70. 7tr, M/LW (pre-set on LW for the Light Programme). £30.0s.0d. plus £5.5s.11d. P.T. 1967.

Royal 72. 9tr, MW/FM portable. £24.0s.0d. plus £5.2s.8d. P.T. 1968. (Mains adaptor, extra).

Royal 75. MW/FM portable. £28.2s.6d. plus £6.12s.3d. P.T. 1969.

Royal 76. 9tr, MW/FM portable. £46.10s.0d. plus £8.4s.1d. P.T. 1967.

Royal 78. 11tr, MW/FM portable. £60.0s.0d. plus £12.16s.8d. P.T. 1968. (Mains adaptor, extra).

Royal 80G. 8tr, MW pocket portable. £14.15s.11d. including P.T. 1964.

Royal 85. 8tr, MW pocket portable. £14.15s.11d. including P.T. 1965.

Royal 92. 13tr, MW/FM portable. £54.0s.0d. plus £11.11s.0d. P.T. 1968. (Mains adaptor, extra).

Royal 94. 11tr, 3S/MW/FM portable. £60.0s.0d. plus £10.11s.9d. P.T. 1967. (Mains adaptor, extra).

Royal 97. 8tr, S/MW/LW portable. £60.0s.0d. plus £10.11s.9d. P.T. 1967. (Complete with direction finder and tuning meter. Mains adaptor, extra).

Royal 125. 6tr, MW pocket portable. £18.5s.7d. plus £5.5s.7d. P.T. April 1962.

Royal 130. 6tr, MW pocket portable. £16.0s.3d. including P.T. 1964.

Royal 150. 6tr, MW pocket portable. £18.5s.1d. plus £6.9s.2d. Purchase Tax. August 1961.

Royal 180G. 8tr, MW pocket portable. £16.0s.3d. including P.T. 1964.

Royal 185. 8tr, MW pocket portable. £16.0s.3d. including P.T. 1965.

Royal 280G. 8tr, MW pocket portable. £19.11s.8d. including P.T. 1964.

Royal 285. 8tr, MW pocket portable. £19.11s.8d. including P.T. 1963.

Royal 400. 7tr, M/LW pocket portable (pre-set on LW for the Light Programme). £25.8s.10d. plus £8.19s.6d. P.T. October 1961.

Royal 500E. 8tr, MW pocket portable. £28.10s.0d. plus £10.1s.2d. P.T. September 1959.

Royal 500H de Luxe. 8tr, MW pocket portable. £33.13s.6d. plus £11.17s.9d. P.T. October 1961. (As Royal 500E but with larger loudspeaker).

Royal 500L-G (de Luxe). 8tr, MW portable. £29.11s.10d. including P.T. 1964. ("Complete with de Luxe gift box ensemble, including earpiece attachment for private listening, full set of batteries and carrying case").

Royal 555-G (Sun Charger). 8tr, MW portable. £41.15s.6d. including P.T. 1965. (Complete with 4 solar cells, or mains rechargeable cells. The first solar-rechargeable transistor radio to be put on the market in Britain).

Royal 625. 6tr, M/LW portable (pre-set on LW for the Light Programme). £25.8s.10d. plus £8.19s.6d. P.T. August 1959.

Royal 645. 6tr, M/LW portable (pre-set on LW for the Light Programme). £22.12s.7d. including P.T. 1964.

Royal 650. 6tr, M/LW portable (pre-set on LW for the Light Programme). £19.10s.0d. plus £5.12s.7d. P.T. April 1962.

Royal 670. 6tr, M/LW portable (pre-set on LW for the Light Programme). £29.10s.6d. including P.T. 1964.

Royal 675. 6tr, MW portable. £37.10s.3d. including P.T. 1959.

Royal 675LG. 6tr, M/LW portable (pre-set on LW for the B.B.C.'s Light Programme). £25.8s.10d. plus £7.6s.11d. P.T. November 1961.

Royal 710LG. 7tr, M/LW portable (pre-set on LW for the Light Programme). £32.13s.8d. plus £11.10s.9d. P.T. November 1959.

Royal 710LM. 7tr, M/LW portable (pre-set on LW for the Light Programme). £30.0s.0d. plus £5.5s.11d. P.T. 1965.

Royal 755LG. (8tr version of Royal 710). £36.7s.6d. plus £12.16.9d. P.T. November 1959.

Royal 780YG. 8tr, M/LW portable. £44.5s.0d. plus £15.12s.4d. P.T. November 1959.

Royal 790YG. 8tr, S/M/LW portable. £60.18s.5d. including P.T. 1963.

Royal 790YM. 8tr, S/M/LW portable. £60.0s.0d. plus £10.11s.9d. P.T. 1965. (Complete with tuning meter and direction-finder. Mains adaptor extra).

Royal 810. 9tr, MW/FM pocket portable. £30.0s.0d. plus £5.5s.11d. P.T. 1965.

Royal 820. 9tr, MW/FM portable. £53.19s.2d. including P.T. 1964.

Royal 880. 12tr, MW/FM portable. £59.18s.7d. including Purchase Tax. November 1962.

Royal 950. 7tr, MW portable/clock radio on pedestal swivel stand. £70.14s.4d. plus £25.11s.1d. P.T. August 1959.

Royal 990. 11tr, 3S/MW/FM portable. £60.0s.0d. plus £10.11s.9d. Purchase Tax. 1966.

Royal 1000D. 9tr, 7xS/M/LW portable. £175.9s.6d. including P.T. August 1959. (Hinged front holds world-time chart and log chart).

Royal 2000 Trans-Symphony. 10tr, MW/FM. £87 plus £30.14s.1d. P.T. May 1960.

Royal 3000. 12tr, 6S/M/LW/FM portable. £154.3s.3d. including P.T. January 1963. (Hinged front holds world-time chart and log chart. Mains adaptor, extra).

Royal 7000. 17tr, 7S/M/LW/FM mains/battery portable. £180.0s.0d. (no Purchase Tax). 1969. (Complete with built-in mains adaptor, battery/tuning meter and navigation charts).

Transistors in Radio Circuits up to 1970 *(dates refer to start of common useage)*

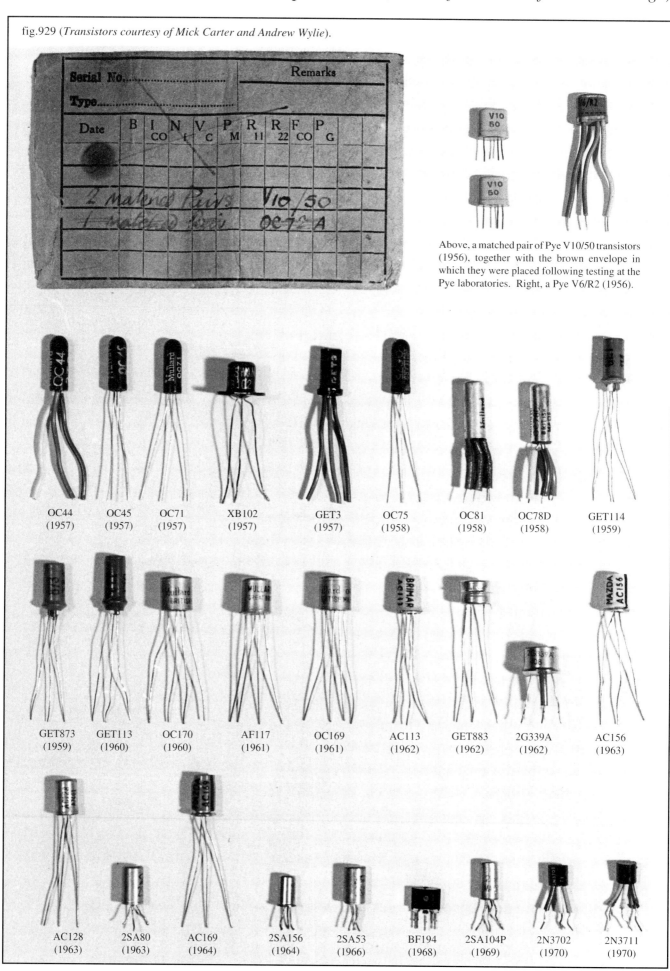

fig.929 (*Transistors courtesy of Mick Carter and Andrew Wylie*).

Above, a matched pair of Pye V10/50 transistors (1956), together with the brown envelope in which they were placed following testing at the Pye laboratories. Right, a Pye V6/R2 (1956).

OC44 (1957)　OC45 (1957)　OC71 (1957)　XB102 (1957)　GET3 (1957)　OC75 (1958)　OC81 (1958)　OC78D (1958)　GET114 (1959)

GET873 (1959)　GET113 (1960)　OC170 (1960)　AF117 (1961)　OC169 (1961)　AC113 (1962)　GET883 (1962)　2G339A (1962)　AC156 (1963)

AC128 (1963)　2SA80 (1963)　AC169 (1964)　2SA156 (1964)　2SA53 (1966)　BF194 (1968)　2SA104P (1969)　2N3702 (1970)　2N3711 (1970)

Typical Transistor Line-ups, pre-1956 to 1960

Examples of the function of transistors used in radio circuits	Examples of the types of transistors used in radio circuits
pre-1956 **Type** — **Function** TI-223 — Conv. Oscillator TI-221 — 1st I.F. Amplifier TI-221 — 2nd I.F. Amplifier TI-210 — Output *Regency Model TR-1 — 4tr MW pocket portable*	**TI-223**, **TI-221**, **TI-221**, **TI-210**, (CK706A or TS117 Diode) [Regency TR-1]. World's first transistor radio (U.S. 1954). GET1, (point-contact type, for general purposes). GET2, (point-contact type, low-level AF amplifier). EW70, (output type). OC10, (low-level AF amplifier for hearing aids). OC12, (output type). OC15, (output type). OC50, (point-contact type, low-level AF amplifier). OC51, (point-contact type, for switching circuits).
1956 **Type** — **Function** V6/R3 — Oscillator V6/R3M — Mixer V6/R3 — 1st I.F. Amplifier V6/R2 — 2nd I.F. Amplifier V6/R2 — Detector V10/30A — A.F. Amplifier V10/30A — Push-Pull Output V10/30A — Push-Pull Output *Pam Model 710 — 8tr M/LW portable*	GET3 and GET4, (low-level AF amplifiers, experimentally introduced in the Spring). GET5, (output type, experimentally introduced in the Spring. Replaced EW70). GET6, (low-level AF amplifier, experimentally introduced in the Spring). OC16, (experimental output type, replaced OC15), OC45, (RF and IF amplifier). OC70, (low-level AF amp. Replaced OC10), OC71, (Output. Replaced OC12), OC72. V6 (RF range), V10 (audio and IF range), V15, V30 and V50 (power range). XA101, (IF amp. - Ediswan 'top-hat'), and XA102, (frequency changer/local oscillator). XB102 and XB103, (low-level AF amps.), and XC101, (output type). The transistors listed below illustrate typical line-ups found in the circuits of British and imported transistor radios from 1956 onwards. **BOLD TYPE** indicates an early use in a radio circuit. **V6/R3**, **V6/R3M**, V6/R3, **V6/R2** (x2), **V10/30A** (x3) [Pam 710]. First British tr. radio.
1957 **Type** — **Function** OC44 — Oscillator/Mixer OC45 — 1st I.F. Amplifier OC45 — 2nd I.F. Amplifier OC71 — A.F. Driver OC72 — Push-Pull Output OC72 — Push-Pull Output *K-B Model OP21 — 6tr M/LW portable*	**OC44**, **OC45** (x 2), **OC71** (x 2) [Akkord Peggie]. OC44, OC45 (x2), OC71, **OC72**, (OA70 diode) [Perdio PR1]. OC44, OC45 (x2), OC71, OC72 (x2), (OA79 diode) [Cossor 546]. OC44, OC45 (x2), OC71, OC72 (x2), (OA70 diode) [K-B OP21]. OC72 (x2) (preceded by DK96, DF96 and DAF96 valves) [H.M.V. 1410]. **OC604** (x2), **OC612** (x2), **OC613** [Telefunken Partner]. **V6/R4M**, **V6/R4**, V6/R2, **V10/50B**, V10/30A (x 2), (CG6E di.) [Pye P123BQ]. **XA102**, **XA101** (x3) (OA70 x2 diodes) [Cossor 561]. XA102, XA101 (x 2), **XB103**, **XC101** (x 2) [Vidor CN440, Gem]. XA102, XA101 (x2), **XB102** (x2), XC101 [Ace Courier 257]. XA102, XA101 (x2), **GET3** (x3) [G.E.C. 1650].
1958 **Type** — **Function** XA102 — Oscillator/Mixer XA101 — 1st I.F. Amplifier XA101 — 2nd I.F. Amplifier XB103 — A.F. Driver XC101 — Push-Pull Output XC101 — Push-Pull Output *Ekco Model BPT333 — 6tr M/LW portable*	OC44, OC45 (x2), **OC78D**, **OC78** (x2), (OA72 diode) [Emerson 888]. OC44, OC45 (x2), OC71, OC72, (OA70 diode) [Perdio PR2]. OC44, OC45 (x2), OC71, OC72 (x2) [Berec Demon]. OC44, OC45 (x2), OC71, OC72 (x2) [Cossor 569]. OC44, OC45 (x2), OC71, OC72 (x2) [Roberts RT1]. OC44, OC45 (x2), OC71, OC72 (x2), (OA70 x2 diodes) [Channel Transette 30]. OC44, OC45 (x2), **OC75**, OC72 (x2), (OA70 diode) [Braun KT3]. OC44, OC45 (x2), **OC81D**, **OC81** (x2) [Dansette RT60]. V6/R4M, **V6/R1** (x2), V10/30A, V10/50B, (OA70 diode) [Pam Gayplay III]. XA102, XA101 (x2), XB103, XC101 (x2), (CG12E diode) [Ekco BPT333]. XA102, XA101 (x2), XB103, XC101 (x2), (CG12E diode) [Ferranti PT1010].
1959 **Type** — **Function** GET874 — Oscillator/Mixer GET873 — 1st I.F. Amplifier GET873 — 2nd I.F. Amplifier GET114 — A.F. Driver GET114 — Push-Pull Output GET114 — Push-Pull Output *G.E.C. Model BC502 — 6tr M/LW portable*	**GET874**, **GET873** (x2), **GET114** (x3), (GEX11 diode) [G.E.C. BC502]. GET874, GET873 (x2), GET114 (x3), (GEX34 diode) [Beaumont Arundel]. OC44, OC45 (x2), OC78D, OC78 (x2), (OA81 diode) [Amplion A226]. OC44, OC45 (x2), OC78D, OC78 (x2), (OA70 diode) [Argosy TA1]. OC44, OC45 (x2), OC78D, OC78 (x2) (OA70 diode) [Emerson 555]. OC44, OC45 (x2), OC78D, OC78 (x2) (OA70 diode) [Ferranti PT1030]. OC44, OC45 (x2), OC71 (x2), **V15/10P** (x2) (OA70, OA79 diodes) [Perdio PR73]. OC613, OC612 (x2), OC604, OC604 (x2), (OA174 x2 diodes) [Goldhorn Amor]. **OC614**, OC612, OC604 (x3), OC604 (x2) (OA160, OA172 diodes) [Perth K766]. XA102, XB102, XB103, XA101 (x2), **XC131** (x2), (CG6E, CG12E diodes) [Dynatron TP11]. **1**, **2**, **3**, **4**, **5** (x2) Pye White Circle type transistors [Invicta 31].
1960 **Type** — **Function** 2SC73 — Oscillator/Mixer 2SC76 — 1st I.F. Amplifier 2SC76 — 2nd I.F. Amplifier 2SD65 — A.F. Driver 2SD65 — Push-Pull Output 2SD65 — Push-Pull Output *Sony Model TR620 — 6tr MW pocket portable*	**GC282**, **GC283**, **GC284**, **GC286**, **GC285** (x2), (1N87G diode) [Zenith Royal 50]. **GET693** (x3), **GET113**, GET114 (x3), **GET851** (x2), (GEX34 x2 ds) [G.E.C. BC562]. OC44, OC45 (x2), OC71, OC78D, OC78 (x2), (OA70 diode) [Bush TR90]. OC44, OC45 (x2), OC71, OC78D, OC78 (x2) [Cossor CR1301T]. OC44, OC45 (x2), **OC82D**, **OC82** (x2), OA70 diode) [Ever Ready Car Portable]. **OC170**, OC45 (x2), **OC602**, OC72 (x2) (OA70 x2 diodes) [Braun T4]. **OC171** (x5), OC71, **OC74** (x2), (OA70 x3, OA79 x2 diodes) [Braun T22]. **TK1000C** (x3), GET113, GET114 (x2), (CG64 diode) [K-B RP21]. XA102, XA101 (x2), **XB113**, XC131 (x2) [Berec Musketeer]. **2N217** (x4), **2N218** (x2), 2N217, (1N34A x2 diodes) [Eumig OKay]. **2SC73**, **2SC76** (x2), **2SD65** (x3), (1T23G diode) [Sony TR620].

283

Typical Transistor Line-ups, 1961 to 1966

Examples of the function of transistors used in radio circuits	Examples of the types of transistors used in radio circuits
1961 **Type** — **Function** AF117 — Oscillator/Mixer AF117 — 1st I.F. Amplifier AF117 — 2nd I.F. Amplifier OC81D — A.F. Driver OC81 — Push-Pull Output OC81 — Push-Pull Output *Alba Model Swift 44 — 6tr M/LW portable*	**AF114, AF115, AF116**(x3), OC71, OC81D, OC81 (x2) (OA79 x2, OA90ds.) [Bush VTR103]. **AF117** (x3), OC81D, OC81 (x2), (OA70, OA79 diodes) [Alba Swift 44]. GET874, GET873 (x2), GET113 (x3), [K-B TR11]. **NKT152, NKT153, NKT154, NKT254, NKT251** [Invicta 332]. **OC169** (x3), OC71, OC72 (x2), (OA90 diode) [Luxy 5910]. **OC615** (x2), **AF105** (x3), OC602, OC604, A105 (x2) [Telefunken Kavalier 3291L]. **T1832, T1833, T1657** (x3), GET114, GET113, GET114 (x2), (GEX12 x2, GEX13 di.) [G.E.C. BC563]. XA102, XA101 (x2), XB113, **XC171** (x2) [Ever Ready Sky Prince]. **2N1742, 2N1743, 2N1747**(x3), GET114, GET113, GET114(x2), (GEX12x2, GEX13 diodes) [G.E.C. BC563].
1962 **Type** — **Function** AF127 — Oscillator/Mixer AF127 — 1st I.F. Amplifier (A.G.C.) AF127 — 2nd I.F. Amplifier AC113 — A.F. Driver AC114 — Push-Pull Output AC114 — Push-Pull Output *Ferguson Model 3102 — 6tr M/LW personal portable*	AF117 (x3), OC71, OC81D, **OC81M/AC127**, (OA70 di.) Mullard trans. [Fidelity Floret]. **AF127** (x3), **AC113, AC114** (x2), (OA70 diode) [Ferguson 3102]. AF127 (x3), **PXB133, PXC181** (x2) (OA70 diode) [Philco 5100]. **GET884, GET883** (x2), GET113, **S5** (x2) (GEX12 diode) [McMichael M110]. NKT152, NKT153, NKT154, **NKT258, NKT257/NKT751**, (OA90 diode) [Ekco PT399]. OC44, OC45 (x2), **GET118, GET119**, (GEX12 diode) [G.E.C. G808]. **S50T, S51T** (x2), **S10T, S11T** x2, (OA91 diode) [Perdio PR33]. **T2067** (x3), OC81D, OC81, (OA90 diode) [Ferguson 3108]. **2SA122**, 2SC76 (x2), 2SD65 (x2), **2SB49** (x2), (1T23G x3 diodes) [Sony TR710B]. **2G417** (x3), 2G371A (x2), **2G381/2G339**, (OA70 diode) T.I. trans. [Fidelity Floret].
1963 **Type** — **Function** AF102 — FM R.F. Amplifier AF115 — FM Freq. Changer AF116 — FM I.F./AM Freq. Changer AF116 (x2) — I.F. Amplifiers NKT255E — A.F. pre-Amplifier NKT258 — A.F. Driver NKT753/NKT251 Comp. Sym. Output *Pye Model 1353 — 9tr M/LW/FM portable*	**AF102**, AF115, AF116(x3), NKT255E, NKT258, NKT753/NKT251, (OA70x3) [Pye 1353]. AF102, AF115 (x2), AF116 (x2), AC126 (x2), **AC128** (x2) [B&O 609FM Export II]. AF114, AF115, AF116 (x3), **AC125** (x2), AC128 (x2), (OA90, E25C5, BA102, OA79 x4 di.) [Cossor CR7225T]. AF117 (x3), **AC155**, AC113, **AC154** (x2) (OA79, OA90 diodes) [H.M.V. 2114]. **AF124, AF125**, AF116 (x3), **AC156**, AC113, AC154 (x2) (OA90 x2 diodes) [H.M.V. 2116]. OC44, OC45 (x2), OC81D, OC81 (x2) (OA70 diode) [Ever Ready Skylark]. **2G415** (x3), 2G417 (x2), 2G371/B, 2G339/B, 2G371/B, 2G381A, **2G399/A, Y159** (x2) [Fidelity Fairline]. **2N1632, 2N1526, 2N1524** (x3), **2N406, 2N408** (x2) R.C.A. transistors [Zenith 285]. **2SA80, 2SA12** (x2), **2SB75, 2SB77, 2SB156**, (1N34A x3 diodes) [Hitachi W752].
1964 **Type** — **Function** AF117 — Oscillator/Mixer AF117 — 1st I.F. Amplifier AF117 — 2nd I.F. Amplifier AC155 — A.F. Amplifier AC113 — A.F. Driver AC154/AC157 Comp. Sym. Output *Marconiphone Model 4112 — 7tr M/LW portable*	AF102, AF115, AF116 (x3), NKT255E, NKT258, **NKT703**, NKT251 (OA70 x3 diodes) [Ferranti PT1100]. AF114, AF115, AF116 (x3), OC71, OC81D, OC81 (x2), (OA91, OA90, OA91 x2 diodes) [Sobell S316]. AF114, AF116 (x4), OC71 (x2), OC74 (x2), (OA79 x2 diodes) [Stella 430]. AF117 (x3), OC81D, OC81 (x2), (OA79, OA90, AA129 diodes) [Roberts R300]. AF117 (x3), NKT255, NKT258, NKT251, NKT753, (OA70, OA90 diodes) [Pye 1352]. AF117 (x3), AC155, AC113, AC154/**AC157**, (OA70, AA120 di) [Marconi. 4112]. AF117 (x4), AC155, AC113, AC154 (x2), **AC169**, (OA90 diode) [Ultra 6116]. **2SA286, 2SA155, 2SA156, 2SB112** (x2), **2SB56** (x2) [Magnavox 7P22L].
1965 **Type** — **Function** AF117 — Oscillator/Mixer AF117 — 1st I.F. Amplifier AF117 — 2nd I.F. Amplifier AC127 — A.F. Driver OC81 — A.F. Driver AC127 — Output OC81 — Output *Baird Model 103 — 7tr M/LW portable*	AF115, AF117 (x2), AC127, OC81D, OC81, AC127, (OA90 di.) [G.E.C. G825]. AF115 (x2), AF117 (x2), OC71, OC81D, OC81 (x2), (OA90) [Bush TR116]. AF117 (x3), AC127, OC81, AC127, OC81, (OA79, OA90 diodes) [Baird 103]. AF117 (x2), AC127, OC81D, OC81, AC127, (OA79, OA90 diodes) [Ever Ready Sky Baby]. AF117 (x2), OC71, OC81D, OC81 (x2), (OA79 diode) [Philips 232]. AF124, AF125, AF116 (x3), AC155, AC113, AC169, AC154 (x2), (OA90 x5 di.) [Ferguson 3138]. AF127 (x3), **OC304, OC305, AC117, AC175** [Grundig Transonette 60]. **AF180**, AF115, AF114 (x3), OC71, OC81D, OC81 (x2) [Decca TP90/A]. **2SA235**(x2), **2SA234, 2SA233**(x2), 2SB75 (x2), 2SB156(x2), **2SA12C**, (1N34A x5 di.) [Sharp FYL119].
1966 **Type** — **Function** AF117 — Oscillator/Mixer AF117 — 1st I.F. Amplifier OC71 — 2nd I.F. Amplifier OC81D — A.F. Driver OC81 — Output OC81 — Output *Cossor Model CR1315T — 6tr M/LW portable*	AF102, AF115 (x2), AF116 (x2), OC71, OC75, AC128 (x2), (OA79, SFD107, 1N542 x2 di.) [Pam 5224]. AF115, AF117 (x2), NKT275P, **NKT775, NKT272A, NKT773**, NKT271A, (OA90 di.) [Dynatron TP36]. AF117 (x2), OC71, OC81D, OC81 (x2), (OA79 diode) [Cossor CR1315T]. **AF178**, AF115 (x2), AF116 (x2), OC75, AF117, AC128 (x2), **AC176** [Ferranti A1143]. AF180, AF114 (x4), AF117 (x3), OC71, OC75, AC127, OC81D, AC127, OC81, (AA119 x5, BA102, OA90, BA114 diodes) [Roberts R700]. **2SA73, 2SA49, 2SA53, 2SB54**, 2SB56 (x2), (1N60 diode) [Pye 1366]. **2SA440**(x2), **2SA203AA, 2SA324, 2SA321**(x2), **2SB185AA, 2SB186, 2SB22**(x2)(1N60x4) [Alba 131].

284

Typical Transistor Line-ups, 1967 to 1972

Examples of the function of transistors used in radio circuits	Examples of the types of transistors used in radio circuits
1967 **Type** — **Function** AF106 — FM R.F. Amplifier AF125 — FM Oscillator/Mixer AF115 — AM Mixer/1st AM/FM I.F. Amplifier AF116 — AM Oscillator AF116 (x2) — 2nd and 3rd AM/FM I.F. Amplifiers BC150 — A.F. Amplifier AC113 — Audio Driver AC176/AC128 — Comp. Sym. Output *H.M.V. Model 2148 — 10tr S/M/LW/FM portable*	**AF106**, AF125, AF115, AF116 (x3), BC150, AC113, AC176/AC128, (AA120, OA90 x4, OA79 x2 diodes) [H.M.V. 2148]. AF117 (x3), OC71, AC128 (x3), (OA90 diode) [Murphy B822]. **BF153UB, BF153UA, SA254, SA253, SA255, SA251, SA252,** (AA119 x2 diodes) [G.E.C. G835]. **C688D** (x2), **2SA222**, 2SA321 (x2), **A440A**, 2SB185, 2SB186, **2SB272**, (1S188 x8, 1S552 diodes) [Murphy B842]. **2SA201A, 2SA202D, 2SA198P, TG48, 2SB270** (x2), **2SB187** (x2), (1S426 diode) [Ekco PT302]. **2SA455, 2SB383** (x2), **2SA454, 2SC401** (x2), **2SC403** (x3), **2SC402**, (IT26 x3, IT2403, IT23 diodes) [Sony 5F94L].
1968 **Type** — **Function** AF115 — Oscillator/Mixer AF117 — 1st I.F. Amplifier AF117 — 2nd I.F. Amplifier AC155 — A.F. Amplifier AC113 — Audio Driver AC154/AC157 — Comp. Sym. Output *Ferguson Model 3164 — 7tr S/M/LW portable*	AF115, AF117 (x2), AC155, AC113, AC154/AC157, (OA70, AA120 diodes) [Ferguson 3164]. AF115, AF117 (x2), NKT275P, NKT775, NKT272A, NKT773, NKT271A (OA90 diode) [Dynatron TP40]. AF180, AF115, AF114 (x3), OC71, OC811D (x2), (OA79 x2, OA91, SF0107 diodes) [Magneta PTR/2]. **BF185** (x2), **BF194**, BF194B, BF195C, BF195D, **BC149**, AC128, AC127, AC128 [Alba 636]. **TAD 100** (integrated circuit), OC44/45, AC187, AC188, (BA114 diode) [Roberts RIC-1]. 2SC535B, 2SC525A, 2SC460A, 2SC460B (x2), 2SC460C, 2SC458B, 2SC458C, 2SB156C (x2), (1N34A, 1N60 x4 diodes) [Ferguson 3167].
1969 **Type** — **Function** 2SC645B — R.F. Amplifier 2SC645A — FM Conv. 2SA1028A — AM Conv. 2SA104P — 1st AM/FM I.F. Amplifier 2SC829BB — 2nd AM/FM I.F. Amplifier 2SC829BY — 3rd FM I.F. Amplifier 2SB175A/B — 1st and 2nd A.F. Amplifiers 2SB475E (x2) — Push-Pull Output *Bush Model VTR125 — 10tr MW/FM portable*	AF117 (x3), OC81D, OC81 (x2), (OA70, OAZ202, STC57 diodes) [Philips 272]. AF178, AF115, AF116 (x3), **NKT267D**, AC187, AC188, BC108, (AA119 x4 diodes) [Dynatron TP43T]. BC113, **BF222** (x2), **BF251** (x2), **U14552/2** (4tr + 1 diode module), (OA90, AA119 x3 diodes) [G.E.C. G838]. **BC195C** (x2), BF194B, BF195D, **BC159** (x2), BC149, AC128, AC127, (AA119 x3, AA129 diodes) [Fidelity Rad 15]. 2SA440 (x2), 2SA324, 2SA321 (x2), **2SP185** (x3), **2SP187** (x2), (1S188 x7 diodes) [Alba 675]. **2SC645B, 2SC645A, 2SA1028A, 2SA104P, 2SC829BB, 2SC829BY, 2SB175A, 2SB175B, 2SB475E** (x2) (OA90 x4 diodes) [Bush VTR125].
1970 **Type** — **Function** AF117 — Oscillator/Mixer AF117 — 1st I.F. Amplifier AF117 — 2nd I.F. Amplifier AC125 — A.F. Amplifier AC126 — Audio Driver AC128 — Push-Pull Output AC128 — Push-Pull Output *Bush Model TR122 — 7tr M/LW portable*	AF117 (x3), AC125, AC126, AC128 (x2) (OA79 diode) [Bush TR122]. AF124 (x2), AF121 (x3), AC127, AC128 (x3) [Pye 1404]. BF194 (x3), **BC172**, 2N3702, AC187K, AC188K (OA90, D3 diodes) [Ferguson 3170]. BF195 (x2), **ME3001, ME4012, ME3011, ME6002**, AC127, AC128 (AA119 x3 diodes) [Fidelity Rad 19]. BF273, BF194 (x5), **D1569, 2N3711, 2N3702, AC142K, AC141K**, (OA90 x5, D3 diodes) [Ultra 6169]. **BX201** (integrated circuit), 2SC403A, 2SD187, **2SB136**, IT26 (x2) [Sony ICR-120]. **TAA 840** (integrated circuit), AC127, AC128 [Philips IC-103]. 2SC535B, 2SC535A, 2SC460C, 2SC454B (x2), 2SC460B, 2SC458C, 2SB75B, 2SB77B (x2), (1N60 x6 diodes) [Murphy B865].
1971 **Type** — **Function** BF115 — FM R.F. Amplifier BF115 — FM Oscillator/Mixer BF121 (x3) — 1st, 2nd and 3rd FM I.F. Amplifiers BC154 — A.F. Amplifier BC148B — Audio Driver AC117P — Push-Pull Output AC175P — Push-Pull Output *Bang & Olufsen Model Beolit 400 — 9tr FM portable*	BF115 (x2), BF121 (x3), **BC154**, BC148B, AC117P, AC175P, (1N4148 x3, BA138, AA119 diodes) [Bang & Olufsen Beolit 400]. BF194 (x3), **MPS6522, U3540**, 2N3702, AC142, AC141, (OA90 x2, D3 diodes) [Marconiphone 4174]. **TAA 450** (integrated circuit), BF194 (x2), BF195, BC147, BC108, AC187, AC188 [Decca PR204]. TAD 100 (integrated circuit), BC158, **T2**, AC188, AC187, BC148 [Hacker RP73]. 2SC535B (x2), 2SC460B (x3), 2SC454B (x2), 2SC458B (x2), 2SB370C (x2), (1N34A x4, 1S85, 1N60 x2, 15990 x2 diodes) [Bush VTR165]. 2SC645, **2SC829A** (x5), 2SA101X, 2SB171A, 2SB175, 2SB324B (x2), (SD-46 x3, 5D461 x2 diodes) [Murphy B868].
1972 **Type** — **Function** BF194 — FM R.F. Amplifier BF195 — FM Oscillator/Mixer BF194B — AM Mixer/1st AM/FM I.F. Amplifier BF195 — AM Oscillator BF195C — 2nd AM/FM I.F. Amplifier BC159 — A.F. Amplifier BC149 — Audio Driver AC188/AC187 — Push-Pull Output *Fidelity Model Rad 21 — 9tr S/M/LW/FM portable*	BF194, BF195, BF194B, BF195, BF195C, BC159, BC149, AC188, AC187, (AA119 x3, AA129, BA102 diodes) [Fidelity Rad 21]. BF194, **BF274** (x4), BC159, BC148LC, **ME4101, BC303, SMV560** (x2), (AA112 x4, C1063 x2, 1S44, 1S970 x2, TAA611B diodes) [H.M.V. 2176]. BF195 (x2), T2, AC188, AC187, BC148, BF194, (AA119 x2 diodes) [Hacker RP71]. **BF255** (x2), **BF241** (x4), **BC252B**, BC172B (x2), AC187, AC188, (ITT210, AA143 x5 diodes) [Murphy B844]. 2SA455 (x2), 2SC403 (x3), 2SC401, 2SB136 (x2), (IT26 x3, IT23 diodes) [Sony TFM8251]. **2SC1047**, 2SC829A (x9), **2SC828**, 2SB175 (x2), **2SB178** (x2), (1S8S, VD1212, 1N34 diodes) [Standard RF-950E].

The TR-1 — The World's First Transistor Radio, 1954

fig.930. The Regency TR-1, housed in a black two-piece moulded polystyrene case — initially also available in ivory, mandarin red and cloud grey (later in forest green and 'mahogany' colours too).

Covering the medium waveband only, the dial is marked from '5.5' to '16' (550kHz to 1600kHz), but also shows little red triangles at 640 and 1240kHz. These were Civil Defence markings and indicated the position of emergency U.S. broadcasting stations which would give out Government and other official announcements in the event of a nuclear attack from Russia. The TR-1 was launched well into the 'cold war' period which existed between the west and the Soviet Union and it was seen as an ideal emergency receiver for 'the atomic age'. Original price: $49.95, battery $1.15, optional earphone $7.50 and leather case $3.95. *(Photo: actual size 5" x 3").*

The world's first transistor radio was made in America in 1954. *"America?"* I hear you say . . . *"Surely you mean Japan?!"* Well, you may be forgiven for thinking this for it's a common belief that a country so good at producing this type of product would be the one to have the idea in the first place. But over 40 years ago, the world's first transistor radio was put into production by the Regency division of Industrial Development Engineering Associates (I.D.E.A.) in Indianapolis, who test-launched model TR-1 in the New York and Los Angeles areas just in time for Christmas 1954.

It was a bold step. At a time when the thermionic valve completely dominated radio circuits you could buy a pretty good valve table model for $15, whereas the battery-operated TR-1 cost $49.95. Since their invention in 1947 at Bell Laboratories (the research arm of A.T. & T.), the only commercial application of component transistors had been in

hearing aids, and apart from a few 'amateur' circuits published in American journals and one or two radio manufacturers' laboratory experiments, the transistor radio as a ready-to-listen-to commercial product was a complete innovation. But the TR-1's success was immediate, and so popular was it in its trial areas, that soon it began to appear on the black market in other cities all over the United States and within a year around 100,000 had been sold.

Designed by I.D.E.A.'s Richard Koch, the main advantage that the TR-1 possessed right from the outset was its small size and therefore its extreme portability. Furthermore, the low power consumption of the set's transistorised superheterodyne circuit meant that its battery would last from between 20 and 30 hours, compared to around 4 to 5 hours with a miniature valve portable. All the TR-1's components including loudspeaker, power source and ferrite core aerial were built into a plastic case measuring just 5" x 3" x 1 1/4". Advertisements boasted that it could slip easily into a shirt pocket. Mind you, it had to be a man's quality dress shirt pocket — and not the slightly smaller pockets of cheaper shirts. It was immediately of appeal to a wide audience eager for a lightweight portable set for listening to live radio entertainment 'in the great outdoors' through its miniature 2 3/4" loudspeaker. In addition, the TR-1 was provided with an optional earphone for discrete 'personal listening' — long before the days of the Walkman.

The original idea of producing a radio using transistors was conceived by Patrick Haggerty, then Executive Vice President of Texas Instruments, who saw it as a way for his company to expand into the semiconductor market. T.I. made and supplied the 4 component transistors (n-p-n grown junction germanium triodes), and I.D.E.A. was given the task of designing, producing and marketing the TR-1. While some U.S. manufacturers had been putting out the occasional pocket valve portable since the mid-1940s (notably the Belmont Boulevard, 1945, and the Privat-ear, 1951), few had ever attempted to produce such a small radio receiver with a built-in loudspeaker before and none with a circuit using transistors.

With the TR-1, many firms co-operated in specially manufacturing the miniature components needed: the loudspeaker was produced by Jensen of Chicago; the tuning condenser by the Radio Condenser Company of New Jersey; the intermediate frequency transformers by the Vokar Corporation of Michigan; the volume control by the Chicago Telephone Supply Corporation of Indiana; the ceramic capacitors by Centralab of Milwaukee, and the two-piece polystyrene plastic case by the Chicago-based industrial design company Painter, Teague and Petertil.

In terms of marketing, the production of the TR-1 was a brilliant move for it gave Texas Instruments the world stage highlighting their ability to manufacture and develop reliable transistors (later including superior silicon types) — factors which would eventually turn them into the world's largest producer of

semiconductors for external sale. Despite the TR-1's tinny and relatively poor sound quality (a characteristic fault that seems to be endemic to this type of radio), in relation to radio history, the TR-1 as the world's first transistor radio and the world's first pocket one at that, was a formidable milestone. Its basic slim rectangular form set the mould of a thousand-and-one other pocket transistors which were eventually to follow it. Yet, for a few years, other U.S. radio manufacturers entering the transistor portable field generally favoured the bigger 'lunch-box' style (horizontal rectangular case with a carrying handle). Favoured it, that is, until Japanese radio manufacturers discovered the ideal target for pocket transistors - the teenage market!

fig.931. Far left, (*photo actual size*), one of Texas Instrument's n-p-n, grown junction, germanium type transistors as used in the TR-1 in 1954 — the very first application of a transistor in a commercial radio. Back in 1952 though, Texas Instruments was already beginning to get involved in small scale transistor production — an archive copy of an original T.I. sales order dated 31st December 1952 shows the sale of ten TI-101 point-contact transistors to the Gruen Watch Company for experimental use with electronic movements. The TI-101, above, right, (*photo actual size*) was the first component transistor produced by Texas Instruments and it used mechanical parts purchased from Bell Labs., along with information on construction and use. Western Electric, the manufacturing arm of A.T. & T. who held the original patents for the component transistor, was now selling these patents under licence for $25,000 to 'all-comers' interested in getting involved experimentally in transistor manufacture. Apart from T.I. and Western Electric themselves, these included R.C.A., Philco and Raytheon — the latter having produced small scale runs of transistors as far back as 1949 and who by the end of 1952 had managed to encourage a few hearing-aid manufacturers to use the new component.

In 1953, W.E. signed a provisional agreement with a Japanese telecommunications engineering company, the action of which was to have far reaching and devastating effects on the whole consumer electronics industry in the western world. That company was Tokyo Tsushin Kogyo Ltd. — within a few years though, it was known by a much more manageable name.... the SONY Corporation. By June 1954, T.T.K. Ltd. had begun to make their own component transistors and the following year produced their first portable transistor radio using 'Sony' as a brand-name, the TR55 (a re-styled version of an un-released prototype known as model TR52). In 1957, worldwide sales of their first pocket transistor, the TR-63, topped more than 500,000 (a large proportion of these imported into the U.S.), by which time other Japanese firms making transistor radios (Hitachi, Toshiba and Matsushita) had joined them and the Japanese and Far Eastern competition, in the U.S. at least, was well under way. The U.K. radio industry, meanwhile, was able to enjoy a short respite (*see page 198*).

fig.932 (*above*). The internal layout of the TR-1, snug and well-fitting, but not impossibly cramped (*photo actual size*). Its designer, Richard Koch, had worked very hard to get an original 6-transistor 6" x 3" prototype circuitboard down to a 4-transistor receiver that would fit into a shirt pocket, and weigh just 12 ounces. Several different companies worked on the TR-1 project to produce the miniature components needed.

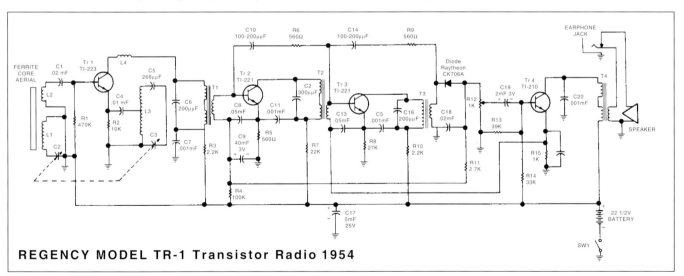

REGENCY MODEL TR-1 Transistor Radio 1954

fig.933. The layout of the TR-1's superheterodyne circuit. The germanium transistors employed here were as follows: TI-223 (converter oscillator), TI-221 (first IF amplifier), TI-221 (second IF amplifier) and TI-210 (output audio amplifier), plus a Raytheon CK706A or Tungsol TS117 (germanium diode detector). At the time, germanium was the only material used to make semiconductors, although it was known to produce relatively unstable transistors whose performance could be greatly affected by heat. However, in May 1954, T.I. took the first steps in the production of temperature tolerant silicon transistors, and although they were not ready for use with the TR-1, it was with the development of this new superior type of transistor that T.I. was able to establish a commanding lead in the semiconductor field.

Special thanks to Texas Instruments, to Ann Westerlin (Manager, Corporate Archives, T.I.) and to Ed Millis (Manager, Artifacts Program, T.I.) for their help with this section on the TR-1.

The Pam 710 - The First British All-Transistor Radio, 1956

Britain's first all-transistor portable radio receiver was released by Pam (Radio & Television) Ltd. at the end of March 1956. Model 710 employed an 8-transistor, 2-waveband circuit covering 176-568 metres on the medium waveband, and 1500 metres on the long waveband (fix-tuned to the B.B.C.'s Light Programme). Compared to the 12 ounce TR-1 (*see pages 280-281*), the 710's weight was colossal — 5 pounds including batteries!

The size of a small handbag, the style of the Pam 710 was similar to that of many other portables already being produced by manufacturers around the mid1950s - even with the advent of transistors, with a few minor exceptions, (*ie.* Perdio), British designers tended to opt for larger cabinets with larger speakers and better sound quality, rather that go for the poorer, sometimes 'tinny' sound of small pocket sets which were seen at first as a bit of a lightweight novelty. Listed at £22.14s.10d plus £8.15s.2d Purchase Tax, the Pam 710 was twice the price of a comparable valve portable and a risky and heavy investment for anyone wanting to try out this milestone in British receiver design.

There was an initial reluctance by the public to accept transistors and this is illustrated by a story told to me by a sales assistant who worked at Install Radio & Television Service at High Wycombe in 1956. Being an authorised Pam dealer, the shop had decided to stock the Pam 710 — albeit just one model — and had proudly put this on show in the window. It was soon spotted by a well-healed regular customer who, for several consecutive days, came to and fro, asking questions and generally teetering on the edge of a purchase, while the assistants held their breath (in those days, a 30 guinea radio would show good profit). At last, and much to everyone's relief, he said he would buy it. But just moments after he left the

MODEL 710

WHAT IS A TRANSISTOR ?

The transistor is simply a tiny crystal of the rare element "Germanium" enclosed in a hemetically sealer container. It is minute in size and colossal in its potentialities. The transistors in the Pam 710 perform all the functions of the normal radio valve — but are infinitely more economical, stronger and more reliable in every way.

SIZE  ACTUAL

BEAUTIFUL APPEARANCE

The PAM 710 has a stoutly-constructed luxury cabinet. It comes in a beautiful ivory and tan finish, set off with gold metallic strips and a real leather carrying handle.

ECONOMY IN RUNNING

The model 710 works entirely off four U2 batteries. The estimated playing life of these batteries, on one set, is 750 hours. By using the set for a period of 4 hours a day, 6 months use is obtained at the extraordinarily low cost of only 2s.4d.

OUTSTANDING REPRODUCTION

The space-saving properties of the transistor and the small batteries used in the set make possible the use of a large High Flux permanent magnet Elliptical Speaker (6" x 4"). This gives perfect reproduction and makes the Transistor Portable outstanding amongst other battery portables.

fig.934. A 1956 advertising leaflet for the Pam Model 710.

shop with the Pam 710 tucked safely under his arm, he changed his mind and brought it back, only to catch the assistants, and the manager, still revelling in the sale and dancing around the counter!

Pam was a subsidiary of Pye Ltd. of Cambridge. As a long established and highly respected radio manufacturing company, Pye, headed by C.O. Stanley, was hesitant about risking its reputation on such an untried innovation as a transistorised radio, and although the 710 was actually designed in Pye's own research laboratories, as a safeguard Pye had its subsidiary company test the market for them and the 710 was therefore brought out under the Pam label.

It is not known how many were produced, or how many were sold, but the 710's reception within the radio industry and in the trade press was very favourable, and within a short time other manufacturers began to bring out their own transistor radios having been shown the way. Pye themselves followed the 710 with their own version early in 1957 - the medium and longwave (fix-tuned) model P123BQ (*figs. 939 and 941*) which employed

many of the physical parts of the 710 but used only 6 transistors, (*see also the recently discovered 'Pye 710', fig. 940*).

With the Pam 710 occupying such an important place in the development of radio, it is, naturally, the subject of a great deal of interest from collectors anxious to acquire one. But there seem to be very few surviving examples - one is on display in a cabinet in the Science Museum at South Kensington, and there are only half a dozen others known in private U.K. collections. Can this number really be a true representation of those that were produced or will other ones come to light?

The team of research scientists who were working towards the development of a transistor radio circuit at the Pye laboratories in the mid-1950s was led by Dr. Lax, a short rotund East European with a liking for Players Navy Cut cigarettes. The youngest member of the team was 22 year old Mick Carter, then in his fifth year as apprentice with Pye and who has kindly supplied me with the following recollections which provide a fascinating insight into the working practices of the company's Transistor Section.

[Journal entry, June 13th 1955]. *Today I moved into the Transistor Section and am now working for Dr. Lax. The others being Carlo Rossi and Amal Roy. It was terribly hectic and I didn't know whether I was coming or going. Dr. Lax just scrawled out a little bit of circuit and said "Make it and see what happens".* Dr Lax came to this country in the 1930's, possibly from Czechoslovakia. I believe he once told us that he had worked for the state railways before the war. He was a very jolly person with twinkling eyes and heavy jowls which wobbled whenever he shook his head. I have a mental picture that he somewhat resembled Alfred Hitchcock. He smoked untipped cigarettes, often sending me (the youngest) out to buy him a packet of ten which he generously handed around while we worked, so that he never had any and was always asking everyone "Give me cigarette please" in his accented voice. Standards of cleanliness in laboratories have certainly changed since those days. At a guess, Dr. Lax would be nearly 90 years old now.

There were others in the Transistor Section at Pye whose names I have now forgotten. After so long it's hard to remember what the others were doing. I do know that, simultaneously with the development of a transistor radio circuit, the team, under Amal Roy, was working on a battery operated record player and, under Carlo Rossi, a deaf-aid (a prototype version of which I unofficially used on my motorbike as an intercom to my pillion passenger during a holiday trip down to Cornwall). I remember Rossi getting an ear infection from repeatedly transferring the deaf-aid's earpiece from the dusty bench into his ear. He was medically advised to keep the outer part of the device immersed in antiseptic solution. However, it dissolved the plastic moulding into a jelly!

[Journal entry, August 10th 1955]. *At work I have really got settled in with Transistors, although I do not know very much about them theoretically. Today after much trouble we have the oscillator, mixer, IF and detector stages working properly on a Bakelite 'chassis' similar to a printed circuit.* The local oscillator invariably stopped working at the high frequency end of the medium waveband due to the low gain of these early germanium junction transistors. Even those that did initially work failed to do so if the battery voltage was a bit low.

[Journal entry, August 10th 1955, continued]. *Dr. Lax is great fun, once you get to know him and his ways, and now we have moved up into the hut on the flat roof we enjoy fresh air and sunshine all day. It's terrific and we do far more work up there, it's easy to concentrate.* The move to the roof was to get away from radio interference generated by the machinery and television soak testing in the factory. This allowed more representative measurements to be made with the B.B.C.'s regular broadcasts. Leastways, that was our excuse, even though we had a screened Faraday cage in the laboratory for precise field strength measurements.

The transistor radio circuit being developed in Dr. Lax's department was an amplitude modulated (AM) superheterodyne receiver covering the medium and long wavebands. We made several versions, and from one of these later emerged a "production engineered" version which became the Pam 710. The circuits we designed had the standard Intermediate Frequency (IF) of 470 kHz. One of my first tasks was the electrical design and mechanical construction of the prototype IF transformers. The first ones were made from a cylindrical ferrite tube, approximately 0.5 inch diameter, surrounding the coil, with a tuning slug in the middle and a paxolin base, with

fig.935. A rare sight indeed . . . . two Pam 710's together! On the left is shown the very neat layout of this important set, easily disassembled for servicing by removing four bolts hidden beneath the volume and tuning controls. The cabinet was designed by Alan Bedmall, whose brief (ordered by C.O. Stanley himself) was to adopt a clean, honest, no-frills line, and to promote "big-sound" — hence the large 6" x 4" loudspeaker.

fig.936. A close-up of the Pam 710's push-pull output transistors (these are V10/15A's, alternatives to V10/30A types). The one on the right is marked '7 56' indicating that it was made in July 1956, just 4 months after the set first appeared on the market.

connection pins, glued to the ferrite tube. I used available parts rather than specially manufactured items — parts that I was familiar with from my apprenticeship in various departments in the Pye factory. The ferrite cylinder was pushed into a cup shaped nylon clip, originally intended to hold electrolytic capacitors on end in a metal chassis. The clip had an external central boss with a small concentric hole in the middle whose function was to insulate one of the axial leads and to secure the capacitor by deforming the boss with a hot tool after it had been pushed through a hole in the chassis. However, for my transformer, a screw thread was tapped into the clip's central hole for adjusting the internal slug which was constructed from a piece of ferrite rod glued to a brass screw. The clip, now containing the ferrite tube, coil and slug, was pushed into a cylindrical aluminium can such that the boss and its screw protruded through a hole at the top end, thus allowing tuning adjustment. The aluminium can had tabs at its open end to secure it to the paxolin base. A later version had a dust iron core and rectangular aluminium can, with the parallel tuning capacitor fitted inside. The terminals were made from brass dressmakers' pins because their heads could be pressed down flat into the paxolin base to keep them out of the magnetic circuit, and their flat domes allowed their coil wires to be soldered (British innovation at its best!).

However, when the prototype unit was passed down to the production engineers, they wanted to use 'proper' components, so they discarded the brass pins, amongst other items, and put in longer steel ones which protruded into the magnetic field. This had the effect of lowering the circuit 'Q' and widening the IF bandwidth. In order to maintain a suitable gain/bandwidth for acceptable adjacent channel separation, they had to lower the IF to a non-standard 120 kHz.

This was one of the reasons which prompted me to ask Dr. Lax if, before being called up for National Service, I could have a free hand in designing a different radio circuit using the latest knowledge that we had acquired. At that time my fellow students, apprentices and friends were very much into the new age of tape recording and hi-fi. One aspect which interested us very much was loudspeaker enclosures. It was the era of large Wharfdale speakers in Briggs sandfilled corner cabinets, Quad and Leak amplifiers, Connoisseur turntables with lightweight pickups, Wearite tape decks and Vortexion tape recorders. At that time, Pye was producing the Black Box record player and coining the phrase "high-fidelity". It was also the beginning of microgroove long play records using vinyl. There were scientific lectures demonstrating multi-speaker arrays and the Ionophone with its zero inertia ionised air driver using a quartz tube with a modulated high voltage. Pye had also just started to produce its own record label, and was experimenting with electrostatic loudspeakers, one of which I saw was the size of a door.

These things are mentioned only to illustrate the new attitudes to acoustics and quality audio reproduction that were emerging at that time and which influenced me in the design of the new radio. My objective was to produce a portable radio with a long battery life, efficient audio output with low distortion even at maximum volume, high signal sensitivity with good adjacent channel separation, and an aesthetically pleasing appearance. The radio was to be capable of being held in one hand. Basically, all the attributes I thought desirable but had never seen in one device. I named this receiver the "Mark-Five" as it was the fifth experimental transistor radio design that the Transistor Section team had put together, except that this one was solely my own creation. It was made with only the medium waveband. Although the Light Programme was broadcast on 1500 metres longwave, it was also on medium wave (on 247 metres), along with the B.B.C.'s Home Service and Third Programme and there were few foreign medium wave stations to cause interference. Therefore I felt there was little incentive to have a long waveband with the added complexity of secondary aerial and local oscillator windings, or switches, or additional capacitors to pad out the tuning capacitor. Nowadays, the B.B.C. has almost abandoned the medium wave. It is now cluttered with overlapping channels. Whatever happened to the International agreements on transmitter power and bandwidth separation? Come back Lord Hill, all is forgiven!

[Journal entry, October 5th 1955]. *Work is going well and at the moment I am making a Mark-Five transistor receiver . . . . . We are also making a transistorised TV set but as yet I have had nothing to do with it.*

[Journal entry, December 5th 1955]. *Even at work I can no longer do things properly. I have always made mistakes, but just lately, there have been more than ever. Dr. Lax doesn't say anything, then I don't think he ever would, he just looks hurt.* Not everything went well as this entry indicated. At the same time as working as part of the Transistor Section, I was also studying hard at night school for my H.N.C. finals and Endorsement subjects for Grad. I.E.E. (two years work in one). The 'mistakes' refer to blowing-up or otherwise damaging a transistor. These days this would not cause more response other than an expletive or two and a quick trip to the stores for a replacement. But in 1955, the loss of a transistor meant that the project would be held up until a new transistor with the same characteristics could be made.

The germanium junction transistors that we used then were literally made by hand in an experimental department at Pye. Ones with good high-frequency gain were few and far between. We had already obtained some from America, at vast expense, and these were religiously unsoldered or removed from their miniature three-pin sockets and locked away in the night safe at the end of each working day! Commercial low frequency audio transistors (OC71 and OC72) from Mullard did not become available to us until the summer of 1956, and then only in limited numbers.

Manufacture (if that is the right word?) of transistors at Pye began, I was told, when the then Managing Director, Mr. C.O. Stanley, came back from the U.S.A. in the early 1950s with information that the Americans had invented an amplifying device called a "Transistor" that would replace thermionic valves. He gave orders to make some. A small amount of germanium was obtained and sliced up in the factory on the diamond wheels, which were normally used for cutting the quartz crystals for high frequency oscillators (the crystal cutting department subsequently became the 'Cathodeon' subsidiary). The pieces of germanium

then had blobs of indium put on opposite faces, and were put into a small oven for a period of time. This caused the indium to diffuse into the germanium to form a three pole junction. Each one was tested to determine its frequency gain characteristic before being put into a small brown paper envelope on which the test data was handwritten. Although I was not involved in that side of development, I do remember that it was a bit of a hit and miss process — very crude by today's standards.

The man in charge of transistor development was also from Eastern Europe, Poland I think. He was of similar build to Dr. Lax, but younger. Although there is no mention of it in my journal, I do remember the excitement when he (the Pole), came bounding into our department waving a brown paper envelope and shouting gleefully that they had produced a transistor with a Beta cut-off greater than 1 mHz. Dr. Lax couldn't wait to try it out and I had to remove the local oscillator from our circuit immediately and put in this new one. Everyone gathered around to hear if it would work over the whole waveband. It did so, successfully. That early transistor work grew into the 'Newmarket Transistor' company.

I was called up for National Service in November 1956 and by that time had seen one of the circuit designs we had been working on develop into the Model 710. I must say I was proud to be associated with the design and production of Britain's first transistor radio but at the same time I was disappointed. Not by the quality of its circuit, for that worked very well indeed, but by the cabinet it was housed in. I was young and go-ahead and was hoping for something a little more different, a little more modern to go with this new modern technology. Instead we got a set which looked like any other portable around at the time.

Of my own design (the "Mark-Five") I don't think it went any further than the prototype stage — even though C.O. Stanley took one with him on holiday to Ireland to try it out. That one I never saw again, nor the one I made for Dr. Lax, but I still have another version. It used three associated 'high' frequency Pye transistors (V6/R3 devices, as in the 710) in short rectangular cans with rounded ends, painted red. Pye AF transistors were painted grey-green. These germanium junction transistors had such a high internal collector-to-base capacitance, that each of the IF stages had to have a neutralising feedback capacitor to prevent high frequency instability. These capacitors had to be selected on test to get the right balance. It says a lot for the skill of the guys who made these transistors at Pye that, after all these years, they do not seem to have drifted at all. The set works as well today as it did the day it was made.

Mick Carter, Aldershot, Hampshire. 8/96.

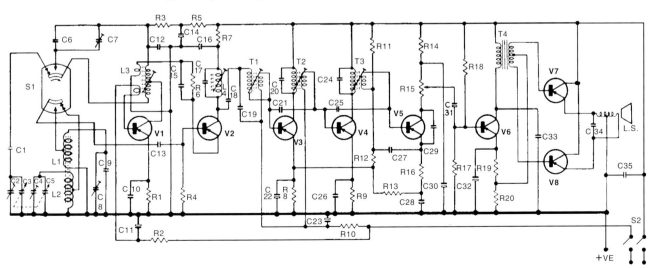

fig.937. The circuit of Pam 710. The transistor line-up comprises: **V1** Oscillator V6/R3 (V6/R6), **V2** Mixer V6/R3M (V6/R6M), **V3** 1st IF V6/R3 (V6/R6), **V4** 2nd IF V6/R2 (V6/R3), **V5** Detector V6/R2 (V6/R3), **V6** AF Amplifier V10/30A (V10/50A), **V7** Output V10/30A (V10/15A or V10/50A), **V8** Output V10/30A (V10/15A or V10/50A). Transistors in brackets show alternatives.

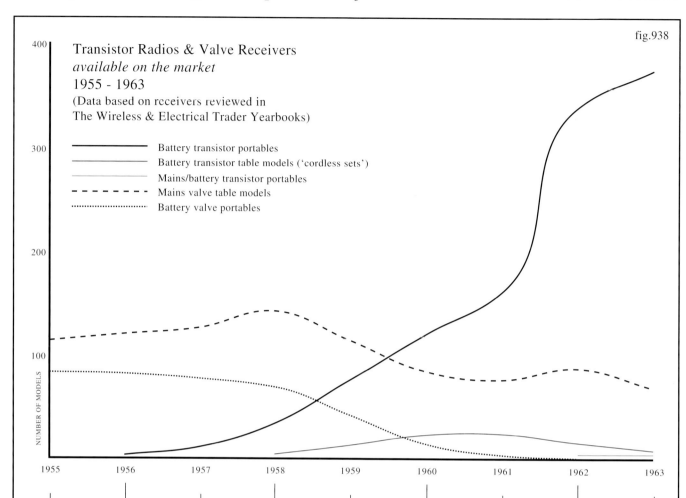

fig.938

Transistor Radios & Valve Receivers
available on the market
1955 - 1963
(Data based on receivers reviewed in
The Wireless & Electrical Trader Yearbooks)

——————— Battery transistor portables
——————— Battery transistor table models ('cordless sets')
——————— Mains/battery transistor portables
– – – – – Mains valve table models
·················· Battery valve portables

NUMBER OF MODELS

By 1955, the world had already seen the launch of the first transistor radios from both the West and the East — the U.S. Regency TR-1 (1954) and the Japanese Sony TR55 (1955). Both these radios exhibited characteristics destined to become hallmarks of the future development of transistors — small size and portability.

In Britain, G.E.C. and Mullard Ltd. were manufacturing transistors for experimental use and several firms were using these to develop prototype radio circuits — for a while, though, hearing-aids remained the only practical application of transistors in British consumer products.

Books like *"Practical Transistors & Transistor Circuits"* by J.S. Kendall (Bernards Publishers Ltd., 1954) appeared giving amateurs instructions for making not only transistor radios, but also the actual transistors themselves.

The first all-British transistor radio, the Model 710, was introduced in 1956 by Pam [Radio & TV] Ltd., a subsidiary of the radio-giant, Pye Ltd. Shunning miniaturisation, this was a beefy handbag-type radio, echoing a style already established in Britain by battery valve portables. It was twice the price of a comparable valve model and sales were slow because of this, and because customers were initially suspicious of this departure from familiar technology. But it was beautifully designed and solidly built and it did work extremely well — a very creditable first offering from the new transistor era.

In January, Ever Ready announced their 'PP' series of batteries (PP1 to PP9) specifically for powering transistorised circuits. By December, less than a dozen transistor radios (all portables) had been introduced on the market in Britain, plus three valve/transistor hybrids (Grundig 200, H.M.V. 1410, and Marconiphone P60B). The industry, however, began to invest heavily in this new branch of electronics with expectations of great improvement and reliability of the components. G.E.C., Mullard, Ediswan and Pye (Newmarket) were now all involved in component transistor production. One newcomer to radio manufacturing, Perdio Ltd., was so confident about the future of the transistor that they specialised solely in transistorised products, launching their first radio, the PR1, in June 1957.

With mass production, component transistors were getting cheaper and Mullard, Ediswan and other suppliers were able to reduce their prices substantially. There was a marked increase in the number of transistor sets, particularly pocket portables. While most of these covered the medium and long wavebands, the 'Trawler Band' (c.90-180 metres) was introduced in some models (ie. the Perdio Continental and the Pye P444). Out of a total of 1,800,000 sets sold in Britain in 1959, just 3% were imported — these mainly coming from Europe and from Scandinavia. By 1963, this had risen to 36% (see right).

A new class of transistor radio was introduced in 1958 — the battery table model. The first two released were the Dansette RT60 and the Pam 365. Because they imitated mains valve table models — only without having a trailing power cable with a plug on the end of it — they were soon known as 'cordless sets'. As a class of receiver they were never very numerous and by 1963 were well in decline, soon to be superseded by mains-only transistorised table models (like the B.&O. 900K of 1964), and quality transistorised hi-fi tuners.

The transistor portable was still being generally regarded as a rather expensive novelty with the lowest-priced model (the Perdio PR4) for sale at £13.13s.0d including P.T. However, by the end of 1958, sales and confidence had very much improved and just two years after their introduction, the number of transistor portables released onto the market had for the first time overtaken valve portables (soon destined to vanish forever — see 1961, right).

A typical transistor circuit line-up (ie. Cossor 569) comprised Mullard OC44 [frequency changer], OC45 (x2) [IF amplifiers], OC71 [AF driver] and OC72 (x2) [output pair], although Ediswan's 'top hat' range (XA102, XA101 etc.) was also popular amongst manufacturers and often specified as an alternative line-up in their circuits.

A new Anglo-Japanese trade agreement was signed and the first wave of Japanese transistor radios started to appear in Britain, headed by Sony (with model TR620) and Toshiba (with model 6TP-354). Within a few years, the popularity of transistor products from Japan and the Far East would have a devastating effect on our long-established radio industry.

The development of VHF component transistors (ie. the Mullard OC170 and OC171) resulted in several AM/FM and FM-only transistorised battery table and portable models being introduced. This reflected the growing number of VHF stations coming on the air as part of the B.B.C.'s expanding plans for FM broadcasting.

Mullard's OC44 and OC45 were still leading the line-up in medium and longwave transistor portable circuits.

Car aerial sockets were a feature on many transistor radios for the first time, enabling them to be used while motoring as well as at home.

The Mullard AF117 high-frequency alloy-diffusion transistor was introduced and immediately became popular for mixer and IF stages.

Just one battery valve portable circuit was designed and produced during 1961 — put out by Ever Ready as the Sky Captain and by their subsidiary, Berec Radio Ltd., as the Buccaneer. Only two other battery valve portables were listed by *The Wireless & Electrical Trader Yearbook* as current, but both these, (the Ever Ready Sky Queen and the Kolster-Brandes QB20) dated from 1959. The year 1961, therefore, saw the end of the battery valve portable — a type familiar to listeners since the very earliest days of broadcasting.

Bandspread coverage of the pop station Radio Luxembourg (on 208 metres) now featured on many sets, reflecting the growing importance of the teenage market.

4,500,000 sets were sold in 1963 and 36% of these were imported — mainly transistor portables produced in Japan and the Far East.

The first transistorised mains/battery portables appeared, led by Ekco MBT414. As a class of receiver they never really took off — the buying public generally preferring a battery transistor radio for round-the-house listening or for outdoor use. Where quality in home listening was demanded, mains-only transistorised table models (available from 1964) and FM tuners (mostly all transistorised by the end of the 1960s) were selected — these included in radiograms, hi-fi systems, or (from 1969) incorporated into Music Centres.

Alloy-diffusion transistors, like the Mullard AF117 introduced in 1961, were now being used by a great many set manufacturers, and were quickly superseding the older alloy-junction types such as the Mullard OC45. The alloy-diffusion transistor had made possible full shortwave coverage and many more models incorporating this waveband were now appearing.

Several manufacturers (Alba, Ferranti, Fidelity, Ekco and Pye in particular) brought out small portable transistor receivers which incorporated a 'complimentary symmetry transformerless output stage'. This used matched pairs of n-p-n/p-n-p transistors, permitting class 'B' output without the need for driver or output transformers.

Mullard, Newmarket and Texas Instruments all introduced suitable matched pairs of n-p-n/p-n-p transistors for these receivers including OC81M/AC127, NKT 257/NKT 751 and 2G381/2G339 (see the Ekco PT399, the Ferranti PT1076 and the Fidelity Floret).

Some Notable Transistor Radios

mixer and oscillator stages, and by replacing the transistor detector stage with a crystal diode.

fig. 940 (above). Recently, an intriguing Pam 710/Pye P123BQ 'crossbreed' has come to light. It has all the features of a Pam 710 (including an 8-transistor chassis marked 'Pam 710'), except that it bears a *Pye* badge on the front where the word 'PAM' should be, and has a strip of green flock around the top, bottom and sides of its cabinet — a decoration, up till now, found only on the P123BQ. This seems to be a genuine and totally unrecorded '*Pye 710*', and with further investigation may itself turn out to be Pye's first transistor radio.

fig.939 (above). The first transistor radio issued under the Pye label? (*see under fig.940, right*) — the model P123BQ of January 1957, housed in a cream textured cloth-covered wooden cabinet with a machined brass fascia and a green flock surround. This set relied heavily on the Pam 710 for many of its physical parts including the wave-change switch and the on/off volume and tuning controls, all of which are positioned facing the front, as opposed to being mounted on top of the set as with the 710 (*see fig.935, page 289*). Instead of eight transistors, the P123BQ was able to use only six by combining

fig.941 (below), the P123BQ makes a fitting retirement present. Mr. Richard Amey, centre wearing glasses, being presented with a brand-new model upon his retirement after 50 years service with the G.N.E.R. (Great North Eastern Railway). Photo, courtesy K.Amey, taken in the station buffet at Letchworth (gingham tablecloth just visible on the right!). Other retiring employees, presumably of lesser standing, have already received their gifts of a book token and a mantle clock and are trying not to look too disappointed.

fig.942 (*left*). The H.M.V. Model 1410 battery portable; an interesting hybrid receiver marking the changeover from valves to transistors with its three-valve/two transistor circuit.

Tuning to the medium and the long waveband, the receiver was produced in either a blue case (1410B) or in a green case (1410G), and cost £9.16s.5d. plus Purchase Tax.

Other valve/transistor hybrids noted in this book are the Braun T1 (1956), the Bush ETR82 (1959), the Grundig Model 200 (1957) and the Marconiphone P60B (*see below*).

fig.943 (*below*). The H.M.V. Model 1410 hybrid, with a pair of Mullard OC72 output transistors in push-pull on the right, following conventional valve circuitry (using Mullard DK96, DF96 and DAF96 valves). At this stage in its development, the component transistor was still generally incapable of equalling valve performance, especially at high frequencies, and was ideally suitable only for handling relatively low powers. Because of this, a few transistor radios of this period were produced as hybrids, with valves in the HF and IF stages, and transistors only in the output stage. The 1410 chassis was also used by the Marconiphone Company for their model P60B which is housed in a similar moulded plastics cabinet. Both models were issued at the same time — June 1957.

fig.944 (*above, left*). The Sony model TR72. The actual set illustrated above, left, was exported to America from Japan in 1957 but soon found its way into England via an American airman stationed on one of the U.S. air-bases in East Anglia. This was three years before Sony transistor radios were first officially placed on the market in the U.K. in 1960 (*see Sony TR620, page 276, also cover flap*). Sony-brand radios were first made in 1955 by Tokyo Tsushin Kogyo Ltd. who quickly established a market for their products in the U.S. In January 1958, they wisely changed their long and difficult-to-pronounce name to something more manageable — the Sony Corporation.

fig.945 (*above, right*). A manufacturer's label attached to the chassis of the TR72. As a general rule of dating early Sony-brand radios, those bearing the manufacturer's name Tokyo Tsushin Kogyo Ltd. (as illustrated here), were made prior to January 1958. Note also the Sony-brand transistor, just above the label.

fig.946. Perdio model PR4, made in 1958 and housed in a blue plastics case with 'gold' fittings and trim. Perdio (derived from PERsonal raDIO) was a new, outgoing company established in 1955 by Derek Willmott and J.D. Heslop and wholly committed to the latest technology of transistors (they never made valve sets!). During the company's lifetime, they produced an enormous number of transistor radios in varying degrees of taste (all are now highly collected) and even branched out into television. Unfortunately, they went into liquidation in 1965 — as with many other British firms in the mid-1960s, Perdio found difficulty in coping with fierce foreign competition, especially from the Far East. Following their demise, Perdio-brand sets were, ironically, made in Hong Kong and bore the legend *"Empire Made"*.

fig.947 (*above*). Hacker Herald (model RP10), introduced in April 1960 — appropriately named, for it was the very first model off the production line of Hacker Radio Ltd. of Maidenhead. Although established in name in 1941 (see above, right), it had lain, inactive, until 1959, when brothers Ron and Arthur Hacker revived it with the intention of producing a range of top quality transistor radios.

Ron and Arthur already had a long involvement in the radio industry, for in 1927 with the help of their father Harry, they had set up H. Hacker & Sons which soon began producing the first in a long line of superbly engineered radios, radiograms and other audio products under the brand-name 'Dynatron'. In 1936, the company changed its name to Dynatron Radio Ltd. and a year later a second company was formed (The Keates-Hacker Co. Ltd.) principally to compete with the American Scott company who were targeting the luxury end of the British market. Keates-Hacker, controlled by the

Hacker brothers, J. Monck-Mason and J. Wilen-Finn, offered sophisticated radiograms in beautifully finished hardwood cabinets, selected or commissioned to order by the customer. These contained the top of the range Dynatron chassis, specially chromed and finished.

The company lasted until 1941 when the Hacker brothers bought out the other two directors and changed the name to Hacker Radio Ltd. This new company then lay dormant for nearly 20 years. In the mid-1950s, Ekco took the Dynatron company over, but retained the brothers as joint Managing Directors. In September 1959, they parted company with Ekco and revived Hacker Radio Ltd., which continued on into the 1970s until economic decay forced it into the hands of the Receiver in May 1977. (Ekco, meanwhile, had merged with Pye at the end of 1960, which was then absorbed by Philips in 1967. Eventually deciding that they had little interest in the company, Philips sold Dynatron to Roberts Radio Co. Ltd. in 1981. Ironically, Roberts Radio had been Hacker's fiercest rival!). For a more complete picture of the Hacker/Dynatron/Roberts connection, try the excellent little publication *Hacker Radio* by Geoffrey Dixon-Nuttall and Gordon Bussey, published by GDN Publications of Cobham, Surrey in 1993 (ISBN 0 9522197 0 0).

fig.948 (*below*). Ancient and modern Roberts' radios. On the left, their first transistor portable, the RT1 of April 1958, and on the right, paying homage to the past, the Roberts Revival model 200 of August 1993, a 3-waveband mains/battery portable (original price £100, including a mains adaptor). A slightly larger version with the addition of a tone control and a bigger loudspeaker (model 500) was also released at the same time, price £130. Both models were available in either a red or claret Rexine-covered MDF case and although manufactured at the Roberts' works at West Molesey, they used a ready-made circuit imported from the Far East which employed a Toshiba TA8117N microchip. Roberts Radio was taken over by Glen Dimplex in 1994, and following a move to the parent company's headquarters in Yorkshire early in 1996, the 200 and 500 were renamed the 250 and 550 respectively, and were brought out in claret, green and blue finishes with no price change.

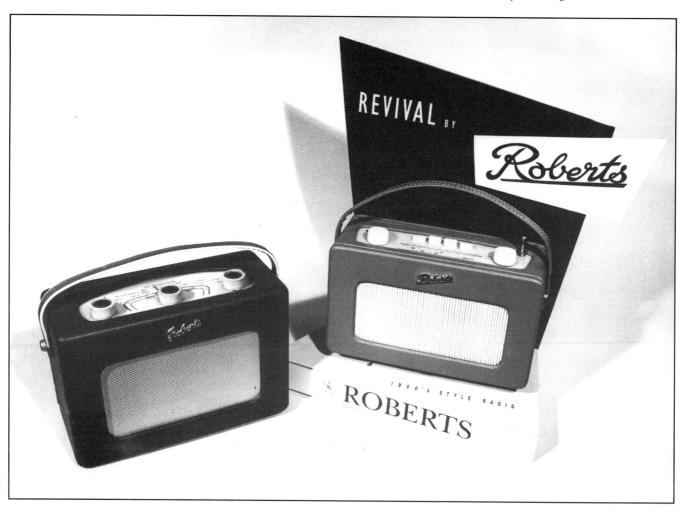

fig.949. The Grundig Micro-Boy of July 1960. A 6-transistor pocket portable for outdoor use which, when docked into its own larger home-based loudspeaker (housed in a matching long, low look cabinet), converts into a table model. An ingenious idea which boosted the quality and gave depth to the somewhat tinny sound of the transistor's own loudspeaker.

fig.950. (*below, left*). Minivox Clock Radio (model RR-34), made by Minivox S.A., Nepro Watch Division of Switzerland in 1963. This little alarm clock (watch movement) transistor radio is probably the finest of its type ever to be made, both in terms of quality and of design. Everything about the RR-34 is exquisite and carefully thought out — right from its moulded black and white case with gold lettering and trim, down to its red and gold presentation box lined with ivory coloured silk.

The circuit components were made by Toshiba in Japan, and then shipped to Switzerland for assembly by Minivox, who added their own watch movement.

fig.951 (*below, right*). The set bears the name of a long-established American company, but the Motorola X21 pocket portable of 1963 was actually made in Japan. Radio companies on both sides of the Atlantic were by now suffering from competition from foreign imports and sometimes it seemed more sensible to western manufacturers to have their sets made cheaply in the Far East and then simply put their own badge on. The X21 was distributed in the U.K. by World Radio Ltd. of London NW2 and, with its gold-plated fascia inset with paste diamonds, was typical of the type of set which proved so irresistible to the younger market in the early to mid 1960s.

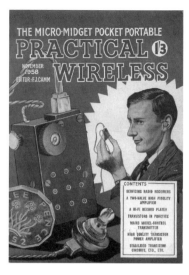

In 1962, when compulsive inventor Clive Sinclair founded Sinclair Radionics in Islington, London, he was already well known to readers of *Practical Wireless* through an article that had been published in November 1958 detailing the construction of his Micro-Midget 3-transistor portable receiver (*fig.952, left*). In addition, he had contributed to *Bernards Radio Manuals* through a series of booklets he had edited on transistor circuits. It was with this fairly new technology coupled with some rather interesting methods of cramming it into very small spaces, that Sinclair was to make his name — a name famous for giving the world miniature transistor radios and hi-fi equipment, hand-held tvs, a PLL tuner, pocket calculators, digital watches, the ZX80 and ZX81 home computers, and of course, that famous 3-wheeled vehicle, the C5.

SINCLAIR MICRO-6, 1964

The Micro-6 kit was even smaller than its predecessor, the Slimline, even though it had one extra transistor. This was mainly due to the use of two *"pill-size"* Mallory cells (ZM312 @ 1s.11d) instead of the bigger-sized PP5. The Micro-6 was housed in a white plastics case with stick-on facia and tuning control labels and employed 3 micro alloy transistors in a six stage circuit - 2 R.F., double diode detector and 3 A.F. Costing £2.19s.6d for the complete set of parts including earpiece, it tuned to the medium waveband only and switched on automatically when the earpiece plug was inserted. A companion amplifier kit, the Sinclair TR750 @ £1.19s.6d (kit) and £2.5s.0d (ready-built), was brought out at the same time and enabled the Micro-6 to be upgraded into a car radio or portable speaker set. Size 1 3/4" x 1 1/4" x 1/2" (approx.). ('Transrista' nylon strap to convert the Micro-6 into a wrist-radio, price 7s.6d. Amplifier kit, model TR750, for use with Micro-6, price £1.19s.6d.).

SINCLAIR MICRO FM, 1965

Hailed by Sinclair as *"the world's first pocket-size FM Tuner/ Receiver"*, the Micro FM was designed to be used with a hi-fi amplifier or tape recorder, or as a self-contained pocket FM receiver for personal listening. The complete kit of parts cost £5.19s.6d, and included a telescopic aerial, 7 transistors, 2 diodes, printed circuit, plastic case with polished and brushed 2-tone aluminium front panel, spun aluminium tuning control (covering 88-108 Mc/s) and a lightweight earpiece. Size 3" x 1 3/4" x 3/4" (approx.).

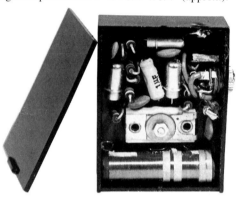

SINCLAIR MICROMATIC Mk.I, 1967

The circuit of the Micromatic Mk.I miniature 3-transistor radio kit (*fig.955, above, actual size*), was very similar to the Micro-6, but was re-styled in a black plastics case with brushed aluminium fascia and dial. Price £2.19s.6d. complete with earpiece. (Ready-built and tested, price £3.19s.6d.). In 1969, the circuit was modified to two transistors (Micromatic Mk.II), and the earpiece socket was moved from the left across to the right hand side (*fig.956, below, actual size*). The price by then had already dropped to £2.9s.6d. (for the kit). In this form, it was still being sold (price £2.48p) when Britain went decimal in 1971.

SINCLAIR SLIMLINE, 1963.

Soon moving his company to Cambridge, Sinclair's first commercial product was the Slimline transistor radio (*figs.953 and 954, above, actual size*). This was a very basic 2-transistor kit set (micro alloy transistors) for use with an earpiece, and covering the medium-wave only — despite its simplicity, advertisements assured potential purchasers that it gave a *"choice of British and European programmes with staggeringly good quality . . . Home, Light, Third, Luxembourg and dozens of continental transmissions"*. The Slimline cost £2.9s.6d plus 1/6d p&p and was powered by an internal Ever Ready PP5 9V battery which took up a lot of room within the case (nearly 25%). It could be put together in under 2 hours and came complete with an easy-build printed circuit board, miniature ferrite rod aerial, plus a deep royal blue plastic case embellished with gold lettering, and a calibrated dial in white on red, *"both designed by a professional artist"*. Size 1 3/4" x 3" x 3/4" (approx.).

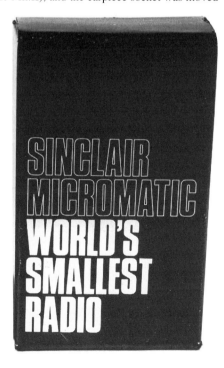

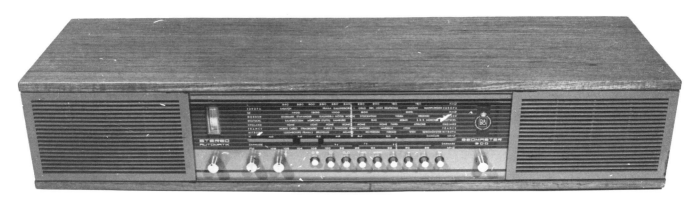

fig.957 (*above*). The magnificent Beomaster 900K of 1964 — one of the first stereo transistor radios to be released onto the market in this country. It was made in Denmark by Bang & Olufsen and imported by Aveley Electric Ltd. of South Ockendon in readiness for the launch of the B.B.C.'s stereophonic radio broadcasting service which was eventually inaugurated on Saturday July 30th 1966. The 900K was also one of the first mains-only transistorised table models to be introduced, and (as with most of B & O's products) was of superb quality.

At first, stereo broadcasts were only available in the London area and in the South East of England (*see page 205*). Because it was also available as a mono receiver, it meant that listeners outside the range of the B.B.C.'s new stereo service could easily upgrade their 900K receivers by means of an adaptor (purchased as an optional extra) as and when stereo broadcasts reached their particular part of the country.

fig.958 (*above*). Roberts RIC-1, the first British-made transistor radio to employ an integrated circuit. Released in August 1968. Normally, it was presented in a much plainer cabinet finish embellished in either red, Oxford blue, conifer green or black Rexine leathercloth as standard. However, it was also available in a very trendy 'Sixties' yellow/orange/green Paisley cloth covering, exclusively from Harrods in Knightsbridge, London — obviously, the aim was to attract some very upmarket Hippies!

The RIC-1 used a TAD100 integrated circuit, developed by Mullard, which housed 11 transistors and 11 resistors in an area occupying just less than 1/500th part of a square inch. This was supplemented by an OC44/5 transistor as the audio driver, with an AC187 and an AC188 as the complementary output pair, and a BA114 was employed as the oscillator diode. In all, some 77,967 sets were produced (figure from the excellent *History of Roberts Radio* by Keith Geddes and Gordon Bussey, published by Roberts Radio Co. Ltd. of West Molesey, Surrey in 1987 (ISBN 0 9512590 0 8).

fig.959 (*above*). Binatone Kissinger (left), a 9-transistor mains/battery portable of 1971 housed in an integral saddle-stitched leatherette case. This style of receiver, very popular throughout the 1970s, resembles an overgrown pocket transistor of the 1960s (the saddle-stitched case of the 1964 Holiday pocket set is shown above on the right for comparison). The Kissinger, and sets like it, were so deceptively light that it would often be a shock to pick them up — they were made to look substantial and impressive, but were in fact comparatively empty and lightweight.

fig.960 (right). And finally . . . . a sloping panel bright-emitter set which plugs into the mains? Not really, for this is the latest in the 1996 'Nostalgic Radio' range of solid state radios from Steepletone, model Valve 1, a MW/LW/FM table model. The five small 'valves' along the front merely light up to indicate which waveband has been selected *etc.*, while the two large 'bright-emitter valves' on top of the set provide a light source, which is something else people used to use bright-emitters for in the 1920s! (*see page 38*).

BayGen Clockwork Radio, 'Freeplay' Model BGR-1, 1995

A clockwork radio, needing no batteries and only a few turns of a winding handle to get it going, seems an obvious idea but it took nearly 100 years of radio development before an ex-circus escapologist living on an island in the middle of the Thames came up with this simple idea for a battery-less radio.

Trevor Baylis, once known as Rameses II when working for a Berlin Circus and now a swimming pool manufacturer and part-time inventor, had the idea while watching a television story in 1993 about the problems associated with the spread of AIDS in Africa. The radio was seen as one of the best ways of communicating health information and educating the population about the disease. However in many regions of Africa, particularly in outlying country areas, there was no electricity and batteries for radios were expensive and often difficult to obtain. Also they didn't last very long — perhaps two or three weeks if used fairly often.

A radio that used no mains electricity or batteries, seemed to Trevor Baylis to be the answer to this problem and he felt sure he could help. The first thing he did after the programme finished was to go into his studio/workshop at the back of the house he built himself in the 1970s on Eel Pie Island in the Thames and rig up a little hand powered generator. *"I knew that an electric motor could be used as a generator of electricity if you reversed it. So I found a very small motor which I put into a hand drill and connected the two wires from the motor to the battery terminals of a very cheap transistor radio. When I turned the handle of the drill the radio barked into life . . . and that really was my Eureka! moment".*

It took him three or four months playing around with different types of springs and gears to get a working prototype clockwork radio together. Based around a pocket transistor called a Pine CQ, and integrated within a large black box containing a fairly powerful spring, gearbox and a small generator mechanism, his prototype radio would work for about 15 minutes following a two minute wind - not yet practical enough to market as a product but sufficiently workable to market as an idea. In order to find support for his project he tried writing to several large companies - to Marconi's, to Philips, to British Petroleum, to National Power and to the Design Council, but they all turned him down flat. *"When I was turned down so many times the feeling of rejection was awful, and in some cases humiliating, and I began thinking to myself that perhaps I had got it wrong after all and that I should give up".*

However, news of his invention had filtered through to the B.B.C. and it was thought important enough to be included as an item by reporter Bob Carter on the 6pm News on Radio 4 on Friday January 7th 1994. Trevor Baylis also appeared the following Wednesday (January 12th 1994) on Radio 4's *Mid-Week* programme. But the next programme to cover the story and which was to prove so crucial was an edition of *Tomorrow's World* which went out on April 15th 1994. *"As soon as the programme was over I was deluged with phone calls from all sorts of people who simply wanted to say* Well done! *and those people really gave me the encouragement to carry on".*

Watching that item on *Tomorrow's World* was Christopher Staines, an accountant with wide experience in product development and in what can make or break a commercial venture. He thought the idea of a clockwork radio was a very good one and went round to visit Trevor Baylis the following Sunday and agreed to help him.

By coincidence, Christopher Stains had a business partner in South Africa, Rory Stears, who upon hearing about the radio became absolutely convinced that this was the set for Africa, and that anything that obviated the need for batteries or electricity on a Continent of 600 million people, most of whom were fairly poor without access to electricity, was certainly going to be beneficial. A Johannesburg radio station ran the story and by chance it was heard by Hylton Appelbaum over his car radio as he drove in to work. Mr Applebaum was head of the Liberty Life Group, a foundation investing in projects which made a social difference, and which gave away around £5M of its profits each year to worthwhile causes. Mr Appelbaum was immediately struck by the relevance the clockwork radio had to South Africa and arranged a meeting with Rory Stears.

Intrigued by the idea, Mr Appelbaum travelled to England to meet Trevor Baylis and to see the prototype in action. He suggested that disabled people could assemble the radio and on his return to South Africa, got in contact with Dr. William Rowland who was President of *Disabled People South Africa*. Mr Appelbaum agreed to fund a group of organisations for the disabled if they agreed to become partners in the venture, Liberty Life then putting up a total of £750,000 to get the project going.

One of the first things that had to be done was some market research and so Christopher Stains and Rory Stears took the prototype around South Africa to gauge people's reactions which were to prove very positive and enthusiastic. Christopher Stains had been worried about how they were going to miniaturise the product, but almost without exception the comments were that people preferred a radio that was big, heavy and robust, and which would play very loud.

On Christopher Stains' return to England, the prototype was taken to Bristol University Electronic Engineering Department to be analysed and every component part measured for its effectiveness. A new member of the growing Baylis team, David Butlion, had now been placed in charge of the technical development of the radio and he was anxious to see how loud it could play. The Head of the project at Bristol University, Dr. Duncan Grant gave the disappointing news that there simply was not enough power being generated by the spring and gears to drive the circuit properly and that every time the radio was turned up, the power distorted. David Butlion then set about redesigning the gearbox and the spring mechanism with the help of a firm of development engineers, *Process Analysis & Automation Ltd.* of Farnborough, and by doubling the spring size and cutting down the number of gear bearings and axles (thus cutting down on energy-wasting friction), the idea worked. With a new redesigned circuit and gearbox, plus a new plastic moulded cabinet, the original prototype had changed out of all recognition by the time the first models rolled off the production lines of the BayGen Power Company's factory in Johannesburg in the Summer of 1995. Trevor Baylis was there to see it, and he was so overcome, and probably relieved too, at the sight of his clockwork radio finally being manufactured (and manufactured by disabled men and women), that he broke down. His visit ended with a meeting with President Nelson Mandela who thought the radio was *"a fantastic achievement".*

CLOCKWORK RADIO MARKETED IN BRITAIN

A few months later in September, the full story of the development of Trevor Baylis' clockwork radio was featured on the B.B.C.'s *QED* programme and, although principally aimed at the African market, it was announced in the *Radio Times* of September 30th that 1,000 of these new radios would also be made available to U.K. readers for £59.95 plus £2.95 p&p from JEM Marketing of Cranleigh in Surrey. Even with a Press-launch on Thursday November 2nd, the initial supplies did not actually begin to arrive in England from the South African factory until late November 1995 by which time the *Radio Times* offer had been seriously oversubscribed - demand was phenomenal and quite unexpectedly so, and although by January 1996 JEM had managed to secure and send out a total of 2,000 radios, their waiting list was growing daily. For those with an extra £20 or so to spare and who couldn't wait, the other outlets were Harrods in Knightsbridge who at this time still had *"several left at £79.95 plus £7 p&p"*, Conrans and John Lewis, Oxford Street.

On July 1st 1996, Trevor Baylis shared the B.B.C. Designer of the Year Award in recognition of his work on the clockwork radio. By this time, a major shipment of some 5,000 sets had been allocated to the former Yugoslavia by the British Red Cross, aided by the British Government who paid for the purchase. These have subsequently been used mainly in Western Croatia by people living in isolated communities cut off without electricity and without any form of communication. In Africa, one of the first countries to receive the clockwork radio has been Eritrea which has been ravaged by war for the last 30 years. With few people having access to either electricity or batteries, the Baygen was seen as the first stepping stone to bring information and communication to the local population.

One puzzle, though, is that the instructions say quite clearly that the set should be protected from the sun and from humidity. For a radio designed with the African market uppermost in mind, I hope it will stand the climate!

SPECIFICATIONS & PERFORMANCE

The BayGen clockwork radio, 'Freeplay' Model BGR-1 (*fig.961, below*), is manufactured by BayGen Power Company (PTY) Ltd., 89 St. Patrick Road, Houghton, Johannesburg 2198, South Africa. It covers the FM (88-108 mHz), MW (520-1600 kHz) and SW (3-12 mHz) bands with a telescopic aerial for FM and SW, and a built-in ferrite rod aerial for MW. The set is powered by a B-Motor carbon steel spring, driving a generator through a transmission. Although essentially a hand-wound clockwork radio, it nevertheless has provision for an optional power source using an external AC 3V-9V/200mA mains adaptor (centre positive).

Giving the maximum 60 turns of the easy-to-wind foldout handle on the right hand side of the radio winds up the coiled spring which under tension drives a small generator providing enough electricity to power the set for just over 30 minutes (although 40 minutes is claimed in the *Radio Times*). On test, the reception on all three wavebands was very good, even on FM where the chosen test reception area (Bampton, Devon) is classed by the B.B.C.'s Engineering Department as 'unserviceable' because

of its hill and valley location. There was, however, quite a noticeable and constant rhythmical background noise (like the gentle chugging of steamboat engine - fans of the film *African Queen* will instantly know what I mean) produced by the internal mechanism, plus occasional and annoying creaking as the coiled spring slipped. Also experienced was 'motor-boating', a stuttering distortion occurring when the volume control was turned up full, something noticed with the prototype when tested at Bristol University and, along with the other problems noted, something which will need ironing out in the future.

The switches on the left hand side of the set provide on/off and FM/MW/SW selection, with controls for volume and tuning. There is an edgewise fine-tuning wheel control just above the yellow and blue plastic tuning dial at the front. The whole set is robustly housed in a moulded black ABS plastic cabinet with integral carrying handle, and features a decent 3 1/2", 5 Watt (maximum) loudspeaker. Within the first week of use, the problems encountered in the test and noted above were added to by a constant squeaking coming from the spring-winding mechanism . This continued to rotate and squeak even when the set was switched off — with all the above faults developing so soon after purchase, I suspect that the BayGen was pushed out too early and I wonder how many will be returned, or have been already.

Having said that, it is certainly one of the most exciting radio products to appear on the market for many, many years and its novel clockwork generator drive might lead to developments in other directions - perhaps in radios designed for boats, or as an independent power source in other electrical applications.

[Clockwork was used to power Marconi's magnetic detector in 1902 (*see fig.13, page 18*) and the idea of a generator was previously tried out by the Marconi Company in the late 1920s with their human-powered tandem generator cycle for use by our chaps out in the African Colonies. There is a picture in a wireless magazine of this period showing a white man lazing outside on his verandah listening to his wireless set while two black natives pedal away in the hot sun to provide enough power for it. *"These happy fellows certainly seem to enjoy their work . . . "* runs the caption . . . I expect they did!].

fig.961

Directory of Radios Illustrated and/or Described in *Radio! Radio!*
(*See also Directory of Transistor Radios & Foreign Imports, 1956-72*)

A.J.S. —
4-Valve Battery Receiver (1923), 35
F6 (1925), 4-v batt., *fig.166,* 81
F6 Model TM2 (1925), 4-v batt., *fig.186,* 84
Z (1925), 2-v batt., *fig.171,* 82
Symphony Two (1926), 2-v batt., *fig.200,* 86

A.T.E. —
A.T.E. (1924), cr.set, *fig.160,* 80

A.T.M. —
Aircraft Receiver Mk.III (1917), 3-v batt., *fig.29,* 28
Mark III Short Wave Tuner (1916), cr.set, *fig.27,* 27

ABBIPHONE —
Abbiphone Type CRO (1923), cr.set, *fig.98,* 72

ABBONPHONE —
Abbon-Daventry (1926), cr.set, *fig.203,* 86
Abbonphone (1926), 2-v batt., *fig.208,* 87

ACE —
Model 357 (1960), 4-v +R AC, *fig.803,* 199
Model BS4 (1936), 5-v +R AC, *fig.525,* 145

ADEY —
Adey 4 (1932), 4-v batt. port., *fig.363,* 127
Cigar Box Portable (1930), 1-v batt. port., *fig.289,* 118
De Luxe (1931), 4-v batt. port., *fig.326,* 122

AERODYNE —
Model 302 (1945), 4-v +R AC/DC, *fig.650,*172
Nightingale (1935), 3-v batt., *fig.515,* 144

ALBA —
Model 52 (1933), 3-v +Bar DC, *fig.423,* 133
Model 472 (1946), 4-v +R AC, *fig.663,* 173
Model 870 (1936), 4-v +R AC, *fig.549,* 148
Model 880 (1935), 5-v +R + TI AC, *fig.503,* 143
Model AC 810 (1939), 3-v +R AC, *fig.624,* 156
Model C112 (1947), 4-v +R AC/DC, *fig.696,* 177

AMBASSADOR —
Type 548 (1948), 4-v +R AC/DC/bookcase, *fig.703,* 178

AMPLION —
2-v +MetR AC, *fig.297,* 119
Alternative (1939), 3-v +R AC/batt. port., *fig.626,* 156
Amplion Six (1931), 5-v +R AC, *fig.323,* 122
Amplion Two-Valve All Mains (1930), 2-v +MetR AC, *fig.297,* 119
Delegate Model HU610, (1947), 4-v +R +Bar AC/DC, *fig.681,* 175
Table Model (1932), 3-v +MetR AC, *fig.388,* 129

ANODE —
Table Model (1922), v batt., 42

ASHLEY —
L.F. Amplifier (1923), 2-v batt. amp., *fig.121,* 75

ASTROPHONE —
Astrophone (1923), cr.set, *fig.118,* 75
Astrophone Deluxe (1923), cr.set, q.v. *fig.118,* 75

B.R.C. —
Radio Exchange (1927), 59

B.S.A. —
Model 4V (1926), 4-v batt., *fig.201,* 86
Model 5010 (1926), 3-v batt., *fig.192,* 85

B.T.H. —
2-Valve Portable (1920), 2-v batt. portable, *fig.33,* 30

Bijou (1923), cr.set, *fig.108,* 73
Model VR2 (1923), 2-v batt., *fig.109,* 73
Radiola 1 Type VC (1923), 1-v batt./cr.set, *fig.111,* 74
Type C Form A (1922), cr.set, *fig.74,* 68
Type VA1 Form AB (1925), 1-v batt. amp., *fig.180,* 83
Type VA2 (1925), 2-v batt. amp., q.v. *fig.183,* 83
Type VR2 Form BA (1925), 2-v batt., *fig.183,* 83
Type VR2 Form C/A (1928), 1-v batt., *figs.241, 241a,* 91
Type VR3 Form A (1927), 3-v batt., *fig.222,* 88

BANG & OLUFSEN —
Beomaster Model 900K (1964), 23-tr mains stereo table model, *fig.957,* 299

BASSETT LOWKE —
Oracle (1922), cr.set, fig.78, 69

BAYGEN —
Freeplay Model BGR-1 (1995), tr clockwork/mains port., 300, 301, *fig 961,* 301

BÉBÉPHONE —
Bébéphone (1924), cr.set, q.v. *fig.96,* 71

BEETHOVEN —
Major Model S.G.4 (1934), 4-v batt. port., *fig.456,* 137
Model 77 (1935), 4-v +R AC, *fig.484,* 140
Model AD770 (1938), 4-v +R AC/DC transp., *fig.601,* 153
Model SG2730 Screen Grid Four (1929), 4-v batt. port., *fig.258,* 93
Model U3038 (1947), 3-v +R AC/DC, *fig.694,* 177
Super Minor (1935), 4-v batt. port., *fig.479,* 140
Transportable (1932), 3-v +R AC transp., *fig.374,* 128

BELMONT —
Model 746 (1936), 6-v +R +TI AC, *fig.539,* 146

BENSON —
Model 420 (1936), 4-v +R AC/DC, *fig.553,* 148

BEREC —
Pioneer (1959), 4-v batt. kit, *fig.801,* 197

BINATONE —
Kissinger (1971), 9-tr mains/batt. port., *fig.959,* 299

BLIGH —
Bligh (1924), 4-v batt., *fig.131,* 76

BRITANNIA —
Britannia (1933), 3-v batt., *fig.400,* 131

BROWN —
Crystal Amplifier (1926), 2-stage mic.amp., *fig.209,* 87
Crystavox (1923), l/s./mic.amp, *fig.827,* 209, 212
Frenophone (1923), l/s./reed amp., *fig.829,* 209, 212
Junior Wireless Set (1927), cr.set/1-stage mic.amp., *fig.219,* 88
Microphone Amplifier Type C (1923), 1-stage mic.amp., *fig.120,* 75

BROWNIE —
Brownie Wireless (1923), cr.set, *fig.99,* 72
Brownie Wireless (1923), cr.set kit, *fig.100,* 72
Brownie Wireless (1924), cr.set, *fig.136,* 77
Model No.2 (1925), cr.set, *figs.188 & 196,* 84, 85
Model No.3 (1927), cr.set, *fig.227,* 89
Two Stage Note Magnifier (1926), 2-v batt.amp., *figs.195,196,* 85

Two Valve Receiver (1927), 2-v batt., *fig.221,* 88

BRUNSWICK —
Model BPU/1 (1937), 5-v +R AC, *fig.575,*150

BRUTON —
Bruton (1937), 5-v +R +TI, *fig.563,* 149

BURGOYNE —
Class B.3 (1933), 3-v batt., *fig.418,* 133

BURNDEPT —
Burndept 1 (1921), 1-v batt., *fig 37,* 33
De Luxe Model 1850 (1930), 3-v +R AC, q.v. *fig.286,* 118
De Luxe Model 1851 (1930), 3-v +R AC, *fig.286,* 118
Ethodyne (1926), 7-v batt., *fig.199,* 86
Ethophone No.1 (1922), cr.set, *fig.73,* 68
Ethophone III (1924), 3-v batt., *fig.207,* 87
Ethophone III, MkIII (1925), 3-v batt., *fig.177,* 83
Ethophone V, MkV (1925), 4-v batt., *fig.172,* 82
Ethophone Duplex (1924), 2-v batt., *fig.138,* 77
Mobile Radio (1935), 4-v +R +Bar AC/DC transp., *fig.499,* 142
Model 252 (1936), 3-v +R AC/DC, q.v. *fig.544,* 147
Screened Ethophone (1928), 3-v batt., *fig.244,* 91
Screened Four (1928), 4-v batt., *fig.252,* 92
Screened Suitcase Portable (1928), 4-v batt. port., *fig.240,* 90
Short Wave Receiver MkIV (1927), 3-v batt., *fig.226,* 89
Universal Screened Five (1929), 5-v +R +MetR AC, *fig.260,* 93

BURTON —
Empire 3 (1929), 3-v batt., *fig.278,* 95
Empire Speaker Three (1931), 3-v batt., *fig.347,* 125
Empire Two (1930), 2-v batt., *fig.294,* 118

BUSH —
Model AC3 (1932), 3-v +R AC, *fig.360,* 126
Model AC91 (1946), 4-v +R AC, *fig.668,* 174
Model DAC10 (1950), 4-v +R AC/DC, *fig.730,* 190
Model DAC90 (1946), 4-v +R AC/DC, *fig.652,* 172
Model DAC90A (1950), 4-v +R AC/DC, *fig.729,* 190
Model BP90 (1946), 4-v batt. port., *fig.672,* 174
Model PB50 (1938), 4-v +R AC, *fig.595,* 153
Model PB51 (1938), 4-v +R AC, *fig.609,* 154
Model SAC5 (1934), 4-v +R +West +TI, *fig.470,* 138
Model SAC25 (1935), 4-v +R AC, *fig.504,* 143
Model TR82B (1959), 7-tr.+cr.di. batt. port., 181, *fig.800,* 197
Model TR91 (1960), 7-tr. batt., *fig.804,* 199
Model VHF41 (1954), 6-v +R AC, *fig.766,* 194
Model VHF64 (1957), 6-v +R +TI AC, *fig.787,* 196
Model VHF90A (1958), 6-v +MetR AC/DC, *fig.794,* 197

BUTLER —
No.111 (1922), cr.set, *fig.72,* 68

C.T. —
Model No.1 (1923), cr.set, *fig.103,* 72
Model No.1 (1923), cr.set kit, q.v. *fig.103,* 72

CARLTON —
The Carlton Model SG4 (1931), 3-v batt., *fig.335,* 123

CEE BEE —
Model No.3 (1922), cr.set, *fig.75,* 68

302   Radio Directory A - C

CHACKOPHONE —
Model No.1B (1926), 3-v batt., *fig.202*, 86
Junior 2 MkII (1927), 2-v batt., *fig.234*, 90
Junior Three (1927), 3-v batt., *fig.228*, 89
Junior Four (1929), 4-v batt. port., *fig.272*,
  95

CHAMPION —
Model 750B (1951), 4-v +R AC, *fig.743*, 191
Model TRF 784 (1952), 3-v +R AC, *fig.746*,
  192
Venus (1947), 4-v +R AC/DC, *fig.691*, 176

CLARION —
Old Lager (1935), 3-v +R AC, *fig.482*, 140

CLARKE —
Atlas Model 7-5-8 (1934), 4-v +R AC, *fig.434*,
  134

CLASSIC —
Super-Two (1931), 2-v batt., *fig.350*, 125

CLEARTRON —
Lodge 'N' Circuit Receiver (1926), 2-v batt.,
  fig.191, 85

CLEMENS & TAYLOR —
All Wave Receiver F.B. (1922), 2-v batt.,
  fig.58, 65

CLIMAX —
All Mains Four (1931), 3-v +R AC, *fig.348*,
  125
Climax (1927), 3-v batt., *fig.220*, 88
Model S5 (1934), *fig.437*, 135

CLYDELCO —
Clydelco (1923), cr.set, *fig.95*, 71

COLUMBIA —
Model 303a (1929), 5-v batt. port., *fig.269*, 94
Model 309 OC (1930), 2-v +MetR AC, *fig.301*,
  119
Model 359 (1935), 3-v +R AC, q.v. *fig.518*,
  144

CONSOLIDATED —
AC Receiver (1932), 3-v +R AC, *fig.385*, 129

COSMOS —
Met-Vick 5 (1927), 5-v batt., *fig.232*, 90
Radiophone Type C4 (1925), cr.set, *fig.174*, 82
Radiophone Type VR2 (1923), 2-v batt.,
  fig.91, 70
Radiophone Type VR3/A5 (1924), 5-v batt.,
  fig.143, 78
Type VR4 (1925), 3-v batt., *fig.185*, 84
Type VR4 (1925), 3-v + cr.batt., q.v. *fig.185*,
  84

COSSOR —
All Electric Melody Maker (1931), 3-v +R AC,
  fig.328, 122
All-In (1929), 2-v +R AC, *fig.274*, 95
Melody Maker (1927), 3-v batt. blueprint, 58
Melody Maker (1928), 3-v batt. kit, *fig.248*, 91
Melody Maker Model 334 (1932), 3-v batt.,
  fig.361, 126
Melody Maker Model 335 (1932), 3-v batt.,
  q.v. *fig.361*, 126
Melody Maker Model 342 (1933), 3-v batt.,
  fig.428, 134
Melody Maker Model 494 (1949), 4-v +R AC,
  fig.716, 179
Melody Portable (1956), 4-v batt. port.,
  fig.781, 195
Model MR 133 (1930), 2-v +R AC, *fig.307*,
  120
Model MR 331 (1930), 3-v +R AC, q.v.
  fig.307, 120
Model 77 (1939), 3-v + 2v AC, q.v. *fig.613*,
  155
Model 77B (1939), 3-v + 2v AC, *fig.613*, 155
Model 364 (1935), 4-v +R AC, *fig.498*, 142
Model 366A (1935), 4-v batt., q.v. fig.498, 142
Model 367 (1935), 3-v +R AC, *fig.501*, 142
Model 368 (1935), 3-v +R, *fig.513*, 144
Model 464 (1946), 4-v +R AC, *fig.662*, 173
Model 469 (1947), 4-v batt. port., *fig.685*, 176
Model 470AC (1947), 4-v +R AC, *fig.701*, 177
Model 484 (1937), 3-v +R AC, *fig.579*, 151
Model 527/X (1955), 4-v batt., *fig.773*, 195

Model 565 (1957), 3-v +R AC/DC, *fig.784*,
  196
Model 575PC (1958), 5-v +R AC/DC, *fig.796*,
  197
Model 579 (1958), 5-v +R +TI AC/DC, q.v.
  fig.796, 197
Model 732 (1931), 4-v batt., *fig.345*, 124
Silvertone (1930), 2-v batt., *fig.293*, 118
Silvertone (1930), 3-v batt.kit, *fig.310*, 120

CROMWELL —
Universal (1933), 3-v +Bar AC/DC, *fig.410*,
  132

DANIPAD —
Popular Regional Three (1929), 3-v batt.,
  fig.275, 95

DECCA —
Deccette (1953), 4-v batt. port., *fig.754*, 193
Double Decca (MW/LW) (1946), 3-v AC/DC/
  batt. port., q.v. *fig.684*, 176
Double Decca (SW/MW/LW) (1947), 3-v AC/
  DC/batt. port., *fig.684*, 176
Double Decca (SW/MW) (1949), 3-v AC/DC/
  batt. port., q.v. *fig.684*, 176
Home & Car (1935), q.v. *fig.478*, 140
Model 55 (1937), 4-v +R +Bar AC/DC transp.,
  fig.556, 148
Model 66 (c.1937), 4-v +R +Bar AC/DC,
  fig.555, 148
Model 77 (1937), 4-v +R AC, *fig.573*, 150
Model 222 (1932), 4-v +R AC, *fig.359*, 126
Model 919 (1935), 3-v +R AC, *fig.478*, 140
Model TPW70 (1961), 6-tr., *fig.808*, 200
Radio Model (1930), 5-v batt. port., *fig.306*,
  120

DEFIANT —
Model M900 (1935), 3-v +R AC, *fig.481*,
  140

DELAPHONE —
Delaphone No.2 (1924), cr.set, *fig.129*, 76

DENCO —
Maxi-Q Transistor Six (1961), 5-tr. batt. port.,
  fig.809, 201

DERWENT —
International Five (1935), 4-v +R AC, *fig.512*,
  144

DIBBEN —
All-Clear Type 44 (1926), v batt., 54

DULCI —
Model MSU4 (1947), 3-v +R AC/DC, *fig.686*,
  176

DYNAMERGY —
Mains Supply Receiver (1925), 3-v DC unit,
  52

EDDYSTONE —
Scientific Four (1927), 4-v batt., *fig.224*, 89
Short-Wave Converter (1933), 2-v +R AC,
  fig.397, 130

EDISON BELL —
Bijou (1926), 2-v batt., *fig.198*, 86
Gem (1925), 2-v batt., q.v. *fig.198*, 86
Type B (1923), cr.set, *fig.97*, 71

EDISWAN —
Model 1924B (1924), cr.set, *fig.139*, 78
Model 1924P (1924), cr.set, q.v. *fig.139*, 78

EELEX —
Short-Wave Converter (1931), 1-v batt.,
  fig.327, 122
Short-Wave Converter (1931), 1-v +R AC, q.v.
  fig.327, 122
Short-Wave Converter (1931), 2-v +R AC, q.v.
  fig.327, 122

EFESCAPHONE —
Nelson (1923), 3-v batt., *fig.144*, 78
Nelson Grand (1923), 3-v batt., q.v. *fig.144*,
  78
Nelson Grand (1924), 3-v batt., *fig.144*, 78
Rodney (1923), 3-v batt., q.v. *fig.134*, 77
Rodney (1924), 3-v batt., *fig.134*, 77

EKCO —
Ekcolectric Model SGP3 (1929), 3-v +MetR
  AC, *fig.273*, 95
Model 21 Braidio (1946), 4-v +R AC, *fig.661*,
  173
Model 157 (1934), 4-v +R AC/DC, *fig.433*,
  134
Model 312 (1930), 2-v +MetR AC, *fig.303*,
  120
Model 313 (1930), 3-v +MetR AC, *fig.304*,
  120
Model A22 (1945), 3-v +R AC, *fig.644*, 172,
  216
Model A23 (1946), 4-v +R AC, *fig.671*, 174
Model A28 (1946), 4-v +R +TI AC, *fig.655*,
  173
Model A147 Festival (1951), 4-v +R AC,
  fig.738, 191
Model AC64 (1933), 4-v +R AC,
  fig.416, 133
Model AC74 (1933), 4-v +R +TI AC, *fig.413*,
  132
Model AC85 (1934), 5-v +R AC, *fig.431*, 134
Model AC86 (1935), 5-v +R AC, *fig.473*, 139
Model AC97 (1936), 4-v +R +TI AC, *fig.533*,
  146
Model ACT96 (1935), 6-v +R AC transp.,
  fig.488, 141
Model AD36 (1935), 3-v +R AC/DC, *fig.485*,
  140, 216
Model AD38 (1937), 3-v +R AC/DC, q.v.
  fig.569, 150
Model AD65 (1934), 3-v +R AC/DC, *fig.448*,
  136, 216
Model AD75 (1940), 3-v +R AC/DC, *fig.635*,
  171
Model AD75 (1946), 3-v +R AC/DC, q.v.
  fig.635, 171
Model AD76 (1935), 4-v +R AC/DC, *figs.477*,
  477a, 139, 216
Model ADT 95 (1934), 5-v +R AC/DC transp.,
  fig.468, 138
Model AW70 (1939), 3-v +R AC, *fig.614*, 155
Model AW119 (1938), 4-v +R AC, *fig.599*,
  153
Model B38 (1937), 3-v batt., *fig.569*, 150
Model B54 (1933), 4-v batt., q.v. *fig.416*, 133
Model B85 (1934), 5-v batt., q.v. *fig.431*, 134
Model B86 (1934), 5-v batt., q.v. *fig.473*, 139
Model BAW71 (1939), 3-v batt., q.v. *fig.614*,
  155
Model BAW78 (1937), 4-v batt., q.v. *fig.565*,
  149
Model BV78 (1937), 4-v batt., q.v. *fig.565*,
  149
Model C389 (1938), 6-v +R AC, q.v. *fig.591*,
  152
Model M23 (1931), 3-v +MetR AC, *fig.318*,
  121
Model PB189 (1938), 6-v +R AC, *fig.591*, 152
Model PB510 (1939), 4-v +R AC, *fig.625*, 156
Model RR 484 (1934), 3-v +R AC/DC, *fig.451*,
  136
Model RS2 AC (1931), 3-v +MetR AC, q.v.
  fig.318, 121
Model RS3 (1931), 4-v +R AC, *fig.314*, 121
Model SH25 (1932), 5-v +R AC/DC,
  q.v. *fig.314*, 121
Model SW86 (1934), 5-v +R AC, q.v. *fig.473*,
  139
Model U29X (1946), 4-v +R AC/DC, *fig.669*,
  174
Model U76 Consort (1948), 4-v +R AC/DC,
  fig.711, 178
Model U243 (1955), 5-v +R +TI AC/DC,
  fig.779, 195
Model UAW 78 (1937), 4-v +R AC/DC,
  fig.565, 149

ELECTRADIX —
CRYSTAL SET (C.1950), cr.di. cr. set,
  fig.728, 190

ELWELL —
Aristophone 160 (1924), 4-v batt., *fig.147*,
  79
Panel No.11 (1922), cr.set, *fig.66*, 67
Statophone Model S50 (1925), 3-v batt./cr.set,
  51
Statophone Model S60 (1925), 4-v batt, 51

EMOR —
Globe (1946), *fig.678*, 175

ENSIGN —
Model C (1927), cr.set, *fig.229*, 89

ERICSSON —
Four Valve Receiver (1923), 4-v batt., *fig.83*, 69
Super Three Valve (1923), 3-v batt., *fig.80*, 69
Two Valve Receiver (1922), 2-v batt., *fig.53*, 65

EUROPHONE —
The Europhone (1928), 2-v batt., *fig. 249*, 91

EVER READY —
Model 5218 (1939), 4-v batt., *fig.623*, 156
Model C (1946), 4-v batt. port., *fig.653*, 172
Model C/A (1947), 4-v batt. port., q.v. *fig.653*, 172
Model C/E (1948), 4-v batt. port., q.v. *fig.653*, 172
Model H (1949), 2-v batt., *fig.715*, 179
Model N (1951), 4-v batt. port. *fig.741*, 191
Saucepan Special (1949), 4-v batt., *fig.720*, 179
Sky Captain (1961), 4-v batt. port., *fig.805*, 200
Sky Casket (1957), 4-v batt. port., *fig.783*, 196
Sky Countess (1958), 4-v batt. port., *fig.795*, 197
Sky Emperor (1958), 8-v +TI batt. port., *fig.793*, 197
Sky Princess (1956), 4-v batt. port., *fig.780*, 195
Sky Queen (1953), 4-v batt. port., *fig.752*, 192
Table Model (1946), 4-v batt., *fig.673*, 174

EVERYMAN —
Everyman Four (1927), 4-v batt., q.v. *fig.190*, 84, 85

EXCELOPHONE —
Excelophone Type 4C (1925), 4-v batt., *fig.187*, 84

FAERITONE —
Faeritone (1923), cr.set, *fig.114*, 74
Faeritone (1923), cr.set kit, q.v. *fig.114*, 74

FELCOURT —
Dual Station Receiver (1926), v batt., 54

FELLOCRYST —
Fellocryst Super (1922), cr.set, *fig.71*, 67

FELLOPHONE —
Little Giant Four (1925), 4-v batt., *fig.169*, 81
One Valve Receiver (1923), 1-v batt., *fig.119*, 75
Portable Three (1923), 3-v batt. port., *fig.104*, 73
Super Two (1923), 2-v batt., q.v. *fig.87*, 70
Super Two Amplifier (1923), 2-v batt. amp., q.v. *fig.87*, 70
Two Valve Receiver (1922), 2-v batt., *fig.54*, 65

FELLOWS —
Little Giant Three (c.1927), 3-v batt., *fig.225*, 89

FERGUSON —
Model 352U (1955), 3-v +R AC/DC, *fig.770*, 194
Model 366 (1936), 4-v +R, *fig.547*, 147
Model 383A (1956), 5-v +MetR AC, *fig.782*, 195
Model 909 (1939), 4-v +R, *fig.621*, 155
Model 3140 Autotwin Mk.II (c.1965), 9-tr. batt. port./car radio, *fig.815*, 205

FERRANTI —
Model 005 (1950), 4-v +R AC, *fig.734*, 191
Model 045 (1954), 5-v +R +TI AC, *fig.760*, 193
Model 32 (1930), 3-v +R AC, *fig.292*, 118
Model 32 (1931), 3-v +R AC, *fig.340*, 124

Model 32 (1931), 3-v +R AC, *fig.343*, 124
Model 139 (1939), 4-v +R AC, *fig.618*, 155
Model 145 (1945), 4-v +R AC, *fig.643*, 171
Model 146 (1946), 4-v +R AC, *fig.656*, 173
Model 215 (1951), 4-v +R AC, *fig.737*, 191
Model 239 (1939), 4-v +R AC, *fig.620*, 155
Model 245 (1954), 4-v +R AC, *fig.764*, 194
Model 248 (1948), 5-v +R AC, *fig.708*, 178
Model 255 (1955), 5-v +R AC, *fig.771*, 194
Model 347 (1947), 4-v +R AC, *fig.693*, 177
Model 515 (1951), 4-v +R AC/DC, *fig.740*, 191
Model 545 (1954), 4-v +R AC/DC transp., *fig.765*, 194
Model 546 (1946), 4-v +R AC/DC, *fig.657*, 173
Model 547 (1947), 4-v +R AC/DC, *fig.699*, 177
Model 815 (9151), 4-v batt. port., *fig.742*, 191
Model 837 (1937), 3-v +R AC, *fig.574*, 150
Model 945 (1954), 6-v +MetR AC/batt., *fig.761*, 193
Model 1037 (1937), 3-v +R AC, *fig.580*, 151
Model 1137 (1937), 3-v +R AC, *fig.584*, 151
Model 1737 (1937), 4-v +R +TI AC, *fig.577*, 151
Model A1 (1932), 6-v +R AC, *fig.384*, 129
Model B815 (1951), 4-v batt. port., *fig.735*, 191
Model M55 (1955), 4-v +R AC/DC, *fig.775*, 195
Model PT1010 (1958), 6-tr. batt. port., *fig.798*, 197
Type 31 (1929), 3-v +R AC, *fig.270*, 94
Arcadia (1936), 4-v +R AC, *fig.548*, 147
Arcadia Console (1935), 4-v +R AC, *fig.487*, 141
Arcadia Model T1/AC (1934), 4-v +R AC, *fig.463*, 138
Arcadia Model T2/AC (1934), 4-v +R AC, q.v. *fig.463*, 138
Gloria (1933), 6-v +R AC/clock, *fig.390*, 130
Gloria (1934), 5-v +R AC/clock, *fig.432*, 134
Kit Receiver (1932), 4-v +R AC kit, *fig.356*, 126
Lancastria (1933), 4-v +R AC, *fig.426*, 134
Lancastria (1934), 3-v +R AC, *fig.465*, 138
Lancastria (1935), 3-v +R AC, *fig.516*, 144
Lancastria Magna (1933), 4-v +R AC, *fig.394*, 130
Nova Consolette (1935), 3-v +R AC, *fig.489*, 141
Parva (1936), 3-v batt., *fig.520*, 144

FIDELITY —
Model 2546 (1947), 4-v +R AC/DC, *fig.688*, 176

FLINDERPHONE —
Flinderphone (1925), cr.set, *fig.182*, 83

GAMAGES —
Atlantic (c.1910), spk.trans/rec., *fig.17*, 21
Crystal Receiver (1923), cr.set, *fig.124*, 75
Two Valve Receiver (1926), 2-v batt., *fig.211*, 87
Polaris Maxiwaver (1920), tuner, *fig.34*, 31
Polaris Mediwaver (1919), 1-v batt., *fig.34*, 31
Polaris Miniwaver (1919), tuner, *fig.34*, 31

GAMBRELL —
Baby Grand AC (1926), 2-v + AC unit, *fig.206*, 55, 87
Baby Grand DC (1925), 2-v + DC unit, 52

GECOPHONE/G.E.C. —
5445 (1954), 4-v +R AC, *fig.759*, 193
AC 37 (1936), 3-v +R AC, *fig.541*, 147
BC 635 (1935), 4-v batt., *fig.511*, 143
BC 1002, Model No:1 (1922), cr.set, *fig.39*, 39
BC 1385 (1925), wavemeter, *fig.179*, 83
BC 1501, Model No:2 (1922), cr.set, *fig.76*, 68
BC 2001 (1922), 2-v batt., *figs.56, 56a*, 65
BC 2010 (1923), 4-v batt., *fig.116*, 46, 74
BC 2050 (1924), 5-v batt., *fig.151*, 79
BC 2580 (1922), 2-v batt. amp., *fig.56a*, 65
BC 2740 (1926), 4-v batt., *fig.213*, 54, 87
BC 2820 (1926), 2-v batt., *fig.205*, 86
BC 2930 Victor 3 (1928), *fig.250*, 92
BC 2940 (1928), 4-v batt., *figs.236, 236a*, 90
BC 3032R (1929), 3-v batt., *fig.255*, 92
BC 3047R, Portable Screened 4 (1929), 4-v batt. port., *fig.266*, 94
BC 3130 (1930), 3-v +R AC, *fig.287*, 118
BC 3235 (1931), 3-v +R AC, *fig.322*, 122
BC 3240 (1931), 4-v +R AC, fig.325, 122
BC 3250 (1924), 2-v batt., *fig.126*, 76
BC 3300 (1924), 3-v batt., *fig.164*, 81
BC 3400 (1922), 4-v batt., *fig.56a*, 65
BC 4040 (1939), 4-v +R AC, *fig.619*, 155
BC 4644 (1954), 4-v +MetR AC, *fig.769*, 194
BC 4650 (1946), 4-v +R AC, *fig.658*, 173
BC 4750 (1947), 4-v +R AC, *fig.692*, 176
BC 4835R (1947), 5-v +R AC/DC, *fig.698*, 177
BC 4941 (1948), 4-v batt. port., *fig.706*, 178
BC 5639 (1950), 4-v +R AC, *fig.733*, 190
BC 7000 (1927), 7-v batt. port., *fig.218*, 88
AC Mains Four (1935) 3-v +R AC, *fig.494*, 142
All-Wave Super-Six (1937), 5-v +R AC/DC, *fig.585*, 151
Compact Three (1934), 3-v batt., *fig.436*, 135
Junior (1925), cr.set, *fig.168*, 81
L & D Model (1926), v batt., 54
New Viking IV (1932), 4-v +R AC, *fig.383*, 129
Osram 4 Music Magnet (1930), 4-v batt. kit, *fig.290*, 118
Osram Thirty-Three, New Music Magnet (1932), 3-v batt., *fig.379*, 128
Overseas Model (1933), 4-v +R AC, *fig.407*, 132
Superhet 5 (1933), 4-v +Bar DC, *fig.425*, 133
Superhet-Five, Model DC5 (1934), 4-v +Bar DC, fig.458, 137
Telephone Wireless Aircraft Mk.II (1917), 2-v trans., *fig.28*, 28
Universal Mains Three (1934), 2-v +R +Bar AC/DC, *fig.435*, 135

GENERAL —
3V (1927), 3-v batt., *fig.223*, 88
G.R.C.4 (1922), cr.set, *fig. 62*, 66
G.R.C.13 (1923), 2-v batt. amp., *fig.93*, 71
G.R.C.16 (1923), 2-v batt., *fig.93*, 71
Type 15 (1926), 2-v batt., *fig.194*, 85

GENT —
Four Valve Receiver (1924), 4-v batt., *fig.149*, 79

GOBLIN —
Time Spot Model CR (1947), 4-v +R AC, *fig.682*, 175

GOLTONE —
Goltone Super (1925), cr.set, *fig.167*, 81

GOOD LISTENING —
Good Listening Table Model (1935), 4-v +R AC, *fig.519*, 144

GRAFTON —
Uncle Tom (1924), cr.set, *fig.135*, 77

GRAVES —
Aerial AC s.het (1937), 4-v +R AC, *fig.581*, 151
Model B3 (1932), 3-v batt., *fig.362*, 126
National (1933), 3-v batt., *fig.420*, 133
National (1934), 3-v +R AC, *fig.449*, 136
Regional (1929), 3-v batt., *fig.268*, 94
Vulcan (1926), 2-v batt., *fig.197*, 85

GRUNDIG —
Hastings Model 2035/WD/3D (1955), 6-v +MetR +TI AC, *figs.767, 768*, 194
Micro-Boy (1960), 6-tr batt. pocket port./table model, *fig.949*, 297

HACKER —
Herald, Model RP10 (1960), 7-tr batt. port.,
fig.947, 296

H.M.V. —
Model 360 (1935), 3-v +R AC, *fig.518,*
144
Model 425 (1936), 5-v +R AC, *fig.531,*
145
Model 435 (1931), 3-v +R AC, *fig.316,*
121
Model 456 (1938), 5-v +R +TI AC/DC,
fig.611, 154
Model 463 (1934), 5-v +R AC, *fig.462,*
138
Model 654 (1938), 4-v +R AC/DC,
fig.612, 155
Model 1124 (1953), 4-v +R AC, *fig.748,*
192
Model 1127 (1955), 4-v +R AC/clock,
fig.774, 195
Model 1360 (1954), 5-v +R AC, *fig.762,*
193
Model 1406 (1940), 5-v batt. port.,
fig.632, 160
Model 1410G (1957), 3-v + 2tr. port.,
(green), *fig.786,* 196, *figs.942, 943,* 294
Model 1410B (1957), 3-v + 2tr. port.,
(blue), q.v. *fig.786,* 196
Model 5201 (1949), 4-v +R +TI AC/DC,
fig.717, 179
Greenwich Superhet Five (1934), 4-v +R
AC/clock, *fig.443,* 135

H.P.R. —
Simplex No.493 (1922), 1-v batt., *fig.55,* 65

HALCYON —
Battery Portable (1928), 3-v batt. port., *fig.237,*
90

HAMLEY'S —
Crystal Receiver (1924), cr.set, *fig.153,* 80

HAMPTON —
Table Model (1931), 4-v +Bar. DC, *fig.337,*
123

HARLIE —
Harlie Melody Maker (1928), 3-v batt. kit, q.v.
fig.248, 91

HAVENWOOD —
Model 151 (1932), 4-v +R AC, q.v. *fig.377,*
128

HEAYBERD —
AC Table Model (1935), 4-v +R AC, *fig.490,*
141

HENDERSON —
Broadcast Receiver (1924), 5-v batt., *fig.140,*
78

HERMES —
Radio Tourist (1947), 4-v batt. port., *fig.683,*
175

HOLIDAY —
Holiday (1964), 6-tr. port., *fig.814,* 204,
fig.959, 299

HOME-CONSTRUCTED —
1-valve/crystal receiver (1923), *fig.113,* 74
2-valve receiver (orig.1929), 2-v, cigarette
cards, *fig.254,* 92
3-valve receiver (1928), 3-v batt., *fig.243,* 91
3-valve receiver (c.1931), 3-v batt., *fig.336,*
123
4-valve unit type (c.1922), 4-v batt., *fig.65,* 67
4-valve receiver (1926), 4-v batt., *fig.204,* 86
5-valve receiver (1927), 5-v batt., *fig.233,* 90
5-valve receiver (1928), 5-v batt., *fig.242,* 91
Berec Pioneer (1959), 4-v batt. kit, *fig.801,*
197
Cossor Melody Maker (1927), 3-v batt.
blueprint, q.v. 58
Cossor Melody Maker (1928), 3-v batt. kit,
fig.248, 91
Crystal set (pre-WWI), cr.set, *fig.22,* 24
Crystal set (orig.1923), cr.set, cigarette cards,
fig.92, 71
Crystal set (1924), cr.set, *fig.161,* 80

Edwardian Amateur Wireless Station
(1911-1913), *figs.915-920,* 234-237
Everyman Four (1926), 4-v batt., blueprint,
fig.190, 84, 85
Ferranti Kit Receiver (1932), 4-v +R AC kit,
fig.356, 126
Grid Leak's Pocketphone (1937), 3-v batt.
blueprint, q.v. *fig.559,* 149
Harlie Melody Maker (1928), 3-v batt. kit, q.v.
fig.248, 91
Osram 4 Music Magnet (1930), 4-v batt. kit,
fig.290, 118
Premier Midget Radio Kit (1948), 3-v +R AC/
DC kit, *fig.709,* 178
ST 400 (1932), 4-v batt., blueprint, *figs.355,*
355a, 126
ST 900 (1937), 5-v batt., blueprint, *fig.586,*
152
Silvertone (1930), 3-v batt.kit, *fig.310,*
120
Skyscraper (1932), 3-v batt. kit, *fig.366,*
127
Skyscraper 3 (1932), 3-v batt. kit, q.v.
fig.366, 127
Skyscraper 4 (1933), 4-v batt. kit, *fig.393,*
130
Sinclair Micro-6 (1964), 3-tr miniature
batt. port. kit, 298
Sinclair Micro-FM (1965), 7-tr miniature
batt. port. kit, 298
Sinclair Micro-Midget (1958), 3-tr
miniature batt. port. (circuit design/
article), *fig.952,* 298
Sinclair Micromatic Mk.I (1967), 3-tr
miniature batt. port. kit, *fig.955,* 298
Sinclair Micromatic Mk.II (1969), 2-tr
miniature batt. port. kit, *fig.956,* 298
Sinclair Slimline (1963), 2-tr miniature
batt. port. kit, *figs.953, 954,* 298
Transatlantic Five (1924), 5-v batt.
blueprint, q.v. *fig.140,* 78
Tri-ang Tri-onic Kit A (1961), tr. kit,
fig.806, 200
Tri-ang Tri-onic Kit A/B (1962), tr. kit,
q.v. *fig.806,* 200
Unidyne (1924), 2-v batt. blueprint,
fig.*152,* 79
Unidyne (1924), 2-v batt. kit, fig.*152,* 79
Three In One (1935), 3-v batt. port. blueprint,
figs.486 & 486a, 141

HOROPHONE —
Horophone Type 'A' (1913), cr.set, *fig.23,* 24,
figs.922, 923, 925, 926, 238-241
Horophone Type 'B' (1913), cr.set, *fig.921,*
238

I.E.C. —
Model IEC (1922), cr.set, *fig.69,* 67

IGRANIC —
Neutrosonic Seven (1927), 7-v batt., *fig.216,*
88

IVALEK —
De Luxe (1950s), cr.di. cr.set., *fig.726,* 190

JEWEL —
Jewel (1957), 4-v +R AC/batt., *fig.785,* 196

K-B —
Brandeset IIIA (1929), 3-v batt., *fig.277,* 95
Kobra Model 305 (1931), 3-v +R AC, *fig.344,*
124
Kobra Junior (1931), 3-v batt., *fig.313,* 121
Masterpiece (1930), 2-v batt., *fig.298,* 119
Masterpiece (1931), 3-v batt., *fig.346,* 125
Model 169 (1929), 3-v +R AC, fig.271, 95
Model 321 (1932), 3-v +R AC, *fig.373,* 128
Model 333 (1933), 3-v batt., *fig.405,* 131
Model 428 (1935), 4-v +R AC, *fig.510,* 143
Model 433 (1935), 2-v +R AC, *fig.508,* 143
Model FB10 (1950), 4-v +R AC, *fig.725,* 190
New Pup Model 362 (1934), 3-v batt., *fig.460,*
137
New Pup Model 397 (1934), 2-v +R AC, q.v.
fig.460, 137
Pup (1930), 2-v batt., q.v. *fig.341,* 124
Pup (1931), 2-v batt., *fig.341,* 124
Pup (1931), 2-v +R AC, q.v. *fig.341,* 124
Rejectostat (1933), 5-v +R AC, *fig.415,* 132
Rejectostat Model 430 (1935), 3-v +R AC,
fig.509, 143

Rejectostat Model 666 (1933), 5-v +R AC,
fig.414, 132
Rejectostat Model 888 (1933), 7-v +R AC,
fig.417, 133
Rejectostat Universal Model 381 (1934), 4-v
+R AC/DC, *fig.442,* 135
Sonata (Model SP31), (1961), 6-tr port.,
fig.928, 243

KABILOK —
Cabinet housing (1928), *fig.239,* 90

KENMAC —
Kenmac Book (1925), cr.set, *fig.175,* 82

KLEINEMPFANGER —
Deutscher Kleinempfanger (1938), Twin triode
+R AC, *fig.604,* 154

KUDOS —
Model No.7 (1925), 3-v batt., 51

LISSEN —
Lissen (1924), cr.set, *fig.156,* 80
Model 8039 (1933), 3-v +R AC, *fig.419,* 133
Model 8214 (1936), 3-v +R AC, *fig.550,* 148
Skyscraper (1932), 3-v batt. kit, *fig.366,* 127
Skyscraper 3 (1932), 3-v batt. kit, q.v. *fig.366,*
127
Skyscraper 4 (1933), 4-v batt. kit, *fig.393,* 130
Two Valve AC Receiver (1931), 2-v +R AC,
fig.333, 123

LOEWE —
Model OE 333 (1926), 1-v batt., *fig.193,* 85
Model RO 433 (1929), 1-v batt., q.v. *fig.193,*
85

LOTUS —
3 Valve All Electric (1931), 3-v +R AC,
fig.342, 124
Bud (1932), 2-v +MetR, *fig.375,* 128
Double Pentode Universal Receiver Type 33
(1933), 2-v +R +Bar AC/DC, *fig.411,* 132

LUMOPHON —
Lumophon (1931), 4-v +R AC, *fig.339,* 124
Model AC3 (1930), 3-v +R AC, *fig.299,* 119

MAGNUM —
Hampshire (1947), 3-v +R AC, *fig.687,* 176
Magnum Crystal Set (1930), cr.set, *fig.309,*
120
Model 3V (c.1937), 3-v +MetR AC, *fig.560,*
149

MAJESTIC —
Model 49C (1933), 4-v +R AC, *fig.389,* 130
Screen-Grid Superhet Model 15 (1932), 4-v +R
AC, *fig.377,* 128

MANUFACTURER UNKNOWN —
A1 Radio (1923), cr.set, *fig.96,* 91
Bijou Radio Card (1924), cr.set, *fig.133,* 77
Headphone/Crystal Set (1923), cr.set, *figs.79 &*
79a, 69
PAL (1924), cr.set, *fig.158,* 80
Triood Radiophone (1924), cr.set, *fig.155,* 80

MARCONI —
3-valve receiver (1922), 3-v batt., *fig.57,* 65
Aircraft Telephony Transmitter (1915), 1-v
batt., *fig.24,* 26
Crystal Receiver No:1 (c.1910/11), q.v.
fig.927, 241
Magnetic Detector (1902), *fig.13,* 18
Marconi-Fleming Valve Receiver (c.1910),
2-v batt., *fig.19,* 22
Multiple Tuner (1907), *fig.16,* 20
Portable Magnetic Receiver (c.1906/7), q.v.
fig.927, 241
Wireless Telephony Arc Trans/Rec. (1910),
fig.18, 22

MARCONIPHONE —
Baby (1923), cr.set, *fig.117,* 75
Cabinet 32A (1927), 3-v batt. q.v. *fig.217,* 88
Chelmsford Baby (1924), cr.set, q.v. *fig.117,*
75
Crystal A, Type RB3 M2 (1922), cr.set, *fig.64,*
66
Crystal Junior, Type RB2 (1922), cr.set, *fig.68,*
67

Model 34 (1928), 3-v batt., *fig.235*, 90
Model 42AC (1931), 3-v +R AC, *fig.315*, 121
Model 47 (1929), 4-v +R AC, *fig.276*, 95
Model 55 (1929), 5-v batt. port., *fig.265*, 94
Model 66 (1931), 4-v batt. port., *fig.334*, 123
Model 219 (1936), 5-v +R AC, *fig.522*, 144
Model 235 (1935), 3-v +R AC, *fig.480*, 140
Model 238 (1935), 3-v +R AC, q.v. *fig.480*, 140
Model 240 (1935), 3-v +R AC, q.v. *fig.518*, 144
Model 248 (1932), 2-v batt., *fig.376*, 128
Model 276 (1933), 6-v +R AC, *fig.430*, 134
Model 282 (1932), 3-v batt., *fig.378*, 128
Model 283 (1933), 3-v batt., *fig.409*, 132
Model 296 (1934), 4-v +R +TI AC, *fig.440*, 135
Model 537 (1937), 6-v +R +TI AC, *fig.583*, 151
Model 562 (1937), 6-v batt. transp., *fig.576*, 150
Model 855 (1938), 4-v +R AC, *fig.593*, 152
Model 878 (1939), 4-v +R AC, *fig.631*, 157
Model 895 (1940), 5-v batt. port., q.v. *fig.632*, 160
Model 911 (1940), 4-v +R AC, *fig.639*, 171
Model P17B (1947), 4-v batt. port., *fig.700*, 177
Model P20B (1948), 4-v batt. port., *fig.704*, 178
Model P60B (1957), 3-v + 2tr. port., q.v. *fig.786*, 196
Model T15DA (1947), 4-v +R AC/DC transp., *fig.702*, 177
Model T43DA (1955), 3-v +R AC/DC, *fig.776*, 195
Round Six (1927), 6-v batt., 59
Type 23 (1928), 2-v batt., *fig.238*, 90
Type 31 (1925), 3-v batt., *fig.178*, 83
Type 32 (1927), 3-v batt., *fig.217*, 88
Type 39 (1929), 3-v batt., *fig.267*, 94
Type 44 (1928), 62
Type 53 (1928), 5-v batt. port., *fig.245*, 91
Type 81 Straight 8 (1925), 8-v batt., fig.173, 82
Type 220 (1930), 2-v +R AC, *fig.291*, 118
Type 246 (1931), 2-v +R AC, *fig.317*, 121
Type A2 (1924), 2-v batt. amp., *fig.142*, 78
Type B2 (1924), 2-v batt. amp., *fig.141*, 78
Type NB2 (1922), 2-v batt. amp., q.v. *figs.60, 142*
Type RB10 (1923), 1-v batt./cr.set, *fig.112*, 74
Universal Baby (1924), cr.set, q.v. *fig.117*, 75
V1 (1924), 1-v batt., fig.165, 81
V2 (1922), 2-v batt. (spade tuning), *fig.60*, 66
V2 (1925), 2-v batt., (rotary tuning), *fig.170*, 82
V2A (1923), 2-v batt., q.v. *fig.60*, 66
V3 (1923), 3-v batt., *fig.82*, 69

MASTER —
Junior (1923), cr.set, *fig.86*, 70

MASTERADIO —
Model D110 (1946), 4-v +R AC/DC, *fig.667*, 174
Sandown Star (1951), 4-v +R AC/DC, q.v. *fig.667*, 174

MCMICHAEL —
AC Superhet (1934), 4-v +MetR AC, *fig.444*, 136
Autodyne (1925), 7-v batt. kit, *fig.176*, 83
Battery 3 (1930), 3-v batt. q.v. *fig.296*, 119
Bijou Portable (1938), 4-v batt. port., q.v. *fig.587*, 152
Colonial Receiver (1931), 4-v batt., *figs.311 & 312*, 121
Duplex Four Type C (1932), 4-v batt. transp., *fig.381*, 129
Duplex Four Type CMC (1933), 4-v batt. transp., *fig.398*, 131
Duplex Four Type S (1932), 4-v batt. port., *fig.368*, 127
Duplex Mains Four Transportable (1932), 4-v +MetR AC transp., *fig.380*, 129
Duplex Super Five (1933), 5-v batt. transp., *fig.396*, 130
Duplex Transportable (1934), 5-v batt. transp., *fig.454*, 137
Mains Three (1930), 3-v +MetR AC, *fig.296*, 119
Model 135 (1935), 4-v +R AC, *fig.474*, 139

Model 137 (1937), 4-v +R +TI AC, *fig.567*, 150
Model 151 (1951), 6-v +R AC, *fig.736*, 191
Model 235 (1935), 3-v +R AC, *fig.514*, 144
Model 361 (1936), 3-v +R AC, *fig.551*, 148
Model 362 Console (1935), 4-v +R AC, *fig.536*, 146
Model 362 Table Model (1935), 4-v +R AC, *fig.540*, 147
Model 367 (1936), 4-v batt. port., *fig.538*, 146
Model 368 (1936), 4-v batt., *fig.545*, 147
Model 374 (1937), 5-v +R +TI, *fig.557*, 148
Model 380 (1938), 4-v +R AC, *fig.589*, 152
Model 381 (1938), 4-v +R AC, *fig.606*, 154
Model 388 (1938), 4-v batt., q.v. *fig.606*, 154
Model 389 (1938), 4-v batt., q.v. *fig.589*, 152
Model 394 (1939), 4-v +R AC, *fig.630*, 156
Model 435 (1935), 5-v +R AC, *fig.507*, 143
Model 451 (1946), 3-v +R AC, *fig.654*, 173
Model 463 (1946), 4-v batt. port., *fig.666*, 174
Model 498 Supervox (1949), 4-v +R AC/DC, *fig.718*, 179
Model 535U (1935), 3-v +R AC/DC, q.v. *fig.514*, 144
Model 808 (1938), 4-v +R AC transp., *fig.587*, 152
Moving Coil Mains Receiver (1931), 3-v +MetR AC, *fig.324*, 122
Radiomac Crystal Mark III (1922), cr.set, 42
Superhet (1926), 7-v batt., *fig.210*, 87
Superhet Mains Transportable (1934), 4-v +R AC, *fig.455*, 137
Super-Screened Portable Four (1929), 4-v batt. port., *fig.261*, 93
Twin Speaker Superhet (1934), 4-v +R AC, *fig.452*, 136
Twin Supervox RV8 (1933), 4-v +MetR AC, *fig.422*, 133

MECOPHONE —
Mecophone (1923), 1-v batt., *fig.94*, 71

MIDGETRONIC —
Model EMU 4214 (1950), 3-v +R AC/DC, *fig.727*, 190

MIDWEST —
New Imperial (1938), 14-v +R AC, *fig.597*, 153

MILLET —
Millet A (1925), cr.set, q.v. *fig.64*, 66
Millet Junior (1925), cr.set, q.v. *fig.64*, 66

MILNES —
Diamond Type D (1936), 7-v batt., *fig.532*, 146
Emerald Type E (1936), 6-v batt., q.v. *fig.532*, 146
Pearl Type P (1936), 5-v batt., q.v. *fig.532*, 146
Ruby Type R (1936), 6-v +R AC, q.v. *fig.532*, 146

MINIVOX —
Model RR-34 (1963), 6-tr batt. pocket port. clock radio, *fig.950*, 297

MONARCH —
Cadet (1931), 2-v +R AC, *fig.351*, 125

MOTOROLA —
X21 (1963), 6-tr batt. pocket port., *fig.951*, 297

MULLARD —
Model MAS4 (1936), 4-v +R AC, *fig.524*, 145
Model MAS90 (1939), 3-v +R AC, *fig.628*, 156
Model MB3 (1934), 3-v batt., *fig.467*, 138
Model MB4 (1935), 4-v batt., *fig.500*, 142
Model MB3A (1935), 3-v batt, q.v. *fig.467*, 138
Model MU35 (1935), 5-v +R +Bar AC/DC, *fig.493*, 141

MURPHY —
Model 188C (1949), 5-v +R +TI AC, *fig.713*, 179
Model A3 (1931), 3-v +R AC, *fig.338*, 124
Model A3A (1932), 3-v +R AC, q.v. *fig.338*, 124
Model A4 (1933), 3-v +R AC, *fig.408*, 132
Model A8 (1932), 8-v +R AC, *fig.367*, 127
Model A24 (1934), 4-v +R AC, *fig.439*, 135

Model A26 (1935), 4-v +R AC, *fig.502*, 142
Model A30 (1936), 3-v +R AC, *fig.542*, 147
Model A34 (1937), 3-v +R +TI AC, *fig.566*, 149
Model A46 (1938), 4-v +R AC, *fig.596*, 153
Model A48 (1938), 4-v +R AC, *fig.603*, 153
Model A50 (1938), 5-v +R +TI AC, *fig.590*, 152
Model A52 (1938), 8-v +R +TI AC, *fig.592*, 152
Model A70 (1939), 4-v +R AC, *fig.622*, 156
Model A72 (1939), 4-v +R +TI AC, *fig.616*, 155
Model A76 (1939), 5-v +R +TI AC, *fig.617*, 155
Model A90 (1940), 5-v +R AC, *fig.637*, 171
Model A92 (1940), 5-v +R AC, *fig.641*, 171
Model A100 (1946), 4-v +R AC transp., *fig.665*, 174
Model A100F (1946), 4-v +R AC transp., q.v. *fig.665*, 174
Model A104 (1946), 4-v +R AC, *fig.651*, 172
Model A122 (1947), 4-v +R AC, *fig.689*, 176
Model A122C (1947), 4-v +R AC, *fig.690*, 176
Model A372 (1955), 5-v +R AC, *fig.777*, 195
Model AD32 (1937), 3-v +R AC/DC, *fig.558*, 149
Model AD94 (1940), 4-v +R AC/DC, *fig.633*, 160
Model B4 (1930), 4-v batt. transp., q.v. *fig.365*, 127
Model B4 (1932), 4-v batt. transp., *fig.365*, 127
Model B5 (1933), 3-v batt., q.v. *fig.408*, 132
Model B97 (1945), 5-v batt., *fig.646*, 172
Model B385 (1961), 8-tr +2-Cr.d. batt. port., *fig.807*, 200
Model BA228 (1954), 6-v +2MetR AC/batt., *fig.756*, 193
Model D4 (1933), 3-v +Bar DC, q.v. *fig.408*, 132
Model U472 (1958), 5-v +R AC, *fig.797*, 197
Type B93 (1940), 5-v batt. port., *fig.638*, 171
Wartime Civilian Receiver (1944), 4-v batt., *fig.909*, 218
Wartime Civilian Receiver (1944), 3-v +R +West AC, *fig.908*, 218
Wartime Civilian Receiver (1945), 3-v +R +West AC (MW/LW), *fig.912*, 219

NEW WILSON —
Magnetic Microphone Bar (1925), mic.amp., *figs. 50 & 51*, 53

NIRVANAX —
Duo Coupling Receiver (1922), cr.set, *fig.67*, 67

OMNIAPHONE —
Omniaphone (1924), cr.set, *fig.154*, 80
The Homeplayer (1926), 2-v batt., fig.212, 87

ORMOND —
Model 608 (1935), 4-v +R AC, *fig.505*, 143

ORR —
Model D3 (1933), 3-v batt., *fig.403*, 131

OTB —
Type A (1923), cr.set, *fig.123*, 75
Type B (1923), cr.set, q.v. *fig.123*, 75

PADDON —
Model 1 (1924), 4-v batt., *fig.150*, 79

PAM —
Model 607 (1949), 3-v +R AC, *fig.719*, 179
Model 710 (1956), 8-tr. port., *fig.724*, 186, *figs.934, 935, 936, 937*, 288-291

PEGASUS —
Table Model (1934), 4-v +R AC, *fig.459*, 137
Table Model (1935), 4-v +R AC, *fig.497*, 142

PELMERSET —
Pelmerset (1923), 2-v batt., *fig.87*, 70
Pelmerset Two Valve Amplifier (1923), 2-v batt. amp., *fig.87*, 70

PERDIO —
Model PR4 (1958), 4-tr. batt. port., *fig.946,* 295
Model PR22 (1960), 7-tr. batt. port., q.v. *fig.802,* 197
Model PR25 (1961), 7-tr +cr.di. batt. port., *fig.811,* 201
Model PR73 Continental (1959), 7-tr. batt. port., *fig.802,* 197

PETER PAN —
Peter Pan (1931), 3-v +R AC, *fig.320,* 122

PETO SCOTT —
Broadcast Major (1922), 2-v batt., 37
Transatlantic V (1924), 5-v batt., q.v. *fig.140,* 78
Type H51 (1946), 4-v +R AC, q.v. *fig.674,* 172
Type H52 (1946), 4-v +R AC, *fig.674,* 172

PHILCO —
Model 100 (1958), 5-v +R AC/DC, *fig.792,* 196
Model 260 (1933), 4-v +R, q.v. *fig.391,* 130
Model 269 People's Set (1936), 3-v +R AC, *fig.523,* 145
Model 333 People's Set (1936), 3-v batt., *fig.526,* 145
Model 444 People's Set (1936), 3-v +R AC, *fig.535,* 146
Model 600 (1938), 7-v +R AC, *fig.600,* 153
Model 1260 Baby Grand (1933), 4-v +R +TI, *fig.391,* 130
Model A9BG (1940), 4-v +R AC, *fig.642,* 171
Model A527 People's Set (1937), 4-v +R AC, q.v. *fig.535,* 146
Model B537 People's Set (1937), 4-v +R AC, q.v. *fig.535,* 146
Model D531 Empire Automatic (1938), AC, q.v. *fig.607,* 154
Model D521 Empire Automatic (1938), 4-v +R AC, *fig.607,* 154
Model P527 People's Set (1937), 5-v batt., q.v. *fig.535,* 146
Model S521 Empire Automatic (1938), batt., q.v. *fig.607,* 154
Model U427 People's Set (1937), 3-v +R +Bar AC/DC, q.v. *fig.535,* 146
Model U527 People's Set (1937), 4-v +R +Bar AC/DC, q.v. *fig.535,* 146
Model U647 (1937), 5-v +R +Bar AC/DC, *fig.561,* 149
Model V537 People's Set (1937), 4-v +R +Bar AC/DC, *fig.562,* 149
Model X521 Empire Automatic (1938), AC/ DC q.v. *fig.607,* 154
Table Model (1934), 3-v +R AC, *fig.457,* 137

PHILIPS —
274A (1934), 4-v +R AC, *fig.453,* 137
372B (1934), 6-v batt., *fig.464,* 138
470A (1938), 3-v +R AC, *fig.605,* 154
472A (1934), 5-v +R AC, *fig.471,* 139
474B (1948), 6-v batt., *fig.707,* 178
577A (1935), 5-v +R AC, *fig.506,* 143
580A (1935), 5-v +R AC, *fig.492,* 141
585U (1935), 5-v +R AC/DC, *fig.491,* 141
587U (1935), 6-v +R AC/DC, *fig.475,* 139
588A (1934), 5-v +R AC, *fig.469,* 138
630A (1932), 5-v +R AC, *fig.357,* 126
634A (1933), 4-v +R AC, *fig.395,* 130
636A (1933), 7-v +R AC, *fig.404,* 131
745A (1936), 4-v +R AC, *fig.554,* 148
787AX (1937), 6-v +R AC, *fig.571,* 150
795A (1936), 4-v +R AC, *fig.543,* 147
830A (1932), 4-v +R AC, *fig.358,* 126
834A (1933), 3-v +R AC, *fig.402,* 131
838U (1934), 3-v +R +Bar AC/DC, *fig.472,* 139
930A (1931), 3-v AC, *fig.321,* 122
940A (1935), 2-v +R AC, *fig.476,* 139
2511 (1929), 4-v +R AC, *fig.263,* 93
2514 (1928), 3-v +R AC, *fig.247,* 91
2515 (1928), 2-v +R AC, *fig.251,* 92
2531 (1930), 3-v +R AC, *fig.302,* 119
2607 (1931), 5-v +R AC, *fig.329,* 123
2634, Radioplayer (1931), 3-v +R AC, *fig.319,* 121
V5A (1936), 4-v +R AC, *fig.528,* 145
Model 141U (1954), 4-v +R AC/DC transp., *fig.758,* 193

Model 186A (1946), 4-v +R +TI AC, *fig.675,* 175
Model 310A (1952), 4-v +R AC, *fig.745,* 192
Model 342A Music Maid (1954), 4-v +R AC/ clock, *fig.757,* 193
Model 411A (1952), 4-v +R +TI AC, *fig.744,* 192
Model 462A (1947), 3-v +R AC, *fig.695,* 177
Model 543A (1954), 6-v +R AC, *fig.763,* 194
Type 291 U/15 (1949), 3-v +R AC, *fig.721,* 179

PILOT —
Model BT530 (1938), 3-v +R AC, *fig.610,* 154
Model U385 (1937), 6-v +R +TI AC, *fig.568,* 150
Model U650 (1936), 5-v +R +TI AC, *fig.530,* 145
Little Maestro (1939), 4-v +R AC/DC (wood), *fig.627,* 156
Little Maestro (1940), 4-v +R AC/DC (bakelite), *fig.640,* 171
Major Maestro (1940), 4-v +R AC/DC, *fig.636,* 171
Major Maestro (1946), 4-v +R AC/DC, q.v. *fig.636,* 171

POLAR —
Polar Twin (1925), 2-v batt., *fig.189,* 84

PORTADYNE —
Challenger (1932), 4-v batt. transp., *fig.386,* 129
Model PB5 (1933), 5-v batt. transp., *fig.392,* 130
Model S (1933), 4-v +R AC, *fig.421,* 133
Princess (1953), 3-v +R AC, *fig.753,* 192
Table Model (1945), 4-v +R AC/DC, *fig.647,* 172

PREMIER —
Midget Radio Kit (1948), 3-v +R AC/DC kit, *fig.709,* 178

PYE —
15A (1945), 3-v +R AC, *fig.648,* 172
25 (1927), 5-v batt. port., *fig.231,* 89, 215
25C (1929), 5-v batt. port., *fig.257,* 93, 215
47X (1948), 3-v +R AC/DC, *fig.705,* 178
128B, Slim Six (1958), 6-tr batt., fig.789, 196
222 (1926), 2-v batt., *fig.214,* 87
232 (1929), 2-v batt., *fig.256,* 92
275 (1929), 2-v +MetR AC, *fig.262,* 63, 93, 215
333 (1927), 3-v batt.
460 (1929), 4-v batt., *fig.259,* 93
520 (1923), 2-v batt.
530 (1923), 3-v batt., *fig.122,* 75
540 (1923), 4-v batt.
547 (1924), 4-v batt., *fig.145,* 78
550 (1923), 4-v batt.
555 (1925/7), 5-v batt. port., *fig.184,* 51, 84
'710' (1956), 8-tr batt. port., *fig.940,* 293
720 (1924), 2-v batt.
730 (1924), 3-v batt.
740 (1924), 4-v batt.
750 (1927), 5-v batt., *fig.215,* 87
811 (1938), 4-v +R AC, *fig.594,* 152
830 (1925), 3-v batt.
AC4D (1930), 3-v +R AC Trans., *fig.305,* 120, 215
B4D (1930), 4-v batt. port., *fig.295,* 119
E (1933), 5-v +MetR AC, *fig.401,* 131, 215
G (1932), 3-v +MetR AC, *fig.369,* 127, 215
K (1932), 2-v +MetR AC, *fig.370,* 127, 215
L75B (1946), 4-v batt. port., *fig.677,* 175
M78F (1948), 4-v batt. port., *fig.712,* 178, 215
MM (1931), 3-v +MetR AC Trans., *fig.332,* 123, 215
O (1933), 4-v batt. port., *fig. 406,* 131
P (1933), 5-v +MetR +West AC Trans, *fig.399,* 131, 215
P75A (1953), 4-v +R AC, *fig.751,* 192
P123BQ (1957), 6-tr batt. port., *figs.939, 941,* 293
P160 PQ (1959), 6-tr batt. port., *fig.799,* 197
PE80 Cambridge International (1953), 7-v +R AC, *fig.749,* 192
PE/98U/LW (1953), 4-v +R AC/DC, *fig.747,* 192
PU118 (1958), 4-v +R AC/DC, *fig.791,* 196
Q (1931), 4-v batt. port., *fig.349,* 125, 215
QAC3 (1937), 3-v +R AC, *fig.572,* 150

QAC5 (1937), 5-v +R AC, *fig.578,* 151
S (1932), 6-v + MetR AC, *fig.371,* 127, 215
SE/U (1934), 4-v +MetR AC/DC, *fig.446,* 136
T/M (1935), 3-v +R AC, *fig.495,* 142
Baby Q (1937), 4-v batt. port., *fig.564,* 149, 215
Desk Tuner Unit (1955), 6-v +R AC, *fig.778,* 195
New Baby Q (1939), 4-v batt. port., *fig.629,* 156
Selector Three (1927), 3-v batt.
Selector Five (1927), 5-v batt.

R.A.P. —
International (1935), 4-v +R AC, *fig.483,* 140
Table Model (1946), 4-v +R AC, *fig.670,* 174
Table Model (1947), 3-v +R AC, *fig.680,* 175
Transatlantic (1935), 4-v +R AC, *fig.517,* 144
Transatlantic (1936), 3-v +R AC, *fig.534,* 146

R.G.D. —
Model 625 (1936), 5-v +R +TI AC, *fig.527,* 145

R.I. —
Madrigal (1929), 3-v +R AC, *figs.253 & 253a,* 92
Model No.1 (1922), cr.set, *fig.77,* 68, 69
Ritz Airflo (1934), 4-v +R AC, *fig.450,* 136
Ritz Airflo (1947), AC, q.v. *fig.450,* 136
Type V2A (1923), 2-v batt., *fig.110,* 73
Type V3A (1923), 3-v batt., *fig.105,* 73
Type V.I.M (1922), 1-v batt. amp., *fig.59,* 65

R.K. —
Penthouse (1934), 3-v +R AC/DC, *fig.447,* 136
Radio Keg (1935), 4-v +R AC, q.v. *fig.482,* 140

RADIAX —
Vest Pocket Receiving Set (1923), cr.set, *fig.47,* 45
Model 24P (1923), 2-v batt. kit, *fig.89,* 70

RADIECO —
Simplex (1922), 1-v batt., *fig.61,* 66

RADIO EQUIPMENT —
Dainty (1924), cr.set, *fig.148,* 79

RADIO RENTALS —
Model 61 (1950), 4-v +R AC, *fig.732,* 190
Model 157 (1934), 4-v +R AC/DC, *fig.433,* 134
Model 216 (1955), 4-v +R AC/DC, *fig.772,* 194
Model RR 57 (1947), 4-v +R AC, *fig.679,* 175
Model RR 484 (1934), 3-v +R AC/DC, *fig.451,* 136

RADIONETTE —
Junior (1924), cr.set, *fig.159,* 80
Popular Model (1924), cr.set, *fig.132,* 76

RADIOPHONE —
Straight Two (1931), 2-v batt., *fig.331,* 123

RAYMOND —
Model F55 (1950), 4-v +R AC, *fig.731,* 190

READ & MORRIS —
Mains Four (1925), 4-v + AC (or DC) unit, 52
Simplicity Five (1925), 5-v + AC (or DC) unit, 52

RED STAR —
Red Star (1930), 2-v batt., q.v. *fig.308,* 120
Red Star (1930), 3-v batt., *fig.308,* 120

REES-MACE —
Super Four (1927), 4-v batt. port., *fig.230,* 89
Type RMC (1943), 4-v batt., *fig.634,* 162

REGENCY —
Model TR-1 (1954), 4-tr pocket port., q.v. *fig.724,* 186, *figs.930, 931, 932, 933,* 286-287

REGENTONE —
Model B/35 (1934), 3-v batt., *fig.466,* 138
Quadradyne Band-Pass Four (1933), 3-v +R AC, *fig.427,* 134
Transportable Five (1938), 4-v +R AC transp., *fig.602,* 153

REID —
Grid Leak's Pocketphone, Type DB/P (1937), 3-v batt. port., *fig.559,* 149

REVOPHONE —
Revo Little Gem (1924), cr.set, *fig.130,* 76
Revophone (1923), *fig.101,* 72

REXOPHONE —
Rexophone (1923), cr.set, *fig.102,* 72

ROBERTS —
Junior (1949), 4-v batt. port., *fig.722,* 179
Model MB4 (1936), 4-v batt. port., *fig.537,* 146
Model R77 (1957), 4-v batt. port., *fig.788,* 196
Model RIC-1 (1968), integrated circuit batt. port., *fig.958,* 299
Model RT1 (1958), 6-tr batt. port., *fig.948,* 296
Revival Model 200 (1993), tr m/batt. port., *fig.948,* 296
Revival Model 250 (1996), tr m/batt. port., q.v. *fig.948,* 296
Revival Model 500 (1993), tr m/batt. port., q.v. *fig.948,* 296
Revival Model 550 (1996), tr m/batt. port., q.v. *fig.948,* 296

ROMAC —
Model 106 (1946), 4-v batt. port., *fig.659,* 173
Model 126 (1947), 4-v batt. port., q.v. *fig.659,* 173
Model 136L (1948), 4-v batt. port., q.v. *fig.659,* 173
Model 136S (1948), 4-v batt. port., q.v. *fig.659,* 173
Model 236L (1949), 4-v batt. port. + AC unit, q.v. *fig.659,* 173
Model 236S (1949), 4-v batt. port. + AC unit, q.v. *fig.659,* 173

ST —
Model ST 400 (1932), 4-v batt., blueprint, *figs.355, 355a,* 126
Model ST 900 (1937), 5-v batt., blueprint, *fig.586,* 152

SCOTT —
Allscott (1928), 3-v batt., *fig.239,* 90

SELECTOR —
All-Electric Transportable (1929), v AC transp., 63
Cabinet Portable (1929), 4-v batt. port., *fig.264,* 94
Super Model U32 (1928), 7-v batt. port., *fig.246,* 91

SERVIS —
Servis Junior (1930), 2-v batt., q.v. *fig.293,* 118

SHOPERTUNITIES —
De-luxe (1972), 6-tr. batt., *fig.816,* 208

SIEMENS —
Type 125 (1923), cr.set, *fig.115,* 74
Type CV (1922), 1-v./cr.set, *fig.63,* 66

SINCLAIR —
Micro-6 (1964), 3-tr miniature batt. port. kit, 298
Micro-FM (1965), 7-tr miniature batt. port. kit, 298
Micro-Midget (1958), 3-tr miniature batt. port. (circuit design/article), *fig.952,* 298
Micromatic Mk.I (1967), 3-tr miniature batt. port. kit, *fig.955,* 298
Micromatic Mk.II (1969), 2-tr miniature batt. port. kit, *fig.956,* 298
Slimline (1963), 2-tr miniature batt. port. kit, *figs.953, 954,* 298

SOBELL —
Model 439 Sobellette (1949), 3-v +R AC/DC transp., *fig.714,* 179
Model 516 (1946), 4-v +R AC, *fig.676,* 175
Model 615 (1945), 5-v +R AC, *fig.645,* 172

SONY —
TR72 (1957), 10-tr. batt. port., *fig.944,* 295

SPARTA —
Sparta (1924), cr.set, *fig.146,* 79

STANDARD —
Micronic Ruby Model SR-G430 (1962), 7-tr. +cr.di. port., *figs.812, 813,* 202

STEEPLETONE —
Valve 1 (1996), tr mains table model, *fig.960,* 299

STELLA —
Stella (1951), 4-v +R AC, *fig.739,* 191

STERLING —
Anodion Type 1592 (1924), 4-v batt., *fig.127,* 76
C.W. Mk.III Transmitter (1917), 2-v batt., *fig.31,* 29
Mk.II Front Receiver (1917), 2-v batt., *fig.30,* 29
One Anodion Type R1586 (1924), 1-v batt., *fig.157,* 80
R1533 (1923), 1-v batt. amp., *fig.107,* 73
Regina Type 1618 (1924), 4-v batt., *fig.125,* 86
Sterling No.1 (1922), cr.set, q.v. *fig.73,* 68
Threeflex Model R1590 (1923), 3-v batt. + cr., *fig.81,* 69
Tuner Aircraft Mk.III (1917), *fig.29,* 28
Type R1588 (1923), *fig.88,* 70
W.T. Spark Transmitter No.1 (1915), *fig.25,* 26

STRAD —
Model 471 (1947), 4-v +R AC, *fig.697,* 177

SUNBEAM —
Model 22 (1934), 3-v +R AC/DC, *fig.438,* 135
Model 55 (1934), 4-v +R AC/DC, q.v. *fig.445,* 136
Model 57 (1934), 4-v +R AC/DC, *fig.445,* 136

SYNCHRONOME —
Horophone Type 'A' (1913), cr.set, *fig.23,* 24, *figs.922, 923, 925, 926,* 238-241
Horophone Type 'B' (1913), cr.set, *fig.921,* 238

T.M.C. —
Model No.2 (1923), cr.set, q.v. *fig.163,* 81
Model No.2 (1924), cr.set, *fig.163,* 81

TELSEN —
Model 474 (1933), 3-v +R AC, *fig.429,* 134
MacNamara (The Golden Voice) (1932), 3-v +R AC, *fig.353,* 125

TEMPOVOX —
Grandmother Clock Radio (1938), 4-v +R +Bar AC/DC/clock, *fig.608,* 154

TEMPUS —
Tempus Crystal Set (1921), cr.set, *fig.927,* 241

TINGEY —
Cabinet Set (1922), 5-v batt., *fig.41,* 40
Valve Tuner No.22 (1920), 1-v batt. port., *fig.35,* 31

TINOL —
Tinol Electric Mains Set (1925), 2-v + cr. + DC unit, 52

TONYPHONE —
Tonyphone Super Two (1924), 2-v batt., q.v. *fig.87,* 70

TRI-ANG —
Tri-onic Kit A (1961), tr. kit, *fig.806,* 200
Tri-onic Kit A/B (1962), tr. kit, q.v. *fig.806,* 200

ULTRA —
Model 22 (1934), 3-v +R AC, *fig.441,* 135
Model 26 (1936), 3-v +R AC, *fig.546,* 147
Model 48 (1936), 4-v +R AC, *fig.529,* 145
Model 66 (1935), 3-v +R AC/DC, *fig.496,* 142
Model 101 (1936), 3-v +R AC, *fig.521,* 144
Model 102 (1936), 3-v AC/DC, q.v. *fig.521,* 144
Model 103 (1936), 3-v batt., q.v. *fig.521,* 144
Model 115 (1937), 3-v +R AC, *fig.582,* 151
Model 125 (1937), 3-v +R AC, q.v. *fig.582,* 151

REID —
Model 122 (1937), 3-v +R AC/DC, *fig.570,* 150
Model 201 (1938), 4-v +R AC, *fig.598,* 153
Model 309 (1939), 3-v +R AC, *fig.615,* 155
Model 310 (1939), 3-v +R AC, q.v. *fig.615,* 155
Model 400 Teledial (1938), 4-v +R +TI, *fig.588,* 152
Model DC3 (1930), 3-v DC, *fig.288,* 118
Model T401 (1946), 3-v +R AC, *fig.660,* 173
Model T406 (1945), 3-v +R AC, *fig.649,* 172
Model TR80 (1961), 6-tr. batt., *fig.810,* 201
Blue Fox (1932), 2-v +R AC, *fig.364,* 127
Model R786 Coronation Twin (1953), 4-v +MetR AC/DC batt., *fig.750,* 192
Model R906 Coronation Twin (1953), 4-v +MetR AC/DC batt., q.v. *fig.750,* 192
Lynx (1933), 3-v +R AC, *fig.424,* 133
Tiger (1932), 4-v +MetR AC, *fig.382,* 129
Tiger Three (1931), 3-v +R AC, *fig.330,* 123
Transistor Six (1958), 6-tr. batt. port., *fig.790,* 196

UMELLO —
Five Valve Receiver (1930), 5-v batt., *fig.300,* 119
Umello (1932), 3-v +R AC, *fig.354,* 126

UNIDYNE —
Unidyne (1924), 2-v batt. blueprint, q.v. *fig.152,* 79
Unidyne (1924), 2-v batt. kit, q.v. *fig.152,* 79

UNIQUE —
Unique Beer-Barrel (1954), 4-v +R AC/DC, q.v. *fig.482,* 140

UTILITY —
See *Wartime Civilian Receiver* under **Murphy**

VIDOR —
Model 254 (1936), 3-v +R AC/DC, *fig.544,* 147
Model 349 Chanson (1946), 4-v +R +TI AC, *fig.664,* 173
Model CN213 (1934), 3-v +R +Bar AC/DC, *fig.461,* 137
Model CN429 Lady Margaret (1954), 4-v batt. port., *fig.755,* 193

VIKING —
Model 810 (1932), 3-v +MetR AC, *fig.352,* 125

W.M.C. —
New Type Crystal Set (1924), cr.set, *fig.162,* 81

WADE —
Decee-Acee (1932), 3-v +MetR AC/DC, *fig.372,* 128

WATES —
Cabinet Set (1922), 42

WAYFARER —
Major (1936), 4-v batt. port., *fig.552,* 148

WEMCO —
Wemco No.1 Valve/Crystal Receiver (1923), 1-v batt./cr.set, *fig.106,* 73

WESTERN ELECTRIC —
Loud Speaking Amplifier (1923), 2-v batt. amp., *fig.90,* 70
Model 44001 (1922), cr.set, *figs.70 & 85,* 67, 70
Model 44002 (1924), 7-v batt., *fig.128,* 76
Superhet Kit (1925), 6-v batt. kit, *fig.181,* 83
Weconomy LF Amplifying Unit (1923), 2-v batt. amp., *figs.84 & 85,* 70
Weconomy Tuner (1924), 2-v batt., *fig.137,* 77

WESTMINSTER —
Model SG3 President (1932), 3-v +R AC, *fig.387,* 129
Model ZA 818 (1948), 6-v +R +TI AC, *fig.710,* 178

WHITLEY & HOLROYD —
Rum Barrel Novelty Radio (1958), 4-v +R AC/DC, q.v. *fig.482,* 140 ∎

Brand Names Used by Valve and/or Crystal Set Manufacturers
(For Transistors, see Directory of Transistor Radios & Foreign Imports, 1956-72)

A.J.S. —
A.J. Stephens & Co. (1914) Ltd., Walsall St., Wolverhampton

A.T.E. —
Parkside Electric & Radio Supplies, 89/91 Rusholme Rd., Manchester

A.T.M. —
Automatic Telephone Man. Co.Ltd., London

Abbiphone —
Abbey Industries Ltd., Abbey Wood, SE2

Abbonphone —
R.R. & Co.Ltd., Birmingham

Ace —
Ace Radio, 2-5 Dingley Place, London EC1
Ace Radio Ltd., Pound Rd., London NW10

Adey —
Adey Radio Co.Ltd., Union Mews, 99 Mortimore St., London W1

Aerodyne —
Aerodyne Radio Ltd., Aerodyne Works, Tottenham, London N17
Aerodyne Ltd., Platina St., London EC2

Alba —
A.J. Balcombe Ltd., 52-58 Tabernacle St., London EC2

Ambassador —
R.N. Fitton Ltd., Hutchinson Lane, Brighouse, Yorkshire

Amplion —
Graham Amplion Ltd., Slough, Buckinghamshire
Amplion (1932) Ltd., 230 Tottenham Court Road, London W1

Anode —
Anode Wireless & Scientific Instruments Ltd., London EC

Ashley —
Ashley Wireless Telephone Co.Ltd., 69 Renshaw St., Liverpool

Astrophone —
Amplifiers Ltd.

B.R.C —
British Radio Corporation

B.S.A. —
B.S.A. Radio Ltd., Birmingham

B.T.H. —
British Thompson-Houston Co.Ltd., Aldwych, London WC2

Bassett Lowke —
Bassett Lowke Ltd.

Bébéphone —
Rooke Bros.Ltd.

Beethoven —
Montague Radio Inventions & Development Co.Ltd., Gt. College St., London NW1
Beethoven Radio Ltd., Chase Rd., North Acton, London NW10
Beethoven Electric Equipment Co.Ltd., Chase Rd., North Acton, London NW10

Belmont —
British Belmont Radio Ltd., Ridgemont St., London WC1

Benson —
Benson & Co., U.S.A.

Berec —
Berec Radio Ltd., Hercules Place, Holloway, London N7

Bligh —
Manufacturer unknown

Britannia —
Britannia Batteries Ltd., Union St., Redditch, Worcestershire

Brown —
S.G. Brown Ltd., Victoria Rd., North Acton, London W3

Brownie —
J.W.B. Wireless Co.Ltd., 19 Garrick St., London WC2
J.W.B. Wireless Co.Ltd., 310a-312a Euston Rd., London NW1
Brownie Wireless Co. (of Gt. Britain) Ltd., Nelson Street Works, Mornington Crescent, London NW1

Brunswick —
Brunswick Ltd., 1-3 Brixton Rd., London SW9

Bruton —
Bruton & Co., U.S.A.

Burgoyne —
Burgoyne Wireless (1930) Ltd., York Rd., Kings Cross, London N1

Burndept —
Burnham & Co., Deptford, London SE
Burndept Ltd., Aldine House, Bedford St., Strand, London WC2
Burndept Wireless Ltd., Eastnor House, Aerial Works, Blackheath, London SE3
Burndept Wireless (1928) Ltd., Blackheath, London SE3
Burndept Ltd., Erith, Kent

Burton —
C.F. & H. Burton Ltd., Progress Works, Bernard St., Walsall
Burton Products Ltd., Bernard St., Walsall

Bush —
Bush Radio Ltd., Woodger Road, Shepherd's Bush, London W12
Bush Radio Ltd., Power Road, Chiswick, London W4

Butler —
H.D. Butler & Co.Ltd., 222 Gt. Dover St., London SE1

C.T. —
C.T. Ltd., 26 Church St., Soho, London W1

Carlton —
Fred Bulmer, 4 Carlton Terrace, Scarborough

Cee Bee —
City Battery & Wireless Co., London SE11

Chackophone —
Eagle Engineering Co.Ltd., Eagle Works, Warwick

Champion —
Champion Electric Corporation Ltd., Drove Road, Newhaven, Sussex

Clarke —
H. Clarke & Co. (Manchester) Ltd., Atlas Works, Patricroft, Lancashire

Classic —
Hustler, Simpson & Webb Ltd., Aerodyne Works, 317 Hoe St., Walthamstow, London E17

Cleartron —
Cleartron Radio Ltd., 1 Charing Cross Rd., London SW1

Clemens & Taylor —
Clemens & Taylor, Pershore, Worcestershire

Climax —
Climax Radio Electric Ltd., Quill Lane, Putney, London SW15

Clydelco —
Clyde Electrical Co., Palm St., Glasgow

Columbia —
Columbia Graphophone Co.Ltd., Newcastle-upon-Tyne

Consolidated —
Consolidated Radio Co.Ltd., 75 Kilburn Lane, London NW6

Cosmos —
Metropolitan Vickers Electrical Co.Ltd., Trafford Park, Manchester
Metro-Vick Supplies Ltd., Trafford Park, Manchester

Cossor —
A.C. Cossor Ltd., Cossor House, Highbury Grove, London N5

Cromwell —
William Dibben & Sons Ltd., 80 St.Mary's Road, Southampton

Danipad —
Danipad Rubber Co.Ltd., 5/7 Market Street, Finsbury, London EC2

Decca —
Decca Gram. Co.Ltd., 1-3 Brixton Rd., SW9
Decca Record Co.Ltd., 1-3 Brixton Rd., SW9

Defiant —
Co-operative Wholesale Society Ltd., 1 Balloon Street, Manchester

Delaphone —
T.W. Thomson, 39 London St., Greenwich, SE10

Denco —
Denco (Clacton) Ltd., Old Rd., Clacton-on-Sea, Essex

Derwent —
Central Equipment Ltd., Wadsworth Road, Perivale, Middlesex

Dibben —
William Dibben & Sons Ltd., 80 St. Mary's Road, Southampton

Dulci —
Dulci Radio Ltd., 97 Villiers Rd, London NW2

Dynamergy —
Dynamergy Mains Supply Co., Staines

Dynatron —
H. Hacker & Sons, Ray Lea Rd., Maidenhead.
Dynatron Radio, Maidenhead, Berks.

Eddystone —
Stratton & Co.Ltd., Balmoral Works, Bromsgrove St., Birmingham

Edison Bell —
Edison Bell Ltd., Glengall Rd., London SE15

Ediswan —
Edison Swan Electric Co., 123-125 Queen Victoria St., London EC4

Eelex —
J.J. Eastick & Sons, Eelex House, 118 Bunhill Row, London EC1

Efescaphone —
Falk, Stadelmann & Co.Ltd., 83-87 Farringdon Rd., London EC1

Ekco —
E.K. Cole Ltd., Ekco Works, London Road, Leigh-on-Sea, Essex
E.K. Cole Ltd., Ekco Works, Southend-On-Sea

Electradix —
Leslie Dixon & Co., London SW8

Elwell —
C.F. Elwell Ltd., Craven House, Kingsway, WC2

Emor —
Emor Radio Ltd., 45 Kilburn High Rd.,
London NW6
Ensign —
Ensign Radio Co., 15 Strand, London WC2
Europhone —
Europhone Radio Co., Birmingham
Ever Ready —
Ever Ready Co. (Great Britain) Ltd., Hercules
Place, Holloway, London N7
Everyman —
Eagle Engineering Co.Ltd., Warwick
Excelophone —
Excelsior Motor Co.Ltd., King's Rd.,
Tyseley, Birmingham

Faeritone —
Mechanical Utilities Co.
Felcourt —
Felcourt Products Ltd., East Grinstead, Sussex
Fellocryst —
Fellows Magneto Co.Ltd., Cumberland Ave.,
Park Royal, Willesden, London NW10
Fellophone —
Fellows Magneto Co.Ltd., Cumberland Ave.,
Park Royal, Willesden, London NW10
Fellows —
Fellows Manufacturing Co.Ltd., Cumberland
Ave., Park Royal, Willesden, London NW10
Ferguson —
Universal Radio Distributers Ltd., London
Ferguson Radio Corporation Ltd., 105 Judd
St., London WC1
Ferguson Radio Corporation Ltd., Enfield,
Middlesex
Ferranti —
Ferranti Ltd., Moston, Manchester
Ferranti Ltd., Hollinwood, Lancashire
Ferranti Radio & Television Ltd.
(subsidiary of E.K.Cole Ltd.)
Fidelity —
Fidelity Radio Ltd., 11 Blechynden St.,
North Kensington, London W11
Flinderphone —
Flinders (Wholesale) Ltd., 18 Butt Rd.,
Colchester, Essex

Gamages —
A.W. Gamage Ltd., Holborn, London EC
Gambrell —
Gambrell Bros. Ltd., Merton Rd.,
Southfields, London SW18
Gecophone/G.E.C. —
General Electric Co.Ltd., Magnet House,
Kingsway, London WC2
General —
General Radio Co.Ltd., Twyford Abbey
Works, Acton Lane, London NW10
Gent —
Gent & Co.Ltd., Faraday Works,
Leicester
Goblin —
British Vacuum Cleaner & Engineering
Co.Ltd., Goblin Works, Leatherhead, Surrey
Goltone —
Ward & Goldstone, Pendleton, Manchester
Good Listening —
Manufacturer unknown - no information
available
Grafton —
A.B. Jones & Sons Ltd., Grafton China Works,
Longton, Staffordshire
Graves —
J.G. Graves, Hallamsgate Works,
Crooks Rd., Sheffield

Grundig —
Grundig (Gt.Britain) Ltd.,
Newlands Park, London SE26

H.M.V. —
The Gramophone Co.,
Hayes, Middlesex
H.P.R. —
H. Powell Rees (designer)
Halcyon —
Halcyon Wireless Supply Co.Ltd.,
110 Knightsbridge, London SW1
Hamley's —
Hamley Bros.Ltd., 86/87 High Holborn,
London WC1
Hampton —
Hampton Radio Ltd. 103 Vicarage Rd.,
Hampton Wick, Kingston-On-Thames
Harlie —
Harlie Bros. Ltd., Balham Road,
London N9
Havenwood —
Grigsby-Grunow Co., Chicago, Illinois, U.S.A.
Heayberd —
F.C. Heaberd & Co., 10 Finsbury St.,
London EC2
Henderson —
W.J. Henderson & Co.Ltd.,
351 Fulham Rd., London SW10
Hermes —
Hermes, Brooke & Co.,
Cobham, Surrey
Horophone —
Synchronome Company Ltd.,
32-34 Clerkenwell Road, London EC

I.E.C. —
International Electric Co., London
Igranic —
Igranic Electric Co.Ltd., Elstow Works,
Bedford
Ivalek —
Ivory Electric Ltd., 45 Grafton Way, London
W1

Jewel —
Jewel Radio Ltd., Pitsea, Basildon, Essex

K.B. —
Kolster-Brandes Ltd., Cray Works,
Sidcup, Kent
Kabilok —
W. & T. Lock Ltd., St.Peters Works, Bath
Kenmac —
Kenmac Radio Ltd., Dalling Rd.,
Hammersmith, London W6
Kleinempfanger —
Siemens and various German manufacturers
Kudos —
Christie & Hodgeson Ltd., Sheffield

Lissen —
Lissen Ltd., 18-22 Friars Lane, Richmond,
Surrey
Lissen Ltd., Lissenium Works, Worple Road,
Isleworth, Middlesex
Loewe —
Loewe Radio A.G., Berlin, Germany
Lotus —
Lotus Radio Ltd., Mill Lane, Liverpool
Lotus Radio (1933) Ltd., 105 Judd St., London
WC1
Lumophon —
British Lumophon Ltd.,
20-22 Parker St., London WC2

Magnum —
Burne-Jones & Co.Ltd., 309-317 Borough
High St., London SE1
Majestic —
Majestic Electric Co.Ltd., Tariff Rd.,
Tottenham, London N17
Marconi —
Marconi Scientific Co.Ltd., 21/25 St.Anne's
Court, Dean St., Soho, London W1
Marconi's Wireless Telegraph Co.Ltd., Hall
St., Chelmsford, Essex
Marconiphone —
Marconi's Wireless Telegraph Co.Ltd., New
St., Chelmsford, Essex
Marconiphone Co.Ltd., 210-212 Tottenham
Court Road, London W1
Marconiphone Co.Ltd., Hayes, Middlesex
Master —
Master Radio Manufacturing Co.Ltd., Carver
St., Old Trafford, Manchester
Masteradio —
Masteradio Ltd., Fitzroy Place, London NW1
McMichael —
L. McMichael Ltd., Slough, Buckinghamshire
McMichael Radio Ltd., Slough,
Buckinghamshire
Mecophone —
Mann, Egerton & Co.Ltd. (Coach Builders),
5 Prince of Wales Rd., Norwich, Norfolk
Midwest —
Midwest Radio (Manufacturing) Co.Ltd.,
16 Old Town, Clapham, London SW4
Midgetronic —
Hale Electric Ltd., Radio Works, Talbot Rd.,
London W13
Millet —
J.M. Millet & Sons, Southampton
Milnes —
Milnes Radio Co.Ltd., Church St., Bingley,
Yorkshire
Monarch —
William Dibben & Sons Ltd., 80 St.Mary's
Road, Southampton
Mullard —
Mullard Wireless Service Co.Ltd., Mullard
House, Charing Cross, London WC2
Murphy —
Murphy Radio Ltd., Welwyn Garden City,
Hertfordshire

New Wilson —
New Wilson Electrical Manufacturing Co., 18
Fitzroy St., Euston Rd., London W1
Nirvanax —
Nirvanax Ltd., 31 Glasshouse St., London W1

OTB —
Harding, Holland & Fry Ltd., 27 Garlick Hill,
London EC4
Omniaphone —
Clarke Bros. (Leicester) Ltd., Leicester
Omniaphone Radio Co., 67 George St., Parade,
Birmingham
Ormond —
Ormond Engineering Co.Ltd., 199-205
Pentonville Road, Kings Cross, London N1
Orr —
Orr Radio Ltd., 63 Lincoln's Inn Fields,
London WC2

Paddon —
M. Paddon & Son, Plumbers & Electricians,
Chulmleigh, Devon
Pam —
Pamphonic Reproducers Ltd., Hendon, NW9

Pam (Radio & Television) Ltd., 295 Regent Street, London W1
Pegasus —
Pegasus Ltd., Lower Mills, Nussy Mill Lane, Lower Wortley, Leeds
Pelmerset —
Fellows Magneto Co.Ltd. for Peronet Ltd., London WC1
Peter Pan —
Jackson-Bell Distributors Ltd., Hammersmith, London
Peto Scott —
Peto Scott Co.Ltd., 77 City Rd., London EC1
Philco —
Philco Radio & Television Corporation of Great Britain Ltd., Aintree Rd., Perrivale, Middlesex
Philco (Gt.Britain) Ltd., Romford Rd., Chigwell, Essex
Philips —
Philips Lamps Ltd., New Road, Mitcham Junction, Surrey
Philips Electrical Ltd., Century House, Shaftesbury Ave., London WC2
Pilot —
Pilot Radio Ltd., 87 Park Royal Rd., North Acton, NW10
Polar —
Radio Communication Co.Ltd., 34-35 Norfolk St., Strand, London WC2
Portadyne —
Portadyne Radio Ltd., Gorst Rd., London NW10
Premier —
Premier Radio Co.Ltd., 169 Fleet Street, London EC4
Pye —
W.G. Pye & Co., Granta Works, Montague Rd., Cambridge.
Pye Radio Ltd., Cambridge.
Pye Ltd., Cambridge.
British Electronic Industries Ltd.
Pye of Cambridge Ltd.

R.A.P. —
Radio Accoustic Products Ltd., 24 Thames Street, Kingston-on-Thames, Surrey
Radio Accoustic Products Ltd., Ferry Works, Thames Ditton, Surrey
R.G.D. —
Radio Gramophone Development Co.Ltd., Newtown Row, Birmingham
R.I. —
Radio Instruments Ltd., 12 Hyde Street, New Oxford St., London WC1
Radio Instruments Ltd., Purley Way, Croydon
R.K.
R.K. Radio Laboratories, Chicago, Illinois, U.S.A.
Radiax —
Radiax Ltd., 10 Radio House, Percy Street, Tottenham Court Road, London W1
Radieco —
Radio Equipment Co., Stilemans Works, High St., Wickford, Essex
Radio Equipment —
Radio Equipment Co., Stilemans Works, High St., Wickford, Essex
Radio Rentals —
Radio Rentals Ltd., 92 Regent Street, London W1
E.K.Cole Ltd., Ekco Works, Southend-on-Sea, Essex
Mains Radio Gramophones Ltd.

Radionette —
Peter Curtis Ltd., 75a Camden Rd., London NW1
Radiophone —
British Radiophone Ltd., 56 Vicarage Lane, Ilford, Essex
Raymond —
Raymond Electric Ltd., London NW10
Read & Morris —
Read & Morris Ltd., 31 East Castle St., London W1
Red Star —
Red Star Radio Ltd., Aston Rd., Birmingham
Regentone —
Regentone Ltd., Worton Rd., Isleworth, Middlesex
Regentone Products Ltd., Worton Rd., Isleworth, Middlesex
Rees-Mace —
Rees-Mace Manufacturing Co.Ltd., 39a Welbeck St., London W1
Reid —
A. Reid Manufacturing Co.Ltd., 14a Clerkenwell Green, London EC1
Regentone —
Regentone Ltd., Worton Road, Isleworth, Middlesex.
Revophone —
Cable Accessories Co.Ltd., Tipton, Staffs.
Rexophone —
Morch Bros.Ltd., 35 Tresham Avenue, London E5
Roberts —
Roberts Radio Co.Ltd., Hills Place, London W1
Roberts Radio Co.Ltd., 41 Rathbone Place, London W1
Roberts Radio Co.Ltd., 35-37 Creek Road, East Molesey, Surrey
Romac —
Romac Radio Corporation Ltd., Hendon, London NW9

ST —
John Scott Taggart (Designer)
Scott —
James Scott & Co.Ltd., of Dunfirmline & Perth, Scotland
Selector —
Selectors Ltd., 1 Dover St., London W1
Servis —
Harris, Williams (Manufacturers) Ltd., Barbican, London EC1
Siemens —
Siemens Bros. & Co.Ltd., Woolwich, London SE18
Sobell —
Sobell Industries Ltd., Slough, Bucks.
Sparta —
Fullers United Electrical Works Ltd., Chadwell Heath, Essex
Stella —
Stella Radio & Television Ltd., 9-15 Oxford St., London W1
Sterling —
Sterling Telephone & Electric Co., W/T Factory, Soho
Sterling Telephone & Electric Co.Ltd., 210-212 Tottenham Court Rd., London W1
Strad —
R.M. Electric Ltd., Majestic Works, Team Valley Estate, Gateshead 11, Durham

Sunbeam —
Sunbeam Electric Ltd., Park Royal Rd., London NW10
Synchronome —
Synchronome Co.Ltd., London EC

T.M.C. —
Telephone Manufacturing Co.Ltd., Hollingsworth Works, Martell Rd., West Dulwich, London SE21
Telsen —
Telsen Electric Co.Ltd., Aston, Birmingham
Tempovox —
British Tempovox Ltd., Holly Road, Hampton Hill, Middlesex
Tempus —
W.J. Badman, Weston-Super-Mare
Tingey —
W.R.H. Tingey, London EC
Tinol —
Totills Ltd., Manchester
Tonyphone —
Fellows Magneto Co.Ltd., for British Engineering Products Ltd., London SW1
Tri-ang —
Minimodels Ltd., Fulford Rd., Havant, Hants.
Truvox —
Truvox Engineering Co.Ltd., Exhibition Grounds, Wembley, Middlesex

Ultra —
Ultra Electric Ltd., Erskin Rd., London NW3
Umello —
Umello Ltd., 55 Gt. Marlborough St., W1
Unidyne —
Bower Electric Ltd., 15 Grape St., London WC2
Popular Wireless
Unique —
Unique Radio Ltd., Chadwell Heath, Essex
Utility —
Murphy Radio Ltd., plus various WWII manufacturers

Vidor —
Vidor Ltd., West Street, Erith, Kent
Viking —
Viking Sales Ltd.

W.M.C. —
Western Manufacturing Co., Lydney, Gloucestershire
Wade —
A.Wade & Co. (Burnley) Ltd., Carlton Rd., Burnley, Lancsashire
Ward & Goldstone —
Ward & Goldstone Ltd., Pendlestone, Manchester
Wates —
Wates Bros.Ltd., 12/14 Great Queen St., Kingsway, London WC2
Wayfarer —
London Electric Appliances Ltd., 62 Glengall Rd., London SE15
Wemco —
Walters Electrical Manufacturing Co., London
Western Electric —
Western Electric Co.Ltd., Connaught House, 63 Aldwych, London WC2
Westminster —
Belcher Ltd., London EC1
Curry's Ltd., 77 Uxbridge Rd., Ealing, Middlesex
Whitley & Holroyd —
Whitley & Holroyd Ltd., Bradford, Yorks. ∎

Subject Index — 19th Century to 1921

Subject Index — 1922 to 1929

AC, 47, 52, 55
DC, 41, 47, 52, 55, 61
Central Electricity Board, 55
National Grid, 55, 63
Maritime vessels —
Berengaria, 61, *Elettra,* 57
Monitoring stations —
Keston, 50, Tatsfield, 50
Morse code, 42

Narborough Workhouse, 54
New York Stock Exchange, 63

Organisations, Conferences & Committees —
British Association, 59
Crawford Committee, 51
Int. Broadcasting Union (I.B.U.), 51
Radio Electrical Conference, 64
Radio Manufacturers Ass. (RMA), 62, 64
Royal Society, 56
Sykes Committee, 43, 45
Valve Manufacturers' Ass. (VMA), 49
Wireless Society of London, 34

Patents action —
Brownie Wireless v Marconi's, 62, 64
Patents, Marconi's, 44
People —
Adams, Godfrey, *fig.52,* 56
'Ariel', 44
Armstrong, E.H., 49
Baird, John Logie, 47, 56, 59, 60, 61, 62
Bull, John, 61
Bull, Sir William, 36
Burnham, Walter W., 36, 39
Burrows, Arthur, 36
Butt, Dame Clara, 48
Cave, Lord, 54
Cooper, Jack, 233
Dempsey, Jack, 36
Dowding, G.V., 49
Eckersley, Peter Pendleton, 34, 50
Fleming, Sir Ambrose, 62
Fulton, Otto, 61
Goodanew, Gwen, *fig.52,* 56
Gordon, R.F., 38
Grant, Winifred, *fig.52,* 56
Hazeltine, Prof., 52
Howe, Robert, 34
Jacomb, Commander W.W., 60
Kellogg, Edward, 53
Kirke, H.L., 56
Langham, James, *fig.52,* 56
Lodge, Sir Oliver, 56
'Lucifer', 54
Luxmore, Mr Justice, 64
Marconi, Guglielmo, 57
Marcuse, Gerald, 57
McMichael, Leslie, 34
Morden, Eric, *fig.52,* 56
Moye, Prof. M., 52
Nipkow, Paul, 47
Plugge, Capt. Leonard F., 50, 58
Reith, John C.W., 36, 48, 49, 50, 56
Rice, Chester, 53
Rogers, K.D., 49
Round, H.J., 59
Scott-Taggart, John, 42
Selfridge jnr., Gordon, 53
Spilsbury, Miss Evelyn, 64
Stropford, C.W., 58
Taylor, Madge, *fig.52,* 56
Taynton, William, 53
Travers, Miss Agnes, 34
Wissenden, J.W., 37
Yeoman Robinson, E., 58
Post Office —
general comment, 34, 36, 37, 44
arc transmitter at Leafield, 34
ban on reaction circuits, 38, 39
commercial wireless communication, 57
licence for experimental television, 56
lifting ban on reaction circuits, 45
Wireless Licence Department, 37
Publications —
Birmingham Post, 63
Daily Mail, 34
Modern Wireless, 42
Pop. Wireless Weekly, 38, 40, 44, 49, 56
Television, 61
The Radio Press, 42
The Radio Times, 44, 61, 63
The Times, 54

The Wireless & Gramophone Trader, 64
The Wireless Constructor, 42
The Wireless Trader, 45, 51, 54, 55, 59
Wireless World, 34, 38, 40, 44, 45, 50,
51, 52, 54, 59, 60, 63
World Radio, 63

Receiver circuits —
general comment, 49
adjustable aerial circuit reaction, 38
band-pass tuning, 63
capacity controlled reaction, 59
grid bias (general), 47, 48, 51, 59
neutrodyne, 39, 44, 52
pre-selected tuning, 54
printed circuit, a distant relative, 62
push-pull, 61
reaction circuit interference, 38, 39
reactionless 'N' circuit, 56
reflex, 42, 51
'ST', 42
supersonic heterodyne circuit, 49
unidyne, 49
Receiver types —
general comment, 38, 49, 51
all-enclosed sets, 42, 51, 52, 63
all-wave, 64, 65
American receivers, 62
'American cabinet' sets, 46
battery valve TRFs, 38, 39, 40, 59, 63
bright/dull-emitter sets, 48
car radios, 41, 42, 58
consoles, 46
crystal sets —
general comment, 39, 48, 51
cat's whisker, 39
crystals, 39, 48
Mark III tuner, 34, 42
permanent detectors, 39
rapid decline in late 1920s, 57
Daventry-only, 51, 53
electric radiograms, 60
'electric wireless', 46
home-constructed, battery, 42, 54
home-constructed, mains, 58
home-construction —
in general, 37, 42, 64
'Melody Maker', *fig.248,* 58, 60, 91
kit sets, 44, 51, 58
'local & Daventry', 54
mains receivers, 47, 52, 59, 61, 63
'no-dial' receivers, 54
outdoor batt. portables, 46, 51, 54, 57, 63
permanently installed, 40, 59, 63
press-button receivers, 54
short-wave only, 57
'smoker's cabinet' sets, 42, 46
suitcase portables, 59
superhets, battery, 51, 59
superhets, kits, 51
superhets, mains, 39, 63
table models, battery, 63
table models, general, 51
table models, mains, 63
transportables, battery, 63
transportables, mains, 63
unit sets, 42
valve/crystal sets, 44, 51
wireless set, the, 40
Reuter's, 37
Round-Sykes Magnetophone, *fig.52,* 56

Television —
B.B.C. involvement, 56
B.B.C. low-def. (30-line) transmissions, 62
Baird, 47, 56, 59, 60, 61, 62
Brookmans Park, 63
companies, 53, 59
first colour demonstrations, 61
first crude experiments, 47
first daylight demonstrations, 61
first detailed living image, 53
first stereoscopic demonstrations, 61
Long Acre studios, 59
Motograph House studios, 56
Royal Society demonstrations, 56
sub-licences, 61
synchronised sound and vision, 63
Television Ltd., 53, 56
Television Society, 61
Televisor, 47, 60
televisors —
first commercial models, 60

home-constructed, 61
transatlantic tests, 60
unofficial use of 2LO transmitter, 56
Tuning dials and controls —
basic types, 43
degree calibrations, 46, 54
disc-drive, 54, 64
drum-drive, 54, 64
drum scale, 54
Ebonite dial controls, 43
edgewise-mounted controls, 54, 60
etholog, 54
illuminated, 59
Indigraph, 52
inductance (sliding), 40, (tapped), 40
metre calibrations, 52, 54, 60, 64
no-dial receiver, 54
plug-in coils, 40, 42
press-button, 54
single-knob control, 64
slow-motion, 52
station names, a selection, 59
super-vernier dials, 52
tuning method, 46
variable condensers —
ganged, 46
square law, 48
straight-line capacity, 40, 48
variometers, 40
vernier condenser, 42
visual tuning indicator, 42
wavelength cards, 46
wavemeter, *fig.179,* 42, 83

Valves —
general comment, 38, 46
general review (1922-1953), 220-221
American-type, 62
anti-microphonic holders, 49, 56
bases —
B4 base, 56, 58, 220
B5 base, 49, 62, 220
battery triodes, 52, 200
bright-emitters, 38, 48
coloured bulbs, 46
directly-heated AC, 61
dome shape, 49
dry cell, 46, 47
dull-emitters, 43, 46, 48
gettering, 46, 220
Hivac, 52
indirectly-htd. (AC), 47, 55, 58, (DC), 47, 59
Mazda, 62
multi-valves, 52, 220
outgassing, 46
oxide coated types, 43, 58
peanut valve, 47
pentode, 61
'pipless', 52, 220
Point-eight, 61
R valve, *fig.38,* 38, 52, 220
rectifiers, 47, 52, 55
screened-grid (batt.), 59, 62, 220 (mains), 61
split-pin legs, 56
slip-coated filaments, 58
thoriated tungsten, 43
top-pip evacuation seal, 38, 52
Tungsram, 62
Wecovalve, 47, 220
AC/G, 58, 62, 220
AC/R, 58, 62
AC/S, 61
DE3, 46, 220
DU5, 55
DU10, 55, 220
K4, 49, 220
KH1, 58, 62
KL1, 55, 58, 62
LS5, 60, 220
LT1, 43
S215, 62
S625, 59, 220
SG 220, 60
U5, 55

Wavebands —
long-wave, 34, 40, 48, 50, 51, 53, 57
medium-wave, 34, 37, 40, 43, 45, 47,
50, 53, 57
short-wave, 57
re-classification of waveband terms, 64
Wireless Industry —
general, 36, 37, 45, 49, 50, 55, 63　■

Subject Index — 1930 to 1939

Subject Index — 1940 to 1949

WARTIME

Acts of Parliament —
Finance (No:2) Act, 1940, 160
Lend-Lease Act (1941), 161
Prices of Goods Act (1940), 160

B.B.C. —
announcers as 'personalities', 160
Broadcasting House,161, 163

Broadcasting Services, Stations & Transmitters —
analysis of B.B.C. stations &
wavelengths, 228-232
Allied Exped. Forces Prog. (B.B.C.), 163
American Forces Network (A.F.N.), 163
Belgian Service (B.B.C.), 161
European Service (B.B.C.), 161, 162
External Services (B.B.C.), 161
Forces Prog. (B.B.C.), 158, 161, 163
Gen. Overseas Service (B.B.C.), 162, 163
'H-Group' transmitters (B.B.C.), 158
Home Service (B.B.C.), 158, 161
I.B.C. Continental Network, 163
N. Afr. & Mid. E. Service (B.B.C.), 162
Overseas Service (B.B.C.), 158
Radio Luxembourg —
'black' broadcasting, 163

Cabinet design —
wartime trends, 158

Companies —
Austerity Radio Ltd., 163
H.M.V., 158
Marconiphone, 158
Murphy Radio Ltd., 158, 162
Philco, 160

Components & Accessories —
batteries —
shortages, 162, stocks run out, 162

International Broadcasting Plans —
Montreux Plan (1940), 116

Licences —
cancellation in vehicles, 160
general review (1904-1971), 225-226
licence figures (1922-1971), 225

Organisations, Conferences & Committees —
American Psychological Warfare
Division, 163
British Radio Valve Manufacturers'
Association, 163
Canadian Broadcasting Corporation, 163
National Council of the Wireless
Retailers' Association, 161
Radio Board, 162
Radio Communications & Electronic
Engineering Association, 163
Radio Component Manufacturers'
Association, 163
Radio Industry Council, 163
Radio Manufacturers' Association, 161
Radio Production Executive, 162

People —
Bush, Irving T., 161
Churchill, 160
Eisenhower, General, 163
Nuffield, Lord, 158
Roosevelt, President, 161
'Thermion', 160

Publications —
Keep It Going, 162
Practical Wireless, 158, 160
The Wireless & Electrical Trader, 162
Wireless World, 158, 161, 162, 163

Radio Programmes —
Ack-Ack, Beer-Beer, 161
Music While You Work, 161
Workers Playtime, 161

Receiver circuits —
battery economy circuits, 158

Receiver types —
all-dry battery portables, 158
car radios (impounded), 160, (released),163
kits, 163
Lend-Lease receivers, 162, 163

midget portables, 158
single valve set, 158
'Wartime Civilian Receiver'
('Utility Set'), 163, 218, 219

Valves —
general review (1922-1953), 220-221
Hivac miniatures, 158
new types, 158
numbers needed by R.A.F., 161
permits during WWII, 117
shortages, 161
small scale release, 162
U.S. replacements, 162

Wireless Industry —
general comment, 161
becomes 'Radio Industry', 162, 163, 164
concentration on Armed Forces, 158
import restrictions, 158, 160
'Industry Set' ('Wartime Civilian
Receiver'), 163, 218, 219
overhaul of sets, 158
production held up, 161
production released, 162
profiteering, 160
public's wartime buying habits, 160, 161
Purchase Tax introduced, 160
role during WWII, 164
shortage of basic materials, 158
shortage of service engineers, 161, 162
shortage of sets, 158, 161
'wireless' as an archaic term, 163

World War Two —
black-out, 161
Blitz, 160
British Expeditionary Force, 158
'dim-out' —
restrictions introduced, 163, 164
restrictions removed, 164
D-Day, 163
Home Front, 158
listening-in under German occupation, 164
North Africa Campaign, 162
'Operation Torch', 162
Pearl Harbour, 161
'V' For Victory Campaign, 161
V1 flying bombs, 163
V2 rockets, 163

Post-WWII

Acts of Parliament —
Lease-Lend Act — terminated, 164

B.B.C.'s third Charter (1947), 167

Broadcasting Services, Stations & Transmitters —
analysis of B.B.C. stations &
wavelengths, 228-232
Allied Exped. Forces Prog. (B.B.C.), 164
'BBC III' (see Third Programme, 167)
'C' Prog. (see Third Programme, 165)
Droitwich transmitter (B.B.C.), 164
Empire Service (B.B.C.), 167
General Forces Programme (B.B.C.),
164, 167
General Overseas Service (B.B.C.), 167
Home Service (B.B.C.), 164
Light Programme (B.B.C.), 164
Overseas Service (B.B.C.), 164
Radio Luxembourg, 166
Third Prog. (B.B.C.), 164, 165, 167
World Service (B.B.C.), 167
Wrotham Hill VHF station (B.B.C.), 169

Cabinet design, 165
Chassis design, 168
Companies —
Bell Telephone Laboratories, 169
Civic Radio Services, 166
Lasky's Radio, 166
Murphy Radio Ltd., 164
John Sargrove Ltd., 168, 169
J. & M. Stone Ltd., 166
Ward, Blenkinsop & Co. Ltd., 169

Components & Accessories —
general comment, 165, 166
'crystal valve', 169

exhibition at Grosvenor House, 166
loud-speakers (extension), 166
silicon crystal rectifier (CS7A), 169
square pin fused plug (B.S.1363), 168
transistors, 117, 169

Exhibitions —
general review (1919-1968), 222-225
Britain Can Make It, 167
Grosvenor House, 166
1947 Radiolympia, 167
1949 Radiolympia, 170

Licences —
general review (1904-1971), 225-226
licence figures (1922-1971), 225
Business Radio Licence (VHF), 170
combined Radio & Television, 166, 226

Organisations, Conferences & Committees —
European Broadcasting Conference, 169
Radio & Electronic Component
Manufacturers' Federation, 169
Radio Component Man. Ass., 169
Radio Industry Council, 167

People —
Bardeen, John, 169
Brattain, Walter, 169
Donegal, Marquis of, 167
Haley, W.J., 164
Shockley, William, 169
Truman, President, 164

Publications —
The Wireless & Elec. Trader, 165,166
Wireless World, 169

Radio Industry —
general comment, 165, 166, 169
electronic equipment, 167, 170
first post-war release of new receivers, 165
Government surplus, 165, 166
— warning about "bargains", 165
near breakdown, 168
production target, 165
Purchase Tax, 165, 168, 169
Radar equipment, 166
'radio' as an up-to-date term, 170
shortage of new receivers, 165
supply situation easing, 170
'wireless' as an out-dated term, 169

Receiver circuits —
printed, experimental, 168, 169

Receiver types —
alarm clock receivers, 168
battery portables, 170
crystal sets, 169
home-construction, 169
kit receivers, 169
Kleinempfanger, 166
mains superhets, 170
'second set', 166, 168, 170
VHF radio telephones, 168, 170
VHF receivers, 166
'Wartime Civilian Receiver'
('Utility Set'), 164

Television —
Alexandra Palace, 166, 170
Lime Grove, 170
re-opening of the B.B.C.'s service, 166
Sutton Coldfield, 170
Television Centre, 170
Wood Lane, 170

Tuning Dials & Controls —
dial markings, 164, 167
fly-wheel, 168
magic-eye tuning indicators, 168
push-button tuning, 168

Valves —
general review (1922-1953), 220-221
B7G, 167, 168
B8A, 168
B9A, 167, 168
G-type octal, 167
GT-type octal, 167
American all-glass miniatures, 167
Rimlock, 168
sub-miniature all-glass, 169 ∎